ADVANCES
IN ORGANIC
GEOCHEMISTRY
1981

ADVANCES IN ORGANIC GEOCHEMISTRY 1981

Proceedings of the 10th International Meeting on Organic Geochemistry,
University of Bergen, Norway, 14–18 September 1981

Organised by the European Association of Organic Geochemists

Edited by
M. Bjorøy *et al.*
Continental Shelf Institute, Norway

A Wiley Heyden Publication

JOHN WILEY & SONS LIMITED
Chichester · New York · Brisbane · Toronto · Singapore

Library of Congress Cataloging in Publication Data:

International Meeting on Organic Geochemistry
    (10th: 1981: University of Bergen)
    Advances in organic geochemistry, 1981.

    'A Wiley Heyden publication.'
    Includes index.
    1. Organic geochemistry–Congresses.
    II. European Association of Organic
Geochemists.   III. Title.
QE516.5.I57   1981   551.9   82-17563
ISBN 0 471 26229 3

British Library Cataloguing in Publication Data:

    Advances in organic geochemistry.—1981
      1. Organic geochemistry—Periodicals
  I. European Association of Organic Geochemistry
      551.9   QE516.5

     ISBN 0 471 26229 3

Typeset by Mid-County Press, London SW15
Printed in Great Britain at The Pitman Press, Bath

Preface

The present volume in the Advances in Organic Geochemistry contains the papers and posters presented at the Tenth International Meeting on Organic Geochemistry which was held at the University of Bergen, Norway, from the 14th to 18th September, 1981. The meeting was held under the auspices of the European Association of Organic Geochemists, and was organised by a committee consisting of M. Bjorøy, K. Bjørlykke, S. Eggen, A. Elvsborg, K. G. Finstad, T. Grønneberg, T. Hægh and F. E. Skaar.

The 231 participants from 23 countries were welcomed to Bergen by E. Bergsager, Norwegian Petroleum Directorate (NPD) and M. Bjorøy, Continental Shelf Institute (IKU). In the opening address, O. J. Kvinnsland, President of the Noroil Group, talked about the future of exploration in the North Sea with special emphasis on the political situation in Norway.

The present volume continues on the lines started with the meeting in Newcastle in 1979. The poster presentations formed an integral part of the meeting and both formal papers and those arising from the poster sessions have been reviewed by referees. In arranging the written texts we have followed closely the order of the formal sessions at the meeting (Organic Geochemistry in Exploration, Migration of Hydrocarbons, Environmental Organic Geochemistry, DSDP/IPOD Organic Geochemistry, Diagenesis/Catagenesis and Organic Geochemistry of Coals and Kerogens, Biomarkers Miscellaneous) and have attempted to allocate each of the poster papers to the most appropriate session topic.

On behalf of the committee of the European Association of Organic Geochemists we thank the following companies for their generous financial support which ensured the scientific and social success of the meeting: BP Petroleum Development of Norway A/S, Superior Oil Company, Norway, Chevron Petroleum Company of Norway, Texaco Exploration Norway A/S, Esso Exploration and Production Norway Inc., Amoco Norway Oil Co., Statoil, Norske Getty Exploration A/S, Norsk Hydro A/S, American Petrofina Exploration Company of Norway, Saga Petroleum A/S, Union Oil Norge A/S, Deminex (Norge) A/S, Kebo-Bredal A/S, Norway, VG Analytical Ltd., England, Mobil Exploration Norway Inc., Elf Aquitaine Norge A/S, Norske Shell A/S and IKU, Norway.

We are most grateful to the large number of referees who undertook the difficult task of refereeing all the papers and to S. C. Brassell for preparing the Subject Index.

Finally, the Association is indebted to the Lord Mayor and to the City of Bergen for a Civic Reception, to the University for its cooperation in making available appropriate facilities, and especially A. Vetti, University of Bergen and M. Granviken, J. Larsen Hawkes, H. Sandvik and other members of the IKU staff for their generous assistance before and during the meeting.

ASSOCIATED EDITORS

Contents

Environmental Organic Geochemistry

List of Participants

Z. Aizenshtat
The Hebrew University
Energy Research Center
Organic Geochemistry
Jerusalem

Israel

P. Albrecht
Université Louis Pasteur de Strasbourg
Institut de Chimie
1, rue Blaise Pascal
67008 Strasbourg Cedex

France

A. K. Aldridge
Masspec Analytical
Woodchester, Stroud
Gloucestershire GL5 5HT

U.K.

R. Alexander
Western Australian Inst. of Techn.
Department of Chemistry
Hayman Road
Bentley

Western Australia

J. Allan
Esso Resources Canada Ltd.
339 – 50th Ave. S.E.
Calgary
Alberta T2G 2B3

Canada

P. Allan
BP Petroleum Development Ltd.
P.O. Box 3077, Mariero
4001 Stavanger

Norway

A. Altebäumer
KFA-Juelich
Inst. for Petr./Org. Geochem.
P.O. Box 1913
D-517 Juelich 1

Germany

F. J. Altebäumer
KFA-Juelich
Inst. for Petr./Org. Geochem.
P.O. Box 1913
D-517 Juelich 1

Germany

A. Amblès
University of Poitiers
Lab. Chimie XII
40 A^c du Recteur Pineau
86022 Poitiers

France

Chantal Andrié
Université P. et M. Curie
Lab. de Phys. et Chimie Marines
Tour 25
4 Place Jussieu
75230 Paris, Cedex 05

France

Tadashi Asakawa
Japan National Oil Corporation
Fukoku Seimei Bld. 18F
2-2-2 Uchisaiwai-Cho
Chiyoda-ku Tokyo 100

Japan

T. Austad
Rogaland Distriktshøgskole
Studiesenteret Ullandhaug
Postboks 2540
4001 Stavanger

Norway

C. C. Bailey
BP Petroleum Development Ltd.
P.O. Box 3077, Mariero
4001 Stavanger

Norway

D. R. Baker
Rice University
Department of Geology
P.O. Box 1892
Houston
Texas 77001

U.S.A.

E. W. Baker
Florida Atlantic University
College of Science
Organic Geochemistry Group
Boca Raton
Florida 33431

U.S.A.

Jacques Barlier
SNEA(P)
Laboratoire de Geologie
Boussens
31360 Saint Martory

France

Mary A. Barnes
University of British Columbia
Dept. Geological Sciences
6339 Stores Road
Vancouver V6T 2B4

Canada

W. C. Barnes
Univ. British Columbia
Dept. Geological Sciences
6339 Stores Road
Vancouver V6T 2B4

Canada

A. J. G. Barwise
BP Research Centre
Chertsey Road
Sunbury-on-Thames
Middlesex TW16 7LN

U.K.

G. S. Bayliss
Geochem Laboratories Inc.
1143 Brittmore Road
Houston
Texas 77043

U.S.A.

Wang Bensham
Academia Sinica
Geochemistry Institute
P.O. Box 91
Guiyang

China

A. Berge
Statoil
Postboks 300
4001 Stavanger

Norway

D. Birk
Petro Canada
Research Laboratory
P.O. Box 2844
Calgary Alberta T2P 1Y6

Canada

K. K. Bissada
Texaco Inc.
Bellaire Research Labs.
P.O. Box 425
Bellaire
Texas 77401

U.S.A.

M. Bjorøy
IKU – Continental Shelf Institute
P.O. Box 1883
7001 Trondheim

Norway

S. R. Blanco
Tenneco UK Inc.
'84 Lower Mortlake Road
Richmond
Surrey TW9 2JG

U.K.

H. Bockmeulen
BP Research Centre
Exploration Division
Chertsey Road
Sunbury-on-Thames
Middlesex TW16 7LN

U.K.

J. J. Boon
Organic Geochemistry Unit
De Vries van Heijstplantsoen 2
2628 RZ Delft

The Netherlands

J. Boulegue
Université de Paris 7
Lab. de Geochimie des Eaux
2 place Jussieu
75251 Paris Cedex 05

France

B. F. J. Bowler
IKU – Continental Shelf Institute
P.O. Box 1883
7001 Trondheim

Norway

S. C. Brassell
University of Bristol
Organic Geochemistry Unit
Cantock's Close
Bristol BS8 1TS

U.K.

J. Brooks
The British National Oil Corp.
Exploration Department
150 St. Vincent Street
Glasgow G2 5LJ

U.K.

P. W. Brooks
VG Analytical
Tudor Road
Altrincham

U.K.

B. Bue
Norsk Hydro A/S
Oljedivisjonen
Postboks 2594 Solli
Oslo 2

Norway

A. L. Burlingame
University of California
Space Sciences Laboratory
Berkeley
CA 94720

U.S.A.

P. Cailleaux
SNEA(P) Boussens
Laboratoire de Géologie
31360 Saint Martory

France

W. S. de Carvalho
IPT – Cidade Universitária 'ASO'
Paulipetro – Consórcio CESP/IPT
Cx. Postal 7141
São Paulo

Brasil

D. J. Casagrande
Exxon Production Research Company
P.O. Box 2189
Houston
Texas 77001

U.S.A.

F. Cassani
Intevep.
Urb. Sta. Rosa-Cos Teques Edo
Miranda Apartado 76343
Caracas 107

Venezuela

R. Cavaliere
AGIP S.p.A.
Serv. Geologie
20097 S. Donato Milanese
Milano

Italy

O. H. J. Christie
Rogalandsforskning
Postboks 2503, Ullandhaug
4001 Stavanger

Norway

P. A. Comet
University of Bristol
Organic Geochem. Unit
School of Chemistry
Cantock's Close
Bristol BS8 1TS

U.K.

J. Connan
Elf Aquitaine
Centre Micoulau,
Dpt. Labo Geologie
64018 Pau, Cedex

France

B. S. Cooper
Robertson Research Intern. Ltd.
Tyn-Y-Coed
Llanrhos
Llandudno
Gwynedd
North Wales LL30 1SA

U.K.

M. J. Cope
Texaco North Sea Norway A/S
1, Knightsbridge Green
London SW1X 7QJ

U.K.

C. Cornford
British National Oil Corporation
150 St. Vincent St.
Glasgow

U.K.

C. Costa Neto
Federal Univ. of Rio de Janeiro
Inst. of Chemistry
Rio de Janeiro

Brazil

H. C. Cox
Delft University of Technology
Organic Geochem. Unit
de Vries van Heystpt.2
2628 RZ Delft

The Netherlands

P. A. Cranwell
Freshwater Biological Association
The Ferry House, Ambleside
Cumbria LA22 0LP

U.K.

S. Creaney
Esso Resources (Canada) Ltd.
2370 – 4th Av. Sw.
Calgary, Alberta

Canada

A. J. Dahle
Norsk Hydro A/S
Research Centre
3901 Porsgrunn

Norway

D. G. Dalton
BP Petroleum Development Ltd.
P.O. Box 3077, Mariero
4001 Stavanger

Norway

J. W. de Leeuw
Delft University of Technology
Organic Geochemistry Unit
de Vries van Heystpl 2
2628 RZ Delft

The Netherlands

Y. Debyser
Institut Francais du Pétrole
1–4 Av. de Bois Préau
92502 Rueil-Malmaison Ced.

France

G. Demaison
Chevron Overseas Petroleum
575 Market Street
San Francisco
California 94105

U.S.A.

A. G. Douglas
University of Newcastle
Organic Geochemistry Unit
Drummond Building
Newcastle upon Tyne NE1 7RU

U.K.

W. G. Dow
Robertson Research (US) Inc.
16730 Hedgecroft
Houston
Texas 77060

U.S.A.

Drozd
Standard Oil Comp.

B. Durand
Institut Francais du Pétrole
BP 311
1–4 Ave. de Bois Préau
92506 Rueil Malmaison Ced.

France

J. H. Durrie
Norske Getty Exploration A/S
Lars Hillesgt.22
5000 Bergen

Norway

M. Dworatzek
Deutsche Texaco Aktiengese..sch.
Lab. für Erdölgewinnung
D-3101 Wietze

Germany

G. R. Dyrkacz
Argonne National Laboratory
9700 S. Cass Ave.
Argonne, IL 60439

U.S.A.

K. L. H. Edmunds
University of Bristol
Organic Geochemistry Unit
Cantock's Close
Bristol BS8 1TS

U.K.

S. Eggen
Norwegian Petroleum Directorate
Lagårdsveien 80
4000 Stavanger

Norway

G. Eglinton
University of Bristol
Organic Geochemistry Unit
School of Chemistry
Cantock's Close
Bristol BS8 1TS

U.K.

M. Eien
Statoil
Postboks 300
4001 Stavanger

Norway

A. Elvsborg
Saga Petroleum A/S
Postboks 9
1322 Høvik

Norway

J. G. Erdman
Phillips Petr. Co.
Research Center
Room 170PL
Bartlesville
OK 74004

U.S.A.

M. Ewald
University of Bordeaux 1
Lab. de Chimie Physique A
351, Cours de la Libération
33405 Talence Cedex

France

A. Ferguson
Sherwin-Williams Company
549 E 115th Street
Chicago, IL 60628

U.S.A.

E. Finnerud
University of Oslo
Geological Institute
P.B. 1047, Blindern
Oslo 3

Norway

A. W. Forsberg
University of Oslo
Geologisk Institutt
Boks 1063 Blindern
Oslo 3

Norway

S. M. Foster
Staveley Electrotechn. Serv. Ltd.
68 Grosvenor Street
Manchester M1 7EW

U.K.

M. Fowler
University of Newcastle-upon-Tyne
Organic Geochemical Unit
Drummond Building
Newcastle-upon-Tyne

U.K.

J. R. Fox
Union Oil Company of California
Research Centre
P.O. Box 76
Brea
California 92621

U.S.A.

Y. Fujita
Teikoku Oil Co. Ltd.
Technical Research Center
9-23-30 Kita-Karasuyama Setagaya-Ku
Tokyo

Japan

R. B. Gagosian
Woods Hole Oceanographic Inst.
Department of Chemistry
Woods Hole
Massachusetts 02543

U.S.A.

E. M. Galimov
Academy of Science of the USSR
Inst. of Geoch. and Anal. Chem.
Vorobjovskoe Shosse 47a
117334 Moscow

U.S.S.R.

K. Garder
Inst. for Energiteknikk
Postboks 40
2007 Kjeller

Norway

J. L. Gevirtz
Tenneco Oil Co.
E&P
P.O. Box 2511
Houston
Texas 77001

U.S.A.

W. Giger
Swiss Federal Institute for Water
Resources and Water Pollution Con.
CH-8600 Dübendorf

Switzerland

P. H. Given
The Pennsylvania State University
Fuel Science Section
408 Walker Building
University Park
Pennsylvania 16802

U.S.A.

J. C. Goff
BP Canada Ltd.
333 Fifth Av. SW
Calgary
Alberta T2P336

Canada

J. R. Gormly
Kernforschungsanlage Juelich
ICH-5
P.O. Box 1913
5170 Juelich

Fed. Rep. of Germany

E. P. Goulart
Paulipetro – Consórcio CESP/IPT
Avenida Engenheiro, Luiz Carlos
Berrini 1461
CEP 04571 Brooklin Novo
Sao Paulo – SP

Brasil

G. van Graas
Delft University of Technology
Organic Geochemistry Unit
De Vries van Heystplantsoen 2
2620 RZ Delft

The Netherlands

P. J. Grantham
Koninklijke/Shell Expl. en Lab.
Volmerlaan 6
Rijswijk (Z.H.)

The Netherlands

K. de Groot
Shell Canada Ltd.
Calgary Research Centre
Station M
Calgary, Alberta T2B 2H5

Canada

T. Grønneberg
University of Oslo
Kjemisk Institutt
Postboks 1033 Blindern
Oslo 3

Norway

K. Hall
VG Analytical
Tudor Road
Altrincham

U.K.

P.B. Hall
IKU – Continental Shelf Institute
P.O. Box 1883
7001 Trondheim

Norway

D. D. Hampshire
Staveley Electrotech. Serv. Ltd.
68 Grosvenor Street
Manchester M17EW

U.K.

T. Handyside
The Univ. of Newcastle-upon-Tyne
Organic Geochemistry Unit
Drummond Building
Newcastle-upon-Tyne

U.K.

J. M. Hayes
Indiana University
Biogeochemical Labs.
Chemistry Building
Bloomington
Indiana 47405

U.S.A.

C. F. Hoffmann
Univ. of Bristol, School of Chem.
Organic Geochemistry Unit
Cantocks Close
Bristol BS8 1TS

U.K.

A. Hollerbach
Aachen Technical University
RWTH-Aachen
Lochnerstr. 4-20
D-5100 Aachen

Federal Rep. of Germany

B. Horsfield
Conoco
P.O. Box 1267
Ponca City
Oklahoma 74601

U.S.A.

V. J. Howell
Bristol University
Org. Geochem. Unit
Cantocks Close
Bristol

U.K.

J. M. Hunt
Woods Hole Oceanographic Institute
Woods Hole
Massachusetts 02543

U.S.A.

A. C. Ibe
NIOMR
PMB 12729 Victoria Island
Lagos

Nigeria

R. Ikan
Hebrew University
Dep. of Organic Chemistry,
Jerusalem

Israel

J. Jacob
Biochem. Inst. für Umweltcarc
Sieyer Landstrasse 19
D-2070 Ahrensburg/Holst

Fed. Rep. Germany

R. Jacquesy
Faculté du Sciences
Laboratorie de Chimie XII
40 Avenue du Recteru
Pineau 86022 Poitiers

France

F. Jiamo
Academia Sinica
Geochemistry Institute
P.O. Box 91
Guiyang

China

R. B. Johns
University of Melbourne
Dept. of Organic Chemistry
Parksville
Victoria

Australia 3052

M. Jones
The University of Newcastle
Organic Geochemistry Unit
Drummond Building
The University
Newcastle-upon-Tyne

U.K.

R. W. Jones
Chevron Oil Field Research Co.
Exploration Dept.
P.O. Box 446
La Habra
California 90631

U.S.A.

I. R. Kaplan
University of California
Dept. of Earth and Space Sci.
Los Angeles
California

U.S.A.

S. P. Kendall
Newcastle University
Organic Geochemistry Unit
Drummond Building
Newcastle-upon-Tyne

U.K.

G. Klar
INTEVEP, S.A.
Apartado No.76343
Caracas 107

Venezuela

J. Klok
Delft University,
Organic Geochemistry Unit
Vries Van Heystplantsoen 2
2628 RZ Delft

The Netherlands

G. C. Koenig
Esso Exploration & Production U.K.
B1 Water House
Portsmouth Road
Esher, Surrey

U.K.

V. Krsmanović
University of Beograd
Dept. of Chemistry
P.O. Box 550
11001 Belgrade

Yugoslavia

K. A. Kvenvolden
U.S. Geological Survey
M/S 99
345 Middlefield Road
California 94025

U.S.A.

Neil A. Lamb
University of Bristol
Org. Geochem Unit
School of Chemistry, Cantock's Close
Bristol BS8 1TS

U.K.

S. R. Larter
Union Oil Research Center
Brea
CA 92621

U.S.A.

T. Lavold
Lavold Masskonsult
Box 26
S-17521 Järfälla

Sweden

L. Leith
University of Newcastle
Organic Geochemistry Unit
Drummond Building
Newcastle-upon-Tyne NE1 7RU

U.K.

R. Leonard
Amoco Norway Oil Co.
Bergjelandsgata 25
4001 Stavanger

Norway

P. Leplat
Labofina S.A.
Centre de Recherches du Groupe
Petrofina Chaussée de Vilvorde, 100
B-1120 Bruxelles

Belgium

J. W. Letcher
VG – Analytical Ltd.
Tudor Road
Altringham
Cheshire WA14 5RZ

U.K.

D. Leythaeuser
Kernforschungsanlage Juelich GmbH
Inst. für Chemie 5
P.O. Box 1913
D-5170 Juelich
FRG

Germany

G. W. M. Lijmbach
Shell Research
Kon./Shell Expl. en Prod. Lab.
Volmerlaan 6
Rijswijk

The Netherlands

H. Lindgren
Danmarks Geologiske Undersøgelse
Thoravej 31
1350 København

Denmark

A. Linsey
University of Newcastle
Organic Geochemistry Unit
Drummond Building
Newcastle

U.K.

S. P. Lowe
Paleochem Ltd., Unit 14
Paramount Ind. Estate
Sandown Road
Watford WD2 4XA

U.K.

A. S. Mackenzie
Geochemistry Branch
BP Research Centre
Chertsey Road
Sunbury-on-Thames
Middlesex TW16 7LN

U.K.

L. B. Magoon
U.S. Geological Survey
345 Middlefield Road
Menlo Park
California

U.S.A.

O. A. Malm
Statoil
Postboks 300
4001 Stavanger

Norway

P. J. Marriott
University of Bristol
School of Chemistry
Organic Geochemistry Unit
Bristol BS8 1TS

U.K.

L. Mattavelli
Agip SpA
Servizio Sgel
20097 S. Donato
Milanese Milan

Italy

J. R. Maxwell
University of Bristol
Organic Geochemistry Unit
Cantock's Close
Bristol BS8 1TS

U.K.

M. A. Mazurek
University of California
Dep. of Earth and Space Sci.
and Ins. of Geophysics and
Planetry Physics
Los Angeles
California 90024

U.S.A.

J. McEvoy
University of Bristol
Organic Geochemistry Unit
School of Chemistry
Cantock's Close
Bristol BS8 1TS

U.K.

T. Meyer
Rogalandsforskning
P.b. 2503, Ullandhaug
4001 Stavanger

Norway

P. A. Meyers
University of Michigan
Atmospheric and Oceanic Science
Ann Arbor
Michigan 48109

U.S.A.

W. Michaelis
University of Hamburg
Geologisch-Paläont. Inst., Bundesstr. 55
2000 Hamburg 13

W. Germany

G. L. Mille
Faculté des Sciences et Techniques
Centre de Spec. Moléculaire
rue Nenri Poincaré
13397 Marseille Cedex 4

France

N. Mills
IKU – Continental Shelf Institute
P.O. Box 1883
7001 Trondheim

Norway

P. R. Mommessin
Shell Development Company
P.O. Box 481
Houston
Texas 77001

U.S.A.

L. E. Mompart Garcia
Corpoven S.A.
Aparthado de Correds 61373
Exploracion
Caracas

Venezuela

J. C. Monin
Institut Francais du Pétrole
1–4 Av. de Bois Préau
92502 Rueil-Malmaison Ced.

France

F. Monnier
Geological Survey of Canada
Inst. of Sedim. and Petr. Geol.
3303 – 33rd Street N.W.
Calgary
Alberta T2L 2A7

Canada

J. Monrozier
Centre de Pedologie Biologique
B.P. 5
17 rue Notre Dame des Pauvres
54500 Nandoeuvre les Nancy

France

A. Nissenbaum
Weizmann Institute of Science
Rehovot 76100

Israel

W. L. Orr
Mobil Research and Dev. Corp.
Field Research Lab.
P.O. Box 900
Dallas
Texas 75221

U.S.A.

E. Osjord
Statoil
Postboks 300
4001 Stavanger

Norway

J. L. Oudin
Compagnie Francaise des Pétroles
114 cours Marechal Gallieni
33404 Talence Cedex

France

P. J. D. Park
BP Research Centre
Chertsey Road
Sunbury on Thames
Middlesex

U.K.

R. Pelet
Institut Francais du Pétrole
1–4 Av. de Bois Préau
92502 Rueil-Malmaison Ced.

France

P. A. Pfendt
University of Beograd
Dept. of Chemistry
Faculty of Sciences
P.O. Box 550
Beograd

Yugoslavia

J. L. Pittion
Total C.F.P.
114 course Gallieni
33404 Talence

France

J. Posthuma
Shell International Research
Kon./Shell Expl. en Prod. Lab.
Volmerlaan 6
Rijswijk

The Netherlands

T. G. Powell
Geological Survey of Canada
Inst. of Sed./Petroleum Geology
3303–33rd St. NW
Calgary
Alberta T2L 2A7

Canada

I. Price
BP Petroleum Development Ltd.
P.O. Box 3077, Mariero
4001 Stavanger

Norway

J. M. E. Quirke
Florida Int. Univ.
College of Arts & Sciences
Dept. of Physical Sciences
Tamiami Trial
Miami
Florida 33199

U.S.A.

M. Radke
KFA-Juelich
Inst. for Petr. and Org. Geoch.
P.O. Box 1913
D-5170 Juelich

Fed. Rep. of Germany

F. Radler de Aquino Neto
Universidade Federal de Rio de Janiero
Instituto de Quimica
Centro de Technologia Bl.A G11
Rio de Janeiro RJ 21914

Brazil

R. H. Reitsema
Marathon Oil Company
P.O. Box 269
Littleton
Colorado 80160

U.S.A.

D. Repeta
Woods Hole Oceanogr. Inst.
Department of Chemistry
Woods Hole
Massachussetts 02543

U.S.A.

T. Ricchiuto
AGIP S.P.A. Servizio SGEL
20097 San Donato Milanese
Milano

Italy

W. Riemer
KFA-Juelich
Inst. for Petr. and Org. Geoch.
P.O. Box 1913
D-5170 Juelich

Fed. Rep. of Germany

G. Rinaldi
Exxon Production Research Co.
P.O. Box 2189
Houston
Texas 77001

U.S.A.

E. Roaldset
Norsk Hydro A/S
Research Center
Kjørbokollen
1301 Sandvika

Norway

R. Rodrigues
Petroleo Brasileiro S.A.
PETROBAS
77 South Audley Street
2nd floor
London W1Y 5TA

U.K.

B. G. Rohrback
Cities Service Company,
P.O. Box 642
Tulsa
Oklahoma

U.S.A.

S. J. Rowland
Bristol University
Organic Geochemistry Unit
Bristol

U.K.

J. Rubinsztain
Hebrew University
Dept. of Organic Chemistry
Lab. of Nat. prod. and Energy
Jerusalem

Israel

J. Rullkötter
KFA-Juelich
Inst. for Petr./Org. Geochem.
P.O. Box 1913
D-5170 Juelich

Germany

G. Saenz
AASA
Geochemistry Dept.
Bruselas 10 3ER
Piso, 6, DF 06600

Mexico

C. Sajgó
Univ. of Bristol
School of Chemistry
Organic Geochemistry Unit
Cantock's Close
Bristol BS8 1TS

U.K.

A. Saliot
Université Pierre et Marie Curie
Lab. de Physique et Chimie
4 place Jussieu
75230 Paris Cedex 05

France

R. Sassen
Getty Oil Company
Houston
Texas

U.S.A.

M. J. Sauer
Geochem Laboratories (UK) Ltd.
The Nutshell
Bretton Lane
Bretton
Chester

U.K.

R. G. Schaefer
KFA-Juelich GmbH
Inst. for Petr./Org. Geochem.
P.O. Box 1913
D-5170 Juelich

Germany

P. A. Schenck
Delft University of Technology
Department of Chemistry
Vries v. Heystpl.2
2628 RZ Delft

The Netherlands

E. J. Schiener
DEMINEX GmbH
P.O.B. 100944
D-4300 Essen 1

Fed. Rep. Germany

J. M. Schmitter
Ecole Polytechnique
Lab. de Chim. Anal. Physique
91128 Palaiseau
Cedex

France

M. Schoell
Bundesanst. Geowissenschaften/Roh.
Stilleweg 2
Hannover

Germany

L. Schou
IKU – Continental Shelf Institute
P.B. 1883
7001 Trondheim

Norway

W. K. Seifert
Chevron Oil Field Research Company
P.O. Box 1627
Richmond
California 94802

U.S.A.

J. Shanchun
Academia Sinica
Geochemistry Institute
P.O. Box 91
Guiyang

China

F. Shanfa
Academia Sinica
Geochemistry Institute
P.O. Box 91
Guiyang

China

B. R. T. Simoneit
Oregon State University
School of Oceanography
Corvallis, OR 97331

U.S.A.

F. E. Skaar
Norsk Hydro A/S
Oljedivisjonen
Postboks 2594 Solli
Oslo 2

Norway

D. J. Smith
School of Chemistry
Organic Geochemistry Unit
Cantock's Close
Bristol BS8 1TS

U.K.

P. Smith
Univ. of Newcastle
Organic Geochemistry Unit
Drummond Building
Newcastle

U.K.

L. Snowdon
Geological Survey of Canada
Inst. of sedim. and petr. geol.
3303 – 33 St. N.W.
Calgary
Alberta T2L 2A7

Canada

H. Solli
IKU – Continental Shelf Institute
P.O. Box 1883
7001 Trondheim

Norway

G. C. Speers
BP Research Centre
Chertsey Road
Sunbury on Thames
Middlesex

U.K.

A. M. Spencer
BP Petroleum Development Ltd.
P.O. Box 3077, Mariero
4001 Stavanger

Norway

B. Spiro
Dept. of Geology
The Hebrew University
Jerusalem

Israel

O. P. Strausz
University of Alberta
Department of Chemistry
Edmonton
Alberta T6G 2G2

Canada

K. R. Sundberg
Phillips Petroleum Company
Phillips Research Center
Bartlesville
Oklahoma 74004

U.S.A.

B. Sundby
Université du Québec à Rimouski
Dépt. d'Océanographie
Rimouski
Québec G5L 3A1

Canada

K. Taguchi
Tohoku University
Inst. of Mineralogy, Petrology
Faculty of Science
Sendai 980

Japan

N. Takeda
Japan Petr. Exploration Co. Ltd
Technical Laboratory
3-5-5 Midorigadka
Hamura
Tokyo

Japan

J. Taylor
Scottish Marine Biological Ass.
Dunstaffnage Marine Res. Lab.
P.O. Box 3
Oban, Argyll PA34 4AD
Scotland

U.K.

S. Taylor
BP Research
Exploration Div.
Chertsey Rd.
Sunbury-on-Thames
Middlesex TW16 7LN

U.K.

M. Teschner
Bundesanst. für Geo. und Rohstoffe
Louise-Schröder Str. 41,
P,O, Box 510153
D-3000 Hannover 61

Germany

J. Thiede
University of Oslo
Department of Geology
P.O. Box 1047, Blindern
Oslo 3

Norway

E. Thomsen
The Geological Survey of Greenland
Øster Voldgade 10
DK-1350 Copenhagen

Denmark

T. O. Throndsen
Saga Petroleum A/S
P.O. Box 550
1301 Sandvika

Norway

B. Tissot
Institut Francais du Petrole
Division Geologie
B.P. 311
Rueil Malmaison
Cedex 92506

France

K. Tjessem
Norsk Hydro A/S
Research Center
Kjørbokollen
1301 Sandvika

Norway

D. J. Toth
Gulf Research & Development Co.
P.O. Drawer 2038
Pittsburgh
PA 15230

U.S.A.

J. Tóth
Hungarian Academy of Science
Petr. Engineering Research Lab
P.O. Box 2
H-3515 Miskolc-Egyetemváros

Hungary

M. Trees
BP Petroleum Development Ltd
P.O. Box 3077, Mariero
4001 Stavanger

Norway

J. G. Trichet
Université d'Orléans
Lab. de Géologie Appliquée
45046 Orleans Cédex

France

J. A. Triguis
Paulipetro – Consórcio CESP/IPT
IPT – Div. Petróleo
Cidade Universitária
Sao Paulo CEP 05508

Brasil

P. Ungerer
Institut Francais du Pétrole
1–4 Av. de Bois Préau
92502 Rueil-Malmaison Ced.

France

E. S. van Vleet
University of South Florida
Dept. of Marine Science
830 First Street South
St. Petersburg
Florida 33701

U.S.A.

M. Vandenbroucke
Institut Frnacais du Petrole
B.P. 311
92506 Rueil Malmaison

France

I. Veto
Geological Survey of Hungary
Nepstadion Ut. 14
1142 Budapest

Hungary

O. Vikane
Rogaland Distriktshøgskole
Studiesenteret Ullandhaug
P.B. 2540, Ullandhaug
4001 Stavanger

Norway

D. Vitorović
University of Beograd
Inst. of Chemistry, Techn.
and Metallurgy
P.O. Box 550
11001 Beograd

Yugoslavia

F. W. Vlierboom
Occidental Exploration
Production Company
5000 Stockdale Highway
Bakersfield
California 93309

U.K.

J. K. Volkman
Woods Hole Oceanographic Inst.
Department of Chemistry
Woods Hole
Massachusetts 02543

U.S.A.

S. G. Wakeham
Woods Hole Oceanographic Inst.
Department of Chemistry
Woods Hole
Massachusetts 02543

U.S.A.

A. M. K. Wardroper
The Univ. of Bristol
School of Chemistry
Cantock's Close
Bristol BS8 1TS

U.K.

H. Wehner
Bundesanst. für Geo. und Rohstoffe
D-3000 Hannover 51

Germany

D. I. Welch
The Univ. of Newcastle
Organic Geochemistry Unit
Drummond Bldg.
Newcastle-upon-Tyne

U.K.

D. H. Welte
KFA-Juelich
Inst. for Petr. and
Org. Geoch.
P.O. Box 1913
D-5170 Juelich

Fed. Rep. of Germany

B. G. Williams
BP Petroleum Development Ltd.
P.O. Box 3077, Mariero
4001 Stavanger

Norway

P. F. V. Williams
University of Newcastle
Organic Geochemistry Unit
Department of Geology
Drummond Building
Newcastle NE1 7RU

U.K.

R. E. Winans
Argonne National Laboratory
9700 S. Cass. Ave.
Bldg. 200
Argonne, IL 60439

U.S.A.

J. C. Winters
Amoco Production Company
Research Department
P.O. Box 591
Tulsa
Oklahoma 74102

U.S.A.

G. Woodhouse
Western Australian Inst. of Techn.
Dept. of Chemistry
Kent Street
South Bentley 6102

Australia

P. A. Wrang
Grønlands Geologiske Undersøgelse
Øster Voldgade 10
1350 København

Denmark

M. P. Wyglendacz
Exploration Logging U.K.
9 Horton Road
Datchet, Slough
Buckinghamshire

U.K.

J. Zumberge
Cities Service Co.
ERG Research Lab.
4500 S. 129th E. Ave.
Box 3908 Tulsa
OK 74102

Organic Geochemistry
in Exploration

Advances in Organic Geochemistry 1981, pp. 3–6
© *John Wiley & Sons Limited, 1983*

State of the Art of Organic Geochemistry in Petroleum Exploration

J. C. Winters

Amoco Production Company, Research Center, PO Box 591, Tulsa, Oklahoma 74102, USA

INTRODUCTION

Most keynote addresses usually contain very little of lasting importance because they review the past and then add a few guesses about the future. I will try not to disturb that tradition. However, in addition to giving this meeting time to get started, I will also try to leave you with a few thoughts about organic geochemistry. I hope that the geochemists in the audience will forgive me if I talk about things they already know, but perhaps I may make a few personal observations about the future of petroleum geochemistry that will give them something to debate later this week.

It is difficult to define organic geochemistry. Part of the reason is that most of the people who work in the field received their academic training in so many different disciplines; for example, geology, petrology, paleontology, organic and physical chemistry, atmospheric and space science, biology and microbiology, oceanography, engineering, and environmental sciences. Practical applications of organic geochemistry are at least as broad but, for this meeting, we must restrict our discussions to the geochemistry of petroleum exploration. Petroleum geochemistry is the study of the factors affecting the thermochemical reactions that occur during conversion of kerogen to petroleum in the natural environment.

HISTORY

I doubt if anyone knows exactly when organic geochemistry began. Early explorers must have been among the first geochemists when they speculated on the origin of oil that they saw bubbling from the earth. The promoters of the first commercial oil well in the United States over a hundred years ago sent samples of the oil for analysis to Professor Silliman at Yale University. His data and optimistic evaluation reports added to earlier speculation about the origin of the petro-oleum or rock oil. Drillers and investors began to feel that if they understood how oil is formed, they could be more successful in their search for oil.

Ideas about the origin of petroleum have gone through many fasionable theories with similar theories repeating about once per generation. The present ideas that, thanks to modern analytical chemistry, must surely be much closer to the truth, are not basically different from some of the earliest theories. Nearly sixty years ago, the American Petroleum Institute started the historical API Research Project 6 to determine the composition of Ponco City Crude Oil. Their efforts lead to additional research projects in industry. I became associated with such an effort in 1950.

However, most literature references attribute the real beginning of modern organic geochemistry to Alfred Treibs who, in Germany in 1934–1936, isolated and elucidated the structure of chlorophyll-like, metal-containing prophyrins in petroleum. This provided the link between photosynthetic organisms and organic material found in sedimentary deposits in the earth and petroleum. As Chairman of the Organic Geochemistry Division of the Geochemical Society, I will again this year recognize this landmark discovery by presenting the Alfred Treibs award medal to an outstanding organic geochemist. It may interest this audience that, to date, all announced recipients of the award are either citizens of Europe or European-trained. Last year's winner of the Alfred Treibs award was Dr Bernard Tissot of the Institute Française du Petrole.

For much of its early history, organic geochemistry was absorbed in using increasingly sophisticated analytical methods and instruments to analyze the major components in the tens of thousands of compounds present in crude oil. More recently, attention has turned to the much more complicated organic mass that is the source from which petroleum is generated. This insoluble organic matter in sediments is known as kerogen.

Crude oil, and its precursor, kerogen, represent very different levels of difficulty when it comes to both analyzing and interpreting the analyses in a way that will be useful to oil exploration. If everything in the scientific world happened in a logical sequence, we would have first studied kerogen. After that, we would have studied the reaction product, crude oil. However, it did not happen in this way.

TYPES OF DATA

Most of the old and new analytical methods work best on volatile liquids and poorest, or not at all, on complex solids. For this reason, oils were the first to be studied. Consequently, the oils are the source of most of the information in our data banks. The early methods measured properties such as density, pour point, viscosity, sulfur and distillation range. These are still used today, because there have been generations of experience in interpreting what these properties reveal about the source of crude oil and its maturation level and later environmental history. This led to an expanded list of tests that was, until recently, the standard menu from which petroleum geochemists could select data to make their interpretations.

For the oils, this list usually includes the type of properties the USBM and the IP have used for years viz:

> API gravity;
> Pour point;
> Percent sulfur;
> Distillation.

In addition, petroleum exploration companies usually measured:
> Percent paraffins, aromatics, polar compounds;
> Distribution of *n*-paraffins in mid-boiling ranges;
> Composition of light ends;
> Gas chromatographic profile.

Some also used:

> Carbon, hydrogen and sulfur isotope ratios;
> Optical rotation;
> Infrared spectra of aromatics;
> Isoprenoid profiles.

The analyses near the top of the list have been used to make geochemical correlations for many years. They require relatively simple apparatus, and they are reproducible. Some toward the bottom of the list are more dependent upon technique and a higher level of expertise, but they are within the boundaries of proven technology. The later methods tend to measure compounds that are fragments from thermochemical reactions of kerogen and, therefore, they are thought to reflect more directly the composition of the kerogen from which the oil was formed.

We believed that we understood what these results were indicating. They provided a common basis for discussion and, more importantly, for making decisions. Properly applied, cross correlation of these properties can tell whether two oils are from the same or different type of source rock; whether the source is relatively more marine or non-marine; the approximate stage of thermal maturity; whether there has been bacterial degradation in the reservoir; perhaps indicate whether there has been physical separation in the reservoir; and many other interpretations. Every company has its favorite combination of geochemical properties that it prefers because they believe their set works better than those used by their competitors.

At the present time, several organizations are trying to develop a new generation of instruments and to interpret the results in a way that will be useful for exploration. Any discussion of these would necessarily include topics such as Fourier transform infrared spectroscopy, nuclear magnetic resonance spectroscopy of solids and combined pyrolysis/capillary gas chromatography/computer-

assisted mass spectroscopy. These new techniques are on the leading edge of modern science. They are offering solutions to problems that only recently seemed as though they might never yield a solution. However, they may also be creating problems that have little to do with science. I would like to delay further discussion of this until the end of my talk in order to complete discussion of the present generation of methods.

GEOCHEMISTRY APPLIED TO EXPLORATION

It is difficult to compile a significant record of practical geochemical applications to exploration. No one likes to talk about his failures and if there has been a successful application most organizations are reluctant to discuss it in the belief that they possess some competitive advantage over other companies. However, I would like to illustrate the point that it does not always require expensive sophisticated instruments and a large staff to derive some very helpful clues for exploration. A few relatively simple data in the hands of a skilled and dedicated geologist who knows how to use such facts can provide valuable exploratory guidance. I will try to illustrate this point with a simplified version of how conventional petroleum geochemistry assisted Amoco Europe in defining the main target for exploration in the North Sea.

Geochemical subsidence profiles showed that there must be major oil-generating source beds at a pre-Tertiary level to account for the amount of oil discovered in Ekofisk in 1969. Geochemical results of value to North Sea exploration only began to be obtained in 1970, at the time that exploration interests had turned to Central Tertiary Basin oil, though the first evaluations concerned the Southern English Zechstein Basin.

The first part of the picture came from geochemical correlations that showed that several of the gas and gas condensates from the Lower Permian Rotliegendes were related to a common source, probably non-marine, and inferred that it is Upper Carboniferous (Pennsylvanian). Some of the Upper Permian Zechstein oils and condensates came from different sources.

Later that year, the Amoco discovery at Montrose Field was geochemically shown to be unrelated to southern North Sea oil and condensates. The Montrose oil seemed to be more geochemically related to oils from the Norwegian Sector of the Central Tertiary Basin. However, during this period, major contamination from diesel oil added to the drilling mud prevented correlation of oil to the source rock. Obtaining uncontaminated samples of Tertiary and older source rocks became a crucial problem by the end of 1970.

Shortly after that, part of the problem was overcome with sidewall coring in the Tertiary section. Geochemical measurements on these cores conclusively placed the peak hydrocarbon generation zone at about 9000 ft, but oil-generating kerogen was not found in the Tertiary Section.

Shales were obtained from onshore outcrops that showed the Jurassic to be a likely oil source if it were located deeper in the basin. Then shales from the Upper

Jurassic in new Amoco wells in the Norwegian sector of the Central Tertiary Basin were geochemically judged to be good oil sources but diesel fuel contamination still prevented correlation until uncontaminated shale samples were obtained from a discovery well in the southern part of the Norwegian Sector. Extracts of these Jurassic source rocks provided excellent geochemical correlation with the produced oil. This geochemical information clearly defined the target for integrated geological, geochemical and geophysical exploration as those areas incorporating organic-rich Kimmeridgian shales buried sufficiently deep to have reached peak generation and expulsion.

Remember that the period covered by this chronological log of events was 1970 to early 1971. This limits the type of oil and kerogen data to that obtainable from relatively simple, well-established traditional analyses that became the standard menu of techniques used by all oil companies. These analyses eventually were supplied by all commercial geochemical service companies at a reasonable price. Even though these simple geochemical parameters have been readily available to everyone for over a decade, there still is little information available as to how much reliance has been placed on them by various organizations.

STATE OF THE ART

There may very well be differences in the value of geochemistry to exploration programs among different companies. However, once the interpretation techniques became fairly well established in the industry, any advantage enjoyed by one company does not depend so much on a unique method or magical combination of methods. It depends more upon the degree of talent and experience and confidence of those who interpret and apply the results to actual exploration. However, geochemists have not been uniformly successful in obtaining appreciation of their exploration management for what geochemistry can and cannot do for them. While the quality of most geochemical interpretations and recommendations may have been rather good, the confidence placed in them, and consequently the use of geochemistry, has been much more erratic.

What then is the state of the art of petroleum geochemistry? The scientific basis of organic and petroleum geochemistry is very good indeed. It is the utilization of organic geochemistry in petroleum exploration that is not in a uniformly healthy condition. A dichotomy exists where some exploration organizations do not believe geochemistry can be used for exploration, others use it as a secondary source of information, others use it to very profitable advantage, while some are racing ahead with a whole new generation of sophisticated and expensive geochemical research that they believe will yield a high return.

PROBLEM AREAS

How did an industry that is to much alike in other respects arrive at this situation? Among the various approaches used today to evaluate exploration prospects, organic geochemistry probably stands alone as an academic subject that is not required or even available to apply to a degree in geology. In many universities where organic geochemistry is taught, it often presents a naiive picture of petroleum geochemistry and is lacking in examples of practical application. Fortunately, there are universities where graduate students may receive an outstanding education in the fundamentals of organic geochemistry and do excellent research in the field. However, the number of graduates from these institutions is small compared with the needs of industry.

Within the industry, there are also exceptions to the rule that geologists lack sufficient working knowledge or interest in organic chemistry and biochemistry and chemists generally lack any useful knowledge of geology. Most petroleum geochemists are industry-retrained people who see the need to bridge this discipline gap. But once they bridge this gap, they must then persuade their management to bridge the same gap. Where petroleum geochemistry is effectively applied today, you can usually find that it is due to a single dedicated individual who is a very talented evangelist, in addition to his scientific talent. He has made it part of his profession to sell his management on incorporating geochemistry into the scheme of petroleum exploration.

Because the successful application of geochemistry frequently depends upon the abilities of one or a few special individuals, we should expect the highly varied pattern of application that we find in the industry.

FUTURE

Where are we likely to go from here? I believe there will be a growing disparity among petroleum exploration organizations in their use of geochemistry. There is an explosive proliferation of very sophisticated, very expensive, large team research efforts that rely on advanced physical instruments and data handling systems. A select few industry, government, and academically based research teams are striving for a new level of unified understanding of the occurrence of organic matter in the geological environment and the thermochemical and biological transformations of this material at depth in the earth: in other words, petroleum geochemistry.

Why will there be only a select few who will do this work? Because the number of people that are competent to do this work is limited and the programs are expensive by any measure, and the number of organizations willing to bring together the proper people, facilities and financing is limited. They are likely to be those industry groups that have a history of successful application of geochemistry or government academic combines that have a very high incentive to catch up with or surpass industry efforts.

Should this be happening today? Should some organizations be racing ahead to new, higher levels of technology while others are still trying to decide whether they should even try the simplest geochemical approaches to exploration? I suspect that this is exactly what will happen for the next decade. By then we may have some clues as to whether the science and technology has outpaced the ability of the industry and government decision makers to assimilate this new technology. We will also know whether they will be willing to make important exploration decisions on an equal basis among geochemistry, geophysics, structural geology, stratigraphy, and others. Unless that happy situation can be achieved, the efforts would better be turned toward improving our ability to apply the more limited knowledge that we have today.

This has been an important opportunity to talk with this audience about what has happened in petroleum geochemistry during the last generation. Some commercial exploration organizations have used modern geochemistry. They found that it can significantly reduce the risk of failure by indicating where occurrences of petroleum are unlikely, by indicating where the probability of success is much higher, and whether it is likely to be mainly oil or gas. Some countries have supported a central research effort in geochemistry for the general good of the industry. A few examples are the Institut Française du Petrole, the United States Geological Survey, several institutes in Germany and your own Continental Shelf Institute in Trondheim. What will happen to petroleum geochemistry is in the hands of the people in this audience. I am talking to the exploration geologists and the management people. The costs of exploration are so high that I do not see how you can avoid utilizing every source of help that you can get. I believe the present record of petroleum geochemistry is a good one. Whether the exciting new generation of geochemical information will improve our exploration record will be up to you and what approach you choose to use. May you choose wisely.

Advances in Organic Geochemistry 1981, pp. 7–15
© *John Wiley & Sons Limited, 1983*

Petroleum Generation in Mesozoic Sediments of the Moray Firth Basin, British North Sea Area

K. K. Bissada

Bellaire Research Laboratories, Texaco Inc., Bellaire, P.O. Box 425, Texas 77401, USA

Geochemical data for the Lower Cretaceous, Upper Jurassic and Middle Jurassic rocks from the British sector of the North Sea provided insights into the origin of oil in the Moray Firth Basin. The Jurassic units were found to be the richest potential generative sequences in the area. Hydrogen-rich, oil-prone kerogens are present in the Kimmeridgian Shale and in pre-Kimmeridgian Upper Jurassic shales, especially in the northwest part of the area. Relative abundance of this type of kerogen decreases from northwest to southeast. In contrast, the Lower Cretaceous sediments are characterized, generally, by low organic carbon contents and by hydrogen-poor, gas-prone kerogens and coals. Oil-to-oil and oil-to-rock correlations, together with the geochemical observations on the Mesozoic rocks, indicate that the oils from Blocks 14 and 15 probably had their origin in Jurassic source beds, with the Kimmeridgian Shale being the primary candidate. Minor differences in wax contents of the crudes reflect the regional variation in kerogen types displayed by the Kimmeridgian source rocks. Thermal maturation data suggest that the Jurassic attains optimum maturity for effective oil generation and release below a depth of about 10 000 feet. A significant correlation exists between known occurrences of oil in the Moray Firth area and the distribution of thermally mature Jurassic source rocks. Time/temperature considerations allowed the reconstruction of the maturation history of the Mesozoic Sequence in this area. This reconstruction suggests that expulsion of oil from the Kimmeridgian shale may have started some forty-five million years ago and is probably proceeding vigorously at the present time.

INTRODUCTION

The occurrence of petroleum in Tertiary and Mesozoic reservoirs in the British sector of the North Sea, and the geologic and geometric relationships of these hydrocarbon accumulations to the organic-rich Kimmeridgian Shale, evoke important questions concerning provenance, generation, and the timing of hydrocarbon migration and entrapment. To investigate these questions, a geochemical study was undertaken utilizing data from oil and rock samples from several wells in Blocks 14 and 15 of the British North Sea (Fig. 1). The wells are located in a northwest–southeast trending area extending a distance of about 100 km. The area lies within the eastern Moray Firth Basin in the northern North Sea where numerous oil fields have been discovered. An excellent example of such an accumulation is found at Piper Field (Fig. 2) which is estimated to contain over 1.5 billion barrels of 36° API gravity, low-sulfur oil (Williams *et al.*, 1975). Upper Jurassic Oxfordian/Kimmeridgian marine sandstones constitute the major reservoir facies at Piper and adjacent fields. The sandstones grade upward into siltstones and organic-rich black shales of Kimmeridgian age. These are overlain successively by Lower Cretaceous Barremian shales, then Albian/Aptian shales and marls.

Specifically, the study was undertaken to: (1) establish the relationships among the crude oils within the study area; (2) assess the quality and distribution of potential source rocks within the Mesozoic section in the area; (3) determine where and under what circumstances potential source beds have undergone adequate maturation for effective hydrocarbon generation; (4) identify the effective source or sources of the associated petroleum acccumulations; and (5) determine the probable timing of petroleum expulsion from the source rocks in the Moray Firth Basin.

Samples for the study included six crude oils from Cretaceous and Jurassic reservoirs penetrated by five wells and over two hundred and fifty rock samples from thirteen wells. The rock samples represented the Lower Cretaceous marls and shales, the Kimmeridgian Shale, the Lower Kimmeridgian/Oxfordian shales, and the Middle Jurassic non-marine lignitic shales and siltstones. The relative depths of the sampled intervals in most of these wells are illustrated in Fig. 3. Sample coverage is incomplete in some wells for the Lower Cretaceous and Middle Jurassic units.

ANALYTICAL PROCEDURES

Aliquots of the crude oils were analyzed by thermovaporization and gas chromatography for their C_4–C_7 isomer

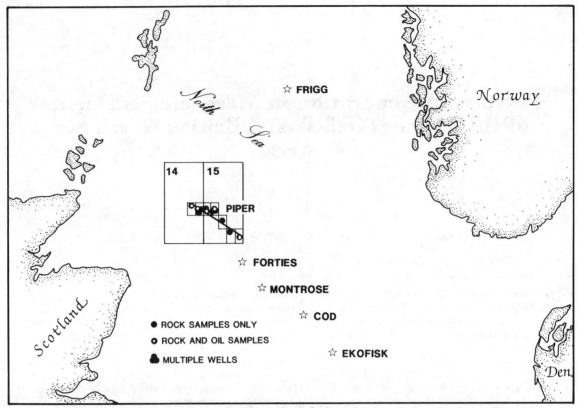

Fig. 1. Geographic setting of the Moray Firth Basin and index of oil and rock samples.

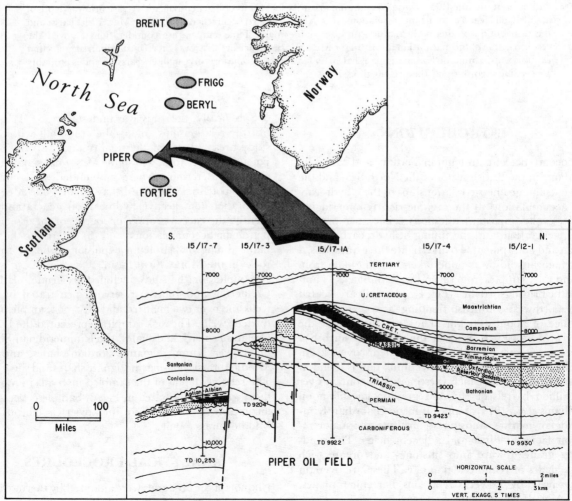

Fig. 2. North .South structural cross section of Piper Oil Field (after Williams *et al.*, 1965).

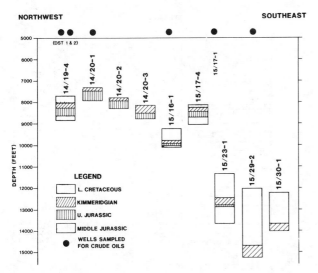

Fig. 3. Relative depths of intervals sampled for organic carbon analysis and visual assessment of kerogen. Solid black circles indicate oil sampling sites.

distribution. The $C_{15}+$ constituents of similar aliquots were fractionated by deasphalteneing and liquid chromatography into saturate hydrocarbons, aromatic hydrocarbons, resins and asphaltenes. The saturate fractions were analyzed by gas chromatography for their n-paraffin distributions. The saturate and aromatic fractions were analyzed further by mass spectrometry for their stable carbon isotopic compositions.

The rock samples used in the study consisted of ditch cuttings of mixed lithologies. Samples were washed and lithlogically upgraded by hand-picking. Analyses were performed on shale lithologies only. All rock samples were analyzed first for total organic content, subsequent to carbonate removal, using the standard Leco method. Selected samples were examined further for kerogen characterization. The kerogen was isolated from the rock matrix by the HCl/HF acid digestion method of McIver (1967). Isolated kerogen was examined microscopically to determine kerogen type and degree of thermal maturity. Numerous kerogen isolates were analyzed chemically to determine their elemental compositions. Some rock samples were analyzed for bitumen content and composition using soxhlet extraction and liquid chromatography. The extractable $C_{15}+$ saturate hydrocarbon fractions of these samples were analyzed by gas chromatography to determine their n-paraffin distributions.

RESULTS AND DISCUSSION

Crude oil characterization

The analytical data pertaining to the crude oils will be discussed first in order to determine whether there are any significant differences which might suggest multiple, rather than common, source beds. Analyses of the crude oils indicate that, with only minor differences, the six oils appear sufficiently similar in molecular composition to suggest that they may have been sourced from the same or similar source beds.

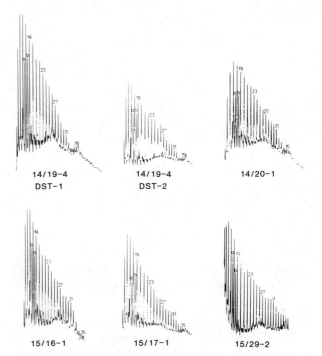

Fig. 4. Gas chromatograms of $C_{15}+$ saturate hydrocarbons isolated from six crude oils from the Moray Firth Basin.

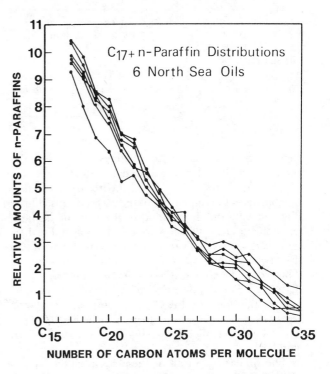

Fig. 5. n-Paraffin distribution patterns of crude oils from the Moray Firth Basin.

The similarities are manifested in the character of the $C_{15}+$ saturate hydrocarbon chromatograms of Fig. 4, which are typified by the presence of a slight sterane–terpane hump. The six crudes all show unusually high paraffin:naphthene ratios. The n-paraffin distribution patterns displayed in Fig. 5 are also quite similar, being characterized by long-chain n-paraffins extending to at least C_{35}. Waxes (defined here as n-paraffins with chain lengths greater than C_{22}) are quantitatively significant,

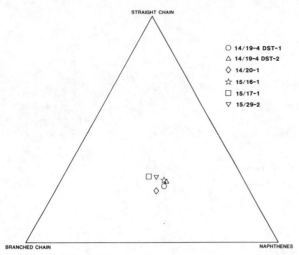

Fig. 6. Distribution of C_7 straight-chain, branched chain and cyclic (non-aromatic) compounds in the Moray Firth crudes.

Table 1

Stable carbon isotopic composition of saturate and aromatic fractions of selected North Sea oils

Crude oil	Carbon isotope composition ($\delta^{13}C$, ‰)	
	Saturate hydrocarbons	Aromatic hydrocarbons
14/19-4 (DST-2)	−29.6	−29.0
14/20-1	−29.0	−28.4
15/16-1	−29.6	−28.7
15/17-1	−29.5	−28.8

a $\delta^{13}C$ relative to the PDB-standard.

suggesting a contribution from higher-plant material to the total oil (Powell and McKirdy, 1975).

Detailed analysis of the C_4–C_7 hydrocarbons further demonstrates the similarities of the six crude oils. This is illustrated by the distribution of the heptane isomers, excluding toluene, which is presented in Fig. 6. Furthermore, the saturate and aromatic fractions of the oils also display very similar stable carbon isotopic compositions. These data for four of the crudes are summarized in Table 1. The total range of variation in isotopic composition for both the C_{15}+ saturate and aromatic fractions is not considered to be geochemically significant, being only slightly over 0.5‰ (relative to the PDB standard).

The similarities in all of these compositional parameters suggest that all of the crudes examined in this study were derived from similar types of organic matter, deposited in comparable environments. It is, therefore, possible that they have been derived from the same source beds.

Organic enrichment and hydrocarbon generation potential of the mesozoic section

Total organic carbon content of rocks can provide an approximation of the rock's potential to generate hy-

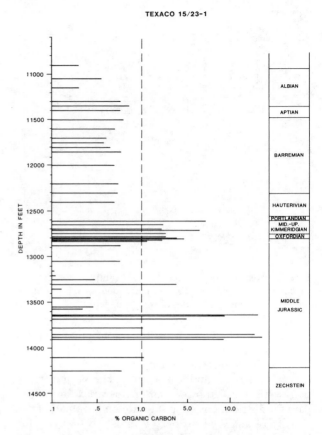

Fig. 7. Example of organic carbon content variation in the Mesozoic section, Texaco No. 15/23-1, British North Sea.

drocarbons upon adequate thermal maturation. The organic carbon data are of interest here because they suggest significant variations in organic enrichment among the sampled units. Figure 7 illustrates this variation for a typical section in Block 15. Average organic carbon contents (calculated excluding coals and quantitatively insignificant shale lithologies) are summarized in Table 2 and Fig. 8. These data indicate that organic enrichment within the sampled units is areally variable, but that no regional trends are discernible. All the examined Mesozoic units display average to above-average organic enrichment relative to the world-wide distribution of organic matter in sedimentary rocks (Bissada, 1981).

The Lower Cretaceous shales and marls are characterized by organic carbon contents averaging about 1.0%. This is interpreted to signify only fair petroleum-sourcing potential. The Kimmeridgian, pre-Kimmeridgian Upper Jurassic, and the Middle Jurassic sediments are characterized by organic carbon contents which average over 2.0% by weight. This is interpreted to signify a very good potential for hydrocarbon generation, provided the kerogen is of the hydrogen-rich variety.

Distribution of kerogen types

The total amount of hydrocarbons that can be generated and the relative proportion of oil and gas depends on the

Table 2
Average organic carbon contents for units penetrated and sampled in the British North Sea wells

Unit	NORTHWEST								SOUTHEAST
	Average for unit	14/19-4	14/20-1	14/20-2	14/20-3	15/16-1	15/17-4	15/23-1	15/29-2	15/30-1
Lower Cretaceous	1.0	0.6	n.d.[a]	n.d.	n.d.	1.4	1.1	0.9	1.1	0.9
Kimmeridgian shale	2.2	2.7	3.7	1.1	2.2	1.6	3.8	1.9	1.6	1.0
Upper Jurassic	3.3	8.8	3.7	1.2	1.5	1.4	4.7	1.8	n.d.	n.d.
Middle Jurassic	2.0	2.3	n.d.	n.d.	n.d.	1.4	2.7	1.4	n.d.	n.d.

[a]n.d. — No Data.

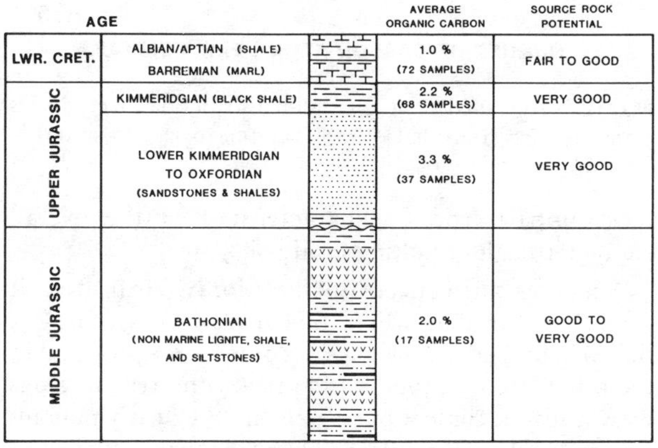

Fig. 8. Average organic carbon contents in Mesozoic rocks, Moray Firth Basin.

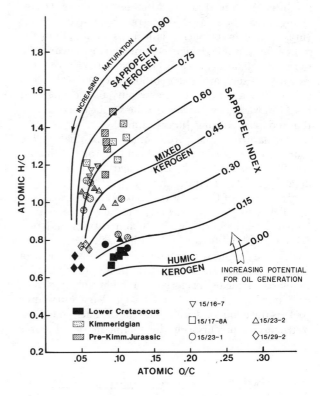

Fig. 9. Elemental composition of kerogen from Mesozoic rocks of the Moray Firth Basin. Increasing values of the 'Sapropel Index' signify an increasing potential for oil generation.

composition of the parent kerogen in a petroleum source bed (Staplin, 1969; Tissot *et al.*, 1974). Elemental analysis and visual assessment of kerogen provide insights into the abundance of oil-prone, hydrogen-rich, amorphous organic matter of lower plant origin relative to the more gas-prone, hydrogen-deficient, structured organic matter of higher plant origin.

Variations in the elemental composition of the kerogens isolated from the Mesozoic rocks of the Moray Firth Basin are illustrated in Fig. 9. This modified form of the van Krevelen-type diagram translates the atomic H:C and O:C ratios into a 'Sapropel Index'. Increased sapropel index values signify an increased contribution from hydrogen-rich, lower-plant kerogens (remains of algae and bacteria) and consequently an increased potential toward oil generation.

The regional distributions of kerogen types within the sampled units are summarized in Fig. 10. These data indicate that the Lower Cretaceous, where encountered, is dominated by hydrogen-poor, gas-prone, woody kerogens in all but the most northwestern well. Amorphous, oil-prone kerogens are dominant, or share dominance with higher-plant kerogens, in all but the two southeasternmost Kimmeridgian Shale sections examined. In the latter sections, hydrogen-poor, higher-plant kerogens predominate. Similarly, amorphous, lower-

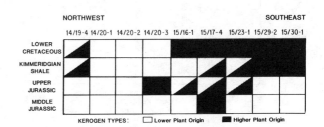

Fig. 10. Regional distributions of major kerogen types within the Mesozoic, Moray Firth Basin.

plant kerogens are dominant, or share dominance with woody kerogens, in the pre-Kimmeridgian Upper Jurassic sediments in most wells where they have been sampled, except the most southeastern well where coaly kerogen predominates.

It can be concluded, therefore, that the Lower Cretaceous sediments are probably gas- or condensate-prone. Within the Kimmeridgian and pre-Kimmeridgian Jurassic units the kerogen tends to be hydrogen-rich and oil-prone. Coupled with the already noted higher organic carbon contents, the kerogen data point to the Kimmeridgian and possibly the pre-Kimmeridgian Jurassic units as probable source-beds for the reservoired oil. However, it is important to note the regional variation in kerogen character. To the extent that the visual assessment and limited elemental analysis data are representative, we would postulate that the tendency of kerogen to generate oil decreases toward the southeast within these Jurassic units. These lateral changes may be related to the relative proximity of a Jurassic land mass. Such a land mass would act as the source for the noted higher-plant detritus toward the southeast. Paleogeographic reconstructions are consistent with such an interpretation. Ziegler (1975), has shown that a southeastern extremity of the Shetland Platform was emergent toward the southeast portion of the study area during Jurassic time.

The nature of the parent organic material in the source rocks exerted a profound influence on the character of the generated and accumulated petroleum in this area. Figure 11 illustrates the southeasterly increase in concentration of $C_{22}+$, 'waxy' n-paraffins in the oils in parallel with the southeasterly increase in content of higher-plant kerogens in the Kimmeridgian and pre-Kimmeridgian Jurassic rocks. Lijmbach (1975), comparing the chemical characteristics of hydrocarbons of crude oils with those released during experimental pyrolysis of algae, bacteria and higher-plant waxes, concluded that the algal and bacterial mass in source rocks is the common basis of all crudes. The presence of other specific precursors in the organic matter of source

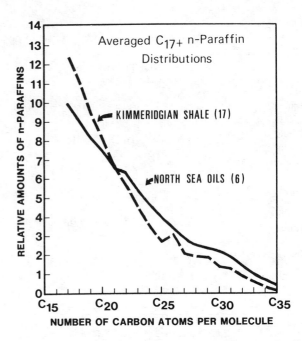

Fig. 12. Averaged $C_{17}+$ n-paraffin distributions in crude oils and extracts from shale samples (oil-to-rock correlation).

rocks imparts specific characteristics to the overall character of the resulting crude oil.

Applying this concept to the Moray Firth area, it would appear that where higher-plant kerogens, enriched in higher-plant waxes, become more significant in the otherwise oil-prone source rocks, the resulting oils show a higher content of long-chain (> 22 carbon atoms per molecule) n-paraffins. Thus, the sympathetic regional variation of compositional parameters of the examined oils with the regional variation of kerogen types in the Upper and Middle Jurassic rocks can be taken as a further indication that the oils have their origin in these rocks.

Oil-to-rock correlation

The data reviewed thus far provide circumstantial evidence that the Kimmeridgian shales, and possibly the pre-Kimmeridgian Jurassic units, are the likely source for the oils of Blocks 14 and 15 of the British North Sea. More specific evidence to confirm this conclusion can be drawn from similarities in compositional parameters for the oils and the soluble bitumens of the suspected source rocks. Unfortunately, interpretation of bitumen data is complicated by very severe oil staining and/or diesel fuel contamination from the drilling fluid additives. In an effort to circumvent these problems, seventeen samples of Kimmeridgian shale, which appeared to be uncontaminated, were selected for this study. The averaged C_{17} + n-paraffin distributions for this select group of rock samples and for the oils are virtually identical (Fig. 12). Considering an experimental error factor (+ 10%) and possible diesel-range hydrocarbon contamination of even these select samples, the correlation between the Kimmeridgian shales and the associated oils is strong enough to imply a genetic relationship.

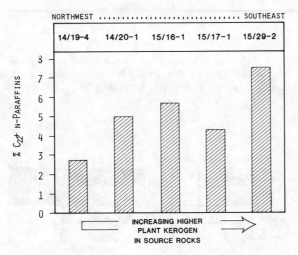

Fig. 11. Increase in 'waxy' n-paraffin content of crude oils as a function of the increasing proportion of higher-plant kerogens in organic matter of Kimmeridgian rocks.

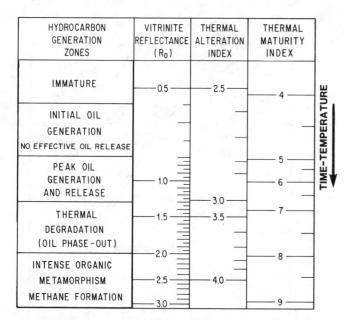

Fig. 13. Organic maturation and hydrocarbon generation and alteration as a function of time and temperature. TAI and R_0 are based on petrographic examination of kerogen properties; 'Thermal Maturity Index' is a theoretical index computed from time–temperature considerations.

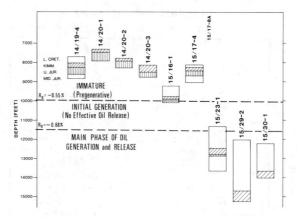

Fig. 14. Approximate depths to zones of hydrocarbon generation and expulsion, Moray Firth area, British North Sea.

Organic maturity and petroleum generation

It is generally accepted that kerogen will not release significant amounts of hydrocarbons until it has reached sufficient levels of thermal maturity. Figure 13 summarizes our concept of crude oil genesis and 'extinction' in response to increased temperature and time. According to this concept, five zones of hydrocarbon generation and degradation can be recognized in the subsurface. In young, shallow, immature sediments, non-reservoir rocks do not contain detectable quantities of indigenous, oil-like hydrocarbon mixtures. With increasing burial of organic matter, a depth/temperature threshold is reached at which generation of oil-range hydrocarbons, through mild alteration of kerogen, becomes perceptible. With increased thermal maturation of kerogen, the concentration of generated hydrocarbons increases, first gradually, then more rapidly. However, oil will not be expelled effectively from the source rock until a quantity of hydrocarbons greater than that which can be retained by the rock and the parent organic matter has been formed (Philippi, 1965; Welte, 1965), and until the volume of generated fluids exceeds that necessary for overpressuring and consequential microfracturing within the source system (Momper, 1978). This critical oil-release threshold marks the principal zone of oil generation and release. During continued burial, lighter and lighter hydrocarbons are generated at the expense of kerogen and unexpelled heavy hydrocarbons. Eventually all $C_{15}+$ hydrocarbons disappear giving rise to condensate- and wet gas-range molecules (Vassoevich *et al.*, 1970). Ultimately, complete carbonization of organic matter occurs, with methane being the only hydrocarbon that can be preserved in deeply buried, 'expended' source beds.

The onset of generation and the threshold of oil release in a stratigraphic sequence can be characterized best by a set of direct indices of maturity based on bitumen and hydrocarbon composition, abundance, and degree of similarity to average crude oils. Derivation of direct evidence from the bitumen data gathered for the Moray Firth study, however, was not possible because the samples were severely contaminated with diesel oil and other non-indigenous hydrocarbons. Only indirect indices based on manifestations of increasing levels of thermal maturation of kerogen could be used reliably. These manifestations include progressive color changes in discrete kerogen particles (thermal alteration index, TAI) and increased reflectivity of polished vitrinite particles (vitrinite reflectance, R_0). In our working scheme, shown in Fig. 13, we maintain that perceptible hydrocarbon generation should begin at maturation levels equivalent to vitrinite reflectance values of 0.55% and TAI values of about 2.5 to 2.6. Significant expulsion of oil should begin at maturation levels equivalent to vitrinite reflectance of 0.68% and a TAI value of about 2.8.

Maturation levels for Jurassic kerogens from the Moray Firth wells were found to increase as a function of depth (Fig. 14). The sediments from the six northwesternmost wells represent an immature, largely pregenerative sequence. The kerogens encountered in these wells at depths less than 10 000 feet are characterized by TAI values no higher than 2.6 and R_0 values near 0.6%. Jurassic kerogens from the three southeasternmost wells are interpreted to be adequately mature for effective hydrogen generation. The kerogens from these wells are characterized at depths of about 11 500 ft to 15 000 ft by TAI values ranging between 2.6 and 3, and R_0 values ranging between 0.68% and 1.2%.

Maturation levels were estimated also using computations based on time–temperature considerations. The mathematical model used is one based on computer adaptation of the classical 'Time–Temperature Index' procedure of Lapotin (1971). We applied this procedure to several wells in the Moray Firth Basin. The input included stratigraphic (burial history) and geothermal information. The output for one well is illustrated in Fig. 15. The results indicate that the explusion threshold should occur at about 9000 ft to 9500 ft in areas where

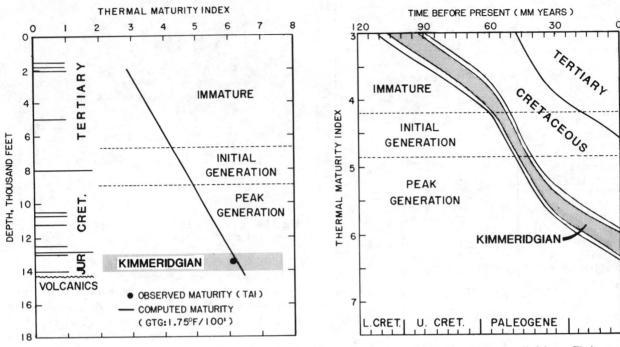

Fig. 15. Computed thermal maturity profile, and maturation history for the Jurassic, Texaco 15/23-4 well, Moray Firth area. Constant geothermal gradient: 1.75°F/100 ft.

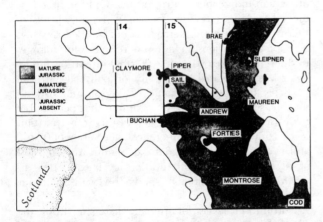

Fig. 16. Relation between production and distribution of thermally mature Jurassic source rocks in the North Sea.

the geothermal gradient exceeds 1.75 °F/100 ft. The computed 'Thermal Maturity Index' for the Kimmeridgian shale compares favorably with the observed maturation level of the unit at its depth of occurrence of about 13 000 ft in this well. Furthermore, tracing of the maturation history of the Kimmeridgian provides an estimate of timing of peak hydrocarbon generation and expulsion. For the conditions stipulated in Fig. 15, explusion of the hydrocarbons from Kimmeridgian source beds commenced some 45 million years ago and is possibly proceeding vigorously at the present time.

Having estimated, both from measured kerogen maturity levels and from maturation modeling, that the depth to the top of the peak generation window lies generally between 9500 and 11 500 ft (average 10 500 ft) in the Moray Firth area, a map of this threshold on the base of the Middle Jurassic section was constructed (Fig. 16). This map outlines the areas of favorable, thermally mature, Jurassic source sediments in the northern North Sea Basin. It is interesting to note that most of the major fields in the basin lie within the confines of these areas, or on their fringes. It is logical to deduce that the Moray Firth oils were generated and released during the past 40 to 50 million years from mature, deeply buried Jurassic source-beds and migrated to their present positions in crestal reservoirs where they were trapped.

CONCLUSIONS

This study indicates that the Kimmeridgian shale and possibly the other organic-rich pre-Kimmeridgian Upper Jurassic and Middle Jurassic shales are the source rocks for much of the eastern Moray Firth Basin oils. Organic facies tend to become more gas-prone toward the southeast. Measurements of organic maturity, together with time/temperature considerations, suggest that these rocks generally become effective source rocks at depths of about 10 000 to 11 000 ft in the study area. It is of exploratory significance to note that reservoirs situated in traps undip from drainage areas containing mature Jurassic sediments should be the most prospective for oil. Reservoirs in traps not associated with drainage areas of mature source rocks are less attractive prospects.

Acknowledgments

Appreciation is expressed to the Management of Texaco Inc. for permission to publish this paper. The author wishes to thank Dr R. Sassen for assistance in the regional interpretation of some of these data. Appreciation is also extended to Mr John A. Boyd of Texaco

International Exploration Company for valuable discussions.

REFERENCES

Bissada, K. K. (1981) Geochemical constraints on petroleum generation and migration — A review. Paper presented at the 1981 ASCOPE Conference, October 1981, Manila, Philippines.

Lijmbach, G. W. M. (1975) On the Origin of Petroleum. *Proc. 9th World Pet. Cong* **2**, 357–369.

Lopatin, N. V. (1971) Temperature and geologic time as factors in coalification. *Izv. Akad. Nauk. SSR. Ser. Geol.* No. 3, 95–106. (In Russian, English translation by N. H. Bostick, Illinois Geological Survey, 1972.)

McIver, R. D. (1967) Composition of kerogen — clue to its role in the origin of petroleum. *Proc. 7th World Pet. Congr.* **2**, 25–36.

Momper, J. A. (1978) Oil migration limitations suggested by geological and geochemical considerations. In *Physical and chemical constraints on petroleum migration*, AAPG Course Note Series 8, B-1–B-60.

Philippi, G. T. (1965) On the depth, time and mechanism of petroleum generation. *Geochim. Cosmochim. Acta* **29**, 1021–1049.

Powell, T. G. and McKirdy, D. M. (1975) Crude Oil composition in Australia and Papua-New Guinea. *Am. Assoc. Pet. Geol. Bull.* **59**, 1176–1197.

Staplin, F. L. (1969) Sedimentary organic matter, organic metamorphism, and oil and gas occurrence. *Bull. Can. Pet. Geol.* **17**, 47–66.

Tissot, B., Durand, B., Espitalie, J. and Combaz, A. (1974) Influence of nature and diagenesis of organic matter in formation of petroleum. *Am. Assoc. Pet. Geol. Bull.* **58**, 499–506.

Vassoevich, N. B., Korchagina, J., Lopatin, N. V. and Chernyshev, V. V. (1970) Principal phase of oil formation. *Mosk. Univ. Vestnik* No. 6, 3–26. (In Russian, English translation: *Int. Geol. Rev.* **12**, 1276–1296).

Welte, D. H. (1965) Relation between petroleum and source rocks. *Am. Assoc. Pet. Geol. Bull.* **49**, 2246–2268.

Williams, J. J., Conner, D. C. and Peterson, K. E. (1975) Piper oilfield, North Sea. Fault-block structure with Upper Jurassic beach/bar reservoir sands. *Am. Assoc. Pet. Geol. Bull.* **59**, 1585–1601.

Ziegler, W. H. (1975) Outline of the Geological History of the North Sea. In *Geology of the North–West European Continental Shelf*, ed. by Naylor, D. and Mounteney, S. N. Graham Trotman Dudley Publishers, London, Vol. 1, pp. 165–187.

Advances in Organic Geochemistry 1981, pp. 16–27
© *John Wiley & Sons Limited, 1983*

Organic Geochemical Analysis of the First Two Wells in the Troms 1 Area (Barents Sea)

M. Bjorøy

Continental Shelf Institute, PO Box 1883, N7001 Trondheim, Norway

B. Bue

Norsk Hydro A/S, PO Box 2594 Solli, Oslo 2, Norway

A. Elvsborg

Statoil, PO Box 300, N4001 Stavanger, Norway

Wells 7119/12–1 and 7120/12–1 were the first to be drilled in the Troms 1 area off Northern Norway. An extensive geochemical study has been carried out on samples from cuttings, sidewall cores and conventional cores. Mesozoic sediments from an interval of approximately 3000 m in 7120/12–1 and 2000 m in 7119/12–1 were analysed. The abundance of organic carbon and extractable organic matter varies greatly in both wells. The best source rocks were found in Jurassic sediments. The maturity of the two wells differs; whereas in well 7119/12–1 it reaches a level at the lower end of the oil window, in 7120/12–1 it reaches a level in the moderately mature zone.

INTRODUCTION

The Norwegian Continental Shelf, North of 62 °N was closed for oil exploration until 1980, when three 'blocks' were awarded for drilling, one at Haltenbanken and two in the Troms 1 area (Fig. 1). This paper reports the organic geochemical analyses of the first two wells, 7120/12–1 and 7119/12–1, drilled during the summer of 1980 in the Troms 1 area by Norsk Hydro and Statoil respectively. Hydrocarbons were detected in Jurassic reservoir rocks in well 7119/12–1. With these wells being the first to be drilled in this area, the results have given important information concerning the source rock potential for oil and gas of the penetrated sequences.

Basin Geology, Troms 1

In the Troms 1 area (Fig. 2), five main structural elements can be distinguished (Fig. 3):

(1) Senja Ridge: a N–S trending, structural high in the westernmost part of the area.
(2) Tromsø Basin: a very deep N–S trending basin containing thick developments of Mesozoic and Tertiary deposits. The structural style in this basin is primarily halokinetic. The salt is probably of Late Paleozoic age.
(3) Hammerfest Basin: an E–W trending basin, limited in the south by the Troms/Finnmark Fault Zone and in the north by the Loppa Ridge (outside the Troms 1 area). The structural style is dominated by tensional tectonics. This basin has so far been penetrated by three wells, 7120/12–1, 7120/12–2 and 7120/8–1.
(4) Transition Zone, Hammerfest/Tromsø Basin: this zone is dominated by extensional forces, resulting in a number of N–S trending fault blocks. Two wells, 7119/12–1 and 7119/12–2, have been drilled in this zone.
(5) Troms/Finnmark Fault Zone: a NWW–SEE normal fault zone separating the Hammerfest basin from the less deformed area to the south.

Stratigraphy and lithology of wells 7119/12–1 and 7120/12–1

The main stratigraphy and lithology of the two wells is illustrated in Fig. 4. The lithology of the geological sequence is quite similar for the two wells. The main stratigraphic differences are the considerably increased thickness of the Cretaceous sediments in 7119/12–1, and the Kimmerian unconformity, which is at a far greater depth in 7119/12–1 than in 7120/12–1.

The Tertiary and Upper Cretaceous sequences consist mainly of claystone. The upper part of the Lower Cretaceous sequence in both wells is composed of grey claystone with some carbonate and sandstone stringers.

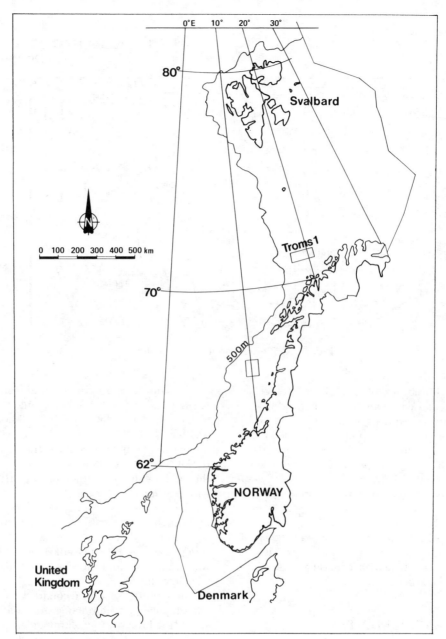

Fig. 1. Map of Northern Norway and Barents Sea.

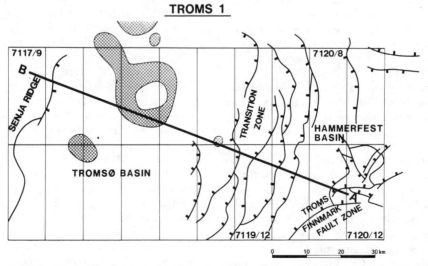

Fig. 2. Map of Troms 1 area with major faults and showing the seismic line AB.

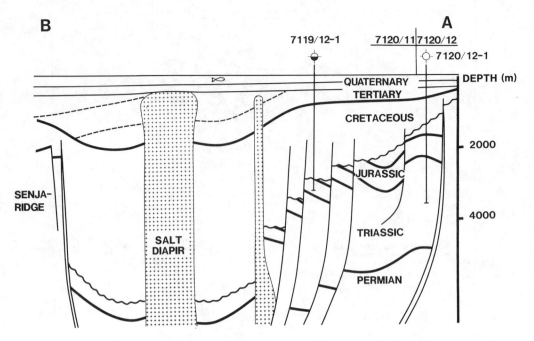

Fig. 3. Geological profile of Troms 1 area.

By contrast, the lower part of the Lower Cretaceous sequence consists of a dark claystone in both wells.

The Upper Jurassic sequence is similar in both wells — a dark grey claystone. The Middle Jurassic sequence is thin in both wells and is characterized by a dark claystone in the uppermost part and sandstones below. The Lower Jurassic sequence consists mainly of sandstone with several layers of dark claystone and thin coals.

Well 7119/12–1 terminated in the Lower Jurassic whereas well 7120/12–1 penetrated more than 1000 m of Triassic sediments. This Triassic sequence consists of grey or red–brown claystone with increasing proportions of sandstone in the lower part.

EXPERIMENTAL

To examine the source rock potential for the different intervals cuttings samples from both wells, and sidewall cores from 7120/12–1 were analysed at the Continental Shelf Institute's organic geochemical laboratory.

The headspace gas (1 ml aliquot) from sealed cans was analysed on a Carlo Erba 2150 Fractovap gas chromatograph fitted with a 1 m × 1/8 inch stainless steel column packed with 80–120 mesh Porapak Q. The analyses were performed isothermally at 100 °C using N_2 as carrier gas. For cuttings gas, a sample of the washed 1–2 mm fraction was crushed in water using a ball mill. One ml of the headspace in the ball mill was analysed gas chromatographically using the same conditions described above.

After being washed in temperate water, the samples were dried at ambient temperature. They were then described sedimentologically and appropriate lithologies were picked for further analysis. The organic carbon content was determined for all picked samples using a Leco EC 12 carbon analyser.

The samples were ground in a centrifugal mill to a particle size <125 μm and extracted with dichloromethane (DCM) using a flow-through system (Radke *et al.*, 1978). Activated copper was used to remove free sulphur from the extracts. The solvent from the DCM extraction was evaporated under nitrogen and the total amount of extractable organic matter (EOM) was determined.

The EOM was then separated into saturated hydrocarbons, aromatic hydrocarbons and 'resinous' compounds by medium pressure liquid chromatography using hexane as eluant (Radke *et al.*, 1980). The hexane was evaporated and the weight of the various fractions was determined.

The saturated hydrocarbon fraction was analysed by glass capillary gas chromatography (GC)[2] using a Carlo Erba 2150 Fractovap gas chromatograph fitted with a 25 m × 0.25 mm glass capillary column coated with OV–101 (helium as carrier gas). The oven was programmed from 80 °C to 260 °C at 4 °C/min and the samples were injected in the splitless mode.

The kerogen was isolated by treating the rock matrix with hydrochloric and hydrofluoric acids. Acid-insoluble minerals were separated using $ZnBr_2$. The organic residues were mounted in glycerine jelly and were examined by microscopy in transmitted light. The composition of the total organic residues was expressed as visual estimates of the volume of marine plant remains (i.e. amorphous matter or sapropel and cysts of algae) in relation to the volume of terrestrial plant remains (i.e. cuticles, pollen grains, spores, woody structures, coaly fragments and finely dispersed or indeterminate herbaceous matter) (Staplin, 1969). For a more refined subdivision of the material, screened residues (particles >15 μm) were studied separately to support the investigation of the total residues. The colour index or thermal alteration index (TAI) was estimated visually from exinite colour (Burgess, 1974).

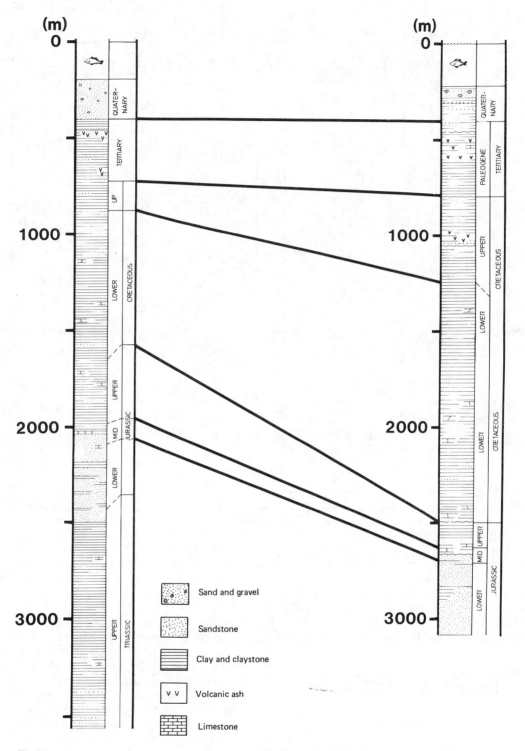

Fig. 4. Simplified lithological log with stratigraphical zonation of wells 7119/12–1 and 7120/12–1.

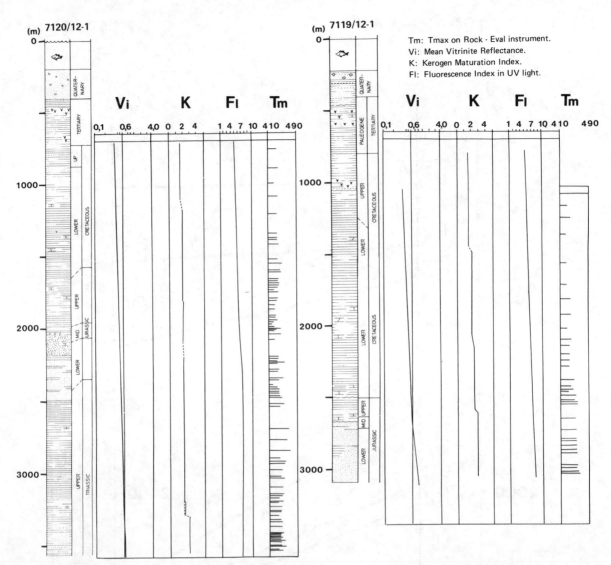

Fig. 5. Vitrinite reflectance, spore colouration, spore fluorescence and T_{max} measurements for wells 7119/12–1 and 7120/12–1.

Rock-Eval pyrolysis was carried out using 100 mg aliquots of freshly crushed samples.

Vitrinite reflectance measurements were undertaken mainly on whole rock samples. The fluorescence was measured on the same samples using a UV source and the colour of the exinite fluorescence was estimated.

RESULTS AND DISCUSSION

Maturation

The evaluation of the maturity data is based on the criteria given by Vassoevich *et al.* (1974), Burgess (1974), Espitalié *et al.* (1977) and Jones (1980). A total of 90 samples composed of a mixture of cuttings samples, sidewall cores and conventional core chips from well 7120/12–1, and 35 cuttings samples from well 7119/12–1 were analysed. The maturity parameters as deduced from vitrinite reflectance, visual kerogen, fluorescence and pyrolysis results show good agreement (Fig. 5).

Well 7120/12–1 is immature down to the Lower Jurassic, where it is considered to be moderately mature. In the Triassic at about 3200 m, the sequence reaches a maturity in the upper part of the oil window. The variation in the vitrinite reflectance data in the lower part of the Lower Cretaceous in 7120/12–1 is probably due to heavy reworking. The reflectance data from the upper part of Triassic are unreliable due to the low content of organic carbon in this interval. In the lower part of this sequence the data is more reliable.

Well 7119/12–1 reaches moderately mature sediments in the Lower Cretaceous, while the Upper Jurassic is fully mature at a depth of about 2600 m.

The rate of increase in maturity with depth throughout the Jurassic of well 7119/12–1 is higher than in the upper part of the well. But even the gradient of the upper part of well 7119/12–1 is higher than found throughout well 7120/12–1. A possible explanation for this difference between the wells lies in the different well locations. Well 7119/12–1 is located in the transition zone towards the Tromsø Basin and is therefore closer to the deep basin than well 7120/12–1.

TOTAL ORGANIC CARBON

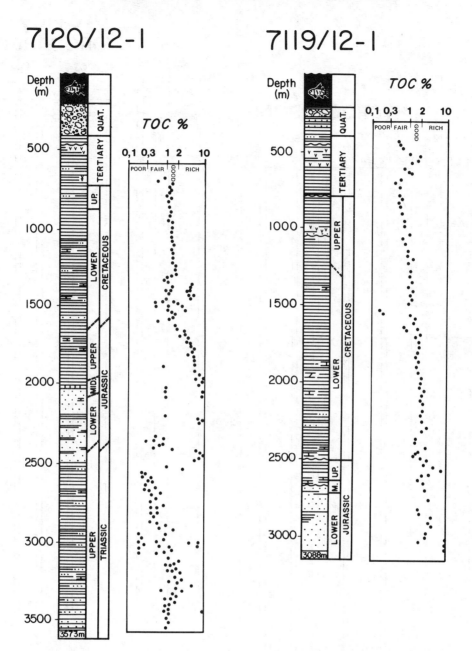

Fig. 6. Total organic carbon measurements on samples from wells 7119/12–1 and 7120/12–1.

Source rock evaluation

The richness classification used in this study follows the lines normally used by the Continental Shelf Institute (Bjorøy, 1977).

Total organic carbon

The results of the total organic carbon (TOC) determinations are shown in Fig. 6. The organic carbon content of the Tertiary and the Upper Cretaceous claystones ranges from 0.5% to 2%. A general increase in carbon content was found throughout the Cretaceous

sequence, and the dark claystones of the lower part of Lower Cretaceous contained more than 2% organic carbon.

The dark grey claystone in the Upper Jurassic sequence showed a marked increase in the abundance of organic carbon compared to the grey claystone in the Lower Cretaceous sequence. In both wells, most of the samples from the Upper Jurassic were found to have TOC values of 4–8% indicating that this sequence has a rich potential as a source rock. Only one claystone sample from the Middle Jurassic sequence of well 7119/12–1 was analysed and it was found to have a TOC value of approximately 3%. This is markedly lower than

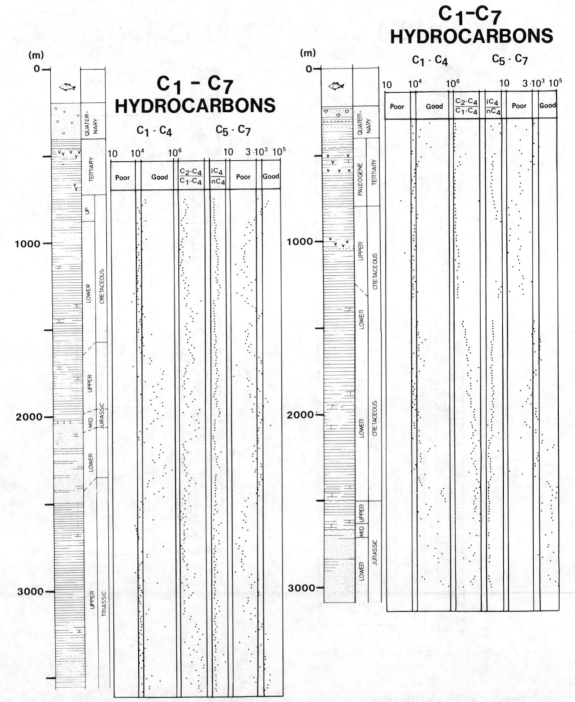

Fig. 7. Gas analyses of canned samples from wells 7119/12–1 and 7120/12–1.

in the claystone samples from the Middle Jurassic sequence in well 7120/12–1. These were found to have very high TOC values which probably reflects the occurrence of coal stringers within the claystone.

The TOC content of the dark claystones of the Lower Jurassic sequence in well 7119/12–1 showed large variation. Most of the samples had a rich abundance of organic carbon — this being particularly high towards the terminal depth of the well. The interbedded dark grey coaly claystone in the lower part of the Lower

Jurassic in well 7120/12–1 gave TOC values indicative of a rich potential as a source rock.

The Triassic claystones have a variable abundance of organic carbon. The upper part of the Triassic sequence has a fair abundance while the lower part contains a good-to-rich abundance of organic carbon.

Light hydrocarbon measurements

Headspace gas and occluded gas analyses were

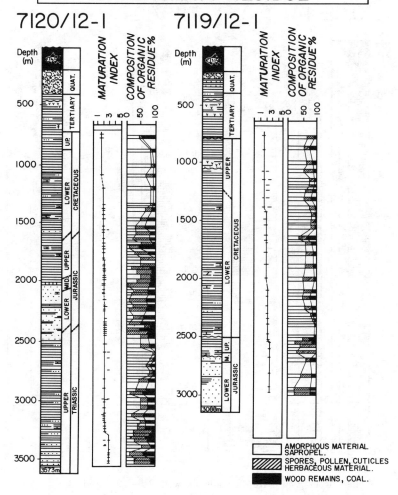

Fig. 8. Visual kerogen examination in transmitted light for wells 7119/12–1 and 7120/12–1.

undertaken on canned samples (Fig. 7). The abundances of C_1–C_4 hydrocarbons are similar throughout the Cretaceous whereas the C_5–C_7 hydrocarbons of the Lower Cretaceous are more abundant in 7119/12–1 than in well 7120/12–1. The wet gases (C_2–C_4) are also more abundant in the Lower Cretaceous sequence in well 7119/12–1. This indicates a higher maturity for well 7119/12–1 than 7120/12–1.

The abundance of C_1–C_7 hydrocarbons increases considerably in both wells in the Jurassic sequence compared to the Cretaceous. The wetness of the gas and the abundance of C_5–C_7 hydrocarbons is far higher in the Jurassic sequence of 7119/12–1 than of well 7120/12–1, while the iC_4/nC_4 ratio is reversed. These analyses clearly indicate that the Jurassic shales in both wells have a source rock potential and that the maturity of the Jurassic sequence in 7119/12–1 is higher than in 7120/12–1. The relatively high abundance of C_5–C_7 hydrocarbons in 7119/12–1 may, in addition, indicate the presence of free hydrocarbons. A relatively low abundance of higher molecular weight hydrocarbons is found in the Triassic, but a slight increase present in the lower part of the sequence which may indicate the occurrence of free hydrocarbons.

Composition of kerogen

In the present study, kerogen type was determined by visual examination in transmitted light (Burgess, 1974) and by Rock-Eval pyrolysis (Espitalié *et al.*, 1977), with additional support from extraction and chromatographic results.

The visual kerogen examination of the Cretaceous samples from well 7119/12–1 indicated approximately 50% amorphous material and 50% various terrestrial material with little variation (Fig. 8). Rock-Eval pyrolysis (Fig. 9) produced a rather low H-index and a high O-index typical for kerogen type III throughout the Cretaceous in both wells. The low hydrogen indices found for these samples are usually more compatible with a higher percentage of terrestrial material than that found in the present samples (Tissot and Welte, Part II, 1978). It is probable that the 'amorphous-like' material is sapropelized terrestrial material.

Similar results were found for samples from the Upper Cretaceous sequence in well 7120/12–1, but the upper part of this sequence has an even higher percentage of amorphous material and a very low hydrogen index. From approximately 1400 m, an increasingly greater

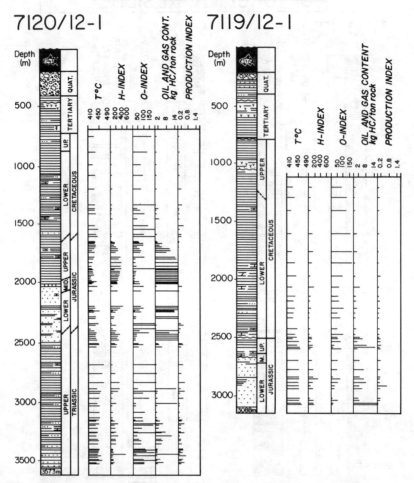

Fig. 9. Rock-Eval pyrolysis results for wells 7119/12–1 and 7120/12–1.

input of terrestrial material is observed in transmitted light examination, but there is no evidence of any change in the hydrogen index. This may be due to a lesser degree of sapropelization of the terrestrial material in the lower part of the Lower Cretaceous samples in well 7120/12–1 compared to that in the remainder of the analysed Cretaceous samples from the two wells. A similar variation in kerogen characteristics is also found in Cretaceous formations on Svalbard (Bjorøy and Vigran, 1979 and 1980).

The Upper Jurassic sequence in both wells contains a mixture of amorphous and terrestrial material with a high proportion of cuticles. The pyrolysis analysis shows a relatively high hydrogen index and low oxygen index (Figs 8 and 9), both being far more pronounced in well 7120/12–1 than in well 7119/12–1. The kerogen in the samples from the Upper Jurassic sequence in both wells is of type II and the sequence has a rich potential as a source rock for oil and gas. The Upper Jurassic sequence in well 7119/12–1 has already reached the principal zone of oil formation whereas in well 7120/12–1 it is still immature.

None of the Middle Jurassic samples in well 7119/12–1 were analysed, but the samples from well 7120/12–1 were found, both by Rock-Eval pyrolysis and by visual kerogen examination, to vary considerably (Figs 8 and

9). The percentage of claystone cuttings in the samples was very low and there is a possibility that the results are unreliable due to the influence of caved material.

The visual kerogen examination of the Lower Jurassic sequence of well 7119/12–1 revealed a lower proportion of amorphous material whereas the Rock-Eval pyrolyses produced a relatively uniform hydrogen index (*ca.* 200 mg HC/g org C) and a high oxygen index. The corresponding sequence in well 7120/12–1 is completely different. Here the samples were found to contain predominantly terrestrial material, often a high percentage of coal and cuticle (Fig. 8). Rock-Eval pyrolysis shows rather variable results (Fig. 9), probably due to variation in the amount of coaly particles present in the samples. The high hydrogen index in some samples is due to a very high percentage of cuticular material.

The upper part of the Triassic sequence contains mainly amorphous material, whereas the samples from approximately 2900 m to TD contain a far higher percentage of terrestrial material (Fig. 8). Results of the Rock-Eval pyrolysis show a similar trend, with a relatively high hydrogen index for the upper part of the sequence and a generally lower hydrogen index below approximately 2900 m (Fig. 9).

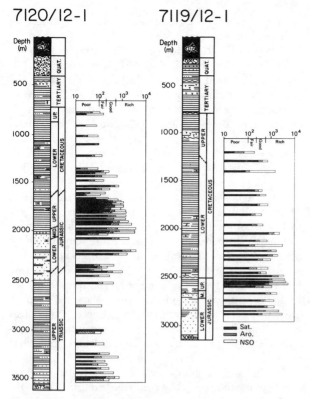

Fig. 10. The abundance of extractable organic matter (EOM) and hydrocarbons (HC) in analysed samples from wells 7119/12–1 and 7120/12–1.

Extractability of organic matter

The extractability of the various samples was evaluated according to the criteria normally used at the Continental Shelf Institute (Bjorøy, 1977).

The abundance of extractable hydrocarbons and extractable organic matter was found to differ significantly between the two wells, both in absolute terms and when normalized to organic carbon (Figs 10 and 11).

The samples from the *Upper Cretaceous* sequence were found to have a poor abundance of extractable hydrocarbons. One sample from 7119/12–1 (1320–1335 m) gave a good abundance of extractable hydrocarbons and a smooth *n*-alkane distribution indivative of contamination by free heavy hydrocarbons (i.e. not originating from the kerogen in the sample).

Most of the samples from the *Lower Cretaceous* section in well 7119/12–1 were found to have a good abundance of extractable hydrocarbons while three samples had a rich abundance (Fig. 10). These three samples were also found to have a high extractability when normalized to organic carbon (Fig. 11). The gas chromatograms of the saturated hydrocarbon fractions are typical for moderately mature hydrocarbons of type III kerogen (Fig. 11) and do not indicate contamination by free hydrocarbons.

Most of the samples from the Lower Cretaceous section of well 7120/12–1 were found to have a poor or

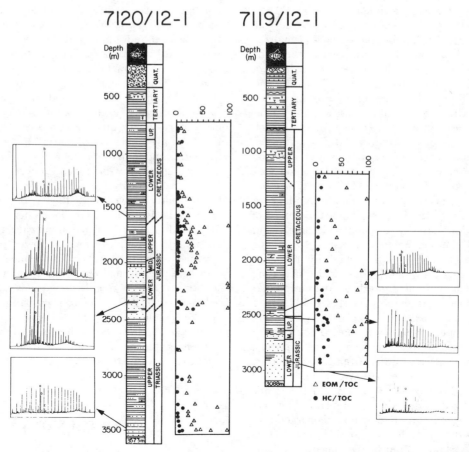

Fig. 11. The extractability of EOM and HC, normalized to organic carbon, in wells 7119/12–1 and 7120/12–1, with gas chromatograms of saturated hydrocarbons from the Cretaceous, Jurassic and Triassic sequence.

fair abundance of extractable hydrocarbons with exception of the sample from 1524–40 m and those from between 1660 m and the base of Cretaceous, which were found to have a good abundance (Fig. 10). The same trend was also present for the carbon-normalized values (Fig. 11). The gas chromatograms of the saturated hydrocarbon fractions of the samples with high extractability show features typical of immature terrestrial material (high CPI value and high pristane/nC_{17} ratio) (Fig. 11). For the other samples, the main difference found is the variation in the heavy end fraction and in the isoprenoid ratio (pr/nC_{17}). A feature (a large unresolved envelope) noted in some of the Lower Cretaceous samples is also present in the Lower Cretaceous sediments on Andøya (Bjorøy et al., 1980) and on Svalbard (Bjorøy and Vigran, 1979 and 1980). It is probably caused by strong weathering and oxidation during deposition. The saturated hydrocarbons from samples in the Lower Cretaceous sequence (Fig. 11) clearly emphasize the difference in maturity encountered for the two wells; higher CPI values and higher pristane/nC_{17} ratios are noted for well 7120/12–1 compared to well 7119/12–1.

The Upper Jurassic sequence in both wells clearly provides the richest source rock. The samples from well 7119/12–1 were found to have a rich abundance of hydrocarbons (Fig. 10). The same is seen for the carbon-normalized results (Fig. 11). The gas chromatograms of the saturated hydrocarbon fraction are typical for mature hydrocarbons from type II kerogen (Fig. 11).

The samples of Upper Jurassic age from well 7120/12–1 have a good to rich abundance of extractable hydrocarbons (Fig. 10). The organic carbon-normalized values are somewhat lower due to the low maturity. The analysed sediments have still not reached a level of maturity within the principal zone of oil formation and the extractability is therefore low. With increasing maturity the extractability will increase and the Upper Jurassic sequence may be considered as a potentially rich source rock for oil should it attain a maturity within the oil window. The gas chromatograms for the saturated hydrocarbon fractions of the analysed samples show very high pristane/nC_{17} and phytane/nC_{18} ratios together with a relative high CPI values and a high abundance of steranes and triterpanes (Fig. 11). These are typical of samples with a low maturity. The high molecular weight n-alkanes and the steranes and triterpanes, i.e. the geochemical fossils, have a relatively high abundance at the observed maturity level, but with increasing maturity this will diminish. A gas chromatogram similar to the one found for the same sequence in well 7119/12–1 would then be expected.

A few claystone samples from the *Middle Jurassic* sequence in both wells were analysed (Figs 10 and 11). When compared with the samples from Upper Jurassic, they were found to have a lower abundance of extractable hydrocarbons. However, the organic carbon-normalized values were similar. The gas chromatograms of the saturated hydrocarbon fraction of the samples in the two wells vary considerably. In well 7119/12–1 they show a front-biased, smooth n-alkane distribution typical for mature hydrocarbons (Fig. 11), whereas for well 7120/12–1 they show an n-alkane

pattern typical of a moderately mature sample of terrestrial origin (Fig. 11).

Some of the interbedded claystone samples from the *Lower Jurassic* sequence in both wells were analysed. The samples from well 7119/12–1 had a rich abundance of extractable hydrocarbons, decreasing slightly with increasing depth. This trend is also found for the organic carbon-normalized values (Figs 10 and 11). The samples from the Lower Jurassic sequence in well 7120/12–1 show a distinct decrease in the abundance of extractable hydrocarbons with an increase in depth (Fig. 10). This is far more pronounced than in well 7119/12–1. The organic carbon-normalized values are very erratic (Fig. 11), probably due to contamination by free hydrocarbons, especially in the samples below 2200 m.

The gas chromatograms of the saturated hydrocarbon fraction vary considerably. The samples from well 7119/12–1 show a pattern typical of mature hydrocarbons (Fig. 11). Some of the samples from well 7120/12–1 gave chromatograms showing typical immature terrestrial features while others gave a clear indication of a mixed source (a smooth front-biased n-alkane distribution and a low input of high molecular weight n-alkanes with a high CPI). The medium molecular weight n-alkanes are either from diesel oil added to the mud or from a condensate migrated into the sequence.

As mentioned previously, only well 7120/12–1 was drilled into *Triassic* sediments. Some of the claystone samples, especially in the lower part of the well, have a fair-to-good abundance of extractable hydrocarbons. Some core-chip samples at approximately 3520 m were also analysed and found to have a good abundance of extractable hydrocarbons. The variation observed in the abundance of extractable hydrocarbons is also clearly seen in the organic carbon-normalized values. The gas chromatograms of the saturated hydrocarbon fraction vary only slightly (each showing a large input of high molecular weight n-alkanes with a low CPI value (Fig. 11)), and are indicative of mature hydrocarbons from terrestrial source material.

The significant difference between the carbon-normalized results for the two wells (i.e. a far higher extractability in well 7119/12–1 compared with well 7120/12–1), is partly due to the higher maturity of the 7119/12–1 samples. The maximum values for both wells are found in samples from the lower part of Lower Cretaceous and the Jurassic. The tremendous variation seen in the normalized values must be due to contamination by free hydrocarbons present in the sediments of 7119/12–1. This is probably the case both for the Cretaceous and the Jurassic sediments. High normalized hydrocarbon values in the lower part of the Triassic sequence also indicate the possibility that migrated hydrocarbons are present in the Triassic interval of 7120/12–1.

CONCLUSIONS

The main difference in the organic geochemistry of the two wells is the higher maturity encountered in the

Jurassic sequence in well 7119/12–1. This may be a result of the well being located closer to the Troms Basin and thus having a higher geothermal gradient.

Although the *Upper Cretaceous sequence* in well 7119/12–1 is thicker than in well 7120/12–1, organic geochemically it is found to be similar. There is a slight discrepancy between the various analyses for determining the kerogen type; this is caused by sapropelization of terrestrial material. The Upper Cretaceous sequence in both wells is found to be immature with a fair potential as source rock for gas. Fluorescence analysis indicates the presence of free hydrocarbons in some samples at the top of the sequence in well 7119/12–1.

The upper part of the *Lower Cretaceous* is found to have a good potential as source rock for gas. In well 7119/12–1, it is found to be moderately mature, whereas in 7120/12–1 it is mature.

The various richness parameters show that the source rock richness is higher for the dark claystone in the lower part of the Lower Cretaceous compared to that for the light grey claystone in the upper part. The organic carbon content in the dark grey claystone in well 7120/12–1 is higher than for the dark claystone in the same zone in well 7119/12–1. A difference is also seen in the kerogen, which is found to contain more terrestrial material in well 7120/12–1 than in 7119/12–1. In both wells, the dark grey claystone in this zone has a rick potential for gas and, possibly, heavy oil. The zone in well 7119/12–1 is found to be moderately mature to mature, whereas the zone in well 7120/12–1 is still immature. None of the samples from 7120/12–1 show any sign of free hydrocarbons, although these were encountered in the samples from 7119/12–1.

The claystone from the *Upper Jurassic* sequence has a rich potential as source rock for gas and heavy oil. It is found to be slightly more oil-prone in well 7119/12–1 compared to well 7120/12–1. The Upper Jurassic sequence in well 7120/12–1 is still immature whereas it is mature in well 7119/12–1. The sandstone in both wells shows clear evidence of the presence of free hydrocarbons.

The organic geochemistry of the Upper Jurassic sequence differs between the two wells. The difference encountered in the hydrogen index (from Rock-Eval pyrolysis) is probably the result of a higher degree of maturity rather than a change in the kerogen type. The very high oxygen indices encountered for the samples from well 7119/12–1 could be due to a release of CO_2 from the carbonate in the samples.

The claystone beds in the *Middle and Lower Jurassic* may also have a rich source potential but are more gas-prone than the Upper Jurassic. The sequence is moderately mature to mature in 7120/12–1 but has an oil window maturity in well 7119/12–1, where the sand layers show clear indications of the presence of free hydrocarbons.

The *Triassic* sediments may also have a favourable source potential; the lower part contains a good-to-rich abundance of organic carbon. The kerogen is mainly gas-prone terrestrial material.

There was no *significant* evidence for migrated hydrocarbons in the sandstone intervals throughout the Triassic sequence but examination in UV light showed fluorescence due to the presence of free hydrocarbons.

The various geological intervals penetrated in the two wells were found to have similar organic geochemical properties to the Mesozoic sequences on Svalbard (Bjorøy and Vigran, 1979 and 1980) and on Andøya (Bjorøy et al., 1980).

Summary; source rock evaluation, Troms 1

1. Large volumes of source rocks are present.
2. Lower Cretaceous source rocks are mainly gas prone. Upper Jurassic source rocks are oil and gas prone.
3. Depth to oil window maturity varies from 2500–3200 m.

Acknowledgement

The authors would like to thank Statoil and Norsk Hydro and their partners on the two licences for allowing us to present these results. These are on block 7119/12: Esso Exploration and Production Norway; Saga Petroleum A/S & Co.; Deminex (Norge) A/S; Hispanoil (Norway) A/S. On block 7120/12: Norske Conoco A/S; Amoco Norway Oil Co. A/S.

REFERENCES

Bjorøy, M. (1977) Organic geochemistry in search of petroleum. *IKU Publication No. 93* (ISSN 0332-5288).

Bjorøy, M. and Vigran, J. O. (1979) *Organic geochemistry of the Lower Cretaceous of Andøya and Spitsbergen*, Norwegian Petroleum Society, NSS/25/79.

Bjorøy, M. and Vigran, J. O. (1980), Geochemical study of the organic matter in outcrop samples from Agardhfjellet, Spitsbergen. *Advances in Organic Geochemistry 1979* ed. by Douglas, A. G., Maxwell, J., 141–147, Pergamon Press.

Bjorøy, M., Hall, K. and Vigran, J. O. (1980) An organic geochemical study of Mesozoic shales from Andøya, North Norway. *Advances in Organic Geochemistry 1979* ed. by Douglas, A. G., Maxwell, J., 77–91, Pergamon Press.

Burgess, J. D. (1974) Microscopic examination of kerogen (dispersed organic matter) in petroleum exploration. *Geo. Soc. Amer. Spec. Paper 153*, 19–30.

Espitalié, J., Madec, M., Tissot, B., Leplat, P. and Menning, J. J. (1977) Source rock characterization method for petroleum exploration. *Inst. Franc. Petrole*. Ref. 24843.

Jones, J. M. (1980) Relationship between vitrinite reflectance and spore colouration. *Personal communication*.

Radke, M., Sittardt, H. G. and Welte, D. H. (1978) Removal of soluble organic matter from rock samples with a flow-through extraction cell. *Anal. Chem.* **50**, 663–665.

Radke, M., Willsch, H. and Welte, D. H. (1980) Preparative hydrocarbon group type determination by automated medium pressure liquid chromatography. *Anal. Chem.* **52**, 406–411.

Staplin, F. L. (1969) Sedimentary organic matter, organic metamorphism and oil gas occurrence. *Bull. Canad. Petrol. Geol.* **17**, 47–66.

Tissot, B. P. and Welte, D. H. (1978) Petroleum Formation and Occurrence. Springer-Verlag, Berlin, Heidelberg.

Vassoevich, N. B., Akramkhodzhaev, A. M. and Geodekyan, A. A. (1974) Principal zone of oil formation. In: *Advances in Organic Geochemistry 1973* ed. by Tissot, B. and Bienner, F., 309–314, Technip. Paris.

Advances in Organic Geochemistry 1981, pp. 28–38
© *John Wiley & Sons Limited*, 1983

Petroleum Geochemistry of the North Slope of Alaska: Time and Degree of Thermal Maturity*

Leslie B. Magoon

U.S. Geological Survey, Menlo Park, California, USA

George E. Claypool

U.S. Geological Survey, Denver, Colorado, USA

The North Slope of Alaska, which contains the largest oil reserves in the United States, lies on the south flank of a ridge system that rifted sometime during Early Cretaceous time to form the Canada basin on the north, and deepened the east–west-trending Colville trough on the south. The Barrow arch, the south flank of the rifted ridge, forms a regional high between the Canada basin and the Colville trough. The arch, which trends west–northwest, has been a focus for migrating oil from Early Cretaceous through Cenozoic time. Previous work has identified at least two types of oils associated with the arch and several source rock units for at least one of these two oils. Even though the potential source rock units occur in the Colville trough and in places drape over the Barrow arch, there still remains the question of when in geologic time the oils could have originated and at which geographic position they could have issued. Temperature-sensitive analytical data and observed temperatures are here used to determine the threshold of oil and gas generation, and Lopatin's method is used to determine the time of maturity for source rock units penetrated in the Inigok No. 1 well. Vitrinite reflectance, gas wetness and present-day subsurface temperatures are compared along two regional cross sections: a north–south cross section from the Barrow arch to the Colville trough and a west–east cross section from the South Barrow gas field through the Kuparuk and Prudhoe Bay oil fields to the western edge of the Wildlife Range. There is good agreement among these three types of data for comparable thermal history along the two cross sections except where uplift has occurred. In the case of uplift, high vitrinite reflectance and associated gas-wetness values occur at a much shallower depth than that of the present-day subsurface temperatures. Thermal maturity data also indicates that the oil and gas in the Barrow field has undergone long-distance migration: organic matter in the shales is thermally immature for some distance away from the field area. For the Inigok No. 1 well there is good agreement among the temperature-sensitive analytical data for the 'onset of oil generation' and the 'wet gas preservation deadline,' to the present-day temperatures suggesting that the well has been drilled in sedimentary rocks that are near maximum depth of burial. Using time–temperature index values that correspond to the measured vitrinite values in conjunction with burial curves of selected stratigraphic horizons, we solved, by the trial-and-error method, for the geothermal gradients that prevailed during geologic time at the Inigok locality. The observed vitrinite reflectance v. depth–age profile requires lower geothermal gradients during the Tertiary, and higher geothermal gradients throughout the late Paleozoic and prior to the Early Cretaceous. The time of the decrease in thermal gradient coincides with the time of rifting.

INTRODUCTION

In 1977, the Department of the Navy turned the Naval Petroleum Reserve No. 4 (NPR-4) over to the Department of Interior to be the National Petroleum Reserve in Alaska (NPRA). The Department of Interior designated the U.S. Geological Survey (USGS) as the organization to continue the exploration effort initiated by the Navy in 1974. In preparation for this sizeable exploration program, the USGS began in late 1976 to plan studies for assessment of the petroleum potential of NPRA. A petroleum–geochemistry study was initiated to evaluate currently drilling wells, to aid in the selection of new well locations, and to contribute to the hydrocarbon-resource estimates for NPRA.

Previous geochemical work on oils and organic matter in rocks from the North Slope is summarized by Magoon and Claypool (1981). Major studies have included investigations of oil geochemistry (McKinney *et al.*, 1959; Jones and Speers, 1976; Young *et al.*, 1977; Magoon and Claypool, 1981), rock geochemistry (Morgridge and Smith, 1972; Magoon and Claypool, 1979; Claypool and Magoon, 1980a–d; Magoon and Claypool, 1980a–f), and oil–rock correlation (Seifert *et al.*,

* Any use of trade names is for descriptive purposes only and does not imply endorsement by the USGS.

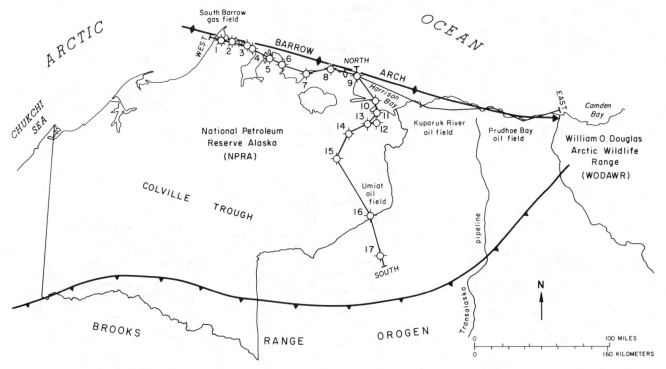

Fig. 1. Map of the North Slope of Alaska showing some of the wells (numbered) sampled for our petroleum geochemical anlyses. Numbers correspond to wells listed in Table 1.

Table 1

Name, API number and total depth for the wells shown on Figs 1, 4 and 5

Map No.	Name	API No.	Total depth (ft)
1	South Barrow No. 13	50-023-20008	2535
2	South Barrow No. 17	50-023-20011	2382
3	Tulageak No. 1	50-023-20018	4015
4	West Dease No. 1	50-023-20014	4173
5	North Simpson No. 1	50-023-10004	3774
6	East Simpson No. 2	50-279-20007	7504
7	Drew Point No. 1	50-279-20002	7946
8	Dalton No. 1	50-279-20006	9367
9	W. T. Foran No. 1	50-103-20010	8864
10	Atigaru Point No. 1	50-103-20008	11 535
11	South Harrison Bay No. 1	50-103-20007	11 290
12	Fish Creek No. 1	50-103-10001	7020
13	West Fish Creek No. 1	50-103-20009	11 427
14	North Inigok No. 1	50-103-20017	10 170
15	Inigok No. 1	50-279-20003	20 102
16	Seabee No. 1	50-287-20007	15 611
17	Grandstand No. 1	50-057-10001	7020

Table 2

Routine analytic program for wells drilled in NPRA from 1977 to 1981. Samples were taken at 30 ft intervals

Analysis	Interval (ft) for analytical program A	B
Sample preparation	60	60
C_1–C_7 headspace gas	60	60
C_1–C_7 cuttings gas	60	60
C_4–C_8 gasoline-range	300	300
TEA-FID	300	60
Organic carbon	60	60
Total carbon	300	60
Vitrinite reflectance	600	300
Visual kerogen	300	300
TAI	300	300
C, H, N and ash of kerogen	600	300
O, S of kerogen	600	300
$\delta^{13}C$ of CH_4 in headspace gas	600	300

Program A is for the Brookian sequence rocks
Program B is for the Ellesmerian sequence rocks

1979). The present report is part of this continuing effort to evaluate the hydrocarbon systems on the North Slope; it includes data on the average organic-carbon values for certain stratigraphic horizons, the thermal history along two regional cross sections, and the geologic time of maturation of selected rock units penetrated in the Inigok No. 1 well.

This report is a preliminary discussion of selected data from North Slope wells. The vitrinite reflectance, gas wetness, and present-day subsurface temperatures are used to interpret the thermal history of the basin along two geologic cross sections. A major objective is to determine whether the South Barrow and the Prudhoe Bay fields are indeed in thermally mature geologic settings, as has been implied by Morgridge and Smith (1972) and Bushnell (1981), and indicated by the

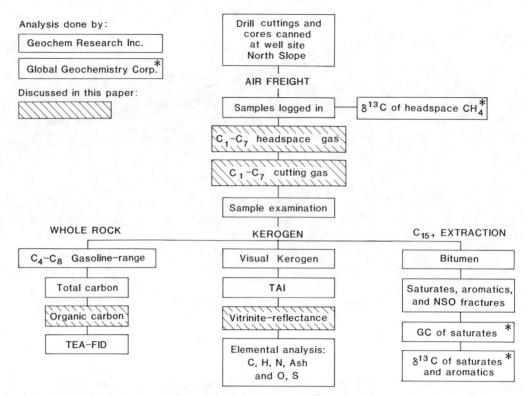

Fig. 2. Outline of geochemical program for canned samples. Whole rock, kerogen and C_{15}+-extraction analyses are shown and are attributed to a laboratory, Geochem Research or Global Geochemistry. Of this analytical program, only the C_1–C_4 gas data from the C_1–C_7 gas analysis, vitrinite reflectance and organic carbon content are discussed in this paper.

geochemical data of Seifert *et al.* (1979). In addition, the present-day subsurface temperatures are used in conjunction with Lopatin's method of calculating the integrated time–temperature index (TTI) from vitrinite reflectance (Waples, 1980) to estimate the earliest geologic time when certain stratigraphic horizons penetrated by the Inigok No. 1 well, one of the deepest wells on the North Slope, would have been sufficiently mature to generate hydrocarbons.

ANALYTICAL PROGRAM

Rock samples from 17 wells drilled on the North Slope of Alaska (Fig. 1; Table 1) have been analyzed by means of various types of petroleum-geochemical techniques. Drill cuttings were collected every 30 ft, washed carefully and sealed in quart cans. Conventional cores were sampled every 5 ft and also canned. Sidewall cores (2 shots each) were acquired at selected depths and canned. Canned drill cuttings samples were selected for analysis as outlined in Table 2. All the analytical work was performed under contract to the USGS by Geochem Research, Inc., the prime contractor, and Global Geochemistry Corp. The kinds of analyses performed are indicated in Fig. 2. At prescribed intervals, analyses (Table 2) were ordered before the samples arrived. To match the thicknesses of stratigraphic units, two sampling programs were established. Analytical program A, of widely spaced analyses, was designed for the Brookian

sequence rocks whereas sample program B, of closely spaced analyses, was designed for the generally thinner rock units in the Ellesmerian sequence.

SAMPLING AND ANALYTICAL PROCEDURE

At the well site, drill cuttings are carefully washed with water to remove the drilling fluid and then are collected in quart cans. When enough cuttings are available, the can is filled about two-thirds full. Enough water is added to submerge the cuttings and leave a $\frac{1}{2}$ in airspace or 'headspace' at the top of the can. A bactericide (zephiran chloride) is added to the water to prevent biological activity in the samples. The can is sealed airtight with a metal lid and three lid clips to insure that the lid will not come loose during shipment. The cans are shipped by air freight to Geochem Research, Inc. in Houston, Texas for analysis (Fig. 2).

A 2 ml sample of headspace gas was analyzed on a 1 ml gas sample loop attached to a gas chromatograph equipped with a $\frac{1}{8}$ in by 8 ft alumina-packed column and flame ionization detector. The gas was analyzed for methane (C_1), ethane (C_2), propane (C_3), iso- and normal butane (i-C_4 and n-C_4), and, if present, the $C_{2=}$, $C_{3=}$ and $C_{4=}$ olefinic hydrocarbons. After *n*-butane elution, the C_5–C_7 hydrocarbons are eluted as a single backflush composite chromatographic peak. The concentration of each hydrocarbon was computed from its peak area. These volumes of airspace, water and rock (drill cuttings) were used to calculate the concentration of each hydrocarbon component in standard volumes of gas per million volumes of sediment (ppm).

After the headspace gas composition is determined, the can is opened and a 10 ml aliquot of wet cuttings is taken for the C_1–C_7 cuttings gas analysis. The sample is disaggregated in a specially designed blender for 2–3 min. Degassed water (2 ml) is injected with a syringe into the 10 ml air space at the top of the blender and an equal amount (2 ml) of the gas withdrawn. This 2 ml gas sample is analyzed in the manner described above. The 10 ml aliquot of cuttings and the 10 ml volume of air space are used for calculation of the standard volumes of C_1–C_7 hydrocarbon components released per million volumes of rock disaggregated. The gas-wetness value is based on the combined headspace and cuttings-gas analyses of the C_1–C_4 data; the C_5–C_7 data was not used in this paper. Gas wetness in per cent is calculated as 100 × $(C_2$–C_4/C_1–$C_4)$.

Solid organic matter dispersed in the rock sample is concentrated, mounted in plastic and polished before vitrinite reflectance is measured. After removal of contaminants, a 30–50 g sample is impact-crushed to 1–2 mm particle size and then digested by excess amounts of 6N hydrochloric acid and 70% hydrofluoric acid to release the kerogen from the inorganic residue. A representative aliquot of the kerogen concentrate is mixed with bioplastic and is mounted in a predrilled hole in a lucite plug. After curing overnight in a drying oven, the surface of the vitrinite plug is polished using different grades of alumina powder from coarse to fine. The plug containing randomly oriented vitrinite is examined under reflected light, and the optical reflectance of first-cycle vitrinite is measured. Wherever the abundance of first-cycle vitrinite permits, 50 vitrinite readings are measured and recorded for each sample. If a sample contains little vitrinite, all the vitrinite particles are measured, even if they appear to be second- or third-cycle material. A description of the plug is part of the vitrinite report and includes (a) polish quality, (b) ease of selecting first-cycle vitrinite, (c) list of all reflectance measurements and (d) qualitative estimate of pyrite abundance. A more complete discussion of the samples and analytical procedure, as well as information for 13 NPRA wells, is available in publications by Claypool and Magoon (1980a–d) and Magoon and Claypool (1980a–f).

GEOLOGY

Physiographically, the North Slope of Alaska can be subdivided into three major provinces: the brooks Range, the foothills and the coastal plain. Gross structural features that correspond to these provinces are, from south to north: (1) Brooks Range orogen, (2) Colville trough or fore deep and (3) Barrow arch (Carter *et al.*, 1977; Grantz *et al.*, 1979; Bird, 1981). Major stratigraphic sequences have been proposed for the Yukon Territory in Canada by Lerand (1973) and extended to northern Alaska by Grantz *et al.* (1975) to

		SYSTEM	ROCK UNIT		ORGANIC CARBON (WT. %)
BROOKIAN SEQUENCE		TERTIARY	Sagavanirktok Formation (M)		1 – 4, Coaly
		CRETACEOUS	Colville Group	sandstone (L)	1 – 4, Coaly
				shale (K)	1 – 2
			Nanushuk Group (J)		1 – 4, Coaly
			Fortress Mountain (H) Formation / Torok Formation (I)		1 – 2
			Pebble shale unit (G)		2 – 4
ELLESMERIAN SEQUENCE		JURASSIC	Kingak Shale (F)		2 – 3
		TRIASSIC	Sag River Sandstone (E)		0 – 3
			Shublik Formation (D)		2 – 5
		TRIASSIC AND PERMIAN	Sadlerochit Group (C)		0 – 1
		PERMIAN TO MISSISSIPPIAN	Lisburne Group (B)		0 – 0.5
		MISSISSIPPIAN AND DEVONIAN	Endicott Group (A)		1 – 4, Coaly
		PRE-DEVONIAN	Basement complex		

Fig. 3. Stratigraphy of the Ellesmerian sequence and Brookian sequence. Two regional unconformities are shown: one at the base of the pebble shale unit, and the other between the basement complex (Franklinian) and the Endicott Group. The average organic-carbon contents for the rocks drilled on the North Slope of Alaska, exclusive of the Wildlife Range, are indicated. The letters shown adjacent to the rock units are the key to stratigraphic units on Figs 4 and 5.

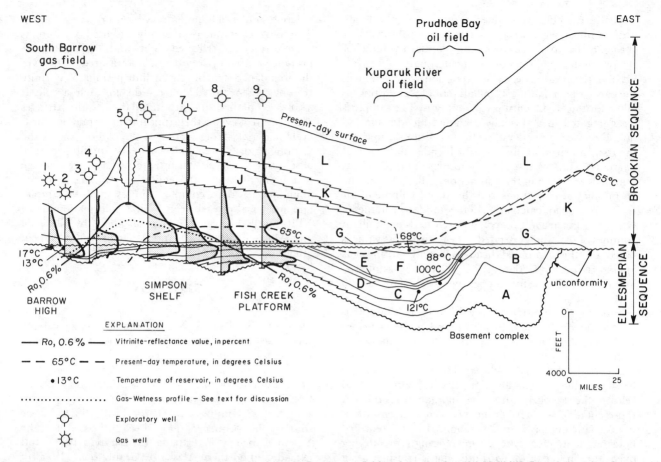

Fig. 4. The west-to-east stratigraphic cross section from the Barrow gas field to the west edge of the Wildlife Range (location shown on Fig. 1). Datum is the regional unconformity immediately beneath the pebble shale unit. The uppermost, undulating surface is the present-day surface. Numbers refer to wells that are named on Table 1 and the letters refer to rock units that are named on Fig. 3. Reservoir temperatures of 68°C is from the Kuparuk River oil field while the other three temperatures (88°C, 100°C and 121°C) are from the Prudhoe Bay oil field.

include the Franklinian sequence, here referred to as the basement complex, the Ellesmerian sequence and the Brookian sequence. The major orogenic episode that separates the basement complex from the Ellesmerian is the Ellesmerian (Antler) orogeny (Grantz *et al.*, 1979). The rifting of northern Alaska from northern Canada is related to the formation of the ancestral Brooks Range as outlined by Grantz *et al.* (1979) and is the major orogenic episode that separates the Ellesmerian from the Brookian sequences. Grantz *et al.* (1979) propose that rifting may have started as early as Early Jurassic time east of Camden Bay and in the Chukchi Sea but that it began in this part of Alaska (Barrow sector) sometime during the Late Jurassic through Early Cretaceous time. Molenaar (1981) further restricts the age of rifting to post early Neocomian (earliest Cretaceous) time as the age of the uppermost part of the Kingak shale in the Inigok No. 1 well is early Neocomian.

The Ellesmerian sequence contains sedimentary rocks that range in age from Late Devonian to Early Cretaceous (Bird, oral communication, 1981); see Fig. 3. The sedimentary rocks include shelf carbonate rocks, and marine and nonmarine siliciclastic rocks whose pro-

venance is generally north of the present coastline. The sandstone included within this sequence is quartz rich. Important reservoir rocks in this sequence are within the Lisburne (carbonate) and Sadlerochit Groups, the Sag River Sandstone and the Kuparuk River sands. The Shublik Formation (2–5 wt % organic carbon (OC)), the Kingak Shale (2–3 wt % OC), and the pebble shale unit (2–4 wt % OC) include shale beds rich in the oil-generating type of organic matter. The basin geography prior to rifting was a simple ramp dipping south, with a coastline trend similar to the present one but with the positions of water and land reversed. Generally as shown on the north–south cross section (Fig. 5), all units within this sequence thicken to the south. The west–east cross section (Fig. 4) indicates these units also thicken to the east before being eroded and lap on to the Barrow arch to the west.

The Brookian sequence, of Early Cretaceous through Tertiary age, includes rock units whose provenance is the Brooks Range orogen. The progradation of the Brookian sequence — a basin-filling deltaic and in-terdeltaic sequence that includes deep-water marine sandstone and shale (Ahlbrandt, 1979) prograded north-

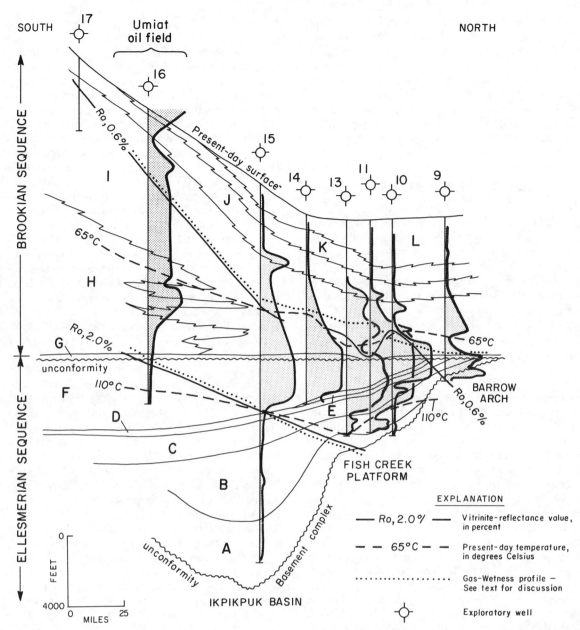

Fig. 5. North-to-south stratigraphic cross section from the Barrow arch to the Colville trough (location shown on Fig. 1). Datum is the regional unconformity immediately beneath the pebble shale unit. The uppermost, undulating surface is the present-day surface. Numbers refer to wells that are named in Table 1 and the letters refer to rock units that are named on Fig. 3.

east from the deep Colville trough over the Barrow arch in the Prudhoe Bay area into the Arctic Ocean basin — is important in providing the overburden to mature older Ellesmerian shales and deeper Brookian shales. When compared to the Ellesmerian sequence, the sandstone within this sequence is quartz poor (Bartsch-Winkler, 1979; Molenaar *et al.*, 1981). Potential reservoir rocks in this sequence are included in the Fortress Mountain Formation, Nanushuk and Colville Groups of Cretaceous age and the Sagavanirktok Formation of Cenozoic age. Brookian shales include at least two marine-shale intervals rich in organic carbon, i.e. Torok Formation (1–2 wt % OC) and shales of the Colville

Group (1–2 wt % OC), both of which contain significant amounts of nonmarine organic matter (Magoon and Claypool, 1979), as is typical of a prograding deltaic sequence.

The rifting of the northern Alaska petroleum province is an important event. The rifted margin first was uplifted, block-faulted and eroded; then it subsided and was overlapped by the pebble shale unit, a condensed marine shale and an important regional petroleum seal. This event was followed by the progradation of the thick Cretaceous and Tertiary siliciclastic rocks of the Brookian sequence. Rifting also appears to have favored formation of petroleum source rocks. For example, the pebble shale unit, deposited during the rifting event, has a higher organic-carbon content and contains more oil-generating amorphous kerogen than do either the Kingak Shale or Torok Formation. Rifting in northern Alaska directly influences conditions for petroleum accumulation. The age (timing), distribution and quality of reservoir rocks are affected by rifting, as are the position of regional seals, and the thermal maturation and expulsion of oil from petroleum source rocks.

GEOCHEMICAL DATA

Both vitrinite reflectance and the gas composition (wetness) are sensitive to the thermal maturity of organic matter in sedimentary rocks. Our data from the North Slope indicates that a vitrinite reflectance value of 0.6% is the beginning point for significant petroleum-hydrocarbon generation. Evidence for this is a significant increase in gas wetness, usually above 25%. Where vitrinite reflectance values of 2.0% occur there is an absence of significant amounts of hydrocarbons larger than methane, due to destruction by thermal cracking or loss due to earlier expulsion. This degree of thermal maturity is also indicated by very low gas wetness beneath a zone of consistently wet gas. Gas composition or wetness also can be influenced by the presence of migrated petroleum in rocks that contain thermally immature organic matter. For this reason, vitrinite reflectance is used as the primary indicator of thermal maturity, and other geochemical properties (in this case gas wetness) are used to confirm or reinforce the interpretation based on vitrinite reflectance. In the present case, a discrepancy between vitrinite reflectance and gas wetness indicates the presence of migrating hydrocarbons.

The geochemical data are shown on two cross sections (Figs 4 and 5). The datum for these two cross sections is the regional unconformity immediately beneath the pebble shale unit. The unconformity, identifiable by well logs and paleontology, is very close to the division between the Ellesmerian sequence and the Brookian sequence, and shows vividly the truncation of the Ellesmerian sequence. Most importantly, these sections force the reader to view the geology more nearly as it was in the geologic past when hydrocarbons migrated and accumulated. To view these sections in their present-day structure, adjust the datum to the almost flat, present-day surface.

The regional correlations of vitrinite reflectance, gas wetness and present-day temperatures are shown in Figs 4 and 5. Reservoir temperatures given in Fig. 4 for the South Barrow gas field (Lantz, 1981) and the Kuparuk (McMillian, 1981) and Prudhoe Bay (Wadman *et al.*, 1979) oil fields are taken from the literature. The isotherms east of Prudehoe Bay were derived by correcting the publicly available bottom-hole temperatures of the wells along the cross section. The gas-wetness profiles shown in Figs 4 and 5 are plotted as solid lines adjacent to each well bore with the intervening shaded area representing C_2–C_4 content; each profile is correlated from well to well with two dotted lines. The shallowest dotted line represents the onset of oil generation, as is indicated

by gas-wetness values that are consistently high, usually above 25%, and the deepest dotted line represents the end of oil generation and is indicated by the decrease in gas wetness to values near zero.

On the north–south cross section (Fig. 5) there is good correlation in the Inigok well among the deeper 2.0 percent vitrinite reflectance, zero gas wetness, and 110 °C temperature horizons. At the southern edge of NPRA, at the Grandstand No. 1 and the Seabee No. 1 wells, the 65 °C isotherm lies about 4500 ft deeper than the 0.6% vitrinite reflectance, which is interpreted as the beginning point for significant wet-gas generation. The 2.0% vitrinite reflectance and zero-wetness values are shallower in the Seabee No. 1 than the 110 °C isotherm by 1500 ft. These relations suggest uplift of this area by an amount equal to the offset of the 65 °C and 110 °C isotherms, or from 1500 to 4500 ft. Acceptable vitrinite-reflectance analyses were not obtained on the cuttings samples from the West Fish Creek No. 1 well, so the depth of 0.6% vitrinite reflectance indicated for this locality is based on analyses of core samples from the adjacent Fish Creek No. 1 well (Fig. 1; Table 1). Good correlations between the 65 °C isotherm, the 0.6% vitrinite reflectance and significant wet-gas generation exists at Inigok No. 1, West Fish Creek No. 1 and Atigaru Point No. 1 wells, but the depth of 0.6% vitrinite reflectance appears to be 1000–2000 ft below the depth of both the 65 °C isotherm and the significant wet-gas generation line at South Harrison Bay No. 1 and W. T. Foran No. 1 wells. In addition, there is poor correlation between the shallow 110 °C isotherm and the 2.0% vitrinite reflectance which intersects the basement complex on the Fish Creek platform. The gas-wetness values on the Fish Creek platform and Barrow arch are also difficult to interpret. However, at this time we do not feel justified in attaching any particular geologic significance to this lower degree of correlation at these two localities.

On the west–east cross section (Fig. 4), the subsurface temperature and the degree of thermal maturity of organic matter in NPRA is such that 110 °C temperatures, 2.0% vitrinite reflectance and the transition at depth from wet to dry gas do not occur in rocks above the basement complex. Only the shallower transitions, indicated by the 65 °C isotherm, 0.6% vitrinite reflectance and depth of significant wet-gas generation, are present. There is good correlation between the selected critical value for vitrinite reflectance and gas wetness in the wells from South Barrow No. 13 to Dalton No. 1. The apparent depth depression of the 0.6% vitrinite-reflectance value at the W. T. Foran No. 1 well (the well that is shown on both cross sections) was pointed out earlier. At North Simpson No. 1 and Tulageak No. 1 further west, the 0.6% vitrinite-reflectance value is very shallow in comparison with the projected present-day depth of 65 °C temperature. This discrepancy suggests uplift and erosion of about 3000–5000 ft of the section. This estimate of uplift and erosion is supported by geologic evidence on this cross section: the reader can visually extend the Torok Formation, Nanushuk Group and the Colville Group to the west over the Barrow area.

The thermal maturity of rocks rich in organic matter is demonstrated on the two cross sections (Figs 4 and 5). The lower part of the Torok Formation, much of the pebble shale unit, the Kingak Shale and the Shublik Formation are in the 'oil window' (Pusey, 1973); the latter two units are also in the 'gas window'. The pebble shale unit is immature in the Barrow field area. The Barrow gas field produces methane gas with a carbon-isotope ratio as (δ^{13}C) of $-40‰$ v. the PDB standard, indicating that the gas originated in rocks with vitrinite reflectance values above 1% (Stahl and Carey, 1975). In addition, oil has been recovered from thermally imma-ture rocks in the South Barrow wells Nos 12, 13, 17, 19 and 20, which indicates long-range migration for this gas and oil.

Seifert *et al.* (1979) have demonstrated on the basis of TAI and biomarker geochemistry that the sedimentary rocks encasing the Kuparuk River oil field, whose reservoir temperature is presently 68 °C, are immature. This conclusion is supported by the depth of the 0.6% vitrinite-reflectance horizon, which plunges toward the Kuparuk field from the North Simpson No. 1 to the W.

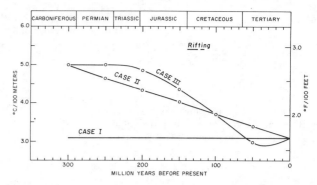

Fig. 6. The change in the geothermal gradient through time is shown for each of the three possible scenarios: in Case I, geothermal gradient is constant; in Case II, the gradient decreases linearly from 325 million years ago to the present; and in Case III, a high geothermal gradient prevailed to the end of Jurassic time followed by a rapid gradient drop in Cretaceous and Tertiary times.

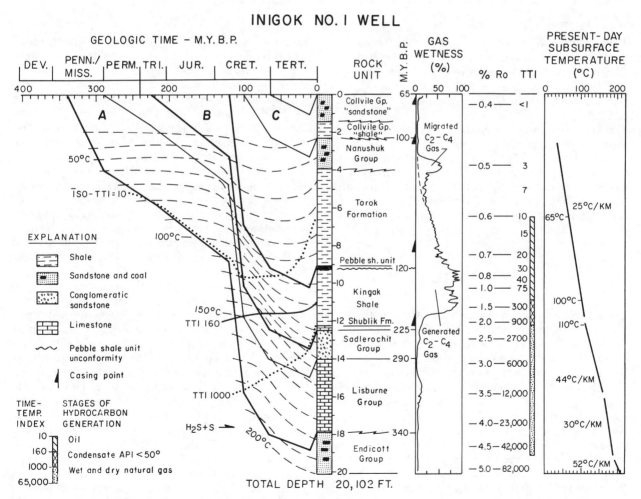

Fig. 7. Burial and thermal history for the Inigok No. 1 well. Three scenarios for geothermal gradients were used to calculate three time-temperature indices (TTI), producing burial paths A, B, and C, respectively. Rock units, the ages assigned to certain horizons, gas wetness, vitrinite reflectance and the present-day corrected subsurface temperature profile are shown. The TTI as calibrated by Waples (1980) is shown next to the vitrinite reflectance data acquired from the Inigok well. The dashed isotherms, every 10°C, are shown for case III superimposed on the burial paths.

Table 3

Time–temperature index calculations for three cases

Stratigraphic Horizon	Age (million yr)	Trial TTI calculations			Observed TTI
		Case I	Case II	Case III	
C Pebble shale unit unconformity	120	25	45	25	30
B Shublik Fm.-Sadlerochit Gp. contact	225	215	340	900	1500
A Lisburne Gp.-Endicott Gp. contact	340	18 000	24 000	34 000	35 000

Table 4

Earliest time that a stratigraphic horizon can achieve a certain TTI

Stratigraphic horizon	Age (million yr)	Time when TTI was achieved (million yr before present)		
		10[a]	160[b]	1000[c]
C pebble shale unit unconformity	120	45	—	—
B Shublik Gp.-Sadlerochit Gp. contact	225	100	80	10
A Lisburne Gp.-Endicott Gp. contact	340	215	110	100

[a] Onset of oil generation (modified from Waples, 1980).
[b] End oil generation (Waples, 1980).
[c] Upper TTI limit for occurrence of oil with API gravity $<50°$ or to begin wet gas generation (Waples, 1980).

T. Foran No. 1 wells and (if one discounts erosion west of the Dalton No. 1 well) parallels the present-day surface. The interpreted depth of increased gas wetness shows a similar trend but plunges less severely toward the Kuparuk field. As would be expected, the 65 °C isotherm parallels the present-day surface.

Whether the rocks that encase the Prudhoe Bay field are mature is questionable. Seifert *et al.* (1979) indicate, on the basis of the data mentioned above, that the rock units are marginally mature. Even though the depth of burial is greater and the reservoir temperatures are higher at Prudhoe when compared to the Kuparuk field, the overburden is largely Tertiary, so the effective time of maturity is short.

THERMAL HISTORY

To illustrate the use of geochemical data in the interpretation of the geologic time of oil and gas generation for this area, the vitrinite-reflectance profile of the Inigok No. 1 well was used in conjunction with burial-history curves and the Lopatin-calculation method described by Waples (1980) to solve for the geothermal-gradient history at the Inigok location during the 350-million-year period in which these rocks accumulated; the results of these geothermal-gradient calculations are summarized in Fig. 6. The burial–history curves for selected horizons in the Inigok No. 1 well are shown in the geologic–time v. depth plot at the left of Fig. 7. These burial curves are determined by the measured depths, the ages and the assumptions regarding the timing and magnitude of uplift. To the right of the depth column appears the stratigraphic sequence of named rock units together with the ages of the horizons for which burial curves are constructed. The predominant lithology for each rock unit is shown to the left of the depth column. The three columns on the right-hand side of Fig. 7 show the gas-wetness v. depth curve, the observed vitrinite reflectance, and the time–temperature index values that correspond to the measured vitrinite-reflectance values at the depth shown. The TTI values are taken from Waples' (1980, Table 4) discussion of Lopatin's method with the modification that the 'onset of oil generation' occurs at a somewhat lower TTI of 10, compared with a TTI of 15 as given by Waples (1980). Except for this modification, we accept the calibration as given by Waples, and use the TTI values given by measured vitrinite reflectance together with the burial curves for selected stratigraphic horizons in order to solve, by trial-and-error method, for the geothermal gradients that could have prevailed during geologic time in the Inigok locality.

Independent confirmation of the maturity calibration given by Waples (1980) is provided by the gas-wetness profile shown in Fig. 7. The inflections of the gas-wetness curve is not the result of caved samples (drill cuttings from shallower depths) because the casing points, shown here as solid triangles adjacent to the wetness profile, do not occur at the points where gas values change, but rather they occur above or below the major changes in gas wetness. The point predicted by theory for the onset of oil generation at TTI 10 ($R_0 = 0.6\%$) occurs at about 6500 ft depth in the Inigok No. 1 well. This corresponds very closely to the depth (6150 ft) at which the gas-wetness curve reaches the twenty-five per cent level and after which the curve remains consistently above that level. The 'upper TTI limit for occurrence of oil with API gravity $<50°$ of Waples (1980) at approximately TTI 1000 occurs in the Inigok well at about 12 200 ft, or below the depth where gas wetness has decreased abruptly from 75% (at 11 300 ft) to less than 20% (at 12 000 ft). 'Peak-oil generation' (TTI 75) occurs about midway between gas-wetness values that exceed 75% and the 'end-of-oil generation' (TTI 160) occurs at the lower end of these high gas-wetness values. The high gas-wetness values at relatively shallow depths (3400–4200 ft) in the Nanushuk Group are disregarded because this depth interval has reservoir rock character, and the gas-wetness values probably represent migrating hydrocarbons. The Nanushuk Group sandstone is the reservoir rock for the Umiat and Simpson oil fields.

Most of our calculations were based on the burial history of three stratigraphic horizons: the contact between the Lisburne and Endicott Groups (340 million yr); the contact between the Shublik Formation and the Sadlerochit Group (225 million yr); and the unconformity at the base of the pebble shale unit (120 million yr). The isotherms shown superimposed on the burial–history curves of Fig. 7 represent the solution (Case III in Fig. 6) that most accurately reproduces the range of observed thermal maturities of organic matter in the Inigok well.

The three general approaches that were used in our calculations are summarized in Fig. 6 and Table 3. TTI values were calculated on the basis of the assumption that the present-day geothermal gradient has prevailed throughout geologic time (Case I). This gradient reproduces the present-day thermal maturity or TTI of the pebble shale horizon, but gives relatively immature or low values for the two deeper horizons. A geothermal gradient that decreases linearly with time (Case II) was used to calculate TTI values for the three stratigraphic horizons. This gave thermal maturities that were too high for the pebble-shale horizon and too low for the Lisburne–Endicott and the Shublik–Sadlerochit horizons. The third assumption (Case III) shown in Figs 6 and 7 of high $(50°C\ km^{-1})$ geothermal-gradient during the late Paleozoic decreasing during the Mesozoic to a low $(28°C\ km^{-1})$ geothermal gradient during the Tertiary best reproduces the present-day TTI. We believe that the heat flow associated with rifting in Early Cretaceous time was higher than normal, as is currently observed in analogous tectonic settings. However, we have not eliminated the alternative interpretation that the apparent change in thermal gradient is due to differences in lithology, as illustrated by the fact that the gradient through the deeper carbonate and sandstone section is higher than that through the shallower shale section. Regardless of the reason, this solution shows good agreement between the TTI values calculated from burial history and assumed thermal gradients, and the TTI values derived from the measured vitrinite reflectance.

For Case III, the earliest times that oil and gas generation could have taken place for the rock units on either side of the three burial paths (A, B and C) are shown on Fig. 7 and outlined in Table 4. The Endicott Group, a rock unit containing coaly 'gas-prone' organic matter, encountered subsurface temperatures sufficient to generate oil during the Triassic (215 million yr) and sufficient to generate wet gas by middle Cretaceous time (100 million yr). The Shublik Formation and lower part of the Kingak Shale reached thermal maturity (TTI 10) during middle Cretaceous time (100 million yr), stopped generating oil during Late Cretaceous time (80 million yr), and is presently at the end of the wet-gas generation

stage (TTI 1500). The lower part of the Torok Formation, pebble shale unit, and upper part of the Kingak Shale are presently generating some oil, as these rocks experienced the onset of oil generation (TTI 10) in Tertiary time (45 million yr).

SUMMARY AND CONCLUSIONS

Preliminary interpretation of selected organic-geochemical analyses conducted on rock samples from wells drilled on the North Slope of Alaska shows that several rock units have contents of oil-generating organic matter sufficient to qualify them for consideration as possible oil source rocks — the pebble shale, the Kingak Shale and the Shublik Formation. Organic matter in the shales of the Colville Group and the Torok Formation is for the most part hydrogen-deficient, and so these may be important gas-source rocks with lesser oil-source-rock potential.

Cross sections and maps showing regional patterns of thermal maturity will be developed on the basis of this geochemical data, and have important implications for oil and gas occurrence. Organic matter in rocks sampled across the northeast edge of NPRA and into Prudhoe Bay field is thermally immature above depths of about 3000 ft in the Barrow area, immature above 8500 ft in the Harrison Bay area, and immature above 7000 ft in the Prudhoe Bay area. In analyzed rocks from wells in a north–south direction from the Harrison Bay region to the Umiat oil field, the depth of thermally mature organic matter shallows considerably, going from 8500 to 3300 ft. The possible oil-source rocks in the Prudhoe Bay region do not have sufficient thermal maturity to account for the quantity of oil present, and migration from the south (the direction of increasing thermal maturity) probably is required to account for the oil.

Thermal maturity of organic matter can be used together with the burial history given by thicknesses and ages of the rock units to estimate the earliest time of oil and gas generation. At the location of the Inigok No. 1 well, the thermal gradient was high from the Carboniferous $(50°C\ km^{-1})$ to the end of the Jurassic $(42°C\ km^{-1})$. The prevailing geothermal gradient at the Inigok locality decreased during the Cretaceous to a low value of 32 °C km^{-1} at the Cretaceous–Tertiary boundary. Since that time the gradient has decreased slightly to the present measured value of 31 °C km^{-1}. The thermal-gradient history provided by the thermal maturity of the organic matter and the burial history indicates that organic matter in the Shublik Formation and Kingak Shale were thermally mature by middle Cretaceous time and that the pebble shale unit, presently at 9000 ft, started to generate oil in Tertiary time.

Acknowledgments

We appreciate and acknowledge the people who made significant contributions to the completion of this paper: Kenneth J. Bird provided the well depths for the rock units shown on Figs 4, 5 and 7; David C. Blanchard generously provided all the corrected present-day subsurface temperatures; Dennis Weitzman of Petroleum

Information did the computer programming that displayed the data used for this paper; Theresa A. Coit typed the manuscript and made valuable comments which, in many cases, were incorporated into the paper. We also thank our reviewers, Keith A. Kvenvolden and Kenneth J. Bird for their extremely helpful comments and suggestions on content and organization.

REFERENCES

Ahlbrandt, T. S. (1979) Introduction to geologic studies of the Nanushuk Group, North Slope, Alaska. In *Preliminary geologic, petrologic, and paleontologic results of the study of Nanushuk Group rocks, North Slope, Alaska*, ed. by Albrandt, T. S. U.S. Geological Survey Circular 794, pp. 1–4.

Bartsch-Winkler, S. (1979) Textural and mineralogical study of some surface and subsurface sandstones from the Nanushuk Group, western North Slope, Alaska. In *Preliminary geologic, petrologic, and paleontologic results of the study of Nanushuk Group rocks, North Slope, Alaska*, ed. by Ahlbrandt, T. S. U.S. Geological Survey Circular 794, pp. 61–76.

Bird, K. J. (1981) *Petroleum exploration of the North Slope in Alaska, U.S.A.* U.S. Geological Survey Open-File Report 81-0227, 43 pp.

Bushnell, H. (1981) Unconformities — key to North Slope oil. *Oil Gas J.* **79**, 114–118.

Carter, R. D., Mull, C. G., Bird, K. J. and Powers, R. B. (1977) *The petroleum geology and hydrocarbon potential of Naval Petroleum Reserve No. 4, North Slope, Alaska.* U.S. Geological Survey Open-File Report 77-475, 62 pp.

Claypool, G. E. and Magoon, L. B. (1980a) *Vitrinite reflectance and C_1–C_7 hydrocarbon data for North Kalikpik No. 1 well, North Slope, Alaska.* U.S. Geological Survey Oil and Gas Investigations Chart OC-96.

Claypool, G. E. and Magoon, L. B. (1980b) *Vitrinite reflectance and C_1–C_7 hydrocarbon data for Cape Halkett No. 1 well, North Slope, Alaska.* U.S. Geological Survey Oil and Gas Investigations Chart OC-97.

Claypool, G. E. and Magoon, L. B. (1980c) *Vitrinite reflectance and C_1–C_7 hydrocarbon data for Drew Point No. 1 well, North Slope, Alaska.* U.S. Geological Survey Oil and Gas Investigations Chart OC-100.

Claypool, G. E. and Magoon, L. B. (1980d) *Vitrinite reflectance and C_1–C_7 hydrocarbon data for Kugrua No. 1 well, North Slope, Alaska.* U.S. Geological Survey Oil and Gas Investigations Chart OC-101.

Grantz, A., Eittreim, S. and Dinter, D. A. (1979) Geology and tectonic development of the continental margin north of Alaska. *Tectonophysics* **59**, 263–291.

Grantz, A., Holmes, M. L. and Kososki, B. A. (1975) Geologic framework of the Alaskan continental terrace in the Chukchi and Beaufort Seas. In *Canada's continental margin and offshore petroleum exploration*, ed. by Yorath, C. J., Parker, E. R. and Glass, D. J. Canadian Society of Petroleum Geologists Memoir 4, pp. 669–700.

Jones, H. P. and Speers, R. G. (1976) Permo-Triassic reservoirs of Prudhoe Bay field, North Slope, Alaska. In *North American oil and gas fields*, ed. by Braunstein, J. American Association of Petroleum Geologists Memoir 24, pp. 23–50.

Lantz, R. J. (1981) Barrow gas fields — N. Slope, Alaska. *Oil Gas J.* **79**, 197–200.

Lerand, M. (1973) Beaufort Sea. In *The future petroleum provinces of Canada — their geology and potential*, ed. by McCrossan, R. G. Canadian Society of Petroleum Geologists Memoir 1, pp. 315–386.

Magoon, L. B. and Claypool, G. E. (1979) Hydrocarbon source potential of the Nanushuk Group and the Torok Formation, A preliminary report. In *Preliminary geologic, petrologic, and paleontologic results of the study of Nanushuk Group*

rocks, North Slope, Alaska, ed. by Ahlbrandt, T. S. U.S. Geological Survey Circular 794, pp. 54–60.

Magoon, L. B. and Claypool, G. E. (1980a) *Vitrinite reflectance and C_1–C_7 hydrocarbon data for South Simpson No. 1 well, North Slope, Alaska.* U.S. Geological Survey Oil and Gas Investigations Chart OC-92.

Magoon, L. B. and Claypool, G. E. (1980b) *Vitrinite reflectance and C_1–C_7 hydrocarbon data for South Harrison Bay No. 1 well, North Slope, Alaska.* U.S. Geological Survey Oil and Gas Investigations Chart OC-93.

Magoon, L. B. and Claypool, G. E. (1980c) *Vitrinite reflectance and C_1–C_7 hydrocarbon data for W. T. Foran No. 1 well, North Slope, Alaska.* U.S. Geological Survey Oil and Gas Investigations Chart OC-94.

Magoon, L. B. and Claypool, G. E. (1980d) *Vitrinite reflectance and C_1–C_7 hydrocarbon data for West Fish Creek No. 1 well, North Slope, Alaska.* U.S. Geological Survey Oil and Gas Investigations Chart OC-95.

Magoon, L. B. and Claypool, G. E. (1980e) *Vitrinite reflectance and C_1–C_7 hydrocarbon data for Atigaru Point No. 1 well, North Slope, Alaska.* U.S. Geological Survey Oil and Gas Investigations Chart OC-98.

Magoon, L. B. and Claypool, G. E. (1980f) *Vitrinite reflectance and C_1–C_7 hydrocarbon data for South Barrow Nos 14, 16, 17, and 19 wells, North Slope, Alaska.* U.S. Geological Survey Oil and Gas Investigations Chart OC-99.

Magoon, L. B. and Claypool, G. E. (1981) Two oil types on North Slope of Alaska — Implications for exploration. *Am. Assoc. Pet. Geol. Bull.* **65**, 644–652.

McKinney, C. M., Garton, E. L. and Schwartz, F. G. (1959) *Analyses of some crude oils from Alaska.* U.S. Bureau of Mines Report of Investigations 5447, 29 pp.

McMillian, W. H. (1981) Reservoir engineering. In *Kuparuk River field, North Slope, Alaska field rules*, Arco Alaska, Inc. Testimony before the Alaska Oil and Gas Conservation Commission, March 25, 1981, pp. III 1–III 9.

Molenaar, C. M. (1981) *Depositional history and seismic stratigraphy of Lower Cretaceous rocks, National Petroleum Reserve in Alaska and adjacent areas.* U.S. Geological Survey Open-file Report 81-1084, 42 pp.

Molenaar, C. M., Egbert, R. M. and Krystinik, L. F. (1981) *Depositional facies, petrography, and reservoir potential of the Fortress Mountain Formation (Lower Cretaceous), central North Slope, Alaska.* U.S. Geological Survey Open-File Report 81-967, 32 pp.

Morgridge, D. L. and Smith, W. B., Jr. (1972) Geology and discovery of Prudhoe Bay field, eastern Arctic Slope, Alaska. In *Stratigraphic oil and gas fields*, ed. by King, R. E. American Association of Petroleum Geologists Memoir 16, pp. 489–501.

Pusey, W. C. (1973) How to evaluate potential gas and oil source rocks. *World Oil* **175**, 71–75.

Seifert, W. K., Moldowan, J. M. and Jones, R. W. (1979) Application of biological marker chemistry to petroleum exploration. In *Proceedings of the 10th World Petroleum Congress*, pp. 425–440.

Stahl, W. and Carey, B. D., Jr. (1975) Source-rock identification by isotope analyses of natural gases from fields in the Val Verde and Delaware Basins, West Texas. *Chem. Geol.* **16**, 257–267.

Wadman, D. H., Lamprecht, D. E. and Mrosovsky, I. (1979) Joint geologic/engineering analysis of the Sadlerochit reservoir, Prudhoe Bay field. *J. Pet. Technol.* 1979, 933–940.

Waples, D. W. (1980) Time and temperature in petroleum formation: Application of Lopatin's method to petroleum exploration. *Am. Assoc. Pet. Geol. Bull.* **64**, 916–926.

Young, A., Monaghan, P. H. and Schweisberger, R. T. (1977) Calculation of ages of hydrocarbons in oils — physical chemistry applied to petroleum geochemistry I. *Am. Assoc. Pet. Geol. Bull.* **61**, 573–600.

Advances in Organic Geochemistry 1981, pp. 39–48
© *John Wiley & Sons Limited, 1983*

Crude Oil Geochemistry of the Gulf of Suez

B. G. Rohrback

Cities Service Company, Energy Resources Group, International Exploration, Houston, Texas

Crude oil samples from the major producing fields in the Gulf of Suez were geochemically assessed to determine the number of genetically related families of oils and to evaluate maturity and migration trends. Multiple analytical parameters used to characterize the petroleum samples included liquid chromatographic separation, gas chromatography, gas chromatography–mass spectroscopy, and stable isotope mass spectroscopy. Combined gas chromatography–mass spectroscopy was used to characterize the variation in distribution of sterane and terpane molecular fossils. Even though these oils are reservoired in strata spanning more than 300 million years of geologic record (Miocene to Devonian in age), all of the oils analyzed from the Gulf of Suez are part of the same genetic family, suggesting the same or highly similar source rocks. The oils reflect a marine origin, show no apparent biodegradation, and display similar carbon isotope ratios (approximately $-29‰$ for the saturate and $-28‰$ for the aromatic hydrocarbons). Their source similarity thus allows a detailed evaluation of chemical and molecular changes that occur as a function of maturity and migration. The maturity variation observed in the Gulf of Suez oils is large, ranging from immature (API gravity 13°) to very mature (API gravity 45°). Migration distances can be very short through juxtaposition of source rock and reservoir bed, or can involve 500 square kilometer drainage patterns.

INTRODUCTION

The Gulf of Suez is a highly faulted rift environment in which successful petroleum exploration has occurred over the past 50 years. Production from the 30 active oil fields of the Gulf and the onshore rift valley extensions, currently projects producible reserves in excess of five billion barrels. These fields span the length and width of the rift zone (an area roughly 250 km × 50 km) with the vast majority of production in the central third of the Gulf (between 28° and 29° north latitude).

A major point of geochemical interest in the Gulf of Suez is the diversity of crude oil parameters in evidence for the region. For example, there is a wide range of crude oil compositions and maturity ranges from very high specific gravity (low API gravity) crudes to oil condensates (high API gravity). In addition, oil reservoirs exist throughout the stratigraphic section (Devonian to Miocene).

The purpose of this paper is to investigate a diverse suite of crude oils collected from the Gulf of Suez rift zone for information related to the environment of deposition and maturity of the source strata responsible for the accumulations. To that end, 52 crude oils from 16 fields and two wildcat wells were analyzed for composition, stable isotope values, and biomarker information. Figure 1 displays a map locating each of the fields assessed in this paper.

The assignation of distinct source rocks (Miocene, Eocene, Cretaceous, and possibly Carboniferous strata) feeding separate reservoirs in the Gulf of Suez have been made by Weeks (1952), Holmquest (1966), Azim

(1970), Girgis and Faris (1970), and Girgis (1975). Because distinct source rocks imply different families of oil, the primary emphasis of this research endeavour was to determine the number of geochemically distinct crude oil families in the Gulf. Secondary emphasis was to examine maturity and migration trends within specific oil families using gas chromatography, gas chromatography–mass spectroscopy, and stable isotope mass spectroscopy.

METHODS

Samples

The 52 crude oils examined in this study represent 16 fields and two non-commercial oil shows (Shukheir Marine 2 and Wadi Dara Marine 1). Samples were

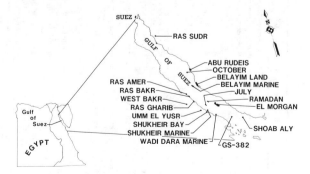

Fig. 1. Field locations for all crude oil samples from the Gulf of Suez.

Table 1

Crude oil sample descriptions and bulk geochemical compositions

FIELD	WELL #	AGE/FORMATION	DEPTH (m)	API GRAVITY	$\%<C_{15}$	$\%\,C_{15}^+$	% S	PARAFFIN	NAPHTHENE	AROMATIC	NSO	ASPHALT	$\delta^{34}S$	$\delta^{13}C$ SAT	$\delta^{13}C$ AR	$\delta^{13}C$ NSO	$\delta^{13}C$ ASPH
Ras Sudr	1	E. Miocene/Rudeis	892	21.7	17.7	82.3	2.1	20.1	22.8	37.5	3.7	15.9	----	-27.78	-26.56	----	----
Ras Sudr	3	Eocene/------	---	22.4	16.3	83.7	2.0	16.8	22.9	33.2	10.8	16.3	----	-27.67	-26.41	----	----
Abu Rudeis	5	E. Miocene/Rudeis	---	24.1	20.6	79.4	2.2	17.7	21.6	37.3	10.3	13.1	----	-28.79	-27.93	----	----
Abu Rudeis	8	E. Miocene/Rudeis	---	25.6	11.7	88.3	2.3	11.7	17.1	24.4	29.3	17.5	+2.6	-29.07	-28.10	-27.77	-28.05
October (GS-195)	A2B	------/Nubia	---	26.6	23.3	76.7	2.0	19.8	23.3	34.1	9.0	13.8	----	-28.54	-27.88	----	----
Belayim Land	?	M. Miocene/Belayim	Zone II	21.2	14.3	85.7	3.2	10.6	17.8	31.2	25.0	15.4	+3.5	-29.11	-28.56	-28.08	-28.23
Belayim Land	112-1	M. Miocene/Belayim	Zone IV	21.1	8.4	91.6	3.2	9.3	14.6	31.4	28.3	16.4	+2.4	-29.30	-28.55	-28.24	-28.18
Belayim Land	112-7	M. Miocene/Zeit	Zone I	20.4	10.4	89.6	3.4	9.2	16.3	31.3	20.8	22.4	+2.7	-29.23	-28.57	-27.85	-28.28
Belayim Land	112-9	E. Miocene/Kareem	Zone IVA	23.0	12.9	87.1	2.8	7.1	13.3	23.3	20.9	35.4	+1.9	-29.10	-28.52	-27.94	-28.22
Belayim Land	112-33	M. Miocene/S. Gharib	Zone IB	19.9	16.1	83.9	3.5	6.4	12.1	27.7	33.7	20.1	+3.4	-29.18	-28.62	-28.14	-28.16
Belayim Land	112-37	E. Miocene/Rudeis	Zone V	17.4	9.4	90.6	2.2	8.5	14.6	26.0	18.4	32.5	+1.2	-29.15	-28.43	-28.11	-28.11
Belayim Land	113-A6	E. Miocene/Rudeis	Zone V	21.4	16.6	83.4	3.3	8.3	14.0	30.4	33.0	14.3	----	-29.22	-28.59	-28.11	-28.20
Belayim Marine	B-M-14	E. Miocene/Rudeis	Zone V	27.1	14.8	85.2	2.0	13.5	24.5	32.4	19.7	9.9	+3.9	-28.80	-28.47	-27.75	-28.10
Belayim Marine	113-M4	Cenomanian/------	---	26.8	22.5	77.5	2.0	11.8	25.3	24.5	22.1	16.3	+3.7	-28.85	-28.22	-27.82	-28.02
Belayim Marine	113-M6	------/------	---	28.0	24.9	75.1	1.9	19.1	22.1	37.3	14.3	7.2	----	-28.59	-27.93	----	----
Ras Amer	4	Eocene/------	1274-1360	21.0	14.5	85.5	4.7	9.2	17.1	28.6	28.7	16.4	+4.4	-28.79	-28.23	-28.03	-28.06
Ras Bakr	24	Turonian/------	816-907	21.5	13.1	86.9	4.0	8.8	17.4	26.6	26.5	20.7	+4.5	-29.06	-28.38	-28.12	-28.18
Ras Bakr	77	Eocene/------	1161-1174	19.6	16.7	83.3	5.3	8.0	15.7	29.7	26.7	19.9	+3.0	-28.97	-28.28	-28.42	-28.09
Ras Bakr	84	Devonian/Nubia "C"	1173-1195	12.8	6.0	94.0	4.7	5.8	7.4	24.8	32.3	29.7	+2.3	-29.71	-28.88	----	-28.35
West Bakr	EPK-2X	E. Miocene/Rudeis	382-393	17.9	12.1	87.9	3.7	12.9	12.8	41.4	11.7	21.2	----	-29.00	-28.35	----	----
Ras Gharib	97	Devonian/Nubia "C"	493-519	17.6	19.6	80.4	2.3	11.3	21.5	30.2	22.8	14.2	+3.2	-28.95	-28.25	-27.55	-28.23
Ras Gharib	200	Turonian/------	580-594	17.2	18.1	81.9	2.5	12.8	21.7	30.2	24.2	11.1	+6.8	-28.92	-28.30	-27.76	-28.00
July	1	------/Nubia	---	33.2	34.2	65.8	1.0	23.5	33.0	33.9	7.3	2.3	----	-28.52	-27.53	----	----
July	4	Cretaceous/------	---	23.2	28.5	71.5	----	25.6	34.0	30.3	5.5	5.6	----	-28.63	-27.63	----	----
July	10	E. Miocene/Rudeis	2865	29.8	25.8	74.2	1.3	14.7	22.6	19.1	28.6	15.0	+0.5	-28.79	-27.99	-27.43	-27.84
July	10-14	E. Miocene/Rudeis	2620	31.7	24.1	75.9	1.2	17.4	28.1	27.8	12.9	13.8	+0.6	-28.69	-27.84	-27.23	-27.67
July	15	E. Miocene/Rudeis	---	25.9	27.7	72.3	----	23.6	30.5	27.4	13.9	4.6	----	-28.54	-27.59	----	----
July	16	E. Miocene/Rudeis	---	27.6	35.0	65.0	----	25.0	30.2	30.2	9.9	4.8	----	-28.52	-27.63	----	----
July	19	E. Miocene/Rudeis	---	25.4	26.4	73.6	----	24.8	30.2	28.0	11.9	5.1	----	-28.48	-27.66	----	----
July	20	E. Miocene/Rudeis	---	30.0	36.6	63.4	----	27.1	23.9	26.1	9.8	13.1	----	-28.58	-27.69	----	----
July	33	E. Miocene/Rudeis	---	26.0	28.9	71.1	----	22.4	28.6	28.8	15.7	4.5	----	-28.80	-28.05	----	----
Ramadan	6	------/Nubia	---	20.6	34.7	65.3	----	22.5	26.9	27.4	11.9	11.3	----	-28.84	-28.16	----	----
Ramadan	8	------/Nubia	---	24.8	24.9	75.1	----	28.9	27.3	27.1	11.3	5.4	----	-28.85	-27.71	----	----
Ramadan	10	------/Nubia	---	30.8	27.7	72.3	1.0	26.9	26.8	31.1	9.8	5.4	----	-28.63	-27.47	----	----
Ramadan		------/Nubia	---	25.9	21.5	78.5	----	27.1	28.6	31.2	7.1	6.0	----	-28.73	-27.65	----	----
Ramadan	6-13	Devonian/Nubia "C"	3475	28.7	22.0	78.0	1.0	20.0	31.6	19.7	25.5	3.2	+0.3	-29.02	-27.84	-27.09	-27.98
El Morgan	7	E. Miocene/Kareem	---	25.9	24.5	75.5	----	22.7	27.7	35.2	8.3	6.1	----	-28.50	-28.09	----	----
El Morgan	16	E. Miocene/Kareem	---	21.9	22.5	77.5	----	24.2	23.3	30.6	14.7	7.2	----	-28.13	-27.79	----	----
El Morgan	27	M. Miocene/Belayim	---	17.5	25.5	74.5	----	16.5	21.7	32.1	14.0	15.7	----	-29.24	-28.58	----	----
El Morgan	51	E. Miocene/Kareem	---	27.2	27.8	72.1	----	20.6	22.6	32.0	17.8	7.0	----	-28.56	-28.05	----	----
El Morgan	59	E. Miocene/Kareem	---	26.5	27.4	72.6	----	19.5	24.1	32.7	14.4	7.7	----	-28.55	-28.19	----	----
El Morgan	62	E. Miocene/Kareem	---	28.1	27.4	72.6	----	19.2	24.1	34.0	15.6	7.1	----	-28.73	-27.99	----	----
El Morgan	64	E. Miocene/Kareem	---	32.7	31.2	68.8	1.4	25.5	32.3	32.5	4.9	4.8	----	-28.33	-27.92	----	----
El Morgan	64	E. Miocene/Kareem	---	22.6	20.8	79.2	----	20.8	22.4	29.2	15.8	6.5	----	-28.20	-27.77	----	----
El Morgan	85	M. Miocene/Belayim	---	24.6	23.3	76.7	----	17.9	17.5	37.6	16.9	10.1	----	-29.30	-28.59	----	----
El Morgan	36-60	E. Miocene/Kareem	---	26.2	25.0	75.0	----	14.7	38.0	34.7	5.5	7.1	----	-28.32	-28.09	----	----
Umm el Yusr	25	E. Miocene/Rudeis	---	21.1	16.7	83.3	2.9	14.3	16.9	39.2	14.2	15.4	----	-29.31	-28.45	----	----
Shukheir Bay	1	E. Miocene/Rudeis	1660	29.1	25.5	74.5	1.3	22.7	27.7	31.9	10.9	6.8	----	-28.46	-28.09	----	----
Shukheir Marine	2	E. Miocene/Kareem	1925	41.2	47.3	52.7	0.3	24.8	35.2	20.4	12.2	7.4	+4.2	-26.80	-24.90	----	----
Wadi Dara Marine	1	E. Miocene/Rudeis	1570	44.6	42.4	57.6	0.4	26.2	37.3	20.8	8.8	6.9	-.3	-28.50	-27.57	-27.04	-27.65
GS-382	1B	------/Nubia	3131	29.7	28.3	71.7	1.3	25.0	25.9	30.7	8.7	9.7	----	-27.33	-26.90	----	----
Shoab Aly	B-6	------/Nubia	---	33.0	36.0	64.0	1.7	23.9	24.8	35.1	10.7	5.5	----	-27.50	-27.50	----	----

1 Normalized weight percent of C_{15}^+ fraction.

2 Isotope ratios in permil relative to PDB and CD standards.

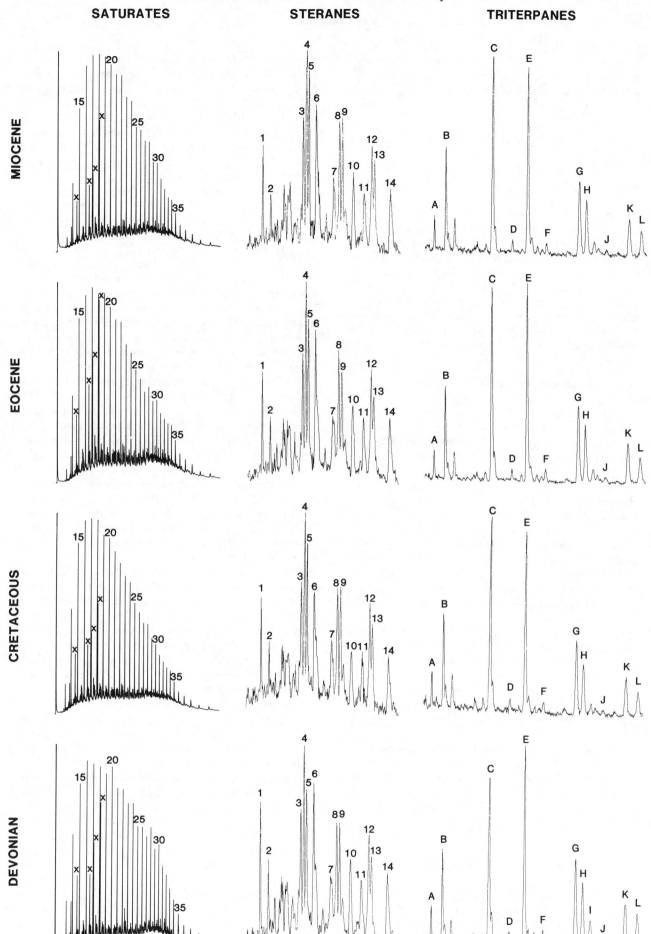

Fig. 2 Saturate hydrocarbon gas chromatograms and sterane ($m/z = 217$) and triterpane ($m/z = 191$) mass chromatograms for four Gulf of Suez crude oils of different reservoir ages: Miocene (Belayim Land 112-33), Eocene (Ras Amer 4), Cretaceous (Belayim Marine 113-M4), and Devonian (Ras Bakr 84). Numbers on the saturate GC traces mark the elution of the straight-chain paraffins of those carbon numbers, x's mark the C_{16}, C_{18}, C_{19} (pristane), and C_{20} (phytane) isoprenoid alkanes. Labelled peaks on the sterane and triterpane traces are identified in Table 2.

collected by the Egyptian General Petroleum Corporation, General Petroleum Company, the Egyptian Army Oil Analysis Laboratory, and Cities Service International.

Analytical procedures

Oils were evaporated to constant weight at 70 °C to quantify the low molecular weight (less that C_{15}) fraction. After evaporation, the residual (C_{15+}) fraction was deasphalted by precipitation in *n*-pentane, and subsequently separated into saturates, aromatics, and polar NSO compounds by column chromatography. The columns were packed with 1:1 (by weight) alumina overlying silica gel such that the weight of the asphalt-free C_{15+} fraction was 2% of the combined weight of the column packing materials. Successive elution with *n*-pentane, toluene, and methanol yielded saturated hydrocarbon, aromatic hydrocarbon, and NSO nonhydrocarbon fractions, respectively.

Instrumental techniques

Gas chromatography of the saturated hydrocarbon fraction was performed on a Hewlett Packard 5880 equipped with a 12.5 meter fused silica SP-2100 capillary column and a flame ionization detector. Oven temperature was programmed from 100 to 280 °C at 8 °C min^{-1}. The gas chromatograph was interfaced to a Hewlett Packard 3354 automation system for data storage, chromatogram drafting, and computation of paraffin/naphthene ratios.

Gas chromatography–mass spectroscopy (GC–MS) analysis was performed by Global Geochemistry Corporation using a Finnigan 4000 quadrupole mass spectrometer. The GC was programmed from 35 to 280 °C at 4 °C min^{-1} and employed a 30 m fused silica SE-54 capillary column.

Carbon and sulphur stable isotope values were measured relative to the PDB and CD standards on separate Micromass 602D dual-collecting isotope ratio mass spectrometers. Carbon isotope samples of petroleum fractions were prepared by the method of Sofer (1980) in our laboratory; sulphur isotope values were measured by Geochron Laboratories on whole crude oils.

Percent sulphur determinations were made on whole crude oils using a Philips X-ray fluorescence spectrograph, PET crystal, and proportional detector.

API gravities were obtained by measuring specific gravity on a Westphal balance and normalizing to 60 °F (15.6 °C).

RESULTS AND DISCUSSION

Table 1 lists reservoir information, crude oil composition measurements, and stable isotope ratios for the 52 samples analyzed. The oils are grouped by field from Ras Sudr in the northern Gulf to Shoab Aly in the south. Well number, formation, and depth information are reported, if supplied by the sample collector. Reservoir

ages range from Middle Miocene (Zeit Formation) to Devonian (Nubia Formation sandstone). The Nubia Formation is a grab bag of sandstone of mixed age (from Cretaceous to Devonian — or perhaps older). In accordance with Pomeyrol (1968), the only oils assigned in Table 1 to the Devonian age classification are those unambiguously collected from the Nubia 'C' horizon. The Nubic 'C' is a sandstone unit that unconformably underlies a Carboniferous shale.

Two of the crude oils listed in Table 1 have duplicates: Ramadan 10 and El Morgan 64. In both cases, the sample listed first was collected near the onset of production from that well, whereas the second sample is more recent. In both wells, the C_{15+} composition and stable isotope ratios of the C_{15+} fractions are similar, but the API gravity values and molecular weight distributions (as represented by $% < C_{15}$ and $%C_{15+}$) are substantially different. Earlier-produced crude oil has a lower average molecular weight and higher API gravity (lower specific gravity), suggesting either that reservoirs are not homogeneous or that production mechanics alter some bulk crude oil composition parameters.

A wide range in values of crude oil parameters exists in the data of Table 1. For example, Gulf of Suez oils span the entire crude oil portion of the API gravity scale ranging from 12.8° (very immature or biodegraded) to 44.6° (mature oil or condensate). In accordance with this range in API gravity, the low molecular weight fraction $(% < C_{15})$ varies between 6% and 47% by weight. Percent sulphur in the crude oils analyzed varies between 0.3% to 5.3% by weight. The C_{15+} composition in the Suez oils range from having a dominant non-hydrocarbon fraction (NSO plus asphaltene) to bring highly enriched in saturated hydrocarbon components (paraffin and naphthene).

Despite the diversity of composition data listed in Table 1, the detail of the geochemistry of these samples strongly suggests a single source for all crude oil reservoired in the Gulf of Suez. Figure 2 displays the notion of common origin for oils produced from Devonian, Cretaceous, Eocene, and Miocene reservoirs. Gas chromatograms of the saturate hydrocarbon fraction, plus patterns from sterane and triterpane mass ion plots ($m/z = 217$ and 191, respectively) are extremely similar and are not dependent on reservoir age.

The saturate gas chromatographic traces for all oils studied from the Gulf of Suez display the same marine-source signature as shown in Fig. 2. Naphthenic unresolved complex mixtures are broad, slightly bimodal humps representing more than 50% by weight of the saturate fraction. Isoprenoid hydrocarbons (denoted by x's in Fig. 2) exhibit consistent patterns in sample comparisons and typically yield pristane/phytane ratios of 0.7. The total range of pristane/phytane ratios observed is 0.6 to 1.0 and is correlatable to the maturity level of the crude: pristane/phytane increased with increasing API gravity. The predominance of phytane relative to pristane and the slight even normal-paraffin preference suggests an extremely reducing environment of source rock deposition (Welte and Waples, 1973). Because the suspected source beds are Tertiary or Cretaceous lime-stones and marls, the carbonate-catalyzed beta cleavage

Table 2
List of identified steranes and triterpanes

Label	Sterane	Label	Triterpane
1	13β(H), 17α(H) diacholestane (20S)	A	18α(H), 21β(H)-22, 29, 30-trisnorhopane
2	13β(H), 17α(H) diacholestane (20R)	B	17α(H), 21β(H)-22, 29, 30-trisnorhopane
3	5α(H) cholestane (20S)	C	17α(H), 21β(H)-30-norhopane
4	5α(H), 14β(H), 17β(H) cholestane (20R)	D	17β(H), 21α(H)-30-normoretane
5	5α(H), 14β(H), 17β(H) cholestane (20S)	E	17α(H), 21β(H)-hopane
6	5α(H) cholestane (20R)	F	17β(H), 21α(H)-moretane
7	5α(H) ergostane (20S)	G	17α(H), 21β(H)-30-homohopane (22S)
8	5α(H), 14β(H), 17β(H) ergostane (20R)	H	17α(H), 21β(H)-30-homohopane (22R)
9	5α(H), 14β(H), 17β(H) ergostane (20S)	I	gammacerane
10	5α(H) ergostane (20R)	J	17β(H), 21α(H)-30-homomoretane
11	5α(H) stigmastane (20S)	K	17α(H), 21β(H)-30, 31-bishomohopane (22S)
12	5α(H), 14β(H), 17β(H) stigmastane (20R)	L	17α(H), 21β(H)-30, 31-bishomohopane (22R)
13	5α(H), 14β(H), 17β(H) stigmastane (20S)		
14	5α(H) stigmastane (20R)		

reaction observed by Shimoyama and Johns (1972) may also be effecting the n-paraffin distribution.

The API gravity of the Devonian-reservoired Bakr 84 oil was the lowest value measured for the suite of Suez crude oils, but the saturate gas chromatogram of this oil (Fig. 2) does not display any significant biodegradation. Therefore, the Bakr field appears to be the result of crude oil migration from an immature source rock.

The sterane and triterpane distributions in Fig. 2 are also extremely similar for this 350 million year span of reservoir ages. Identified components are labelled with numbers from 1 to 14 for steranes and letters A through L for triterpanes. A listing of these identifications appears in Table 2. Gammacerane (triterpane peak I) was identified in the Gulf of Suez crude oil samples, but in most cases, remained at a very low concentration level (approximately 1%) of the total triterpanes. The exception is the Ras Bakr oil of Devonian reservoir age in Fig. 2. Although the significance of the presence or absence of gammacerane in a crude oil has not been fully investigated, the three-fold higher concentration of this compound in only the Devonian Ras Bakr oil may be significant. This variation suggests the possibility that some triterpane components have been provided by the terrestrially derived Carboniferous black shale that forms the caprock of this reservoir.

Further evidence for the similarity in source rocks for oils of diverse reservoir age is presented in Fig. 3. This

figure plots the relative abundance of the 5α(H), 14α(H), 17α(H) 20R and 20S isomers of the C_{27}, C_{28}, and C_{29} steranes. The 20R isomers have been used by Seifert and Moldowan (1978) and MacKenzie (1980) as sensitive indicators of source input because the ratios of C_{27}, C_{28} and C_{29} 20R isomers are relatively unaffected by maturation and migration processes.

The data of Fig. 3 are calculated from the sterane mass chromatograms of Fig. 2 for Devonian, Cretaceous, Eocene, and Miocene oil samples. Quantitation based on peak height yields a tight clustering of data for both 20S and 20R isomers around a composition of 50% C_{27}, 25% C_{28}, and 25% C_{29} and, therefore, suggests a single source. The relatively low abundance of C_{29} steranes (stigmastanes), characteristic of higher land plant input, is further support for the marine origin of the Gulf of Suez crude oils.

Because the Gulf of Suez oils appear to share a common marine source, detail of maturity trends within a single oil family can be examined. Figure 4 plots three crude oil composition parameters against API gravity (as a measure of maturity level) for all oils in this study. These plots chart the following general trends: with an increase in API gravity, there is a corresponding

1. increase in the low molecular weight $\% < C_{15}$ fraction;
2. increase in the ratio of saturated to aromatic hydrocarbons; and
3. decrease in the percent sulphur.

These trends are consistent with maturity relationships reported by Nelson (1968) and Milner *et al.* (1977).

The saturate to aromatic ratios and the hydrocarbons to non-hydrocarbon ratios presented in Fig. 4 are calculated for the C_{15+} fractions and therefore disregard the light ends ($< C_{15}$) of the oils; this minimizes the effects of sample collection and storage which can result in a depletion of the low molecular weight range components.

The sulphur content reported in Fig. 4 is total crude oil sulphur and is, therefore, the combination of elemental sulphur, sulphides or disulphides, mercaptans and thiophenes. Percent sulphur in Gulf of Suez crude oils decreases in a regular fashion with an increase in maturity. The sulphur values and

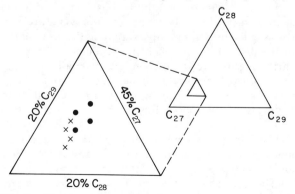

Fig. 3. Ternary diagram showing relative abundance of C_{27}, C_{28}, and C_{29} 5α(H), 14α(H), 17α(H) steranes (● = 20R isomers, x = 20S isomers).

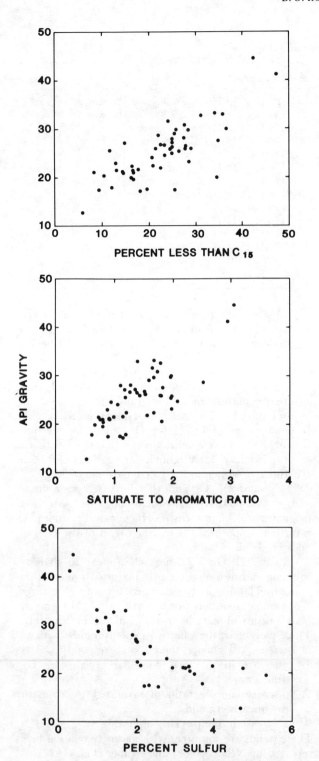

Fig. 4. Crude oil composition parameters as a function of API gravity.

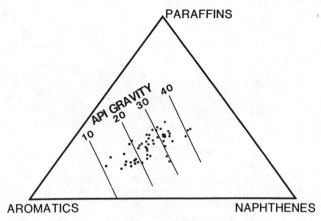

Fig. 5. Ternary diagram illustrating the effect of increasing maturity level (increasing API gravity) on hydrocarbon composition for oils of a common marine source.

relationship to specific API gravity levels are consistent with data reported by Elzarka (1975).

Sulphur isotope values ranged from +0.3‰ to +6.8‰ relative to the Canyon Diablo troilite (Table 1), and did not display any consistent trend with increased API gravity. This lack of dependence of sulphur isotopic composition on maturity level is consistent with observations of Thode *et al.* (1958) and Thode and Monster (1965). The sulphur isotopes also show no

dependence on age, inorganic facies or temperature of the reservoir rock — suggesting that reservoir effects, as applied to Big Horn Basin oils by Orr (1974), are not effective in the Gulf of Suez. At present, the geochemical processes controlling the sulphur isotope ratios are unknown.

The relationship between C_{15+} hydrocarbon composition and maturity is depicted in Fig. 5. The relative amounts of paraffins, naphthenes, and aromatics are plotted for all 52 oils studied from the Gulf of Suez. Superimposed on the ternary composition diagram is the API gravity scale and the approximate position of four benchmark maturity levels. With increasing maturity, the C_{15+} hydrocarbon fraction changes from aromatic fraction dominance (65% aromatics) to saturated hydrocarbon dominance (75% paraffins plus naphthenes). The paraffin to naphthene ratio remains unchanged with increasing maturity, maintaining a paraffin/naphthene ratio of approximately 1 to 2.

There are slight regional variations in Gulf of Suez oils based on stable carbon isotope ratios of the C_{15+} crude oil fractions (Table 1). The deviations from isotopic norm (typically 1–2‰ more positive) are only found in crude oil fractions of the extreme north (Ras Sudr) and the extreme south (Shukheir Marine, GS-382, and Shoab Aly). These differences are most likely due to subtle changes in the micro-environment during source rock deposition in the extreme ends of the Suez rift.

Stable carbon isotope values of oils reservoired in the central portion of the Gulf of Suez oil province are very consistent. The slight isotopic variations that are evident in the data of Table 1 can be attributed to maturity effects. Figure 6 relates carbon isotope data to maturity level for selected central Gulf oils. The basis for selection was that measurements were carried out on both hydrocarbon and nonhydrocarbon fractions of plotted oil samples.

The four graphs of Fig. 6 depict the $\delta^{13}C$ values of the four C_{15+} organic fractions (saturates, aromatics, NSOs and asphaltenes) plotted relative to API gravity. The Gulf of Suez oils show the expected carbon isotope trend (kinetic isotope effect) for all four component fractions: as thermal maturity level increases (higher API gravity), the isotopic ratios increase to less negative values. Thus,

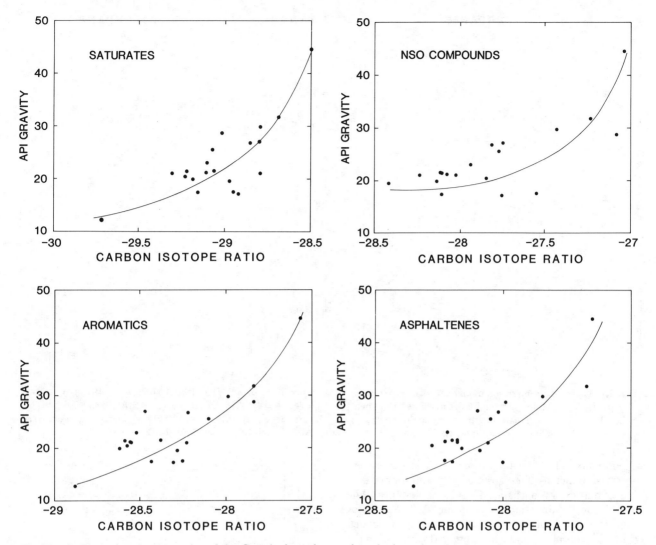

Fig. 6. Stable carbon isotope ratios of the C_{15+} hydrocarbon and nonhydrocarbon fractions related to maturity level (API gravity).

saturate hydrocarbons range from $-29.7\permil$ for the least mature oil (Ras Bakr 84) to $-28.5\permil$ for the most mature sample (Wadi Data Marine 1). Similar maturity ranges were observed for the other three fractions: $-28.9\permil$ increasing to $-27.6\permil$ for the C_{15+} aromatics; $-28.4\permil$ increasing to $-27.0\permil$ for the NSO compounds; and $-28.4\permil$ increasing to $-27.6\permil$ for the asphaltene fraction.

The effects of maturity on sterane and terpane distributions are illustrated in Fig. 7. Mass chromatograms are displayed for three oil samples: Ras Bakr 84 is immature with an API gravity of 12.8°; Abu Rudeis 8 is moderately mature and has an API gravity of 25.6°; Wadi Dara Marine 1 is highly mature with a 44.6° API gravity.

These three oils accurately reflect the changes noted among all eight oil samples studied by GC–MS. Both di- and triterpane mass chromatograms in Fig. 7 monitor $m/z = 191$, whereas the sterane distribution is based on $m/z = 217$. Sterane and triterpane identifications are the same as shown in Fig. 2 and listed in Table 2.

The diterpane distribution in Gulf of Suez crude oil does not change dramatically during thermal stress, but several subtle trends can be observed. Four diterpane

components posted a consistent increase in their abundance relative to the total diterpane concentration with increasing maturity level: C_{19} (peak a), C_{20} (peak b), C_{21} (peak c) and C_{24} (peak f). The suggestion is that these compounds are either thermodynamically more stable than other diterpenoid hydrocarbons or they represent breakdown products of higher molecular weight diterpane homologs or triterpanes. Compound e (C_{23} diterpane) is the most abundant diterpane in Gulf of Suez oil but decreases in its relative importance with increasing thermal stress (a similar decrease in abundance was noted for peak d, a C_{22} diterpane). Relative amounts of compounds g, h, and i (the C_{25} and C_{26} diterpanes) do not change appreciably with thermal stress in this case.

The increasing maturity level of the sterane mass chromatograms of Fig. 7 display a decrease in the total sterane content of the crude oil (as noted by the decreasing signal-to-noise ratio) as well as a preferential degradation of the C_{28} and C_{29} steranes compared with C_{27} components and diasteranes. The $5\alpha(H)$, $14\alpha(H)$, $17\alpha(H)$ isomers are notably less stable than the $5\alpha(H)$, $14\beta(H)$, $17\beta(H)$ isomers for C_{27}, C_{28} and C_{29} steranes. This trend was noted by Mackenzie *et al.* (1980) for the

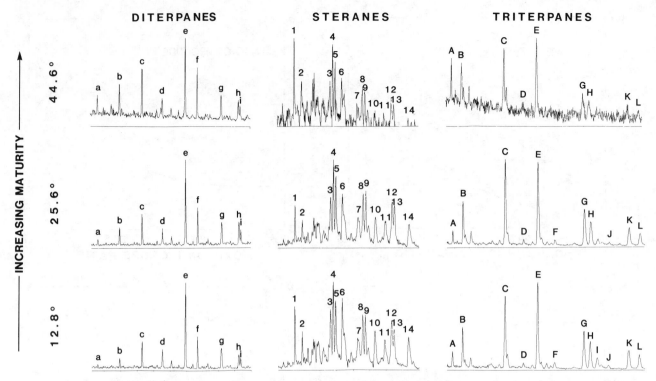

Fig. 7. Mass spectrometric ion monitoring of diterpanes ($m/z = 191$), steranes ($m/z = 217$) and triterpanes ($m/z = 191$) as a function of maturity level. Molecular weights of diterpane components are: a = 262; b = 276; c = 290; d = 304; e = 318; f = 332; g = 346; h, i = 360. Sterane and triterpane identifications are listed in Table 2. Maturity levels are ordered by API gravity and are represented by the following samples: 12.8° = Ras Bakr 84; 25.6° = Abu Rudeis 8; 44.6° = Wadi Dara Marine 1.

C_{29} isomers. The $20S/20R$ ratios of $\alpha\alpha\alpha$ steranes were observed to increase for ergostane (C_{28}) and stigmastane (C_{29}), but show no change for C_{27} cholestanes. The magnitude and direction of change for $20S/20R$ ratio for stigmastane are consistent with observations by Schoell *et al.* (this volume). The lack of observed variation in the $20S/20R$ ratio for cholestanes may be due to overlap of diasteranes in the m/e 217 trace.

The triterpanes shown in Fig. 7 show expected maturity trends in hopane series $22S/22R$ ratios (Seifert and Moldowan, 1978): homohopane $22S/22R$ (G/H) increases from 1.3 to 1.5 and bishomohopane $22S/22R$ (K/L) increases from 1.3 to 2.0. This starting ratio of 1.3 for $22S/22R$ ratios represents immature oils and is the same as found for the beginning of the oil window in Mahakam Delta source rocks by Schoell *et al.* (this volume). The $18\alpha(H)/17\alpha(H)$ trisnorhopane ratio (A/B) is insensitive to low and to moderate levels of thermal stress, but rapidly increases in the most mature oils studied. The trisnorhopanes show no change in the Gulf of Suez oils up to an API gravity of 27°; the A/B ratio rapidly increases at higher API maturity levels, progressing from 0.4 to 1.0 at 44.6° API. Moretanes (peaks D, F and J) are minor components, but are preserved in all crude oil samples studied regardless of oil maturity.

Figure 8 is a crossplot of two C_{29} sterane ratios; the $20S/20R$ ratio for $\alpha\alpha\alpha$ stigmastanes and the $\alpha\beta\beta/\alpha\alpha\alpha$ stigmastane $20R$ ratio. This format has been used by Seifert and Moldowan (1981) to separate the effects of maturation and migration for related crude oils. The curve drawn through the data represents a trend in the C_{29} sterane ratios, unencumbered by effects of

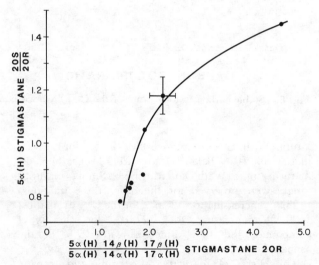

Fig. 8 Maturity–migration plot of C_{29} steranes (after Seifert and Moldowan, 1981). Data points represent the following oils: Ras Bakr 84; Belayim Land 112–33; Ras Amer 4; Abu Rudeis 8; Belayim Marine 113-M4; Shukheir Bay 1; July 10–14; and Wadi Dara M-1. Uncertainty in the ratio measurement for the July 10–14 stigmastanes is noted by error bars.

migration; deviations from the curve to the lower right are reported to be caused by migration effects (Seifert and Moldowan, 1981). Figure 8 suggests that geochemically assessable migration effects in this suite of Gulf of Suez crude oils are small: this observation is consistent with the play concept in the Gulf (i.e. reservoirs exist in small tilted fault blocks fed by source rocks within the block or from adjacent strata). The largest deviation from the strict maturity line is the oil sample from Belayim Marine field. Of the samples studied by GC–MS, the Belayim Marine field effectively drains the largest areal extent (approximately 500 square kilometers) due to the distance separating major faults and, therefore, would be expected to show the largest geochemical deviation in the data presentation of Fig. 8.

CONCLUSIONS

An extensive series of crude oil samples from the Gulf of Suez, Egypt were studied by a variety of organic geochemical techniques. These oils were found to share a common marine source rock regardless of the age of reservoir. Because of this common origin, detailed maturity effects can be examined. Observed maturity trends include:

1. a transition from C_{15+} nonhydrocarbon dominance relative to C_{15+} hydrocarbons (2:1) to a nearly 10:1 hydrocarbon dominance;
2. a progression from aromatic to saturate C_{15+} hydrocarbon prepotency (65% aromatic to 75% saturate);
3. a 1.5‰ maximum variation in $\delta^{13}C$ of C_{15+} crude oil fractions strictly attributable to maturity; and
4. a decrease in percent sulphur from 5.3% to 0.3%.

No apparent biodegradation is evident for this suite of Gulf of Suez crude oils. This conclusion is based on gas chromatography (preservation of normal paraffins), combined gas chromatography–mass spectroscopy (lack of biodegradative effects on steranes and terpanes — Seifert and Moldowan, 1979; Goodwin *et al.*, this volume), and stable carbon isotope mass spectroscopy (based on observations described by Sofer, 1981). The reason for this regional lack of biological activity may be that the high salinity of formation waters provides a barrier against invasion by meteoric waters (Elzarka, 1975).

The occurrence of the lowest API gravity oil in the oldest reservoir of the Ras Bakr field is most likely the result of migration at an immature stage of source rock categenesis. The contention that a low apparent maturity level might be related to escape of the low molecular weight fraction due to ineffectively sealed traps (Gilboa and Cohen, 1979) is not supported by the biomarker or carbon isotope data.

Apparent geochemical migration effects are small for a subset of eight Gulf of Suez crude oils. This conclusion is supportive of the exploration play concept (draining of the same or adjacent small fault blocks) currently accepted for the Suez rift.

Acknowledgements

I thank Cities Service Company Energy Resources Group and Egyptian General Petroleum Corporation for permission to publish this study. I appreciate Dr M. K. El Ayouty, Mr G. Hanter, Dr E. Shaltout, Mr R. T. El Adl, and Mr J. F. Keith for their interest in this project and for their assistance in obtaining samples. I am indebted to J. Heard, A. Jones, C. Schiefelbein, and Dr Z. Sofer for technical analyses. Special thanks are due to Dr J. Maxwell for sterane isomer identifications and Drs C. Sutton and J. Zumberge for critically reviewing the manuscript.

REFERENCES

Azim, M. F. A. (1970) Crude oil composition — a clue to its migration in the Gulf of Suez region. *Proceedings of the Seventh Arab Petroleum Congress, Kuwait*, 16–22 March 1970.

Elzarka, M. H. (1975) Geochemical relations of fluids in oil fields of Gulf of Suez, Egypt. *Am. Ass. Petrol. Geol. Bull.* **59**, 1667–1684.

Gilboa, Y. and Cohen, A. (1979) Oil trap patterns in the Gulf of Suez. *Israel J. Earth Sci.* **28**, 13–26.

Girgis, G. F. (1975) About oil generation and accumulation in the abundant carbonate rocks of the sedimentary section in Arab Republic of Egypt. *Proceedings of the Ninth Arab Petroleum Congress, Dubai*, 10–16 March 1975.

Girgis, G. F. and Faris, M. I. (1970) Presence of some local source sediments within the oil-producing Eocene limestones in the western coast of Gulf of Suez. *Proceedings of the Seventh Arab Petroleum Congress, Kuwait*, 16–22 March 1970.

Goodwin, N. S., Park, P. J. D. and Rawlinson, T. (1981) Crude oil biodegradation. *Adv. Org. Geochem.* (ed. M. Bjorøy) in press.

Holmquest, H. J. (1966) Stratigraphic analysis of source bed occurrences and reservoir oil gravities. *Am. Ass. Petrol. Geol. Bull.* **50**, 1478–1486.

Mackenzie, A. S. (1980) Application of biological marker compounds to subsurface geological processes. PhD Thesis, University of Bristol.

Mackenzie, A. S., Patience, R. L., Maxwell, J. R., Vandenbroucke, M. and Durand, B. (1980) Molecular parameters of maturation in the Toarcian shales, Paris Basin, France I. Changes in the configurations of acyclic isoprenoid alkanes, steranes and triterpanes. *Geochim. Cosmochim. Acta* **44**, 1709–1721.

Milner, C. W. D., Rogers, M. A. and Evans, C. R. (1977) Petroleum transformations in reservoirs. *J. Geochem. Explor.* **7**, 101–153.

Nelson, W. L. (1968) Sulfur in crude oils around the world. *Oil Gas J.* **66**, 96–98.

Orr, W. L. (1974) Changes in sulfur content and isotopic ratios of sulfur during petroleum maturation: A study of Big Horn Basin Paleozoic oils. *Am. Ass. Petrol. Geol. Bull.* **58**, 2295–2318.

Pomeyrol, R. (1968) Nubian Sandstone. *Am. Ass. Petrol. Geol. Bull.* **52**, 589–600.

Schoell, M., Teschner, M., Wehner, H., Durand, B. and Oudin, J. L. (1981) Maturity related biomarker and stable isotope variations and their application to oil/source rock correlation in the Mahakam Delta/Kalimantan. *Adv. Org. Geochem.* (ed. M. Bjorøy) in press.

Seifert, W. K. and Moldowan, J. M. (1978) Applications of steranes, terpanes and monoaromatics to the maturation, migration and source of crude oils. *Geochim. Cosmochim. Acta* **42**, 77–95.

Seifert, W. K. and Moldowan, J. M. (1979) The effect of biodegradation on steranes and terpanes in crude oils. *Geochim. Cosmochim. Acta* **43**, 111–126.

Seifert, W. K. and Moldowan, J. M. (1981) Paleoreconstruction by biological markers. *Geochim. Cosmochim. Acta* **45**, 783–794.

Shimoyama, A. and Johns, W. D. (1972) Formation of alkanes from fatty acids in the presence of $CaCO_3$. *Geochim. Cosmochim. Acta* **36**, 87–91.

Sofer, Z. (1980) Preparation of carbon dioxide for stable carbon isotopes of petroleum fractions. *Anal. Chem.* **52**, 1389–1391.

Sofer, Z. (1981) Isotopic composition of heavy (C_{15+}) saturate and aromatic fractions of crude oils. *Am. Ass. Petrol. Geol. Bull.* **65**, 995.

Thode, H. G. and Monster, J. (1965) Sulfur-isotope geochemistry of petroleum, evaporites, and ancient seas. Fluids in subsurface environments: *Am. Ass. Petrol. Geol. Mem.* **4** (Ed. by Young, A. and Galley, J. E., pp. 367–377.

Thode, H. G., Monster, J. and Dunford, H. B. (1958) Sulfur isotope abundances in petroleum and associated materials. *Am. Ass. Petrol. Geol. Bull.* **42**, 2619–2641.

Weeks, L. G. (1952) Factors of sedimentary basin development that control oil occurrence. *Am. Ass. Petrol. Geol. Bull.* **36**, 2071–2124.

Welte, D. H. and Waples, D. (1973) Uber die Bevorzugung geradzahliger *n*-Alkane in Sedimentgesteinen. *Naturwiss.* **60**, 516–517.

Advances in Organic Geochemistry 1981, pp. 49–59
© *John Wiley & Sons Limited, 1983*

Organic Geochemical Studies of the Devonian to Triassic Succession on Bjørnøya and the Implications for the Barent Shelf

M. Bjorøy, A. Mørk and J. O. Vigran

Continental Shelf Institute, PO Box 1883, N-7001 Trondheim, Norway

Bjørnøya (Bear Island) is situated on the western margin of the Barents Shelf and comprises three main geological elements: the Hecla Hoek basement, Upper Devonian to Permian clastic and bioclastic sediments, and Triassic shales and siltstones. The Upper Devonian and Lower Carboniferous formations consist of coarse clastics, shales and coals derived from material deposited in various alluvial environments. The Middle and Upper Carboniferous sandstones, conglomerates and limestones were deposited in marginal marine to marine, tectonically influenced environments. The Permian limestones reflect two transgressive episodes. The attenuated Triassic deposits in the lower part consist of near-shore/open marine shales, while those in the upper part consist of a regressive coarsening upwards sequence. The oil and gas potential, as evaluated by organic geochemical techniques, differs between the various formations. The values for total organic carbon content of the Paleozoic rocks (except for the few shale and coal units) is mostly low, in the range 0.4%–1%, whereas for Triassic samples, the values are in the range of 0.6%–2%. The Paleozoic rocks have a maturity-level on the boundary between the gas and the oil window, whereas the Triassic rocks are at maturity-level in the lower part of the oil window. The kerogen in most samples indicates a potential for gas only, although some also have a potential for oil. The variation in the maturity-level in the Upper Paleozoic sequence indicates the formation of a minor graben in the middle and western parts of the island, and downfaulting of the formations during the time of maximal depth of burial. The observed occurrence of migrated hydrocarbons in the Triassic siltstones is probably due to local migration, but a lateral migration from stratigraphically younger (downfaulted?) rocks cannot be completely excluded. The faulting may reflect reactivation of earlier N–S trending fault lineaments, common throughout Svalbard, and related to tensional forces present prior to the opening of the Norwegian Sea.

INTRODUCTION

Bjørnøya is situated on the southwestern edge of the Barents Shelf between Norway and Spitsbergen. This small island (approximately 180 km²) is comprised of rocks of considerable significance for an understanding of the offshore sediments of Svalbard and of the Barents Sea. The geology of Bjørnøya was described by Horn and Orvin (1928); the main geological elements (Fig. 1) are, Hecla Hoek basement (approx. 1200 m), Upper Devonian to Permian (approx. 1200 m) and Triassic (approx. 200 m). A tectonic control on sedimentation for the succession comparable to sedimentation patterns observed in sequences on Spitsbergen has been postulated (Cutbill and Challinor, 1965; Gjelberg and Steel, 1979; Knarud *et al.*, in press).

The objective of this study was to examine the Paleozoic and Mesozoic shales on Bjørnøya and to determine their source rock potential, and to study the coarser clastic lithologies to determine if they contain migrated hydrocarbons. Samples which were found to contain migrated hydrocarbons would be examined further, with the objective of determining their source.

GEOLOGY

The Upper Paleozoic succession of Bjørnøya has been the subject of many previous papers (Andersson, 1900; Horn and Orvin, 1928; Cutbill and Challinor, 1965; Krasilscikov and Livsic, 1974; Worsley and Edwards, 1976). The present study is based mainly upon the general geological subdivision and environmental interpretations as given by Worsley and Edwards (1976). Datings of the different units are given in Fig. 2.

Røedvika Formation

(100 m thickening to approx. 360 m.) Two main facies groups are identified in the lower *Vesalstranda Member* (Gjelberg, 1978); a floodplain association and a probable deltaic lacustrine association. Local thin coals are found in both facies groups. An overall time-trend of sedimentation from deltaic to fluvial environments suggests a general progradational, lacustrine basin-filling episode. In the *Kapp Levin Member* (80 m) cross-stratified sandstones and conglomerates are interpreted

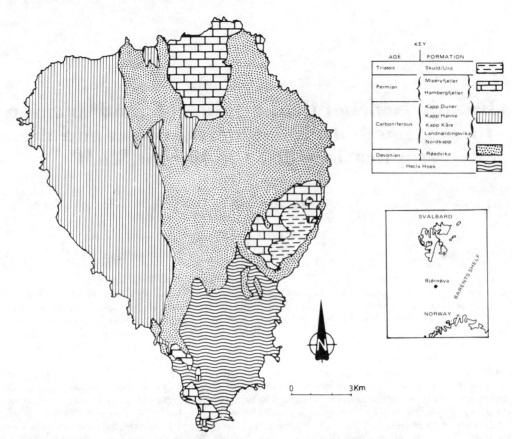

Fig. 1. Simplified geological map of Bjørnøya.

as braided stream deposits. The sandstone-dominated *Tunheim Member* (80 m) contains local conglomerates and coals attributed to deposition by streams meandering northwards across a densely vegetated flood-plain. The coal seams of this member were mined from 1916 to 1925 and although they show thick development in some outcrops, they rapidly thin in a lateral direction.

Nordkapp Formation

(Thickening from 110 m to 230 m northwards.) The formation is dominated by cross-bedded sandstones, the orientation of which suggests deposition by north-eastward-flowing braided streams (Gjelberg, 1981). The formation contains numerous thin coals, all of local origin.

Landnørdingsvika Formation

(Thickness 120–145 m.) The lower part of the formation suggests deposition on coastal alluvial plains. Alluvial fan conglomerates are again built out eastwards, probably as a result of renewed faulting along N–S trending lineaments. A mixed development in the uppermost part of the unit marks a regional marine transgression (Gjelberg, 1981). No organic-rich lithologies are present.

Kapp Kåre Formation

This formation has been subdivided into three members (Kirkemo, 1979). The mixed sandstones, shales and limestones of the *Bogevika Member* (95 m) occur as small-scale coarsening and fining upwards sequences indicating deposition in tidally influenced, marginal marine environments with minor deltaic progradations. There are local, thin, organic-rich shales. The *Efuglvika Member* (70 m) was deposited in normal marine environments and the *Kobbebukta Member* (8 m to 45 m) consists of interbedded marine limestone and intraformational carbonate and chert conglomerates. Organic-rich lithologies are not found in the two upper members.

Kapp Hanna Formation

(100 m.) This unit consists of sandstones, conglomerates, shales and dolomites. Marginal marine to tidal flat and lagoonal sequences are eroded by westward-flowing, braided streams depositing thick sandstones and conglomerates (Agdestein, 1980).

Kapp Duner Formation

(50 m, top not exposed.) The massive to well-bedded dolomites and limestones were deposited on a carbonate shelf characterized by the development of bioherms, biostromes and patch reefs (Agdestein, 1980). Lagoonal sequences (behind these structures?) may have been deposited in hypersaline environments (Siedlecka, 1972, 1975). Individual thin, highly bituminous beds occur together with porous biohermal structures which have also been observed in units of comparable age in central Spitsbergen.

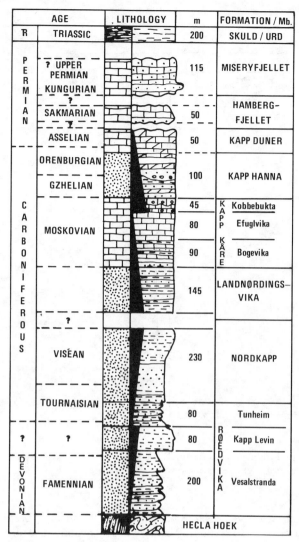

AGE		LITHOLOGY	m	FORMATION / Mb.	
℞	TRIASSIC		200	SKULD / URD	
P E R M I A N	? UPPER PERMIAN		115	MISERYFJELLET	
	KUNGURIAN				
	?				
	SAKMARIAN		50	HAMBERG- FJELLET	
	?				
	ASSELIAN		50	KAPP DUNER	
C A R B O N I F E R O U S	ORENBURGIAN		100	KAPP HANNA	
	GZHELIAN				
	MOSKOVIAN		45	K A P P K Å R E	Kobbebukta
			80		Efuglvika
			90		Bogevika
			145	LANDNØRDINGS- VIKA	
	?				
	VISÉAN		230	NORDKAPP	
	TOURNAISIAN		80	R Ø E D V I K A	Tunheim
?	?		80		Kapp Levin
D E V O N I A N	FAMENNIAN		200		Vesalstranda
				HECLA HOEK	

Fig. 2. Stratigraphical column from Bjørnøya. (Modified from Worsley and Edwards, 1976).

Hambergfjellet Formation

(Max. 50 m.) This unit occurs as an onlapping wedge found only in the southernmost mountains of Bjørnøya. Basal sandstones are overlain by sandy limestones passing upwards into marine limestones. The organic carbon content of this coarse clastic–bioclastic sediment is low.

Miseryfjellet Formation

(115 m.) This formation rests unconformably on various older units. The basal sandstones pass up into sandy and partially silicified biosparites with brachiopod faunas typical of the Tempelfjorden Group on Svalbard. The sandy biosparites and fossil content suggest deposition in high energy, shallow marine environments and consequently there is a low potential for the preservation of organic material.

Triassic

The succession is approximation 200 m thick and for-mational units have been formally defined by Knarud *et*

al. (in press) (Fig. 3a). Following the proposal of Pcelina (1972), they subdivided the Triassic into a lower Urd Formation and an upper Skuld Formation. A remanier phosphatic conglomerate, the Verdande Bed, separates the formations and is regarded as the remnant of a Middle Triassic unit. Reliable datings are available only for the upper Carnian part (Böhm, 1903). The condensed sequence indicates deposition on an Upper Palezoic high.

The Urd Formation

(65 m.) Consists of a siltstone–sandstone with reworked Permian material in the lowermost part. It rests with a sharp contact on massive Permian limestone. Dark grey shales contain abundant thin siltstone beds deposited in a marine environment, the siltstone beds indicating storm episodes.

The Skuld Formation

(140 m.) Resting on the Verdande Bed, consists of dark shales with red, weathered, siderite nodules. The shale grades up into a thick siltstone unit with abundant plant remains and bivalves. A marginal marine nearshore depositional environment seems probable. A similar development is found in the southern part of Spitsbergen (Buchan *et al.*, 1965; Pcelina, 1972; Knarud *et al.*, in press).

METHODS

Evaluation of source rock potential was based upon results from the following analyses; total organic carbon (TOC) content, total extractable organic matter (EOM), content of saturated and aromatic hydrocarbons, Rock–Eval pyrolysis, gas chromatography of saturated hydrocarbons, vitrinite reflectance and examination of kerogen concentrates in transmitted light. More detailed information concerning these analyses may be found in Bjorøy, Bue and Elvsborg (this volume).

Thiourea non-adducts from 13 hydrocarbon fractions were analysed by computer-assisted gas chromatography–mass spectrometry (GC–MS), using a Varian 3700 gas chromatograph coupled via an all-glass line to a VG Micromass 7070H double-focusing magnetic spectrometer. Data acquisition and manipulation was performed by a VG Datasystems 2035 data system. Gas chromatographic analysis was performed using a 25 m × 0.3 mm i.d. glass capillary column coated with OV-1, temperature programmed from 120° to 260 °C at 3 °C min^{-1}. Helium carrier gas flow-rate = 0.7 ml min^{-1}. The mass spectrometer was operated in the multiple ion detection (MID) and sequential scanning modes, monitoring the ions with m/z = 191 (triterpanes) and $m/z = 217$ (steranes). The sequential scanning was performed at 1 s/decade and the MID recording at 200 ms dwell time per ion.

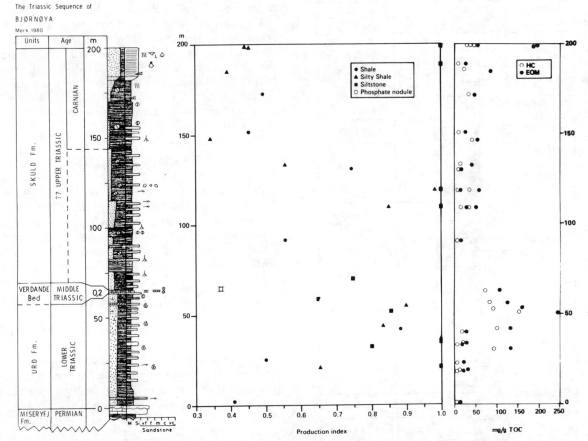

Fig. 3. The Triassic sequence at Bjørnøya. (a) Lithological column. (b) Production index from Rock-Eval pyrolysis. (c) Extraction results.

RESULTS AND DISCUSSION

Organic carbon content was determined in a total of 94 samples; the results were very variable and dependent on the lithology (Table 1). Based on these results, a total of 57 samples (25 Paleozoic and 32 Triassic) were selected for extraction.

Of the Paleozoic samples, only a few (all siltstones or fine sandstones) gave high values for extractable hydrocarbons when normalized to organic carbon (Table 1). At the maturity-level encountered, the potential source rocks (the shales and coaly shales) have already produced and expelled hydrocarbons from the kerogen. The present petroleum potential for most of the shales and coaly shales is therefore low. The expelled hydrocarbons occur mainly in the coarser lithologies (the siltstones and sandstones), although small quantities are still present as free hydrocarbons in the shales and coaly shales. The distribution patterns of the saturated hydrocarbons vary considerably although a front-biased distribution of n-alkanes, typical of well-matured hydrocarbons (Fig. 4b and f), is consistently found in all shale and shaly coal samples. In the coarser lithologies, the gas chromatograms of the saturated hydrocarbons show a definite loss of the light-to-medium-weight hydrocarbons, probably due to diffusion (Fig. 4c and d). The large unresolved complex mixture in the high molecular weight region of many of the gas chromatograms (e.g. Fig. 4a and e), in conjunction with

the selective loss of n-alkanes, has frequently been ascribed to weathering and/or heavy oxidation of the samples (Powell, 1978; Clayton and Swetland, 1978; Bjorøy et al., 1980).

Most of the extracted Triassic samples were found to have high values for extractable hydrocarbons, both in absolute terms and when normalized to organic carbon (Table 1). Where shales and siltstones were located in close proximity, samples of each lithology were extracted. The siltstones were found to have far higher organic carbon-normalized extraction values than the shales, indicating the presence of free hydrocarbons which are probably migrated from the interbedded shale units.

The gas chromatograms of the saturated hydrocarbons show considerable variation in the different samples. Some of the siltstones have lost most of the light- and medium-weight hydrocarbons, probably due to diffusion (Fig. 5b and d). Others show the front-biased distribution typical of a high maturity-level (Fig. 5c and d). At this high maturity-level, the bimodal distribution (Fig. 5a and f) seen for a large number of shale samples suggests that the hydrocarbons originated either from terrestrial material or a mixture of terrestrial and amorphous material. The unresolved complex mixture encountered in the gas chromatograms of many of the Paleozoic samples was found only in the lowermost part of the Triassic succession.

The maturity of the samples was measured using

Table 1

Sample	FORMATION/Member	Lithology	TOC %	EOM	Sat	Aro	HC	H_I	O_I	a S_1+S_2	b $\frac{S_1}{S_1+S_2}$	Ro	Kerogen colour	Kerogen composition
533A	SKULD	siltstone	.4	65	28	5.5	33	0	385	.12	1.00	1.10(20)	3-	He,Cut,WR!,W,P/Am,Cy
533B	SKULD	silty shale	.6	193	31	8.3	39	24	279	.26	.46			
526	SKULD	siltstone	.8	197	54	8.5	62	47	112	.64	.45			
522	SKULD	siltstone	1.1	31	11	3.1	14	0	171	.12	1.00		3-	He,WR!,W,P,S/Am,Cy
512	SKULD	siltstone	.8	137	20	8.7	28	94	139	1.27	.39	1.19(20)		
510	SKULD	shale	2.0	31	8	8.5	17	-	-	-	-	1.19(20)		
506	SKULD	shale	.9	48	35	3.3	38	9	113	.16	.50		3-	He,Cut,W,P,S/Am,Cy
485A	SKULD	shale	1.1	25	9	2.4	11	13	136	.26	.46	0.92(3)		
485B	SKULD	silty shale	1.2	146	75	25.9	101	-	-	-	-			
481	SKULD	silty shale	1.3	56	33	11.2	44	28	157	.53	.34	0.84(9) 0.95(11)	3-	W,He/Am
467	SKULD	silty shale	1.0	33	15	1.0	16	13	86	.27	.56			
464	SKULD	shale	1.2	18	11	1.3	13	3	109	.16	.75			
452A	SKULD	silty shale	1.3	17	7	1.5	8	1	432	.22	.95			
452B	SKULD	siltstone	.2	61	32	7.0	39	0	2011	.04	1.00			
445	SKULD	silty shale	.7	76	45	6.9	52	-	-	-	-	1.08(20)		
443A	SKULD	silty shale	1.1	31	12	2.3	15	5	450	.37	.86			
443B	SKULD	siltstone	.3	55	25	6.7	32	0	1806	.45	1.00			
442	SKULD	shale	.8	231	25	11.5	37	146	97	2.48	.32	0.85(7) 1.19(13)	3-	W,He,P,S/Am
425	SKULD	shale	1.1	23	11	2.2	14	14	344	.37	.57	1.22(20)	3-	Am/Cut,He,W,WR!,P
422	SKULD	shale	1.3											
409	SKULD		.5	-	-	-	-	2	67	.04	.75			
408	Verdande	phosph.nod.	1.1	116	55	12.8	68	10	88	.18	.39	1.04(4)	2+/3-	He/Am
392	URD	siltstone	.4	138	83	6.5	89	33	605	.40	.65			
387	URD	silty shale	.4	164	80	13.5	94	7	169	.31	.90			
385	URD	siltstone	.7	248	52	92.8	145	9	53	.37	.84	0.8(1) 1.15(1)	3-	He/Am
377	URD	silty shale	.5	131	68	16.0	84	21	327	.60	.83			
375	URD	shale	1.0	33	22	3.0	25	2	210	.13	.85			
369A	URD	silty shale	.7	49	27	1.1	28	0	383	.07	1.00			
369B	URD	siltstone	.5	44	7	2.4	9	0	556	.08	1.00	0.99(20)	3-	W,He/Am
365	URD	siltstone	.4	143	68	13.5	81	21	174	.38	.79			
358	URD	shale	1.8	25	4	1.8	6	10	178	.37	.51			
354A	URD	silty shale	1.5	21	4	.9	5	5	219	.21	.67			
354B	URD	siltstone	.5	38	14	1.6	16	0	1515	.06	1.00			
M345	URD	siltstone										1.21(8)		
334	URD	shale	.6	7	1	1.0	2	29	95	.29	.41	1.14(21)	3-	?Am/He,W
BR3 59	MISERYFJ.	sparitic limest.	.4	47	13	8	21	-	-					
BR2 11.0	MISERYFJ.	fine sandstone	.4									0.88(5)	NDP	Ox
BR2 5.0	MISERYFJ.	sparitic limest.	.8										3	Am/He,Cut,WR!
JS 6.5	MISERYFJ.	sandstone	.4									1.13(20)		
BR2 1	MISERYFJ.	sparitic limest.	.8	69	23	17	40	33	32	.45	.41			
H 12.0	MISERYFJ.	f.-v.f. sst.	.3									0.88(1) 1.38(20)	(3-/3)	He,WR!/Am
BR3 12.5	MISERYFJ.	limestone	.5	328	93	22	115	2	43	.03	1.00			
BR3 3.0	MISERYFJ.	sparitic limest.	.5	-	-	-	-	8	47	.08	.50	0.68(1) 1.10(22)		
BR 5.7	MISERYFJ.	siltst.-v.f. sst.	.5	171	16	10	26	63	83	.52	.44			
BR 0.25	MISERYFJ.	siltst.-v.f. sst.	.6	112	45	16	61	28	122	.33	.50			
DW 6	HAMBERGFJ.	sandy limestone	.9	13	2	0	2	18	51	.32	.53			
DW 5	HAMBERGFJ.	silty shale/limest.										1.12(11)	3-/3	Cut,H,W,S/Am
D4 5.5	KAPP DUNER	arenaceous limest.	.4									NDP		Am/(Cut,He,W)R!
D2 12	KAPP DUNER	silty limestone	.2									NDP	NDP	AM/(Cut,W)R!
D2 11.5	KAPP DUNER	arenaceous limest.	.3									0.40(4) 11.5(2)	NDP	Am/WR!
H4 14	KAPP HANNA	silty calc. shale	1.6	25	3	7	10	52	24	1.38	.41	0.73(3) 1.04(18)	3-	Cut,W/Am
C5A 42.5	KAPP KARE	black shale	2.1	28	3	7	10	17	27	.78	.55	1.21(20)	3	Am/He,S
C5A 20.3	KAPP KARE	black shale	2.3	35	6	12	18	22	12	.80	.37	0.73(3) 1.04(18)	3	?Am/He
C5A 9.5	KAPP KARE	black shale	2.5	9	1	1	2	15	11	.68	.47	1.40(20)	3/3+	W,He
DW 4	NORDKAPP	dark shale	2.1	20	3	5	8	20	7	.76	.43	1.45(21)	2+/3- 3-/3	He,W,WR!,Cut,S/Am
DW 3	NORDKAPP	coal/shale	41.6	-	-	-	-	54	3	23.4	.05	1.54(22)	3-/3	He,W,S/Am
DW 2	NORDKAPP	m. sandst.	.6	75	13	3	16	85	90	1.49	.66			
Gj 6	NORDKAPP	black silty shale	1.7	16	0	4	5	39	9	.93	.29		2+/3- 3-/3	Am/W,WR!,Cut,S,P
Gj 9	NORDKAPP	black colay shale	22.7	-	-	-	-	29	8	7.28	.09		3-/3	W,WR!He/Am
246	Tunheim	dirty coal	25.9	11	1	4	5	70	2	20.5	.12	1.34(21)	?3-	W(Coal)
3	Tunheim	shale	4.5	30	7	6	13	-	-	-	-	1.34		
5	Tunheim		1.2									1.4(6)	2+/3-	He/Am
8	Tunheim	siltstone	1.2	53	12	12	24	59	9	1.28	.45	1.07(21)		
9	Tunheim	coal-carbarg.	23.5	10	1	4	5	-	-	-	-	1.13(21)		
15	Tunheim	shale	1.1	-	-	-	-	46	10	.98	.48	1.08(15) 1.63(14)		
73/13	Tunheim	shale										1.23(20)		
229	Tunheim	carbargillite										1.25(20)		
225	Tunheim	siltstone										1.24(21)		
217	Tunheim	shale	1.4	24	4	7	11	54	2	1.24	.38			
186	Tunheim												3-/3	P,S,He,Cut,W
187	Tunheim	siltst. w. coal fr.	2.3	39	7	11	19	43	221	1.37	.27	1.24(20)		
55	Tunheim	shale	3.5	17	2	3	5	55	9	2.78	.31	1.40(21)		
53	Tunheim	shale										1.23(25)		
40	Tunheim	shale	10.8	9	1	5	6	90	3	11.1	.13	1.27(19)		
90	Tunheim	carbarg.	20.3	7	0	3	3	1	1	.65	.61	1.21(21)		
89	K.Levin	shale										1.21(21)		
156	K.Levin	siltstone	.7	-	-	-	-	63	54	.81	.49			
80	K.Levin	siltstone	.5									1.26(20)	3-/3	* P,S,Cut,He,W,R
143	K.Levin	siltstone	.7	-	-	-	-	71	36	.99	.50			
137	K.Levin		1.7											* Cut,W,He,P,S
135	K.Levin	siltst. w. coal fr.	1.7	33	3	9	11	-	-	-	-	1.30(21)		
128	Vesalstr.											1.35(20)	3-/3	* Cut,He,P,S,W
124	Vesalstr.	shale	5.7	-	-	-	-	65	8	4.83	.24			
120	Vesalstr.	carbarg.	16.4	15	1	6	8	124	4	23.3	.12	1.25(20)		
118	Vesalstr.	pyritic shale	6.0	18	1	9	10	21	7	1.79	.29	1.13(22)		
104	Vesalstr.	siltstone	0.3									1.43(20)	3-/3	* P,S,Cut,He,W
Gj 3	Vesalstr.	coal and carbarg.										1.45(22)		
Gj 8	Vesalstr.	carbarg.										1.26(22)		
Gj 5	Vesalstr.	shale w. coal fr.	10.5	-	-	-	-	89	6	10.7	.12	1.16(22)	3	Am/He,Cut,W,S
Gj 1	Vesalstr.		0.5	167	95	22	117	-	-	-	-			
Gj 10	Vesalstr.	silty shale	0.3									0.8(2) 1.18(19)		

a Petroleum potential = S_1+S_2 b Production index = $\frac{S_1}{S_1+S_2}$

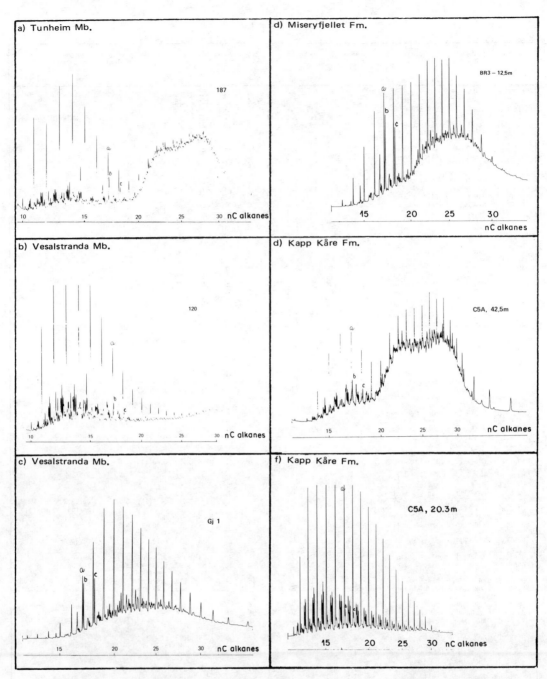

Fig. 4. Gas chromatograms of saturated hydrocarbon fraction of Paleozoic samples.

different methods, and the results are in good agreement. All samples from the Paleozoic sequence were at a maturity-level between the oil window and the gas window (Vassoevich *et al.*, 1974; Burgess, 1974; Espitalié *et al.*, 1977), while the samples from the Triassic sequence were found to have a maturity-level in the lower part of the oil window (Table 1).

With the maturity-level being high for most of the analysed samples, the original differences between the principal kerogen types, as usually manifest by Rock–Eval pyrolysis, have disappeared. The main emphasis for the determination of the kerogen types is, therefore, put on kerogen examination in transmitted light. These analyses show predominantly terrestrial residues for most of the Paleozoic samples. Amorphous material

was recorded in the few analysed samples from Kapp Duner, Kapp Hanna and Kåre formations (Table 1). The samples from the lower part of the Triassic succession contained a mixture of amorphous and herbaceous material, while in the upper part of the succession a predominance of mixed terrestrial and amorphous material was found (Table 1).

Migration of hydrocarbons

Migration of hydrocarbons can, to a certain extent, be measured by traditional organic geochemical techniques. Two such techniques were used in this study: Extraction with organic solvents, followed by

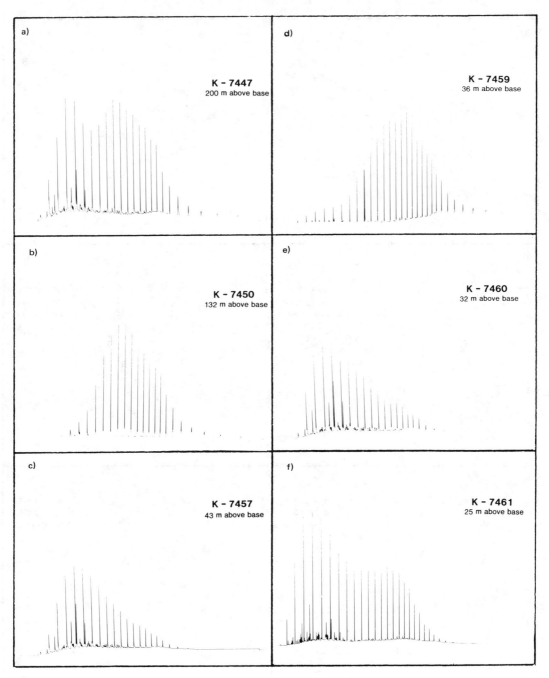

Fig. 5. Gas chromatograms of saturated hydrocarbon fraction of Triassic samples.

correlation of the extracted hydrocarbons, and a study of the production index obtained from Rock–Eval pyrolysis.

A very high abundance of extractable hydrocarbons (normalized to organic carbon) was found for three of the Paleozoic samples (Gj 1 fine sandstone, Vesalstranda Member; BR 0.25 fine sandstone and BR3 12.4 limestone, Miseryfjellet Formation). The high extractability of these samples is indicative of the presence of migrated hydrocarbons, in good agreement with the high production indices (0.5 and higher) from Rock–Eval analysis. The high production indices recorded for a large number of the siltstones indicate that many of the coarser lithologies contain migrated hydrocarbons.

Some of the Triassic siltstones have a high extractability when normalized to organic carbon (Table 1, Fig. 3c). When comparing the Triassic shales with the interbedded siltstones, the latter always have higher extractabilities (Table 1). This, together with the very high production indices found for the siltstones (Table 1, Fig. 3b), indicates that they contain migrated hydrocarbons, probably sourced by the interbedded shale layers.

Gas chromatography–mass spectrometry (GC–MS) analysis

GC–MS analysis of the saturated hydrocarbon fractions was undertaken in an effort to correlate the extracts from

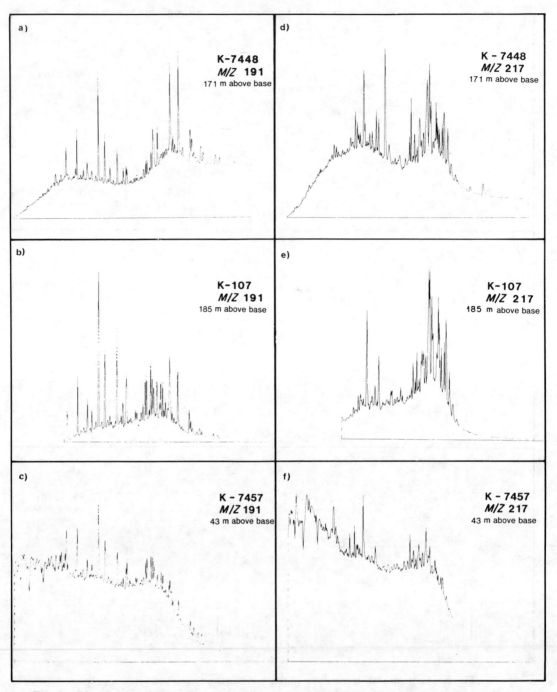

Fig. 6. Mass fragmentograms (m/z 191 and m/z 217) of saturated hydrocarbons of Triassic samples.

the siltstones and the interbedded shale samples. Biomarkers, most frequently steranes and triterpanes, are commonly used for correlation purposes (Mackenzie *et al.*, 1980a and b; Seifert, 1977, 1978; Seifert and Moldowan, 1978, 1979 and 1980; Seifert *et al.* 1980). Twelve Triassic samples, including shales, interbedded silty shales and siltstones, were selected for GC–MS analysis. The silty shales were selected on the basis of Rock–Eval pyrolysis and extraction data, ensuring that they contained free hydrocarbons. The samples contained very small amounts of steranes and triterpanes and the reliability of the analyses is therefore somewhat dubious. GC–MS analysis was attempted in both the total data collection mode (TDC) and in the selected ion

recording mode (SIR). The abundance of steranes/triterpanes was insufficient to allow analysis in the TDC mode and a *positive*, direct identification of the different compounds was therefore not possible. However, an identification of the different compounds and a correlation between the samples was attempted on the basis of pattern recognition techniques.

The large peaks found in the first part of the $m/z = 191$ fragmentogram (Fig. 6) are believed to represent diterpanes. The hopane series, found to be ubiquitous in sedimentary samples (Kimble *et al.*, 1974; van Dorsselaer *et al.*, 1974) was identified by pattern recognition in a few samples only. Individual steranes could not be identified and a correlation between the samples is therefore based mainly on the $m/z = 191$ fragmentograms. Three distinct groups of samples can be recognized:

Group 1, with a distinct hopane pattern (Fig. 6a) as found in the grey shales from levels 464 and 506.

Group 2, with the very complex triterpane pattern (shown in Fig. 6c), found for the silty shales from levels 485 and 377, and the grey shale from level 375.

Group 3, with a triterpane pattern which appears to be a mixture of the two former series (Fig. 6b), found for the silty shales and siltstones from levels 452, 467, 512, 522, 526 and 533.

Although the steranes, represented by the $m/z = 217$ fragmentograms, are less distinct than the triterpanes, the general patterns formed allow a tentative division into the same three series (Fig. 6d–f).

The results indicate that the free hydrocarbons of the silty shales and siltstones in the lower part of the section have migrated from the local interbedded shales. The hydrocarbons present in the silty shales and siltstones of the middle and upper part of the section have probably migrated from shales in both the upper and the lower part of the section.

The burial history of Bj∮rn∮ya

The maturity data derived from the vitrinite reflectance measurements fall into three groups: Sediments of Carboniferous formations in the middle of the island show R_0 values in the range 1.3 to 1.5%, which is higher than the formations on either side, which have R_0 values in the range 0.9 to 1.2%. The similarity in R_0 values of samples from the eastern and western part of the island indicates a similarity in burial history. The higher reflectance values of the Carboniferous formations in the middle of the island may be a result of early oxidation, although a slightly greater depth of maximum burial may also be a possible explanation.

Geological evidence suggests syndepositional fault control on sedimentation from the R∮edvika Formation (Famennian) through to the Kapp Hanna Formation (Gzhelian) (Kirkemo, 1979; Agdestein, 1980; Gjelberg, 1978; Gjelberg and Steel, 1979; Worsley, personal communication). Two fault lineaments are postulated; the earlier west of Bj∮rn∮ya, the latter intersecting the island. The outcrop areas in the middle of the island (with somewhat higher reflectance values than elsewhere) contain units which were deposited in a small trough, initially east and subsequently west of uplifted blocks. The maturity of the Triassic sequence suggests a post-Triassic overburden in the range of a few kilometres thickness. The higher maturation in the central area may have resulted from reactivation along the late Carboniferous fault lineament intersecting the island, and downwarping of the middle and western parts of the island at the time of maximum burial (late Mesozoic/early Tertiary?); the reactivation resulting from tensional forces operating prior to the opening of the Norwegian Sea. Downwarping in the order of only a few hundred metres would produce the higher maturation observed today. It should be noted here that the base of the Miseryfjellet Formation now outcrops between 200 and 350 m above sea level to the east of this postulated lineament, whereas the outcrop is at sea level on the northern coast to the west of the lineament.

The Barents Sea

The presence of Mesozoic beds (mainly the Jurassic/Cretaceous Janusfjellet Formation) is postulated from observations on sea bottom samples (Edwards, 1975, Bj∮rlykke *et al.*, 1978). A pronounced seismic reflector observed in the Barents Sea is thought to represent the upper Permian (R∮nnevik and Motland, 1979). Mesozoic successions have been found in wells drilled on Troms∮flaket (SW-Barents Shelf) (Bjor∮y, Bue and Elvsborg; this volume). A small downfaulted block of Jurassic–Cretaceous sediments is present on And∮ya, Northern Norway (Dalland, 1975). The Palaeozoic and Mesozoic sedimentation on Svalbard is tectonically controlled by movement along lineaments trending N–S (Gjelberg and Steel, 1979; M∮rk and Worsley, 1979; Knarud *et al.*, in press).

At the Continental Shelf Institute we have, over the last four years, analysed over 100 sea-floor samples from the Barents Sea and the Norwegian Sea. Seventy of these samples were from the Troms I area, Svalbardbanken and the Eastern Barents Sea. Six samples were of Triassic age, the remainder were of Jurassic age or younger (Bjor∮y and Vigran, 1979, 1980b, c and d). All Triassic samples were found to have an oil window maturity and a large variation in their kerogen composition. The Jurassic samples from the Eastern Barents Sea were found to be immature ($R_0 = 0.3$–0.4%) while those from the Svalbard bank were of a higher maturity, (approximately $R_0 = 0.6$–0.7%). The samples from the Troms I area were immature ($R_0 = 0.4$–0.5%).

Organic-rich Lower and Middle Triassic beds (120–700 m) occur on Svalbard, Barents∮ya and Edge∮ya, together with several hundred metres of Jurassic–Cretaceous deposits (Janusfjellet Formation) Knarud *et al.*, in press; Forsberg and Bjor∮y, this volume).

The occurrence, both in land areas surrounding the Barents Shelf and in sediments of the Barents Shelf, of Mesozoic rocks (mainly shales) of a maturity which is never below the oil/gas window suggests that good source rocks may exist on the Barents Shelf. The Upper Paleozoic sequences have some source potential (mainly for gas), if the maturity is not too high.

CONCLUSIONS

The analysed samples represent many formations and different depositional environments. General conclusions cannot be drawn for the whole sequence and each formation or member will therefore be discussed separately. Source rock ratings are referred to by Bjor∮y (1977).

The Paleozoic succession

The Paleozoic samples were found to have a maturity-level bordering the oil window and the condensate window.

The lowermost section, the *Vesalstranda Member* of the *Røedvika Formation*, contains numerous thin coal layers and minor amounts of organic-rich shales. The member has been estimated to have a fair potential as a source for gas and heavy oil. The coarser lithologies of the overlying *Kapp Levin Member* show clear evidence of free, migrated hydrocarbons. The abundant coals in the *Tunheim Member* have a good to rich potential as a source for gas.

The samples from the *Nordkapp Formation* are comparable to those of the *Røedvika Formation*. The minor shale sequences are found to have a rich potential for gas and oil, and the siltstone and sandstone sequences contain free, migrated hydrocarbons.

The red beds of the *Landørdingsvika Formation* have very poor abundance of organic carbon; detailed analyses were therefore not performed. The formation has no source rock potential for hydrocarbons.

The black shale samples from the *Bogevika Member* of the *Kapp Kåre Formation* have kerogen of mixed amorphous and herbaceous character. The deltaic to marginal marine deposits are therefore expected to have a rich potential as source rocks for oil and gas. No organ-rich lithologies were found in the two upper members of this formation.

Calcareous sandstones and silty shales dominate the *Kapp Hanna Formation*. The analysed silty calcareous shales are atypical for the formation, but show a good abundance of organic carbon and a mixture of amorphous and herbaceous kerogen. The samples analysed are found to have a good potential as source rock for oil and gas.

The limestone from the *Kapp Duner Formation* has a poor abundance of organic carbon. Although containing mainly amorphous kerogen, the formation has a poor potential as a source rock. However, highly bituminous limestones are known at similar levels in this formation on Spitsbergen.

The samples analysed from the *Hambergfjellet Formation* are mainly limestones. They resemble the samples from the *Kapp Duner Formation* and are given the same (poor) source rock potential as this unit.

The samples from the *Miseryfjellet Formation* are comprised of siltstones, limestones and silty sandstones. The kerogen consists of amorphous, herbaceous and woody material but the unit has a low content of organic carbon and a poor potential as source rock for gas and oil. One of the samples (BR3 12.5) shows traces of migrated hydrocarbons.

Triassic

Samples from the Triassic sequence have a maturity-level at the lower end of the oil window.

The high extractability and the high production indices found for the silty shales and siltstones indicate the presence of migrated hydrocarbons in these samples. These hydrocarbons are probably sourced within the formation by small-scale migration from the shales to the interbedded siltstones, as suggested by Rock–Eval pyrolysis and GC–MS analysis. The GC–MS analysis also indicates that the migrated hydrocarbons

encountered in the lower part of the section have their source in the interbedded shales. The migrated hydrocarbons in the middle and upper part of the section have mixed sources, probably the interbedded shales of both the lower *and* the upper part of the section.

Heavy oxidation has affected many of the analysed samples. Leythaeuser (1973) and Clayton and Swetland (1978) showed a loss of up to 50% in both total organic carbon (TOC) and extractable organic matter (EOM) in samples from arid areas. Forsberg and Bjorøy (this volume) have shown that the TOC values in samples from Svalbard are not affected by weathering, whereas the EOM and (especially) the aromatic compounds are modified. The EOM results should therefore not be weighed too heavily when evaluating the richness of the samples. Taking these considerations into account, the shale sequences of the Triassic sequence on Bjørnøya may be described as having a fair/good potential as source rocks for oil and gas.

Acknowledgements

Much of the Upper Paleozoic succession has been the subject of investigations by research groups from the Universities of Oslo and Bergen. Samples and unpublished information utilized in the present study have been supplied by geologists involved in these research projects. We especially acknowledge the assistance of D. Worsley, T. Agdestein, J. Gjelberg, T. Hellem, K. Kirkemo and the crew of the Bjørnøya Radio Station. The very capable technical assistance of the staff of the Geology and Organic Geochemistry Departments at the Continental Shelf Institute (Norway) is also gratefully acknowledged. M. B. Edwards collected most of the samples from the Røedvika Formation.

REFERENCES

Agdestein, T. (1980) *En stratigrafisk og diagenetisk undersøkelse av Karbon-Perm sedimenter (Kapp Hanna Formasjonen og Kapp Duner Formasjonen), på Bjørnøya, Svalbard*. Thesis, Univ. of Oslo.

Andersson, J. G. (1900) Über die Stratigraphie und Tektonik der Bären Insel. *Bull. geol. Inst. Univ. Uppsala*, **4**, 243–280.

Bjorøy, M. (1977) Organic geochemistry in search of petroleum. *IKU Publ. 93.*

Bjorøy, M., Bue, B. and Elvsborg, A. (this volume) Organic geochemical analyses of the first two wells in the Troms I Area (Barents Sea).

Bjorøy, M., Hall, K. and Vigran, J. O. (1980) Organic geochemical study of Mesozoic shales from Andøya, North Norway. In *Adv. Org. Geochem.*, 1979. Ed. by Douglas, A. G. and Maxwell, J. R. Pergamon Press, Oxford. pp. 77–91.

Bjorøy, M. and Vigran, J. O. (1979) Source rock studies on outcrop samples from the Norwegian Continental Shelf I. *IKU project report P215/1/78.*

Bjorøy, M. and Vigran, J. O. (1980a) Source rock analysis of selected samples from the Norwegian Continental Shelf II. *IKU project report P160/1/80.*

Bjorøy, M. and Vigran, J. O. (1980b) Organic geochemical analyses of samples from Barents Sea. *IKU project report P160/3/80.*

Bjorøy, M. and Vigran, J. O. (1980c) Organic geochemistry of drift material from Svalbardbanken. *IKU project report P160/5/80.*

Bjorøy, M. and Vigran, J. O. (1980d) Geochemical study of the organic matter in outcrop samples from Agardhfjellet, Spitsbergen. In *Adv. Org. Geochem.,* 1979. Ed. by Douglas, A. G. and Maxwell, J. Pergamon Press, Oxford. pp. 141–147.

Bjørlykke, K., Bue, B. and Elverhøi, A. (1978) Quaternary sediments in the northwestern part of the Barents Sea and their relation to the underlying Mesozoic bedrock. *Sedimentol.* **25,** 227–246.

Böhm, J. (1903) Uber die obertriadische Fauna der Bäreninsel. *Vet.-Ak. Hande. Stock.* **37,** 1–76.

Buchan, S. H., Challinor, A., Harland, W. B. and Parker, J. R. (1965) The Triassic stratigraphy of Svalbard. *Norsk Polarinst. Skr.* **135,** 1–94.

Burgess, J. D. (1974) Microscopic examination of kerogen (dispersed organic matter) in petroleum exploration. *Geo. Soc. Am. Spec. Paper,* **153,** 19–30.

Clayton, J. L. and Swetland, P. J. (1978) Subaerial weathering of sedimentary organic matter. *Geochim. Cosmochim. Acta* **42,** 305–312.

Cutbill, J. L. and Challinor, A. (1965) Revision of the stratigraphical scheme for the Carboniferous and Permian rocks of Spitsbergen and Bjørnøya. *Geol. Mag.* **102,** 418–439.

Dalland, A. (1975) The Mesozoic rocks of Andøya, northern Norway. *Nor. Geol. Unders.* **316,** 271–287.

Edwards, M. B. (1975) Gravel fraction on the Spitsbergen bank, NW Barents Shelf. *Norg. geol. Unders.* **316,** 205–217.

Espitalié, J., Madec, M., Tissot, B., Leplat, P. and Menning, J. J. (1977) Source rock characterization method for petroleum exploration. *Inst. Franc. Pétrole, Ref. 24843.*

Forsberg, A. and Bjorøy, B. (this volume) A sedimentological and organic geochemical study of the Botneheia Formation, Svalbard, with special emphasis on the weathering effect.

Gjelberg, J. (1978) Facies analysis of the coal-bearing Vesalstranda Member (Upper Devonian) of Bjørnøya. *Norsk Polarinst Årbok 1977,* 71–100.

Gjelberg, J. (1981) Upper Devonian (Famennian) — Middle Carboniferous succession of Bjørnøya. *Norsk Polarinst. Skr.* **174,** 1–67.

Gjelberg, J. and Steel, R. (1979) Middle Carboniferous sedimentation in relation to tectonic, climate and sea level changes on Bjørnøya and Spitsbergen. *Norwegian Sea Symposium, Norwegian Petroleum Society.* NSS/27. 1–25.

Horn, G. and Orvin, A. K. (1928) Geology of Bear Island, *Skr. Svalb. og Ishavet* **15,** 152 pp.

Kimble, B. J., Maxwell, J. R., Philp, R. P. and Eglinton, G. (1974) Identification of steranes and triterpanes in geolipid extracts by high-resolution gas chromatography and mass spectrometry. *Chem. Geol.* **14,** 173–198.

Kirkemo, K. (1979) *En sedimentologisk undersøkelse i Kapp Kåre Formasjonen (Moscov), Bjørnøya.* Thesis, Univ. of Oslo.

Knarud, R., Mørk, A. and Worsley, D. (in press): Depositional and diagenetic environments of the Triassic and Lower Jurassic of Svalbard. Canad. Soc. Petr. Geol. Mem. 8.

Krasilscikov, A. A. and Livsic, J. J. (1974) Tectonika ostrova Medvezij (Tectonics of Bjørnøya). *Geotektonika 1974* No. 4, 39–51. (In Russian.)

Leythaeuser, D. (1973) Effects of weathering on organic matter in shales. *Geochim. Cosmochim. Acta* **37,** 113–20.

Mackenzie, A. S., Quirke, J. M. E. and Maxwell, J. R. (1980a) Molecular parameters of maturation in the Toarcian shales, Paris Basin, France II. Evolution of metallaporphyrins. In *Adv. in Org. Geochem. 1979.* Ed. by Douglas, A. G. and Maxwell, J. R. Pergamon Press, Oxford. pp. 239–248.

Mackenzie, A. S., Patience, R. L. and Maxwell, J. R. (1980b) Molecular parameters of maturation in the Toarcian shales, Paris Basin, France I. Changes in the configurations of a cyclic isoprenoid alkanes, steranes and triterpanes. *Geochim. Cosmochim. Acta* **44,** 1709–21.

Mørk, A. and Worsley, D. (1979) The Triassic and Lower Jurassic succession of Svalbard: a review. *Norwegian Sea Symposium, Norwegian Petroleum Society,* NSS/29, 1–22.

Pcelina, T. M. (1972) Triasovye otlozenija ostrova Medvez'ego (Trias deposits of Bjørnøya). In *Mezozoijskie otlozenika Sval'barda (Mesozoic deposits of Svalbard).* Ed. by Sokolov and Vasilevskaja. NIIGA, Leningrad. pp. 5–20. (In Russian.)

Powell, T. G. (1978) An assessment of the hydrocarbon source rock potential of the Canadian Artic Island. *Geol. Surv. Canada, Paper, 78/12.*

Rønnevik, H. C. and Motland, K. (1979) Geology of the Barents Sea. *Norwegian Sea Symposium, Norwegian Petroleum Society,* NSS/15, 1–34.

Seifert, W. K. (1977) Source rock/oil correlations by C_{27}–C_{30} biological marker hydrocarbons. In *Adv. Org. Geochem., 1975.* Ed. by Campos, R. and Goni, J. Enadimsa, Madrid. pp. 21–44.

Seifert, W. K. (1978) Steranes and triterpanes in kerogen pyrolysis for correlation of oils and source rock. *Geochim. Cosmochim. Acta* **42,** 473–784.

Seifert, W. K. and Moldowan, J. M. (1978) Application of steranes, terpanes and monoaromatics to the maturation, migration and source of crude oils. *Geochim. Cosmochim. Acta* **42,** 77–95.

Seifert, W. K. and Moldowan, J. M. (1979) The effect of biodegradation on steranes and terpanes in crude oils. *Geochim. Cosmochim. Acta* **43,** 111–126.

Seifert, W. K. and Moldowan, J. M. (1980) The effect of thermal-stress on source rock quality as measured by hopane stereochemistry. In *Adv. Org. Geochem. 1980.* Ed. by Douglas A. G. and Maxwell, J. R. Pergamon Press, Oxford. pp. 229–237.

Seifert, W. K., Moldowan, J. M. and Jones, R. W. (1980) Application of biological marker chemistry to petroleum exploration. *Proc. 10th World Petroleum Congress,* Bucharest. Heyden & Sons Ltd, London.

Siedlecka, A. (1972) Length-slow chalcedony and relicts of sulphates: evidences of evaporitic environments in the Upper Carboniferous and Permian beds of Bear Island, Svalbard. *J. Sediment. Petrol.* **42,** 812–816.

Siedlecka, A. (1975) The petrology of some Carboniferous and Permian rocks from Bjørnøya, Svalbard. *Norsk Polarinst. Årbok 1973,* 53–72.

van Dorsselaer, A., Ensninger, A., Spyckorelle, C., Dastillung, M., Sieskind, O., Arpino, P., Albrecht, P., Ourisson, G., Brooks, P. W., Gaskell, S. J., Kimble, B. J., Philp, R. P., Maxwell, J. R. and Eglinton, G. (1974) Degraded and extended hopane derivatives (C_{27} to C_{35}) as ubiquetous geochemical markers. *Tetr. Lett.,* 1349–1352.

Vassoevich, N. B., Akramkhodzhaev, A. M. and Geodekyan, A. A. (1974) Principal zone of oil formation. In *Adv. Org. Geochem. 1973.* Ed. by Tissot, B. and Bienner, F. Technip, Paris. pp. 309–314.

Worsley, D. and Edwards, M. B. (1976) The Upper Palaeozoic succession of Bjørnøya, *Norsk Polarinst. Årbok 1974,* 17–34.

Advances in Organic Geochemistry 1981, pp. 60–68
© *John Wiley & Sons Limited, 1983*

A Sedimentological and Organic Geochemical Study of the Botneheia Formation, Svalbard, with special Emphasis on the Effects of Weathering on the Organic Matter in Shales

A. Forsberg

University of Oslo, Norway

M. Bjorøy

Continental Shelf Institute, Trondheim, Norway

Samples from three sections through the Middle Triassic sedimentary succession on Svalbard were analysed using standard sedimentological and organic geochemical techniques including field logging, XRD, thin-section microscopy, total organic carbon determination, high resolution gas chromatography, Rock-Eval pyrolysis, vitrinite reflectance and visual kerogen examination. The sections were located along an approximately 200 km WNW–ESE traverse from Tschermakfjellet, by Isfjorden on Spitzbergen, to Veidemannen, in the south of Edgeøya. Vitrinite reflectance decreased from $R_0 = 0.9\%$ in the west (Festningen) to $R_0 = 0.4\%$ in the east (Veidemannen). The potential of the Botneheia Formation as a source-rock for oil and gas was rated as 'good' in the West Spitzbergen section and 'rich' in the Central and East Spitzbergen sections and on Edgeøya. In a study of the effects of weathering on the organic matter from the organic-rich Botneheia Formation, samples obtained by shallow core-hole drilling were compared with stratigraphically equivalent, weathered outcrop samples. The main effect of weathering was to reduce the amount of extractable organic matter and the relative amounts of saturated and aromatic hydrocarbons; the total organic carbon content was little affected.

INTRODUCTION

A geological and geochemical study of Svalbard may provide a key to an understanding of the sedimentary record of the vast shelf area of the Barents Sea. A Mesozoic sedimentary sequence is exposed on all major islands of the archipelago and has been divided into three major lithostratigraphic units or Groups; Sassendalen, Kapp Toscana and Adventdalen. The Sassendalen Group on Spitzbergen has been divided into three Formations; the Vardebukta and the Sticky Keep Formations of Lower Triassic age, and the Botneheia Formation of Middle Triassic age (Buchan *et al.*, 1965).

The present study concerns samples of the Botneheia Formation taken mainly from three sections; the Tschermakfjellet and Stensiöfjellet sections, representing the central/eastern outcrop belt on Spitzbergen, and the Veidebreen/Veidemannen composite section on southern Edgeøya. For the purpose of comparison with the western outcrop belt, some data from the Festningen section are included. Organic geochemical studies were undertaken in an effort to correlate the quality of the organic matter with the sedimentological information, and to describe the

source-rock potential of the sediments. Details concerning maturity, organic-richness and typing of organic matter are given elsewhere (Forsberg, 1981).

As most of the samples available for this study were outcrop samples, it was important to investigate the effect of weathering on the organic matter. Several authors (Leythaeuser, 1973; Clayton and Swetland, 1978) have shown that, in areas with a warm arid climate, severe weathering can effect changes up to several metres into the outcrop. Bjorøy *et al.* (1980) and Bjorøy and Vigran (1980) have described the effect of weathering on organic matter in colder, more humid areas. As part of the present study, samples obtained by shallow core-hole drilling were compared with outcrop samples collected at stratigraphically equivalent levels.

GEOLOGICAL SETTING

At Festningen, a transgressive event marks the base of the Middle Triassic Botneheia Formation by the development of black phosphatic shales. The Formation shows a single coarsening-upwards sequence with the black shales grading upwards via oolitic carbonate

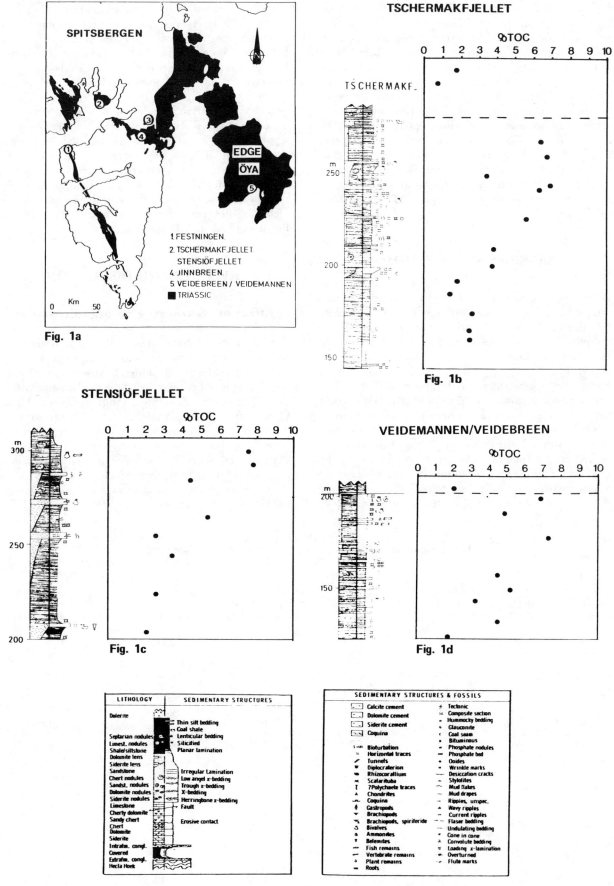

Fig. 1. (a) Map of Svalbard showing location of Triassic sediment outcrops and sampling sites. (b), (c), and (d) Lithostratigraphic and total organic carbon (TOC) content profile of the Botneheia Formation at Tschermakfjellet (b), Stensiöfjellet (c) and Veidemannen/Veidebreen (d).

deposits into highly bioturbated siltstones and sandstones representing delta top facies. During deposition of the Middle Triassic, renewed activity along old north/south-trending faultlines occurred. This tectonism created a sea-bottom with a varied topography in the central/eastern area. Upwelling of water from below the photic zone gave a steady supply of phosphate and nutrients. This caused phosphoritization of the sediments and a high primary productivity in the water column. The finely laminated, often papery, shales of the Botneheia Formation, and the thin interbedded layers of bioturbated siltstones, indicate that the environment of the sea-bottom was usually stagnant with occasional periods of more oxic conditions.

SAMPLES AND METHODS

During outcrop sampling, efforts were made to obtain samples which were as unweathered as possible, usually by digging into the outcrop. The location of the sampling sites is shown in Fig. 1a. Eight fresh, unweathered samples were obtained by shallow core-hole drilling through part of the organic-rich Botneheia Formation at a location near Jinnbreen (Fig. 1a). The core samples were obtained using a Winkie GW-15 drill fitted with a propane water heater to avoid freeze-in of the drill pipe caused by the permafrost. The bedding plane at the drill-site dips only 2–3° and the core was drilled on the edge of a canyon, perpendicular to the bedding. Eight outcrop samples were collected at approximately equivalent stratigraphic levels on the face of the cliff below the drill site. As the average core

recovery was only 70%, sampling from equivalent stratigraphic levels was, of necessity, only approximate.

The sedimentological interpretations were mainly based on sections logged in the field on a 1:100 scale. Further analyses were performed in the laboratory and included X-ray diffractometer (XRD) analysis and microscope studies of thin-sections. The organic geochemical analysis included the determination of total organic carbon, Rock–Eval pyrolysis, chromatographic separation, gas chromatographic analysis and examination of kerogen concentrates in transmitted light. Vitrinite reflectance, spore coloration in uv light and T_{max} values from Rock–Eval pyrolysis data were used to determine the maturity of the organic matter. Details of these procedures are given elsewhere (Bjorøy, Bue and Elvsborg; this volume).

RESULTS AND DISCUSSION

Effect of weathering on organic matter

Various authors have shown that weathering can seriously affect the content and composition of organic material in shales and siltstones. Leythaeuser (1973) has shown that weathering reduced the total organic carbon (TOC) content of surface samples of the Upper Cretaceous Mancos Shale (Utah) by up to 25%. Similarly, Clayton and Swetland (1978) reported that outcrop and shallow (<2 feet) core samples of the Permian Phosphoria Formation contained an average of 60% less TOC than deeper samples. Both studies also demonstrated a 50% loss of extractable organic matter (EOM) in weathered samples compared to

Table 1.
Extraction results on core-hole and outcrop samples from Jinnbreen.

Sample number	Sample depth (m)	Organic carbon (TOC-wt%)	Extractable organic matter (mg g^{-1} C_{org})	Saturated HC: aromatic HC	Pristane to n-C_{17} ratio	Prist.+phyt. to n-C_{17}+n-C_{18} ratio
8580[a]	core	3.4[a]	88.6[a]	1.44[a]	0.41	0.33
8605[a]	1.0	3.7[a]	82.6[a]	1.86[a]	0.35	0.28
K 1301	core	3.9	85.28	2.40	0.96	0.79
K 1404	2.3	4.2	81.10	1.88	1.08	0.89
K 2860	core	3.6	87.22	1.48	0.31	0.28
K 1250	4.0	4.3	70.51	1.88	1.57	1.21
K 2130	core	4.5	77.73	1.04[a]	0.33	0.28
K 1405	4.3	5.0	69.48	1.24	1.51	1.17
K 2861	core	5.5	78.02	1.10	0.40	0.33
K 1249	6.0	4.5	83.91	1.48	0.43	0.36
K 2125	core	5.2	81.15	1.27	0.37	0.31
K 1406	6.3	4.6	77.0	1.82	8.00	5.69
K 2862	core	4.4	82.93	0.94[a]	0.36	0.31
K 1248	8.0	5.2	75.38	1.45	0.39	0.33
K 2863	core	2.9	102.39	1.59	0.42	0.35
K 1247	10.0	4.5	73.64	1.62	0.75	0.60

[a] Analysed at KFA Jülich.

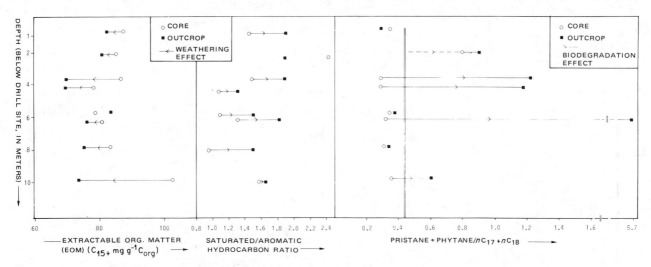

Fig. 2. Effect of weathering/biodegradation on various organic geochemical parameters as determined by a comparison of core samples and outcrop samples.

OUTCROP   CORE

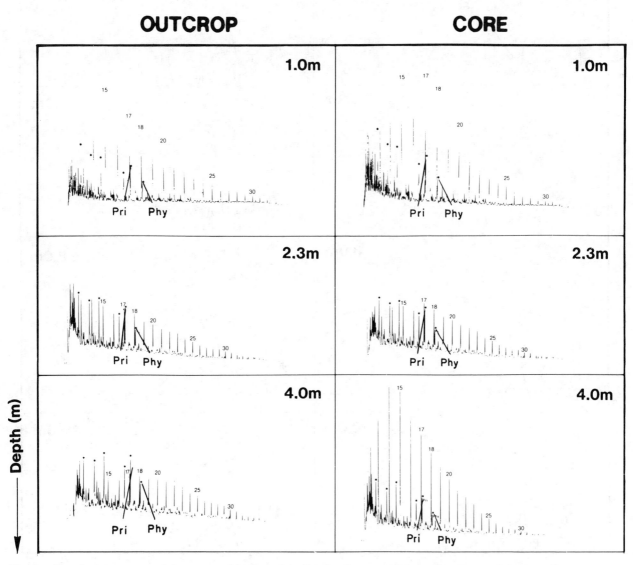

Fig. 3. Gas chromatograms of the saturated hydrocarbon fraction from core-hole and outcrop samples from Jinnbreen. (Pri = pristane, Phy = phytane, numbers denote carbon number of *n*-alkane).

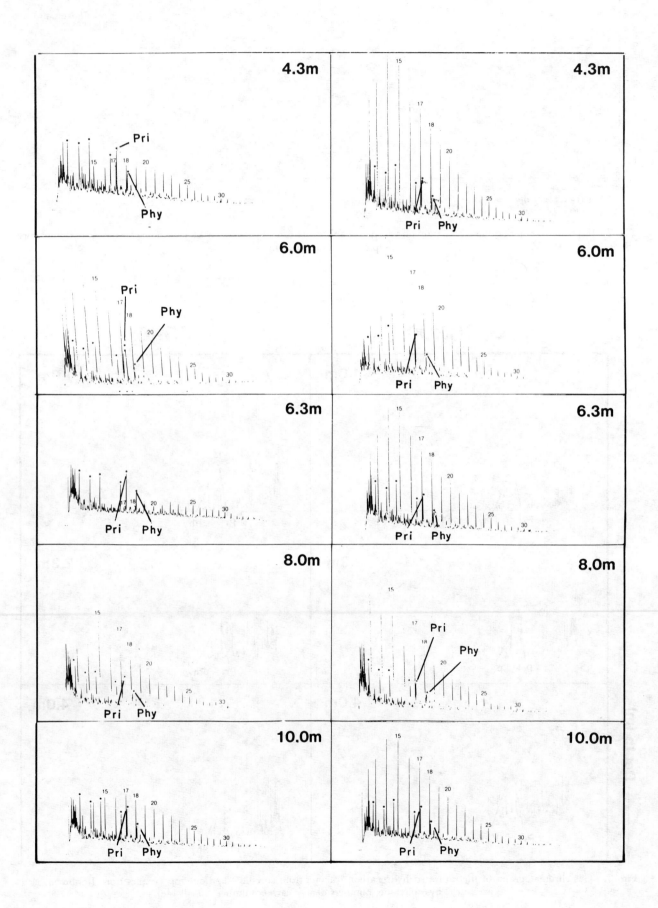

unweathered. This supports the study by Radchenko *et al.* (1951) in which a 39% loss of EOM was observed in outcrop samples compared to stratigraphically equivalent, unweathered subsurface samples.

In the present study, the increasing discrepancies for the organic carbon content between the equivalent sample pairs with increasing depth (Table 1) may be due to failure to obtain samples from exactly equivalent stratigraphic levels. Rock–Eval pyrolysis and visual examination of kerogen concentrates in transmitted light did not show any variation in the type of kerogen throughout the 11.4 m deep core-hole. Values for total organic carbon content were in the range 2.9–5.5%, with the highest values being found in samples from the central part of the cored section (Table 1). The cliff outcrop appeared to be a relatively fresh exposure and only two of the core samples gave organic carbon values higher than the corresponding outcrop samples. It is therefore suggested that weathering of the organic material in the Botneheia Formation at this location has been relatively mild and has not severely affected the content of organic material.

Clear trends are seen in the yield of extractable organic matter. With the exception of that from 6.0 m, the outcrop samples show a clear decrease in the amount of extractable organic matter compared to the core samples (Table 1, Fig. 2), indicating that even mild weathering affects the yield. The average loss of EOM in the outcrop samples compares with the core samples is approximately 10%. There is a preferential loss of aromatic compounds from the extracts in the outcrop samples compared to the core samples (Table 1, Fig. 2). The sample from level 2.3 m, however, shows the opposite trend. The composition of the saturated hydrocarbons in this sample suggests strong biodegradation effects (Table 1, Fig. 3) (see also Clayton and Swetland, 1978).

Various authors have shown that bacteria degrade *n*-alkanes before isoprenoids (Bailey *et al.*, 1973; Deroo *et al.*, 1974; Ho *et al.*, 1974; Burns *et al.*, 1975; Powell, 1978). An indication of the degree of biodegradation may be obtained from the capillary gas chromatographic analyses of the saturated hydrocarbons, which show a clear separation of the *n*-alkanes and isoprenoids (Fig. 3). The ratios pristane:nC_{17} and pristane + phytane:$nC_{17} + nC_{18}$ indicate the degree of biodegradation (Table 1, Fig. 2). The surface samples analysed show a reduction of the *n*-alkane content and a relative enrichment of the isoprenoids and branched alkanes compared with core samples (Fig. 2). Biodegradation effects vary drastically within the sample series (Fig. 2). It is most severe in the samples from 6.3 m; relatively strong at 4.0 m and 4.3 m; moderate at 10.0 m and almost absent at 1.0 m, 6.0 m and 8.0 m.

The effect of biodegradation is clearly seen in the gas chromatograms of the saturated hydrocarbons (Fig. 3). With the exception of that from 2.3 m, the core sample extracts give gas chromatograms showing a smooth, front-biased *n*-alkane distribution typical of well-matured hydrocarbons (Tissot and Welte, 1978). Most outcrop samples (i.e. not those from 1.0 m, 6.0 m and 8.0 m) show chromatograms in which the isoprenoids and branched alkanes are predominant. Although the gas

chromatograms of the outcrop samples from 1.0 m, 6.0 m and 8.0 m are basically similar to those of the stratigraphically equivalent core samples, they show a significant reduction in the ratio of the saturated to aromatic hydrocarbons (Table 1).

At least two different mechanisms may be responsible for the weathering of the organic matter in the shales at this site, namely, subaerial oxidation, which is known to remove aromatics preferentially from crude oils and sediment extracts (Aksnes, 1979; Clayton and Swetland, 1978), and bacterial activity, which removes *n*-alkanes before isoprenoids (Bailey *et al.*, 1973; Deroo *et al.*, 1974; Ho *et al.*, 1974; Burns *et al.*, 1975; Clayton and Swetland, 1978; Powell, 1978). It is suggested that depletion of *n*-alkanes relative to isoprenoids in the outcrop samples at Jinnbreen is due to biodegradation and that this process has been effective since the last ice-age. The shales at the outcrop site are finely laminated and fissile, often with a papery appearance. This would provide a large contact area between penetrating/percolating surface water and the shale, thereby facilitating the access of bacteria to the organic matter contained in the shale.

Biodegradation of hydrocarbons in the core samples is mainly apparent at 2.3 m (Table 1, Figs 2 and 3). Percolation of water (and hence bacteria) along fractures penetrating deep into the outcrop may provide an explanation for this observation. The mechanism and duration of the biodegradation processes occurring in these Botneheia shales is unclear. The presence of permafrost at this location and the severe arctic climatic conditions would tend to reduce bacterial penetration and metabolic rate.

Maturity and source rock potential

On the basis of the scale devised by Vassoevich *et al.* (1974), the vitrinite reflectance values (R_0) found for the Middle Triassic rocks in the west (Festningen) ($R_0 = 0.9\%$) indicate these samples to have an oil-window maturity. Samples from the two locations in the central/eastern part of Spitzbergen gave lower reflectance values ($R_0 = 0.5$–0.6%), indicating moderate maturity. A decrease in maturity is also seen on going from eastern Spitzbergen to Edgeøya, where all parameters indicate the organic matter to be immature ($R_0 = 0.4\%$). The trend of increasing maturity on going from east to west probably reflects the effect of increasing overburden. A higher heatflow, related to the Tertiary orogenesis of Western Spitzbergen, could be an additional explanation for the relatively high maturity at Festningen.

Kerogen type was determined using data from Rock–Eval pyrolysis of whole rock (Espitalié *et al.*, 1977) supported by visual examination of kerogen concentrates in transmitted light. In each of the four sections analysed, the Botneheia Formation was found to be dominated by an input of marine organic matter resulting in the formation of a type II kerogen (Fig. 4).

The abundance of total organic carbon shows a clear, general correlation with lithology (Fig. 1b, 1c, 1d). The coarser the sediments, the less organic carbon they

ROCK-EVAL PYROLYSIS

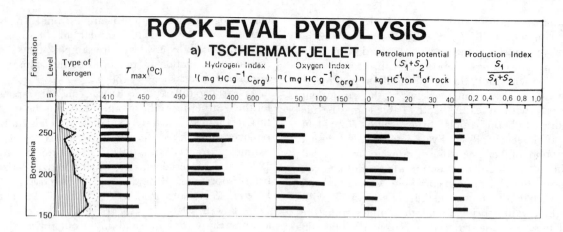

a) TSCHERMAKFJELLET

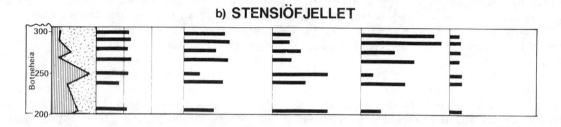

b) STENSIÖFJELLET

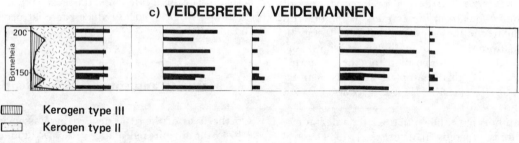

c) VEIDEBREEN / VEIDEMANNEN

▓▓▓ Kerogen type III
▒▒▒ Kerogen type II

Fig. 4. Depth profile of Rock-Eval pyrolysis data from samples of the Botneheia Formation: Tschermakfjellet section (a), Stensiöfjellet section (b), Veidebreen/Veidemannen section (c).

contain. Samples from Festningen, in the west, contained less organic carbon than the samples from the equivalent beds in the central/eastern exposure belt on Spitzbergen and on Edgeøya. The phosphatic black shales of the Botneheia Formation at Festningen gave TOC values in the range 1.3–2.9%; the sandstones in the upper part of this Formation gave TOC contents of 0.4% and lower.

The fining-upwards trend of the Triassic sediments in the eastern exposure belt and on Edgeøya correlates with a gradual increase in the abundance of organic carbon. An increase in the organic carbon content is observed within the Botneheia Formation going from west to east, the maximum value being 7.5%. The uppermost section of the Botneheia Formation in both the Tschermakfjellet and the Veidebreen/Veidemann section shows no decrease in abundance of organic carbon, in contrast to that observed in the deltaic top at Festningen.

To a certain extent, the abundance of extractable hydrocarbons showed the same trends as those found for the abundance of organic carbon. The samples from the Botneheia Formation at Festningen were found to contain 500–1500 ppm of extractable hydrocarbons and at Stensiöfjellet the samples contained 700–2000 ppm. When normalised to organic carbon, the samples from the Botneheia Formation at Stensiöfjellet gave extractable hydrocarbon values in the range 14–60 mg HC g^{-1} C_{org}. The values for the same formation in the Tschermakfjellet profile were in the range 100–1000 ppm (2–15 mg HC g^{-1} C_{org}), while the samples from the Viedemannen/Veidebreen composite profile gave values in the range 1300–4300 ppm (25–58 mg HC g^{-1} C_{org}).

The gas chromatograms of the saturated hydrocarbon fractions show significant differences between samples from the western and the central/eastern areas. Most of the samples from the Botneheia Formation at Festningen show a smooth front-biased distribution (Fig. 5a) although a few contain a large unresolved envelope (Fig. 5b) which is typical of weathered and/or biodegraded samples (Bjorøy et al., 1980).

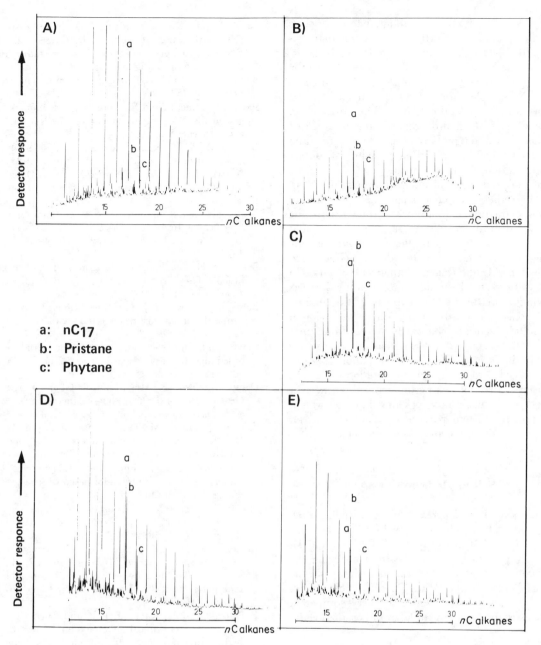

Fig. 5. Gas chromatograms of the saturated hydrocarbon fraction from samples of the Botneheia Formation at Festningen (a — 'unweathered' pattern; b — slightly weathered) and at Stensiöfjellet (c — lower, weathered; d — upper, 'unweathered'; e — upper, biodegraded).

The distribution of saturated hydrocarbon from samples of the Botneheia Formation at Stensiöfjellet was more variable. The samples from the lower part of the section contained abundant geochemical fossils (steranes/triterpanes) (Fig. 5c), indicating the organic matter to be immature (Tissot and Welte, 1978). In the upper part of the section, some samples showed a front-biased, smooth n-alkane distribution typical of mature hydrocarbons of marine origin (Fig. 5d), whereas others contained abundant isoprenoids (Fig. 5e). The latter may be the effect of bacterial activity (Evans *et al.*, 1971; Powell, 1978). The saturated hydrocarbon distributions in samples from the Tschermakfjellet and the Veidemannen/Veidebreen sections were similar to those from the Stensiöfjellet section.

The distribution of saturated hydrocarbons in many samples was indicative of a far higher maturity of the

hydrocarbons than that of the kerogen (Tissot and Welte, 1978). This, together with the relatively high abundance of extractable hydrocarbons in these samples (when the low maturity is taken into account), indicates that some samples are impregnated by migrated hydrocarbons. As several samples gave saturated hydrocarbon distribution patterns typical of mature hydrocarbons and others gave patterns typical of biodegraded hydrocarbons, it is concluded that biodegradation occurred subsequent to migration.

CONCLUSION

The degree of weathering of outcrop samples of the Botneheia Formation shales at Jinnbreen is too low to have significantly affected the abundance of organic carbon; the abundance of extractable organic matter is only slightly affected, with an average loss of 10%.

The aromatic hydrocarbons are more affected by weathering than the saturated compounds, a feature also reported for samples from warmer, more arid areas (Clayton and Swetland, 1978). The degree of biodegradation of the hydrocarbons in the investigated shales is variable and is probably dependent on the ratio between the area of the surficial water–sediment contact and on the volume of the sediment.

If care is taken during collection, outcrop samples can be useful in studies of source rock potential. However, in evaluating extraction and chromatographic results, the possibility of degradation of the organic material should be taken into account. With these reservations, the following conclusions may be drawn concerning maturity of the Middle Triassic Botneheia Formation in central Svalbard: the Festningen profile in the west has an oil-window maturity. The maturity of the organic matter decreases eastwards; in the Triassic succession in central Spitzbergen it is moderately mature to mature, whereas in the eastern part it is immature.

The Middle Triassic Botneheia Formation contains marine-sourced kerogens which increase in abundance in an easterly direction. At Festningen, the Formation has a good potential as source rock for gas and oil, and in the central and eastern parts of Spitzbergen and on Edgeøya it has a rich potential as source-rock for these hydrocarbons.

Acknowledgements

The authors wish to express their gratitude to D. Leythaeuser (KFA, Jülich) for valuable discussions during the course of this project. W. Benders and D. Leythaeuser provided technical assistance during the drilling programme and we are grateful to Statoil for the provision of logistic support during the 1979 field season. Finally, we wish to acknowledge the very competent technical assistance given by the laboratory staff at IKU.

REFERENCES

Aksnes, G. (1979) Kjemisk nedbrytning av olje. FOH Rapport nr. 1.

Bailey, N. J. L., Krouse, H. R., Evans, C. R. and Rogers, M. A. (1973) Alteration of crude oil by waters and bacteria: Evidence from geochemical and isotope studies. Bull. Am. Ass. Petrol. Geol. 57, 1276.

Bjorøy, M., (1977) Organic geochemistry in search of petroleum. IKU Publ. 93.

Bjorøy, M., Bue, B. and Elvsborg, A. (this volume). Organic geochemical analyses of the two first wells in the Troms 1 area (Barents Sea).

Bjorøy, M., Hall, K. and Vigran, J. O. (1980) Organic geochemical study of Mesozoic shales from Andøya, North Norway. In Adv. Org. Geochem., 1979. Ed. by Douglas, A. G. and Maxwell, J. R. Pergamon Press, Oxford. pp. 77–110.

Bjorøy, M. and Vigran, J. O. (1980) Geochemical study of the organic matter in outcrop samples from Agardhfjellet, Spitsbergen. In Adv. Org. Geochem., 1979. Ed. by Douglas, A. G. and Maxwell, J. R. Pergamon Press, Oxford. pp. 141–147.

Buchan, S. H., Challinor, A., Harland, W. B. and Parker, J. R. (1965) The Triassic stratigraphy of Svalbard. Norsk Polarinst. skr. 135, 1–94.

Burns, B. J., Hogarth, J. T. C. and Milner, C. W. D. (1975) Properties of Beaufort Basin liquid hydrocarbon. Bull. Can. Petrol. Geol. 23, 295–303.

Clayton, J. L. and Swetland, P. J. (1978) Subaerial weathering of sedimentary organic matter. Geochim. Cosmochim. Acta 42, 305–312.

Deroo, G., Tissot, B., McCrossan, R. G. and Der, F. (1974) Geochemistry of the heavy oils of Alberta. In Oil Sands Fuel of the Future. Can. Soc. Petrol. Geol. Mem., 3, 148–167.

Espitalié, J., Madec, M., Tissot, B., Leplat, P. and Menning, J. J. (1977) Source rock characterization method for petroleum exploration. Inst. Franc. Pétr. Ref. 24843.

Forsberg, A. (1981). Em sedimentologisk og organisk undersøkelse av Barentsøya formasjanen (trias), Svalbard. Thesis, Univ. of Oslo.

Ho, T. Y., Rogers, M. A., Drushek, H. V. and Koons, C. B. (1974) Evolution of sulphur compounds in crude oils. Bull. Ass. Petrol. Geol., 58, 2338–2348.

Leythaeuser, D. (1973) Effects of weathering on organic matter in shales. Geochim. Cosmochim. Acta 37, 113–20.

Powell, T. G. (1978) An assessment of the hydrocarbon source rock potential of the Canadian Arctic Islands. Geol. Surv. Canada, Paper, 78/12.

Radchenko, O. A., Karpova, I. P. and Chernysheva, A. S. (1951) A geochemical investigation of weathered and highly altered mineral fuels from South Fergana. Tr. Unigri. New Ser. 5. Contrib. Geochem. 2/3, 180–202.

Vassoevich, N. B., Akramkhodzhaev, A. M. and Geodekyan, A. A. (1974) Principal zone of oil formation. In Adv. Org. Geochem. 1973. Ed. by Tissot, B. and Bienner, F. Technip. Paris. pp. 309–314.

Advances in Organic Geochemistry 1981, pp. 69–71
© John Wiley & Sons Limited, 1983

Aromatic Hydrogen Exchange in Petroleum Source Rocks

R. Alexander, R. I. Kagi, A. V. Larcher and G. W. Woodhouse

School of Applied Chemistry, Western Australian Institute of Technology, Kent Street, Bentley, 6102, Western Australia, Australia

The exchange of aromatic hydrogen in petroleum source rocks has been studied by measuring the rate of detritiation of 2-methoxy[1-^{3}H]naphthalene in the presence of petroleum-containing sediments obtained from various temperature zones of a sedimentary sequence. The use of a highly activated substrate enabled the reactions to be studied at 138 °C. The catalytic effects observed in the laboratory experiments have been proposed as being representative of those occurring in sediments under natural geological conditions. The results have been used to estimate the rate of exchange of aromatic hydrogen in petroleum aromatics with clay-rich sediments and indicate that the reactions are fast on a geological time-scale.

INTRODUCTION

Clays are an important component in the mineral matrix of source rocks in many sedimentary basins (Hunt, 1979; Tissot and Welte, 1978a). Many of the organic reactions which occur in sedimentary environments are believed to be influenced or catalysed by the clay minerals present. Examples include the formation of petroleum hydrocarbons (Galwey, 1972), the aromatization of terpenes (Frenkel and Heller-Kallai, 1977), the rearrangement of sterols (Sieskind *et al.*, 1979), and the exchange of aromatic hydrogens (Alexander *et al.*, 1981a). Clay minerals, particularly the smectites, have acid properties: this acidity has been attributed to the dissociation of water molecules associated with the hydration spheres of exchangeable cations (Frenkel, 1974; Benesi and Winquist, 1978). These acid properties play a role in the catalysis of many of the reactions of petroleum generation and maturation, in particular the acid-catalysed aromatic hydrogen exchange reaction

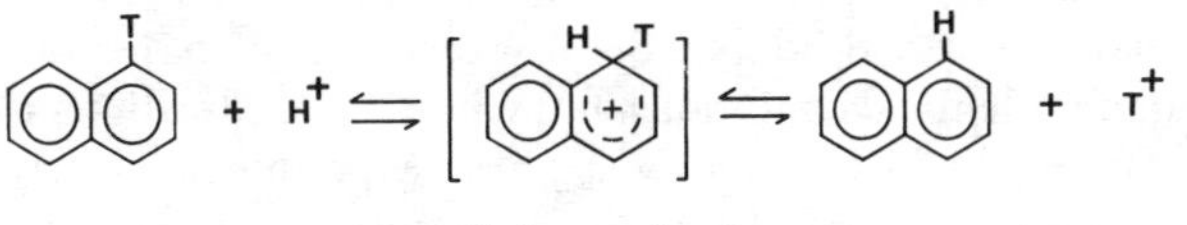

Scheme 1

(Scheme 1) which occurs in homogeneous and heterogeneous systems via an intermediate arenium ion typical of electrophilic aromatic substitution reactions (Ansell *et al.*, 1977; Venuto and Landis, 1968). In this paper we report the reactivity of aromatic hydrogens in the presence of a range of petroleum source rocks obtained from different temperature zones of the sedimentary column.

In carrying out laboratory-based maturation studies one is confronted with the problem of causing reactions to proceed within a practical time scale. This is usually accomplished by carrying out the experiments at temperatures greatly above those found in the geological situation. Because of the obvious risk of gross modifications to the system occurring at such elevated temperatures, for example, alteration of the catalytic properties of the mineral matrix (Mortland and Raman, 1968) extrapolation to the geological system is usually a very uncertain matter. An alternative option is the selection of a more reactive compound for use as a model for the petroleum organics. The use of the highly reactive 2-methoxy [1-^{3}H]naphthalene in this study allowed the hydrogen exchange reaction at 138°C to be monitored conveniently by loss of tritium.

EXPERIMENTAL

Sediment samples

The samples selected for study consisted of organic-rich shales and siltstones obtained in the form of cuttings from oil-drilling operations in the Carnarvon Basin of Western Australia. Each sample was washed with water, air-dried and crushed to pass through a 125 μm sieve.

Soluble organic matter (SOM)

A portion of the crushed and dried sample was extracted with a dichloromethane:methanol (9:1) solvent mixture using ultrasonic vibration for two hours. The combined weight of the saturate, aromatic and polar fractions obtained after subjecting the extract to column chromatography (Alexander *et al.*, 1981b) was reported as soluble organic matter.

Table 1
Geochemical and kinetic data

Sample	Temp[a] (°C)	SOM (% w/w)	Rate constant $k \times 10^7$ s^{-1}	Sample	Temp[a] (°C)	SOM (% w/w)	Rate constant $k \times 10^7$ s^{-1}
Well A				Well C			
1	44	0.01	700	1	103	0.02	682
2	46	nd[b]	319	2	122	0.05	567
3	47	nd	375	3	134	0.07	554
4	54	nd	378	4	139	0.18	464
5	56	0.04	383	5	140	0.12	651
6	61	0.11	16.9	6	144	0.10	529
7	73	0.16	5.72	7	155	0.06	461
8	76	0.15	14.31	8	157	0.03	450
9	79	0.13	7.19				
10	80	0.14	9.06	Well D			
11	81	0.15	13.08	1	41	0.06	636
				2	49	0.03	580
Well B				3	52	0.08	608
1	93	0.17	494	4	60	0.20	682
2	99	0.07	347	5	64	0.12	594
3	119	0.10	405	6	68	0.08	580
				7	73	0.11	430
				Well E			
				1	149	0.20	259

[a] Subsurface sediment temperature determined from well-log data.
[b] Not determined.

Preparation of tritium-labelled compounds

2-methoxy[1-^{3}H]naphthalene was prepared by treatment of the appropriate Grignard reagent with tritiated water (Eaborn et al., 1968).

Hydrogen-exchange experiments

Rates of hydrogen exchange were obtained by measuring the decrease in activity of 2-methoxy[1-^{3}H]naphthalene intimately mixed with a sample of sediment at a temperature of 138 °C. Sediment-organic mixtures were prepared by mixing the crushed and dried sediment sample (5 g) with finely divided, labelled 2-methoxynaphthalene (0.15 g). The mixture was sealed in a glass ampoule and placed in a constant temperature oven (± 1 °C). Ampoules were removed at appropriate time intervals, cooled, the contents extracted with pentane using ultrasonic vibration for 20 minutes and the 2-methoxynaphthalene isolated from the extract using silicic acid chromatography (Alexander et al., 1981b). The purity of the recovered 2-methoxynaphthalene was determed by gas chromatography and in all cases greater than 99% one peak was observed. The activity of the 2-methoxynaphthalene was then measured by liquid scintillation.

Rate constants were calculated from the experimental data using the following integrated form of the first-order rate equation.

$$\ln A = -kT + A_0$$

where A_0 and A are the activity of the 2-methoxy[1-^{3}H)naphthalene at time (t) zero and at time t. The rate constant (k) for each reaction was obtained as the slope from the plot of $\ln A$ versus t. Experimental measurements were made within the first two half-lives of

reaction to reduce problems associated with the reincorporation of displaced tritium.

RESULTS AND DISCUSSION

The rate of detritiation of 2-methoxy[1-^{3}H]naphthalene was determined at 138 °C in the presence of sediment samples which had been obtained from different depths (temperatures) from five sedimentary sequences in the Carnarvon Basin of Western Australia. Table 1 contains geochemical and kinetic data for the sediment samples. Most contain sufficient soluble organic matter to be classified as petroleum source rocks and they have been recovered from geological formations with subsurface sediment temperatures typical of those where petroleum formation and maturation processes occur (Tissot and Welte, 1978b). The results of the reaction rate measurements show that reaction takes place readily on the mineral surfaces with rate constants ranging from 700 $\times 10^{-7}$ s^{-1} (half-life of 2.8 hours) to 5.72×10^{-7} s^{-1} (half-life of 336 hours). Blank experiments carried out under identical conditions, but without added sediment, showed no loss in activity. These experiments clearly demonstrate that the sediment samples are catalytic towards this hydrogen exchange reaction. Since the sample treatment and reaction conditions were identical for all samples, differences in reactivity reflect only the differing catalytic abilities of the sediment samples.

The use of naphthalenes as model compounds for petroleum aromatics is appropriate not only because naphthalenes are major constituents of petroleum aromatics but also because their reactivity towards exchange is intermediate between that of the slower mononuclear aromatics and the faster polynuclear aromatic systems (Ansell et al., 1977; Ansell and Taylor,

1977). Further, because the presence of a methoxy substituent greatly increases the reactivity of naphthalene (Alexander *et al.*, 1981a; Eaborn *et al.*, 1968), appreciable exchange can be observed over time intervals convenient for laboratory experiments at temperatures similar to those which result in exchange of the unsubstituted compounds over extended time intervals under geological conditions. The differences in reactivity observed between sediment samples should therefore reflect the differing ability of the mineral matrices to catalyse aromatic hydrogen exchange of typical petroleum aromatics under geological conditions.

The reactivity of the parent compound naphthalene towards hydrogen exchange with the mineral matrix can be estimated from the experimental results. We recently reported that [1-^{3}H]naphthalene reacts faster than 2-methoxy[1-^{3}H]naphthalene on bentonite clay by a factor of 4.8×10^3 at 100 °C (Alexander *et al.*, 1981a). Assuming that this reactivity difference is maintained when reaction occurs on the mineral matrix of the sediment sample and at the higher temperature (138 °C) the half-life of exchange for [1-^{3}H]naphthalene ($t_{1/2}$) may be calculated as follows:

$$t_{1/2} = \frac{0.69}{k/(4.8 \times 10^3)}$$

where k is the experimentally determined rate constant for 2-methoxy[1-^{3}H]naphthalene. Such calculations show that the half-life for hydrogen exchange at the 1 position of naphthalene ranges from a few years to approximately two hundred years for the range of source rocks studied. Clearly, this is a fast reaction when considered in the context of a geological time-scale. These results suggest that aromatic hydrogens in the complex mixture of aromatic compounds usually found in petroleum will undergo appreciable exchange with the clay-rich matrix in source rocks.

Acknowledgements

The authors wish to thank the Department of Medical Technology of the Western Australian Institute of Technology for providing radio-counting facilities. This work was supported by grants from the National Energy Research Development and Demonstration Council of Australia.

REFERENCES

Alexander, R., Kagi, R. I. and Larcher, A. V. (1981a) Clay catalysis of aromatic hydrogen-exchange reactions. *Geochim. Cosmochim. Acta* **46**, 219–222.

Alexander, R., Kagi, R. I. and Woodhouse, G. W. (1981b) Factors affecting the evolution of aromatics during pyrolysis of an immature Australian crude oil. *J. Anal. Appl. Pyrol.* **3**, 59–70.

Ansell, H. V., Hirschler, M. M. and Taylor, R. (1977) Electrophilic aromatic substitution. Part 18. Protiodetritiation of anthracene, coronene, and triphenylene in anhydrous trifluoroacetic acid. *J. Chem. Soc. Perkin Trans.* **2**, 353–355.

Ansell, H. V. and Taylor, R. (1977) Electrophilic aromatic substitution, Part 19. Protiodetritiation of 1,2-diphenylethane and 9,10-di-hydrophenanthrene: Effect of Strain on aromatic reactivity. *J. Chem. Soc. Perkin Trans.* **2**, 866–872.

Benesi, H. A. and Winquist, B. H. C. (1978) Surface acidity and solid catalysts. *Adv. Catal.* **27**, 97–182.

Eaborn, C., Golborn, P., Spillet, R. E. and Taylor, R. (1968) Aromatic reactivity. Part XXXVII. Detritiation of substituted 1- and 2-tritionaphthalenes. *J. Chem. Soc. B*, 1112–1123.

Frenkel, M. (1974) Surface acidity of montmorillonites. *Clays Clay Miner.* **22**, 435–441.

Frenkel, M. and Heller-Kallai, L. (1977) Aromatization of limonene — a geochemical model. *Org. Geochem.* **1**, 3–5.

Galwey, A. K. (1972). The rate of hydrocarbon desorption from mineral surfaces and the contribution of heterogeneous catalytic-type processes to petroleum genesis. *Geochim. Cosmochim. Acta* **36**, 1115–1130.

Hunt, J. M. (1979) *Petroleum Geochemistry and Geology.* Freeman, Oxford, pp. 124–130.

Mortland, M. M. and Raman, K. V. (1968) Surface acidity of smectites in relation to hydration, exchangeable cation, and structure. *Clays Clay Miner* **16**, 393–398.

Sieskind, I., Jolly, G. and Albrecht, P. (1979) Simulation of the geochemical transformations of sterols: super acid effect of clay minerals. *Geochim. Cosmochim. Acta* **43**, 1675–1679.

Tissot, B. P. and Welte, D. (1978a) *Petroleum Formation and Occurrence.* Springer-Verlag, Heidelberg, pp. 179–180.

Tissot, B. P. and Welte, D. (1978b) *Petroleum Formation and Occurrence.* Springer-Verlag, Heidelberg, pp. 96, 195.

Venuto, P. B. and Landis, P. S. (1968) Organic catalysis over crystalline aluminosilicates. *Adv. Catal.* **18**, 259–371.

Advances in Organic Geochemistry 1981, pp. 72–75
© John Wiley & Sons Limited, 1983

The Spectral Fluorometric Analyses of the Soluble Organic Matter Applied to Hydrocarbon Source Rock Evaluation

H. W. Hagemann and A. Hollerbach

Lehrstuhl für Geologie, Geochemie und Lagerstätten des Erdöls und der Kohle, Aachen Technical University, D-5100 Aachen, FRG

It is known that there are direct relations between the degree of maturity of the organic matter and the hydrocarbon genesis in sediments. Due to this, the degree of maturity is normally determined by means of microscopic measurements of the reflectance on vitrinitic particles. Since this method is very time consuming, a rapid method was developed for the hydrocarbon exploration which is based on fluorometric measurements of the soluble organic matter for the determinations of the degree of maturity of source rocks.

INTRODUCTION

Fluorometric analyses have already been applied to many exploration projects, although this new method of microscopic measurements of the fluorescence spectra on polished surfaces cannot yet be regarded as a well established standard procedure. Apart from the detection of the type and quantity of the primary and secondary liptinite macerals of hydrocarbon source rocks, these analyses deal primarily with the characterization of the fluorescence properties of these components as maturity parameters in rocks poor in huminite or vitrinite respectively (Teichmüller, 1974, 1979; Teichmüller and Teichmüller, 1975; Teichmüller and Ottenjann, 1977; Teichmüller and Wolf, 1977; Alpern and Cheymol, 1978; Robert, 1979, 1980; Leythaeuser *et al.*, 1980; Alpern, 1980).

The main aims of the present fluorometric study are as follows

(a) In addition to the known spectra measurements of fluorescence on liptinites, the extracts of rocks from five wells in a depth range from approximately 2000 to 6000 m should be analysed by fluorescence microscopy in order to test the efficiency of the extracts for the determination of the degree of maturity.

(b) To gain characteristics indicating formation and migration of hydrocarbons.

METHODOLOGY

Principles of fluorometric analysis of the extracts

Apart from other factors, hydrocarbons can only be formed in source rocks within a certain temperature range, i.e. from 50 to 150 °C. In addition to microscopic measurements of reflectance, this range can also be covered by microscopic investigations of their fluorescence. The latter appear particularly appropriate for the liptinites, if huminitic or vitrinitic components, on which the reflectance measurements are carried out, are missing in the source rocks.

Unfortunately, it is not yet clear which figured liptinites in the source rocks are particularly suitable for the determination of the degree of maturity by means of fluorometric analysis. Furthermore, the question arises as to whether the valuation criteria which are known for the rank determination of coals can also be fully applied to the liptinitic particles of the source rocks or their mineral-bituminous groundmass. In order to avoid these difficulties, which are caused primarily by the diversity of the liptinites in one sample fluorescing with different colours and intensities, Hagemann and Hollerbach (1980, 1981) chose an alternative method of analysis. Their method does not refer to the macerals of the liptinite group, but to the soluble organic matter (extract) of coals and source rocks. Similarly to the macerals of the liptinite group, the extracts also change their fluorescence colour and intensity with increasing degree of maturity of the sediments. As an analogy, the position of the maximum of the spectrum changes from about 450 nm wavelength to peaks of 700 nm wavelength in anthracites. The red-green ratio, i.e. the ratio of the fluorescence intensity between 650 nm and 500 nm wavelength, is augmented with increasing rank, from values smaller than 0.50 in peats to approximately 9.00 at the anthracitic stage of maturity.

Hagemann and Hollerbach also used a new parameter for the evaluation of fluorescence spectra. This parameter is composed of the quantitative coefficients of the corresponding fluorescence colours, such as tristimulus values and, especially, the trichromatic coor-

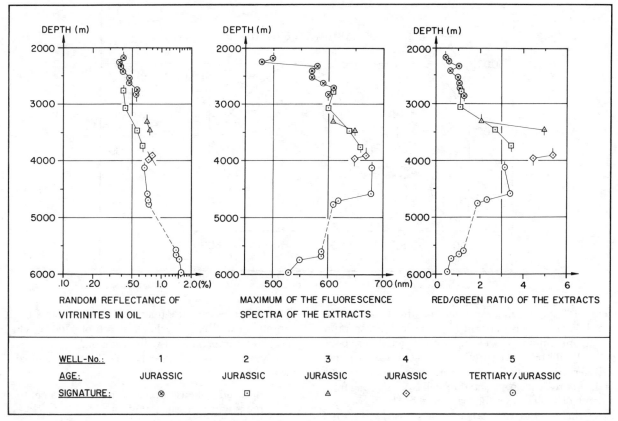

Fig. 1. Variation of rank parameters with increasing depth.

dinates x,y of the ICI system, which can be computed from the spectral curves. The trichromatic coordinates are plotted on a two-dimensional chromaticity diagram, where the shade and the saturation of colours of the emitted fluorescent light can be determined.

This new analytical method was first tested on extracts of a well known series of coals with increasing rank, i.e. from the peat to the anthracite stage, and also on samples of known source bed formation. The shade of colour of the extracts changes with increasing maturity from blue, through green, yellow and orange, to red, simultaneously with increasing saturation.

Analytical procedures and samples

The analytical procedures used in this study followed practices commonly used in petroleum geochemistry and organic petrology. Ground rock samples were extracted with dichloromethane by the Soxhlet method. After the evaporation of dichloromethane the extract was obtained under reduced pressure.

In order to obtain comparable results it is necessary to fix a definitive concentration of the extracts on a surface. Therefore, the extracts were dissolved in a mixture of toluene/methanol (3:1) with a ratio of 10 μl mg^{-1} extract. A glass slide covered with Kieselgur G was placed in this solution for 10 min to equilibrate. After evaporation of the solvent the glass slide with the extract is ready for fluorometric measurements to be carried out in the same way as for the figured liptinites. For this study, 24 samples were selected from five wells to cover a wide range of depths from 2000 to 6000 m.

RESULTS

It is known that rocks which contain a certain amount of finely dispersed organic matter can form hydrocarbon only at a certain degree of maturity and thus be a source rock. The reflectance of the vitrinitic particles proved very useful for the determination of rank. Figure 1 shows the variation of the vitrinitic reflectance values from 0.37% to 1.61% in a depth range of 2000 to 6000 m, which appears in the five wells under investigation. As can be seen, many of the samples are to be found within the range of the so-called 'oil window'. Parallel with this, the corresponding fluorescence parameters of the extracts, such as the position of the maximum of the spectrum and the red–green ratio, are shown. Up to a depth of approximately 4600 m the two parameters increase more or less continuously. These are known regularities which are, in a similar way, also true of the figured liptinites. They clearly show that the two fluorescence parameters mentioned above can also be applied to the determination of the degree of maturity of the soluble organic matter (extracts).

Similar interrelations are apparent when the trichromatic coordinates x,y are plotted in the chromaticity diagram (Fig. 2). The shade of colour of the extracts changes with increasing depth from green (line No. 20–21) to orange (line No. 3–4), simultaneously with increasing saturation (from curve No. 1–2 to curve No. 5–6). It can be noted that very small differences in colour are detected by means of this internationally accepted standard method. As a reason for this the intensities over the entire spectrum of 420–700 nm wavelength (in single

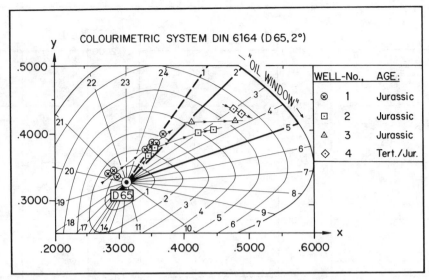

Fig. 2. Shade and saturation of colour of extracts from different rock samples.

steps of 5 or 10 nm) account for the trichromatic coordinates. This is different from the red–green ratio and the maximum peak of the spectrum which are both defined only by two respectively selected wavelengths.

Referring back to Fig. 1, we can observe an inversion of the fluorescence parameters in well No. 5 starting from a depth of 4700 m after the maximum has been reached. Nevertheless, the reflectance values clearly increase. Figure 3, showing the relationship between the fluorescence parameters of four oils of different maturities, explains this behaviour. With increasing maturity of the oils from A to D (hydrocarbon content varying from 30% to 90%) the position of the maximum of the spectrum is shifted towards shorter wavelengths. The red–green ratio decreases accordingly. Thus, the crude oils behave with increasing maturation in an exactly opposite way to the rock extracts (Hagemann and Hollerbach, 1981). This fact has not yet been explained. However, it accounts for the inversion and the more-or-less con-tinuous decrease of the fluorescence parameters in the samples of well No. 5 below a depth of 4700 m which have to be impregnated with crude oil.

These crude oil marks can basically be explained in two ways:

(a) the crude oil has formed from the kerogen in those rocks where it was found, or
(b) it can be formed in source rocks of some strata which have not been investigated here and migrates over greater or lesser vertical or horizontal distances.

Since fluorescence parameters of the extracts of coals and selected rocks of known source bed formations (Hagemann and Hollerbach, 1981) never decrease up to the overmature stage (anthracitic stage), the present criteria support the view that there are migrated crude oil marks in well No. 5.

SUMMARY

The main object of this paper has been to highlight the application of fluorescence analysis of hydrocarbon extracts as a complement to microscopic rank studies on dispersed organic particles in reflected normal and/or fluorescent light. It results in a simple application to the characterization of the stages of maturation, i.e. the hydrocarbon release in the oil maturation phase, called 'oil window'. In applying this method the diversity of the liptinites fluorescing with different intensities and colours in the polished surfaces does not have to be taken into account. Furthermore, this method helps us to evaluate the migration of liquid hydrocarbons and the maturity of the formed crude oils.

Acknowledgements

This investigation was submitted by financial support of the Deutsche Forschungsgemeinschaft. For technical assistance with the analyses we are grateful to the staff of the Lehrstuhl 'Erdöl und Kohle' (Aachen Technical

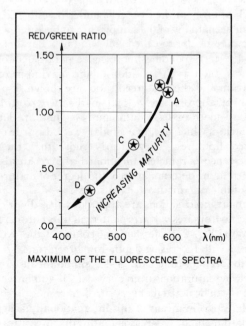

Fig. 3. Variation of fluorescence parameters of crude oils.

University) especially to A. Gölden, E. Noppeney, I. Schwartz and R. Mildenberger.

REFERENCES

Alpern, B. (1980) Pétrographie du kérogene. In *Kerogen, insoluble organic matter from sedimentary rocks*, ed. by Durand, B. Editions Technip, Paris, pp. 339–370.

Alpern, B. and Cheymol, D. (1978) Réflectance ou fluorescence des organoclastes du Toarcien du Bassin de Paris en fonction de la profondeur et de la température. *Revu. Inst. Fr. Pét.* **33**, 515–535.

Hagemann, H. W. and Hollerbach, A. (1980) Spektralfluorometrische Analysen von Sediment-Extrakten. *Erdöl Kohle* **33**, 577.

Hagemann, H. W. and Hollerbach, A. (1981) Spectral fluorometric analysis of extracts, a new method for the determination of the degree of maturity of organic matter in sedimentary rocks. *Bull. Cent. Rech. Explor. Prod. Elf-Aquitaine* **5**, 635–650.

Leythaeuser, D., Hagemann, H. W., Hollerbach, A. and Schaefer, R. G. (1980) Hydrocarbon generation in source beds as a function of type and maturation of their organic matter: a mass balance approach. *Proceedings of the Tenth World Petroleum Congress* Vol. 2. Heyden, London, pp. 31–41.

Robert, P. (1979) Classification des matieres organiques en fluorescence. Application aux Roches-Meres pétrolieres. *Bull. Cent. Rech. Explor. Prod. Elf-Aquitaine* **3**, 223–263.

Robert, R. (1980) The optical evolution of kerogen and geothermal histories applied to oil and gas exploration. In *Kerogen, insoluble organic matter from sedimentary rocks*, ed. by Durand, B. Editions Technip, Paris, pp. 385–412.

Teichmüller, M. (1974) Über neue Macerale der Liptinit-Gruppe und die Entstehung von Micrinit. *Fortschr. Geol. Rheinl. Westfalen* **24**, 37–64.

Teichmüller, M. (1979) Beispiele für die Anwendung fluoreszenzmikroskopischer Methoden bei der Erdölprospektion. *C.R. 8ᵉ Congr. Int. Strat. Géol. Carbonifere* **4**, 79–89.

Teichmüller, M. and Ottenjann, K. (1977) Liptinite und lipoide Stoffe in einem Erdölmuttergestein. *Erdöl Kohle* **30**, 387–398.

Teichmuller, M. and Teichmüller, R. (1975) Inkohlungsuntersuchungen in der Molasse des Alpenvorlandes. *Geol. Bavarica* **73**, 123–142.

Teichmüller, M. and Wolf, M. (1977) Application of fluorescence microscopy in coal petrology and oil exploration. *J. Microsc.* **109**, 49–73.

Advances in Organic Geochemistry 1981, pp. 76–79
© *John Wiley & Sons Limited, 1983*

Variation in the Ratio of Isomeric Butanes with Sediment Temperature in the Carnarvon Basin of Western Australia

R. Alexander, R. I. Kagi and G. W. Woodhouse

Petroleum Geochemistry Group, School of Applied Chemistry, Western Australian Institute of Technology, Kent Street, South Bentley 6102, Western Australia

The variation in the ratio of isobutane to normal butane over a sediment temperature range of 42–152°C has been determined by analysis of the cuttings gas from 248 sediment samples recovered from five exploration wells drilled in the Carnarvon Basin of Western Australia. In the 42–58°C temperature zone, the value for the ratio increases systematically from 1.8 to a maximum value of 14.0 and then decreases to 1.6, and these changes are attributed to selective removal of *n*-butane by micro-organisms. At temperatures greater than 58 °C the ratio initially decreases from a value of 1.6 to a minimum value of 0.46 and then increases to a value of 0.55 with increased temperature. This trend indicates an initial predominance of free radical processes which preferentially produce the normal isomer, but with increased temperature there is a progressive increase in the importance of carbonium ion reactions which favour the more stable isobutane.

INTRODUCTION

The isomeric butanes, along with other low molecular weight hydrocarbons, are known to occur in sediments over a wide range of temperatures (Hunt, 1979; Tissot and Welte, 1978). Up to the present time detailed reports of i-C_4/n-C_4 ratios are restricted to reservoired natural gas and crude oil deposits (Thompson and Creath, 1966). Previous investigations of the change in this ratio in sediments have been restricted either to small numbers of samples or to limited temperature ranges (Hunt, 1963; Thompson and Creath, 1966; Durand and Espitalié, 1972; Thompson, 1979). In a recent study (Hunt *et al.*, 1980) the change in the i-C_5/n-C_5 ratio with sediment temperature was examined in detail for U.S. Gulf Coast, Black Sea, and Paris Basin sediments.

Pyrolysis studies suggest that, in petroleum formation processes, straight-chain *n*-alkanes are formed predominantly by free radical reactions, whereas the branched isoalkanes arise mainly via carbonium ion reactions (Eisma and Jurg, 1969; Almon and Johns, 1977). Further, it is well established that microbiological attack on petroleum leads to preferential removal of *n*-alkanes, the branched isoalkanes being more resistant to attack (Bailey *et al.*, 1973; Philippi, 1977). The determination of the ratio i-C_4/n-C_4 over a range of temperatures in a sediment column might, therefore, be expected to provide useful insights into the processes influencing the composition of petroleum in that column.

Isomeric butane ratios for sediments can often be obtained from mud log reports routinely prepared for exploration wells. Even if accurate data are not available from such reports, determination of the ratio by gas chromatographic analysis of the headspace gas in canned cuttings or the gas obtained by grinding cuttings in a sealed blender is a straightforward analytical procedure (Le Tran, 1975). Consequently, if the change in the i-C_4/n-C_4 ratio with sediment temperature is a source of useful information, data can be readily obtained.

In the present study, i-C_4/n-C_4 ratios were measured using an extensive series of sediments from five exploration wells drilled in the Carnarvon Basin of Western Australia. The results are interpreted in terms of diagenetic and catagenetic processes likely to occur at various depths and temperatures in the sediment profile.

EXPERIMENTAL

Samples

The 248 samples selected for study were organic-rich siltstones, shales and claystones obtained as ditch cuttings from oil-drilling operations in the Carnarvon Basin of Western Australia. The cuttings were sealed in cans immediately after recovery from the well and were analysed within 20 days of recovery.

Gas analysis

Cuttings were transferred to the blender bowl of a Kenwood electronic blender with the lid modified to incorporate a septum, and then water at 75 °C was added to leave a headspace of 160 ml and the mixture was blended for 2 min at maximum speed. Following a 2 min settling period, 1 ml of the headspace gas was sampled and then analysed by gas chromatography as follows: instrument — Varian 1440 equipped with an FID; column — 3 m × 3.2 mm Chromosorb 102 (60–80 mesh); carrier gas — nitrogen (22 ml min^{-1}); temperature program — 70 °C for 2 min, then 70–140 °C at 15 °C min^{-1}. The amount of sample gas was quantified by comparing the areas for each of the C_1–C_4 components in the sample to the areas for the corresponding components of a known volume of a standard gas.

Determination of soluble organic matter (SOM)

A series of samples from Well 1 were extracted and the extracts were fractionated by column chromatography according to previously described procedures (Alexander *et al.*, 1980).

Determination of total organic carbon (TOC)

Determination of TOC was carried out using a LECO induction furnace equipped with a gravimetric carbon analyser.

RESULTS AND DISCUSSION

Figure 1 contains a logarithmic plot of the values of the isomeric butane ratios against sediment temperature for

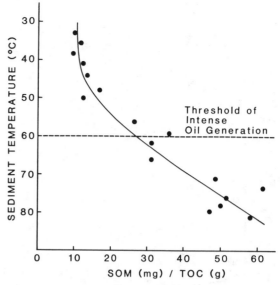

Fig. 2. A plot of SOM(mg)/TOC(g) against sediment temperature for Well 1 showing the onset of oil generation.

five wells in the Carnarvon Basin of Western Australia. In this Fig., Line A is a trend line for the values of the ratio at temperatures greater than 58 °C obtained by regression analysis (Nie *et al.*, 1975). Piecewise linear and multiple non-linear models were tested ($r^2 = 0.6$ in each case). However, the non-linear model, $\log_{10}$ (i-C_4/n-C_4 $= 2.328 + 121.60/$Temp$ + 0.008262$ Temp, gave a more parsimonious statistical account of the data than the linear regressions. Line B represents the change with temperature of the equilibrium value of the ratio, calculated from free energy of formation data (Rossini *et al.*, 1953; Stull *et al.*, 1969). To minimize the possibility of including samples containing significant quantities of migrated gas, only fine-grained siltstones, shales, or claystones were used in this study. Figure 2 is a plot of SOM(mg)/TOC(g) against temperature for Well 1 in this study. This plot shows that the threshold of intense oil generation occurs at about 60 °C, which in turn suggests that the zone of catagenesis commences at a temperature between 50 °C and 60 °C in this basin. The i-C_4/n-C_4 versus temperature profile shown in Fig. 1 will be discussed in two parts: that for temperatures less than 58 °C and that for temperatures greater than 58 °C, broadly corresponding to zones of diagenesis and catagenesis respectively.

The isomeric butane ratio increases from 1.8 at 42 °C to a maximum value of 14.0 at 55 °C, and then decreases rapidly to a value of 1.6 at about 58 °C. The plots shown in Fig. 3 of the amounts of n-butane and of total C_1–C_4 alkanes in these sediments between 52 °C and 65 °C show minima in the vicinity of 54 °C corresponding to the maximum in the i-C_4/n-C_4 curve. Preferential depletion of the n-alkanes may arise from the action of microorganisms (Bailey *et al.*, 1973; Philippi, 1977) entrained in the sedimentary material.

In the zone of catagenesis, the i-C_4/n-C_4 ratio shows a steady decrease from about 1.6 at 58 °C to a value of about 0.46 at the point of inflection in the region 100–120 °C, then there is a steady increase to a value of about 0.55 at 152 °C. It would seem that these results are not unique to the Carnarvon Basin: the values are consistent

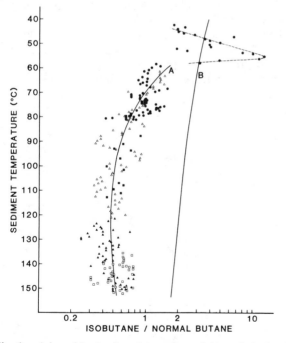

Fig. 1. A logarithmic plot of the values of the mole ratio of isobutane to normal butane against sediment temperature. Line A shows the trend for measured values for sediments from the Carnarvon Basin (● Well 1, △ Well 2, ▲ Well 3, □ Well 4, ■ Well 5). Line B represents calculated equilibrium values.

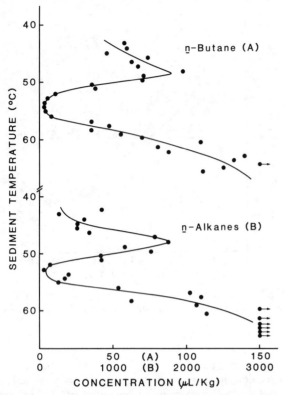

Fig. 3. A plot showing the change in both the amount of *n*-butane and total C_1–C_4 *n*-alkanes in the sediments with increasing sediment temperature for Well 1.

observed in the ratio. However, for two reasons, we do not believe that this is a major factor. The first is that our results are obtained from five wells: if variations in source type were a factor, one might expect to observe significant discontinuities in the plots from well to well, but this is not the case. Secondly, capillary gas chromatography of SOM obtained from selected samples reveals no marked changes in organic material with depth. The isomer ratio for a particular temperature is more likely to be determined by the net effects of the major processes influencing butane concentrations in sediments which are summarized in Fig. 4. Isobutane and normal butane may be produced either directly from kerogen or from soluble organic compounds which may themselves have been formed from cracking of kerogen. In the formation of butanes from soluble organic matter, both free radical and carbonium ion processes may occur. Since free radicals cannot rearrange (March, 1977), free radical reactions proceed by scission of carbon–carbon bonds to give unrearranged fragments which reflect the structure of the source material and hence, if the SOM contains appreciable amounts of *n*-alkanes, these processes will tend to give rise mainly to *n*-butane. Carbonium ion reactions, on the other hand, are often accompanied by rearrangement and will give rise predominantly to the more stable isobutane (Eisma and Jurg, 1969; Almon and Johns, 1977). Formation of petroleum from kerogen is referred to as a thermal cracking process (Espitalié *et al.*, 1980; Horsfield and Douglas, 1980; Hunt, 1979), probably involving mainly free radical processes: electron spin resonance studies have shown that the concentration of free radicals in kerogen increases significantly up to temperatures of at least 120 °C (Marchand and Conrad, 1980), and further, we believe it is unlikely that solid kerogen is sufficiently mobile to locate catalytically active sites on clay minerals to form carbonium ions. Alkanes cracked from kerogen by free radical processes will reflect the structure of the kerogen moiety from which they are cracked: *n*-alkanes will therefore be formed in large quantities if the kerogen

with those reported for several hundred natural gases and approximately 100 crude oils from North America (Thompson and Creath, 1966). In these gas and oil samples, the ratios were found to be usually in the vicinity of 0.5 and seldom greater than 1.0. In the region 90–150 °C, where the greatest proportion of oil and gas are formed (Tissot and Welte, 1978) our trend line varies from 0.46 to 0.59.

Changes in the nature of the organic material in the source rocks could, of course, contribute to the changes

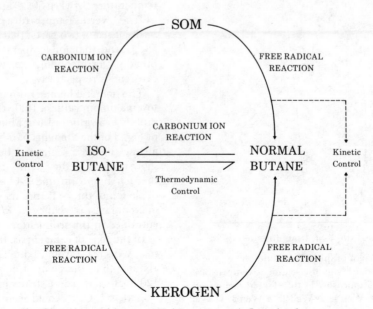

Fig. 4. A summary of the major formation and interconversion processes influencing butane concentrations in sediments.

contains substantial amounts of unbranched material. Finally, apart from *de novo* generation from kerogen or SOM, the butanes may also be interconverted via a carbonium ion mechanism.

The i-C_4/n-C_4 versus temperature profile shown in Fig. 1 can therefore be interpreted as follows. Kerogen and SOM contains a substantial proportion of unbranched material (Durand, 1980; Tissot and Welte, 1978) so that free radical processes will give rise mainly to *n*-butane. The steady decrease of the isomeric butane ratio at temperatures greater than 58 °C can therefore be attributed to free radical processes being predominant in this region. As temperatures increase with greater burial depth, however, carbonium ion processes become increasingly important: cracking of SOM, and catalytic isomerization of butanes by the mineral matrix, lead to the formation of an increasing proportion of isobutane, and so the i-C_4/n-C_4 ratio steadily approaches the thermodynamic values shown by Line B.

We attribute the lack of carbonium ion processes in the initial stages of catagenesis to deactivation of the catalytic sites on the mineral matrix by SOM. At a more advanced stage of catagenesis, corresponding to temperatures of 95–105 °C, active sites are generated, possibly by desorption of hydrocarbons or by dehydration processes, giving Lewis acid sites which promote carbonium ion processes. Recent work by Espitalié *et al.* (1980) and additional data provided by us in another paper in this volume support this interpretation.

CONCLUSIONS

Variations observed in the ratio i-C_4/n-C_4 with sediment temperature (depth) for a range of sediments from five wells in the Carnarvon Basin of Western Australia are interpreted in the following manner. In the 42–58 °C temperature zone, some very high values for the ratio are observed due to the selective removal of *n*-butane by micro-organisms. In the zone of temperatures greater than 58 °C the ratio initially decreases due to the dominance of free radical processes which produce mainly *n*-butane from the linear moiety of kerogen and soluble organic matter. At greater depth and temperature, as the number of catalytically active sites on the mineral matrix increases, a steady increase in the ratio is attributed to a progressive increase in the importance of carbonium ion processes which tend to favour the more stable isobutane.

ACKNOWLEDGEMENTS

Mr W. S. Perriman is gratefully acknowledged for his assistance with the regression analyses. This work was supported by grants from the National Energy Research Development and Demonstration Council of Australia.

REFERENCES

Alexander, R., Gray, M. D., Kagi, R. I. and Woodhouse, G. W. (1980) Proton magnetic resonance spectroscopy as a technique for measuring the maturity of petroleum. *Chem. Geol.* **30**, 1–14.

Almon, W. R. and Johns, W. D. (1977) Petroleum-forming reactions. The mechanism and rate of clay catalyzed fatty acid decarboxylation. In *Advances in Organic Geochemistry* (1975). Ed. by Campos, R. and Goni, J. Enadimsa, Madrid. pp. 157–172.

Bailey, N. J. L., Jobson, A. M. and Rodgers, M. A. (1973) Bacterial degradation of crude oil: comparison of field and experimental data. *Chem. Geol.* **11**, 203–221.

Durand, B. (1980) *Kerogen, Insoluble Organic Matter from Sedimentary Rocks*. Editions Technip, Paris, 519 pp.

Durand, B. and Espitalié, J. (1972) Formation et évolution des hydrocarbures C_1 à C_{15} et des gaz permanents dans les argiles du toarcian du bassin de Paris. In *Advances in Organic Geochemistry* (1971). Ed. by v. Gaertner, H. R. and Wehner, H. Pergamon Press, Braunschweig. pp. 455–468.

Eisma, E. and Jurg, J. W. (1969) Fundamental aspects of the generation of petroleum. In *Organic Geochemistry, Methods and Results*. Ed. by Eglinton, G. and Murphy, M. T. J. Springer-Verlag, Berlin, pp. 675–698.

Espitalié, J., Madec, M. and Tissot, B. (1980) Role of mineral matrix in kerogen pyrolysis: influence on petroleum generation and migration. *Am. Ass. Petrol. Geol. Bull.* **64**, 59–66.

Horsfield, B. and Douglas, A. G. (1980) The influence of minerals on the pyrolysis of kerogens. *Geochim. Cosmochim. Acta* **44**, 1119–1131.

Hunt, J. M. (1963) Geochemical data on organic matter in sediments. In *Reports of the 3rd International Scientific Conference on Geochemistry, Microbiology and Petroleum Chemistry*, volume II part I Geochemistry and Microbiology. Terv Nyomda, Budapest.

Hunt, J. M. (1979) *Petroleum Geochemistry and Geology*. W. H. Freeman and Company, San Francisco, 617 pp.

Hunt, J. M., Whelan, J. K. and Huc, A. Y. (1980) Genesis of petroleum hydrocarbons in marine sediments. *Science* **209**, 403–404.

Le Tran, K. (1975) Analyse et étude des hydrocarbures gazeux occlus dans les sédiments: examples d'application à l'exploration pétrolière. *Bull. Centre Rech. Pau* **9**, 223–243.

March, J. (1977) *Advanced Organic Chemistry; Reactions, Mechanisms, and Structure*. McGraw-Hill, New York.

Marchand, A. and Conrad, J. (1980) Electron paramagnetic resonance in kerogen studies. In *Kerogen, Insoluble Organic Matter from Sedimentary Rocks*. Ed. by Durand, B. Editions Technip, Paris. pp. 243–270.

Nie, N. H., Hull, C. H., Jenkins, J. G., Steinbrenner, K. and Bent, D. H. (1975) *Statistical Package for the Social Sciences*. McGraw-Hill, New York, 675 pp.

Philippi, G. T. (1977) On the depth, time and mechanism of origin of the heavy medium-gravity naphthenic crude oils. *Geochim. Cosmochim. Acta* **41**, 33–52.

Rossini, F. D., Pitzer, K. S., Arnett, R. L., Braun, R. M. and Pimental, G. C. (1953) *Selected Values of Physical and Thermodynamic Properties of Hydrocarbons and Related Compounds*. Carnegie Press, Pittsberg.

Stull, D. R., Westrum, E. F. Jr. and Sinke, G. C. (1969) *The Chemical Thermodynamics of Organic Compounds*. John Wiley and Sons, New York.

Thompson, K. F. M. (1979) Light hydrocarbons in subsurface sediments. *Geochim. Cosmochim. Acta* **43**, 657–672.

Thompson, R. R. and Creath, W. B. (1966) Low molecular weight hydrocarbons in recent and fossil shells. *Geochim. Cosmochim. Acta* **30**, 1137–1152.

Tissot, B. P. and Welte, D. H. (1978) *Petroleum Formation and Occurrence, A New Approach to Oil and Gas Exploration*. Springer-Verlag, Berlin, 538 pp.

Advances in Organic Geochemistry 1981, pp. 80–86
© John Wiley & Sons Limited, 1983

Effect of Geologically Rapid Heating on Maturation and Hydrocarbon Generation in Lower Jurassic Shales from NW-Germany

F. J. Altebäumer, D. Leythaeuser and R. G. Schaefer

Institute for Petroleum and Organic Geochemistry (ICH-5) KFA-Jülich, PO Box 1913, D-5170 Jülich, Federal Republic of Germany

A comparison of geochemical data between the Lias δ shales around the igneous intrusion of the 'Bramsche Massiv' in NW-Germany and Upper Cretaceous source rock-type shales from the Douala Basin (Cameroon) reveals the influence of heating rate on hydrocarbon generation and maturation: for the rapidly heated shale series the liquid window interval is shifted and extended into a maturity stage of $1.75\%R_0$. This is obvious from maturity-trends of extract and hydrocarbon yields as well as of the composition of the extractable hydrocarbons, e.g. CPI values. Also, long-chain n-alkanes are generated up to a maturity level of $1.7\%R_0$. These observations lead to the conclusion that the vitrinite reflectance reaction responds in a more sensitive way to the conditions of very rapid heating than hydrocarbon generation processes. Finally, pre- and post-intrusive palaeotemperatures calculated for some sampling locations reveal the degree of temperature and maturity increase with the intrusion of the 'Bramsche Massiv'.

INTRODUCTION

A wealth of geochemical data leads to the conclusion that the bulk of the petroleum hydrocarbons have been generated by thermal degradation of the organic matter in source rocks during burial and geologic time. Time–temperature relationships controlling the maturation stage of organic matter are important factors for generation of hydrocarbons (Philippi, 1965; Connan, 1974; Hood et al., 1975; Waples, 1980). The influence of increasing temperatures on amount and composition of hydrocarbons generated in source rocks can be demonstrated on the basis of geochemical analyses of the organic matter in samples from sediments:

1. which have experienced a normal burial history in a basin (Philippi, 1965; Tissot et al., 1971; Albrecht et al., 1976),
2. which occur in the immediate vicinity of sills and dykes (Dow, 1977; Perregaard and Schiener, 1979; Simoneit et al., 1981), and
3. subjected in the laboratory to stepwise pyrolysis experiments (Espitalié et al., 1977; Ishiwatari et al., 1976, 1977, 1978).

Both 1 and 3 represent extreme end members, with respect to differences in heating rate. An intermediate situation can be expected to occur in sediments around a large-size igneous intrusive body. Here, at intermediate distances from the igneous contact, rates of heating and cooling can be expected to be slower than in the vicinity of sills and dykes of limited thickness. The 'Bramsche Massiv' in N.W. Germany is a deep-seated subsurface intrusion which is documented, e.g. by a pronounced maturation anomaly in the iso-reflectance contour maps for Mesozoic strata in the Lower Saxonian basin of N.W. Germany (Fig. 1). Also, initial results of the effects of this intrusion on maturation and hydrocarbon generation on the Lower Jurassic Lias δ shales have been reported (Leythaeuser et al., 1980). In this study, the effect of the 'Bramsche Massiv' intrusion on hydrocarbon generation processes in Lias δ shales was investigated. Comparison of the igneous heat-influenced Lias δ shales and a source rock series of the Douala Basin has allowed the differences in the hydrocarbon generation processes due to different time–temperature relationships to be evaluated. In addition, the burial history of the Lias δ shale at some locations has been reconstructed and pre- and post-intrusive temperatures and maturation levels have been calculated according to the method of Waples (1980).

SAMPLES AND METHODS

Forty-nine samples of the Lower Jurassic-age Lias δ shale were selected partly from conventional cores of exploration wells, material from shallow core holes and also from outcrops. To avoid alteration effects of the organic matter due to surface weathering processes (Leythaeuser, 1973; Clayton and Swetland, 1978) samples from quarries were taken by digging deeply into the outcrops. The Lias δ shale unit consists of an about 100 m thick sequence of grey to dark grey, calcareous shales.

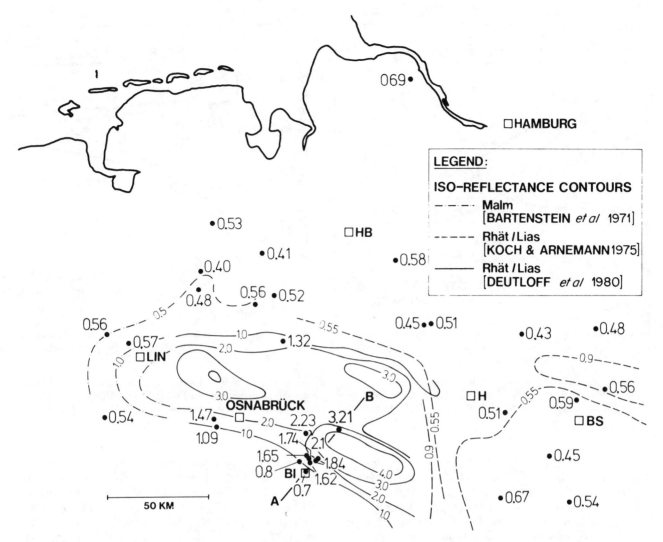

Fig. 1. Sampling locations and mean vitrinite reflectance values for Lower Jurassic-age Lias δ shales in relation to iso-vitrinite reflectance contours for Jurassic strata in NW-Germany (modified according to Bartenstein *et al.* 1971; Koch and Arnemann, 1975; and Deutloff *et al.* 1980). Note reflectance anomaly near city of Osnabrück caused by the deep-seated igneous intrusion of the 'Bramsche Massiv' in contrast to low maturity values (below 0.7% $\bar{R}_0$) for the Lias δ throughout the northern part of the Lower Saxonian Basin.

Organic carbon contents of the Lias δ shales vary between 0.7 and 1.5%. All samples contain, according to Rock–Eval pyrolysis data, a hydrogen-lean kerogen of a uniform type III nature (Tissot *et al.*, 1974; Espitalié, 1977).

Most analytical procedures of this study follow common practices in organic geochemistry and have been discussed elsewhere: extraction of ground rock samples with dichlormethane by a slightly modified flow-blending method (Radke *et al.*, 1978), medium pressure liquid chromatography (Radke *et al.*, 1980), glass capillary gas chromatographic analysis of the C_{15+}-saturated hydrocarbons, extraction and capillary gas chromatographic analysis of the light hydrocarbons (C_2–C_8) by the hydrogen stripping technique combined with a thermovaporization step (Schaefer *et al.*, 1978), pyrolysis yield measurements by the Rock–Eval method (Espitalié *et al.*, 1977), determination of organic carbon by the Leco method and measurement of mean vitrinite reflectance values (% $\bar{R}_0$) at 546 nm on kerogen concentrates.

RESULTS AND DISCUSSION

Effect of igneous heat on evolution of C_{15+}-soluble organic matter

The generation of C_{15+}-soluble organic matter with increasing maturity in Liassic shales is shown in Fig. 2a. At a maturity level of about 0.6% $\bar{R}_0$ an increase of the carbon-normalized extract yields is interpreted as an indication for the onset of hydrocarbon generation. Highest extract yields (about 60 mg g^{-1} organic carbon) occur around the maturity level of 1.5% $\bar{R}_0$. Between 1.5 and 2% $\bar{R}_0$ the amount of extractable organic matter and total hydrocarbons decreases rapidly to values below 5 mg g^{-1} organic carbon. This indicates that high molecular weight extractable components are being converted by cracking to low molecular weight compounds. Obviously, these observations represent a major deviation from the classical generation versus maturity relationship established for many source bed

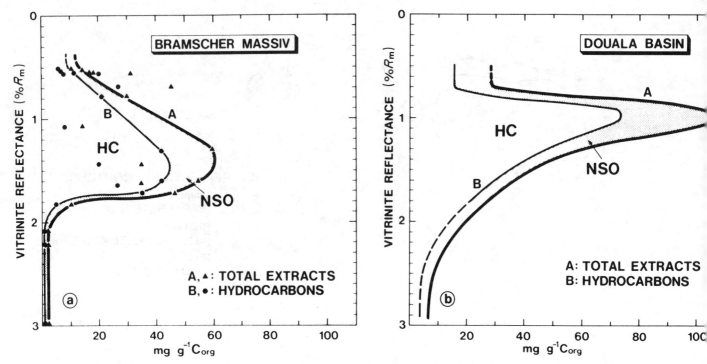

Fig. 2. Evolution of total C_{15+}-soluble organic matter (A, ▲) and hydrocarbons (B, ●) with increasing maturity: (a) for Lias δ shales around the 'Bramsche Massiv', (b) Upper Cretaceous-age source rock-type shales from the Douala Basin (Albrecht *et al.* 1976; Durand and Espitalié, 1976). Note that the liquid window for the Lias δ shales around the 'Bramsche Massiv' is extended up to a maturity level of 1.75% $\bar{R}_0$.

sequences which experienced heating by normal burial (Albrecht *et al.*, 1976; Tissot and Welte, 1978; Hunt, 1979). The comparison of the 'Bramsche Massiv' data with a source bed sequence of this type is shown in Fig. 2b. Here, Upper Cretaceous/Tertiary source rock-type shales have experienced thermal maturation due to normal subsidence in the Douala Basin (Cameroon) (Albrecht *et al.*, 1976). This comparison is justified, since samples of both series bear a very similar kerogen-type, i.e. uniformly hydrogen-lean type III kerogens, which are predominantly derived from residues of terrestrial vegetation. In the Douala Basin, the onset of hydrocarbon generation is observed at a maturation stage around 0.6 or 0.7% $\bar{R}_0$ (Fig. 2b). In contrast to the above-reported results on hydrocarbon generation in Lias δ shales, the amount of extract yields for the Douala Basin series increases rapidly only up to a rank level of 0.95% $\bar{R}_0$ (106 mg g^{-1} organic carbon). The comparison of both series (Fig. 2a v. 2b) shows clearly a shift of hydrocarbon generation maximum from 0.95% $\bar{R}_0$ in the Douala Basin series towards 1.5% $\bar{R}_0$ in the Lias δ shales in the area surrounding the 'Bramsche Massiv'. In summary, in the Lias δ shale series the liquid window interval or the 'principal zone of oil formation' is shifted and extended up to a maturation stage of 1.75% $\bar{R}_0$.

Thermal evolution of saturated hydrocarbons

The compositional changes of the saturated hydrocarbons in the Lias δ shales with increasing maturity are shown in Fig. 3 by six selected capillary gas chromatograms. For the maturity interval shown here, a

change is evident from a bimodal *n*-alkane distribution envelope at 0.52% $\bar{R}_0$ to a smooth front-end biased *n*-alkane distribution at 1.32% $\bar{R}_0$. The pronounced predominance of odd-carbon numbered *n*-alkanes in the molecular range $C_{23}-C_{35}$ decreases slightly between 0.52 and 1.09% $\bar{R}_0$ and with maturity increase more rapidly in order to disappear around 1.32% $\bar{R}_0$. A similar trend with maturity is observed for the ratios pristane/*n*-C_{17} and phytane/*n*-C_{18}. Whereas these ratios remain unchanged in the maturation interval 0.52 to 1.09% $\bar{R}_0$ they decrease sharply in the subsequent maturity interval.

In addition to the changes in relative compositions discussed above, the absolute quantity for each individual *n*-alkane has been calculated for the C_{15+}-hydrocarbons and for a selected range of light hydrocarbons (C_2-C_8). However, due to analytical limitations, there is a gap in the molecular range C_9 to C_{14} as well as for methane. Figure 4 shows the carbon-normalized absolute concentrations for C_2 to C_{36} *n*-alkanes of four selected samples from the Lias δ shale series. At 0.56% $\bar{R}_0$, low absolute concentrations of high molecular weight *n*-alkanes were obtained (less than 40 μg g^{-1} organic carbon for individual components), and only traces of light hydrocarbons were present. The sample at 0.8% $\bar{R}_0$ exhibits a distinct increase in *n*-alkane concentration in the total observed molecular range. The *n*-alkane with the highest concentration is *n*-pentadecane with about 280 μg g^{-1} organic carbon. Highest concentrations for the light hydrocarbons occur at 1.74% $\bar{R}_0$ (585 μg g^{-1} organic carbon). However, at this maturation stage, the absolute concentrations of C_{23} to C_{36}-*n*-alkanes are lower than ta 0.8% $\bar{R}_0$. This trend

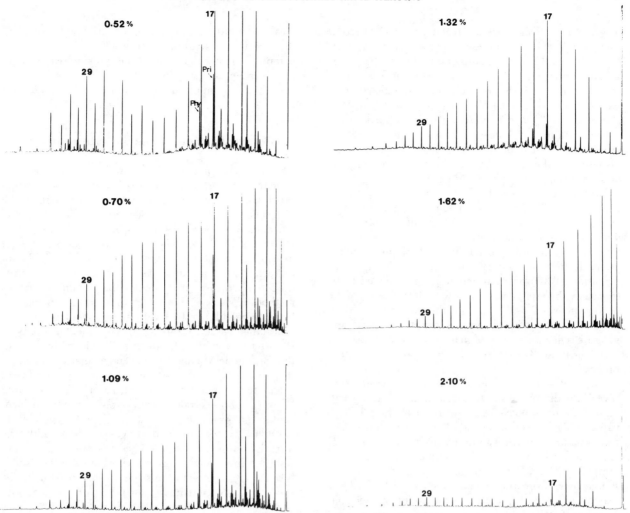

Fig. 3. Capillary gas chromatograms of the C_{15+}-saturated hydrocarbons for selected samples of Lias δ shales, arranged in sequence of increasing mean vitrinite reflectance (% $\bar{R}_0$-values indicated). Selected *n*-alkanes indicated by carbon numbers. Pri = Pristane; Phy = Phytane.

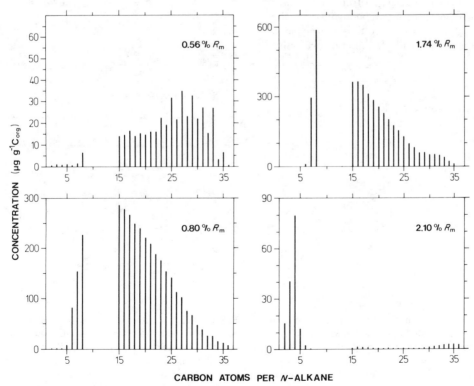

Fig. 4. Absolute concentrations of *n*-alkanes C_2–C_{36} for four selected samples of Lias δ shales from the study area.

appears to reflect cracking reactions which become increasingly effective at these higher maturity levels. At 2.1% $\bar{R}_0$, small concentrations of only low molecular n-alkanes remain. Furthermore, it is obvious from Fig. 4 that a pronounced shift of the peak in the distribution pattern from n-C_{27} at 0.56% $\bar{R}_0$ to n-C_{15} at 0.80% $\bar{R}_0$ to n-octane at 1.74% $\bar{R}_0$ occurs. At 2.1% $\bar{R}_0$ the peak in the concentration envelope is displaced to n-butane. However, the real peak may even be below butane, because of the possibility of ethane and propane depletion during sampling and storage.

In summary, in the Lias δ series from the 'Bramsche Massiv', the highest yields of soluble organic matter (Fig. 2) and highest concentrations of n-alkanes are found in samples above 1.3% $\bar{R}_0$. These observations indicate a shift and an extension of the liquid window interval up to a maturity level of 1.75% $\bar{R}_0$. This extension of hydrocarbon generation is believed to be caused by the rapid heating rate with the intrusion of the 'Bramsche Massiv'. Presumably, the chemical reactions and structural changes which result in increasing vitrinite reflectance respond in a more sensitive way to a high heating rate than hydrocarbon generation processes.

The CPI versus vitrinite reflectance relationship reveals for the Lias δ shale series a similar shift towards higher maturity levels. A comparison of the CPI_{25-29}-values with those of the Douala Basin series shows that, throughout the maturity range considered, lower CPI values occur in the Lias δ shales than in Douala Basin samples (Fig. 5). For example, in the normally heated source rocks from the Douala Basin a CPI of 1.08 is reached at 0.95% $\bar{R}_0$, whereas in the rapidly heated Lias δ shales a CPI of 1.08 occurs not before a maturity level of 1.65% $\bar{R}_0$ (Fig. 5).

The most likely explanation for these observations is that the rate of the reaction causing vitrinite reflectance to increase is more temperature-dependent than the rates of the cracking reactions controlling hydrocarbon generation and the CPI trend. In kinetic terms this

means that, although the processes are highly complex, the effective activation energy (E_a) of the vitrinite reaction is higher than that of the cracking reactions (in the Arrhenius equation, $\ln k = -E_a/RT + \ln A$, E_a defines the temperature-dependence of the reaction rate).

Determination of palaeotemperatures

The influence of temperature and heating time is of primary importance for hydrocarbon generation processes. Several methods are used to recognize the influence of time and temperature on vitrinite reflectance (Lopatin, 1971; Lopatin and Bostik, 1973; Hood and Castaño, 1974; Buntebarth, 1979). Lopatin developed a 'time–temperature index' (TTI) of maturity using a numerical summation to integrate time–temperature increments. Based on Lopatin's method, Waples (1980) established a correlation between calculated TTI values and measured vitrinite reflectance values. Utilizing Waples' method the post-intrusive temperature for the sampling locations around the 'Bramsche Massiv' have been calculated. Likewise, the pre-intrusive temperature and maturation level were calculated, based on a reconstruction of their burial histories and certain assumptions of the palaeo-geothermal gradients.

Obviously, the difference between post- and pre-intrusive temperatures gave an estimate of the heat input resulting from the intrusion itself. Figure 6 shows in a NE/SW cross section across the 'Bramsche Massiv' the pre- and post-intrusive vitrinite reflectance and

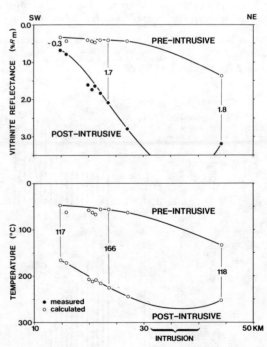

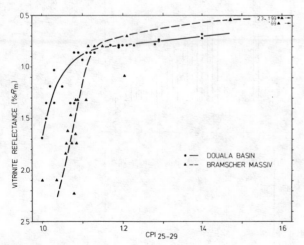

Fig. 5. $CPI_{(25-29)}$ versus maturity for the Lias δ shales around the 'Bramsche Massiv' intrusion in comparison with the Upper Cretaceous source rock series from the Douala Basin (Albrecht *et al.*, 1976). The difference between the two trends is interpreted to reflect the influence of heating rate and heating time.

Fig. 6. NE/SW cross section (A/B in Fig. 1) with calculated pre- and measured post-intrusive reflectance and temperature levels. Difference between present % $\bar{R}_0$ and pre-intrusive % $\bar{R}_0$ reveals effect of igneous heat input. Pre-intrusive % $\bar{R}_0$ and post-intrusive temperature calculated according to Waples (1980).

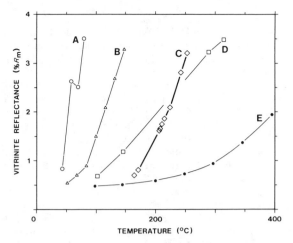

Fig. 7. Vitrinite reflectance versus temperature for several sample series which have experienced different burial and temperature histories: A — carboniferous rocks, Arkoma Basin, Oklahoma; B — Upper Cretaceous source rock series, Douala Basin, Cameroon; C — Lias δ shales, 'Bramsche Massiv', N.W. Germany; D — Salton geothermal field rocks, California; E — Pyrolysis experiments (heating period of one month); (trends A, D, E after Bostik, 1979; trend B calculated after Tissot and Espitalié, 1975). Vitrinite reflectance of sample series A and B is the result of normal burial and temperature history with subsidence in a basin. In case D rapid heating in a high geothermal area prevailed.

temperature values for a number of Lias δ sampling locations. Obviously, the temperature and maturity progress increases towards the center of the intrusion. According to our calculations the temperature and vitrinite reflectance values were low in the Lias δ shales prior to the time the intrusion occurred (<0.4–$0.7\% R_0$ and <48–$134\ °C$). With the intrusion, the temperatures increased very rapidly. Maximum temperatures were presumably reached about 500 000 years after the intrusion was emplaced (Buntebarth and Teichmüller, 1979). As shown in Fig. 6, in the Lias δ shales near the centre of the intrusion a temperature increase from 106 °C to 271 °C has produced an increase in vitrinite reflectance from 0.78 to 4.2$\% \bar{R}_0$.

The vitrinite reflectance versus temperature relationship for suites of samples which have experienced vastly different heating rates is shown in Fig. 7. The influence of heating time is obvious from this diagram: at a given temperature, the reflectance of vitrinite particles exposed to heat for millions of years with normal subsidence is much higher (trends A and B in Fig. 7) than the reflectance in those sample series which were heated rapidly and only over short periods (trends C, D, E). Laboratory pyrolysis experiments show that a temperature of about 360 °C is necessary for one month to raise the reflectance of vitrinite particles up to 1.5$\%$ $\bar{R}_0$. It is interesting to note that the Lias δ shale samples influenced by igneous heat from the 'Bramsche Massiv' intrusion show a vitrinite reflectance versus temperature relationship which is just intermediate between that for slowly heated sample series and that of pyrolysis experiments.

Acknowledgements

For supplying sample material we are indebted to BEB Gewerkschaften Brigitta und Elwerath Betriebsührungsgesellschaft GmbH, Hannover, FRG, especially Dr E. Plein. Assistance with the experimental work by W. Benders, U. Disko, H. Pooch, B. Schmidl, F. Schlosser, H. Willsch and B. Winden of KFA-ICH 5 is gratefully acknowledged.

REFERENCES

Albrecht, P., Vandenbroucke, M. and Mandengue, M. (1976) Geochemical studies on the organic matter from the Douala Basin (Cameroon). I. Evolution of the extractable organic matter and the formation of petroleum. *Geochim. Cosmochim. Acta.* **40**, 791–799.

Bartenstein, H., Teichmüller, M. and Teichmüller, R. (1971) Die Umwandlung der organischen Substanz im Dach des Bramscher Massivs. *Fortschr. Geol. Rheinld. u. Westf.* **18**, 501–538.

Bostik, N. H. (1973) Time as a factor in thermal metamorphism of phytoclasts (coaly particles). In: *Congrès Internat. Strat. Geol. Carbonif., Compte Rendue* **2**, 183–193.

Bostik, N. H. (1979) Microscopic measurement of the level of catagenesis of solid organic matter in sedimentary rocks to aid exploration for petroleum and to determine former burial temperatures — A review. *SEPM Special Publication* **26**, 17–43.

Buntebarth, G. and Teichmüller, R. (1979) Zur Ermittlung der Paläotemperaturen im Dach des Bramscher Intrusivs aufgrund von Inkohlungsdaten. *Fortschr. Geol. Rheinld. u. Wests.* **27**, 171–182.

Clayton, J. L. and Swetland, P. F. (1978) Subaerial weathering of sedimentary organic matter. *Geochim. Cosmochim. Acta* **42**, 305–312.

Connan, J. (1974) Time–temperature relation in oil genesis. *Am. Ass. Pet. Geol. Bull.* **58**, 2516–2521.

Deutloff, O., Teichmüller, M., Teichmüller, R. and Wolf, M. (1980) Inkohlungsuntersuchungen im Mesozoikum des Massivs von Vlotho (Niedersächsisches Tektogen). *N. Jb. Geol. Paläont. Mh.*, 321–341.

Dow, W. G. (1977) Contact metamorphism of kerogen in sediments from Leg 41 Cape Verde rise and basin. In *Initial Reports of the Deep Sea Drilling Projects.* Ed. by Lancelot, Y., Seibold, E. *et al.* **41**, 839–847.

Durand, B. and Espitalié, J. (1976) Geochemical studies on the organic matter from the Donala Basin (Cameroon). II. Evolution of kerogen. *Geochim. Cosmochim. Acta* **40**, 801–808.

Espitalié, J., Laporte, J. L., Madec, M., Marquis, F., Leplat, P., Paulet, G. and Boutefeu, A. (1977) Méthode rapide de caractérisation des roches mères de leur potentiel pétrolliér et de leur degré d'évolution. *Rev. Inst. Franc. Pétr.* **32**, 23–42.

Hood, A. and Castaño, J. R. (1974) Organic metamorphism. Its relationship to petroleum generation and application to studies of authigenic minerals. *Coordinating Comm. Offshore Prospecting Techn. Bull.* **8**, 85–118.

Hood, A., Gutjahr, C. C. M. and Heacock, R. L. (1975) Organic metamorphism and the generation of petroleum. *Am. Ass. Pet. Geol. Bull.* **59**, 986–996.

Hunt, J. M. (1979) *Petroleum Geochemistry and Geology.* W. H. Freeman and Co., 616 pp.

Ishiwatari, R., Ishiwatari, M., Kaplan, I. R. and Rohrback, B. G. (1976) Thermal alteration of young kerogen in relation to petroleum genesis. *Nature (London)* **264**, 347–349.

Ishiwatari, R., Ishiwatari, M., Rohrback, B. G. and Kaplan, I. R. (1977) Thermal alteration experiments on organic matter from recent marine sediments in relation to petroleum genesis. *Geochim. Cosmochim. Acta* **41**, 815–828.

Ishiwatari, R., Rohrback, B. G. and Kaplan, I. R. (1978) Hydrocarbon generation by thermal alteration of kerogen from different sediments. *Am. Ass. Pet. Geol. Bull.* **62**, 678–692.

Koch, G. and Arnemann, H. (1975) Die Inkohlung in Gesteinen des Rhät and Lias im südlichen Nordwestdeutschland. *Geo. Jb. A* **29**, 45–55.

Leythaeuser, D. (1973) Effects of weathering on organic matter in shales. *Geochim. Cosmochim. Acta* **37**, 113–120.

Leythaeuser, D., Altebäumer, F. J. and Schaefer, R. G. (1980) Effect of an igneous intrusion on maturation of organic matter in Lower Jurassic shales from N.W. Germany. In *Advances in Organic Geochemistry 1979*. Ed. by Douglas, A. G. and Maxwell, J. R. Pergamon Press, Oxford. pp. 133–139.

Lopatin, N. V. (1971) Temperature and geologic time as factors in coalification (in Russian). *Akad. Nauk SSSR Izv. Ser. Geol.* **3**, 95–106.

Lopatin, N. V. and Bostik, N. H. (1973) Geological factors in coal catagenesis. In *Nature of Organic Matter in Recent and Ancient Sediments* (in Russian). *Symph. Nauka*, Moscow.

Perregaard, J. and Schiener, E. J. (1979) Thermal alteration of sedimentary organic matter by a basalt intrusive (Kimmeridgian Shales, Milne Land, East Greenland). *Chem. Geol.* **26**, 331–343.

Philippi, G. T. (1965) On the depth, time and mechanism of petroleum generation. *Geochim. Cosmochim. Acta* **29**, 1021–1049.

Radke, M., Sittardt, H. G. and Welte, D. H. (1978) Removal of soluble organic matter from rock samples with a flow through extraction cell. *Anal. Chem.* **50**, 663–665.

Radke, M., Wilssch, H. and Welte, D. H. (1980) Preparative hydrocarbon group type determination by automated medium pressure liquid chromatograophy. *Anal. Chem.* **52**, 407–411.

Schaefer, R. G., Weiner, B. and Leythaeuser, D. (1978) Determination of sub-nanogram per gram quantities of light hydrocarbons (C_2–C_9) in rock samples by hydrogen stripping in the flow system of a capillary gas chromatograph. *Anal. Chem.* **50**, 1848–1854.

Simoneit, B. R. T., Brenner, S., Peters, K. E. and Kaplan, I. R. (1981) Thermal alteration of Cretaceous black shale by diabase intrusions in the Eastern Atlantic. II. Effects on bitumen and kerogen. *Geochim. Cosmochim. Acta* **45**, 1581–1602.

Tissot, B., Califet-Debyser, Y., Deroo, G. and Oudin, J. L. (1971) Origin and evolution of hydrocarbons in Early Toarcian shales. *Am. Ass. Pet. Geol. Bull.* **55**, 2177–2193.

Tissot, B., Durand, B., Espitalié, J. and Combaz, A. (1974) Influence of the nature and diagenesis of organic matter in formation of petroleum. *Am. Ass. Pet. Geol. Bull* **58**, 499–506.

Tissot, B. and Espitalié, J. (1975) L'évolution thermique de la matière organique des sédiments: Applications d'une simulation mathématique. *Rev. Inst. Fr. Pétrol.* **30**, 743–777.

Tissot, B. and Welte, D. H. (1978) *Petroleum Formation and Occurrence*. Springer Verlag, Berlin, 538 pp.

Waples, D. W. (1980) Time and temperature in petroleum formation: Application of Lopatin's method to petroleum exploration. *Am. Ass. Pet. Geol. Bull.* **64**, 916–926.

Advances in Organic Geochemistry 1981, pp. 87–93
© *John Wiley & Sons Limited, 1983*

An Oil/Oil Correlation Study Utilizing High Resolution GC–MS

M. Bjorøy, P. W. Brooks† and K. Hall‡

*Continental Shelf Institute (Norway); PO Box 1883, 7001 Trondheim, Norway

†VG Analytical, Altrincham, Cheshire, England

‡College of Pharmacy, University of Saskatchewan, Saskatoon, Canada

The application of GC–MS in oil/oil and oil/source correlation analysis is now a routine analytical method utilized by many laboratories involved in oil exploration and pollution control. In this study four oils from the North Sea with the same assumed source but differing characteristics due to varying levels of biodegradation effects have been intensively examined using both high and low resolution GC²–MS techniques. The practical uses of several diagnostic biomarker molecules commonly monitored are discussed with regard to their routine applicability in day-to-day analaysis situations.

INTRODUCTION

The use of C–GC–MS as a routine tool in geochemical evaluation of crude oils and source rocks is well established. The most common classes of compounds investigated are the polycyclic alkanes, steranes and triterpanes (e.g. Reed, 1977; Rubinstein *et al.*, 1977; Seifert and Moldowan, 1979). Such compounds are present in oils and source rocks at low relative abundance but are recognized as useful tools to correlate unaltered crudes (Van Dorsselaer *et al.*, 1977; Seifert and Moldowan, 1978).

Debate exists as to whether these compounds are affected by biodegradation and their usefulness thus limited as correlation parameters. Reed (1977) and Seifert and Moldowan (1979) report that these compounds are destroyed by bacteria while Rubinstein *et al.* (1977) reported that steranes and triterpanes were unaffected either in laboratory experiments or in fossil fuels. In a study of biodegradation of oils in the Aquitaine Basin, Connan *et al.* (1979) supported the conclusions of Rubinstein *et al.* (1977).

Due to the low abundance of steroidal and triterpenoidal alkanes in crude oils and source rocks it is frequently necessary to fractionate the sample, following extraction, into the branched and cyclic alkane fraction. Such fractionation is necessary to obtain sufficient signal/noise of m/z 191 and 217 ions of the cycloalkanes, for reliable quantitation even when operating in the multiple ion detection mode. Further, even after such sample clean-up procedures, a large signal in the m/z 191 and 217 fragmentograms is observed from the gross hydrocarbon matrix, when monitoring by low resolution

(less than 500) mass spectrometry. Such chemical background signals may either completely 'swamp' the compounds of interest as an unresolved complex mixture, in the case of severe biodegradation, or lead to spurious peaks being observed which are neither steranes or triterpanes but which arise from components being present in the mixture having a fragment ion at the same nominal mass as those of interest. If the above problems occur, the organic geochemist is left with little choice but to further purify the samples to concentrate the biomarkers of interest relative to the complex matrix of the oils or shale extracts.

An alternative approach to this problem is to utilize the specificity of high resolution mass spectrometry combined with the separation capabilities of high resolution capillary column gas chromatography on either whole oils or total source rock extracts.

This paper reports on the correlation between four oils K-7080–K-7083 from the Viking Graben. Three of the oils were from separate wells on structure A while the fourth oil originates from a neighbouring structure B on the same acreage. The oils are produced from different reservoir formations (Table 1).

Table 1
Reservoir formation and structure of the four oils

Sample No	Structure	Reservoir formation
K-7080	A	Cook
K-7081	A	Brent
K-7082	B	Statfjord
K-7083	A	Statfjord

Table 2

Accurate mass and elemental composition of ions used for high resolution SIR

Accurate mass of ion used	Elemental composition	Compound class
191.1798	$C_{14}H_{23}$	Triterpenoid alkanes
217.1955	$C_{15}H_{25}$	Steroidal alkanes
178.0782	$C_{14}H_{10}$	Phenanthrene
192.0928	$C_{15}H_{12}$	Methyl phenanthrenes
206.1088	$C_{16}H_{14}$	Dimethyl phenanthrenes
184.0344	$C_{12}H_8S$	Dibenzothiophene
198.0501	$C_{13}H_{10}S$	Methyl dibenzothiophenes
212.0457	$C_{14}H_{12}S$	Dimethyl dibenzothiophenes
212.1560	$C_{16}H_{20}$	Hexamethyl naphthalenes

Table 3

Quantitative correlation between methylphenanthrenes, phenanthrenes and dimethyldibenzothiophenes/methyldibenzothiophenes

	Oil			
Ratio	7080	7081	7082	7083
m/z 192/178	1.46	1.46	1.40	1.45
m/z 212/198	1.00	1.20	1.00	0.08

Experimental

The GC-analyses were performed on a HP5730 gas chromatograph fitted with a 30 m × 0.3 mm fused silica column coated with OV101. The oven was temperature programmed from $-40°-270$ °C at $4°$ min^{-1} using H_2 as carrier gas.

The GC–MS analyses were performed on a VG Analytical 7035 GC–MS–DS combination operated at 70 eV in Electron Impact mode and 4000 resolution (10% valley). A 25 m 0.3 mm fused silica column coated with OV-1 was directly coupled to the source and temperature programmed from 60–270 °C at $5°$ min^{-1}, and 2 ml min^{-1} helium flow rate. The accelerating voltage of the mass spectrometer was switched under data system control to the exact peak centroids of the ions of interest, listed in Table 2.

Discussion

The GC traces of the four oils show three significant different distributions. Samples K-7080 and K-7083 from the Cook and Statfjord Formations on structure A show some similarities. The major difference is that the isoprenoids are more abundant relative to the n-alkanes in sample K-7080 (Cook Formation) than in K-7083. On the whole the two samples show large similarities with other oils from the Viking Graben (Fig. 1). The two other samples are significantly different. The gas chromatogram of sample K-7081 from the Brent Formation on structure A does not show any dominant n-alkanes (Fig. 1). These have been lost probably due to bacteriological activity. The oil from the Statfjord Formation on structure B was found to have a relatively low abundance of low to medium weight hydrocarbons. The n-alkanes have a maximum at nC_{18} (Fig. 1).

Further examination of the whole oils by Selected Ion Recording (SIR) using low resolution, revealed little or no discrete peaks of interest above a large background signal. Thus, each oil was examined again using high resolution SIR (resolution Ca. 4–5000) using voltage switching from peak top at exact mass to the next peak top at exact mass. No voltage span at the mass was performed during data acquisition. The exact masses monitored are shown in Table 2.

Figures 2 and 3 show the SIR outputs over the GC retention time window of interest. For example, Fig. 2 shows the m/z 178.0782 (phenanthrene) traces for the whole oils. Thus, phenanthrene is clearly detected with a good signal to noise ratio in each oil, as indeed are the methyl (m/z 192.0928) and dimethyl (206.1088) isomers. Similarly, Fig. 3 shows the detection and relative distribution of dimethyl dibenzothiophenes (m/z 212.0457). The m/z 212.1560 ($C_{16}H_{20}$) trace in Fig. 3 demonstrates the clear separation obtained between the $C_{16}H_{20}$ compounds, hexamethyl naphthalenes and the $C_{14}H_{12}S$ compounds, dimethyl dibenzothiophenes, which have the same nominal mass.

Visual examination of the traces demonstrates several features:

1. the similarity in relative distribution of compound types, and
2. the advantage of using high resolution for selectivity is clearly seen from the two m/z 212 traces where no contribution from m/z 212.1560 is seen in the m/z 212.0457. Quantitation of total peaks of interest in each trace was achieved by peak area determination. Table 3 demonstrates the quantitative correlation of the methylphenanthrene/phenanthrene and dimethyldibenzothiophene/methyldibenzothiophene ratios again demonstrating the close similarity between the four oils.

Figure 4 shows the m/z 217.1955 (steranes) and m/z 191.1798 (triterpanes), for the four oils, over the chromatographic regions of interest. As for the aromatic components above, the similarity in the relative distributions of steranes and triterpanes for the four oils is readily apparent.

CONCLUSION

The usefulness of capillary GC–high resolution MS, as a single stage procedure for analyses of whole crude oils, is clearly demonstrated. The increased confidence in peak assignment and sensitivity, due to the specificity of the technique, combined with the separating power of the capillary columns allows a rapid sample throughout without fractionation.

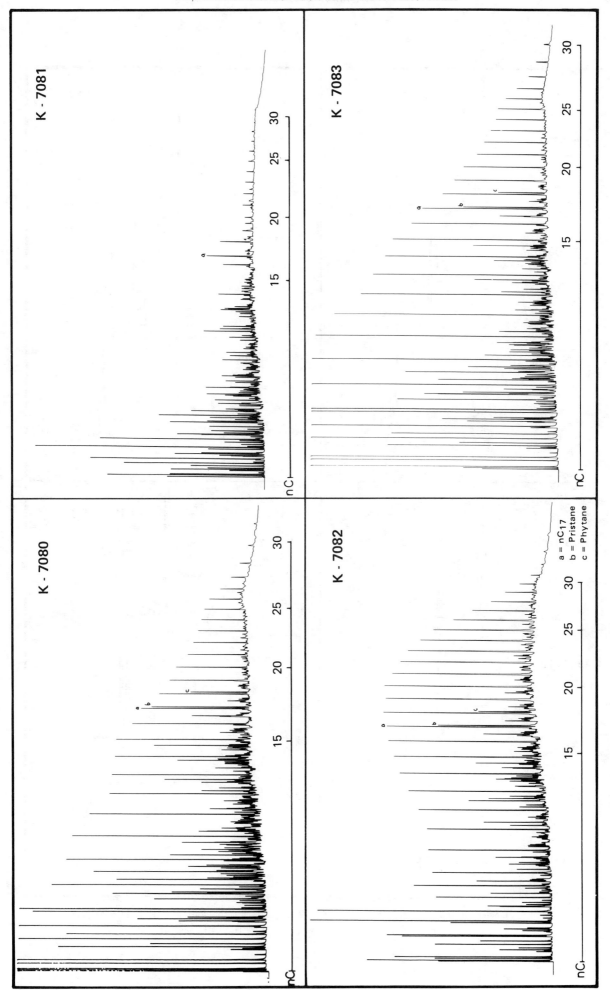

Fig. 1. Capillary GC traces of the four oils. 30 m × 0.3 m OV101, −40–270 °C at 4 °C min.[1], 1 ml min.[1] He flow rate.

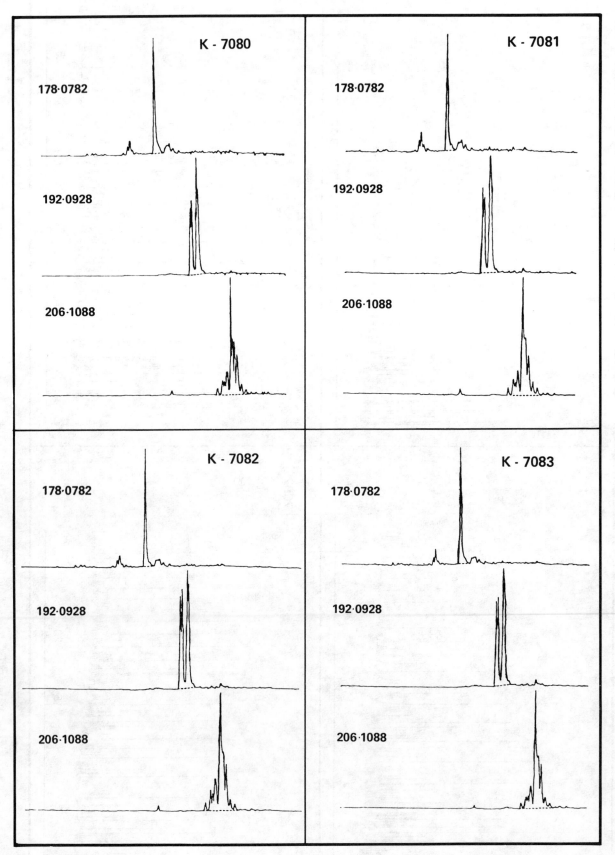

Fig. 2. High resolution Selected Ion recording for m/z 178, 192 and 206 for the four oils. K-7080-K7083. See Table 2.

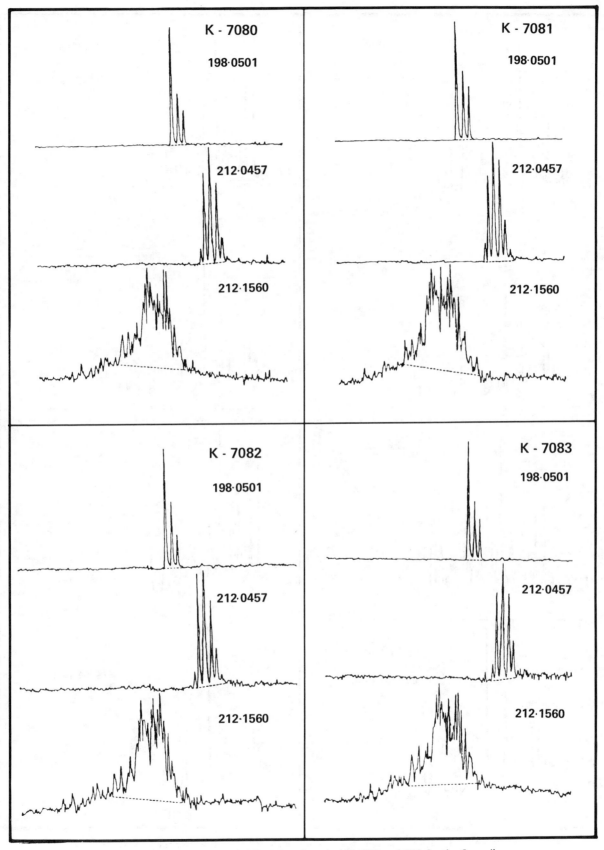

Fig. 3. High resolution S.I.R. traces for *m/z* 198, 212 and 212 for the four oils.

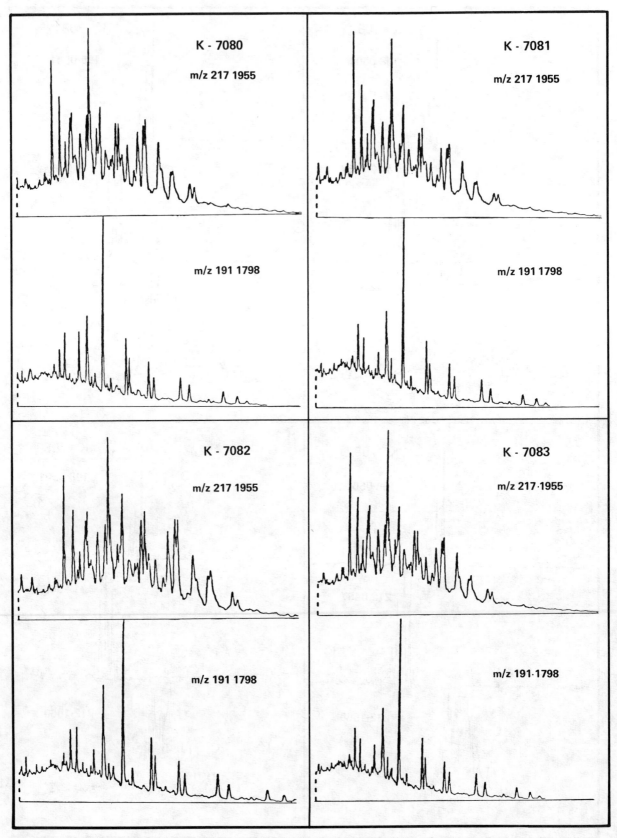

Fig. 4. High resolution S.I.R. traces for *m/z* 191 and 217 for the four oils.

REFERENCES

Reed, W. E. (1977) *Geochim. Cosmochim. Acta.* **41**, 237–247.

Rubinstein, I., Strausz, O. P., Spyckerelle, C., Crawford, R. J. and Westlake, D. W. S. (1977) *Geochim. Cosmochim. Acta.* **41**, 1341–1350.

Seifert, W. K. and Moldowan, J. M. (1979) *Geochim. Cosmochim. Acta.* **43**, 111–126.

Van Dorsselaer, A., Schmitter, J. M., Albrecht, P., Claret, J. and Connan, J. Communication presented at the 8th International Congress of Organic Geochemistry, Mowcow, May 1977.

Seifert, W. K. and Moldowan, J. M. (1978) *Geochim. Cosmochim. Acta.* **42**, 77–95.

Connan, J., Restle, A. and Albrecht, P. (1980). In *Advances in Organic Geochem.* May 1979. Ed. by Douglas, A. G. and Maxwell, J. Pergamon Press. pp. 1–17.

Advances in Organic Geochemistry 1981, pp. 94–98
© John Wiley & Sons Limited, 1983

Increased Vitrinite Reflectance Associated with Uranium Mineralization

R. Sassen

Research Center, Getty Oil Company, Houston, Texas 77042, USA

The effects of radiation exposure on vitrinite were studied in uraniferous coalified logs characterized by the same maceral composition and burial history. The logs were collected in a sandstone facies of the Upper Jurassic Morrison Formation of New Mexico. Uranium contents in the 2.95–5.40% range were associated with coffinite deposition, whereas higher uranium contents (15.50–19.50%) occurred in samples where secondary tyuyamunite was deposited. Mean vitrinite reflectance of samples with lower uranium contents was measured in the 0.41–0.54% range, but was higher (0.63–0.82%) in heavily mineralized samples. Moreover, samples with higher uranium contents showed increased values of Thermal Alteration Index, decreased atomic H/C ratios, and loss of fluorescence. Vitrinite reflectance and other indices of thermal maturity are widely applied in identification of petroleum source rocks. Unless recognized, radiation damage of vitrinite results in significant overestimation of thermal maturity.

INTRODUCTION

A primary application of thermal maturity studies on kerogen is to assist in identification of effective source rocks for petroleum. Vitrinite reflectance and other indices of thermal maturity have been used extensively to estimate the time–temperature exposure of organic matter in sediments. Factors other than time and temperature which influence the reflectance and other properties of vitrinite are of interest to petroleum geochemists.

Increased reflectance as well as other physical and chemical changes within coals have been observed as a consequence of radiation from decay of uranium and daughter products (Teichmüller and Teichmüller, 1958; Jedwab, 1965; Breger, 1974). The present study provides further quantitative data on the extent of vitrinite alteration in relation to measured uranium content.

GEOLOGIC SETTING

Numerous economic deposits of uranium have been discovered in the Grants mineral belt of northwestern New Mexico. This linear trend of ore deposits occurs along the southern margin of the San Juan Basin. Up to 2000 m of sediments are present in this area which range in age from Pennsylvanian to Cretaceous. Nearly all ore deposits have been found in fluvial sandstones of Late Jurassic age in which terrestrial organic matter has played a role in accumulation of uranium.

The present study focuses on samples of uraniferous coalified logs from the now-inactive Poison Canyon Mine in McKinley County, part of the Ambrosia Lake ore district. There, uraniferous logs occur in a sandstone ore body of the Brushy Basin Member of the Upper Jurassic Morrison Formation. Locally, this unit is known as the Poison Canyon sandstone.

Timing of primary mineralization is not known with certainty, but appears to have taken place in the Late Jurassic or Early Cretaceous (Lee and Brookins, 1978). At the Poison Canyon Mine, deposition of coffinite [$USiO_4$] and other minerals occurred in reducing microenvironments associated with terrestrial organic matter (Tessendorf, 1980).

Changes in the distribution and mineralogy of uranium occurred over geologic time at the mine. Fracturing related to formation of the Zuni uplift in the Late Cretaceous permitted access by oxidizing solutions which redistributed much of the primary coffinite (Rapaport, 1963). A second and more intense phase of redistribution occurred as a consequence of erosional unroofing during the Pleistocene (Tessendorf, 1980). The occurrence of tyuyamunite [$Ca(UO_2)_2(VO_4)_2 \cdot 5$–$8 H_2O$] characterized this phase of mineralization. Where redistribution has occurred, uranium is no longer in equilibrium with daughter products.

EXPERIMENTAL

Samples

Discrete coalified logs with varying contents of uranium were collected by the author at the Poison Canyon Mine in 1979. The logs had been buried simultaneously during the Late Jurassic, as shown by their clustered distribution along less than 3 . m of a single bedding surface within the Poison Canyon sandstone. All fossil wood samples have experienced the same time–temperature history since burial.

Analytical approach

Vitrinite of fossil wood was isolated from mineral matter by treatment with HCl and HF. Measurements of mean vitrinite reflectance and observations of fluorescence were performed using a Zeiss Model 01K microscope photometer equipped with a IIIRS vertical illuminator. Aliquots of isolates were also used for estimates of Thermal Alteration Index in transmitted light. In addition, polished sections of mineralized fossil wood were examined in reflected light.

Uranium contents of samples were determined by standard fluorimetric techniques. A scanning electron microscope (AMRAY Model 1200) equipped with an energy dispersive X-ray analysis system (Kevex Corp.) was used for investigation of fossil wood and associated minerals.

Elemental analysis of fossil wood samples was carried out by GeoChem Laboratories, Inc. (Houston, Texas).

RESULTS AND DISCUSSION

Maceral analysis

Macerals of the vitrinite group are the only significant components of each sample. Both telinite (wood tissue) and collinite (amorphous gel) are present within vitrinite fractions. Trace amounts of fungal spores and exinite were observed in some samples.

Table 1
Summary of geochemical data concerning uraniferous coalified logs from the Poison Canyon Mine

Sample no.	Color hand specimen	Dominant mineral	Mean vitrinite reflectance	Number of measure-ments	TAI	% Total uranium	% Soluble[a] uranium	% Organic carbon	Atomic H/C ratio
PCM-1	Brown	Coffinite	0.41 ± 0.06	100	3.0	4.70	0.01	27.5	1.00
PCM-2	Brown	Coffinite	0.50 ± 0.16	100	3.0	2.95	0.01	19.4	0.80
PCM-3	Brown	Coffinite	0.48 ± 0.04	100	3.0	5.40	0.01	24.7	0.78
PCM-4	Brown	Coffinite	0.54 ± 0.05	100	3.0	4.70	0.01	23.9	0.75
PCM-5	Black	Tyuyamunite	0.81 ± 0.16	100	4.0	15.50	0.02	38.8	0.65
PCM-6	Black	Tyuyamunite	0.82 ± 0.12	98	4.0	19.50	0.02	40.5	0.59
PCM-7	Black	Tyuyamunite	0.78 ± 0.11	100	4.0	18.50	0.04	27.9	0.65
PCM-8	Black	Tyuyamunite	0.63 ± 0.12	99	4.0	16.87	0.03	39.5	0.63

[a] This fraction is mainly associated with water-soluble schroekingerite.

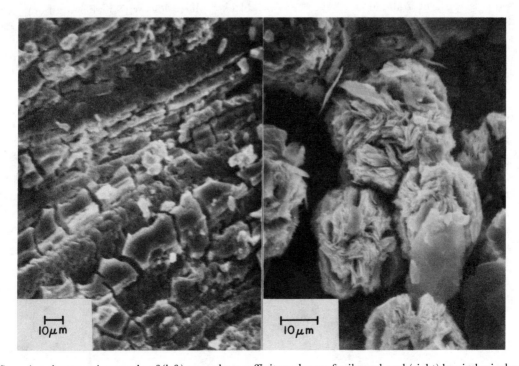

Fig. 1. Scanning electron micrographs of (left) amorphous coffinite on brown fossil wood, and (right) hemispherical aggregates of tyuyamunite crystals on a fracture surface in black fossil wood.

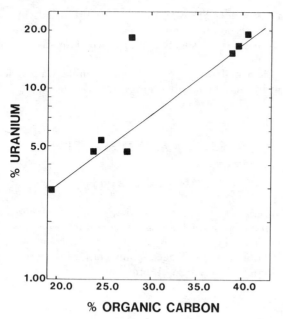

Fig. 2. Plot of organic carbon and uranium contents of uraniferous fossil wood samples.

Distribution of uranium

All coalified log samples are characterized by relatively high contents of uranium (Table 1). However, total uranium contents of samples occur in two groups that correspond to color of fossil wood in hand specimen and to mineralogy. Brown, friable woody material displays a remnant vascular structure and is characterized by total uranium contents in the 2.95–5.40% range. Black fossil wood is harder, denser and richer in uranium (15.50–19.50%). The occurrence of colored uranium minerals in black fossil wood is apparent to the unaided eye.

Scanning electron micrographs of fossil wood and associated uranium minerals are shown in Fig. 1. Brown fossil wood appears to mainly contain dispersed coffinite of poor crystallinity. Although not all uranium minerals in black fossil wood could be identified, tyuyamunite is the major component. The secondary mineral occurs as greenish–yellow concentrations in voids and fractures of the black coalified logs. Schroekingerite [Na Ca$_3$(UO$_2$)(CO$_3$)$_3$(SO$_4$)F·10H$_2$O] was found as rare discrete crystals in black fossil wood but was not a significant component of samples (Table 1).

Organic carbon content of samples is a factor which appears to control uranium concentration (Fig. 2). The observation that uranium content increases with organic carbon content is well recognized (Swanson, 1960; Breger and Brown, 1962).

Increased reflectance of vitrinite

Increased reflectance as a result of radiation damage from uranium decay has been observed as microscopic halos surrounding discrete uranium minerals in coals (Teichmüller and Teichmüller, 1958; Jedwab, 1965); only a small fraction of the total organic matter has been altered in these examples. However, the increased reflectance from radiation effects is much more extensive in highly mineralized samples from the Poison Canyon Mine. Examination of polished sections of highly mineralized samples reveals large coalescent areas of enhanced reflectance rather than isolated halos.

Vitrinite reflectance histograms of each coalified log sample are presented in Fig. 3. In brown logs, mean vitrinite reflectance ranges from 0.41% to as high as 0.54%. Since all samples are likely to have been altered to some extent, the *lowest* mean reflectance (0.41%) provides the best estimate of thermal maturity. The black coalified logs with higher uranium contents are characterized by significantly higher mean reflectance

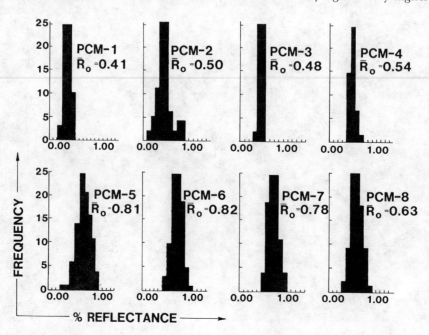

Fig. 3. Vitrinite reflectance histograms of uraniferous fossil wood. The exceptionally high uranium concentrations in samples PCM-5 through 8 (15.50–19.50%) have resulted in extensive alteration of vitrinite.

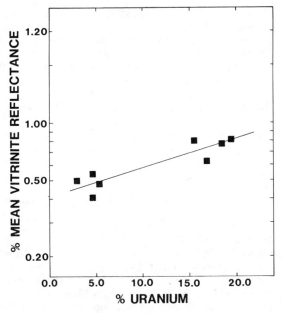

Fig. 4. Plot of mean vitrinite reflectance and uranium content of fossil wood samples.

Thermal alteration index

Increasing time–temperature exposure results in gradual change in color and translucency of organic matter in transmitted light (Staplin, 1969). Thermal Alteration Index (TAI) is based on the progressive shift in color of organic matter from yellow to brown and finally to black at advanced levels of thermal maturity.

As noted above, the mean vitrinite reflectance of 0.41% probably provides the truest estimate of thermal maturity for Poison Canyon Mine samples. This value implies that the colour of vitrinite in transmitted light should be yellow, corresponding to a TAI in the 2–2.5 range (Héroux *et al.*, 1979). However, samples are characterized by higher TAI values than would be predicted (Table 1). Indeed, the highly mineralized black fossil wood displays a black color in transmitted light which is normally associated with a TAI of 4, suggesting advanced thermal maturity.

Radiochemical dehydrogenation

The research summarized by Breger (1974) shows that increased reflectance of uraniferous logs is accompanied by loss of hydrogen. This radiochemical dehydrogenation has evidently also occurred in samples from the Poison Canyon Mine. Although all samples have the same maceral composition and burial history, atomic H/C ratios vary and were measured in the 1.00–0.59 range. As shown in Fig. 5, increasing reflectance of vitrinite is related to decreasing atomic H/C ratio. Although vitrinite reflectance continues to increase, radiation appears to be less effective as an agent of hydrogen loss at higher doses.

values (0.63–0.82%), falsely implying more advanced thermal maturity.

The increased reflectance of the black fossil wood is attributed to radiation effects which have varied in intensity over geologic time. Because of the episodic redistribution of uranium at the mine, radiation dose over time cannot be calculated in a simple manner as done by Leventhal and Threlkeld (1978) for another uranium occurrence in the Grants mineral belt (where only primary mineralization was present). Nevertheless, a semilogarithmic plot of vitrinite reflectance and uranium content yields a good correlation (Fig. 4). The observation that reflectance is related to present-day uranium content suggests that secondary mineralization has been most effective as an agent of alteration.

Fluorescence

The brown fossil wood with lower uranium contents shows some weak yellow and dark brown fluorescence of organic matter. However, no fluorescence could be

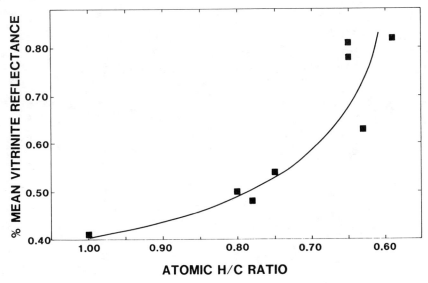

Fig. 5. Plot of mean vitrinite reflectance and atomic H/C ratios of fossil wood samples.

detected in black fossil wood with higher uranium contents.

SUMMARY AND CONCLUSIONS

This study shows that intense radiation exposure over geologic time results in variable but sometimes extensive alteration of vitrinite in coalified logs. The alteration is shown by increased reflectance of vitrinite, increased values of TAI, decreased atomic H/C ratios, and by loss of fluorescence. Each of these parameters is widely used to estimate the thermal maturity of kerogen (Héroux *et al.*, 1979). Unless recognized during interpretation of analytical results, radiation damage of vitrinite results in overestimation of thermal maturity.

Acknowledgements

The writer wishes to express his appreciation to the Getty Oil Company for technical assistance and permission to publish this paper. The cooperation of Reserve Oil and Minerals Corporation in field work and sample collection is also acknowledged. In addition, determinations of maceral distribution and TAI carried out by Dr Pieter van Gijzel of Getty Oil Company, and discussions with Dr I. A. Breger of the US Geological Survey are much appreciated.

REFERENCES

Breger, I. A. (1974) The role of organic matter in the accumulation of uranium: The organic geochemistry of the coal–uranium association. In *Formation of Uranium Ore Deposits*. Ed. by International Atomic Energy Agency, Vienna. pp. 99–124.

Breger, I. A. and Brown, A. (1962) Kerogen in the Chattanooga Shale. *Science* **137**, 221–224.

Héroux, Y., Changnon, A. and Bertrand, R. (1979) Compilation and correlation of major thermal maturation indicators. *AAPG Bull.* **63**, 2128–2144.

Jedwab, J. (1965) Les dégats radiatifs dan le charbon uranifère du Schaentzel. *Geol. Rundsch.* **55**, 445–453.

Lee, M. J. and Brookins, D. G. (1978) Rubidium–strontium minimum ages of sedimentation, uranium mineralization, and provenance, Morrison Formation (Upper Jurassic), Grants mineral belt, New Mexico. *AAPG Bull.* **62**, 1673–1683.

Leventhal, J. S. and Threlkeld, C. N. (1978) Carbon-13/carbon-12 isotope fractionation of organic matter associated with uranium ores induced by alpha-irradiation. *Science* **202**, 430–432.

Rapaport, I. (1963) Uranium deposits of the Poison Canyon ore trend, Grants district. In *Geology and Technology of the Grants Region*. Ed. by Kelley, V. C. New Mexico Bureau of Mines and Mineral Resources Mem. 15. pp. 122–135.

Staplin, F. L. (1968) Sedimentary organic matter, organic metamorphism, and oil and gas occurrence. *Bull. Canadian Petrol. Geol.* **17**, 47–66.

Swanson, V. E. (1960) Oil yield and uranium content of black shales. *US Geol. Surv. Prof. Pap.* 356-A, 1–44.

Teichmüller, M. and Teichmüller, R. (1958) Inkohlungsuntersuchungen und ihre natzanwendung. *Geol. en Mijnb.* **20**, 41–66.

Tessendorf, T. N. (1980) Redistributed ore bodies of Poison Canyon Sec. 18 and 19. T.13N., R.9W, McKinley County. In *Geology and Mineral Technology of the Grants Uranium Region*. Ed. by Rautman, C. A. New Mexico Bureau of Mines and Mineral Resources Mem. **38**. pp. 226–229.

Advances in Organic Geochemistry 1981, pp. 99–107
© *John Wiley & Sons Limited, 1983*

A Geochemical Comparison of some Crude Oils from Pre-Ordovician Carbonate Rocks

D. M. McKirdy*

Organic Geochemistry Unit, School of Chemistry, University of Bristol, Bristol BS8 1TS, England

A. K. Aldridge

Masspec Analytical, Wallbridge, Stroud, Gloucestershire GL5 3JA, England

and P. J. M. Ypma

Department of Economic Geology, University of Adelaide, Adelaide SA 5001, Australia

The occurrence of oils as shows and, less commonly, economic accumulations is widespread in rocks of late Proterozoic and early Palaeozoic age. With a few notable exceptions, little is known of the geochemistry of these very old oils. This study is based on crude oils from Vendian–Cambrian carbonate sequences in Australia (Officer, Arrowie, and Amadeus Basins), Namibia (Etosha Basin), and the USA (North Appalachian Basin). Biomarker techniques and conventional geochemical methods have been used to identify source-related differences between the oils and to discern the effects of subsequent migration, maturation, water-washing inspissation, and biodegradation on their respective C_{12+} compositions. Unusual features of the oils include C_{11} through C_{21} *n*-alkanes in late Precambrian oil from the Etosha Basin and abundant acyclic sesterterpanes and squalane in nonmarine Cambrian oils from the Officer Basin. Despite differences in API gravity (14° to 43°), sulphur content (0.2 to 2.2 per cent), and gross composition (paraffinic to aromatic–naphthenic), the oils have a number of common characteristics. They are isotopically light ($\delta^{13}C_{PBD} = -27$ to $-30\%_0$). The ratio of pristane to phytane is low, and hopanes (C_{27} and C_{29} through C_{35}) are more abundant than steranes, consistent with source material of mainly prokaryotic origin deposited under highly reducing conditions. Sterane distributions (C_{21}, C_{22}, and C_{27} through C_{29}) are much less uniform than those of the hopanes, reflecting the diversity of their algal (including cyanobacterial) precursors and different source maturities at the time of primary migration. The *carbonate-sourced* oils possess apparently diagnostic biomarker signatures (viz. trisnorhopane T_m ($17\alpha H$) $\gg T_s$ ($18\alpha H$); $C_{35} \gg C_{34}$ hopanes; nonrearranged > rearranged steranes; and diacholestane $20S \simeq 20R$). The survival of steranes and triterpanes in ancient oils is unlikely if their reservoir rocks contain anhydrite.

INTRODUCTION

Indications of indigenous petroleum (residual bitumen, oil and gas shows, oil seeps) in sedimentary rocks of mid-Proterozoic to early Palaeozoic age (1600 to 500 m.y.) occur widely throughout North America, Eurasia, Africa, and Australia (Vassoyevich *et al.*, 1971; Palmer, 1980). Commercial or potentially commercial oil and gas accumulations in reservoirs of this age are known from USSR (Maximov and Muromtseva, 1975; Meyerhoff, 1980); USA, Algeria, and Libya (Becker and Patton, 1968); Australia (Anonymous, 1982); and Oman (M. R. Walter, personal communication). Although a younger source has been suggested for the oil and gas in some pre-Ordovician reservoirs (Palmer,

1980), many contain hydrocarbons apparently generated from the remains of aquatic microorganisms preserved in sediments deposited before the appearance of extensive vegetation on land. Land plants originated during the Silurian (Chaloner, 1967), but it was not until early Devonian time that vascular plant residues became a significant potential source of petroleum hydrocarbons (Tissot and Welte, 1978).

Because of their derivation from the lipids of algae and bacteria, indigenous Proterozoic and Cambrian crude oils (and their source rocks) constitute a vast store of geochemical data on the nature of the early marine and lacustrine biomass, in the form of biological marker compounds; e.g. branched, isoprenoid, steroid, and polyterpenoid hydrocarbons (Hollerbach and Welte, 1977; McKirdy and Hahn, 1982). As yet, however, little is known of the biomarker geochemistry of these ancient crude oils, with the possible exception of oil seeping from

* Present address: Australian Mineral Development Laboratories, P.O. Box 114, Eastwood, S.A. 5063, Australia.

Table 1
Geological setting and bulk chemistry of oils

Well/Field	Basin	Formation	Age	API gravity	S content %	Type	Composition of $C_{12}+$ fraction				
							Sat	Arom	ONS %	Asph	$\delta^{13}C_{PDB}$ ‰
Morrow County	N. Appalachian	Knox Dol.	Late $\in$	40.1	n.d.	paraffinic–naphthenic	70.3	13.2	15.6	0.9	−29.5
Alice-1	Amadeus	Giles Creek Dol.	Middle $\in$	43.0	0.2	aromatic–naphthenic	43.8	10.0	45.1	1.1	−28.8
Wilkatana-1	Arrowie	Wilkawillina Lst.	Early $\in$	n.d.	n.d.	paraffinic	54.7	1.1	38.3	5.9	−27.4
Byilkaoora-1	Officer	Observatory Hill Beds	?Early $\in$	14.4	0.3	aromatic–naphthenic (Family A)	23.7	6.4	53.6	16.3	−28.7
				n.d.	n.d.	naphthenic (Family B)	53.4	3.5	42.6	0.5	n.d.
				n.d.	n.d.	aromatic–naphthenic (biodegraded Family B)	24.9	7.7	67.1	0.2	n.d.
Etosha 5-1A	Etosha	Tsumeb Sub-group	Vendian to ? $\in$	29.5	2.2	naphthenic	82.4	10.1	7.2	0.3	−27.1

n.d. not determined

the 1100 m.y. old Nonesuch shale in the White Pine Mine, Michigan (Hoering, 1976); the Siva crude, Volga–Urals Basin (Petrov *et al.*, 1976, 1977; Seifert, 1981; Seifert and Moldowan, 1981) and similar Proterozoic (Riphean–Vendian) oils from the Siberian Platform (Arefev *et al.*, 1980); and oil shows in Cambrian sediments of the Officer Basin, South Australia (McKirdy and Kantsler, 1980; McKirdy *et al.*, 1982).

The present study is based on seven crude oils of diverse and, in some cases, highly unusual composition from Vendian–Cambrian carbonate sequences in Australia, Namibia, and the USA (Table 1). Biomarker techniques (Seifert and Moldowan, 1981, and references cited therein) and conventional geochemical and isotopic methods were used in an attempt to recognize source-related differences between the oils and to document the

Table 2
Biomarker parameters of source, maturation, and migration[a]

Oil	Steranes								
	$C_{27}:C_{28}:C_{29}$ ($\beta\beta$ 20S)			$\dfrac{C_{21}+C_{22}}{C_{29}}$	$C_{29}\dfrac{\alpha\alpha\,20S}{\alpha\alpha\,20R}$	$C_{29}\dfrac{\beta\beta\,20R}{\alpha\alpha\,20R}$	$C_{29}\dfrac{20R\ rearr}{\Sigma\ non\text{-}rearr}$	C_{27} rearr $\dfrac{20S}{20R}$
Morrow Co.	39	18	43	0.52	0.93	1.79	0.50	1.7
Alice	—	—	—	—	—	—	—	—
Wilkatana	30	30	40	0.27	0.70	0.90	0.28	1.6
Byilkaoora (Family A)	10	50	40	0.06	1.14	1.30	0.21	0.91
Byilkaoora (Family B)	12	54	34	0.12	1.34	1.86	0.28	0.91
Byilkaoora (biodegraded Family B)	16	48	36	b	b	b	b	0.90
Etosha	35	28	37	0.39	0.95	1.47	0.13	1.1
Parameter specificity	source			source	maturation	maturation migration	source migration	[source] maturation
Parameter number	1			2	3	4	5	6

subsequent effects of various alteration processes on their respective C_{12+} compositions.

EXPERIMENTAL

The Morrow County oil was topped to 210 °C by distillation before analysis; the remaining samples were oil shows which had already lost their light ends. The bulk geochemistry of the oils (Table 1) was determined as indicated by McKirdy *et al.* (1982). A sample of the C_{12+} aliphatic fraction of each oil was prepared for more detailed analysis, as follows.

Isolation of aliphatic and saturated hydrocarbons

The oil (100 mg) was deasphalted by suspension in light petroleum (nanograde, 30° to 60°) and centrifugation (1000 rpm, 10 min). The aliphatic hydrocarbon fraction was isolated by column chromatography (Al_2O_3 Merck 90, light petroleum eluent), and in the case of the Etosha sample, alkenes were separated from the saturates by argentation thin-layer chromatography (10 per cent $AgNO_3$/silica gel G plate, light petroleum developer).

Gas–liquid chromatography (GLC)

GLC analyses were carried out on a Carlo Erba FTV 4160 gas chromatograph using a glass WCOT column (20 m × 0.3 mm ID) coated with OV-1. The carrier gas was He (0.5 kg cm^{-2}). The temperature programme was

60 to 260 °C at 6 °C per minute, with a 30-second initial hold at ambient.

Combined gas chromatography–mass spectrometry (GC–MS)

GC–MS analyses of the aliphatic hydrocarbon fractions were carried out on a Finnigan 3200 system coupled to a Finnigan 6100 data system. The GLC column (20 m × 0.3 mm ID OV-1 WCOT) was temperature-programmed from 80 to 270 °C at 4 °C per minute after a one-minute hold at ambient. The carrier gas was He (0.8 kg cm^{-2}). The ionizing voltage was 70 eV. The mass spectrometer was scanned from 50 to 450 amu every two seconds.

Structural assignments and compound ratios

The following mass fragmentograms were examined: *m/e* 85 (acyclic alkanes); *m/e* 183 (acyclic isoprenoids); *m/e* 191, 205 (hopanes); *m/e* 217, 218 (steranes, rearranged steranes); *m/e* 231 (4-methyl steranes); and *m/e* 259 (rearranged steranes). In addition, fragmentograms for *m/e* 83 and combined *m/e* 83 + 69 and *m/e* 85 + 71 were used to demonstrate the presence of *n*-alkenes in the Etosha total aliphatic fraction. Mass spectra confirmed the identity of the *n*-C_{16} alkene/alkane doublet. Background-subtracted mass spectra of individual isoprenoids were compared with published spectra (Haug and Curry, 1974; Holzer *et al.*, 1979) and the mass spectra of authentic squalane and C_{25} regular

Table 2
Biomarker parameters of source, maturation, and migration[a]

Hopanes						Acyclic isoprenoids			
$\dfrac{C_{29}}{C_{30}}$	$\dfrac{C_{34}}{C_{35}}$ (22S)	$C_{27}\dfrac{T_m}{T_s}$	$C_{32}\dfrac{22S}{22R}$	$\dfrac{Pristane}{n-C_{17}}$	$\dfrac{Phytane}{n-C_{18}}$	$\dfrac{Pristane}{Phytane}$	$\dfrac{2,6,10\text{-TMTD}}{Pristane}$	Sesterterpanes and squalane
0.69	1.2	0.80	1.4	0.39	0.33	1.7	0.59	—
0.78	—	0.70	1.2	0.20	0.17	2.6	0.96	—
1.0	0.89	0.86	1.2	0.91	0.49	2.0	—	—
0.55	1.1	3.6	1.4	2.7	3.3	0.92	0.72	+ +
0.65	1.3	2.8	1.4	2.3	3.0	0.94	0.51	+ +
0.61	1.4	2.5	1.3	—	—	—	—	—
1.5	0.86	2.9	1.6	0.18	0.34	0.48	1.4	—
source	source	[source] maturation	maturation	source maturation	source maturation	source	maturation	source
7	8	9	10	11	12	13	14	15

— not detected   + + abundant   [b] parameter severely modified by biodegradation   [ ] clay content, as distinct from organic input   2,6,10-TMTD = 2,6,10-trimethyltridecane

[a] The theoretical and/or empirical basis of each parameter is elaborated elsewhere, as follows: (1) Huang and Meinschein (1979), Mackenzie (1980). (2) Suggested by results of present study. (3) Seifert and Moldowan (1981). (4) Seifert *et al.* (1980), Seifert and Moldowan (1981). (5) Seifert and Moldowan (1978), Seifert *et al.* (1980). (6) Mackenzie *et al.* (1980). (7) Pym *et al.* (1975). (8) Suggested by results of present study. (9) Seifert and Moldowan (1978, 1981). (10) Seifert and Moldowan (1980), Seifert *et al.* (1980), Mackenzie (1980). (11), (12) Lijmbach (1975), Connan and Cassou (1980). (13) Powell and McKirdy (1973). (14) McKirdy (1981). (15) McKirdy and Kantsler (1980), McKirdy *et al.* (1982).

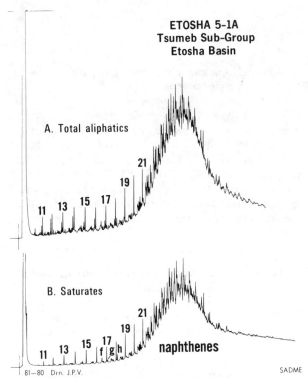

Fig. 1. Gas chromatograms of (a) total aliphatic and (b) saturates fractions of oil which apparently seeped from Proterozoic marine carbonates (Tsumeb Subgroup, Otavi Group) in Etosha 5-1A, Namibia. *n*-Alkenes elute immediately before corresponding *n*-alkanes (numbered according to chain length) in the upper chromatogram.

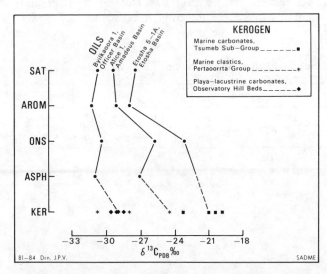

Fig. 2. Carbon isotopic profiles of three pre-Ordovician oils showing source-related differences in their C_{12+} fractions. With the exception of one new Tsumeb value, kerogen δ^{13} C data are from Eichmann and Schidlowski (1975), McKirdy (1977), and McKirdy and Kantsler (1980).

isoprenoid standards. Isoprenoid biomarker ratios (parameters 11 to 14, Table 2) were calculated from GLC peak heights. The structures of the hopanes (Fig. 3) and steranes (Fig. 6) were assigned by comparison of their relative retention times with existing data (Seifert and Moldowan, 1979; Mackenzie, 1980), and the use of molecular ion mass chromatography. Compound ratios

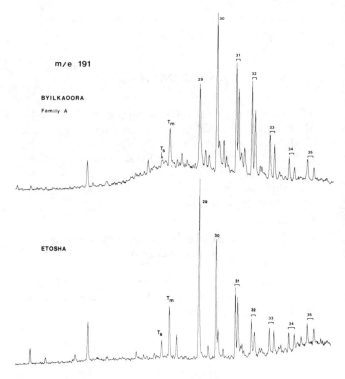

Fig. 3. Terpane (*m/e* 191) mass fragmentograms of mature Byilkaoora (Family A) and Etosha oils in which C_{27} $T_m > T_s$ and $C_{35} > C_{34}$. These oils probably originated in carbonate (rather than shale) source beds. *Key*: T_m and T_s are the C_{27} $17\alpha(H)$ and $18\alpha(H)$ trisnorhopanes of Seifert and Moldowan (1978, 1981); 29 to 35 indicate carbon numbers of $17\alpha(H)$ hopanes; C_{31}–C_{35} doublets comprise 20S (left) and 20R (right) epimers.

for the steranes (parameters 1 to 6, Table 2) and hopanes (parameters 7 to 10, Table 2) were determined by manual quantitation from *m/e* 217, 218, and *m/e* 191 mass fragmentograms.

RESULTS

The geologic setting and bulk geochemistry of the oils is summarized in Table 1. The biomarker parameters used to assess differences in source, maturity, and migration are listed in Table 2.

Etosha Basin, Namibia

During sampling of formation waters in an uncompleted exploration well, Etosha 5-1A, a small amount (< 1 US barrel) of oil was found floating on top of the water table. Geological evidence (Ypma, 1979) suggests that this seepage of naphthenic oil originated in Vendian (to ? Cambrian) marine carbonates (in part stromatolitic) of the Hüttenberg Formation, Tsumeb Subgroup, Otavi Group; and that these organic-rich carbonates probably have been both source and reservoir for the oil.

The composition of the Etosha oil is unusual in several respects. It is one of the rare crude oils in which *n*-alkenes (C_{11} to C_{21}) have been identified (Fig. 1). Unlike those isolated by Hoering (1977) from a Northern Appalachian crude oil (reservoir age, Devonian), the *n*-alkenes in the Etosha oil display a distinct even carbon number predominance. The skewed saturates distribution of the oil (Fig. 1) is characterised by a very prominent naphthene hump in the C_{21}–C_{29} region and a relative lack of *n*-alkanes. This oil also differs from the others examined in having a much higher sulphur content, a lower ratio of pristane to phytane, and a heavier isotopic composition (Table 1). The last feature is consistent with the occurrence of isotopically heavy kerogen in the oil's supposed source beds (Fig. 2).

Hopanoid triterpanes (Fig. 3) and somewhat lesser amounts of steranes (Table 2) are present in the oil. Maturation-dependent biomarker parameters (Nos. 3, 4, 10–12, and 14, Table 2) show that, contrary to a previous interpretation (McKirdy and Hahn, 1982), the Etosha oil is mature. However, the trisnorhopane ratio T_m/T_s (parameter 9, Table 2) is much higher than in mature, shale-sourced crude oils (Seifert and Moldowan, 1980).

The great antiquity and small size of the Etosha oil accumulation fits its appearance of having undergone several episodes of alteration. These include (not necessarily in order of occurrence):

1. Water-washing, which removed the light ends and possibly also some of the more soluble C_{12+} aromatic hydrocarbons and polar compounds;
2. Biodegradation of original *n*-alkanes (note: saturates fraction is isotopically heavier than the aromatic hydrocarbons, Fig. 2); and
3. Late-stage *in situ* maturation of partially biodegraded oil, to produce the present *n*-alkane and *n*-alkene distributions (Fig. 1) via thermal-cracking of *n*-alkyl moieties from asphaltenes, polar compounds, and/or alkylbenzenes.

The Etosha oil is likely to have existed as a discrete hydrocarbon phase since at least Devonian time. Hydrocarbon-bearing fluid inclusions are associated with replacement Pb–Zn deposits of this age in the Otavi carbonate fold belt bordering the Etosha Basin (Ypma, 1979). Among the hydrocarbons identified in these inclusions are low molecular weight (C_2–C_3) alkenes. One possible reason for the well-documented stability of alkenes in fluid inclusions is that they lack access to an effective hydrogen donor, e.g. kerogen or asphaltene. Porosity in certain relatively impermeable carbonate rocks, such as the reservoir formation of the Etosha oil, may be analogous to carbonate-hosted fluid inclusions in its ability to preserve alkenes.

Officer Basin, South Australia

In the northeastern Officer Basin, ?Early Cambrian alkaline playa–lacustrine carbonates of the Observatory Hill Beds are reservoir and source for two families of nonmarine oil, one aromatic–naphthenic and the other naphthenic (Table 1; McKirdy and Kantsler, 1980). Both are rich in C_{15}–C_{25} regular and C_{30} irregular acyclic isoprenoid alkanes (Table 2, Fig. 4), presumably derived from halophilic and/or methanogenic archaebacteria (McKirdy *et al.*, 1982).

Sterane and hopane maturation indices (Table 2) show that the Byilkaoora oils are more mature than the

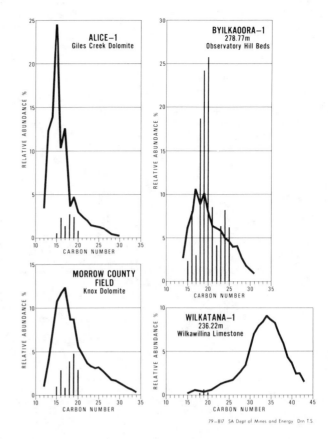

Fig. 4. Comparison of *n*-alkane and regular acyclic isoprenoid distributions in oils from four Cambrian carbonate reservoir rocks.

Etosha crude. Again, $T_m/T_s \gg 1$ (Fig. 3), suggesting that in carbonate source rocks this parameter may be less responsive to thermal stress than it is in shales. Family B oils are more mature, and ostensibly have migrated further (parameters 4 and 5, Table 2), than Family A oils. The latter conclusion assumes migration of the two oil types through carrier beds of similar geochromatographic plateage value.

In drill cores recovered from Byilkaoora-1, oil shows in separate vugs have undergone differing degrees of biodegradation. The relative susceptibility of aliphatic hydrocarbons to bacterial attack appears to be as follows: *n*-alkanes > isoprenoid alkanes > nonrearranged steranes (20R > 20S) > rearranged steranes > hopanes. In this case, therefore, the effects of biodegradation on polycyclic alkanes are similar to those reported by Seifert and Moldowan (1979), with the important additional finding that the 14α(H) 17α(H) and 14β(H) 17β(H) 20R sterane epimers are removed more readily than their 20S counterparts (Fig. 5).

Arrowie Basin, South Australia

Small amounts of 26° API gravity paraffinic oil and associated semi-solid wax occur in marine dolomitic limestones of the Early Cambrian Wilkawillina Limestone in the southern Arrowie Basin (Wopfner, 1970). These hydrocarbons are located in vuggy porosity just below a major unconformity and represent the

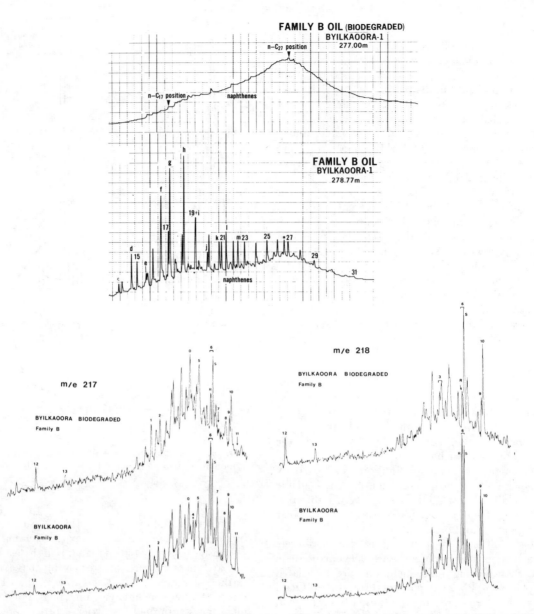

Fig. 5. Alkane gas chromatograms (after McKirdy and Kantsler, 1980) and corresponding sterane (*m/e* 217 and 218) mass fragmentograms of two Byilkaoora (Family B) oils. Severe biodegradation of the upper oil has resulted in a reduced concentration of regular steranes (nonrearranged) relative to diasteranes (rearranged) and the preferential loss of 20R epimers. See Fig. 6 for key.

inspissated and water-washed remains of a deroofed Cambrian oil pool.

The Wilkawillina-hosted sample from Wilkatana-1 (Table 1) is a residual paraffinic reservoir bitumen rich in long-chain *n*-alkanes (C_{15} through C_{43+}, maximum C_{34}) which exhibit a very slight even/odd predominance (Fig. 4). Biomarker maturation parameters (Table 2) confirm that the bitumen is relatively immature. The source of the parent Wilkatana oil has not yet been established. Source-rock data (McKirdy, 1981) indicate that the Wilkawillina Limestone could have been self-sourcing, although the oil's high diacholestane 20S/20R ratio (parameter 6, Table 2) and low T_m/T_s value are perhaps more consistent with an argillaceous source rock.

Amadeus Basin, Northern Territory

A core cut in the middle Cambrian Giles Creek Dolomite in Alice-1, north central Amadeus Basin, contained a show of aromatic–naphthenic oil (Table 1). Although now reservoired in anhydritic dolomite, the oil may have originated in contemporaneous dolomitic shale (T_m/T_s <1, Table 2; Fig. 2; see also McKirdy, 1977). More oxic conditions during source-bed deposition and diagenesis would account for the relatively high pr/ph value (2.6) of the oil. Its low hopane (C_{27} and C_{29}–C_{33}) content and lack of steranes (Table 2) distinguish it from the other oils studied.

North Appalachian Basin, USA

In the Morrow County Field, Ohio, oil is produced from a subunconformity play in the late Cambrian Knox Dolomite (Janssens, 1973). The C_{12} through C_{20} *n*-alkanes of this paraffinic–naphthenic oil, like those in the Officer and Amadeus Basin oils (Fig. 4), display the

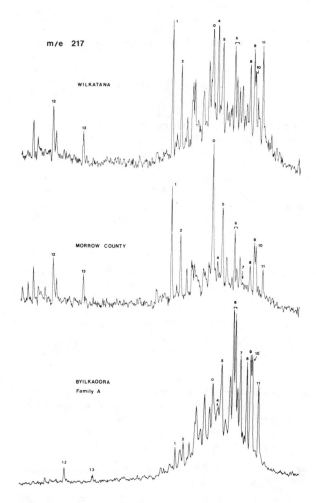

Fig. 6. Sterane (m/e 217) mass fragmentograms of the Wilkatana, Morrow County, and Bilkaoora (Family A) oils showing differences attributable to source, maturation, and migration (see also Table 2). Key: 1. 27S dia; 2. 27R dia; 3. $27\beta\beta R$ and S; 0. 29S dia; 4. $27\alpha\alpha R$; 5. 29R dia; 6. $28\beta\beta R$ and S; 7. $28\alpha\alpha R$; 8. $29\alpha\alpha S$; 9. $29\beta\beta R$; 10. $29\beta\beta S$; 11. $29\alpha\alpha R$; 12. C_{21} sterane; 13. C_{22} sterane. Abbreviations thus: R, S = 20R, 20S epimers; 27S dia = C_{27} (20S) diasterane; $29\alpha\alpha R = C_{29}$ $14\alpha(H)$ $17\alpha(H)$ (20R) regular sterane.

distinct odd/even predominance that is characteristic of many mature pre-Devonian crudes and may be a biological marker of bacterial lipids (McKirdy *et al.*, 1980).

The Morrow County oil is the only sample in the present study which, on the basis of its C_{29} sterane epimer ratios (parameters 3 and 4, Table 2), plots within the field of mature migrated crude oils on the maturation/migration diagram of Seifert and Moldowan (1981, Fig. 10). This oil appears to be a mature shale-sourced crude (cf. $T_m/T_s < 1$, Table 2) which migrated to a contiguous carbonate reservoir.

DISCUSSION

The contrasting sterane distributions of the Morrow County, Wilkatana, and Byilkaoora (Family A) oils

(Table 2, Fig. 6) illustrate at least some of the compositional diversity that is possible in early Palaeozoic crude oils. Primary differences in the steroid, hopanoid, and isoprenoid components of the microbial geolipids incorporated in their source beds have been modified further by maturation (source and reservoir), biodegradation, and to a lesser degree, migration, broadly as described by Seifert (1980), Seifert and Moldowan (1978, 1979, 1980, and 1981), and Seifert *et al.* (1980) for oils in much younger shale–sandstone sequences. However, there are significant differences in the biomarker geochemistry of the present suite of oils that may be diagnostic of their carbonate habitat.

The two most reliable biomarker maturation indices (parameters 3 and 10, Table 2) show that the Wilkatana reservoir bitumen is the least mature oil. Both the Wilkatana and Alice oils appear to be early expulsion products (C_{32} hopane 22S/22R = 1.2), although the latter subsequently has undergone appreciable cracking in the reservoir (2,6,10-TMTD/pr = 0.96, Table 2). The Morrow County oil is of intermediate maturity, whereas the Etosha and Byilkaoora oils are all mature. The maturity of the Byilkaoora crudes exceeds that of the most mature samples in Seifert and Moldowan's (1980) worldwide selection of oils.

The lack of diasteranes relative to nonrearranged steranes, low C_{27} rearranged sterane (diacholestane) 20S/20R values (0.9 to 1.1), and anomalously high C_{27} hopane T_m/T_s ratios (2.5 to 3.6) in the mature Byilkaoora and Etosha oils (Table 2) may be a direct result of their genesis in carbonate source rocks which lacked acidic clay minerals (Seiskind *et al.*, 1979) capable of catalyzing the relevant epimerization and isomerization reactions (e.g., Seifert and Moldowan, 1978, page 81; Mackenzie *et al.*, 1980, page 1719).

With the exception of the Morrow County sample, all the oils plot to the left of the so-called 'correct kinetic path toward petroleum generation' (Seifert and Moldowan, 1981, p. 791). This empirically derived curve is based on C_{29} steranes in a set of predominantly shale-sourced crude oils. In view of the contrasting catalytic activity of carbonate and clay minerals, it is perhaps not surprising that the kinetics of petroleum sterane generation in *carbonate rocks* should also apparently differ from those in *shales*.

The Alice oil is the only one associated with abundant anhydrite. During high-temperature (> 80 to 120 °C) maturation in Fe-poor carbonate reservoirs, anhydrite is thought to react with H_2S (from desulphurization of the oil) to produce elemental sulphur, an active dehydrogenating agent (Orr, 1974). Dehydrogenation (aromatization) of steranes and triterpanes by sulphur (Douglas and Mair, 1965) may well have occurred in the case of the Alice oil, although detailed GC–MS study of its aromatic fraction is required to verify this hypothesis.

CONCLUSIONS

Despite their obvious differences, these ancient oils have a number of common features. They tend to be isotopically light ($\delta^{13}C_{PBD} = -27$ to $-30‰$). Pr/ph values are low (generally $\leqslant 2$), and hopanes are more abundant than steranes, consistent with source organic matter of prokaryotic origin deposited under highly reducing conditions.

Acyclic sesterterpanes and squalane, probable biological markers of archaebacteria, were detected in only the nonmarine Cambrian oils from the Officer Basin. One of these oils is the first reported case of an oil in which the regular sterane 20R epimers can be shown to have been preferentially metabolised during biodegradation.

The C_{12}–C_{20} *n*-alkanes of the oils not affected by water-washing or biodegradation display a distinct odd/even predominance. Sterane distributions are far less uniform than those of the hopanes. They reflect both the diversity of the combined algal and cyanobacterial inputs to late Proterozoic and early Palaeozoic source rocks, and different source maturities at the time of primary migration. This maturity increases in the following order: Arrowie < North Appalachian < Etosha < Officer. High 2,6,10-TMTD/pr values in the Etosha and Amadeus Basin oils indicate extensive cracking in the reservoir. The unusual survival of C_{11}–C_{21} *n*-alkenes, possible artefacts of late-stage thermal alteration, in the Etosha oil is paralleled by the presence of C_2 and C_3 olefins in fluid inclusions within the same carbonate reservoir formation.

These oils with a proven or inferred carbonate source are characterized by a full complement of bacteriohopanes (C_{27} and C_{29}–C_{35}), among which C_{27} $T_m \gg T_s$ and $C_{35} \gg C_{34}$; and sterane distributions in which C_{28} or C_{29} are the major compounds, diasteranes are subordinate to nonrearranged steranes, and epimerization at the C-20 chiral centre in diacholestane is retarded (C_{27} rearr. 20S/20R $\simeq$ 1). Steranes and triterpanes are unlikely to survive in ancient oils if the reservoir contains (or is capped by) anhydrite because of the high probability of their conversion to aromatic compounds following the inorganic reduction of sulphate to elemental sulphur.

Acknowledgements

Oil samples for this study were kindly provided by the South Australian Department of Mines and Energy (SADME), Australian Bureau of Mineral Resources, Etosha Petroleum Company, Dr J. Armstrong (Santos Ltd.), and Dr M. B. Wood (Towner Petroleum Company). We are grateful to the Director General of Mines and Energy, South Australia, for permission to publish analytical data generated by the senior author while a SADME officer. We thank Drs A. S. Mackenzie and J. R. Maxwell (Bristol University) and Dr J. A. Momper (Tulsa) for helpful discussions during the writing of the paper. Thanks are also due to Mr H. W. Sears (Australian Mineral Development Laboratories) for technical assistance; the Publications Drafting Section, SADME, for preparation of some of the figures; Miss R. J. Barnett (Masspec Analytical) for her help with the poster version of the paper; and Conoco Inc. for access to their typing and drafting facilities. This paper is a contribution to IUGS–UNESCO International Geological Correlation Program Project 157: Early Organic Evolution and Mineral and Energy Resources.

REFERENCES

Anonymous (1982) Production tests due at Amadeus Basin strike. *Oil and Gas J.* **80** (2), 56.

Arefev, O. A., Zabrodina, M. N., Makushina, V. M. and Petrov, A. A. (1980) Relic tetra- and pentacyclic hydrocarbons in the old oils of the Siberian Platform. *Izv. Akad. Nauk SSSR, Ser. Geol.* **3**, 135–140 (in Russian).

Becker, L. E. and Patton, J. B. (1968) World occurrence of petroleum in pre-Silurian rocks. *Bull. Amer. Assoc. Petrol. Geologists.* **52**, 224–245.

Chaloner, W. G. (1967) Spores and land-plant evolution. *Rev. Palaeobotan. Palynol.* **1**, 83–93.

Connan, J. and Cassou, A. M. (1980) Properties of gases and petroleum liquids derived from terrestrial kerogen at various maturation levels. *Geochim. Cosmochim. Acta* **44**, 1–23.

Douglas, A. G. and Mair, B. J. (1965) Sulfur: role in genesis of petroleum. *Science* **147**, 499–501.

Eichmann, R. and Schidlowski, M. (1975) Isotopic fractionation between coexisting organic carbon–carbonate pairs in Precambrian sediments. *Geochim. Cosmochim. Acta* **39**, 585–595.

Haug, P. and Curry, D. J. (1974) Isoprenoids in a Costa Rican seep oil. *Geochim. Cosmochim. Acta* **38**, 601–610.

Hoering, T. C. (1976) Molecular fossils from the Precambrian Nonesuch Shale. *Carnegie Inst., Wash., Yearbook.* **75**, 806–813.

Hoering, T. C. (1977) Olefinic hydrocarbons from Bradford, Pennsylvania, crude oil. *Chem. Geol.* **20**, 1–8.

Hollerbach, A. and Welte, D. H. (1977) Uber Sterane und Triterpane in Erdölen und ihre phylogenetische Bedeutung. *Naturwissenschaften* **64**, 381–382.

Holzer, G., Oró, J. and Tornabene, T. G. (1979) Gas chromatographic–mass spectrometric analysis of neutral lipids from methanogenic and thermoacidophilic bacteria. *J. Chromatography* **186**, 795–809.

Huang, W. Y. and Meinschein, W. G. (1979) Sterols as ecological indicators. *Geochim. Cosmochim. Acta* **43**, 739–745.

Janssens, A. (1973) Stratigraphy of the Cambrian and Lower Ordovician rocks in Ohio. *Ohio Geol. Survey Bull.* **64**, 1–38.

Lijmbach, G. W. M. (1975) On the origin of petroleum. *Proc. 9th World Petroleum Congr.*, Tokyo **2**, 357–369.

McKirdy, D. M. (1977) Diagenesis of microbial organic matter: a geochemical classification and its use in evaluating the hydrocarbon-generating potential of Proterozoic and Lower Palaeozoic sediments, Amadeus Basin, central Australia. PhD Thesis, Australian National University.

McKirdy, D. M. (1981) Petroleum geochemistry and source-rock potential of the Arrowie, Pedirka, Cooper, and Eromanga Basins, central Australia. Report for Delhi Petroleum Pty. Ltd. (unpublished).

McKirdy, D. M. and Kantsler, A. J. (1980) Oil geochemistry and potential source rocks of the Officer Basin, South Australia. *Aust. Petrol. Explor. Assoc. J.* **20**(1), 68–86.

McKirdy, D. M. and Hahn, J. H. (1982) The composition of kerogen and hydrocarbons in Precambrian rocks. In *Mineral Deposits and the Evolution of the Biosphere*. Ed. by Holland, H. D. and Schidlowski, M. Dahlem Konferenzen, Springer-Verlag, Berlin. pp. 123–154.

McKirdy, D. M., McHugh, D. J. and Tardif, J. W. (1980) Comparative analysis of stromatolitic and other microbial kerogens by pyrolysis-hydrogenation–gas chromatography

(PH–GC). In *Biogeochemistry of Ancient and Modern Environments*. Ed. by Trudinger, P. A., Walter, M. R. and Ralph, B. J. Australian Academy of Science, Canberra and Sptinger-Verlag, Berlin. pp. 187–200.

McKirdy, D. M., Kantsler, A. J., Emmett, J. K. and Aldridge, A. K. (1982) Hydrocarbon genesis in Cambrian carbonates of the eastern Officer Basin, South Australia. In *Petroleum Geochemistry and Source Rock Potential of Carbonate Rocks*. Ed. by Palacas, J. G. Amer. Assoc. Petrol. Geologists, Mem. (in preparation).

Mackenzie, A. S. (1980) Applications of biological marker compounds to subsurface geological processes. PhD Thesis, University of Bristol.

Mackenzie, A. S., Patience, R. L., Maxwell, J. R., Vandenbroucke, M. and Durand, B. (1980) Molecular parameters of maturation in the Toarcian shales, Paris Basin, France — I. Changes in the configurations of acyclic isoprenoid alkanes, steranes, and triterpanes. *Geochim. Cosmochim. Acta* **44**, 1709–1721.

Maximov, S. P. and Muromtseva, V. A. (1975) Formation of oil pools in Cambrian sediments on the southern margin of the Baltic syneclise. *Geol. Nefti Gaza* **3**, 20–27 (English translation in *Petroleum Geology USSR* (1975) **13** (3), 119–121.

Meyerhoff, A. A. (1980) Geology and petroleum fields in Proterozoic and Lower Cambrian strata, Lena-Tunguska petroleum province, Eastern Siberia. In *Giant Oil and Gas Fields of the Decade 1968–1978*. Ed. by Halbouty, M. T. Amer. Assoc. Petrol. Geologists, Mem. **30**, pp. 225–252.

Orr, W. L. (1974) Changes in sulfur content and isotopic ratios of sulfur during petroleum maturation — study of Big Horn Basin Paleozoic oils. *Bull. Amer. Assoc. Petrol. Geologists* **50**, 2295–2318.

Palmer, A. R. (1980) Cambrian oil and gas: a world review. In *Facts and Principles of World Petroleum Occurrence*. Ed. by Miall, A. D. Can. Soc. Petrol. Geologists, Mem. 6, pp. 975–982.

Petrov, A. A., Pustil'nikova, S. D., Abriutina, N. N. and Kagramonova, G. R. (1976) Petroleum steranes and triterpanes. *Neftekhimiya* **16**, 411–427 (in Russian).

Petrov, A. A., Vorobyeva, N. S. and Zemskova, Z. K. (1977) The peculiarities of the composition and structure of the relict hydrocarbons of Proterozoic oils from the Siva deposit. *Eighth International Congress on Organic Geochemistry, Moscow, Abstracts* **2**, 19–20.

Powell, T. G. and McKirdy, D. M. (1973) Relationship between ratio of pristane to phytane, crude oil composition and geological environment in Australia. *Nature Phys. Sci.* **243** (124), 37–39.

Pym, J. G., Ray, J. E., Smith, G. W. and Whitehead, E. V. (1975) Petroleum triterpane fingerprinting of crude oils. *Anal. Chem.* **47**, 1617–1622.

Seifert, W. K. (1981) The impact of Treibs' discovery of porphyrins on present day biological marker organic geochemistry. *Proc. Treibs Internatl. Symp.*, Munich, July 1979 (in press).

Seifert, W. K. and Moldowan, J. M. (1978) Applications of steranes, terpanes, and monoaromatics to the maturation, migration and source of crude oils. *Geochim. Cosmochim. Acta* **42**, 77–95.

Seifert, W. K. and Moldowan, J. M. (1979) The effect of biodegradation on steranes and terpanes in crude oils. *Geochim. Cosmochim. Acta* **43**, 111–126.

Seifert, W. K. and Moldowan, J. M. (1980) The effect of thermal stress on source-rock quality as measured by hopane stereochemistry. In *Advances in Organic Geochemistry 1979*. Ed. by Douglas, A. G. and Maxwell, J. R. Pergamon, Oxford. pp. 229–237.

Seifert, W. K. and Moldowan, J. M. (1981) Paleoreconstruction by biological markers. *Geochim. Cosmochim. Acta* **45**, 783–794.

Seifert, W. K., Moldowan, J. M. and Jones, R. W. (1980) Application of biological marker chemistry to petroleum exploration. *Proc. 10th World Petroleum Congr.*, Bucharest **2**, 425–440.

Sieskind, O., Joly, G. and Albrecht, P. (1970) Simulation of the geochemical transformation of sterols: superacid effect of clay minerals. *Geochim. Cosmochim. Acta* **43**, 1675–1679.

Tissot, B. P. and Welte, D. H. (1978) *Petroleum Formation and Occurrence — a new approach to oil and gas exploration*. Springer-Verlag, Berlin.

Vassoyevich, N. B., Vysotskiy, I. V., Sokolov, B. A. and Tatarenko, Y. I. (1971) Oil–gas potential of Late Precambrian deposits. *International Geol. Rev.* **13**(3), 407–418.

Wopfner, H. (1970) Early Cambrian paleogeography, Frome Embayment, South Australia. *Bull. Amer. Assoc. Petrol. Geologists*. **54**, 2395–2409.

Ypma, P. J. M. (1979) Mineralogical and geological indications for the petroleum potential of the Etosha Basin, Namibia (SW Africa). *Proc. Kininklijke Nederlandse Akademie van Wetenschappen, Series B* **82**(1), 91–112.

Advances in Organic Geochemistry 1981, pp. 108–113
© *John Wiley & Sons Limited, 1983*

A Preliminary Organic Geochemical Study of the Fushan Depression, A Tertiary Basin of Eastern China

Wang Benshan, Fan Shanfa, Xu Fenfang, Jiang Shanchun and Fu Jiamo

Institute of Geochemistry, Academia Sinica, Guiyang, Guizhou Province, People's Republic of China

Preliminary organic geochemical studies of Tertiary sediments from the Fushan depression and Tongking Bay (E. China) indicate the main source rocks are Oligocene black shales of lacustrine origin. The oil generation threshold is estimated to occur at *ca.* 2500 m.

INTRODUCTION

The most important source rocks in Eastern China are Palaeogene dark mudstones. Because of the non-marine depositional environment and the active tectonics, especially faulting, the nature of the source rock and therefore the oil prospects change over a very small area, such as the Langgu and Raoyang depressions. Although these are very similar in nature and close together, a big oil field has been found in Raoyang, but there is almost no oil in Langgu.

Consequently, it is very important to identify the source rock, its kerogen type and the oil generation threshold precisely, basin by basin. Presented below is a preliminary study of the Fushan depression, Hainan Island, Kwangtung Province (Figs. 1a and b), a very typical basin in Eastern China. In the depression there are thick formations of Palaeogene non-marine sediments and Neogene marine sediments. The main source rocks are Oligocene black shales deposited in a medium deep water lacustrine environment. Samples were collected from the basin (Wells Fu-5, Fu-12, Fu-25) and the adjacent Tongking bay (Well W-2; see Fig. 1). Six potential source rock samples (two from each of the Fu wells) from the same stratigraphic interval, namely the upper part of the Liushagang Unit, buried at different depths were analysed for a detailed maturity study.

RESULTS AND DISCUSSION

After a study of the sedimentary environment, the organic petrography and infrared spectroscopy (IR) of extracts and kerogen, the Tertiary organic matter of the Fushan depression and adjacent area can be divided into the three types (Table 1) — Type I, II and III (Tissot and Welte, 1978).

Type II, a composite of amorphous organic matter and humic debris (Table 1) with small amounts of spore and pollen grains, is widely distributed in the Palaeogene non-marine dark grey shales, forming the main source rock of the area. The IR spectra of the Type II kerogen of the six potential source rock samples from the Fu wells are shown in Fig. 2.

Type I organic matter is mainly distributed in the immature Neogene marine grey mudstones, and Type III in the coal beds interlayered in the Palaeogene formations. Therefore, neither stratigraphic units are likely source rocks. The Upper Oligocene Unit (Ew, Fig. 1) was not examined in detail as the sediments contain very low amounts of organic carbon (see Fig. 3).

The maturity study was conducted on twenty-one samples from well W-2 and the six Fu samples. According to vitrinite reflectance data (R_0), organic carbon data, the amounts of extracts and ratios of hydrocarbon and other fractions in the extracts, the oil generation threshold (OGT) in well W-2 can be set at 2500 m (see Fig. 3). Above this depth, some low maturity oils have been previously found in the Upper Oligocene and Miocene sandstones. It is believed that these oils originated from the Oligocene black shales (Unit E1), on the basis of geological and geochemical data.

Analysis of the six samples collected from the main Oligocene source rock stratum (E1) in the three Fu wells, shows that they can be divided into three groups on the basis of R_0 and $20S/20S + 20R$ — C_{29} ααα sterane parameter (Mackenzie *et al.*, 1980; see Fig. 4). The three groups are (i) R_0 0.30–0.40%, $20S/20\underline{S} + 20\underline{R}\%$ 20–30, (ii) R_0 0.40–0.50%, $20S/20\underline{S} + 20\underline{R}\%$ 30–40, and (iii) R_0 >0.60%, $20S/20\underline{S} + 20\underline{R}\%$ 40–50. Figs. 5 and 6 give an overall impression of the distribution of aliphatic hydrocarbons of these samples. Fig. 7 contrasts R_0 and the

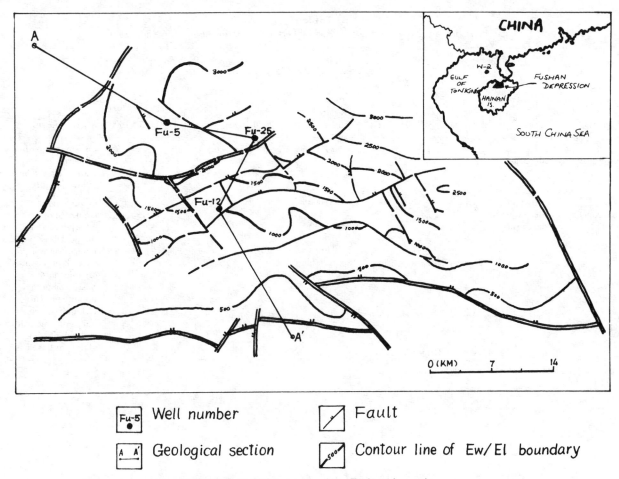

Fig. 1a. Geological map of the Fushan depression.

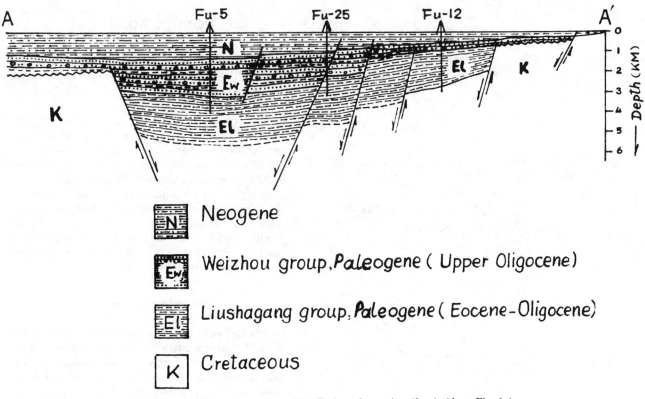

Fig. 1b. Stratigraphic section of the Fushan depression (for A–A′ see Fig. 1a).

Table 1
Characteristics of the organic matter types of Tertiary rocks in the Fushan depression

			Extractables		Kerogen IR data (cm^{-1})			
Type	Facies	Strata	SHC/AHC[a]	Aromatic IR data (cm^{-1})	2920/1600	2920/1715	$\dfrac{2920+2860}{1715+1600}$	Microscope studies
I (Sapropelic)	Marine and deep lake	N	>3.3	1460 ⪢ 1600	>1.5	>2.5	>1.5	Organic matter finely dispersed in rock matrix. Plant debris in low quantity
II (Sapropelic-humic)	Medium deep water lacustrine	E1	≤3.3	1460/1600 =1.5–5 Both 1040–1150 and 1350 are appreciable	1.5	2.5	1.5	Organic matter composed of amorphous and humic debris, the latter accounting for 10–60% of the total organic matter. Small amounts of liptinite present.
III (Humic)	Swamp	Inter-stratified thin coals in Upper E1	n.a.[b]	n.a.[b]	<0.35	<0.5	<0.4	Gelatinized–semigelatinized organic matter with telinites and abundant liptinites.

[a] Ratio of saturated hydrocarbons to aromatic hydrocarbons
[b] Not available.

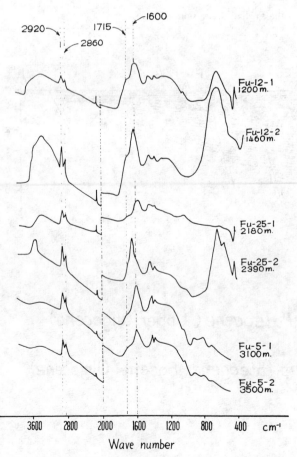

Fig. 2. IR spectra of Type II kerogen of the six Fu samples.

sterane parameter against depth for the six samples. As for well W-2 (Fig. 3), OGT is estimated to be at *c.* 2500 m depth.

CONCLUSIONS

1. Because of the terrestrial sedimentary environment and faulting activity, care must be taken to study the nature and maturity of source rocks in Tertiary basins of Eastern China.
2. According to microscopic and IR data for the kerogen, as well as GC of extracts, the organic matter of the Fushan depression can be divided into the three types, and the main source rocks are Type II Oligocene black shales of lacustrine origin.
3. A study of the Fushan depression and well W-2, Tongking Bay, gives a reasonable maturity model with OGT at *ca.* 2500 m.
4. Further work, particularly detailed molecular analyses of rock and oil samples, is necessary to confirm the preliminary results.

Acknowledgements

We are grateful to Professor G. Eglinton for arranging a visit to the Organic Geochemistry Unit, Bristol, as well as for helpful advice, Dr A. M. K. Wardroper for practical assistance and helpful criticism, Professor Zeng Dingqian for the arrangement of field work and collection of samples, Mr Zeng Xianzhang, etc. and Mrs

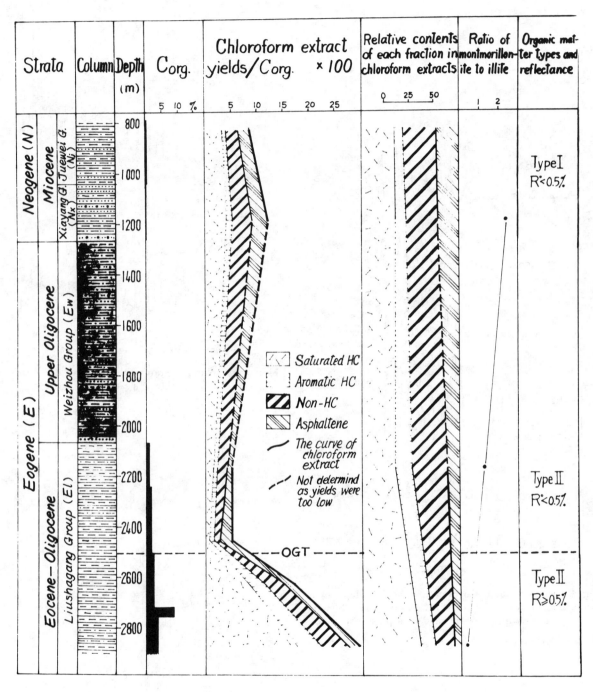

Fig. 3. Geochemical profile of well W-2.

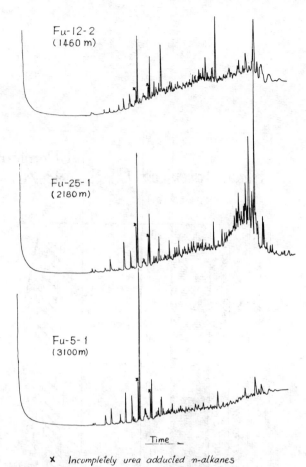

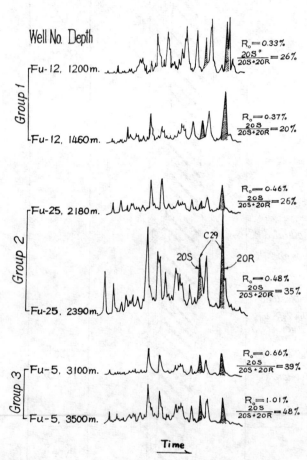

Fig. 4. *m/z* 217 Fragmentograms from the GC–MS analysis of the branched/cyclic alkanes of the six Fu samples. Sterane parameter measured by hand from peak area.

x   *Incompletely urea adducted n-alkanes*

Fig. 5. Gas chromatograms of the branched/cyclic alkanes of three Fu samples.

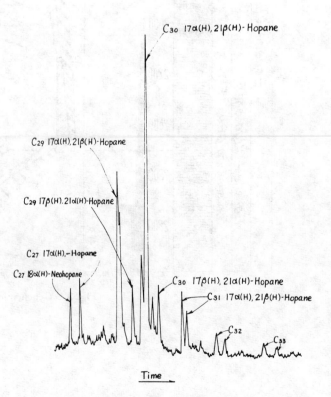

Fig. 6. *m/z* 191 Fragmentogram from the GC–MS analysis of Fu-25-2 (2390 m) branched/cyclic alkanes.

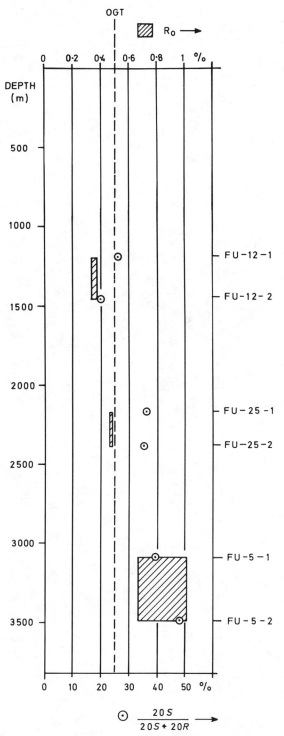

Fig. 7. Depth profile of R_0 and $\underline{20S}/20\underline{S}+20\underline{R}\alpha\alpha\alpha$ C_{29} sterane parameter for the six Fu samples.

A. P. Gowar and Ms V. Howell for assistance with GC–MS work, UNDP for financial assistance (CPR/A/037).

REFERENCES

Tissot, B. and Welte, D. H. Formation and occurrence of petroleum. Springer–Verlag, New York. (1978).

Mackenzie, A. S., Patience, R. L., Maxwell, J. R., Vandenbroucke, M. and Durand, B. (1980) Molecular parameters of maturation in the Toarcian shales, Paris Basin, France — I. Changes in the configurations of acyclic isoprenoid alkanes, steranes and triterpanes. *Geochim. Cosmochim. Acta* **44**, 1709–1721.

Migration of
Hydrocarbons

Advances in Organic Geochemistry 1981, pp. 117–128
© *John Wiley & Sons Limited, 1983*

Present Trends in Organic Geochemistry in Research on Migration of Hydrocarbons

B. Durand

The most important recent change in understanding the phenomenon of migration is probably the preference for expulsion mechanisms in which hydrocarbons constitute a separate phasis over those in which hydrocarbons are carried by water. In the new view, hydrocarbon saturation in the source-rock porous space is an essential parameter; it is primarily determined by the organic matter content, which is in turn determined by the sedimentation style of a sedimentary basin. Research in organic sedimentology is thus of major interest to the advance of our knowledge of migration. In this paper, two styles of sedimentary basins are compared: (1) a slowly subsiding basin in which marine organic matter occurs as discrete organic-rich layers, and (2) a quickly subsiding basin in which organic matter is found throughout the sedimentary column, but in low contents. The above considerations are largely theoretical and need to be supported by more observations. There exist tools at the present time, particularly for observing light hydrocarbons the behaviour of which is for the most part unknown, but good samples are still rare. The strong support of oil companies would be invaluable in increasing the number of suitable samples available to researchers. Contrary to widespread opinion, the generation of hydrocarbons, particularly of light hydrocarbons, is not sufficiently understood for the needs of migration studies, as it is seen in the present-day controversy concerning the 'early generation' of methane and light hydrocarbons. Here again, more observation is needed. Since light hydrocarbons are very mobile, however, simulation, usually conducted by pyrolysis, is advisable. Although the validity of simulation by pyrolysis is moot, the field is obviously developing. The handling of correlations between pooled hydrocarbons/source-rock extracts is poor as compared with analytical means, partly because of the length of time required for analysis. This situation will be improved by the development of GC–MS systems. However, the absence of precise information on the fate of biomarkers in migration, due to generally poor cooperation between chemists and geologists, is mainly responsible for this situation. Notable progress in the use of carbon and hydrogen isotopes is due to extensive activity in recent years.

INTRODUCTION

The description and comprehension of the hydrocarbon migration phenomena in sedimentary basins can evidently be achieved only through collaboration among all the disciplines in the field of geology and also need a great deal of experimental and theoretical work.

Therefore isolating the specific contribution of organic geochemistry may appear to be an artificial task. However, themes can be selected, in which organic geochemistry plays the central role and whose progress has immediate impact on the philosophy of oil exploration. They are: the choice of a mechanism of expulsion from the source-rocks, the observation of migration phenomena, and the correlations between pooled hydrocarbons and source rock hydrocarbons. I would like therefore to bring out the progress and present trends of thought in the three above-mentioned fields.

1. SELECTION OF A MECHANISM OF EXPULSION FROM THE SOURCE-ROCK REPERCUSSIONS IN THE FIELD OF OIL EXPLORATION

A great change in the approach to problems of hydrocarbon migration in sedimentary basins is seen in the gradual relinquishing of mechanisms for describing expulsion from source-rock with combined water and hydrocarbons in one phase.

This trend is due to progress in the field of knowledge on hydrocarbon formation in sedimentary basins; we now know that:

(1) Formation essentially takes place at depths at which most of the water has already been expelled from the sediments, and at which the quantities available to propel the hydrocarbons are therefore low;

(2) Differences in distribution of hydrocarbons between pools and source-rocks are difficult to explain in

cases where the hydrocarbons have been transported by water, since they are mostly reverse of solubilities in water.

These observations, combined with the fact that most hydrocarbons have very low solubility in water, even in subsurface conditions (Price, 1976; McAuliffe, 1980), and the difficulty of conceiving a mechanism of exsolution once the hydrocarbons arrive in the reservoirs, make water transportation very unlikely.

Faced with this situation, proponents of this sort of mechanism have made several suggestions:

(1) Creation of water in the hydrocarbon-formation zone by transforming smectites into illites (Powers, 1967; Burst, 1969; Perry and Hower, 1972), so as to increase the quantities of water available;

(2) Formation of micella (Baker, 1962) or emulsions (Cordell, 1973);

(3) Expulsion at shallow depth of a protopetroleum constituted of functionalized molecules, which are thus soluble in water. These molecules defunctionalize afterwards in reservoirs to form petroleum (Dobryansky et al., 1961; Hodgson, 1980).

(4) Dissent with hydrocarbon-formation schemes, by proposing a formation either at shallow depths (Wilson, 1975) where there is still plenty of water, or at great depths, where the higher temperatures and pressures increase the level of solubility (Price, 1976).

The most widespread opinion at the present is that while these mechanisms may sometimes play a role, and it must not be forgotten that methane and light aromatics are fairly soluble in water, the great majority of cases can only be explained by mechanisms in which the hydrocarbons constitute a separate phase — liquid or gas.

The objection that is generally made to the validity of these mechanisms is that the interfacial tension between the water phase and the hydrocarbon phase creates capillary pressures in the source-rock, where the pores are very fine, which are generally deemed to be greater than the pressures developed by compaction. Several additional mechanisms have therefore been proposed.

The ones that evade the obstacle of interfacial tensions by creating a continuous organic phasis, for instance:

(a) The kerogen content is large enough for its transformation into oil and creates a continuous oil phasis (Meissner, 1978a and b),

(b) The kerogen constitutes a three-dimension organic network which is wettable with oil. It is utilized by the hydrocarbons to get out of the source-rock (McAuliffe, 1980),

(c) An organic film exists on the mineral surface (Yariv, 1976); this idea should be seen in conjunction with the preceding one.

The others result in an increase in pore pressure sufficient to exceed the capillary pressure or even microcrack the rock for instance:

(a) Thermal dilatation of the water (aquathermal effect, Barker, 1972),

(b) Increase in specific volume of the organic matter upon transformation of kerogens to hydrocarbons, particularly to gas (Snarskiy 1962, 1970; Sokolov et al., 1964; Vandenbroucke in Tissot and Pelet, 1971; Hedberg, 1974 and 1980; see also Ungerer et al., this congress),

(c) Partial transmission of the geostatic constraints from the solid to the liquid phase when the kerogen is transformed into hydrocarbon (Meissner, 1978). This transmission also might occur to kerogen, due to its plastic behaviour (Du Rouchet, 1978 and 1981), provoking microfracturation even when kerogen is still in a solid state, thus creating ways for further expulsion of hydrocarbons.

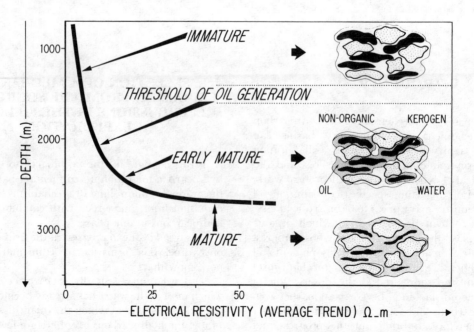

Fig. 1. Bakken formation, after Meissner (1978). *Left*: evolution of resistivity with depth; *Right*: interpretation by increase of pore saturation in oil.

It is possible, however, that the obstacle created by the water/hydrocarbon interfacial tension has been exaggerated. Inaccessible, the source-rock environment is very little understood, and descriptions of its pore space and distribution of organic matter are very abstract. In situ interfacial tension cannot be measured, and the values assumed for calculation are taken from measurements in laboratories on simple systems. Moreover, the source-rock is neither homogeneous nor immutable, and it is modified during compaction. Mineral diagenesis phenomena, some of which occasionally being due to products issued from thermal degradation of kerogen (Moore and Druckam, 1981) may alter the porosity.

To schematize the present trend of thought, let us examine the favourable example of the Bakken formation in the Williston Basin described by Meissner (1978) (see Fig. 1). This formation of lower Mississippian age, is an organic-rich (around 5% wt organic matter) marl. During burial water is expelled from the source-rock before hydrocarbons are formed. If the hydrocarbons are formed from kerogens:

(1) Hydrocarbon saturation of the pores is considerably increased and the hydrocarbons finally constitute in the source-rock a continuous phase which can be expelled without hindrance of water. This phenomenon is shown by the increase in resistivity to very high levels.

(2) The transformation of part of the solid phase (kerogen) to liquid phase (hydrocarbon) results in the partial transmission of the geostatic constraints of the solid phase to the liquid phase. There is thus an increase in pore pressure, which creates in the hydrocarbon phasis pressure gradients favourable to expulsion.

The important fact to retain for oil exploration seems to me to be that unlike the expulsion mechanisms using water transport, separate-phase mechanisms — whatever their proposed variables — depend primarily for their efficacy on the hydrocarbon saturation of the pores of the source-rock.

Hydrocarbon saturation depends initially on the content and distribution of organic matter in the source-rock, and thus on the features of sedimentation in the basin under exploration (the features also determine the gradients of the hydraulic head which define the size and direction of the flows).

By analogy with low permeability reservoirs the flow of hydrocarbons out of the source-rock may be tentatively described by Darcy's law, thanks to the notion of relative permeability.

It should be noted that according to the shape of the relative permeability curves observed for example in the production studies, any increase in hydrocarbon saturation is reflected in a much greater relative permeability to the hydrocarbons. Disregarding, for the moment, the presence of reservoirs capable of receiving the hydrocarbons, the probability of expulsion from the source-rock at a given level of maturity will thus be multiplied, going from a sector which is poor in organic matter to one which is rich, by a factor much greater than the simple ratio of organic matter contents.

Moreover, since the saturation must be above a minimum threshold for the expulsion of the

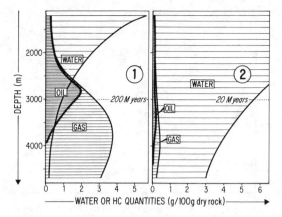

Fig. 2. Comparison of water and hydrocarbons contents in rocks of two sedimentary basins having different sedimentation styles. Basin 1: low sedimentation rate and discrete organic-rich layers. Basin 2: high sedimentation rate and numerous organic-poor layers.

hydrocarbons to be greater than negligible, these mechanisms will not be effective outside certain periods in the history of the source-rock and if its organic-content is too low.

If this line of reasoning is correct, much importance ought to be devoted to organic sedimentological research for the oil exploration industry, particularly research on the source-rock/reservoir systems.* This research is developing (see for example, Demaison and Moore, 1980; the Orgon cruises (CEPM–CNEXO), Tissot *et al.* (1979, 1980), Deroo and Herbin (1980)); but too little attention is given to the aspects I have just exposed. One instrument in the study of organic sedimentology could be a more extensive development of the use of geochemical logs of the Rock Eval type (Espitalié *et al.*, 1977).

Once expelled from the source-rock, hydrocarbons can mobilize by solubilization along their way hydrocarbons formed in other source-rocks which otherwise could not contribute to migration. This mechanism is cited particularly when the initial expulsion takes place in 'gas' phase.† The experimental demonstration of the possibility of such a mechanism was undertaken by Madame Zhuze's team (Zhuze and Bourova, 1975).

The importance of this effect should be highly variable according to the nature of hydrocarbons pathways towards the reservoir-rock. Good efficiency is obtained when under high pressure conditions, hydrocarbons are forced through relatively low permeabilities series containing mature organic matter. It must be noted that the mobilization capabilities of hydrocarbons which would not otherwise be expelled from the source-rocks is not *a priori* restricted to a gas phase, but may also occur in an oil phase.

For a more complete illustration of the preceding ideas, let us examine the schematic comparison of two

---

* I borrowed this expression from G. Demaison.

† Gas phase is the current expression. However 'supercritical fluid phase' would be preferable, since light hydrocarbons are in this case in a supercritical state.

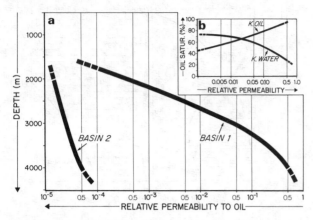

Fig. 3. (a) Evolution of relative permeability to hydrocarbons with depth in Basins 1 and 2 of Fig. 3(b). (b) Curves of relative permeabilities to water and to oil as a function of oil saturation, used to build Fig. 4(a) from water and oil saturation deduced from Fig. 3.

models of sedimentary basins (Fig. 2): the first is a basin of low sedimentation rate (3000 m in 200×10^6 years) with discrete episodes of heavy concentrations of marine organic matter in clay carbonate sediments. Where the porous levels are in sufficient communication with the surface, the slowness of sedimentation and the relative thinness of the fine-grained sedimentation levels make it fairly easy to expel most of the water before the hydrocarbons have begun to form. The second has a high sedimentation rate (3000 m in 20×10^6 years) filled with terrigenous deposits with fairly constant small quantities of organic matter of terrestrial origin throughout the sedimentary column. The sediments still contain a good deal of water when the hydrocarbons form.

In the first model, shortly after their formation the level of saturation of hydrocarbons rapidly rises in the pores rich in organic matter. At the same time, more of the geostatic constraints are transmitted to the liquid phase. The relative permeability of the hydrocarbons and pressure gradients in the hydrocarbons phasis thus rapidly increase, and partial expulsion at the oil stage is likely.

In the second, hydrocarbon saturation remains very low for a long time. Expulsion at the oil stage is unlikely. The oil which is formed is transformed into gas, with a notable increase in pore pressure. Migration, if it takes place, will be later, and will occur preferentially in the 'gas phase'.

Note that in such a basin, the water transport mechanisms can be relatively important, as soon as the hydrocarbons formation reach the gas phase. Organic matter is very dispersed in the sediment, and contact with the water is facilitated. There is a good deal of accessible water compared with the hydrocarbons present. The gaseous hydrocarbons, particularly methane (Bonham, 1978) and the light aromatics are fairly soluble in water under these temperature and pressure conditions.

Figure 3(a) shows the evolution of relative permeabilities to hydrocarbons in basins 1 and 2, estimated from the saturations deduced from curves in Fig. 2 and from the curves of relative permeabilities

versus oil saturation in Fig. 3(b). The values indicated are largely arbitrary, particularly because the curves in Fig. 3(b), extrapolated from a production study (Simlote and Withjack, 1980) have only a distant connection with the actual situations in the sedimentary basins. But it can probably by concluded that, as seen in Fig. 3(b):

1. The relative permeability of source-rocks to hydrocarbons during their expulsion (curves of Fig. 3 do not refer to further drainage and pool formation by secondary migration) is several orders of magnitude lower in basin 2 than in basin 1, although the ratio of concentrations of organic matter is only 1 to 10.

2. This relative permeability increases very rapidly as soon as the hydrocarbons form in basin 1, while it is practically nil to a considerable depth in basin 2.

Basin 1 might be taken as a model for epicontinental platform basins. However the 10% organic carbon content which was used for the making-up of Figs 2 and 3 is rare in such basins. Such a high figure was taken to make a strong contrast with basin 2.

Basin 2 applies for instance to quickly subsiding tertiary basins. Such basins are known for gas occurrence rather than oil occurrence. This feature is widely attributed to the terrestrial nature of organic matter in these basins, which is believed to result in high gas/oil ratios in formation of hydrocarbons during burial (Dow, 1978). Retention of oil and formation of gas by cracking of unexpelled oil seems to me to explain much better the abundance of gas in these basins than do the properties of the organic matter. Indeed, studies of terrestrial kerogens show they form much more oil than gas during burial (Durand *et al.*, in preparation). In this view, the nature of hydrocarbon accumulations (oil or gas) in such a basin should not be very dependent on the nature of organic matter (marine or terrestrial), but much more on organic matter distribution in the sediments. On a large scale, accumulations should be mainly gas ones. However, one should note that in such basins, abnormal pressure zones appear below a certain depth, owing to the high rate of subsidence and the relatively high proportion of clayey sediments in the sedimentary column. Migration of oil will be facilitated, all other things being equal, if hydrocarbon formation takes place in zones where there are high pressure gradients; for example, transition zones near abnormal pressure zones. Also note that percolation in the gas phase across sediments situated above will eventually dissolve part of the hydrocarbon contained therein giving birth to gas-condensate pools or even light oil pools.

Locally, there can be particularly well drained levels, owing to the numerous sand bodies under hydrostatic pressure. There also can be levels with fairly high organic matter-content and even coals (this is the case of many tertiary deltas). These conditions are similar to those of basin 1, and therefore facilitate the precocious expulsion of the hydrocarbons at the oil stage.

Therefore in this view, the nature of hydrocarbon accumulation (oil or gas) in such a basin should not be very dependent on the nature of organic matter (marine or terrestrial), but much more on the organic matter distribution in sediments, and local conditions. On a large-scale, accumulations should be mostly gas ones, owing to a generally poor organic matter content.

After experiments conducted by Bray and Foster (1980), attention was drawn to the role that carbon dioxide might play in the migration of hydrocarbons. These authors showed that slow percolation in an oil bearing rock under the pressure of a water charged with CO_2 permits a greater mobilization of oil than does percolation under the same conditions, but with water free of CO_2. Moreover, the distribution of mobilized hydrocarbons is near that of the oil. It has been concluded by some that the effect of the CO_2 is to increase the solubility of the hydrocarbons in water. In fact, under the experimental conditions, its role appears to be to increase the relative permeability to the oil in the milieu by lowering the interfacial water/oil tension, and the expulsion mechanism is linked up with the mechanisms of migration of the hydrocarbons in separate phase. A qualitatively analogous phenomenon (but quantitatively weaker) would occur by using gaseous hydrocarbons, instead of CO_2. Formation of CO_2 concurrently with that of the hydrocarbons thus appears to be able to facilitate the expulsion of the latter. But CO_2 is probably found only occasionally in great quantities in the source rock at the time when hydrocarbons are formed. Formation of CO_2 from organic matter in fact mostly precedes that of the hydrocarbons. Since it is very soluble in water, most of it is probably expelled with the water, unless it is partially dissolved in the organic matter because of the heavy subsurface pressures. Formation of carbonates is also a sink for CO_2. In some cases, however, the possibility of mobilization of hydrocarbons on the path of the CO_2 from greater depths is not to be excluded (Kvenvolden and Claypool, 1980), in the same way as light hydrocarbons might act (migration in a 'gas' phase).

Let us recall the renewed interests in diffusion mechanisms following the work of Leythaeuser et al. (1980). Without any doubt, diffusion works under subsurface conditions, and its effects reinforce those of all the above-described expulsion mechanisms. It plays a role in equalizing concentrations, and its efficacy, like that of the separate phase expulsion mechanisms, increases with hydrocarbon saturation in the source rock. At the present time, however, its role is usually considered to be minor in the constitution of oil pools owing to very low diffusion coefficients and limitation by low solubilities of hydrocarbons in water and even destructive, given its inherent dispersing effect. It might be more effective in the constitution of gas accumulation, given the higher diffusion coefficients and higher solubilities in water in this case.

2. OBSERVATION OF MIGRATION PHENOMENA

The preceding considerations are largely theoretical, and a realistic discussion of expulsion mechanisms can only be conducted on the basis of precise observation of geological samplings.

The past few years have seen the development of techniques which permit rapid observation of the quantities and distributions of hydrocarbons in sediments. At the forefront of the field are the

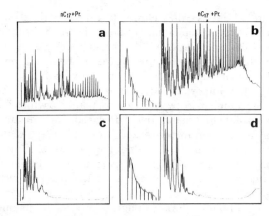

Fig. 4. Comparison of C_1–C_{35} hydrocarbons chromatograms extracted by thermovaporization at 300 °C of: (a) a coal from the Mahakam delta, (c) the same coal mixed at 2% wt with illite. Both chromatograms relate to the same initial weight of organic matter and are recorded with the same shunt. (b) and (d) comparison of hydrocarbons produced by the same samples during a pyrolysis at 470 °C under a nitrogen stream performed after the thermovaporization. The large peak ahead of the chromatograms corresponds to the recording of CH_4.

geochemical logging techniques, such as the Rock Eval (Espitalié et al., 1977) and similar devices (Claypool and Reed, 1976). Thanks to the Rock Eval it is now possible to study the concentrations of free hydrocarbons in rocks, summarily but rapidly — on the well-site for example — and to compare them with the quantities which theoretically should be present according to the characteristics of the kerogen.

Over the same period, techniques known as thermovaporization have been developed, by which the distribution of hydrocarbons in sediments is studied in small samples vaporized at temperature < 300 °C and followed by gas-phase chromatography (Bordenave et al., 1970; Jonathan and Lothe, 1975; Schaeffer et al., 1978; Whelan, 1979; Saint Paul et al., 1980).

These techniques are very useful, because observations of migration phenomena on the sedimentary basin scale can now theoretically be conducted by studying a great number of cheaply obtained samples. These techniques also make it possible to study light hydrocarbons, which are not recovered with the usual extraction techniques using solvent, and after which the solvent is evaporated.

Some reservations are required, however, as to the results obtained through these methods at their present level of technology, which apply for the same reasons to results obtained with the Rock Eval. In some cases, particularly where organic matter contents of samples are low and/or samples are very clayey, heaviest hydrocarbons contained in samples are retained in them and a low-temperature cracking may even occur, the effect of which is to produce in the recovered hydrocarbons distributions which are not that of hydrocarbons contained in samples pores. This is the effect of the mineral matrix described by Espitalié et al. (1980). An example — fortunately extreme — is shown in Fig. 4(a) and (c): in this example mineral matrix effect has been simulated by mixing a coal sample to a large excess of illite (2% weight coal in the mixture).

Figure 4(a) is the chromatogram obtained by thermovaporization of pure coal (method of Saint Paul *et al.*, 1980) and Fig. 4(c) is the chromatogram obtained from the coal–illite mixture. In case of Fig. 4(c), only hydrocarbons up to about C_{10} are recovered.

Another important advance is due to progress in fluorescent microscopy applications, thanks to which it is now possible to visualize the hydrocarbons and to study their distribution in pore space (Robert, 1979). At the same time, it has become possible to make a more realistic description of the pore space and distribution of organic matter in a sediment, although at a relatively large scale.

Let us also note the advantages of progress in making electric logs on fine-grained sediments. I have referred above to the use of resistivity logs made by Meissner (1978) to test his hypothesis on hydrocarbon saturation in a porous environment. The same observations were made for the Bazhenov formation in western Siberia (in Bois and Monicard, 1981). The logging study of the compaction phenomenon, the initial expulsion driving force (Chiarelli *et al.*, 1973; Magara, 1978), is also of great value.

An obstacle to observation, however, is the lack of adequate samples, particularly for observing expulsion, and it would be a good idea for the oil companies to exert an effort in this field. The chances of obtaining accumulated samples are greater than those of obtaining drained samples, because drilling is presumably undertaken in accumulation zones. Moreover, the phenomenon of accumulation can be more clearly observed than the phenomenon of drainage because the surface is presumably smaller, and the mobilized quantities per surface unit larger in accumulation zones than in drainage zones. Samples, incidentally, must be taken very carefully, and current drilling practice (turbodrilling; muds of complex composition, often kept secret) complicate or even hinder research in the field.

Because of all these difficulties, interpretative studies of migration phenomena through geochemical observation, are rarely undertaken, and are usually of limited extent when they are. Examples are Vandenbroucke (1972), Barker (1980), Huc and Hunt (1980), Leythaeuser *et al.* (1980), and during this session, Leythaeuser *et al.*, Schaeffer *et al.*, Schoell *et al.*, and Vandenbroucke *et al.*

The above-cited study by Meissner (1978) on the Williston basin, using the geochemical results of Dow (1974) and Williams (1974), those of Combaz and de Matharel (1978) and Durand and Oudin (1979) on the Mahakam delta, that of Clayton and Swetland (1980) on the Denver basin, that of Basu *et al.* (1980) on the Bombay basin are among the studies which have been able to take into account, on the basis of precise geochemical observations, the three-dimensional aspect of the phenomena and the necessity of integration into the geological framework. None of these studies founded on observation has yet been able to establish the nature of expulsion mechanisms definitively.

One fundamental obstacle to interpretation of observations is that migration phenomena can be clearly shown only if the genetic history of the hydrocarbons is well known. And our knowledge of genetic phenomena is

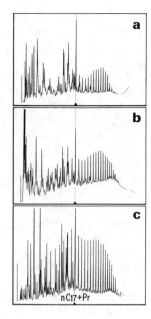
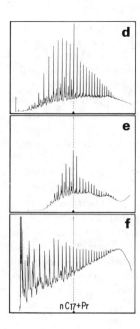

Fig. 5. Comparison of C_1–C_{35} hydrocarbons: (a) of an oil from the Mahakam delta, (b) produced by thermovaporization at 300 °C of a coal from the Mahakam delta at a vitrinite reflectance (in oil) of 0.8%, (c) produced by pyrolysis at 470 °C of a coal from the Mahakam delta at a vitrinite reflectance (in oil) of 0.4% (d), (e), (f) idem for an oil and Lower Toarcian shales from the Paris Basin. Recording of CH_4 produced in cases c and f is not presented here.

still not precise enough, on the quantitative as well as the qualitative level, particularly concerning the formation of light hydrocarbons. I might take as an example that still unresolved controversy on the possible formation processes of light hydrocarbons, notably methane, by thermal degradation of kerogen before the principal zone of oil formation (Powell, 1978: Powell *et al.*, 1978; Snowdon, 1978; Connan and Cassou, 1979; Kubler, 1980). Another example is the very widespread opinion referred to above, which I believe will have to be reexamined, according to which organic matter of terrestrial origin can form almost solely gas.

It will be difficult to establish a very precise scheme of hydrocarbon formation, particularly of light hydrocarbon formation, on the basis of observation alone, precisely because of the element of migration. That is why a correct simulation of the formation phenomenon in the laboratory is needed. This research theme is now highly developed, and pyrolysis in an open milieu under inert atmosphere between 300 and 700 °C is the technique most often used. Many researchers use this technique, in an open or a closed environment, to characterize kerogens (Larter, 1978; Larter *et al.*, 1978; Larter and Douglas, 1980; Philp and Russel, 1980; Van Graas *et al.*, 1980; Van de Meent *et al.*, 1980) but others aim to simulate petroleum formation (Vandenbroucke *et al.*, 1977; Harwood, 1977; Ishiwatari *et al.*, 1978; Peters, 1978; Seifert, 1978; Rohrback, 1979; Peters *et al.*, 1980, Monin *et al.*, 1980).

This technique gives encouraging results, as seen in Fig. 5, which compares for marine and terrestrial organic matters three chromatograms: one is that of an oil (Fig. 5(a) and 5(d)), the other the hydrocarbons obtained by thermovaporization at 300 °C from a sample situated in the principal oil-formation zone Fig. 5(b) and 5(e), and the latter, the hydrocarbons obtained by pyrolysis at 470 °C from an immature kerogen (Fig. 5(c) and 5(f)). Similar patterns are obtained from oil, thermovaporized hydrocarbons and pyrolytic hydrocarbons, however less obviously for marine than for terrestrial organic matter.

Yet the principle of such a simulation is often disputed (Snowdon, 1979). Furthermore, pyrolysis is very sensitive to operating conditions details. The mineral matrix effect is of course observed and may be very important, such as in case of Fig. 5(b) and 5(d) where are compared the hydrocarbons from a pyrolysis at 470 °C of a pure coal and a coal–illite mixture (2% weight of coal in the mixture), so that it is not always wise to pyrolyse organic matter in rock, although pyrolysing isolated organic matter would appear to go against geological logic. In spite of these constraints, it seems to me that the results already obtained encourage the hope of improving the quality of simulations in the near future to a point where the needs of migration studies are satisfied — without, of course, being able to obtain a total similitude of molecular structures in detail. Artificial series will then be close analogous to natural ones and clear tables of correspondence will be established.

In order to do that, experimental techniques will have to be modified. One promising direction seems to be that opened up by Lewan *et al.* (1979) through pyrolysis of pieces of rock in the presence of water at a temperature of about 350 °C. The distributions observed in the hydrocarbon produced are in fact very close to those observed in the oils. Furthermore the production is limited of *n*-olefins, which are also present in large quantities in the experiments conducted in open environments without water, and which are scarce in natural oils.

3. CORRELATION BETWEEN POOLS AND SOURCE-ROCKS

These correlations are founded on the comparative study of distributions of hydrocarbons, in particular those of biomakers. They are mainly used in basins studies for an identification of source-rock beds and most often do not refer explicitly to description and explanation of migration. However, the present wide use of such correlations, which means that some satisfaction is obtained, is an implicit argument in favour of migration in a phase separated from the water phase. Indeed, in water phase transportation, distribution of hydrocarbons in source-rocks and in pools would be so different, due to very different solubilities of hydrocarbons in water as a function of molecular weight and molecular structure, that correlations would be much too delicate to be very popular.

However, besides the classical search for source-rock levels, more work on correlation could do much more for solving migration problems and elucidation of mechanisms than is done now. Typically it should be possible to localize more precisely than is done now the

sections of source rocks from which the hydrocarbons come and to translate more accurately the differences of distribution in terms of expulsion and transportation mechanisms. The panoply of usable biomarkers is wide, and has recently been expanded to include petroporphyrins, which the development of HPLC has made possible to handle. The contrast between the analytical profusion and the relative paucity of application to understanding migration is all the more visible.

In fact, understanding migration through a careful comparison of distribution in source-rocks and pools comes against serious difficulties, some of which are listed below:

1. The oil represents the average composition of a source-rock over its drainage area, and sometimes is a mixture of different sources. In contrast, a specific sample of the source-rock used for correlation studies may represent a specific kerogen facies of limited extent. Also there may be several possible layers of source-rock in a sedimentary basin having close geochemical characteristics. Therefore a large number of sediment samples should be studied in great detail. The complexity and the time needed by the present analytical methods is difficult to reconcile with this requirement. The development of GC–MS coupling sizeably reduces this obstacle.

2. Available sediment samples are not generally those that the oil comes from, simply because drilling presumably takes place in accumulation zones and not in expulsion zones. At best, in many cases, they represent an immature stage of the effective source-rock.

3. The biomarkers used may be dissolved by the oil on its way, and thus correspond to a rock other than the source-rock.

4. Complex molecules such as biomarkers are easily destroyed by maturation. Therefore their concentration (and consequently their significance) in the hydrocarbons generated at depth has very much decreased when the zone of intense generation (the only significant one for constitution of commercial oil pools) is reached.

5. The behaviour of the biomarkers in migration and in the possible alteration of oils in the reservoir is little known.

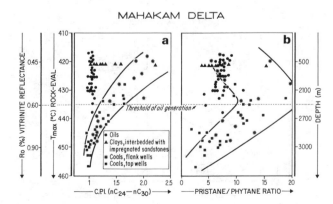

Fig. 6. (a) Evolution of CPI with depth and/or maturation for coals and oils from the Mahakam delta, (b) *idem* for Pristane : Phytane ratio.

As a whole, the effect of migration is previously to lower the concentration of biomarkers in the final oil by 'loss' on the way towards the reservoir-rock, which results in an effect similar to that of maturation and an increased difficulty in interpretation. Moreover, since migration and maturation have presumably similar effects it may be difficult to separate their respective influence on biomarkers distribution.

I might illustrate, with a simple example, certain ambiguities and difficulties relating to the use of markers for migration problems. This example is drawn from the study of the Mahakam delta in Indonesia where the migration phenomena were studied. The organic matter in the delta is of a type which is unique in the sedimentary series. It derives throughout from higher vegetal debris inherited from the continent, and appears either in the dispersed state in clays or in concentration in coal beds (Durand and Oudin, 1979).

Figure 6(a) represents the evolution of the CPI (measured on the n-alkanes in the C_{24}–C_{30} range on oils and $CHCl_3$ extracts of sediments) according to the depth or degree of evolution, which is ascertained by the reflective power of the vitrinite or the T_{max} of the Rock Eval (Espitalié et al., 1977) for: (a) coal samples little affected by migration from the wells situated on the flanks of the Handil and Nilam structures (Vandenbroucke et al., this session), (b) accumulated coal samples from wells situated at the top of the Handil structure, (c) clay samples interbedded between layers of impregnated sandstone, coming from a core taken at shallow depth in the proximity of a reservoir and (d) oil samples taken at different depths.

The CPI of oils is between 0.95 and 1.15. That of coals, whether or not they are accumulated, decreases with evolution and is parallel to that of oils at a degree of evolution corresponding to a T_{max} over 440 °C (or a R_0 of 0.7%). This leads one to believe that the oils were formed at a higher stage of maturity than the one corresponding to this value and that this T_{max} of 440 corresponds to the formation threshold of the oils which may have reached the pools. This result is in agreement with the results obtained through other methods.

The CPI of clays interbedded with impregnated sandstones is highly variable. In the above-described context, the fluctuation in values is interpreted by a greater or lesser impregnation of the samples with oils coming from greater depths.

The CPI of the oil does not appear in the present case to be affected by migration, and the impregnation of the 'accumulated' coals by n-alkanes in the C_{24}–C_{30} range seems minimal, at least at the top of the series (it is impossible to consider in the lower part of the series, because the CPI of the oils and the coals are very close). The values of the Pristane/Phytane ratio (Fig. 6(b)) are too dispersed to be interpretable. A part of this scattering might be due to variations in redox conditions according to variations in the deltaic facies, although the organic matter origin is very constant throughout the whole series. Indeed it is widely accepted that Pristane/Phytane ratio is very sensitive to such variations. Moreover, this ratio — a phenomenon which is now known, at least for organic matter derived from higher plants (Boudou, 1981) — reaches a maximum value in coals little affected by migration (and therefore useful as reference for genetic phenomena) at the end of the immature zone. A low value may thus correspond to two degrees of evolution.

The ratios Pristane nC_{17} and Phytane nC_{18} (Fig. 7(a) and (b)), although they show the disadvantage of reaching maximum values, are less dispersed and more clearly interpretable, once the conclusion is accepted that the oil comes from deep zones:

1. The 'accumulated' coals of the middle and top of the series are there distinguishable from the reference coals, indicating an addition by impregnation by nC_{17}, nC_{18}, Pristane and Phytane from oils coming from the lower depths which add to those generated in situ.

2. The values measured in oils are homogeneous, and correspond to values measured in the deepest coals. An increase in values is observed in the shallowest oils, which suggests that they have dissolved some of the pristane contained in the adjacent rocks during their migration. An interaction, slight but visible, thus takes place with the rocks met on the migration path, which was not the case in the heavy n-alkanes (the behaviour of the oil thus varies according to the fraction under consideration).

These interpretations of markers which are probably the most universally utilized in the geochemical study of sedimentary basins, are here relatively easy, presumably because: (a) it was demonstrated beforehand that the organic matter is of a unique type, (b) the evolution of the markers concentrations with maturation could be defined independently of migration phenomena and (c) the migration phenomena and the geological context were studied elsewhere.

It is evident that the use of these markers in this still simple case, would have been much more delicate if used in interpreting migration phenomena a priori. In more complex cases, for example basins in which organic matter is of several types or of mixed types, difficulties would be even greater, and the instruments for surmounting them even less developed. Here a considerable effort will be required, in a close collaboration of geologists, sedimentologists and geochemists, of a kind which has rarely been carried out heretofore, in three directions:

MAHAKAM DELTA

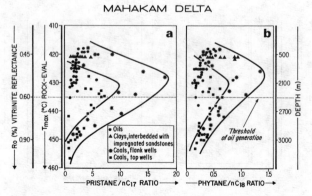

Fig. 7. (a) Evolution of Pristane : n-C17 ratio with depth and/or maturation for coals and oils from the Mahakam delta (b) idem for Pristane : n-C18 ratio.

1. To find easily handled biomarkers, truly specific to the various types of sedimentation. The hopanes exemplify the opposite; having long linked them to higher plants, we are now linking them with bacterial alteration of a ubiquitous character. In this field, the use of n-alkanes derived from cuticle waxes as markers of the continental environment at low stages of evolution, and the abundance of steranes as markers of the marine environment, seem to be the only ones that have withstood the test of time. The work of Baker *et al.* with petroporphyrins, raises some hope; they show (see Baker and Louda, 1981; Louda and Baker, 1981) the great sensitivity of these markers to deposit conditions.

2. To study the evolution of each class of biomarkers with maturation, in homogeneous sedimentary series or by thermal simulation (but thermal simulation might be unrealistic in this particular case since details of molecular structure must be reproduced), so as to be able to extrapolate the results obtained with immature sediments to mature sediments. The following works in the fields of steranes, triterpanes, acyclic isoprenoids and porphyrins are worthy of note: Ensminger (1977), Seifert (1978), Huc (1978), Hajibrahim (1978), Mackenzie (1980), Eglinton *et al.* (1980), Mackenzie *et al.* (1980a and b).

3. To study the fate of the biomarkers in the course of migration or alteration from geological models which have been well studied elsewhere. In this field, we should cite the work of Seifert and Moldowan (1980) on steranes. On the basis of geological examples, these authors indicate that the extent of migration is reflected in the proportions of certain optic isomers in this family of markers. We should also cite the recent work of Connan *et al.* (1980) on the oils of the Aquitaine basin, which confirms more ancient work according to which the distributions of tri-, tetra- and pentacyclic alkanes are not modified by biodegradation unless in extreme cases and might thus serve as correlations in cases of biodegradation.

It would hardly be feasible to follow the paths of gaseous hydrocarbons, particularly methane, with any methods other than isotopic techniques. It is risky, for example, to try to deduce the origin and path of gases from the liquid hydrocarbons which can be associated with them, because, given their vastly different physical properties, it is presumably impossible to be sure that they have come from the same place and at the same time as the gas.

But the isotopic relationships conceal within themselves little information and can thus hardly constitute more than an accessory to the study of migration problems. Also, the factors which determine them, except for the migration phenomena, are numerous, and their respective influence bitterly disputed. These factors are: (a) the nature of the organic matter, (b) the maturity of the organic matter, (c) the genetic process (biogenic gas/thermogenic gas), (d) interaction with the environment (water, CO_2, carbonates in particular).

A good deal of clarification work has been undertaken during the past few years, based on both observation and experimentation. Examples are Schoell (1979), Chung and Sackett (1980), Peters (1980), Redding *et al.* (1980), Fuex (1980), Rice and Claypool (1980). The result is that, in spite of opposing opinions (Neglia, 1979), migration phenomena probably influence the carbon and hydrogen isotopic composition very little. Interactions with the environment also appear to be limited. And the values of $\delta 13 C < -55\%$ are very likely to correspond to biochemical formation processes.

In spite of this simplification, correspondence between the values of isotopic relationships and the nature and stage of maturity of the organic matter, which determine the usefulness of these methods in migration problems by making it possible to localize the gas-formation zones, seem even less sure. As an example, the chart proposed by Stahl (in Schoell, 1979) comparing the degree of maturity of the terrestrial organic matter with the $\delta 13 C$ of the gases that issued from it, does not seem to prove a universal correspondence. One possible explanation, suggested by the work of Redding *et al.* (1980), is that the gas found in the deposits can have different $\delta 13 C$, depending on whether they are directly formed from kerogen (in which case the range of values would be large and the methane issued from overmature samples would be isotopically heavy) or by the succession of two stages: formation of oil then cracking of oil (in which case the range of values would be rather narrow around -50%). Reservoirs could be supplied with those two types of gas in variable proportions according to nature of organic matter and geological conditions. The values reported by Stahl are those of gases in northern Germany, issued from coal levels of complex geological history (Patijn, 1964). The gas may have been formed at an advanced stage of maturity, during a reburial stage, and thus would have come from a direct degradation of coal without the intermediary of oil formation previously eliminated by migration. This would explain the fact that it is isotopically heavy compared to methane, which also issues from terrestrial organic matter but probably through an oil-formation stage. The Mahakam delta is an example (Schoell *et al.*, this session).

Again, it is through the availability of very carefully prepared geological models that such problems may be resolved.

CONCLUSION

Organic chemistry is only one means for understanding hydrocarbon migration in sedimentary basins. But it is an essential instrument. Observation and prediction of the distribution of organic matter in sediments, as well as the quantities and distributions of hydrocarbons and the reconstitution of the history of their formation, make it possible to establish the initial and final conditions of the system, to make mass-balances and to verify the validity of the proposed mechanisms. Through the three themes I have discussed, some recent important progress in the field is indicated, but there are also some weaknesses. Among the advances, from the conceptual point of view, emergence of expulsion mechanisms in which the hydrocarbons constitute a phasis separated from water seems to me to be a progress as important as the explanation of petroleum formation by the kinetics of organic matter degradation, and from the technological point of view, miniaturization of analytical techniques and increase in analytical speed allow the researchers to study migration in its necessary three dimensions and to realize small and easy to handle experimental systems. Progress in fluorescence microscopy observations offers a possibility of knowing the source-rock milieu in a lesser abstract form.

Among the faults: exploitation for migration studies of those new possibilities is still weak. I also note that the knowledge of hydrocarbon formation, which has advanced little in the past five years, is insufficient for the problems posed. There is also still no clear set of instructions for the use of biomarkers in problems of correlation, taking into account the reality of migration. I believe these faults to be because there is insufficient collaboration among geologists, sedimentologists and geochemists, because the oil companies have placed very few satisfactory geological models at the disposal of researchers, and because the teams are too small to treat problems in their proper prospective.

ACKNOWLEDGEMENTS

This paper greatly benefited of criticism by R. Pelet, T. Powell, P. Ungerer and Mrs M. Vandenbroucke.

I also thank my colleagues at IFP, CFP and SNEA (P), whose support is invaluable in the effort for understanding hydrocarbon migration. I feel particularly indebted to Miss Bessereau and A. Chiarelli and J. L. Oudin.

REFERENCES

Baker, E. G. (1962) Distribution of hydrocarbons in solution. Bull. Am. Assoc. Pet. Geol. **46**, 76–84.

Baker, E. W. and Louda, J. W. (1981). Thermal aspects of chlorophyll geochemistry. This volume.

Barker, C. (1972) Aquathermal pressuring: role of temperature on the development of abnormal pressure zones. Bull. Am. Assoc. Pet. Geol. **56**, 2068–2071.

Barker, C. (1980) Distribution of organic matter in a shale clast. Geochim. Cosmochim. Acta **44**, 1483–1492.

Basu, D. N., Banerjee, A. and Tamhane, D. M. (1980) Source Areas and Migration Trends of Oil and Gas in Bombay offshore basin, India. Bull Am. Assoc. Pet. Geol. **64**, 209–220.

Bois, C. and Monicard, R. (1981) Pétrole: peut-on encore découvrir des gisements géants? La Recherche 124, Juillet-Août, pp. 854–865.

Bonham, L. C. (1978) Solubility of methane in water at elevated temperatures and pressures. Bull. Am. Assoc. Pet. Geol. **62**, 2478–2481.

Bordenave, M., Combaz, A. and Giraud, A. (1970) Influence de l'origine des matières organiques et de leur degré d'évolution sur les produits de pyrolyse du kérogène. In Advances in Organic Geochemistry 1966, ed. by Hobson, G. D. and Speers, Pergamon Press, Oxford, pp. 389–405.

Boudou, J. P. (1981) Diagenèse organique de sédiments deltaiques, delta de la Mahakam, Indonésie, thesis, University of Orléans.

Bray, E. E. and Foster, W. R. (1980) A process for primary migration of petroleum. Bull. Am. Assoc. Pet. Geol. **64**, 107–114.

Burst (1969) Diagenesis of Gulf Coast clay sediments and its possible relation to petroleum migration. Bull. Am. Assoc. Pet. Geol. **53**, 73–93.

CEPM–CNEXO (Comité d'Etudes Géochimiques Marines) Géochimie organique des sédiments marins profonds: Orgon I. (1977) Mer de Norvège, ed. by Combaz, A. and Pelet, R.; Orgon II (1979) Atlantique, NE Brésil, ed. by Combaz, A. and Pelet, R.; Orgon III (1979) Mauritanie, Sénégal, îles du Cap Vert, ed. by Arnould, M. and Pelet, R.; Orgon IV (1981) Golfe d'Aden, Mer d'Oman, ed. by Arnould, M. and Pelet, R., Editions du CNRS, Paris.

Chiarelli, A., Serra, O., Gras, C., Masse, P. and Tison, J. (1973) Etude automatique de la sous-compaction des argiles par diagraphies différées. Méthodologie et Applications. Rev. Inst. Fr. Pét. **28**, 19–36.

Chung, H. M. and Sackett, W. M. (1979) Carbon isotope effects during pyrolysis of carbonaceous materials. In Advances in Organic Geochemistry 1979, ed. by Douglas, A. G. and Maxwell, J. R., Pergamon Press, Oxford, pp. 705–710.

Claypool, G. E. and Reed, P. R. (1976) Thermal analysis technique for source-rock evaluation: quantitative estimate of organic richness and effects of lithologic variation. Bull. Am. Assoc. Pet. Geol. **60**, 608–626.

Clayton, J. L. and Swetland, P. J. (1980) Petroleum generation and migration in Denver basin. Bull. Am. Assoc. Pet. Geol. **64**, 1613–1633.

Combaz, A. and de Matharel, M. (1978) Organic sedimentation and genesis of petroleum in Mahakam delta, Borneo. Bull. Am. Assoc. Pet. Geol. **62**, 1684.

Connan, J. and Cassou, A. M. (1979) Properties of gases and petroleum liquids derived from terrestrial kerogens at various maturation levels. Geochim. Cosmochim. Acta **44**, 1–23.

Connan, J., Restle, A. and Albrecht, P. (1980) Biodegradation of crude oil in the Aquitaine basin. In Advances in Organic Geochemistry 1979, ed. by Douglas, A. G. and Maxwell, J. R., Pergamon Press, Oxford, pp. 1–18.

Cordell, R. J. (1973) Colloidal soap as proposed primary migration medium for hydrocarbons. Bull. Am. Assoc. Pet. Geol. **57**, 1618–1643.

Demaison, G. J. and Moore, G. T. (1980) Anoxic environments and oil source bed genesis. Bull. Am. Assoc. Pet. Geol. **64**, 1179–1209.

Deroo, G. and Herbin, J. P. (1980) Bilan des culminations de matière organique pétroligène dans le Crétacé de forages DSDP en Atlantique Nord. Rev. Inst. Fr. Pet. **35**, 327–333.

Dobryansky, A. F., Andreyev, P. F. and Bogomolov, A. I. (1961) Certain relations in the composition of crude oils. Int. Geol. Rev. **3**, 49–59.

Dow, W. G. (1974) Application of oil-correlation and source rock data to exploration in the Williston Basin. Bull. Am. Assoc. Pet. Geol. **58**, 1253–1262.

Dow, W. G. (1978) Petroleum source beds on continental slopes and rises. Bull. Am. Assoc. Pet. Geol. **62**, 1584–1606.

Du Rouchet, J. (1978) Elements d'une théorie géomécanique de la migration de l'huile en phase constituée. Bull. Cent. Rech. Explor. Prod. Elf Aquitaine **2**, 337–373.

Du Rouchet, J. (1981) Stress Fields, a key to oil migration. Bull. Am. Assoc. Pet. Geol. **65**, 74–85.

Durand, B. and Oudin, J. L. (1979) Exemple de migration des hydrocarbures dans une série deltaique: le delta de la Mahakam, Kalimantan, Indonésie. Proceedings of 10th World Petroleum Congress, Bucharest, Sept. 1979, Vol. 1, pp. 3–11.

Eglinton, G., Hajibrahim, S. K., Maxwell, J. R. and Quirke, J. M. E. (1980) Petroporphyrins: structural elucidation and the application of HPLC fingerprinting to geochemical problems. In *Advances in Organic Geochemistry 1979*, ed. by Douglas, A. G. and Maxwell, J. R., Pergamon Press, Oxford, pp. 193–203.

Ensminger, A. (1977) Evolution de composés polycycliques sédimentaires. Thesis, University of Strasbourg.

Espitalié, J., Laporte, J. L., Madec, M., Marquis, F., Leplat, P., Paulet, J. and Boutefeu, A. (1977) Méthode rapide de caractérisation des roches-mères, de leur potentiel pétrolier et de leur degré d'évolution. *Rev. Inst. Fr. Pét.* **32**, 23–42.

Espitalié, J., Madec, M. and Tissot, B. (1980) Role of Mineral Matrix in Kerogen Pyrolysis: Influence on Petroleum generation and migration. *Bull. Am. Assoc. Pet. Geol.* **64**, 59–66.

Fuex, A. N. (1980) Experimental evidence against an appreciable isotopic fractionation of methane during migration. In *Advances in Organic Geochemistry 1979*, ed. by Douglas, A. G. and Maxwell, J. R., Pergamon Press, Oxford, pp. 725–732.

Hajibrahim, S. K. (1978) Applications of petroporphyrins to the maturation, migration and origin of crude oils. Ph.D. Thesis, University of Bristol.

Harwood (1977) Oil and gas generation by laboratory pyrolysis of kerogen. *Bull. Am. Assoc. Pet. Geol.* **61**, 2082–2102.

Hedberg, H. D. (1974) Relation of methane generation to undercompacted shales, shale diapirs and mud volcanoes. *Bull. Am. Assoc. Pet. Geol.* **58**, 661–673.

Hedberg, H. D. (1980) Methane generation and petroleum migration. In Problems of Petroleum Migration, AAPG Studies in Geology, No. 10, ed. by Roberts, W. H. III and Cordell, J. R., pp. 179–207.

Hodgson, G. W. (1980) Origin of petroleum: in transit conversion of organic compounds in water. In *Problems of Petroleum Migration*, AAPG Studies in Geology, ed. by Roberts, W. H. III and Cordell, J. R., No. 10, pp. 89–107.

Huc, A. Y. (1978) Géochimie organique des schistes bitumineux du Toarcien du Bassin de Paris. Thesis, University of Strasbourg.

Huc, A. Y. and Hunt, J. M. (1980) Generation and migration of hydrocarbons in offshore South Texas gulf coast sediments. *Geochim. Cosmochim. Acta* **44**, 1981–1989.

Hunt, J. M., Huc, A. Y. and Whelan, J. K. (1980) Generation of light hydrocarbons in sedimentary rocks. *Nature (London)* **288**, 688–690.

Jonathan, D., L'Hote, G. and Du Rouchet, J. (1975) Analyse géochimique des hydrocarbures légers par thermovaporisation. *Rev. Inst. Fr. Pet.* **30**, 65–98.

Ishiwatari, R., Rohrback, B. G. and Kaplan, I. R. (1978) Hydrocarbon generation by thermal alteration of kerogen from different sediments. *Bull. Am. Assoc. Pet. Geol.* **62**, 687–692.

Kubler, B. (1980) Les premiers stades de la diagenèse organique et de la diagenèse minérale. *Bull. Ver. Schweiz. Pet. Geol. Ing.* **45**, 1–22; **46**, 1–22.

Kvenvolden, K. A. and Claypool, G. E. (1980) Origin of gasoline-range hydrocarbons and their migration by solution in carbon dioxide in Norton Basin, Alaska. *Bull. Am. Assoc. Petr. Geol.* **64**, 1078–1086.

Larter, S. R. (1978) A geochemical study of kerogen and related materials. Ph.D. Thesis, University of Newcastle-upon-Tyne.

Larter, S. R. and Douglas, A. G. (1980) Typing of kerogens by pyrolysis capillary G.C. In *Advances in Organic Geochemistry 1979*, ed. by Douglas, A. G. and Maxwell, J. R., Pergamon Press, Oxford, pp. 579–583.

Larter, S. R., Solli, H. and Douglas, A. G. (1978) Analysis of kerogens by pyrolysis-gas chromatography-mass spectrometry using selective ion detection. *J. Chromatogr.* **167**, 421–431.

Lewan, M. D., Winters, J. C. and McDonald, J. H. (1979). Generation of Oil Like Pyrolyzates from Organic Rich Shales. *Science* **203**, 2, March.

Leythaeuser, D., Schaeffer, R. G. and Yükler, A. (1980) Diffusion of light hydrocarbons through near surface rocks. *Nature (London)* **284**, 522–525.

Louda, J. W. and Baker, E. W. (1981) Geochemistry of tetrapyrrole, carotenoid and perylene pigments in sediments from the San Miguel Gap (Site 467) and Baja California borderland (Site 471), DSDP/IPOD Leg 63. Initial Reports of the deep sea drilling project, Vol. 63.

McAuliffe, C. D. (1980) Oil and gas migration: chemical and physical constraints. In *Problems of Petroleum Migration*, ed. by Roberts, W. H. III and Cordell, J. R., AAPG Studies in Geology, No. 10, pp. 89–107.

Mackenzie, A. S. (1980) Application of biological marker compounds to subsurface geological processes. Ph.D. Thesis, University of Bristol.

Mackenzie, A. S., Patience, R. L., Maxwell, J. R., Vandenbroucke, M. and Durand, B. (1980) Molecular parameters of maturation in the Toarcian Shales, Paris Basin, France I. Changes in the configurations of acyclic isoprenoid alkanes, steranes and triterpanes. *Geochim. Cosmochim. Acta* **44**, 1709–1721.

Mackenzie, A. S., Quirke, J. M. E. and Maxwell, J. R. (1980) Molecular parameters of maturation in the Toarcian Shales, Paris Basin, France. II. Evolution of metalloporphyrins. In *Advances in Organic Geochemistry 1979*, ed. by Douglas, A. G. and Maxwell, J. R., Pergamon Press, Oxford, pp. 239–248.

Magara, K. (1978) Compaction and Fluid Migration. Practical Petroleum Geology. Developments in Petroleum Science 9. Elsevier.

Meissner, F. F. (1978a) Compaction and Fluid Migration. Practical Petroleum Geology. Developments in Petroleum Science 9 Elsevier.

Meissner, F. F. (1978b) Petroleum Geology of the Bakken Formation, Williston Basin, North Dakota and Montana. *Proceedings of 1978 Williston Basin Symposium*, Sept. 24–27, 1978. Montana geological society, Billings, pp. 207–227.

Monin, J. C., Durand, B., Vandenbroucke, M. and Huc, A. Y. (1980) Experimental simulation of the natural transformation of kerogen. In *Advances in Organic Geochemistry, 1979*. ed. by Douglas, A. G. and Maxwell, J. R., Pergamon Press, Oxford, pp. 517–530.

Moore, C. H. and Druckman, Y. (1981) Burial Diagenesis and Porosity Evolution, Upper Jurassic Smackover, Arkansas and Louisiana. *Bull. Am. Assoc. Pet. Geol.* **65**, 597–628.

Neglia, S. (1979) Migration of fluids in sedimentary basins. *Bull. Am. Assoc. Petr. Geol.* **63**, 575–597.

Patijn, R. J. H. (1964) Die Entstehung von Erdgas infolge der Nachinkohlung in Nordesten der Niederlande. *Erdöl Kohle* **17**, 2–9.

Perry and Hower (1972) Late stage dehydration in deeply buried sediments. *Bull. Am. Assoc. Pet. Geol.* **56**, 2013–2021.

Peters, K. E. (1978) Effects on sapropelic and humic protokerogen during laboratory simulated geothermal maturation experiments. Ph.D. Thesis, UCLA.

Peters, K. E., Rohrback, B. G. and Kaplan, I. R. (1980) Laboratory simulated thermal maturation of Recent sediments In *Advances in Organic Geochemistry 1979*, ed by Douglas, A. G. and Maxwell, J. R., Pergamon Press, Oxford, pp. 547–555.

Philp, R. P. and Russel, N. J. (1980) Pyrolysis-gas chromatography mass spectrometry of batch autoclave products derived from coal macerals. In *Advances in Organic Geochemistry, 1979*, ed. by Douglas, A. G. and Maxwell, J. R., Pergamon Press, Oxford, pp. 653–661.

Powell, T. G. (1978) An assessment of the hydrocarbons

source-rocks potential of the Canadian arctic islands. *Geological Survey of Canada*, paper 78–12.

Powell, T. G., Foscolos, A. E., Gunther, P. R. and Snowdon, L. R. (1978) Diagenesis of organic matter and fine clay minerals; a comparative study. *Geochim. Cosmochim. Acta* **42**, 1181–1197.

Powers (1967) Fluid-release mechanisms in compacting marine mudrocks and their importance in oil exploration. *Bull. Am. Assoc. Pet. Geol.* **51**, 1240–1254.

Price, L. C. (1976) Aqueous solubility of petroleum as applied to its origin and primary migration. *Bull. Am. Assoc. Pet. Geol.* **60**, 213–224.

Redding, C. E., Schoell, M., Monin, J. C. and Durand, B. (1980) Hydrogen and carbon isotopic composition of coals and kerogens. In *Advances in Organic Geochemistry, 1979.* ed. by Douglas, A. G. and Maxwell, J. R. Pergamon Press, Oxford, pp. 711–723.

Rice, D. D. and Claypool, G. E. (1981) Generation, accumulation and resource potential of biogenic gas. *Bull. Am. Assoc. Pet. Geol.* **65**, 5–25.

Robert, P. (1979) Classification des matières organiques en fluorescence. Application aux roches-mères pétrolières. *Bull. Centr. Rech. Explor. Prod. Elf Aquitaine* **3**, 223–263.

Rohback, B. G. (1979) Analysis of low molecular weight products generated by thermal decomposition of organic matter in recent sedimentary environments. Ph.D. Thesis, UCLA.

Saint Paul, C., Monin, J. C. and Durand, B. (1980) Méthode de caractérisation rapide des hydrocarbures de C_1 à C_{35} contenus dans les roches sédimentaires et dans les huiles. *Rev. Inst. Fr. Pet.* **35**, 1065–1078.

Schaefer, R. G., Leythaeuser, D. and Weiner, B. (1978) Single-step capillary G.C. method for extraction and analysis of sub-ppb quantities of hydrocarbons (C_2–C_8) from rock and crude oil samples and its application in petroleum geochemistry. *J. Chromatogr.* **167**, 355–363.

Schoell, M. (1980) The hydrogen and carbon isotopic composition of methane from natural gases of various origins. *Geochim. Cosmochim. Acta* **44**, 649–662.

Seifert, W. K. and Moldowan, J. M. (1981) Paleoreconstruction by biological markers. *Geochim. Cosmochim. Acta* **45**, 783–794.

Seifert, W. K. (1978) Steranes and terpanes in kerogen pyrolysis for correlation of oils and source-rocks. *Geochim. Cosmochim. Acta* **42**, 473–484.

Simlote, V. N. and Withjack, E. M. (1981) Estimation of tertiary recovery by CO_2 injection, Springer A Sand, Northeast Purdy Unit. *J. Pet. Technol.* May, p. 810.

Snarski, I. (1962) Primary migration of oil. *Geol. Nefti Gaza* **6**, 700–703 (in Russian).

Snarski, I. (1970) Nature of primary migration of petroleum. *Geol. Nefti Gaza* **8**, 11–15 (in Russian).

Snowdon, L. R. (1978) Organic geochemistry of the upper Cretaceous/Tertiary delta complexes of the Beaufort Mackenzie Sedimentary Basin. Thesis, Rice University.

Snowdon, L. R. (1979) Errors in extrapolation of Experimental Kinetic Parameters to organic geochemical systems. *Bull. Am. Assoc. Pet. Geol.* **63**, 1128–1134.

Snowdon, L. R. (1980) Resinite, a potential petroleum source in the upper Cretaceous/Tertiary of the Beaufort Mackenzie Basin. In *Facts and Principles of World Petroleum Occurence.* Canadian Society of Petroleum Geologists, Calgary, Alberta.

Sokolov *et al.* (1964) Migration processes of gas and oil, their intensity and directionality. *Proceedings of the 6th World Petroleum Congress.* Frankfort 1963, Section 1, pp. 493–505.

Tissot, B. and Pelet, R. (1971) Nouvelles données sur les mécanismes de genèse et de migration. Simulation mathématique et application à la prospection. *Proceedings of the 8th World Petroleum Congress*, Moscow 1971, Vol. 2, pp. 35–46.

Tissot, B., Deroo, G. and Herbin, J. P. (1979) Organic matter in cretaceous sediments of the North Atlantic: contribution to sedimentology and paleogeography. In *Deep Drilling Results in the Atlantic Ocean: Continental Margins and Paleoenvironment*, ed. by Talwain, M., Hay, W. and Ryan, W. B. F. Maurice Ewing Series, 3, Am. Geoph. Union, pp. 362–374.

Tissot, B., Demaison, G., Masson, P., Delteil, J. B. and Combaz, A. (1980) Paleoenvironment and Petroleum Potential of Middle Cretaceous Black Shales in Atlantic Basins. *Bull. Am. Assoc. Petr. Geol.* **64**, 2051–2065.

Vandenbroucke, M. (1972) Etude de la migration primaire: variation de composition des extraits de roche à un passage roche mère/réservoir. In *Advances in Organic Geochemistry 1971*, ed. by Von Gaertner and Wehner, H., Pergamon Press, Oxford–Braunschweig, pp. 547–565.

Vandenbroucke, M., Durand, B. and Hood, A. (1977) Thermal evolution experiments on a kerogen from the Green River Shales formation (Uinta Basin, USA), 8th Int. Meeting on Organic Geochemistry, Moscow.

Van de Meent, D., Brown, S. C., Philp, R. P. and Simoneit, B. R. T. (1980) Pyrolysis-high resolution gas chromatography and pyrolysis–gas chromatography-mass spectrometry of kerogens and kerogen precursors. *Geochim. Cosmochim. Acta* **44**, 999–1014.

Van Graas, G., De Leeuw, J. C. and Schenck, P. A. (1980) Analysis of coals of different rank by Curie pyrolysis/mass spectrometry and Curie point pyrolysis/gas chromatography/mass spectrometry. In *Advances in Organic Geochemistry 1979*, ed. by Douglas, A. G. and Maxwell, J. R., Pergamon Press, Oxford, pp. 485–494.

Whelan, J. K. (1979) C_1 to C_7 hydrocarbons from IPOD Holes 397 and 397 A. *Initial Report DSDP 47*, 531–539.

Williams, J. A. (1974) Characterization of oil types in the Williston Basin. *Bull. Am. Assoc. Pet. Geol.* **58**, 1242–1252.

Wilson, H. H. (1975) Time of Hydrocarbon expulsion, paradox for geologists and geochemists. *Bull. Am. Assoc. Pet. Geol.* **59**, 69–94.

Yariv, S. (1976) Organophilic pores as proposed primary migration media for hydrocarbons in argillaceous rocks. *Clay Sci.* **5**, 19–29.

Zhuse, T. P. and Bourova, E. G. (1977) Influence des différents processus de la migration primaire des hydrocarbures sur la composition des pétroles dans les gisements. In *Advances in Organic Geochemistry 1975*, ed. by Goni, J. and Campos, E., ENADIMSA, Madrid, pp. 493–499.

Advances in Organic Geochemistry 1981, pp. 129–135
© John Wiley & Sons Limited, 1983

Tentative Calculation of the Overall Volume Expansion of Organic Matter during Hydrocarbon Genesis from Geochemistry Data. Implications for Primary Migration

P. Ungerer, E. Behar and D. Discamps

Institut Francais du Pétrole, 92502 Rueill-Malmaison ced France

This study tries to predict organic matter (OM) volume expansion from theoretical calculations. For this purpose, experimental data are derived from pyrolysis of kerogen. They lead to an approximate composition of hydrocarbons (HC). The other products generated (H_2O, CO_2, H_2S ...) are also estimated. A thermodynamic model is then used to determine the equilibrium state of the system (oil and/or gas phase), their composition and their volume. The results show that the expansion depends on the evolution level (low expansion in the oil zone, opposite to high expansion in the dry gas zone), on the type of OM (greater for type III than for type II in the oil zone, greater for type II in the dry gas zone) and on the preservation of mobile compounds (selective escape of CO_2, H_2S, ... makes expansion negligible or non-existent in the oil zone). Additionally, all the HC mixtures are found to be monophasic at depth. It appears that the expulsion of oil is better explained by the high fluid content of kerogen than by the overall volume expansion.

INTRODUCTION

A source rock generally has a very low permeability and numerous mechanisms have been proposed to explain the expulsion of oil or gas towards the reservoir rocks: migration as a separate phase, in water solution, in gas solution or by diffusion are the main ones. The general opinion is now that the major mechanism leading to HC pool formation is the migration as a separate phase. Two processes may add their expulsion effects. The first one is the compaction, that is to say the porosity reduction caused by the overburden and tectonic stress supported by the source rock. The second one, proposed by Snarskii (1970), cited by Tissot and Pelet (1971) and by Momper (1978), is the volume expansion of the OM. The tendency to expansion, hindered by the rock matrix, would cause an increase of the pressure of HC fluids within the pores. Microcracks would open by hydraulic microfracturation and let the HC escape.

If we refer to literature, no experimental measurement of OM volume during HC generation has been achieved. Therefore, the only way to get information about it is to start from theoretical considerations, in spite of important potential uncertainties.

Our computation is made as follows:

(1) Estimation of a weight balance for the products generated from kerogen: heteroatomic compounds (NSO), HC, water and gases (CO_2, H_2S, N_2, ...).

(2) Calculation of the volume of each phase, either from density data (kerogen, NSO, water) or from a thermodynamic model (HC and gases).

These estimations have been performed in various cases, involving two types of organic matter and several evolution levels ranging from diagenesis to metagenesis.

1. Weight balance

Our final purpose is to study HC migration. Thus, we cannot rely on solvent extracts in reference source rocks to estimate the quantity of HC generated, since the amounts of extract are influenced by migration. As a consequence, pyrolysis data appear to be the only way to derive a weight balance. It has to be kept in mind that pyrolysis is not an exact simulation of the natural evolution of OM. Monin *et al.* (1979) point out that it well represents the hydrogen loss of kerogen, but not the oxygen loss as seen on van Krevelen's diagram.

Pyrolysis data. We used Rock-Eval data (peak S_2) and chromatography of pyrolysis products data on immature kerogens or coals. These two techniques consist of a pyrolysis of kerogen with a linear increase of temperature versus time. It is possible to derive an approximate correspondence between the temperature of the end of the pyrolysis and the evolution level (equivalent vitrinite reflectance R_0) as seen in Table 1.

The reference state is taken to be 1 g of organic carbon at $R_0 = 0.5\%$ (immature stage). Two types of OM have been studied, according to the classification of Tissot *et al.* (1974).

Type II Marine origin, mainly planktonic. Principal reference series: Lower Toarcian of Paris Basin.

Type III Terrestrial origin, mainly higher plants. Principal reference: Tertiary of Mahakam Delta, Indonesia.

Table 1

Correspondence between the temperature of the end of pyrolysis and the evolution level in the cases studied

Temperature of the end of pyrolysis	R_0 (%)	Stage in natural evolution
350°C	0.65	Beginning of intense oil generation.
450°C	0.9	Approximate maximum of oil genesis. The secondary cracking of oil into light HC is supposed to be still unimportant.
475°C	1.3	Wet gas zone. An important part of the firstly generated oil and NSO compounds has been cracked into gas.
550°C	2	Metagenesis zone: All HC and NSO compounds have been transformed into dry gas.

Table 2

Average cumulated quantities of HC and NSO compounds formed during pyrolysis

Temperature at the end of pyrolysis		HC and NSO mg/g initial org. C	HC mg/g initial org. C
Type II	450°C	520	300
	475°C	560	320
	550°C	600	340
Type III	450°C	180	140
	550°C	240	190

The quantities of HC generated are given by chromatography of pyrolysis products, while the amount of HC and NSO compounds is given by the Rock-Eval peak S_2 (Table 2). As the Rock-Eval results concern only the last stage of evolution (pyrolysis ends at $T_f = 550°C$), we have supposed that the proportion NSO/HC was the same for $T_f = 450$ °C and $T_f = 475°$. This leads to the results of Table 2.

Secondary cracking. The HC and NSO compounds are not subject to secondary cracking in the pyrolysis experiments because the products are driven away by an inert gas flow as soon as they are formed. Therefore, assumptions have to be made for the stages $R_0 = 1.3\%$ and $R_0 = 2\%$ for which secondary cracking is known to be important in a natural evolution. We based our assumptions on material balance for carbon and hydrogen, in the same way as Orr (1975). For the wet gas stage $R_0 = 1.3\%$, we supposed that a major part (90%) of the NSO compounds and an important part (50%) of the HC formed undergo secondary cracking, yielding to a lighter distribution of HC (Fig. 4). For the dry gas stage, all the HC and NSO compounds are supposed to be cracked into methane. These assumptions may be summarized as follows:

Type II:
$R_0 = 1.3\%$
HC + NSO → HC + NSO + carbonaceous residue
320 mg 240 mg   308 mg 28 mg   234 mg

$$\left. \begin{array}{l} CH_{1.6} + \\ CH_{1.4}(N,S,O)_{0.1} \end{array} \right\} \rightarrow \left\{ \begin{array}{l} CH_{2.2} + CH_{1.4}(N,S,O)_{0.1} \\ + CH_{0.5}(N,S,O)_x \end{array} \right.$$

$R_0 = 2\%$
HC + NSO → HC + carbonaceous residue
340 mg   260 mg   200 mg   400 mg
$CH_{1.7} + CH_{1.4}(N,S,O)_{0.1} \rightarrow CH_4 + CH_{0.5}(N,S,O)_x$

Type III:
$R_0 = 2\%$
HC + NSO → HC + carbonaceous residue
190 mg   50 mg   195 mg   145 mg
$CH_{1.8} + CH_{1.4}(N,S,O)_{0.1} \rightarrow CH_4 + CH_{0.5}(N,S,O)_x$

Of course, these weight balance equations for HC are approximate because we do not really know the cracking reactions involved, especially the resulting composition of the carbonaceous residue (assumed H/C = 0.5) which has an influence on the outcome. In this work we assume an accuracy of 1 mg/g org. C in all cases only for the sake of consistency.

Other products of evolution: H_2O, CO_2, H_2S, N_2... The quantities of CO_2 and water generated have been estimated from mean paths of natural evolution on van Krevelen's diagram, assuming that all the oxygen is lost as H_2O and CO_2. Reference oxygen contents at $R_0 = 0.5\%$ have been taken at O/C = 0.10 (atomic) for type II and O/C = 0.18 for type III.

Type II kerogen is supposed to produce equal amounts of CO_2 and H_2O (in weight). Assuming the oxygen content of the remaining kerogen, it is thus possible to determine the amounts of CO_2 and H_2O produced at the various stages.

Formation of H_2S or N_2 has been quantitatively estimated in the same way, from mean S/C and N/C ratios of kerogen (Monin and Durand, 1980). We supposed that only H_2S and N_2 are formed and that the decrease of S/C, N/C, and O/C is simultaneous.

Figures 1 and 2 present the resulting balance. The amount of kerogen includes the carbonaceous residue formed by secondary cracking and this explains its weight increase for R_0 values higher than 0.9%.

2. Calculation of volumes

Pressure and temperature conditions. We have chosen standard conditions for each evolution level:

$R_0 = 0.65\%$	$P = 300$ bar	$T = 100$ °C
$R_0 = 0.9\%$	$P = 350$ bar	$T = 115$ °C
$R_0 = 1.3\%$	$P = 400$ bar	$T = 130$ °C
$R_0 = 2\%$	$P = 500$ bar	$T = 160$ °C

These conditions may of course be different from one source rock to another, depending on the kinetics of evolution, on the geothermal gradient and pressure situation. Here, they correspond to a gradient of 30°C/km and hydrostatic pressure and a subsidence of about 200 m per million years with average kinetics.

Kerogen volume. Van Krevelen (1962, pp. 314–315) presents density data for two coal macerals, vitrinite and exinite, as a function of carbon content (Fig. 3). It has been assumed that the chemical composition of these macerals was representative of type III and type II kerogen respectively, as well as their density, with carbon contents as shown in Table 3.

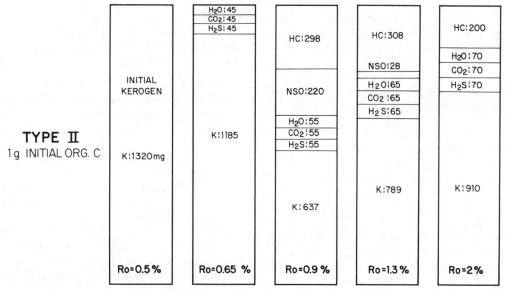

Fig. 1. Material balance for type II kerogen evolution products. The amount of kerogen (K) includes the carbonaceous residue formed for $R_0 = 1.3\%$ and $R_0 = 2\%$ (mg/g initial carbon).

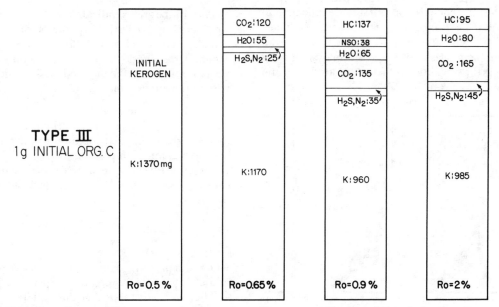

Fig. 2. Material balance for type III kerogen evolution products. The amount of kerogen (K) includes the carbonaceous residue formed for $R_0 = 2\%$ (mg/g initial carbon).

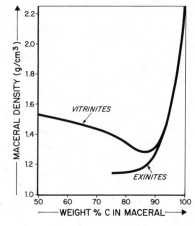

Fig. 3. Density of vitrinite and exinite as functions of carbon content (Redrawn after van Krevelen, 1961.)

Table 3
Assumed carbon content and subsequent density of kerogen used for computations

	R_0 (%)	% C in weight	Density
Type II	0.5	76	1.15
	0.65	85	1.15
	0.9	88	1.20
	1.3	90	1.25
	2	92	1.35
Type III	0.5	73	1.40
	0.65	83	1.30
	0.9	88	1.30
	2	92	1.35

Van Krevelen's densities have been measured under standard conditions of temperature and pressure. Using data on thermal dilation and compressibility of coal (van Krevelen, 1961, pp. 422–425 and p. 408), the density variation at depth ($T = 100$ °C, $P = 800$ bar) has been found to be less than 3% in all cases. Since other potential uncertainties are much larger we did not account for this variation.

NSO compounds volume. As the density of NSO compounds varies between 1.0 and 1.1 (Wuithier, 1965, pp. 605 and 610), we have selected an average value of 1.05 for the calculations.

Water volume. Water specific volume can be estimated from the diagram presented by Barker (1972). It is slightly less than 1.0 in the temperature and pressure conditions considered here.

HC and gases volume.
Composition of the HC generated.

Chromatography of pyrolysis products gives information about the composition of HC: identification of numerous specific compounds like benzene, toluene, xylene and different saturates as well as separation of all the others in major classes. Besides, the analysis of rocks extracts gives the proportions of saturates, aromatics and

naphthenes in the $C_{15}+$ fraction (Vandenbroucke *et al.*, 1976). However, these compositions are not valid if secondary cracking takes place, and they have been modified as follows:

(a) For $R_0 = 0.9\%$, the secondary cracking is supposed to be very minor and pyrolysis products are supposed to be representative of natural evolution (Figs 4 and 5);

(b) For $R_0 = 1.3\%$ (Type II), 90% of the NSO compounds and 50% of the HC produced by pyrolysis have been assumed to crack into light HC (Fig. 4). The composition of the gases C_1–C_4 formed by secondary cracking have been estimated after the experimental results of Harwood (1977). Although propane is the major constituent in weight, methane has the higher molar fraction. Liquid HC (C_5–C_{15}) are also supposed to be formed to a lesser extent, so that the resulting composition corresponds to a wet gas with an important oil fraction;

(c) For $R_0 = 2\%$ only methane is supposed to be formed.

The compositions indicated by Figs 4 and 5 must be considered as realistic hypotheses only. We would actually need much more information to give such an accurate distribution but these assumptions are necessary for the use of the thermodynamic model, since it is based on compositional data.

Thermodynamic model

Volumetric and phase equilibrium properties of the (hydrocarbon and gas) mixtures are determined by a thermodynamic compositional model. This model is based on a new equation of state proposed by Behar *et al.* called the Developed Redlich Kwong (RKD) equation of state.

$$P = \frac{RT}{v-b} - \frac{a}{v(v-b)}\left(1 - \gamma\frac{b}{v} + \delta\frac{b^2}{v^2}\right)$$

where P is pressure, T is temperature, v is molar volume and a, b, γ, δ are temperature dependent parameters.

The main advantages of this equation are its large application range (pressures up to 1000 bar, temperatures from 20 to 200 °C, molar weights from gases to heavy compounds) and the possibility of fitting parameters to any available experimental results. The use of this equation of state for mixtures of hydrocarbons and gases like CO_2, N_2, H_2S ... is possible through adequate averaging process (Behar *et al.*).

In all cases, the mixtures of HC and eventually CO_2, H_2S ... have been found in a monophasic state, and the volume of this phase has been computed.

For $R_0 = 0.9\%$ and $R_0 = 1.3\%$, the HC phase has oil-like densities (0.8 to 1.15) while for $R_0 = 2\%$ the densities are much lower (0.2 to 0.4). The precision of these figures cannot be assessed: as there are no experimental data concerning the mixtures involved, the model is used in a predictive way. However, it has been checked on different fluids that it leads to values that are at least in qualitative agreement with physical reality and which show the proper trends.

Additionally, bubble point and dew point curves have been determined for the mixture corresponding to

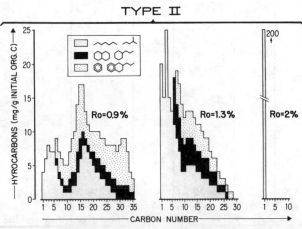

Fig. 4. Assumed compositions of HC generated by type II kerogen (weight amount of each family versus carbon number).

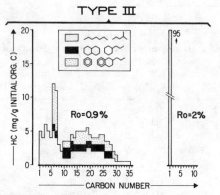

Fig. 5. Assumed compositions of HC generated by type III kerogen (weight amount of each family versus carbon number).

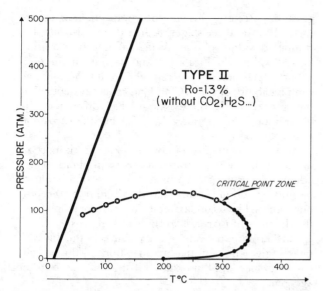

Fig. 6. Bubble point–dew point curves computed for the HC mixture corresponding to $R_0 = 1.3\%$ (type II kerogen). The inner part of the curve represents the conditions of two-phase state. The straight line represents hydrostatic pressure versus temperature, assuming a geothermal gradient of 30 °C/km with a surface temperature of 10 °C.

$R_0 = 1.3\%$ (Fig. 6). Although the results are mostly qualitative, they show that this mixture would be in a two-phase state only for pressures lower than 140 bar that is much less than in all source rocks. Yet this conclusion depends on the basic assumption that the wet gas has a more or less continuous composition as a result of genesis with secondary cracking. If this is not the case, the miscibility pressure (that is, the maximum pressure consistent with two-phase equilibrium) would be higher, in the range of 400–500 bar as found by Zhuze *et al.* (1975) for mixtures of dry gas and oil at 100°C.

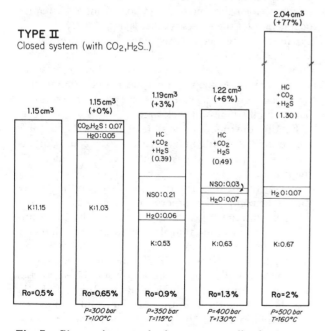

Fig. 7. Phase volumes and subsequent overall volume computed for type II kerogen evolution (closed system).

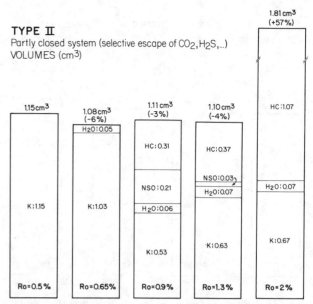

Fig. 8. Phase volumes and subsequent overall volume computed for type II kerogen evolution (partly closed system).

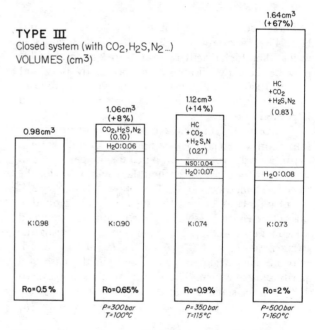

Fig. 9. Phase volume and subsequent overall volume computed for type III kerogen evolution (closed system).

3. Results

The results of the volume calculations are indicated in Figs 7, 8, 9 and 10. Two cases have been considered for each type of OM:

(1)   Closed system: no compound can escape from the system (Figs 7 and 9).

(2)   Partly closed system: (Figs 8 and 10) the most reactive gases (CO_2 and H_2S) can escape selectively from the system, through a migration mechanism other than oil (either diffusion or water solution migration).

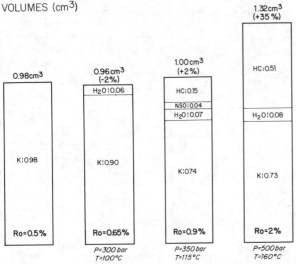

TYPE III
Partly closed system (selective escape of CO_2, H_2S, N_2,.)
VOLUMES (cm^3)

Fig. 10. Phase volume and subsequent overall volume computed for type III kerogen evolution (partly closed system).

geostatic pressure (insufficient compaction of source rock). For the three stages of the catagenesis zone, the computed values of the overall volumes are slightly lower than those of Figs 7, 8, 9 and 10 (the diminution is about 1%) which is merely the result of the low compressibility of the HC and gas phase at depth. For the stage $R_o = 2\%$ there is a marked difference (the diminution is in the range 15–20%) but the expansion remains important.

All these results are of course subject to important uncertainties deriving from all the assumptions made: fidelity of pyrolysis experiments for the simulation of natural evolution, nature and distribution of the products formed by secondary cracking, extrapolation from the densities of macerals to those of kerogens.

Furthermore, the sum of the volumes of the different phases gives only a maximum value of the overall volume, since the fluids may fill the microporosity of kerogen.

4. Implications for primary migration

The main conclusion of this work is that the volume expansion of OM plays probably a minor role in the expulsion of oil. Indeed, the expansion does not exceed 15% of initial volume in the catagenesis zone and even less if CO_2 and H_2S escape selectively as it seems reasonable to suppose. Particularly, a major part of the CO_2 is formed early in the evolution of OM (diagenesis) and the source rocks contain enough water at that stage for the migration in water solution by diffusion.

At the opposite, the expansion may have an important influence at the metagenesis stage, since the dry gas formation brings notable expansion. The experiments of Vandenbroucke (in Tissot and Pelet, 1971) clearly show the possible expulsion mechanism: the pressure builds up until high values are reached — it may exceed the geostatic pressure — and decreases suddenly at the moment when the microfracturation of the rock matrix occurs and let the gas escape. It is noteworthy that this expansion at the metagenesis stage takes place only if the HC are effectively transformed into dry gas, that is to say only in the cases of impossible expulsion at previous stages. This type of expulsion appears to be characteristic of poor source rocks: low oil potential, impermeable flanks, high stiffness of sock matrix.

Finally, the monophasic state of all the HC mixtures considered at depth makes useless to account for interfacial tensions oil/gas which would hinder the migration.

In our mind, the primary migration of oil is mainly due to the compaction process of source rocks. Since the kerogen contains a great proportion of fluids, it seems reasonable to assume that it shows a plastic behaviour under high pressures, in the same way as coal does (van Krevelen, 1961; Gretener, 1979) and that it undergoes deformation under the geostatic stresses. These stresses are thus transmitted to fluids, and Du Rouchet (1981) has shown that the resulting pressure build-up causes their expulsion, either by hydraulic microfracturation of the rock matrix, or by flowing in the pore system. The expulsion occurs in the directions of greatest per-

These are two extreme hypotheses about CO_2 and H_2S. The important water solubility of these gases as well as their high reactivity towards rock minerals (CO_2 may be fixed by silicates as mentioned by Bray and Foster (1980), and H_2S may combine with iron to form pyrite) makes necessary to account for the second hypothesis too.

The distinction of the two cases does not bring about important differences concerning the overall volume expansion: the volumes computed for the partly closed system are 5 to 15% lower than those computed for the closed system, except for the OM of type III at $R_o = 2\%$.

For type II as for type III, the expansion is found to take place continuously along the evolution in a closed system (Figs 6 and 8). It remains moderate during the catagenesis ($R_o = 0.65\%$, $R_o = 0.9\%$, $R_o = 1.3\%$), and it may be even negative (contraction) in the case of a partly closed system. The expansion does not exceed 15% at those stages and at the opposite it reaches very high values (35 to 80%) at the metagenesis stage ($R_o = 2\%$).

When compared to this trend, the influence of the OM type is limited. In the oil formation zone, we have found expansion values slightly greater for type III than for type II (closed system). This is probably the result of the assumed decrease of type III kerogen density which corresponds to the oxygen loss at the end of the diagenesis zone (cf. vitrinite density curve, Fig. 3). In the metagenesis zone, the great amount of methane formed by type II OM explains that the computed expansion is more important for this type than for type III.

These main conclusions would remain about the same if another reference state is chosen in the diagenesis: with $R_o = 0.65\%$ as reference for instance, very little change would occur for type II results and slightly lower expansion for type III in the case of a closed system.

The volume calculations have also been achieved for pressures twice as much as the values considered in Figs 7, 8, 9 and 10, which is supposed to represent the case of

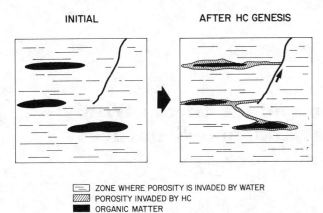

INITIAL   AFTER HC GENESIS

☰ ZONE WHERE POROSITY IS INVADED BY WATER
▨ POROSITY INVADED BY HC
■ ORGANIC MATTER

Fig. 11. Proposed scheme for primary migration: once formed in sufficient amount, HC are expelled from the kerogen by overburden and tectonic stresses in the directions of greatest permeability or easiest microfracturation. Their subsequent migration depends on the development of continuous HC filled channels.

meability or easiest microfracturation (Fig. 11). The subsequent migration depends on the development of a continuous network of oil-wet pores. If the HC phase is discontinuous, its migration is stopped by the water/oil interfacial tensions. This continuity is mostly probable in source rocks of high petroleum potential since the hydrocarbon saturation of the porous medium is important then.

Acknowledgements

We express our thanks to Mrs Vandenbroucke, Mr Durand and Mr Pelet for their useful observations and advice. Special thanks are also due to Mr M. Parratte and Mr M. Espitalié who achieved the experimental work which provided our base.

REFERENCES

Barker, C. (1972) Aquathermal pressuring. Role of temperature on the development of abnormal pressure zones. *AAPG Bull.* **56**, 2068–2071.

Behar, E., Simonet, R. and Peneloux, A. A new non-cubic Redlich Kwong based equation of state. Proposed for publishing to *Fluid Phase Equilibria*.

Behar, E., Simonet, R. and Peneloux, A. Application of the developed Redlich Kwong equation of state to mixtures. Proposed for publishing to *Fluid Phase Equilibria*.

Bray, E. E. and Foster, W. R. (1980) A process for primary migration of petroleum. *AAPG Bull.* **64**, 107–114.

Durand, B. and coworkers (1980) *Kerogen, Insoluble Matter from Sedimentary Rocks*. Editions Technip, Paris, 519 pp.

Du Rouchet, J. (1981) Stress fields, a key to oil migration. *AAPG Bull.* **65**, 74–85.

Gretener, P. E. (1979) *Pore pressure*. AAPG continuing education course note series No. 4, 131 pp.

Momper, J. A. (1978) *Oil migration limitations suggested by geological and geochemical considerations*. AAPG Course Notes No. 8, April 1978, Oklahoma city, 60 pp.

Monin, J. C., Durand, B., Vandenbroucke, M. and Huc, A. Y. (1979) Experimental simulation of the natural transformation of kerogen. Adv. in org. geochemistry. *Proceedings of the 9th Int. Meeting on Org. Geochemistry*, Newcastle 1979. Pergamon Press, Oxford, pp. 517–529.

Orr, W. L. (1975) Geological and geochemical controls on the distribution of hydrogen sulfide in natural gas. *Proceedings of the 7th International Meeting on Organic Geochemistry*, Madrid 1975, pp. 571–597.

Snarskii, A. N. (1970) Nature de la migration primaire du pétrole. *Geol. Nefti Gaz.* **8**, 11–15 (French translation by R. Pelet).

Tissot, B. P. and Pelet, R. (1971) Nouvelles données sur les mécanismes de genèse et de migration du pétrole. Simulation mathématique et application à la prospection. *Proceedings of the 8th World Petroleum Congress*, Vol. 2. Applied Science, London.

Tissot, B., Durand, B., Espitalié, J. and Combaz, A. (1974) Influence of nature and diagenesis of organic matter in formation of petroleum. *AAPG Bull.* **58**, 499–506.

Vandenbroucke, M., Albrecht, P. and Durand, B. (1976) Geochemical studies on the organic matter from the Douala Basin (Cameroun). III. Comparison with the Early Toarcian Shales, Paris Basin, France. *Geochim. Cosmochim. Acta* **40**, 1241–1249.

van Krevelen, D. H. (1961) *Coal*, Elsevier, Oxford, 514 pp.

Wuithier, P. (1965) *Raffinage et génie chimique*, tome 1. Editions Technip, Paris, 934 pp.

Zhuze, T. P., Youchkevitch, G. N. and Tchakhmaxhtchev, B. A. (1973) L'influence de la température et de la pression sur les compositions des phases dans les systèmes huile-gas naturel. *Advances in Organic Geochemistry 1973*, pp. 463–469.

Advances in Organic Geochemistry 1981, pp. 136–146
© *John Wiley & Sons Limited, 1983*

Recognition of Migration and its Effects Within Two Coreholes in Shale/Sandstone Sequences from Svalbard, Norway

D. Leythaeuser, A. S. Mackenzie, R. G. Schaefer, F. J. Altebäumer

Institut für Chemie 5 (Erdöl und organische Geochemie) der Kernforschungsanlage Jülich GmbH, 5170 Jülich, FRG

M. Bjorøy

Institutt for Kontinentalsokkelundersøkelser, Hakon Magnussons gt. 1B, 7001 Trondheim, Norway

Shale and sandstone samples taken from two continuous coreholes (142 and 239 m deep) through the permafrost in Spitsbergen Island have been analysed by established organic geochemical techniques. The gross composition and amounts of the organic matter present were evaluated by Rock-Eval pyrolysis and solvent extraction. Light hydrocarbons and C_{15+}-alkanes were characterized by capillary gas chromatography. Many effects, entirely explicable by redistribution within the sequence, have been observed. The production index of the Rock-Eval pyrolysis technique and the extract yields suggest most sandstones have experienced enrichment by migration of petroleum range hydrocarbons, whilst the shales show a corresponding depletion. In general, the thinner and more fractured a shale is, the greater the extent of depletion. An average expulsion efficiency of 32% was calculated from the production indices of the shales from one corehole. Several small accumulations and an impregnated cap rock have been detected at lithologic boundaries. Clear evidence that fractures serve as channels for the organic components migrating into sandstone bodies was obtained. For the C_{15+}-alkanes, evidence was obtained which suggests that the lower molecular weight components undergo migration more readily, and that n-alkanes migrate faster than isoprenoid alkanes. These fractionation effects are less well demonstrated when migration is via fractures or clean sands. There is tentative circumstantial evidence, which requires further investigation, that the lower boundary of the permafrost could act as a membrane to upward moving hydrocarbons, filtering out and accumulating C_{15+} material.

INTRODUCTION

In the summary session of a recent research symposium on migration organized by the American Association of Petroleum Geologists it was concluded that a major reason why hydrocarbon migration continues to remain to a large extent an enigma is the lack of direct observations of petroleum in the act of moving in the subsurface from one place to another (Roberts and Cordell, 1980). This certainly applies to any chances of witnessing the migration process with the human eye. However, as will be shown in this paper there are a number of geochemical criteria now available, which allow an unequivocal interpretation of the effects of migration. Migration can generally occur in the subsurface in a wide range of concentration levels, which result in a wide range of effects from the visible to the invisible. These range from minute traces, which can only be recognized by sophisticated geochemical analysis, to 'hydrocarbon shows' recorded by standard techniques during exploratory drilling, and ultimately to commercial-size hydrocarbon accumulations.

Initial results of an ongoing study are reported here which demonstrate that hydrocarbon migration processes can effectively be recognized in a column of rocks at a stage, where migration is probably continuing today. Interpretation of certain geochemical criteria in the geological context of the study area has furthermore led to conclusions regarding expulsion efficiency, direction of migration and recognition of intervals of enrichment and of others which suggest depletion by migration. It has also been possible to demonstrate that compositional fractionation effects occur in the C_{15+} molecular range, which are often related to migration distance. The role of permafrost as a limiting factor for migration and the importance of fractures are discussed.

GEOLOGICAL AND GEOCHEMICAL SETTING

Geochemical migration effects are most likely to be unequivocally observed in a geological situation where all of the following are available:

Table 1
Basic geological and geochemical data for coreholes from Svalbard

	Adventdalen	Reindalen
Total depth (m)	239	142
Age	Lower Cretaceous	Palaeocene
Sand/shale ratio	1.25	0.43
Estimated depth of permafrost (m)	80	110
Depth of gas shows (m)	162	141
Mean organic carbon content (%)		
of shales	2.6	1.7
of sandstones	1.4	0.3
Kerogen type (mean hydrogen index in mg HC/g C_{org})		
of shales	77.6	72.7
of sandstones	69.6	34.4
Maturity (mean vitrinite reflectance of coals)	0.85	0.82

(a) Closely spaced samples from a sequence of interbedded source bed-type shales and reservoir sands

(b) Source rocks at optimum maturity levels for generation to occur

(c) Good quality samples for geochemical analysis, i.e. conventional cores, thereby avoiding the interpretation problems commonly encountered with the analytical data of cuttings (caving, contamination by mud additives etc.).

The two deep coreholes 'Adventdalen' and 'Reindalen', drilled in summer 1979 in Svalbard, Norway, appear to meet these conditions. Basic geological and geochemical data for both core holes are listed in Table 1.

At the Adventdalen site a 239 m thick sequence of interbedded shales and sandstones of Lower Cretaceous age was continuously cored. Likewise, a 142 m thick Palaeocene-age sequence of a similar overall lithologic nature was sampled at the Reindalen site. Core recoveries approached 100%. The sands encountered in both coreholes are mainly poorly sorted, clay and silt-rich, fine to medium grained, light to medium grey sandstones, which bear frequent thin interbedded layers of shales or siltstones (mostly between 0.1 and 0.5 m). As evident from their lower mean organic carbon contents (Table 1) the sands of the Reindalen sequence are generally cleaner and less poorly sorted. In both sequences there are clearly defined contacts between the major lithologic units which are shown schematically in Figs 1 and 4. The shales penetrated in both coreholes are dark grey to black, partly massive, partly laminated with varying proportions of silt. Indeed, all transitions between shales and siltstones exist. These were not differentiated, however, in this paper but collectively called shales. The organic carbon content of these shales varies mostly between 1.8 and 6.1% in the Adventdalen, corehole, and between 2.0 and 4.2% in the Reindalen corehole (means of 2.6 and 1.7% respectively).

There is no change in type of organic matter with depth in both sequences. The organic matter remains uniformly of a hydrogen-lean kerogen quality in the sands and shales of both sequences. Based on pyrolysis yield measurements by the Rock-Eval method (Espitalié *et al.*, 1977), the kerogens of all samples analysed were classified as type III (Durand and Espitalié, 1973; Tissot

et al., 1974). The corresponding hydrogen index values for the shale kerogens vary in both cores between 40 and 100 mg hydrocarbons/g C_{org}, with almost identical means of 77.6 and 72.7 for the Adventdalen and Reindalen series respectively. The sandstone kerogens were of similar quality to those of the corresponding shales. In Adventdalen their hydrogen indices ranged between about 40 and 130 mg/g C_{org}, and had an average of 69.6 and in Reindalen, they were slightly lower: varying from about 10 to 70 with a mean of 34.4. In the lower third of each sequence coals were encountered: in Adventdalen two thin layers (0.05 and 0.2 m) and in Reindalen a major seam and several thin layers (1.85 m and 0.1 to 0.25 m). The shales adjacent to these coal layers bear abundant coaly particles.

Both coreholes are located in Svalbard within an area of an extensive trough with a NNW-trending axis, which rapidly subsided during the early Tertiary receiving in excess of 3500 m of clastic sediment in-fill (Manun and Throndsen, 1978). The sediments of both sequences studied here have therefore experienced substantial burial. Consequently, the organic matter finely disseminated in the shales encountered in both coreholes has reached adequate maturity levels for hydrocarbon generation to occur. The 0.85 and 0.82% mean vitrinite reflectances measured for the coal seams of the Adventdalen and Reindalen series respectively indicate that a level of catagenesis close to peak hydrocarbon generation has been attained (Tissot and Welte, 1978). This conclusion is supported by relatively high carbon-normalized yields of extractable organic matter and hydrocarbons, and also by elevated values of the so called 'production index' for those shales encountered in both coreholes, which only bear indigenous hydrocarbons (see below). In view of the shortness of the coreholes no attempts were made to establish maturity gradients with depth; the maturity of the organic matter of all the shales encountered was considered uniform.

The shales penetrated in the Adventdalen and Reindalen sequences can therefore be regarded as source rocks which have generated hydrocarbons. This is further indicated by the gas shows in the reservoir-type sands encountered during drilling in both areas. Corehole Adventdalen penetrated a gas-charged sand around 160 m depth, which was bleeding gas to the surface for a long time after termination of the drilling procedure. A comparatively minor gas show was observed in corehole Reindalen around 141 m depth. Several distinct intervals of fractured rocks were observed in the cores at the Adventdalen location. Samples for geochemical analysis were deliberately selected from these fractured intervals.

Both coreholes are, owing to their high latitude position, located within the area of continuous permafrost (Black, 1954). In both sequences the lower boundary of the permafrost interval was penetrated, so that sediments with frozen and unfrozen pore waters were encountered (A. Stensrud, personal communication). No efforts were made, however, to determine the exact position of the lower contact of the permafrost. According to the definition of permafrost, the pore water present in all rocks within this interval remains frozen all year round.

SAMPLES AND METHODS

At the well sites all core samples selected for this study were placed in gas-tight tin cans immediately upon retrieval of the cores from the core barrel. Also, a detailed lithologic description of each core was made by one of us (FJA). Until analysis in the lab the tin cans were stored in a deep freezer.

Only well established routine geochemical techniques were applied in this study, which are not discussed in detail here: Determination of organic carbon by the Leco method, solvent extraction by a slightly modified flow blending technique (Radke *et al.*, 1978), medium pressure liquid chromatography (Radke *et al.*, 1980), and capillary gas chromatographic analysis of the C_{15+} saturated hydrocarbons, pyrolysis yield measurements by the Rock-Eval method (Espitalié *et al.*, 1977) and determination of mean vitrinite reflectance of polished blocks of coal samples.

RECOGNITION OF MIGRATION PHENOMENA BASED ON GROSS CHEMICAL PARAMETERS

Although little detailed knowledge exists concerning migration mechanisms, it is a widely accepted concept that migration occurs concurrently with the generation of hydrocarbons in source rocks (Tissot and Welte, 1978; Hunt, 1979). For interpretation of geochemical data the problem arises therefore, how to differentiate in a particular geologic situation between indigenous hydrocarbons and migrated hydrocarbons. A fundamental problem is the assessment of the relative directions of migration, i.e. the recognition in a particular geologic situation of the 'source' and the 'sink' of the migrating hydrocarbons. At the 'source', that portion of a source rock which has effectively expelled hydrocarbons, migration causes a depleted zone. Conversely, the sink is represented by an interval, which is enriched in migrated hydrocarbons. If strongly enriched and of sufficient porosity, such intervals can exhibit visible oil staining. Case histories documenting the geochemical effects of this source/sink relationship due to hydrocarbon migration have been discussed in the literature (e.g. Vandenbroucke *et al.*, 1982).

There are several commonly accepted geochemical criteria for the recognition of the above discussed migration phenomena. Anomalously high or low values for the so-called 'production index' calculated from pyrolysis yield measurements can indicate enrichment or depletion respectively (Espitalié *et al.*, 1977). Intervals of enrichment frequently also bear superabundant concentrations of extractable light and/or heavy hydrocarbons. For a proper assessment of these effects the problem invariably arises as to what constitutes an 'anomalous' value. However, as will be shown in the following paragraphs, this question can be resolved if the geochemical parameters chosen are interpreted in the geological context of the samples analysed.

Figure 1 is a depth-plot of the production index for all samples analysed from the Adventdalen series. There appears to be a clear distinction of the samples according to lithology, despite uniform kerogen qualities (Table 1). Most sand samples exhibit production index data in excess of 0.22, whereas most shales remain below this value. This value corresponds exactly, according to Espitalié *et al.* (1977) to the maximum limit for indigenous hydrocarbons of source rocks at a maturity level of 0.85% R_m. Although the conclusion that all production index values, in excess of 0.22 indicate enrichment by migrated hydrocarbons, is probably valid, values below 0.22 (which belong mainly to shales) do not necessarily represent depletion. The great data scatter, which is observed at first glance for the shales in Fig. 1, can, however, be explained if the relative position of individual samples in the stratigraphic sequence is considered. First, the thin interbedded shale layers consistently show markedly lower production index values than their adjacent sand samples. Secondly, many shale samples from thin shale layers interbedded in the sand intervals tend to exhibit somewhat lower production index values than the shale samples from the thicker continuous shale intervals. This trend is especially obvious in the Adventdalen sequence below a depth of 150 m: The nine samples from thin shales interbedded in the sandstone interval 160.8–230 m have a mean production index of 0.14, whereas the samples from the more massive shale intervals directly above and below this sandstone have mean production index values of 0.18 and 0.22 respectively. These observations are interpreted as an indication that thinly interbedded shale layers have, in the course of migration, been more effectively depleted in hydrocarbons than the samples from the more massive shale layers. This effect may be related to differences in the compaction history: thin shale layers wedged in between porous sands have presumably lost their pore fluid content more effectively and hence have experienced a higher degree of compaction.

The observations in the Adventdalen series about frequent differences in production index values between samples from thick versus thin shale intervals lead to a concept for the estimation of expulsion efficiencies during primary migration of hydrocarbons from shale

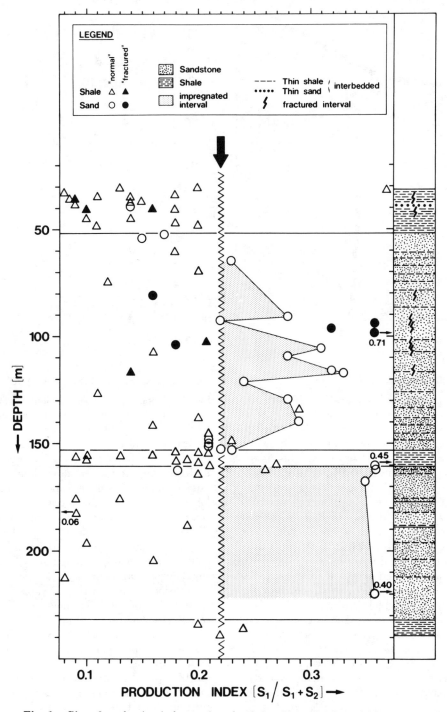

Fig. 1. Plot of production index against depth for the total Adventdalen sequence.

source rocks. For each thin shale interbed the difference between the measured production index and 0.22 as a percentage of 0.22 is proposed to represent the expulsion efficiency. Among the 18 samples analysed from thin shale interbeds encountered in this corehole the expulsion efficiency varies considerably (5 to 73%) and has a mean of 32%. This value of 32% is higher than most previous estimates of the expulsion efficiency (Hunt, 1979). For the Rock-Eval procedure, the production index includes, however, both the light and the heavy hydrocarbons. Thus, the mean expulsion efficiency of 32% determined here applies to the expulsion of both gasoline and petroleum-range products.

Another factor controlling the degree of enrichment, in the Adventdalen series, appears to be the occurrence of fractures. Among the five sand samples analysed from fractured intervals (Fig. 1), three are strongly enriched and two are depleted by migration. It is noteworthy, that the three fractured sands between 93.5 and 99.0 m occur close to the depth of maximum enrichment in the upper massive sand interval encountered in this corehole.

If the above concept for interpretation of production index data is accepted, the overall variation in degree of enrichment in the two thick sand intervals encountered in corehole Adventdalen becomes clear and leads to

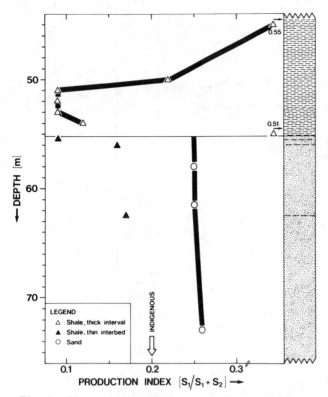

Fig. 2. Plot of production index against depth for the Reindalen sequence between 45 and 75 m.

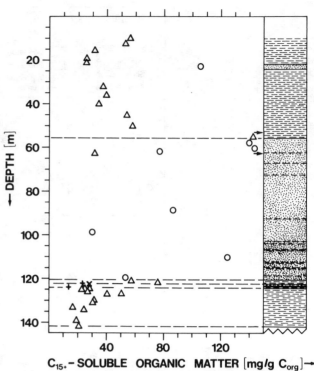

Fig. 3. Plot of C_{15+} solvent extractable organic matter yield against depth for the total Reindalen sequence.

conclusions about the direction of migration. The degree of enrichment in migrated hydrocarbons is highest in the lower sand interval. In the upper sand interval it is highest in the central part dropping sharply towards the upper and lower boundaries of this sand unit. It is particularly revealing that the two highest production index values over the total length of this corehole occur in the sand at 161.5 m (0.45) which is directly below the shale unit which separates the two massive sand units, and secondly in the fractured sandstone interval at 99.0 m depth (0.71). The nearly perfect symmetry of the production index trend which drops with increasing distance away from this fractured sand interval suggests that migrating hydrocarbons were transported into the upper sand unit primarily *via* the fractures between 93.5 and 99.0 m in depth. Furthermore, it is concluded that the shale layer between 153.4 and 160.8 m functioned as a permeability barrier, albeit rather inefficiently, for hydrocarbons migrating upwards in the sand. Thus, a small-size hydrocarbon accumulation was formed below 160.8 m. In this context it appears particularly revealing that gas was violently bleeding into the hole and to the surface upon retrieval of the core interval 153.5–158.2 m.

The evidence for migration of hydrocarbons based on production index is similar in the Reindalen sample series. Figure 2 is a depth-plot of production index data for the depth interval 47–75 m. Based on the above discussed reasoning the critical production index level indicating *in situ* generated hydrocarbons was, due to the slightly lower maturity, given a value of 0.20. Consequently, the sand unit below 55.2 m is thought to be uniformly enriched by migrated hydrocarbons, with the three thin shale interbeds again depleted. Over the

lowermost 5 m interval of the thick shale unit, which extends down to 55.2 m, there is a pronounced gradient of decreasing production index data towards the shale/sand contact. The shale appears to have increasingly lost hydrocarbons to the underlying sand as the contact is approached (but see below). However, the lowermost shale sample at 55.0 m has a high production index value suggesting that this sample at 0.2 m above the shale/sand contact has been impregnated by hydrocarbons from the small accumulation in the sand below. It can, therefore be interpreted as a caprock effect. In summary, interpretation of the data shown in Fig. 2 leads to the conclusion that the sand unit is enriched by migrated hydrocarbons and that the bottom 5 m of the shales above have lost part of their original hydrocarbon content by migration.

Many of the conclusions concerning intervals of enrichment and depletion reached above from production index data receive additional support from data on the yield and gross composition of C_{15+}-soluble organic matter and hydrocarbons. Figure 3 is a depth-plot of carbon-normalized concentrations of C_{15+}-soluble organic matter for samples from the Reindalen core hole. Generally, most of the sand samples exhibit higher C_{15+}-soluble organic matter concentrations than most of the shales. Since kerogen quality remains uniform throughout the whole sequence, this is an indication that most of the sands have received an additional input of hydrocarbons by migration. The maximum concentration of *in situ* generated extractable organic matter is in this case empirically set at a value of 60 mg/g C_{org}. The amount of extract relative to organic carbon of the sample of the shale caprock at 55.0 m depth therefore suggests enrichment by migrated oil. Since the two sand samples immediately below it also exhibit high values (Fig. 3), the conclusion of a small accumulation of oil in the uppermost sand appears to be justified. Within the thick sand unit between 55.2 and 120.5 m the extract concentrations of all except two sand samples suggest enrichment by migrated oil (Fig. 3). The degree of enrichment varies with depth in a fashion, which at present appears random. However, it is suspected that this variation is controlled by relative differences in clay content, porosity and permeability and possibly even by the permafrost (see below). Likewise, the upper shale unit (extending by 55.2 m) and the lowermost sequence of shales and interbedded coals (below 120.5 m) exhibit distinct depth-related patterns for the variation of C_{15+}-soluble organic matter. In the upper shale unit there is a pronounced gradient of decreasing concentrations above and below and towards a thin interbedded conglomeratic sandstone layer at 22.8–23.0 m depth. The sample from the conglomeratic sand itself shows a 5-fold increase in C_{15+}-soluble organic matter when compared to the shale samples immediately above and below. The depth-variation of C_{15+}-soluble organic matter in the sequence below 120.5 m may indicate the presence of another, smaller oil accumulation directly below the lowermost coal layer, as indicated by a gradient of increasing concentrations from around 140 m towards this coal (Fig. 3).

The variation with depth and lithology in the gross composition of the C_{15+}-SOM appears also to be controlled by redistribution effects. This is exemplified by a depth-plot of the hydrocarbon/non-hydrocarbon ratio (Fig. 4). From the bottom to the top of the thick sand unit this ratio increases from around 0.4 to about 0.8, indicating preferential enrichment of hydrocarbons with increasing migration distance. Within the overly-

ing shale unit the conglomeratic sand has one of the lowest hydrocarbon/non-hydrocarbon ratios, suggesting that this layer is not the actual site of an accumulation, but rather has functioned as a transit avenue for migrating organic material. The trend of regularly increasing hydrocarbon/non-hydrocarbon ratios in the shale interval 30–55 m is hard to explain. The two lower shale samples at 50 and 55 m probably represent impregnated caprocks. A similar explanation may apply to the shale sample at 21 m, which immediately overlies the conglomeratic sand.

RECOGNITION OF REDISTRIBUTION PHENOMENA BASED ON COMPOSITIONAL PARAMETERS

Examination of the gas chromatograms (GC) of the C_{15+}-alkanes of the samples suggested redistribution may occur with fractionation as postulated by Vanden-

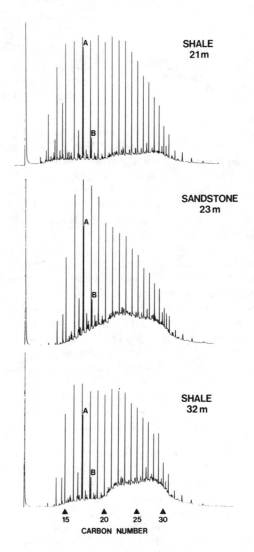

Fig. 5. Capillary gas chromatograms for the C_{15+} alkanes from three samples from the Reindalen sequence: a conglomeratic sandstone and the two shale samples directly above and below it. A is pristane and B is phytane.

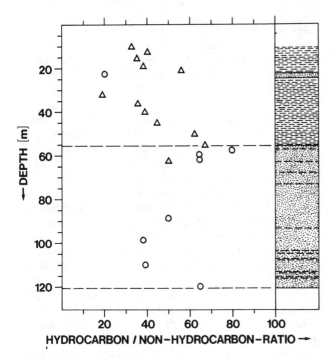

Fig. 4. Plot of hydrocarbon/non-hydrocarbon ratio (multiplied by a factor of 100) against depth for the Reindalen sequence to a depth of 120 m.

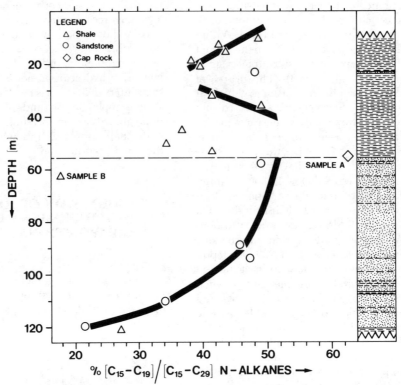

Fig. 6. Plot of the amount of *n*-alkanes with 15 to 19 carbon atoms expressed as a percentage. (%C_{15}–C_{19}/C_{15}–C_{29}) against depth for the Reindalen sequence to a depth of 120 m.

broucke (1972). Certain components, indeed, seem to move more readily than others. Fig. 5 shows the GC traces for the conglomeratic sandstone bed at 23 m in the Reindalen core and those of the shales lying directly above and below it. Gross chemical parameters (see above) suggested that movement of material from the shales to the sandstone had occurred. It appears that the lower molecular weight *n*-alkanes underwent this movement more readily, leading to their relative enhancement in the enriched sand when compared to the depleted shales (Fig. 5). With this initial observation in mind, the proportion of the total C_{15}–C_{29} *n*-alkanes, with 15 to 19 carbon atoms was measured (by peak heights) in all samples above the coal sequence in the Reindalen core and expressed as a percentage. This is shown as a depth plot in Fig. 6. That the depletion/enrichment effect connected with the sandstone at 23 m is associated with fractionation is further substantiated. As the sand body is approached the shales show progressively lower proportions of C_{15}–C_{19} *n*-alkanes, yet the sand has a significantly higher value for the chosen ratio than the adjacent shales.

The sandstone sequence between 55 and 120 m is also included in Fig. 6. Here the gross chemical parameters suggested an upward migration/redistribution *within the sandstone* has led to a small accumulation at the sandstone/shale contact at 55 m. Sample A in Fig. 6 is the siltstone sample referred to earlier which either represents an impregnated caprock or the transition zone between reservoir and seal. At the base of the sand body the sample showing a low production index also has a particularly low relative concentration of the lower molecular weight *n*-alkanes (Fig. 6). Following the

migration pathway a relatively steady increase in the value can be discerned, although the most dramatic changes were detected between 120 and 90 m and between the shallowest sandstone sample examined and the impregnated siltstone caprock (sample A, Fig. 6). This could mean clay content is important for these fractionation effects, since the sandstone interval between 90 and 120 m has a higher clay content and more thin interbedded shales than that between 60 and 90 m. Four selected GC traces from this interval are included in Fig. 7. That the Rock-Eval data suggest movement from the shales above 55 m in the Reindalen core, to the underlying sandstones (Fig. 2), whilst the C_{15+} data suggest movement within the sand towards the shale need not be contradictory. The Production Index of Rock-Eval includes the concentrations of all hydrocarbons from C_1 and clearly the concentrations of the lighter components are much higher in the shales, so encouraging a movement towards the sandstones. This does not prevent the shale acting as a barrier to the upward movement of C_{15+} material *within the sandstone unit*, and so forming a small accumulation.

The only thin shale within the sandstone sequence whose alkanes were examined by GC is that at 62.50 m (sample B in Fig. 6). This depleted sample (on Rock-Eval and extract concentration) shows the predicted low relative concentration of C_{15}–C_{19} *n*-alkanes (Fig. 6).

In order to evaluate further the observed fractionation effects the highly simplified and hypothetical scheme shown in Fig. 8 was constructed as an aid to further interpretation. The basic assumption is always that 50% of the total original *n*-alkane concentration in a sample is lost by migration (although clearly any value

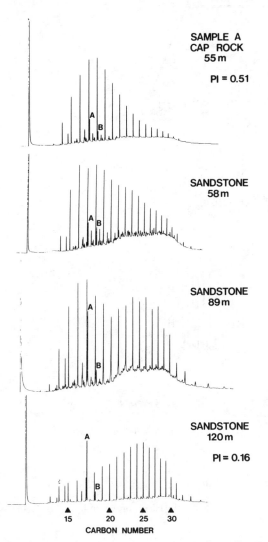

Fig. 7. Capillary gas chromatograms for the C_{15+} alkanes of (i) 3 sandstone samples of the Reindalen sequence, which show increasing relative enrichment in the lower molecular weight *n*-alkanes towards the shale caprock, and (ii) the impregnated caprock. A is pristane and B is phytane.

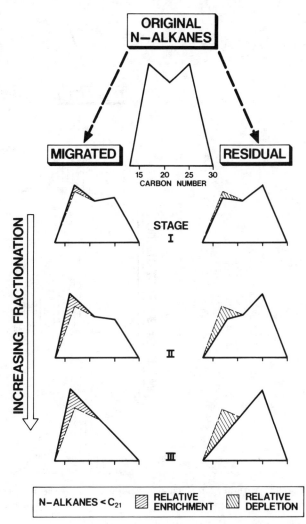

Fig. 8. Hypothetical scheme for the redistribution of *n*-alkanes with fractionation. The scheme assumes that 50% of the total original *n*-alkanes are lost by migration but that the migrated fraction will contain more than 50% of the original $C_{14}-C_{20}$ *n*-alkanes and less than 50% of the original $C_{22}-C_{29}$ *n*-alkanes to an increasing extent. Only the changes in the relative distributions below C_{21} are shown by shading.

between 0 and 100% could have been chosen), giving rise to a migrated *n*-alkane fraction and a residual *n*-alkane fraction. Stages I–III represent increasing extents of compositional fractionation resulting from this 50:50 redistribution. It was assumed that redistribution can lead to a relative enrichment in *n*-alkanes $<C_{21}$ in the migrated fraction which is matched by a relative depletion in the residual fraction or in other words that more than 50% of the original *n*-alkanes $<C_{21}$ underwent migration even though only 50% of the total was redistributed. Similarly, it was also assumed that redistribution can at the same time lead to a relative depletion in *n*-alkanes $<C_{21}$ in the migrated fraction which is matched by a relative enrichment in the residual alkanes, or in other words that less than 50% of the original *n*-alkanes underwent migration even though at least 50% of the total was redistributed. Only the changes in the relative distributions of *n*-alkanes $<C_{21}$ are shown by shading in Fig. 8.

Although in theory good examples of residual alkane distributions should exist in nature, true migrated distributions will be more difficult to detect. The

migrating *n*-alkanes will in most cases be added to the indigenous components. For example a migrated *n*-alkane distribution of stage I in Fig. 8, could represent a 50:50 mixture of the original alkane distribution and stage II migrated distribution. True migrated distributions will only exist when the absolute amount of the migrated material far exceeds that of the indigenous components.

Examples of all seven distributions were, however, seen in this study. One of each was selected from the Reindalen corehole where the difference in organic carbon content between shales and sands is greatest (Table 1) and included in Fig. 9. In comparing Figs 8 and 9 it should be remembered that the pronounced bimodality in the original *n*-alkane distribution imagined in Fig. 8, was never seen in the Reindalen samples. Such bimodality was observed in the Adventdalen core (see below and Fig. 10). With the provisos given above, the designation of the distributions in Fig. 9 as migrated, depleted (residual) or original on the basis of the scheme

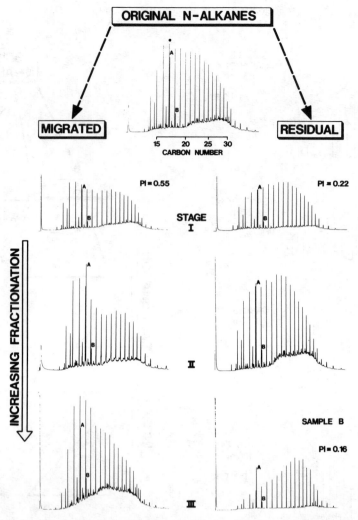

Fig. 9. Natural examples taken from the Reindalen sequence above 120 m to illustrate the effects proposed in Fig. 8. A is pristane and B is phytane.

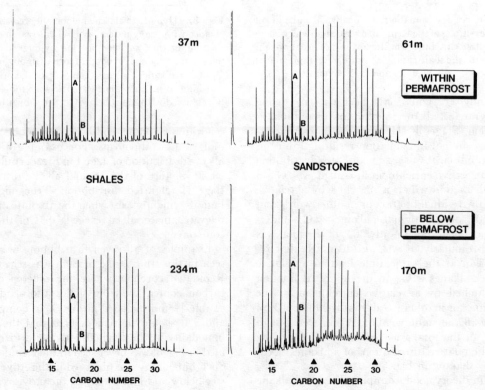

Fig. 10. Comparison of C_{15+}-alkane distributions from sandstones and shales from above and within the permafrost interval of the Adventdalen sequence. A is pristane and B is phytane.

in Fig. 8 is consistent with the geological setting of the samples concerned and, where available, the Rock-Eval data (production indices are shown in Fig. 9). The selected 'original' *n*-alkane trace derives from the first sampled shale interval just below a depth of 10 m and the stage I migrated/residual pair are shales in close proximity to each other, the residual sample having the higher organic carbon value. Whilst the residual (depleted) stage II distribution is from a shale close to the sand body at 23 m, the migrated equivalent is part of the migration sequence in the sandstone discussed previously in connection with Fig. 8. The highly depleted *n*-alkane trace chosen for stage III is that of the thin shale at 62.5 which is within the sandstone sequence (sample B in Fig. 6) whilst the migrated equivalent is the thin conglomeratic sandstone at 23 m which is within the upper shale sequence.

The work of Vandenbroucke (1972) on a Paris Basin borehole suggested that cyclic alkanes were undergoing redistribution less readily than the *n*- and branched alkanes. Detailed study of the distributions shown in Fig. 9 suggests in this case that the *n*-alkanes are in fact migrating more readily than the isoprenoid alkanes of equivalent carbon number. This is particularly striking when the two most depleted samples from the Reindalen core (according to Rock-Eval criteria) are considered — the thin shale in the sandstone sequence (sample B in Fig. 6, distribution shown in Fig. 9) and the sandstone sample from the base of the same sandstone sequence (bottom distribution shown in Fig. 7). Previous to this study such distributions could have been erroneously interpreted as representing biodegradation.

ROLE OF PERMAFROST

Although the level of the lower boundary of the permafrost was only estimated in both sequences and not determined accurately, it is still possible to make certain comparisons between samples from within and below the permafrost. The estimated lower level in the Reindalen sequence (110 m; A. Stensrud, personal communication), unfortunately almost coincides with the beginning of the coal-bearing sequence. Since this is related to a change in lithology comparison of samples from the two environments is difficult. Most of the discussion on the effect of permafrost is therefore restricted to the Adventdalen suite. Here the lower level of the permafrost is thought to occur between 78 and 80 m (A. Stensrud, personal communication).

Ample evidence was provided above for significant movement of both the gasoline and petroleum range products within and outside the permafrost interval in both sequences. However, many of the gross and *n*-alkane fractionation effects observed in the shallow (permafrost) part of the Reindalen corehole were not observed within the permafrost interval of the Adventdalen corehole. For example, many of the Adventdalen shale and sandstones within the permafrost interval show an unmodified hydrocarbon composition, i.e. a classic non-migrated bimodal *n*-alkane distribution (Fig. 10). Of the 12 shales examined above 80 m, 7 contained such

a distribution. The score for the sandstones above 80 m is 3 out of 5. This result contradicts with the Reindalen findings discussed above, and with the interval in the Adventdalen core below 80 m. Here (Fig. 10) 11 out of 17 shales examined still preserved the presumed non-migrated *n*-alkane distribution but 12 of 17 sandstones have a *n*-alkane distribution which on the Reindalen evidence would suggest migration.

There are several possible reasons to explain why the Reindalen sediments within the permafrost interval and the Adventdalen samples below the permafrost show fractionation effects to greater extents than the Adventdalen samples within the permafrost zone. The most obvious is only partly connected with the permafrost. Most of the shallow Adventdalen samples are the only group which are always near abundant fracturing (Figs 1 and 3). When the movement is along fractures many of the adsorption/desorption effects necessary for fractionation may be relatively restricted. A reason why the fractionation features are so well developed in the upper part of the Reindalen core, could be that they are mainly related to a more recent redistribution and that the slowing effect of the permafrost observed previously in a comparison of the light hydrocarbons of other sample suites (Leythaeuser *et al.*, 1980) maximizes the exchange (adsorption/desorption) processes required for fractionation. This, however, is speculation since: (i) the time scale is not known and although the Palaeocene Reindalen sequence is younger than the Lower Cretaceous Adventdalen sequence it must have existed for a significant portion of time without permafrost in order to have attained its present maturity ($0.82\% \, R_0$, see above), and (ii) the greater contrast between sandstones and shale organic carbon contents in Reindalen when compared to Adventdalen, together with the simpler sequence and the better sorted sands at Reindalen could provide alternative explanations for the difference between the results for the upper part of the Reindalen sequence (permafrost), and those of the lower part of the Adventdalen sequence (below permafrost).

The ability of the lower boundary of the permafrost interval to act either as a seal to upward migrating hydrocarbons or as a membrane allowing only the lower molecular weight hydrocarbons to pass on but creating an accumulation of the heavier components, can only partly be addressed in the absence of accurate figures for this lower level. It should, however, be noted that in Reindalen an accumulation of C_{15+} material occurs near the roughly estimated depth for the lower boundary of the permafrost (110 m, Fig. 3) which is not easily explained by the geological setting. The accumulation is not, however, matched by high production indices.

The implications for this observation if correct are two-fold: (i) it implies significant migration has occurred in the sequence since the establishment of the present permafrost interval and (ii) it suggests an interesting new target for energy exploration in polar regions.

In summary, effective redistribution of petroleum-range hydrocarbons and the associated fractionation effects are restricted within the permafrost interval of the Adventdalen core, although the reason for this and the role of the permafrost is not clear. There is tentative circumstantial evidence which suggests the base of the permafrost can act as a membrane towards upward migrating material, filtering out and leading to an accumulation of higher molecular weight components. This should be investigated further.

CONCLUSIONS

(1)   In two deep coreholes drilled through a sequence of interbedded shale source rock and reservoir sands on Spitsbergen Island the following migration effects were observed:

(a)   Based on the production index of Rock-Eval, pyrolysis intervals of depletion and enrichment were detected. Most shales were depleted, whilst most sandstones were enriched. In general the thinner and/or more fractured shales tend to show a higher degree of depletion.

(b)   An estimate of expulsion efficiency based on the production index gave a mean of 32% for the Adventdalen shales.

(c)   Fractures in the sandstones can show strong enrichment suggesting they serve as channels for the migrating organic material.

(d)   Depleted and enriched zones can also be revealed by the extract yield data and these follow the same pattern with the coarser sandstones acting as 'sinks' and showing enriched characteristics whilst the shale 'sources' have lower (depleted) extract yields.

(e)   Several small accumulations of petroleum range hydrocarbons occur at those lithologic boundaries which represent a major permeability decrease upwards. For example, in sandstones overlain by shales (and, perhaps, in shales overlain by coal). In one case an impregnated caprock was observed.

(2)   Compositional fractionation effects were observed as follows:

(a)   Samples showing evidence of a migrated input had, in general, higher hydrocarbon/non-hydrocarbon ratios than average and C_{15+} n-alkanes distributions dominated by the lower molecular weight components.

(b)   Samples which suggested extensive depletion had C_{15+} n-alkane distributions biased to the higher molecular weight end.

(c)   Where it was thought that neither depletion nor enrichment had occurred a bimodal n-alkane distribution was observed.

(d)   On this basis within a thick enriched reservoir sand interval a trend of increasing fractionation approaching the contact with the overlying shale caprock was discerned.

(3)   The fractionation effects clearly suggest that the less polar species undergo migration more readily, which as more data becomes available may help explain the mechanism of the redistribution.

(4)   Fractionation effects are less pronounced when migration was through fractures or clean sands, and possibly when it occurred below the permafrost interval.

(5)   There is tentative evidence that accumulation of petroleum range hydrocarbons can occur at the lower boundary of the permafrost interval.

(6)   The ability of redistribution changes quite dramatically both the relative amount of organic material which can be volatized (by the Rock-Eval procedure) or extracted, and the gross and detailed chemical composition of the extractable fraction over very short distances, means the use of these criteria to assess maturation, nature of the original organic input to a sediment and biodegradation requires extreme caution.

Acknowledgements

We thank the Store Norske Spitsbergen Kulkompani, especially Dr A. Orheim and Mr A. Stensrud, for permission to sample their coreholes for geochemical purposes and for logistic support during the sampling. ASM thanks the Alexander von Humboldt-Stiftung for a fellowship.

REFERENCES

Black, R. F. (1954) Permafrost — a review. *Bull. Geol. Soc. Am.* **65**, 839–856.

Durand, B. and Espitalié, J. (1973) Evolution de la matière organique au cours de l'enfouissement des sédiments. *C.R. Acad. Sci. (Paris)* **276**, 2253–2256.

Espitalié, J., Laporte, J. L., Madec, M., Marquis, F., Leplat, P., Paulet, J. and Boutefeu, A. (1977) Méthode rapide de caractérisation des roches mères, de leur potentiel pétrolier et de leur degré d'évolution. *Rev. Inst. Fr. Pet.* **32**, 23–42.

Hunt, J. M. (1979) *Petroleum Geochemistry and Geology.* W. H. Freeman and Co., 616 pp.

Leythaeuser, D., Schaefer, R. G. and Yuekler, A. (1980) Diffusion of light hydrocarbons through near surface sediments. *Nature* **284**, 522–525.

Manum, S. B. and Throndsen, T. (1978) Rank of coal and dispersed organic matter and its geological bearing in the Spitsbergen Tertiary. *Norsk Polarinstitutt Arbok 1977*, 159–177.

Radke, M., Sittardt, H. G. and Welte, D. H. (1978) Removal of soluble organic matter from rock samples with a flow through extraction cell. *Anal. Chem.* **50**, 663–665.

Radke, M., Willsch, H. and Welte, D. H. (1980) Preparative hydrocarbon group type determination by automated medium pressure liquid chromatography. *Anal. Chem.* **52**, 407–411.

Roberts, W. H. and Cordell, R. J. (1980) Introduction to: *Problems of Petroleum Migration*, AAPG Series in Geology No. 10, ed. by Roberts, W. H. and Cordell, R. J.

Tissot, B. P. and Welte, D. H. (1978) *Petroleum Formation and Occurrence.* Springer-Verlag, Heidelberg, 538 pp.

Tissot, B., Durand, B., Espitalié, J. and Combaz, A. (1974) Influence of the nature and diagenesis of organic matter in the formation of petroleum. *Bull. Am. Assoc. Pet. Geol.* **58**, 499–506.

Vandenbroucke, M. (1972) Etude de la migration primaire: variation de composition des extraits de roche à un passage roche mère/réservoir. In *Advances in Organic Geochemistry 1971*, ed. by von Gaertner, H. R. and Wenner, H. Pergamon Press, Oxford, pp. 547–565.

Vandenbroucke, M., Durand, B. and Oudin, J. L. (1982) Detection of migration phenomena in a geological series by means of C_1–C_{35} hydrocarbon amounts and distributions. In *Advances in Organic Geochemistry 1981*, ed. by Bjøy. John Wiley, Chichester.

Advances in Organic Geochemistry 1981, pp. 147–155
© *John Wiley & Sons Limited, 1983*

Detecting Migration Phenomena in a Geological Series by Means of C$_1$–C$_{35}$ Hydrocarbon Amounts and Distributions

M. Vandenbroucke and B. Durand

I.F.P., Rueil Malmaison, France

J. L. Oudin

TOTAL C.F.P., Talence, France

This paper describes geochemical analyses of samples from various wells in the Mahakam Delta area in Indonesia having different structural positions. One of these wells was partly drilled through an overpressured shale section. Geochemical methods were applied either to coals hand-picked from total cuttings or to kerogens obtained after the acidic destruction of minerals. Analyses include elemental analysis and Rock–Eval pyrolysis of all the samples, as well as more detailed investigation of selected samples, by methods such as extraction and composition of extracts or thermovaporization of free hydrocarbons. The quantitative parameters obtained by these methods are compared for the different wells, and the behaviour of the organic matter is described in relation to the geological environment: formation of hydrocarbons in the source rocks; loss of fractions by migration; and cracking of soluble products if migration does not occur and subsequent formation of both gas and insoluble residues.

GEOLOGICAL SETTING

The Mahakam Delta is situated in Indonesia, on the eastern edge of the Kutei Basin, in south–eastern Borneo (Kalimantan). The exact position of the basement is not known, nor is the age of the first deposits, but deltaic sedimentation is known to have occurred at least since the Middle Miocene, and this eastward prograding series is more than 4000 m thick. The structure of the region is characterized by a succession of NNE–SSW anticlinal axes of decreasing amplitude going from west to east (Fig. 1). Underneath the interbedded clays and sands of the deltaic plain, which are rich in organic matter and coal seams, there are argillaceous platform or prodelta facies, where high-pressure phenomena can occur. Oil fields were discovered along the successive anticlinal axes (Fig. 1). Depending on the case, oil is preferentially found (Handil), which is eventually degraded near the surface (Sanga Sanga) or else gas condensate (Badak). Except for Badak and Nilam, the fields are compartmented by more or less numerous normal faults.

Geochemical analyses in this region have been made on a great many wells (Combaz and de Matharel, 1978; Durand and Oudin, 1979). The results described here have to do with only a portion of these analyses, concerning wells H8, H9bis and H627 of the Handil field and well N25 (formerly Terentang) of the Nilam field.

Their aim is to show how migration phenomena in this type of deltaic sedimentation influence the distribution of hydrocarbons. The position of the wells is shown on the section in Fig. 2. Wells H8 and H9bis, which are next to each other (50 m), are situated at the top of the Handil structure. This structure has a single major fault and mainly contains oil. Well H627 is situated on the eastern flank on the same side of the fault as H8 and H9bis. Well N25 is also situated on the flank of the Nilam structure. This structure is a nose extending towards SW of the Badak structure and having no structural closure above 2200 m. As at Badak, this structure contains mainly gas.

The sedimentary series are characterized from top to bottom by sandy bodies having highly varying sizes and shapes, interbedded with shales (deltaic-plain sedimentation), and then by very fine silty shales (prodelta sedimentation). The hydrocarbons are situated in these sandy bodies. Each reservoir has its own gas/oil and oil/water contact. The Handil field contains hydrocarbons throughout the whole depth where these reservoirs exist, i.e. between 2900 m and almost up to the surface, with a maximum of productive horizons between 1800 and 2450 m. The accumulated oils are lighter and lighter upon approaching the surface.

The prodelta shales are, at the present time, overpressured because subsidence was very fast and the water contained in the porosity was not expelled quickly enough. The transition from well-drained, normal-

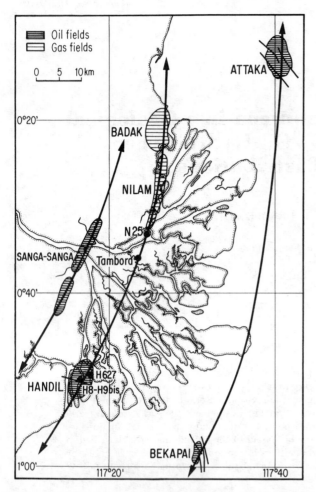

Fig. 1. Regional map of the Mahakam Delta showing the principal oil and gas fields located along parallel anticlinal trends. (Name of the fields in capital letters.)

pressure zones (specific gravity equal to one) to geostatic-pressure zones (specific gravity > 2) occurs in an interval which varies according to the local sedimentological characteristics. It is about 300 m (2850 to 3150 m) at the top of Handil and probably much greater on Nilam and Badak (about 1000 m on the northern side of Badak). The wells examined here penetrated more or less deeply into these zones. For example, well H8 crosses all the way through the transition zone and stops at the top of the high-pressure zone. Well H9bis penetrates 1000 m into this high-pressure zone without reaching the bottom. Well H627 reaches the transition zone at around 3150 m but does not run in very far (less than 100 m). Well N25 penetrates for 180 m into the transition zone (3900 to 4080 m), but the equivalent specific gravity at the bottom of the well is not very high (1.32).

REVIEW OF ANALYTICAL PROCEDURE

This review will be brief. For a detailed description reference is made to the analytical procedure given in various publications dealing with this subject.

Rock–Eval pyrolysis

Samples of 5 to 100 mg are heated quickly (250 to 550 °C at 25 °C min^{-1}) in helium (Espitalié *et al.*, 1977). The hydrocarbons which are released are detected by flame ionization and occur in the form of a first peak caused by the free compounds present in the rock, then by a second peak caused by the pyrolysis of the organic matter. The surface area of the pyrolysis peak related to organic

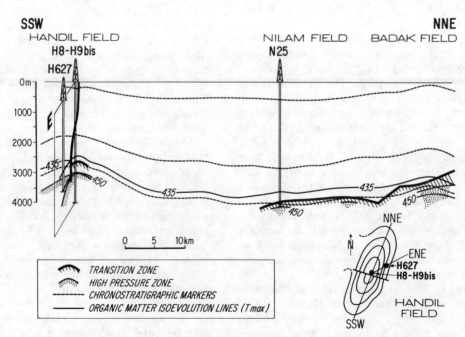

Fig. 2. Section across the Handil–Badak anticlinal trend showing the position of the four wells studied here. Approximate boundaries of transition zone and high-pressure zone are indicated along with isoevolution lines of organic matter (Rock–Eval T_m).

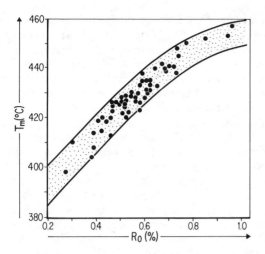

Fig. 3. Correlation between vitrinite reflectance (R_0) and Rock–Eval T_m in Mahakam coals.

carbon, called the hydrogen index, measures the petroleum potential that is still available from the organic matter. The pyrolysis temperature reached at the top of this peak, called T_m, is representative of the maturation state of the organic matter. It gives information equivalent to what is obtained by measuring the reflectance of vitrinite, called R_0, as can be seen in Fig. 3 where the R_0/T_m correlation is given for several Mahakam coals. This parameter T_m, which is obtained faster than R_0, is what we will use hereafter as the common scale of evolution for the wells investigated because the geothermal gradients are relatively variable in the delta. The beginning of oil formation can be roughly situated at about $T_m = 435°C$, the very beginning of gas formation (C_1 to C_5) at around $T_m = 450°C$, and maximum oil formation at around $T_m = 455$–$460°C$.

Solvent extraction

The ground rock is chloroform extracted (Monin *et al.*, 1978). After the solvent has been filtered and evaporated, the extract is fractionated by thin-layer chromatography (Huc *et al.*, 1976; Huc and Rouchaché, 1981) to obtain saturated hydrocarbons, aromatic compounds and NSO compounds. The hydrocarbons are analysed by gas chromatography and, in some cases, by mass spectrometry (Fabre *et al.*, 1972).

Thermovaporization followed by simulated distillation

The analytical system (Saint-Paul *et al.*, 1980) consists of a sample-holder tube in line with a trap followed by direct introduction into a gas-chromatography column. A sliding oven can be moved from the sample-holder tube to the trap. This system is swept by helium, and the chromatograph has a sub-ambient programming device. The phase used (Dexsil 300) and the programming conditions (-15 to $+370°C$, $8°C$ min^{-1}) enable the total hydrocarbons to be analysed from C_1 to C_{35}, thus renewing interest in this technique which, moreover, has been known for a long time (Bordenave *et al.*, 1970; Jonathan *et al.*, 1975; Schaefer *et al.*, 1978). The sample

is quickly heated to 300°C, and the volatilized hydrocarbons are stopped in the trap which is maintained in liquid nitrogen for 15 min. The oven is then moved around the trap. At the same time the temperature programming of the chromatograph is started up. This analysis is thus similar to a chromatographic separation of free hydrocarbons from the first peak in the Rock–Eval method. The distribution of total hydrocarbons (saturated + aromatic) can be calculated along with their amount, between C_1 and C_{35} or in more restricted carbon ranges, by means of a reference standard.

Preparation and analysis of kerogens

The ground and solvent-extracted rock is attacked, under inert gas flow, successively by hydrochloric acid to eliminate the carbonates and then by a hydrochloric-acid/hydrofluoric-acid mixture to eliminate the silicates, and finally by hydrochloric acid once again to destroy the fluorosilicates formed during the preceding stage (Durand and Nicaise, 1980). The pyrite is not attacked during these operations. Between each acid attack, the rock is water washed until it reaches neutrality. Then the organic residue is dried in nitrogen atmosphere. To characterize this kerogen, an elemental analysis is made of C, H, N, O, S and Fe (Durand and Monin, 1980). The organic S is calculated by subtracting from the total S the sulfur belonging to pyrite, this latter being dosed by Fe.

NATURE AND EVOLUTION OF ORGANIC MATTER

Nature of organic matter

Previous publications on this deltaic series (Combaz and de Matharel, 1978; Durand and Oudin, 1979) have already shown that the organic matter it contains comes from higher plants from the continent, that the characteristics of this vegetation have been practically invariable during the entire Tertiary and that there is no difference in either nature or evolution between the organic matter dispersed in the shales and that concentrated in the coals. This is why we have mainly analysed coals here, because analyses can be made on small amounts of these latter samples, easily obtained by hand-picking among cuttings taken at regular intervals in the wells. (Coal is taken here to mean any piece of cutting that can be isolated by tweezers and that can be recognized by its aspect as being mainly made up of pure organic matter. A large proportion of this coal probably comes from the massive coal beds crossed through by the boreholes and spotted by logs.)

These coals were systematically analysed by Rock–Eval pyrolysis and elemental analysis, methods which were also applied to kerogens in the case where coals did not exist in the cuttings. More detailed analyses were made on some coals, in particular the study of distribution of hydrocarbons by thermovaporization or by separation of the chloroform extract. Such analyses are possible only on samples that have not undergone any prior treatment, thus excluding kerogens.

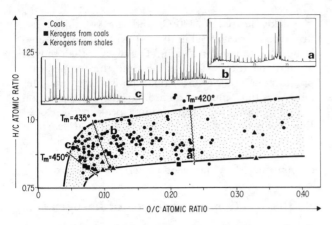

Fig. 4. Evolution of elemental analyses of kerogens and coals in an atomic H/C versus O/C diagram. Some isoevolution lines, indicated by the correspond T_m, are shown. Increasing evolution follows increase of T_m. The chromatograms of saturates from chloroform extracts of coals correspond to increasing evolution from **a** to **c**.

The results of elemental analysis on coals, coal kerogens and shale kerogens coming from the different wells in the Handil field and from well N25 are given in Fig. 4 in the form of a diagram of the H/C versus O/C atomic ratios. The position of these samples is similar to that of other organic matters coming from continental plants and especially with the Type III ones (Tissot *et al.*, 1974; Durand and Espitalié, 1976). The dispersion among coals is in the same range as that between coals and kerogens. Approximate isoevolution lines corresponding to the Rock–Eval T_m of 420, 430 and 450°C are given. Above 450 °C, these isoevolution lines become very close-set on such a diagram.

Formation of hydrocarbons

Figure 4 shows, for three samples having an increasing maturation level and coming from N25, the chromatogram of the $> C_{15}$ saturated hydrocarbons from the chloroform extract. Sample **a**, which is the least evolved, contains very few *n*-alkanes. Some peaks around the *n*-C_{15} and *n*-C_{30} position come from sesquiterpenoids which, in mass spectrometry, give a fragment at m/e = 204, and pentacyclic triterpenoids derived from friedelin (Boudou, 1981). Sample **b** contains mainly $> C_{20}$ heavy *n*-alkanes having a marked odd predominance. The appearance of these alkanes, linked to the decrease in the O/C ratio between stages **a** and **b**, is due to the decarboxylation of vegetal cuticular waxes. In sample **c**, which is the most evolved, the *n*-alkanes have a regularly decreasing distribution, still with a slight odd predominance. This is the type of distribution that is found in a great many oils in the region. It is due to the thermal cracking of the kerogen and hydrocarbons already formed. Further stages of evolution, that are not obtained here because of the lack of more mature samples, but which are known from other investigations (Albrecht *et al.*, 1976), lead to an alkane distribution whose mode is centred around smaller and smaller carbon numbers and which finally leads to methane.

The formation of hydrocarbons in the coals was also examined by thermovaporization followed by simulated distillation. This method has great advantages compared with chloroform-extract analysis. It is much faster, can be performed on a very small sample and is capable of investigating a wider range of carbon atoms. However, it does not distinguish between saturated hydrocarbons and aromatic hydrocarbons and, until now, was limited to coals for analysis problems.

The quantitative results of this investigation for C_1–C_{35}, C_6–C_9, C_{10}–C_{14} and C_{25}–C_{35} carbon ranges are given in Figs 5 to 8, with the evolution being graduated in Rock–Eval peak temperatures (T_m). Although they were also investigated, the C_{15}–C_{19} and C_{20}–C_{24} distributions are not given here, the representative points of the samples from abnormal-pressure zones being widely scattered because of interference with fuel oil from the drilling mud in these carbon ranges. The amounts of hydrocarbons related to organic carbon are given for the four wells examined, two of which are situated on the top (H8 and H9bis) and two on the flank of the structures (H627 and N25). These amounts of hydrocarbons can be seen to have a regular evolution for the samples from the flank wells, with most of the representative points being within the limit curves traced on each figure, whereas the same is not true for the top wells. This regularity, together with the structural position of the wells and the similarity of the values observed, although these wells are quite far away from one another (Fig. 2), lead us to assume that these curves represent the formation of hydrocarbons by autochthonous organic matter without any influence by migration phenomena. The evolution with T_m of the amounts observed in the different classes effectively corresponds to what can be expected with this hypothesis of hydrocarbon formation, i.e. there is a progressive evolution, when T_m increases, of the carbon number of the hydrocarbons formed towards lighter and lighter fractions, with maximum formation moving from $T_m = 435$–440°C for class C_{25}–C_{35}, $T_m = 450$°C for class C_{10}–C_{14} and T_m far more than 450°C for class C_6–C_9. In this last class, as was shown by Bordenave *et al.* (1970) for other types of terrestrial organic matter, most of the products formed up to $T_m = 440$°C are represented by light aromatics, benzene, toluene and xylenes, which can easily be spotted on simulated distillation chromatograms (Fig. 9).

The formation curve for total hydrocarbons, both saturated and aromatic in the C_1 to C_{35} range (Fig. 5) has an 'S' shape, with the maximum amount formed being around 40 to 50 mg of hydrocarbons per g C, i.e. 2–2.5 Mt of HC km^{-3} of rock (assuming a rock with a porosity of 10% containing 2% organic carbon), which correlates effectively with the calculation made by Durand and Oudin (1979) using other geochemical parameters independent of the ones used here. The hydrocarbons formed in the diagenesis zone (420 °C $< T_m < 430$°C) by decarboxylation reactions represent about one fifth of the maximum amount, and they are mainly heavy hydrocarbons, as can be seen by comparing the distributions of the C_6–C_9 (Fig. 6), C_{10}–C_{14} (Fig. 7) and C_{25}–C_{35} (Fig. 8) classes. The inflection point of the total-hydrocarbon curve (Fig. 5), situated at the diagenesis/catagenesis transition ($T_m \sim 435$°C), will be interpreted as indicating the transition in the formation mechanisms of hydrocarbons, from decarboxylation to cracking of carbon–carbon bonds. This transition effec-

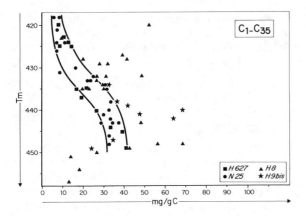

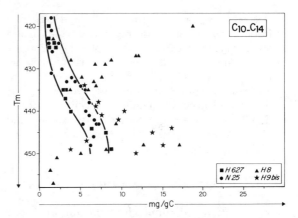

Fig. 5. Variation of the amount of total hydrocarbons in the C$_1$–C$_{35}$ range with increasing evolution (increasing T_m). Data are obtained by thermovaporization on coals from four wells. H8 and H9bis are located on the top of the Handil structure; H627 and N25 are located respectively on the flank of the Handil and Nilam structures.

Fig. 7. Variation of the amount of total hydrocarbons in the C$_{10}$–C$_{14}$ range with increasing evolution (see Fig. 5).

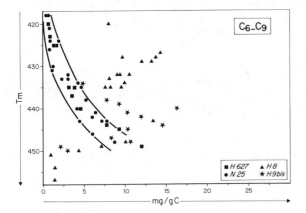

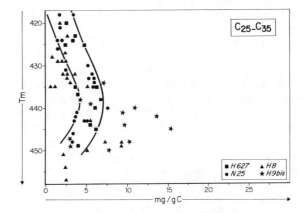

Fig. 6. Variation of the amount of total hydrocarbons in the C$_6$–C$_9$ range with increasing evolution (see Fig. 5).

Fig. 8. Variation of the amount of total hydrocarbons in the C$_{25}$–C$_{35}$ range with increasing evolution (see Fig. 5).

tively corresponds to a maximum value of formation in the C$_{25}$–C$_{35}$ class, the most frequent carbon range in the higher vegetal waxes.

MIGRATION PHENOMENA

If we return to hydrocarbon distributions by carbon classes, as shown in Figs 5 to 8, for the coals from the wells in the top of the Handil structure (H8 and H9bis), we can see that they do not follow the regular curves defined by the coals from wells H627 and N25. In what follows, we will explain why we attribute this deviation to migration phenomena.

Accumulation phenomena

Let us begin by recalling that a great many reservoirs exist at Handil, and that their filling up with hydrocarbons is all the more frequent as we approach the top of the structure. The positive deviation in total hydrocarbon amounts from C$_1$ to C$_{35}$ (Fig. 5) among the coals defining the amount formed *in situ* and some of the coals from H8 and H9bis will thus be interpreted as an

impregnation of these coals by migrated hydrocarbons. This interpretation is based on two observations.

(1) The depth of the impregnated samples, which is not indicated in Fig. 5, corresponds to that of the zones where hydrocarbon accumulations exist in Handil, i.e. $T_m = 420°C$ corresponding to the shallow zone of the reservoirs (850–1200 m), $T_m = 427–430°C$ corresponding to the main zone of the reservoirs (1800–2450 m) and $T_m = 440–443°C$ corresponding to the lower zone (2450–2800 m).

(2) The nature of the hydrocarbons impregnating the coals depends, just as for the oils, on the depth at which they are situated in the series. Indeed, if the amounts by carbon classes (Figs 6, 7 and 8) are compared with the curve for total amounts (Fig. 5), we can see that the accumulation in the upper zones (1200 and 2000–2200 m, $T_m = 420$ and 427–432°C) is mainly due to light hydrocarbons in classes C$_6$–C$_9$ and C$_{10}$–C$_{14}$. Class C$_{25}$–C$_{35}$ is not involved. On the other hand, in the deepest accumulation zone (2600–2800 m, $T_m = 440–443°C$), impregnation involves hydrocarbons from all molecular weights, both light and heavy. The curves assumed to represent the genesis of the different hydrocarbon

classes, based on coals from H627 and N25, are justified by arguments of regularity which is not observed in the accumulated samples. Therefore it is not possible to attribute the hydrocarbons in classes C_6-C_9 and $C_{10}-C_{14}$ from these samples entirely to an in-situ origin. Thus, we must assume that the light hydrocarbons, which were formed at greater depth, may have migrated more easily on account of their lower molecular weight and thus have risen higher up in the series.

Depletion phenomena

If we now examine the samples from the transition zone from wells H8 and H9bis (3000–3140 m, $T_m = 448–457$ °C), we find exactly the opposite phenomenon from the preceding one, i.e. the amounts measured are less than the amounts that would be expected from the model of the formation based on the flank wells, both for the total amounts of hydrocarbons (Fig. 5) and for the amounts by carbon classes (Figs 6–8). This cannot, therefore, be the result of a cracking phenomenon, and the systematic loss of hydrocarbons during handling, which may always occur for class C_6-C_9, is not very probable for class $C_{10}-C_{14}$. Consequently, this phenomenon will be interpreted as a depletion of hydrocarbons resulting from their departure by migration. As was seen previously, this phenomenon is much more appreciable for light hydrocarbons which migrate more easily. Moreover, this loss of the light fraction immediately appears in the comparison of the chromatograms made after the thermovaporization of two coals situated at the top and bottom of the transition zone (Fig. 9). By comparing the amounts remaining in the three deep samples from H8 with the theoretical amounts formed per carbon classes, it is apparent that only one tenth of the C_6-C_9 hy-

drocarbons and one third of the $C_{10}-C_{14}$ hydrocarbons remain. Class $C_{25}-C_{35}$ is almost unaffected.

Interpretation of the above observations in terms of migration thus reveals:

(1) The importance of working with light hydrocarbons ($<C_{14}$) for investigating migration phenomena, and especially for observing depletion phenomena.

(2) The fact that, in the carbon samples considered, the $C_{25}-C_{35}$ hydrocarbons migrate very little. Therefore they are always representative of organic matter in place or from nearby, hence having a similar degree of evolution. Nonetheless, this comment might not be applicable to shales in which migration may be facilitated by interbedding with sandy drains.

(3) The fact that a differentiation exists in the effects of migration, depending on the carbon classes of the hydrocarbons examined. This may be of help in choosing the most plausible migration mechanism in each case. In our conclusion, we will return to the mechanism considered for explaining the formation of the Handil field.

This interpretation allows the justification, *a posteriori*, of the use of samples coming from the flank wells for modeling the formation of hydrocarbons. Impregnation by migrated hydrocarbons is not very probable on the side of the structure except in the case of stratigraphic trapping. Moreover, these wells stopping near the top of the transition zone, the drainage of this zone is still not very apparent, if it exists.

PHENOMENA SPECIFIC TO THE HIGH-PRESSURE ZONE

Of the two wells from the top of the Handil field described here, one of them, H8, crosses through the entire transition zone (zone in which the pressure of the fluids gradually moves away from hydrostatic pressure and approaches geostatic pressure) and stops at the top of the high-pressure zone. The other well, H9bis, was continued for nearly 1000 m in the high-pressure zone. Samples of cuttings were analysed; unfortunately, the use of an oil-base drilling mud prevented any analysis of coals by thermovaporization and simulated distillation. Whenever possible, the coals were isolated by manual sorting of chloroform-washed cuttings, but a great many samples did not contain any coal. Therefore, kerogens were prepared. Elemental analyses and Rock–Eval pyrolysis characterization were done on both coals and kerogens. An x-ray mineralogical analysis was also made of untreated cuttings and their shaly fraction.

Mineralogical analyses as well as the aspect of the cuttings show that the portion of the high-pressure zone situated below 3250 m is different from the upper part by its richness in silts, and that the kaolinite that is found there and makes up most of the shaly fraction is a product of hydrothermal neogenesis. This shows that it is possible for fluids to circulate inside the high-pressure zone. We will return to this point later.

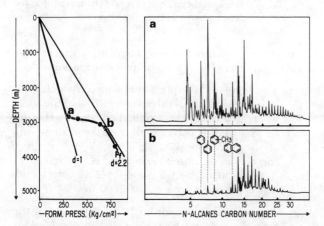

Fig. 9. On the left, evolution of the formation pressure P_f (pressure of the fluids inside the pores) with depth in the top wells of Handil. Equivalent density, d, corresponding to the specific weight of the drilling mud required for equilibrium, is indicated. Normal pressure (hydrostatic pressure) corresponds to $d = 1$. High pressure (geostatic pressure) corresponds to $d = 2.2$. On the right, chromatograms obtained by thermovaporization on coals from Handil top (well H8). Sample **a** (2865 m, 41 mg HC g^{-1} C) located at the normal pressure zone/transition zone boundary is not affected by migration phenomena, whereas sample **b** (3140 m, 13 mg HC g^{-1} C) located at the transition zone/high pressure zone boundary is strongly depleted, mainly in the light carbon range.

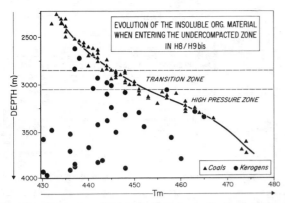

Fig. 10. Evolution of Rock-Eval T_m in the insoluble organic matter (coals and kerogens) from wells H8 and H9bis, when going from normal-pressure zone to high-pressure zone.

The results of Rock–Eval pyrolysis are given in Fig. 10 in the form of a graph showing T_m as a function of depth for coals and kerogens. Whereas in the normal-pressure zone at the top of Handil, including the one not shown here (from 0 to 2250 m), the increase in T_m for both coals and kerogens follows the increase in depth and thus clearly indicates the maturation of the organic matter, a new phenomenon is observed in the abnormal-pressure zone. Coals and some kerogens show a regular and increasing variation of T_m with depth. However, the major part of the kerogens underneath the top of the high-pressure zone (3150 m) does not follow this regular curve, and especially underneath 3250 m. The T_m values may even be lower than 435 °C, i.e. lower than the level of maturation generally considered to be the threshold of the oil generation. Since the succession of the maturation levels of organic matter undergoing increasing burial can, at the most, remain constant but cannot retrograde, this means that there is a change in the nature of the organic matter being analysed. This is confirmed by optical analysis. Beside the humic coals and kerogens showing normal behavior, pyrobitumens appear in the form of finely dispersed amorphous organic particles which are quite recognizable by their optical properties in transmitted and reflected light. These pyrobitumens represent the residual products of thermal and eventually oxidative alteration of a crude oil, besides lighter hydrocarbons which can either migrate toward cooler zones or be again cracked. These pyrobitumens having a less complex and probably less condensed structure than the kerogen are more easily decomposed than this kerogen during Rock–Eval pyrolysis and so have a lower T_m. In fact, in the samples analysed, we observe the result given by the mixture in varying proportions of humic kerogen and pyrobitumens.

The distinction between humic kerogens or coals and pyrobitumens, which appears clearly with methods such as optical observation and Rock–Eval pyrolysis, is much more difficult to detect by elemental analysis. This might be suspected as the result of both the many possible causes of alteration of the measurements (especially for oxygen), and the overall nature of the results obtained. In any case, notwithstanding the many fluctuations, it appears that the H/C ratio of pyrobitumens does not vary and remains around 0.9, whereas the same ratio decreases to 0.7 in coals at the bottom of well H9bis (T_m ~475°C). The maturation level of the autochthonous

organic matter at this depth is thus presently at the threshold of the dry-gas formation zone.

The above observations suggest that the presence of the high-pressure zone has a specific influence on the composition of the hydrocarbons produced by the source rock, on account of the delay it causes in the expulsion of water and hydrocarbons. The heavy hydrocarbons formed by the thermal cracking of kerogen inside the high-pressure zone remain in a dispersed state for a longer time inside the source rock because the main cause of primary migration, which is the pressure gradient in the pores caused by compaction, no longer exists. (On the other hand, this cause is particularly effective in the transition zone.) The effect of time and temperature results in lighter and lighter hydrocarbons by cracking, and only the fraction that has been carried by convection or diffusion to the vicinity of the transition zone will be able to escape.

In the light of the above observations, it appears that a high-pressure zone is not necessarily impermeable, and this seems to be the case below 3250 m at Handil. Considering the high silt content and the special composition of the shales in this zone (kaolinite from neogenesis, in large crystals), fluid circulation may possibly be easy there. In fact, there is no communication between this zone and the overlying zone, and the cause of the overall relative impermeability probably lies in the transition zone.

CONCLUSIONS

Formation of the Handil field

In the light of the general results described above, various hypotheses can be formulated to explain the migration mechanisms which have led to the formation of the Handil field. The geochemical examination of hydrocarbon formation shows that the most favorable zone for the formation of liquid hydrocarbons is the one with a T_m of between 440 and 450°C, i.e. mainly the transition zone. The high-pressure zone, on the other hand, gives rise to the creation of gas on account of the delay it causes in fluid flow. This gas percolates through the transition zone and entrains liquid hydrocarbons exactly as a solvent would do during chromatography. This mechanism is probably superposed on the expulsion of oil by compaction in the transition zone, thus improving, and perhaps appreciably so, the efficiency of migration. Most of the oil thus expelled can be found in the main zone of the Handil reservoirs, i.e. 500 to 1000 m above the zone where it was formed. The light fraction continues to rise in the series and, little by little, becomes trapped in successive reservoirs, locally entraining heavy hydrocarbons over shorter distances. A large portion of the methane probably reaches the surface in this way and is released into the atmosphere. This mechanism, which is similar to elution chromatography, explains why the distribution of oil by specific gravity in this field is the opposite from what would have been expected if source rocks of increasing maturation levels had been in immediate contact with the reservoirs, i.e. lighter and lighter oils with increasing depth. The same mechanism also explains why the distributions by carbon atoms in the oils, in the shallow zone and in this zone only, are bimodal: these oils are largely made up of an allochthonous light fraction which has migrated over long distances, the remainder being an autochthonous heavy fraction.

Ubiquity of migration phenomena

This study finally leads to the conclusion that the spatial distribution and composition of the oils in the different reservoirs of the Handil field are mainly controlled by migration phenomena. In many other petroleum basins it can be supposed that the nature and maturation level of the source rocks also influence the distribution of oils; it is nonetheless obvious that migration is a banal phenomenon which always accompanies the formation of oil fields. Therefore, an analysis of possible migration paths and of migration consequences must always be done together with the identification of source rocks, when examining problems of source-rock/reservoir correlation. If the influence of migration phenomena is not regarded in the case described here, we arrive at a hydrocarbon formation scheme in which the light fractions are formed before the heavy ones. This contradicts both laboratory simulations and observations based on various basins in which little migration is known to have occurred because of the absence of fields.

Dynamic nature of migration phenomena

The different oil fields in the Mahakam Delta make up a specially favorable subject for studying migration phenomena. Indeed, since the series are of recent age, the formation and accumulation of hydrocarbons are presently in full evolution and so show the dynamic nature of the phenomena involved. As was previously mentioned in the paper presented at the World Petroleum Congress in Bucharest (Durand and Oudin, 1979), the nature (oil or gas) and amount of the hydrocarbons accumulated in the different fields of the Mahakam delta depend only on the relative position, related to time, of the hydrocarbon formation zone and of the zone from which these hydrocarbons may have been expelled.

So, the existence of a high-pressure zone plays a specific role in this dynamic process. This zone, whose existence is linked to sedimentological phenomena, probably has boundaries that are relatively independent of the rate of burial but, on the other hand, the pressure attained in this zone closely depends on this rate of burial. Therefore, when high-pressure zones exist, the nature of the hydrocarbons found in the reservoirs will depend not only on the conditions under which the petroleum products were formed but also on their migration possibilities. Practically only gaseous hydrocarbons can be expelled from the high-pressure zone. In the example of the Mahakam Delta presented here, where the same potential source rock is found in a high-pressure zone and in an overlying normal-pressure zone as a result of sedimentological conditions and rate of burial, the nature of the hydrocarbons accumulated will change with time, according to the scheme given in Table 1. This scheme is arbitrarily divided into five stages, focusing mainly on the nature, oil or gas, of the hydrocarbons formed in the source rock but, of course, the composition of hydrocarbons during genesis varies

Table 1

	PRESSURE	INCREASING TIME				
		STAGE 1	STAGE 2	STAGE 3	STAGE 4	STAGE 5
GENESIS IN THE SOURCE ROCK	NP*	Immature	Immature	Oil	Oil + gas	Gas
	HP*	Oil	Oil + gas	Gas	Nothing	Nothing
MIGRATION FROM THE SOURCE ROCK	NP	Nothing	Nothing	Oil	Oil + gas	Gas
	HP	Nothing	Gas	Gas	Nothing	Nothing (or a bit of gas formed in Stage 3)
CONTENTS OF THE RESERVOIRS	NP	Nothing	Gas	Oil + gas	Oil + gas	Gas
EXAMPLE IN MAHAKAM FIELDS		Trend** Dian-Pantuan	Nilam Badak	Handil Attaka		

* NP Normal-pressure zone.
HP High-pressure zone underneath the NP zone.

** Next trend east of Bekapai - Attaka.

continuously from heavy oil to nearly dry methane. Nevertheless, the separation by stages allows to point out the following:

(1) The abundance of gas in this type of situation depends more on migration conditions than on any particular aptitude for gas formation linked to the nature of the source rock.

(2) The chronology for the appearance of hydrocarbons in the reservoirs is also linked to migration conditions and cannot be superposed on the chronology of hydrocarbon formation inside source rocks.

We can thus see to what extent migration conditions can modify in this situation the spatial and temporal distribution in reservoirs of the hydrocarbons produced by a given source rock.

Question

K. de GROOT:

Can you comment on the amount of pseudokerogen, or pyrobitumen found in the overpressured zones?

Answer

M. VANDENBROUCKE:

A distinction between pyrobitumen and autochthonous kerogen is not easy because many geochemical parameters are quite similar. However, optical examination of samples showed that pyrobitumen were abundant, even forming the major fraction of the organic material in some cases. An idea of the amount of pyrobitumen in particular samples, expressed as organic carbon content in the rock, can be deduced from both the lithology and the Rock-Eval data: silts contain mainly allochthonous organic matter, and Rock-Eval T_m allows to distinguish pyrobitumen from kerogens. The carbon content in silts from H9bis below 3500 m and such as $430°C < T_m < 440°C$, is generally around or slightly higher than 1%. If the concentration of pyrobitumen is homogenized in the lower high-pressure zone by convection and migration phenomena, then the total organic carbon, which varies there around a mean value of 2%, is fairly equally distributed between autochthonous kerogen and pyrobitumen.

At last, the composition of an oil, even when accumulated in a reservoir, evolves with time. Indeed, hydrocarbon migration continues both from the source rock where new hydrocarbons are formed and will in part be added to the ones already in place, and through the cap-rock of the reservoir through which the lightest hydrocarbons escape. Therefore, the size and even the existence of an accumulation are linked to the relative rates of arrival and escape of hydrocarbons, i.e. to migration phenomena.

Acknowledgments

We thank all our colleagues at I.F.P. and TOTAL C.F.P. who have taken part in this project, and especially Mesdames Bessereau and Bernon and Messrs Pittion, Albouy, Buton, Espitalié and Paratte. We also thank C.F.P. for having supplied a great many geological documents and Compagnie Total Indonésie for having sent samples and for having been particularly careful in taking cuttings from well H9bis. Finally, we thank these latter companies together with societies Pertamina and Inpex for having authorized this publication.

REFERENCES

Albrecht, P., Vandenbroucke, M. and Mandengué, M. (1976) Geochemical studies on the organic matter from the Douala Basin (Cameroon) — I Evolution of the extractable organic matter and the formation of petroleum. *Geochim. Cosmochim. Acta* **40**, 791–799.

Bordenave, M., Combaz, A. and Giraud, A. (1970) Influence de l'origine des matières organiques et de leur degré d'évolution sur les produits de pyrolyse du kérogène. In *Advances in Organic Geochemistry 1966*, ed. by Hobson, G. D. and Speers, G. C. Pergamon Press, Oxford, pp. 389–405.

Combaz, A. and de Matharel, M. (1978) Organic sedimentation and genesis of petroleum in Mahakam delta, Borneo. *Am. Assoc. Pet. Geol. Bull.* **62**, 1684–1695.

Durand, B. and Espitalié, J. (1976) Geochemical studies on the organic matter from the Douala basin (Cameroon) — II Evolution of kerogen. *Geochim. Cosmochim. Acta* **40**, 801–808.

Durand, B. and Monin, J. C. (1980) Elemental analysis of kerogens (C, H, O, N, S, Fe). In *Kerogen — Insoluble organic matter from sedimentary rocks*, ed. by Durand, B. Editions

Technip, France, pp. 113–142.

Durand, B. and Nicaise, G. (1980) Procedures for kerogen isolation. In *Kerogen — Insoluble organic matter from sedimentary rocks*, ed. Durand, B. Editions Technip, France, pp. 35–52.

Durand, B. and Oudin, J. L. (1979) Exemple de migration des hydrocarbures dans une série deltaïque: le delta de la Mahakam, Kalimantan, Indonesia. *Proc. 10th World Pet. Congr.* **1**, 3.11.

Espitalié, J., Madec, M., Tissot, B., Mennig, J. J. and Leplat, P. (1977) Source rock characterization method for petroleum exploration. OTC paper 2935.

Fabre, M., Leblond, C. and Roucaché, J. (1972) Analyse quantitative par CPG capillaire des *n*-alcanes de C12 à C32 dans les hydrocarbures saturés d'un pétrole brut ou d'un extrait de roche. *Rev. Inst. Fr. Pét.* **27**, 469–481.

Huc, A. Y. and Roucaché, J. G. (1981) Quantitative thin layer chromatography of sedimentary organic matter. *Anal. Chem.* **53**, 914.

Huc, A. Y., Roucaché, J. G., Bernon, M., Caillet, G. and Da Silva, M. (1976) Application de la chromatographie sur couche mince à l'étude quantitative et qualitative des extraits de roches et des huiles. *Rev. Inst. Fr. Pét.* **31**, 67–98.

Jonathan, D., L'Hote, G. and de Rouchet, J. (1975) Analyse géochimique des hydrocarbures légers par thermovaporisation. *Rev. Inst. Fr. Pét.* **30**, 65–98.

Magnier, P. and Ben Samsu (1975) The Handil oil field in East Kalimantan. *Proceedings of the Indonesian Petroleum Association, 4th Annual Convention*, June 1975.

Monin, J. C., Pelet, R. and Février, A. (1978) Analyse géochimique de la matière organique extraite des roches sédimentaires; IV: Extraction des roches en faibles quantités. *Rev. Inst. Fr. Pét.* **33**, 223–240.

Saint-Paul, C., Monin, J. C. and Durand, B. (1980) Méthode de caractérisation rapide des hydrocarbures de C1 à C35 contenus dans les roches sédimentaires et dans les huiles. *Rev. Inst. Fr. Pét.* **35**, 1065–1078.

Schaefer, R. G., Leythaeuser, D. and Weiner, B. (1978) Single-step capillary GC method for extraction and analysis of sub ppb quantities of hydrocarbons (C2–C8) from rock and crude oil samples and its applications in petroleum geochemistry. *J. Chromatogr.* **167**, 355–363.

Tissot, B., Durand, B., Espitalié, J. and Combaz, A. (1974) Influence of nature and diagenesis of organic matter in formation of petroleum. *Am. Assoc. Pet. Geol. Bull.* **58**, 499 . 506.

Trendel in Boudou, J. P. (1981) Diagenèse organique de sédiments deltaïques (Delta de la Mahakam — Indonésie). Thesis, Université d'Orléans, p. 80.

Verdier, A. C., Oki, T. and Suardy, A. (1979) Geology of the Handil field. American Association of Petroleum Geologists' Convention, Houston, March 1979.

Advances in Organic Geochemistry 1981, pp. 156–163
© John Wiley & Sons Limited, 1983

Maturity Related Biomarker and Stable Isotope Variations and Their Application to Oil/Source Rock Correlation in the Mahakam Delta Kalimantan

M. Schoell, M. Teschner and H. Wehner

Bundesanstalt für Geowissenschaften und Rohstoffe, Hannover, FRG

B. Durand

Institut Français du Pétrole, Rueil-Malmaison, France

J. L. Oudin

Compagnie Française des Pétroles, Talence, France

Maturity dependent stereochemical and isotopic parameters have been investigated in extracts from humic (type III) kerogens covering a maturity range between $T_{max} \approx 420$ to 450 °C ($R_0 \approx 0.45$ to 0.8%). The epimerization ratio 22S/22R of the C_{32} hopanes approaches values slightly above unity already at maturities around $T_{max} \approx 425$ °C $R_0 \approx 0.5\%$). Above this maturity no dependence on maturity has been found. The C_{30} hopane/$C_{29} + C_{30}$ moretane ratio (M_H) and the 20S/20R ratio of the C_{29} steranes (M_{SE}) are linearly correlated with maturity:

$$T_{max} = 8 \times M_H + 420$$
$$T_{max} = 23 \times M_{SE} + 416$$

Also the isotopic difference between the NSO extract and the kerogen are strongly dependent on maturity. A corresponding maturity parameter $M = \delta D_{kerogen}/\delta D_{NSO}$ approaches unity at maturities of oil formation. Four crudes of the area revealed sterane and triterpane patterns which are similar to the mature extracts. This is regarded as evidence that the oils are sourced from the humic kerogens in the Mahakam Delta. A quantitative oil to source correlation has been performed using the hopane/moretane maturation parameter M_H which indicates that all oils are derived from a narrow maturity interval ($T_{max} \approx 440$ to 450 °C). The depth of this interval is at Handil around 2800 m. Oils must have migrated between 300 and 1400 m in vertical distance to their reservoirs.

INTRODUCTION

One of the pertinent interests in organic geochemistry applied to petroleum geology is the establishment of reliable internal maturity parameters of organic compounds, which ideally should be quantitative and independent of the organic matter source.

Early attempts using stable isotopes date back to the work of Silverman (1971). Later, Orr (1974) established a maturation index by using the sulphur chemistry of oils and their sulphur isotopic composition. Recent developments in biomarker geochemistry have led to establish a variety of molecular parameters which are sensitive to maturation through transformation of compounds or isomerization at chiral centres (Ensminger *et al.*, 1974; Ensminger *et al.*, 1977; Seifert and Moldowan, 1978, 1980, 1981; Mackenzie *et al.*, 1980).

Cases of chemically uniform source rocks are rare but are a prerequisite if changes of the molecular parameters are to be related to maturity and not to facies changes. Previously published work has concentrated on oils and oil prone kerogen of type II but little information is available on maturity parameters in humic organic matter of type III (Tissot *et al.*, 1974). Moreover, it is desirable to relate more quantitatively stereochemical or isotopic parameters to other quantitative maturation parameters such as vitrinite reflectance or Rock-Eval pyrolysis data.

This paper reports the results of biomarker and isotope analyses performed on sediments from the Mahakam Delta in which only humic organic matter is encountered. These sediments consist of surprisingly uniform facies of alternating sand clay lithology with intercalations of coaly material throughout the delta. The investigated drillholes penetrated undisturbed series of increasing maturity up to levels of the main stage of oil formation.

The purpose of the paper is to investigate parameters, both isotopic and stereochemical, in a uniform series of source rocks of variable maturity. Changes in these parameters should then reflect maturation.

Experimental

Samples from Handil have been prepared for isotope analysis at IFP. The rocks were extracted and demineralized according to standard procedures described by Durand and Nicaise (1980). H/C analyses were carried out following procedures described by Durand and Monin (1980). Carbon and hydrogen isotope analyses were conducted at BGR according to procedures described by Redding *et al.*, 1980. The values are reported in the δ-notation $(\delta = (R_{sample}/R_{standard} - 1) \times 1000(\%_0)$ against the PDB and SMOW standard for carbon and hydrogen respectively. Maturities of organic matter have been determined by Rock-Eval pyrolysis and are reported as T_{max} values, i.e. the temperature of maximum yield of pyrolysate. T_{max} correlated well with the vitrinite reflectance in the Mahakam Delta (Durand and Oudin, 1979; Fig. 3), and therefore, provided a good maturity indicator. The samples from Nilam were processed at the BGR laboratories according to the following procedures.

Column chromatography. Sediments were ground to less than 100 μm, soxhlet-extracted with dichloromethane for 18 h. The deasphaltation procedure involved pouring the sample into a mixture of dichloromethane–petroleum ether (bp 40–60 °C) 1:30 and centrifugation at 800 rpm for 20 min. After removal of the solvent the deasphalted samples were chromatographed on an automatic system consisting of 50 cm × 4 mm ID columns filled with alumina (neutral, activated 2 h at 700 °C) and silica gel (70/230 mesh activated 6 h at 400 °C). Saturated hydrocarbons (SHC) were eluted with *n*-heptane, and the hetero-compound-fraction (NSO) with dichloromethane–methanol (2:1).

GC/MS. The SHC-fraction was subjected to GC using a Hewlett–Packard 5985 A instrument consisting of a 5840 A gas chromatograph, a quadrupole MS and a 21 MXE computer. A 25 m × 0.2 m ID fused silica SP-2100 capillary column was temperature programmed from 100 °C at 10°/min to 170 °C, then at 4°/min to 250 °C and at 2°/min to 280 °C. The MS instrument was directly coupled to the GC and for MS analyses the selected-ion-monitoring mode measuring 200 msec at each mass point (m/e 191.2, 217.2 and two other) with 70 eV electron energy was used. Quantification was performed by electronic integration of the 191.2 — or 217.2 — mass fragmentograms.

AREA OF INVESTIGATION

Basic geochemical data of the Mahakam Delta have been reported by Durand and Oudin (1979). Our

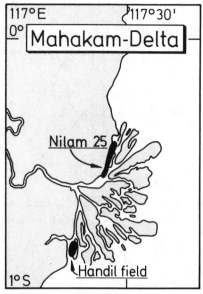

Fig. 1. Area of investigation.

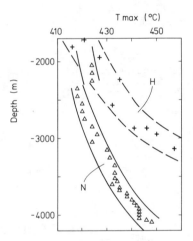

Fig. 2. Maturity/depth relationship at wells of the Nilam (N) and Handil (H) fields.

investigations have been performed on sample material from Handil and Nilam fields which are very close to the area described by Durand and Oudin. We refer therefore to this paper. Two wells at Handil and Nilam have been investigated (Fig. 1). Handil is situated on a structural high where the maturity gradient is higher than at Nilam (Fig. 2). However, the maturity follows in general the chronostratigraphy. For this reason strata of similar maturity are approximately of the same age. So plotting the data versus maturity instead of depth should make the data of both sites comparable.

The kerogens in both drillholes are entirely of humic type, partly forming thin coal seams. H/C ratios range from 0.86 to 0.74 and O/C ratios decrease from 0.3 to 0.07 from immature to mature kerogens.

The organic matter (OM) in all investigated samples is very uniform. No significant changes neither in the type of macerals nor in their amount have been found. On average, 30–40% are amorphous OM, 20 to 30% are coaly particles and 30 to 50% are vegetal debris throughout the investigated depth.

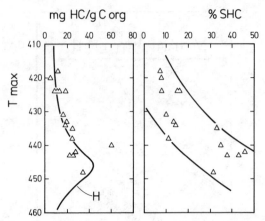

Fig. 3. Extractable organic matter as a function of maturity. (Left: mg hydrocarbons per gram organic carbon; right: amount of saturated hydrocarbons, SHC.) Triangles = Nilam. H = Handil.

In the immature sections, resins are common. The source for the organic matter is tropical forest which has not changed since Miocene time.

Results

Extractable organic matter. In immature sections 3 to 6% of organic matter is extractable whereas 5 to 16% is extractable in the mature section. Both sites, Handil and Nilam, have quite similar quantities of extractable hydrocarbons (Fig. 3 (left)). Saturate contents in extract, (Fig. 3 (right)), an accepted measure of maturity, increases clearly with maturity.

Molecular parameters in extractable OM. C_{32} *hopane epimerization.* The S/R doublet which represents the epimerization at C22 was selected. Figure 4(a) shows that within the T_{max} range investigated, this parameter does not increase linearly with maturity. A sharp increase in the 22S/22R ratio at low maturity levels ($T_{max} \approx 425$ °C) was observed.

C_{29} *steranes.* We have analysed the isomers 5α, 14α, 17α, 20S and 20R of the C_{29} steranes. The ratio of 20S/20R gives the increasing degree of epimerization which has been shown to be dependent on maturity (Seifert and Moldowan, 1981; Mackenzie *et al.*, 1980). 20S/20R ratios (M_{SE}) increase towards unity in mature

Table 1
Analytical data on extracts and stereochemical maturation parameters at a drillhole of Nilam/Mahakam Delta field

Depth	T_{max} (°C)	$\dfrac{\text{Extr.}}{C_{org}} \times 10^2$	HC[a] (mg/g)	SHC (%)	M_{SE}[b]	M_H[c]	M_{HE}[d]
2050	424	3.14	8.64	16.2	0.22	0.24	0.15
2150	424	—	—	—	—	—	—
2250	424	6.81	13.21	7.9	0.18	0.22	0.25
2350	418	—	—	—	—	—	—
2450	418	4.12	11.62	7.1	0.22	0.45	0.20
2550	420	—	—	—	—	—	—
2650	420	2.47	4.74	7.7	0.16	0.56	0.52
2750	421	—	—	—	—	—	—
2850	424	3.04	11.42	9.4	0.48	1.04	1.27
2950	426	—	—	—	—	—	—
3050	424	4.37	18.61	15.1	0.37	1.00	1.17
3150	430	—	—	—	—	—	—
3250	431	4.02	16.05	10.0	0.59	1.18	1.35
3350	433	—	—	—	—	—	—
3450	433	5.28	19.15	13.5	1.04	2.05	1.43
3520	433	—	—	—	—	—	—
3560	434	4.68	18.08	14.4	0.92	1.48	1.43
3600	432	—	—	—	—	—	—
3640	435	5.29	24.47	32.8	0.95	1.67	1.51
3680	435	—	—	—	—	—	—
3720	438	6.88	24.09	11.3	0.87	2.78	1.44
3760	438	—	—	—	—	—	—
3800	440	16.58	71.01	34.9	1.30	2.09	1.46
3840	441	—	—	—	—	—	—
3880	442	4.18	27.12	45.8	0.94	2.42	1.44
3920	443	—	—	—	—	—	—
3960	443	5.40	25.04	43.0	1.08	4.16	1.49
4000	443	—	—	—	—	—	—
4040	443	4.71	21.65	37.7	1.18	3.58	1.42
4065	446	—	—	—	—	—	—
4092	448	8.22	33.85	31.4	1.15	2.89	1.44

[a] Hydrocarbons in extracts as mg per g C_{org}
[b] 5α, 14α, 17α C_{29} sterane epimerization 20S/20R.
[c] Ratio of C_{30} hopane/$C_{29} + C_{30}$ moretanes.
[d] C_{32} hopane epimerization ratio 22S/22R.

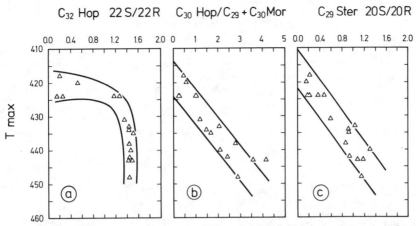

Fig. 4. Variation of stereochemical parameters with maturity (Nilam field). (a) Epimerization ratio 22S/22R of C_{32} hopanes. (b) Ratio of C_{30} hopanes versus $C_{29} + C_{30}$ moretanes (M_H in Fig. 9). (c) Epimerization ratio 20S/20R of C_{29} steranes (M_S)

samples. We found this parameter to correlate well with maturity (Fig. 4(c)). In the case of the Nilam site, the 20S/20R ratio increases linearly with the relationship:

$$T_{max} \approx 23 \times M_{SE} + 416$$

which would, in this case, enable prediction of the maturity from the isomer ratio. We have measured 20S/20R ratios slightly above unity; however, most cases in the literature report 20S/20R ratios levelling off at unity.

Hopane/moretane ratio. Hopane and moretane stereochemistry has been shown by Seifert and Moldowan (1980) to be specifically susceptible to thermal stress. We have selected the C_{30} hopane/C_{29} $+ C_{30}$ moretane ratio (M_H) and found good correlation with maturity (Fig. 4(b)). Again, for Nilam, a relationship between T_{max} and the molecular maturity parameter can be given:

$$T_{max} \approx 8 \times M_H + 420$$

where M_H is the C_{30} hopane/$C_{29} + C_{30}$ moretane ratio.

Stable isotopes. Carbon and hydrogen isotopic composition of extracted NSO compounds at the Handil field revealed a marked trend towards positive values with increasing depth and maturity (Fig. 5). The

shallowest sample from Handil at 280 m has $\delta^{13}C$ and δD values of $-20.8‰$ and $-192‰$. The corresponding kerogen, however, is more positive by 2.0‰ and 77‰ respectively. The deeper, more mature samples become isotopically more similar to the kerogen and indistinguishable at maturities exceeding the level corresponding to $T_{max} \approx 440$ °C or $R_0 \approx 0.7\%$.

Discussion of the results

Homogeneity of organic matter The rationale of this investigation was to select a series of source rocks for which primary differences in the organic matter due to the variation of facies or other parameters can be neglected. This is certainly true in this investigation as regards the principal type of organic matter: All investigated samples were oxygen rich type III and humic kerogens. Paleogeographically, the area has remained unchanged since Miocene and organic matter accumulated from higher plant debris from tropical forests. Kerogen samples show a shift in carbon isotopic composition from oldest to youngest of approximately 2‰ in favour of the ^{12}C isotope. This shift could be attributed either to primary effects such as change of climate or plant species, or to secondary effects such as the maturation of organic matter (Monin *et al.*, in press). Maturation is unlikely to cause a 2‰ change (Redding *et*

Table 2

Isotopic composition of kerogens and NSO extracts at a drillhole of the Handil/Mahakam Delta field

No.	Depth	T_{max} (°C)	NSO Extract		Kerogen	
			$\delta^{13}C$	δD	$\delta^{13}C$	δD
1	280	414	-30.8	-192	-28.8	-115
2	1810	416	-29.1	-174	-28.7	-118
3	1720	421	-28.1	-165	-28.7	-118
4	1280	423	-29.1	-166	-28.5	-106
5	1949	427	-28.7	-145	-28.0	-102
6	2570	432	-28.4	-126	-28.2	-113
7	2236	435	-28.1	-134	-27.7	-102
8	2874	441	-28.0	-124	-27.8	-116
9	2870	446	-27.8	-107	-27.8	-98
10	2965	450	-28.1	-112	-28.1	-98
11	3140	457	—	—	-27.0	-65

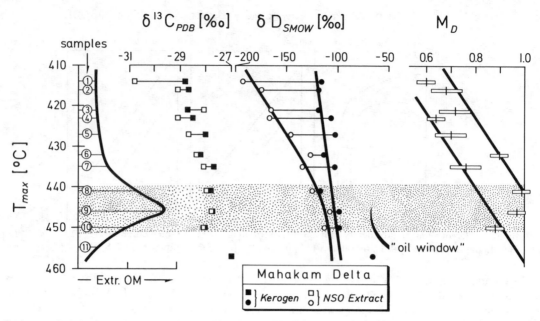

Fig. 5.   Carbon and hydrogen isotopic composition of kerogen and NSO-extracts as a function of maturity. M_D is the ratio of δD
values of NSO extracts versus kerogen and approaches unity at maturities of the oil window.

al., 1980). The major product of maturation is CO_2 and
this should isotopically resemble the kerogen itself
(Galimov, 1980). Climatic changes have been reported
to affect the hydrogen isotopic composition of cellulose
but not carbon isotopic composition (Yapp and Epstein,
1977). Minor changes in the species of higher landplants
may therefore account for the observed shift in isotopic
composition of the kerogen. We regard such minor
changes as insignificant for changes found in extractable
OM. Changes in the various stereochemical parameters
(Fig. 4) and the change in isotopic composition of
heterocompounds (Fig. 5) are interpreted as being
predominantly, if not solely, due to maturation.

Maturation dependent parameters. Epimeri-
zation at C_{22} of the C_{32} hopanes does not seem to react
linearly with maturation, and is therefore not a suitable
maturation parameter. Seifert and Moldowan (1980)
also report only minor changes in this ratio for mature
samples. The other molecular parameters, however,
correlated well with maturity. Mackenzie *et al.* (1980)
found good correlation of C_{20} configuration of C_{29}
steranes with approximately 0.3 at the beginning of the
zone of oil formation.

In the Mahakam Delta the value of 0.3 corresponds to
maturities around $T_{max} \approx 420$ °C ($R_0 \sim 0.47$). Onset of
hydrocarbon generation in Handil is assumed to be
above maturities of $T_{max} \approx 440$ °C ($R_0 \approx 0.7$) (Durand and

Oudin, 1979). This may be a principal difference
between type II and type III kerogens, however, more
data are needed to justify this interpretation.
Hopane/moretane ratios in type III kerogens also seem
to correlate with maturity as was found for type II
kerogen by Seifert and Moldowan (1980) and
Mackenzie *et al.* (1980). A C_{30} hopane/$C_{29} + C_{30}$
moretane ratio of 2.5 is found for the maturity at the
onset of oil formation.

The variation of the isotopic composition of the NSO
fraction with maturity is of specific interest in that the
isotopic similarity between the NSO fraction and
kerogen could be used for oil/source rock correlation
(Stahl, 1980). Figure 5 shows that this would be
applicable only in the mature zone of the Mahakam
Delta. It is not possible to use extracts from immature
outcrop samples for oil to source rock correlation,
because these NSO fractions are isotopically different
compared to mature kerogens. NSO fractions of extracts
are isotopically similar to kerogens in mature rocks, not
only for carbon but also for hydrogen. Therefore
hydrogen isotopes may also be used for oil/source rock
correlation. The ratio $\delta D_{kerogen}/\delta D_{NSO}$ may be defined as
a maturity parameter, M_D, shown in Fig. 5.

Change in isotopic composition of the extractable
NSO compounds could be explained by the fact that the

Table 3

Stereochemical parameters of oils at the Handil field

Reservoir depth	M_{SE}	M_H
~2000 m	0.71	3.74
~2600 m	1.04	4.12
—	1.24	3.40
~1400 m	0.90	2.94

Table 4

Isotopic composition of the NSO fraction of oils at the
Handil/Mahakam Delta field

Reservoir depth	$\delta^{13}C$	δD
~450 m	−27.9	−137
~700 m	−27.8	−126
~1000 m	−28.0	−121
~1400 m	−28.0	−126
~1400 m	−28.0	−131

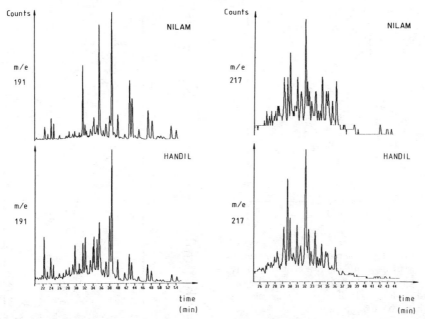

Fig. 6. Sterane (m/e = 217) and triterpane (m/e = 191) patterns in mature extracts (top) and oils (bottom). Explanation see text.

extractable part of immature OM stems to a large extent from the deposited organic matter still possessing the original lipidic material of living organic matter. This assumption is supported by the fact that resins found in lignites had negative δD values (-180 to -216%). The corresponding $\delta^{13}C$ values range between -30.6 and -26.6%. It is conceivable that an appreciable part of immature extractable material, resins and lipids, contribute predominantly to the NSO fraction. Increasing isotopic similarity between NSO fraction and kerogen with higher extract yields reflect the increasing conversion of biological material and the increasing formation of extractable organic matter from maturation reactions of the kerogen itself.

The change of δD values of the NSO fraction would then directly reflect the increasing contribution of thermally produced extracts which are products of the rearrangement of kerogen and therefore are isotopically similar to the kerogen.

Oil/source rock correlation. The extracts of the Mahakam source rocks exhibit some internal stereochemical and isotopic relationships which can be related to maturity. An oil/source rock correlation was attempted using these parameters on oils reservoired at various depths in Handil. It should be noted that the extract results have been obtained from the Nilam field and those of the oils from Handil. We assume here the general applicability of the results from one well to another in this region.

Figure 6 gives a comparison of the general sterane and triterpane pattern from mature extracts and petroleums in the area of investigation. The m/e 217 trace of a mature extract shows great similarity in the elution pattern of C_{29}-steranes (retention times 34 to 37 min) when compared with an oil. A very good match has been found for the 5α, 14α, 17α 20R/20S and 5α, 14β, 17β 20R/20S isomers.

Characteristic to these fingerprints is the very high abundance of presumably 5α, 14α, 17α, 20S-

methylcholestane which is the most prominent peak in both sediment and oil fragmentograms. Rearranged steranes of cholestane type (retention times 26 to 29 min) are of very low concentration which again is a characteristic feature to both fingerprints. Finally the overall shape of the m/e 217-trace (distribution of most prominent peaks, ratio of peak heights or peak areas of adjacent peaks etc.) gives a good comparability.

Hopane is the most abundant triterpane. As can be seen from the ratios of 17α, 21β, 22S/22R-homohopane, C_{31} epimers are similar in both oil and extract. The concentrations of the C_{29}- and C_{27}-hopanes in relation to hopane are a little dissimilar, but both fingerprints show the presence of tricyclic triterpanes and some additional signals from components which elute between 32 and 39 min retention time. Low concentrations are indicated for the moretanes, the C_{30} compound being the most abundant. Characteristic to both mass fragmentograms is the peak, pre-eluting very close to hopane which is probably 18α(H)-oleanane (see Grantham *et al.*, this volume).

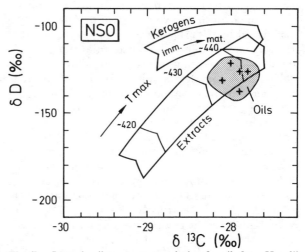

Fig. 7. Isotopic oil to source correlation for oils from Handil field. The oils are isotopically identical to mature extracts.

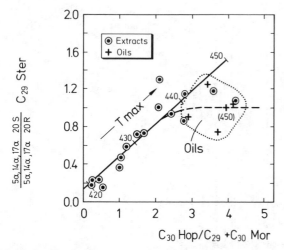

Fig. 8. Cross-plot of two stereochemical maturity parameters. Extracts are used for the calibration of a maturity line in terms of T_{max}. The stippled line indicates that the C_{29} sterane 20S/20R ratio may level off at ~1. Oils plot at maturities above T_{max}~440 °C.

Similarity of triterpane and sterane patterns justifies the general statement that mature kerogens in the Mahakam Delta are potential source rocks for oils found in the reservoirs. This lends support to the general assumption that type III kerogens in the Mahakam Delta are potential source rocks for liquid petroleum, not only for gas (Durand and Oudin, 1979).

Stable isotope ratios of NSO fractions also reveal a positive oil to source correlation (Fig. 7). Oils match fairly well isotopically with the mature extracts, and are also similar to the mature kerogens.

Stereochemical parameters of Fig. 4(b) and 4(c) have been selected for an oil to source correlation. Hopane/moretane ratios (M_H) and C_{29}-sterane 20R/20S ratio (M_{SE}) the latter of which is identical to the ratio III/II of Seifert and Moldowan (1981), have been combined for a cross-plot (Fig. 8) producing a maturity line. Although here the maturity line has been calculated up to values for $M_{SE}=1.5$, Mackenzie *et al.* (1980) note that this parameter levels off around unity (stippled line in Fig. 8). The extract values in Fig. 8 are well correlated along the maturity line but with increasing scatter towards higher maturities. Handil oils plot in the high maturity section but deviate from the constructed line. This probably is due to the fact that M_{SE} approaches unity around maturities of $T_{max} \approx 440°$ and is no longer sensitive to maturation above this level. Taking these considerations into account we conclude from the biomarker maturation plot of Fig. 8 that the oils are originating from source beds at maturities between $T_{max} \approx 440$ °C and 450 °C. This is in agreement with earlier conclusions of Durand and Oudin (1979).

Thus, the hopane/moretane maturation index M_H is more effective in determining source rock maturity (Fig. 9). The values of M_H for all oils are in the range between 3 and 4.5 indicating a maturity of their source above 440 °C ($\approx 0.7\%$ vitrinite reflectance). Using T_{max}/depth relationship to estimate source rock depth at the time of hydrocarbon generation, all oils appear to originate from a narrow depth interval around 2800 m. A comparison of reservoir depth and the depth of the

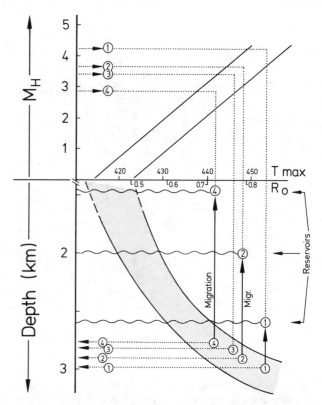

Fig. 9. Oil to source rock correlation using the hopane/moretane maturity parameter M_H (see Fig. 4(b)) of extracts. Oils 1, 2, 3 and 4 (see Table 3) have been analysed for their M_H values. Comparison of M_H of oils (dotted lines) pinpoint the depth in which M_H values of the oils are identical to the M_H values of indigenous extracts, i.e. the zone of oil formation. Comparison with reservoir depth allows an estimate of migration distances.

source rocks results in vertical migration distances of 200 m (oil 1) and 1400 m (oil 4).

The structure in Handil has some deep fault systems which could act as conduits for migration. Long and highly differing migration distances are easily conceivable in this structure.

Acknowledgement

We are indepted to Compagnie Française des Pétroles, Total Indonesie, Inpex Indonesia Ltd. and Pertamina Indonesia for the permission to publish the results.

REFERENCES

Durand, B. and Monin, J. C. (1980) Elemental analysis of kerogens (C, H, O, N, S, Fe). In *Kerogen — Insoluble Organic Matter from Sedimentary Rocks, 1980*, ed. by Durand, B. Paris, pp. 113–142.

Durand, B. and Nicaise, G. (1980) Procedures for kerogen isolation. In *Kerogen — Insoluble Organic Matter from Sedimentary Rocks, 1980*, ed. by Durand, B. Paris, pp. 35–53.

Durand, B. and Oudin, J. L. (1979) Exemple de Migration des Hydrocarbures dans une serie Deltaigue: La Delta de la Mahakam, Kalimatan, Indonesia. *Proceedings of the 10th World Petroleum Congress*, Panel Discussion, pp. 1–9.

Ensminger, A., Albrecht, P., Ourisson, G. and Tissot, B. (1977) Evolution of polycyclic hydrocarbons under effect of burial (early Toarcian shales, Paris basin). In *Advances in Organic Geochemistry 1975*, ed. by Campos, R. and Goni, J. Enadimsa, pp. 45–52.

Ensminger, A., Van Dorsselaer, A., Spyckerelle, C., Albrecht, P. and Ourisson, G. (1974) Pentacyclic triterpanes of the hopane type as ubiquitous geochemical markers: Origin and significance. In *Advances in Organic Geochemistry 1973*, ed. by Tissot, B. and Bienner, F. Editions Technip, Paris, pp. 245–260.

Galimov, R. (1980) C^{13}/C^{12} in kerogen. In *Kerogen, Insoluble Organic Matter from Sedimentary Rocks*, ed. by B. Durand. Editions Technip, Paris, pp. 271–299.

Mackenzie, A. S., Patience, R. L., Maxwell, J. R., Vandenbroucke, M. and Durand, B. (1980) Molecular parameters of maturation in the toarcian shales, Paris Basin, France — I. Changes in the configuration of acyclic isoprenoid alkanes, steranes and triterpanes. *Geochim. Cosmochim. Acta* **44**, 1709–1721.

Monin, J. C., Boudou, J. P., Durand, B. and Oudin, J. L. Variations de la composition isotopique du carbone dans la matiere organique d'une serie sedimentaire en fonction de l'evolution due a l'enfouissement. *Fuel* (in press).

Orr, W. L. (1974) Changes in sulfur content and isotopic ratio of sulfur during petroleum maturation — study of Big Horn basin Paleozoic oils. *Bull. Am. Assoc. Pet. Geol.* **58**, 2295–2318.

Redding, C. E., Schoell, M., Monin, J. C. and Durand, B. (1980) Hydrogen and carbon isotopic composition of coals and kerogens. In *Advances in Organic Geochemistry 1979*, ed. by Douglas, A. G. and Maxwell, J. R. Pergamon Press, Oxford, pp. 711–723.

Seifert, W. K. and Moldowan, J. M. (1981) Paleoreconstruction by biological markers. *Geochim. Cosmochim. Acta* **45**, 783–794.

Seifert, W. K. and Moldowan, J. M. (1980) The effect of thermal stress on source rock quality as measured by hopane stereochemistry. In *Advances in Organic Geochemistry, 1979*, ed. by Douglas, A. G. and Maxwell, J. R. pp. 229–238.

Seifert, W. K. and Moldowan, J. M. (1978) Application of steranes, terpanes and monoaromatics to the maturation, migration and source of crude oils. *Geochim. Cosmochim. Acta* **42**, 77–95.

Silverman, S. R. (1971) Influence of petroleum origin and transformation on its distribution and redistribution in sedimentary rocks. *Proceedings of the 8th World Petroleum Congress* Vol. 2, pp. 47–54.

Stahl, W. J. (1978) Source rock/crude oil correlation by isotopic type curves. *Geochim. Cosmochim. Acta* **42**, 1573–1577.

Tissot, B., Durand, B., Espitalié, J. and Combaz, A. (1974) Influence of nature and diagenesis of organic matter in formation of petroleum. *Am. Assoc. Pet. Geol. Bull.* **58**, 499–506.

Yapp, C. J. and Epstein, S. (1977) Climatic implications of D/H ratios of meteoric water over North America (9500–22000 B.P.) as inferred from ancient wood cellulose hydrogen. *Earth Planet Sci. Lett.* **34**, 333–350.

Advances in Organic Geochemistry 1981, pp. 164–174
© *John Wiley & Sons Limited, 1983*

Generation and Migration of Low-molecular Weight Hydrocarbons in Sediments from Site 511 of DSDP/IPOD Leg 71, Falkland Plateau, South Atlantic

R. G. Schaefer and D. Leythaeuser

Institute for Petroleum and Organic Geochemistry, KFA-Jülich, ICH-5, P.O. Box 1913, D-5170 Jülich, FRG

H. von der Dick

Institut für Geologie, Geochemie und Lagerstätten des Erdöls und der Kohle, RWTH Aachen, Lochnerstr. 4-20, D-5100 Aachen, FRG

Concentration and detailed composition of low-molecular weight hydrocarbons (C_2 to C_8) have been measured in a series of 56 sediment core samples collected between 160 and 605 m depth at Site 511, Leg 71 of the Deep Sea Drilling Project. Analysis was carried out by a combined hydrogen stripping/thermovaporization method and subsequent capillary gas chromatography. Total light hydrocarbon yields, which represent both hydrocarbons dissolved in the pore water and those adsorbed on clay minerals, vary from 24 ng/g of dry weight sediment in the Coniacian/Upper Santonian zeolitic claystones to 17 400 ng/g in the Upper Jurassic 'black shales' (organic-carbon normalized concentrations from 10^4 to 3.5×10^5 ng/g C_{org}). The concentration encountered in the lowermost part of the 'black shales' is in accordance with the quantity of light hydrocarbons generated by type-II kerogen-bearing petroleum source beds in an early maturity stage (0.4–0.5% vitrinite reflectance). Generally, low-molecular weight hydrocarbons in Hole 511 are formed *in situ* and remain at their place of formation. Indications for a redistribution of light hydrocarbons are observed around the Tertiary/Cretaceous unconformity, and at the contact between the 'black shales' and the overlying chalks and claystones. Redistribution patterns are interpreted to reflect a combination of several processes: bulk migration of light hydrocarbons along with moving compaction waters, replenishment of the depleted intervals by mobile, gas-range hydrocarbons possibly by diffusion, and the enrichment of polar compounds such as benzene and toluene in those intervals where an excessive flow of compaction water has occurred.

INTRODUCTION

The occurrence of low-molecular weight hydrocarbons in DSDP cores has been studied in detail by Hunt (1974, 1975, 1978), Faber *et al.* (1978), Hunt and Whelan (1978a,b, 1979), Whelan and Hunt (1978, 1979, 1980), Whelan (1979), Whelan and Sato (1980) and Whelan *et al.* (1980). The main conclusion from their comprehensive studies was that these compounds (C_1 to C_7 molecular range) are generated from kerogen by *in situ* low-temperature degradation reactions in low-maturity sediments. The exception is methane which can, in addition, be formed in large quantities by bacterial action. Recently, the formation of C_4 to C_7 hydrocarbons from bacterial degradation of naturally occurring terpenoids has been demonstrated in laboratory experiments by Hunt *et al.* (1980). Therefore, it seems reasonable to assume a dual origin of low-molecular weight hydrocarbons in low-mature sediments, i.e. from both biological and chemical low-temperature reactions.

Site 511 of DSDP Leg 71 (geographical coordinates 51°00′17″S; 46°58′18″W) is located about 10 km south of Site 330 (DSDP Leg 36, Maurice Ewing Bank, drilled in 1974) in the basin province of the Falkland Plateau (Fig. 1). The site was drilled and continuously cored by D/V *Glomar Challenger* in January 1980 to a sub-bottom depth of 632 m. A schematic cross-section based on seismic data through part of the basin province of the Falkland Plateau along seismic line 142 is shown in Fig. 2. Whereas at Site 330 gneissose and granitic continental basement was reached at the depth of 550 m, at Site 511 coring operations were terminated before reaching the lower contact of the 'black shale' unit due to regulations imposed by the JOIDES Safety Panel. At an estimated sub-bottom depth of 700 m a seismic reflector that was interpreted as the base of the petroliferous claystones would have been reached. Figure 3 summarizes data and

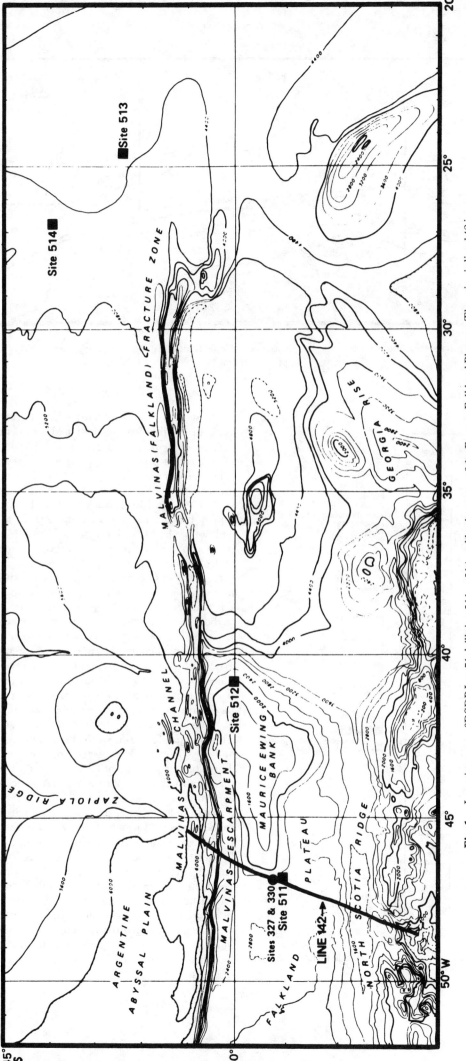

Fig. 1. Location map of DSDP Leg 71 drill sites 511 to 514 and bathymetry of the Eastern Falkland Plateau. The seismic line 142 in Fig. 2 is indicated. (After Ludwig, Krasheninnikov *et al.* (1980) and Ludwig, pers. commun.).

165

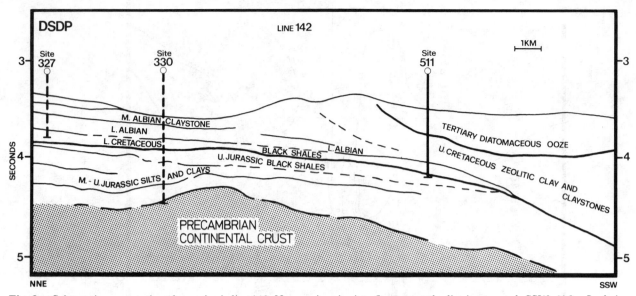

Fig. 2. Schematic cross-section along seismic line 142. Note main seismic reflectors gently dipping towards SSW. (After Ludwig, pers. commun.)

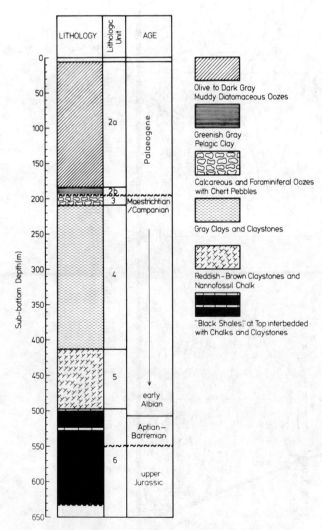

Fig. 3. Lithology and geological age of section penetrated by Hole 511, Leg 71.

conclusions by the shipboard scientists concerning the age and the lithology of the cored sediments.

As documented by previous investigations (von der Dick *et al.*, in press; Schaefer *et al.*, in press) geological conditions for an initial stage of hydrocarbon generation are present in the section penetrated at Site 511. In particular, the 140 m thick section of 'black shales' of Upper Jurassic/Early Cretaceous age, at top interbedded with chalks and claystones, revealed in certain intervals elevated organic carbon contents and a hydrogen-rich kerogen type. Furthermore, the temperature history has been adequate to reach an initial stage of hydrocarbon generation as is evident from a vitrinite reflectance of about 0.5% at TD. Thus, since hydrocarbons are present in significant concentrations in parts of the section, it could be suspected that redistribution phenomena are initiated as concentrations arise with progressive generation. Therefore, the main objective of the present study was to examine if, and to what extent, light hydrocarbons have been redistributed in certain intervals of the section penetrated by Hole 511. Generally, light hydrocarbons have among all constituents of a sediment the highest degree of mobility and hence can be expected to move most readily. Therefore, it was intended to test the hypothesis that such redistribution phenomena have occurred along concentration gradients which exist near contacts between lithologic units of grossly different light hydrocarbon concentrations. Geological situations of this type were encountered at Site 511, e.g., at the contact between the Upper Jurassic/Aptian-age 'black shales' and the overlying organic carbon-lean claystones and chalks of Albian/Turonian age. Furthermore, if such redistribution phenomena could be observed, it would be of interest to deduce information about their origin and mechanism. In order to recognize any depth-related light hydrocarbon redistribution, it was necessary to establish the hydrocarbon generation trend as a function of depth.

In order to meet these objectives a new approach was necessary for sampling and geochemical analysis: the micro-scale technique of hydrogen-stripping/thermovaporization (Schaefer *et al.*, 1978) has permitted the study of small-size sediment samples at a high interval frequency, where necessary, by closely spaced sampling even in the decimetre range. Thus, a total of 56 samples were analysed from Site 511.

EXPERIMENTAL

The small-size (approx. 10 g) sediment samples were collected from the cores immediately after they had been cut into sections on deck. Samples were stored in Teflon-sealed 30 ml aluminium containers in a deep-freezer and remained in deep-frozen condition (approx. -20 °C) until the analysis was performed in the laboratory on-shore. The low-molecular weight hydrocarbons (molecular range C_2-C_8) were analysed by a slightly modified, combined hydrogen-stripping/thermovaporization method described in detail by Schaefer *et al.* (1978). The modification of the method was necessary since the core samples turned out to be extensively contaminated by acetone. An examination of the sampling procedures revealed the cause for this contamination: on-board D/V *Glomar Challenger* acetone is routinely used for sealing each 1.5 m length section of the core by rinsing the plastic caps with this solvent prior to sealing. Obviously the acetone penetrates readily into the sediments and contaminates the cores to a variable degree. This explains our observation that, generally, the contamination is more drastic at the ends of a core section than in the middle. In most samples analysed the concentration of acetone by far exceeded that of the total C_2 to C_8 hydrocarbons. A detailed discussion of this contamination problem will be published elsewhere (Schaefer *et al.*, in press).

The analytical method used in this study comprises both the extraction of hydrocarbons from the rock and subsequent capillary gas chromatography in a single-step procedure carried out in a closed gas-flow system. Briefly, a small portion of the crushed sediment sample (generally between 0.1 and 1.0 gram) is placed in the flow system of a capillary gas chromatograph, the carrier gas serving as the stripping gas. The rock sample is heated to 110 °C for five minutes in a hydrogen flow of 5 ml/min. Thus, the yields obtained by this procedure represent nearly the absolute quantities of hydrocarbons both dissolved in the pore water and adsorbed on the mineral surfaces. Hence, the concentration values obtained cannot easily be compared to light hydrocarbon data obtained by other techniques, e.g., from head-space analyses.

Prior to the chromatographic separation the eluted compounds are passed through a small section of a mixture of dry $CaCl_2$ and silica gel in order to prevent the pore water and the acetone from entering the gas chromatographic column. The analysis is carried out using a 45 m 0.5 mm i.d. support coated open tubular column with squalane stationary phase and hydrogen carrier gas, run isothermally at 55 °C, connected to a flame ionization detector.

Table 1

Low-molecular weight hydrocarbons identified. Numbers refer to the lower gas chromatogram in Fig. 7

Ref. no.	Compound
1	Ethane
2	Propane
3	Methylpropane
4	Methylpropene + 1-Butene
5	*n*-Butane
6	*trans*-2-Butene
7	2,2-Dimethylpropane
8	*cis*-2-Butene
9	Methylbutane
10	*n*-Pentane
11	2,2-Dimethylbutane
12	Cyclopentane
13	2,3-Dimethylbutane
14	2-Methylpentane
15	3-Methylpentane
16	*n*-Hexane
17	Methylcyclopentane + 2,2-Dimethylpentane
18	2,4-Dimethylpentane
19	Benzene
20	Cyclohexane
21	2-Methylhexane
22	2,3-Dimethylpentane + 1,1-Dimethylcyclopentane
23	3-Methylhexane
24	1,*cis*-3-Dimethylcyclopentane
25	1,*trans*-3-Dimethylcyclopentane
26	1,*trans*-2-Dimethylcyclopentane
27	*n*-Heptane
28	1,*cis*-2-Dimethylcyclopentane
29	Methylcyclohexane
30	2,5-Dimethylhexane
31	Ethylcyclopentane
32	1,*trans*-2,*cis*-4-Trimethylcyclopentane
33	1,*trans*-2,*cis*-3-Trimethylcyclopentane
34	Toluene
35	2-Methylheptane
36	*n*-Octane

Organic carbon contents have been measured on the stripped sediment samples after treatment with hot 6N HCl by a combustion method (LECO Carbon Analyser IR 112).

Pyrolysis data (hydrogen indices) were obtained by application of the Rock-Eval procedure (Espitalié *et al.*, 1977) to whole rock samples.

RESULTS AND DISCUSSION

Generation of low-molecular weight hydrocarbons

Low-molecular weight hydrocarbons (C_2-C_8 molecular range) have been analysed in 56 core samples covering the depth interval 159 to 605 m (cores 18 to 68). The hydrocarbons identified, arranged in sequence of increasing retention on squalane as the stationary GC phase, are summarized in Table 1.

Figure 4 is a depth-plot of the hydrocarbon quantities for Hole 511. In this figure the concentration of all

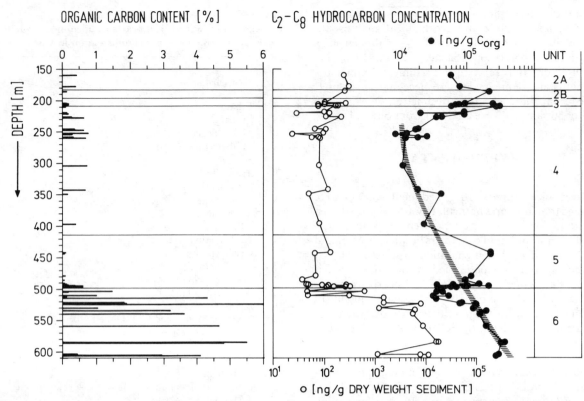

Fig. 4. Organic carbon and low-molecular weight hydrocarbon content (sum of all C$_2$ to C$_8$ hydrocarbons identified in Table 1, except olefins) versus depth for sediment samples of Site 511, DSDP Leg 71. Interpreted hydrocarbon generation trend is marked by hatched signature. Units 2a to 6 refer to lithologic units as defined by Leg 71 shipboard scientists. See Fig. 3.

hydrocarbons identified (except the olefins) is plotted against depth, both in absolute (ng/g of dry weight sediment) and organic-carbon normalized units (ng/g of organic carbon), respectively. Also included is a depth-plot of the organic carbon content (measured on the identical samples). It ranges from about 0.1 to 0.7% in lithologic units 2a to 5, and reaches up to 6% in the 'black shale' unit.

The rock-weight based hydrocarbon concentrations vary over the whole interval by nearly three orders of magnitude. In principle, the entire section drilled in Hole 511 can be subdivided into two main intervals. Low hydrocarbon concentrations (20–300 ng/g dry weight sediment) in lithologic units 2a, 2b, 3, 4 and 5, whereas significantly higher yields are encountered for most of the unit 6 ('black shale' unit), particularly for those intervals with elevated organic carbon contents. Here, almost 20 000 ng/g are reached, e.g., at 585 m depth. The organic carbon normalized values, however, show a somewhat different trend with depth. Concentrations vary from about 10^4 to 3×10^5 ng/g C$_{org}$. The highest values are found, as expected, near the bottom of the hole. However, various samples of lithologic units 5, 3 and 2b also exhibit quite similarly high values of more than 2×10^5 ng/g C$_{org}$. Obviously the uppermost part of this hole down to a depth of 230 m appears to be enriched by low-molecular weight hydrocarbons if compared to the immediately underlying part of unit 4 (250 m to 350 m) where concentrations remain below 20 000 ng/g C$_{org}$. This observation which is interpreted as a redistribution effect will be discussed in more detail in the next section. From approx. 300 m to 605 m an exponential trend (a

nearly straight line in the semi-log plot) of increasing carbon-normalized concentrations can be observed. This trend is interpreted to reflect increasing generation of these compounds from kerogen with increasing thermal stress. A change of the type of organic matter in this interval from lithologic unit 5 to 6, i.e. from a hydrogen-lean kerogen derived from land plant organic matter to a hydrogen-rich marine derived organic material, has only a minor influence on the carbon-normalized C$_2$–C$_8$ hydrocarbon concentrations plotted in Fig. 4. As shown by Leythaeuser *et al.* (1979) type-III kerogen generates predominantly gas and aromatic hydrocarbons, whereas at the same maturity type-II kerogen favours the formation of saturated gasoline-range hydrocarbons C$_5$ to C$_8$. Therefore, in the plot of the total carbon-number range C$_2$ to C$_8$ this influence of kerogen-type is suppressed to a large extent.

A major deviation from the generation trend drawn in Fig. 4 is observed around the contact between lithologic units 5 and 6, i.e. between the Albian chalks and claystones and the Aptian 'black shales'. Whereas the upper-most section of the 'black shales' show significantly lower values than the general trend, the lower part of unit 5 reveals drastically elevated organic-carbon normalized values. As shown in the next section the concentration drop in the upper 30 m of the 'black shales' unit is most probably not due to a slight change of the kerogen type in this interval to a more transitional composition with increasing amounts of inert, partly oxidized organic matter (von der Dick *et al.*, in press).

The concentrations reached in the main part of the 'black shale' unit indicate that considerable quantities of

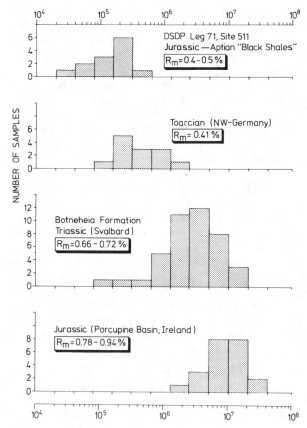

Fig. 5. Saturated light hydrocarbon concentrations (in ng/g C_{org}) in the 'black shales' of Site 511 compared to those of potential oil source rocks of different maturity stages. This comparison indicates additionally the low maturity of the 'black shales'.

gasoline-range hydrocarbons have been generated. However, values of about 3×10^5 ng/g C_{org} are still well below those concentrations encountered in mature ($R_m = 0.8$–0.9%) type-II kerogen bearing source beds. This is exemplified by a comparison with several hydrogen-rich, type-II kerogen bearing petroleum source rocks of different maturity stages in Fig. 5. The range of the concentrations of the C_2–C_8 saturated hydrocarbons (organic-carbon normalized units) encountered in lithologic unit 6 (from 514 m downwards, mean organic carbon content 3.4%, mean hydrogen index $I_H = 278$ mg/g C_{org}) is compared to

(a) Toarcian shales from NW Germany (mean $C_{org} = 9.6\%$, mean $I_H = 890$ mg/g C_{org}, $R_m = 0.41\%$);

(b) The Triassic Botneheia Formation, Svalbard (mean $C_{org} = 4.4\%$, mean $I_H = 261$ mg/g C_{org}, maturity interval $R_m = 0.66$–0.72%);

(c) Jurassic shales, Porcupine Basin, Ireland (mean $C_{org} = 1.5\%$, mean $I_H = 300$ mg/g C_{org}, maturity interval $R_m = 0.78$–0.94%).

Compared with these three petroleum source rocks the 'black shale' unit of Site 511 has low concentrations of light hydrocarbons. Therefore it is concluded, that the maturity of the 'black shales' is relatively low. In terms of light hydrocarbon concentration the maturity stage seems to coincide with the Toarcian of NW Germany, an immature petroleum source rock (vitrinite reflectance $R_m = 0.41\%$). The low maturity of the 'black shales' is further supported by reflectance measurements discussed in detail by von der Dick *et al.* (in press). Mean reflectance values of the huminites/vitrinites are around 0.4–0.5% R_m. A wood fragment encountered in Core 64

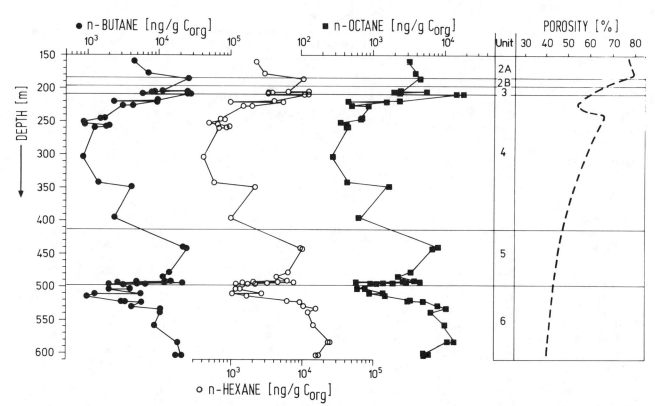

Fig. 6. Selected *n*-alkane (C_4, C_6, C_8) concentrations and mean sediment porosities versus depth for sediment samples of Site 511, DSDP Leg 71. Units 2a to 6 refer to lithologic units as defined by Leg 71 shipboard scientists. See Fig. 3.

(approx. 570 m depth) also revealed a low reflectance value of 0.38%.

Redistribution of low-molecular weight hydrocarbons

It has been shown in the previous section that major deviations from the general trend of organic-carbon normalized C_2–C_8 concentrations (Fig. 4) are observed between 160 m and 230 m depth as well as close to the contact of lithologic units 5 and 6. The elevated carbon-normalized hydrocarbon concentrations from approx. 183 m to 210 m occur around the Tertiary/Cretaceous unconformity at 196 m depth (contact of lithologic units 2b and 3). For example, highest concentrations are encountered in lithologic unit 3 characterized by the occurrence of chert pebbles in grey calcareous and zeolitic foraminiferal oozes. Elevated sand contents of up to 25% are found in the depth interval from 186 m to 225 m. As shown in Fig. 6 this interval coincides with a marked increase of the porosity values from about 50 to 80% (U. Bayer, personal communication).

In summary, the interval of 160–230 m which has elevated carbon-normalized light hydrocarbon concentrations, appears to offer favourable conditions for any movement of mobile phases. Therefore, the interpretation appears likely, that movement of compaction waters through this part of the section has occurred to a significant extent. These compaction waters, which originated at greater burial depths may

have carried some dissolved light hydrocarbons. While these waters continued to move further updip, light hydrocarbons have been preferentially adsorbed on clay mineral surfaces. In this way, the elevated hydrocarbon concentrations, as represented in this figure by n-butane, n-hexane and n-octane can be explained. These three hydrocarbons, although differing considerably in molecular weight and hence mobility, show a remarkable 'in-phase' variation over the complete depth interval. Therefore, it is concluded that no specific enrichment by gas-range hydrocarbons due to diffusion has occurred.

The other depth interval which exhibits a significant deviation from the generation trend (Figs 4 and 6) is between 495 m and 520 m depth. Here, carbon-normalized values of both the sum of C_2–C_8 hydrocarbons or individual compounds exhibit a significant 5- to 10-fold reduction as compared to the overall trend. Although the organic matter changes from a type-II kerogen in the lower part to a partially oxidized, residual kerogen in the upper part of lithologic unit 6, this change cannot account for the drastic differences in the hydrocarbon concentrations. Instead, as shown later, this observation is explained by a redistribution effect.

In situ origin versus short-distance migration

In order to differentiate between the in situ origin of light hydrocarbons in the sediment samples and compositions

Table 2

Comparison between low-molecular weight hydrocarbon concentrations of three selected sample pairs of the 'black shale' unit of Site 511, DSDP Leg 71

	Case A		Ratio	Case B		Ratio	Case C		Ratio
Depth (m)	604.77	604.69		523.93	514.60		503.97	503.92	
Organic carbon content (%)	2.9	0.39	7.4	6.0	4.3	1.4	1.4	0.13	11
Hydrogen index (mg/g C_{org})	223	153	1.5	371	433	0.86	131	41	3.2
Concentration (ng/g dry weight sediment):									
Ethane	117	18.0	6.5	479	139	3.5	60.7	4.8	13
Propane	332	64.1	5.2	369	85.3	4.3	59.4	8.9	6.7
n-Butane	489	80.4	6.1	332	40.8	8.1	27.8	5.0	5.6
n-Pentane	776	114	6.8	554	55.6	10	24.4	2.7	9.0
n-Hexane	482	66.4	7.3	551	71.5	7.7	16.5	1.7	9.7
n-Heptane	324	42.2	7.7	495	97.5	5.1	14.1	1.1	13
n-Octane	172	20.7	8.3	298	64.1	4.7	11.1	0.79	14
Methylpropane	541	88.4	6.1	169	23.6	7.2	19.6	4.6	4.3
2,2-Dimethylpropane	3.1	0.39	8.0	10.1	8.6	1.2	1.5	<0.5	>3
2-Methylbutane	657	94.0	7.0	234	41.8	5.6	28.6	2.7	11
Cyclopentane	54.3	7.9	6.9	45.7	6.4	7.1	4.0	0.04	100
Methylcyclopentane	587	78.3	7.5	336	40.9	8.2	34.6	0.33	105
Methylcyclohexane	321	39.0	8.2	346	65.7	5.3	37.9	—	—
Benzene	129	18.6	6.9	80.0	34.4	2.3	9.7	2.6	3.7
Toluene	586	109	5.4	969	310	3.1	51.3	8.8	5.8

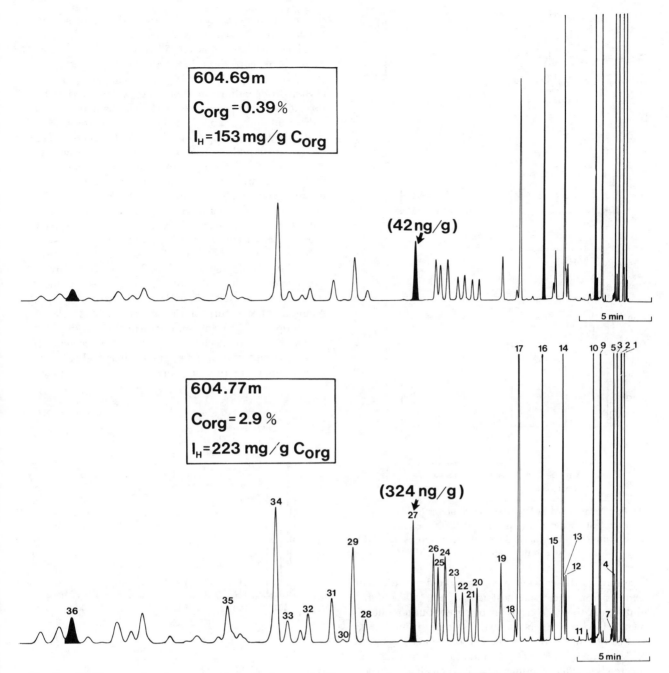

Fig. 7. Capillary gas chromatograms of two closely spaced sediment samples (604.69 and 604.77 m depth, respectively) from the lower part of the 'black shale' unit of Site 511, indicating the *in situ* origin of the low-molecular weight hydrocarbons. *n*-Alkane peaks are marked in black. Peak numbers refer to Table 1. *n*-Heptane (no. 27) concentrations are indicated in both chromatograms for comparison.

which are affected by redistribution effects three sample pairs of the 'black shale' unit have been selected. Light hydrocarbon concentrations, organic carbon contents and hydrogen indices of these samples are shown in Table 2.

Case A represents a closely-spaced sample pair of different organic richness in the lowermost section of the 'black shale' unit. Both samples are only 8 cm apart and differ in their organic carbon contents by a factor of 7.4. Although the hydrogen index is slightly lower in the organic-carbon lean sample (604.69 m depth) both samples bear roughly the same kerogen type. The light hydrocarbon capillary gas chromatograms of these two

samples are shown in Fig. 7. Apparently the hydrocarbon distributions in both samples are nearly identical. The major difference is obvious from Table 2, where the concentrations of several selected compounds and the corresponding concentration ratios for both samples are listed. According to these ratios the organic-carbon richer sample contains for most compounds 6 to 8 times as much hydrocarbons than the organic-carbon lean sample. It is concluded therefore that light hydrocarbons have been generated in both samples in direct proportion of the organic matter present, i.e., that the light hydrocarbons were formed *in situ* and remained at their place of origin.

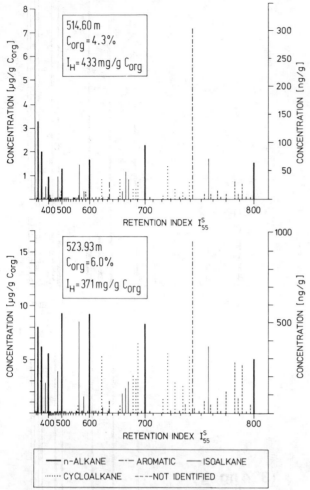

Fig. 8. Normalized hydrocarbon distributions (concentration versus retention index on squalane at 55 °C) of two 'black shale' samples (514.60 and 523.93 m depth, respectively) of the upper part of lithologic unit 6, Site 511.

Following this concept, a comparison of two adjacent samples from the uppermost part of the 'black shale' unit, leads to the conclusion of redistribution phenomena. Two typical 'black shale' samples from 523.93 and 514.60 m depth (organic carbon contents 6.0 and 4.3%, hydrogen index 371 and 433 mg/g C_{org}, respectively) differ considerably in their hydrocarbon concentrations (Case B in Table 2). The corresponding compositions are shown in Fig. 8 where, instead of the chromatograms, normalized hydrocarbon distributions are presented. Although the organic carbon contents differ only by a factor of 1.4, and hydrogen indices are nearly identical, the hydrocarbon concentrations differ in both samples in a characteristic manner. For each individual *n*-alkane the concentration ratio (calculated by dividing the hydrocarbon concentration in the sample from 523.93 m by that of the sample from 514.60 m) varies from 3.5 (ethane) to a maximum value of 10 (*n*-pentane), and decreases again to 4.7 (*n*-octane). Iso-butane and isopentane exhibit ratios which are significantly lower than those of their straight-chain isomers. Likewise, this effect is even more pronounced in the case of neopentane (2,2-dimethylpropane): both samples reveal nearly the same concentration. Whereas the saturated cyclic compounds show comparable values to

the acyclic hydrocarbons, the aromatics (benzene and toluene) reveal very low values of 2.3 and 3.1, respectively. The pronounced difference in overall hydrocarbon concentrations between the two samples is, therefore, interpreted as a preferential loss of hydrocarbons, depending on molecular weight and structure, from the upper part of the 'black shale' unit and a redistribution probably into the overlying strata. Most probably the mechanism of this redistribution is a bulk-type migration along with moving compaction waters. The depletion of the uppermost interval of the 'black shale' unit is most pronounced for the butane to heptane hydrocarbons, including the cycloalkanes of this molecular range. The light gases (ethane, propane and, particularly, neopentane), however, seem to be depleted to a smaller extent. This is explained by a preferential replenishment by diffusion of these compounds from below into the depleted interval. The high mobility of, e.g. neopentane has frequently been observed in DSDP sediments (Whelan, 1979) and is attributed to the highly symmetrical structure of this molecule. The relative enrichment of benzene and toluene in the depleted section is also in accordance with the hypothesis of moving compaction waters. Due to their high polarity these aromatic hydrocarbons remain preferentially ad-

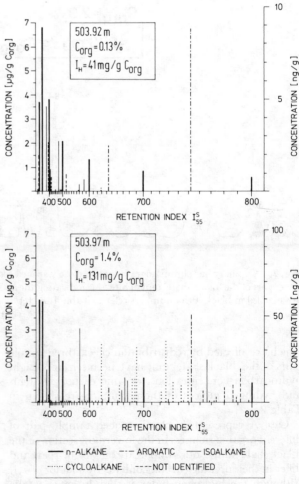

Fig. 9. Normalized hydrocarbon distributions (concentration versus retention index on squalane at 55 °C) of two closely spaced sediment samples of the upper part of lithologic unit 6 of Site 511.

sorbed on clay mineral surfaces resulting in less effective depletion as compared to the saturated hydrocarbons.

In Case C two samples spaced 5 cm apart within the uppermost section of lithologic unit 6 are compared (Table 2, Fig. 9). They both bear type-III kerogens with quite different organic carbon contents of 1.4 and 0.13%, respectively. Since these samples are from that part of the section of lithologic unit 6 discussed in the previous Case B they reflect a more complicated situation. Both *in situ* generated and migrating hydrocarbons have mixed and result in the present compositional pattern. It is logical to assume a more pronounced interference by migrating hydrocarbons in the organic-carbon lean sample (503.92 m depth). This sample seems to be relatively enriched by propane to hexane straight-chain and branched hydrocarbons, as well as by benzene and toluene. The extreme high ratios of cyclopentane and methylcyclopentane have to remain unexplained at the moment. The enrichment by the above mentioned hydrocarbons, particularly benzene and toluene, is, as in the previously discussed Case B, typical for moving hydrocarbon bearing compaction waters. Therefore, the hydrocarbon content and composition of both Cases B and C are explained here as the combined effect of several dynamic processes:

(1) Upward movement of hydrocarbon bearing compaction waters originating from the upper part of the 'black shale' unit and leading into the overlying claystones and chalks.

(2) Replenishment by diffusion, that favours mobile gas-range hydrocarbons.

(3) Polarity-related adsorption effects on clay mineral surfaces, giving rise to relative enrichment of aromatic hydrocarbons.

In order to demonstrate the effect of preferential removal of more polar compounds from moving compaction waters the concentration ratio of toluene to methylcyclohexane has been plotted against depth in Fig. 10. These two compounds have been selected because they are nearly identical with respect to molecular size and boiling point, however, reveal very different polarities. It is obvious from Fig. 10 that this ratio reaches a maximum just at the lithologic boundary between the Albian chalks and claystones and the Aptian 'black shales'. Within each of these lithologic

units the toluene/methylcyclohexane ratio remains fairly constant, reflecting an unmodified condition of light hydrocarbon composition with a value below 5 for this ratio throughout most of the 'black shale' interval, and about 30 in the chalks and claystones above. In contrast, values in excess 100 are only observed in three samples from interval 492 to 494 m. These high values cannot be explained by slight changes in the type of organic matter. Instead, they are believed to reflect the relative enrichment of toluene by preferential adsorption on clay mineral surfaces. The most probable mechanism to explain this effect would again be the upward flow of compaction waters, being most intense at the boundary between lithologic units 5 and 6.

CONCLUSIONS

Light hydrocarbon data of Site 511, Leg 71 indicate a gradual maturity increase in the organic matter throughout the sampled interval down to 605 m. Significant quantities of gas and gasoline-range hydrocarbons have been generated, particularly in the lower section of lithologic unit 6 ('black shales'). However, organic carbon normalized concentrations are more than one order of magnitude lower than usually encountered in type-II kerogen source beds in the main phase of oil generation. Therefore, the light hydrocarbon concentration in the 'black shale' unit is in accordance with low maturity indicated by mean vitrinite reflectance values between 0.4 and 0.5% around 600 m depth (von der Dick *et al.*, in press). Over most of the section penetrated by Hole 511 low-molecular weight hydrocarbons are formed *in situ* and remain at their place of origin. However, redistribution processes can be recognized at certain narrow intervals which are associated with major stratigraphic or lithologic boundaries, i.e. at the Cretaceous/Tertiary unconformity, or at the transition from 'black shales' to the overlying chalks and claystones. The upper part of the 'black shale' unit has been depleted to a significant degree: light hydrocarbons have been removed possibly by expulsion of compaction waters from this section. In summary, redistribution phenomena are restricted in Hole 511 to a narrow interval of 20–30 m, which could only be recognized due to a dense interval spacing of samples.

Acknowledgements

Financial support by the Deutsche Forschungsgemeinschaft (DFG) grant No. Le 469/1–1 and the German Federal Ministry for Research and Technology (BMFT) grant No. 3070B is gratefully acknowledged.

We thank Dr J. Gormly for the organic carbon and Rock-Eval pyrolysis data, as well as Mrs B. Winden, Messrs. U. Disko, J. Höltkemeier, F. Leistner, H. Pooch, B. Schmidl, and K. Schmitt (all at KFA–Juelich) for technical assistance.

Samples were made available by participation of the Deutsche Forschungsgemeinschaft in the DSDP/IPOD programme. We extend thanks to the U.S. National

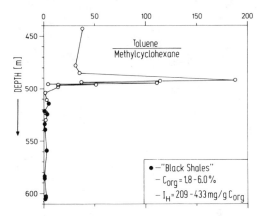

Fig. 10. Toluene/methylcyclohexane concentration ratio versus depth for a selected interval from Site 511.

Science Foundation and to the JOIDES Organic Geochemistry Panel who made possible the participation of one of the authors (H. v. d. D.) on Leg 71.

REFERENCES

Espitalié, J., Laporte, J. L., Madec, M., Marquis, F., Leplat, P., Paulet, J. and Boutefeu, A. (1977) Méthode rapide de caractérization des roches mères, de leur potentiel pétrolier et de leur degré d'évolution. *Rev. Inst. Fr. Pet.* **32**, 23–42.

Faber, E., Schmitt, M. and Stahl, W. (1978) Carbon isotope analyses of head space methane from samples of Leg 42 B, Sites 379, 380, and 381. In *Init Repts. DSDP*, ed. by Ross, D. A., Neprochnov, Y. P. *et al.* Vol. 42, part 2. U.S. Govt Printing Office, Washington, pp. 667–672.

Hunt, J. M. (1974) Hydrocarbon and kerogen studies. In *Init. Repts. DSDP*, ed. by von der Borch, C. C., *et al.* Vol. 22. U.S. Govt Printing Office, Washington, pp. 673–675.

Hunt, J. M. (1975) Origin of gasoline range alkanes in the deep sea. *Nature (London)* **254**, 411–413.

Hunt, J. M. (1978) Light hydrocarbons in Holes 361 and 364, Leg 40. In *Init. Repts. DSDP*, ed. by Bolli, H. M., Ryan, W. B. F., *et al.* Vol. 40 (Supplement). U.S. Govt Printing Office, Washington, pp. 649–650.

Hunt, J. M. and Whelan, J. K. (1978a) Dissolved gases in Black Sea sediments. In *Init. Repts. DSDP*, ed. by Ross, D. A., Neprochnov, Y. P., *et al.* Vol. 42, part 2. U.S. Govt Printing Office, Washington, pp. 661–665.

Hunt, J. M. and Whelan, J. K. (1978b) Light hydrocarbons in sediments of DSDP Leg 44 Holes. In *Init. Repts. DSDP*, ed. by Benson, W. E., Sheridan, R. E., *et al.* Vol. 44. U.S. Govt Printing Office, Washington, pp. 651–652.

Hunt, J. M. and Whelan, J. K. (1979) Volatile organic compounds in Quaternary sediments. *Org. Geochem.* **1**, 219–224.

Hunt, J. M., Miller, R. J. and Whelan, J. K. (1980) Formation of C_4–C_7 hydrocarbons from bacterial degradation of naturally occurring terpenoids. *Nature (London)* **288**, 577–578.

Leythaeuser, D., Schaefer, R. G., Cornford, C. and Weiner, B. (1979) Generation and migration of light hydrocarbons (C_2–C_7) in sedimentary basins. *Org. Geochem.* **1**, 191–204.

Ludwig, W. J., Krasheninnikov, V. *et al.* (Scientific Party of DSDP Leg 71) (1980) Tertiary and Cretaceous paleoenvironments in the southwest Atlantic ocean: preliminary results of deep sea drilling project leg 71. *Geol. Soc. Am. Bull.* part 1, **91**, 655–664.

Schaefer, R. G., Weiner, B. and Leythaeuser, D. (1978) Determination of sub-nanogram per gram quantities of light hydrocarbons (C_2–C_9) in rock samples by hydrogen stripping in the flow system of a capillary gas chromatograph: *Anal. Chem.* **50**, 1848–1854.

Schaefer, R. G., von der Dick, H. and Leythaeuser, D. C_2–C_8 hydrocarbons in sediments from deep sea drilling project leg 71, site 511, Falkland plateau, south Atlantic. In *Init. Repts. DSDP*, ed. by Ludwig, W. J., Krasheninnikov, C., *et al.* Vol. 71. U.S. Govt Printing Office, Washington (in press).

von der Dick, H., Rullkötter, J. and Welte, D. H. Content, type and thermal evolution of organic matter in sediments from the eastern Falkland plateau, deep sea drilling project, leg 71. In *Init. Repts. DSDP*, ed. by Ludwig, W. J., Krasheninnikov, V., *et al.*, Vol. 71. U.S. Govt Printing Office, Washington (in press).

Whelan, J. K. (1979) C_1 to C_7 hydrocarbons from IPOD holes 397 and 397A. In *Init. Repts. DSDP*, ed. by von Rad, U., Ryan, W. B. F., *et al.*, Vol. 47, part 1. U.S. Govt Printing Office, Washington, pp. 531–539.

Whelan, J. K. and Hunt, J. M. (1978) C_1–C_7 hydrocarbons in holes 387A, 380/380A, and 381. In *Init. Repts. DSDP*, ed. by Ross, D. A., Neprochnov, Y. P., *et al.*, Vol. 42, part 2. U.S. Govt Printing Office, Washington, pp. 673–677.

Whelan, J. K. and Hunt, J. M. (1979) C_2 to C_7 hydrocarbons from IPOD hole 398D. In *Init. Repts. DSDP*, ed. by Sibuet, J.-C., Ryan, W. B. F., *et al.*, Vol. 47, part 2. U.S. Govt Printing Office, Washington, pp. 561–563.

Whelan, J. K. and Hunt, J. M. (1980) C_1–C_7 volatile organic compounds in sediments from deep sea drilling project legs 56 and 57, Japan trench. In *Init. Repts. DSDP*, ed. by Honza, E. *et al.*, Vols. 56 and 57, part 2. U.S. Govt Printing Office, Washington, pp. 1349–1355.

Whelan, J. K. and Sato, S. (1980) C_1–C_5 hydrocarbons from core gas pockets, deep sea drilling project legs 56 and 57, Japan trench transect. In *Init. Repts. DSDP*, ed. by Honza, E. *et al.*, Vols. 56 and 57, part 2. U.S. Govt Printing Office, Washington, pp. 1335–1347.

Whelan, J. K., Hunt, J. M. and Berman, J. (1980) Volatile C_1–C_7 organic compounds in surface sediments from Walvis Bay. *Geochim. Cosmochim. Acta* **44**, 1767–1785.

Advances in Organic Geochemistry 1981, pp. 175–182
© *John Wiley & Sons Limited, 1983*

Extracts from the Open and Closed Pores of an Upper Triassic Sequence from W. Hungary:† a Contribution to Studies of Primary Migration

A. Brukner, I. Vetö

Geological Survey of Hungary, H 1442 Budapest Népstadion ut 14 PO Box 106

An investigation of the bulk composition of extracts obtained before and after crushing of samples from a sequence of limestones and marls provides a means of determining the association of extractable components with open and closed pores. Evidence for the accumulation of compounds generated during catagenesis in the open pores is seen from the enrichment of the non-crushed extracts in the less polar and lower molecular weight components. This process of compound redistribution during catagenesis is more efficient in the marls than in the limestones and may, in part, account for the observed hindrance of primary migration from carbonate rocks.

INTRODUCTION

It is a well-known phenomenon that oil is enriched in hydrocarbons compared to the extractable organic matter of source rocks. From the relatively few case histories available (Baker, 1962; Connan and Cassou, 1980; Gimplevich cited by Hunt, 1979; Hunt, 1962; Young and McIver, 1977) the saturates/aromatics ratio is found to be greater in the oils than in the parent source rocks. These differences between oils and source rock extracts can be interpreted to be a result of the sharp contrast in the polarity and molecular weight of the respective molecules or groups of molecules, which cause different absorption and adsorption behaviour.

Primary migration, at least in a source rock with an average organic matter content, must be preceded by the entry of part of the oil generated from the kerogen into the open pores. The question arises whether the above differences between an oil and its source rock extract can be observed in the extracts of the open and closed pores or whether they are produced only after the oil has migrated from the source rock.

We have studied this question on samples from a 200 m Upper Triassic limestone–marl section by a simplified two-step $CHCl_3$ extraction variant of the Beletzkaya method. Beletzkaya *et al.* (1976) pioneered the separate analysis of extracts of open and closed pores. They extracted non-crushed samples with CO_2 under pressure and identical samples with $CHCl_3$ both before and after crushing. In this way they were able to separate the hydrocarbons of open, bitumen-plugged and mineralogically closed pores. They did not find bitumen-plugged pores in source rocks with $<1\%$ C_{org}.

GEOLOGICAL SETTING OF THE SAMPLES

The 26 samples studied cover the 550–750 m depth interval of the Upper Triassic in the Zsámbék No. 14 borehole, located 30 km west of Budapest. The lithology of this interval is shown in Fig. 1. From their microfaunal assemblages the sediments accumulated in brackish and oxygenated water.

The section between 550.0 and 683.4 m is composed mainly of limestone, which often contains chert. This limestone sequence is intercalated with 30 marly beds of a total thickness of 24 m. The limestone is composed of micrite and micropatite, its texture is mainly wackestone; packstone and mudstone textures are rare. The mineralogical composition is shown in Table 1.

The upper limestone section is underlain by a thick calcareous marl stratum (683.4–753.4 m) with limestone intercalations in its lower part. The mineralogical composition of these calcareous marls is similar to that of the marly beds above. From 753.4 m to the bottom of the borehole (890.0 m) a pure, recrystallized dolomite stratum was found.

Visible open fractures are scarce in the section studied. A significant fracture porosity is also highly unlikely on the basis of the resistivity and the neutron–neutron logs. The vitrinite reflectance (R^0) of sediments (300–500 m depth) above the section studied herein is low with values of 0.39–0.42%. The colour and preservation of the palynomorphs in these sediments are typical of the onset of the oil generation (TAI values are 2.5–3.0 on the Correia scale).

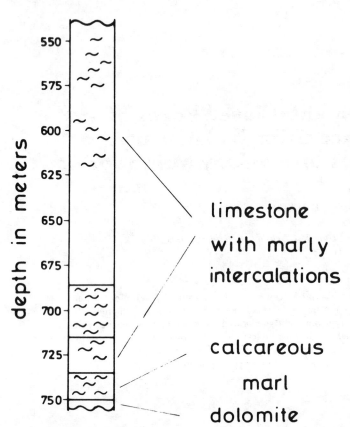

Fig. 1. Lithological column for the section of the Zsámbék No. 14 borehole studied.

Table 1
The mineralogical composition of the Zsámbék limestone.

	Limestone (%)	Marly beds (%)
Calcite	73–94	18–70
Dolomite	2–14	5–34
Quartz	2–18	0–27
Illite	0–12	0–12
Illite–smectite	–	0–10
Smectite	0–6	0–18
Pyrite	max. 1	max. 6

EXPERIMENTAL

Core samples were first checked in UV light. Rock chips (200 g, <30 mm) were subjected to extraction (40 h by Soxhlet with redistilled $CHCl_3$ (300 ml) and their fluorescence remeasured. After crushing (<60 μm) a second extraction was carried out on the rock powder (90 g) with $CHCl_3$ (200 ml). In the following the two types of extract will be referred to as non-crushed and crushed respectively.

The C_{org} content of the extracted rock powder, after decarbonation using HCl, was determined by combustion in a Wösthoff CARMOGRAPH-B apparatus in the Department of Mineralogy at the University of Szeged.

Table 2
Geochemical data for the samples

Depth (m)	HCl-insoluble residue (%)	C_{org} (%)	Total extract (%)	Crushed extract / Non-crushed extract	Extract (mg) / C_{org} (g)
552.6	32.0	0.48	0.028	0.87	58
563.0	9.2	0.11	0.030	5.10	270
573.5	1.2	0.07	0.015	2.20	230
586.5	8.9	0.19	0.036	1.80	190
595.0	26.0	3.40	0.360	0.50	100
602.5	60.0	1.10	0.090	0.11	80
603.0	18.0	0.30	0.028	1.30	93
618.5	4.0	0.24	0.075	3.20	310
620.4	29.0	0.88	0.075	0.28	85
632.0	13.0	0.13	0.020	4.20	150
633.0	27.0	0.53	0.033	0.94	62
638.0	21.0	1.80	0.023	0.89	12
643.0	7.4	0.41	0.120	5.90	280
653.9	14.0	0.43	0.091	0.54	210
658.0	47.0	1.30	0.210	0.23	150
663.5	9.9	0.39	0.100	5.30	260
667.2	40.0	0.92	0.120	1.30	130
674.0	28.0	1.00	0.071	1.70	69
687.0	17.0	0.47	0.038	2.20	80
691.0	30.0	0.46	0.037	1.10	80
693.3	23.0	0.43	0.041	1.70	95
704.3	26.0	0.42	0.034	1.40	81
717.5	30.0	0.72	0.070	0.21	97
726.5	8.5	0.15	0.029	0.69	190
738.0	32.0	0.44	0.033	0.65	75
747.5	34.0	0.55	0.030	0.98	55

Table 3

Composition of crushed and non-crushed extracts. Upper values to left: crushed extracts. Lower values to right: non-crushed extracts

Depth (m)	$\dfrac{E_{1610}}{E_{1470}}$		$\dfrac{E_{1710}}{E_{1470}}$		Saturates (%)		Aromatics (%)		Resins (%)		Asphaltenes (%)	
552.6	0.26	0.20	0.80	0.50		19.0		14.0		53.0		13.0
586.5	0.16	0.11	0.54	0.45		30.0		10.0		48.0	20.0	12.0
595.0	0.13	0.08	0.41	0.37	15.0	28.0	24.0	24.0	51.0	41.0	7.9	3.8
602.5	0.20	0.14		0.39		35.0		12.0		44.0		7.2
603.0	0.22	0.15	0.51	0.45		24.0		17.0		44.0		15.0
618.5	0.20	0.13	0.66	0.61	4.1	12.0	15.0	13.0	50.0	51.0	31.0	25.0
620.4	0.19	0.13		0.28		28.0		19.0		45.0		8.2
633.0	0.15	0.10		0.32		33.0		21.0		37.0		9.5
638.0	0.34	0.14		0.35		33.0		19.0		33.0		8.9
643.0	0.27	0.21	0.61	0.59	6.0	11.0	19.0	15.0	48.0	48.0	27.0	27.0
653.9	0.27	0.17	0.58	0.51	9.5	13.0	11.0	18.0	44.0	49.0	36.0	19.0
658.0	0.39	0.18	0.75	0.40		20.0		21.0		43.0	36.0	14.0
663.5	0.11	0.18	0.13	0.56	5.2	16.0	13.0	13.0	32.0	47.0	37.0	21.0
667.2	0.19	0.12	0.37	0.35	12.0	20.0	23.0	24.0	54.0	45.0	11.0	6.9
674.0	0.19	0.15	0.39	0.37	21.0	37.0	19.0	15.0	49.0	36.0	9.1	5.5
687.0	0.21	0.15	0.39	0.43	21.0	29.0	19.0	17.0	48.0	39.0	12.0	6.4
691.0	0.22	0.17	0.47	0.38		43.0		12.0		33.0	17.0	7.6
693.3	0.19	0.16	0.41	0.41	29.0	46.0	17.0	7.7	44.0	34.0	9.9	6.3
704.3	0.32	0.14	0.56	0.37		31.0		15.0		39.0	17.0	7.8
717.5	0.20	0.16	0.51	0.29		40.0		17.0		36.0		5.1
726.5	0.22	0.40	0.41	0.40		26.0		13.0		47.0		11.0
738.0	0.41	0.29	0.52	0.47		26.0		19.0		39.0		12.0
747.5	0.27	0.24	0.54	0.49		29.0		15.0		40.0		8.2

The IR spectra of the extracts were recorded on a Zeiss-Jena Spekord IR75 spectrophotometer using the KBr disc technique, and evaluated by the baseline method. Extracts were characterized by the following indices: E_{720}/E_{750}, E_{1610}/E_{1470} and E_{1710}/E_{1470}, where for example E_{720} is the extinction coefficient at 720 cm^{-1}.

Asphaltenes were precipitated with a large excess of light petroleum (40–70 °C). The asphaltene-free extract was separated into saturate aromatic and resin fractions by chromatography using light petroleum (40–70 °C), benzene and methanol-benzene (1:1 mixture) as eluents.

RESULTS

Only one sample was contaminated; its drilled surface showed stains with a yellow fluorescence. The stained part of this sample was eliminated.

The limestone matrix always showed a weak yellow or dull brown fluorescence, which did not change after the initial extraction. The limestone samples were characterized by the presence, albeit in insignificant quantity, of fracture-filling calcite with bright yellow fluorescence. This fluorescence only weakened in three samples after the initial extraction.

The analytical data are summarized in Tables 2 and 3. The C_{org} content and the total extract vary from 0.065–3.400% and 0.015–0.360% respectively. The crushed to non-crushed extract ratios vary from 0.11 to 5.90. The extract to C_{org} ratio also shows a large variation (12–310 mg g^{-1}).

The extracts can be characterized as follows:

IR spectra (26 pairs of extracts). The E_{720}/E_{750} ratio i.e. the ratio of aliphatic chains ($n > 4$) to certain substituted aromatic structures is generally greater in the crushed extracts. The E_{1610}/E_{1470} ratio which reflects the

ratio of aromatic C=C bonds to methylene groups is usually higher in the crushed extracts (Table 3). The absence of ester groups among carbonyl-containing compounds is characteristic of the non-crushed extracts, in contrast to the crushed ones. The E_{1710}/E_{1470} ratio which reflects the ratio of carbonyl to methylene groups is nearly always higher in the crushed extracts (Table 3). The IR spectra of a pair of extracts is shown in Fig. 2.

Extract fractions. The crushed extracts have higher asphaltene contents, lower saturates contents, lower saturates to aromatics ratios and lower hydrocarbons to NSO-compounds ratios than the non-crushed ones (either 13 or 9 pairs of extracts); see Table 3. The aromatic and resin contents of the two extract types do not show any major or systematic differences (Table 3, Fig. 3).

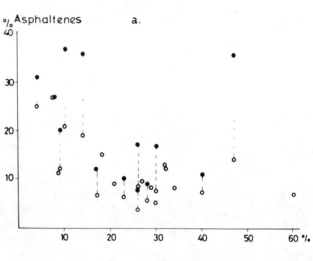

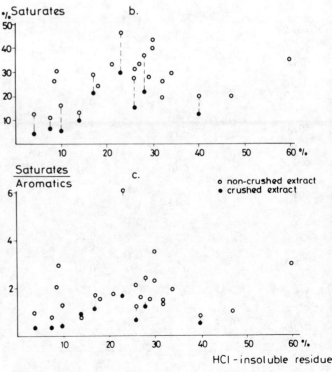

Fig. 3. Plots of the asphaltenes (a) and saturates (b) contents, and of the saturates/aromatics ratios (c) for crushed and non-crushed extracts *v.* HCl-insoluble residues.

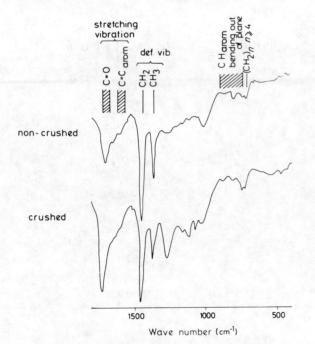

Fig. 2. IR spectra of crushed and non-crushed extracts; Zsámbék No. 14 borehole, 602.4 m depth.

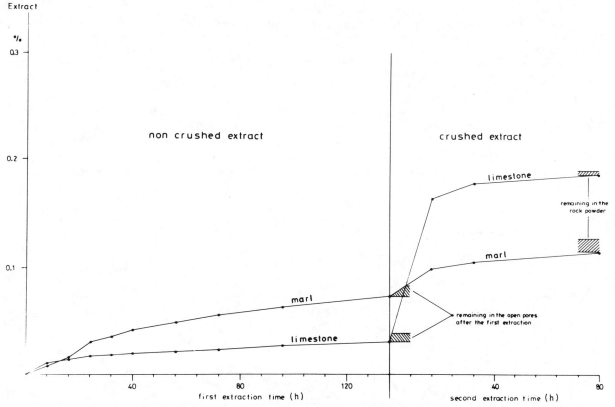

Fig. 4. Plot of the progress with time of the two extractions.

DISCUSSION

Contamination

Pre-laboratory contamination was found in only one case on the basis of sample fluorescence. As redistilled solvents and pre-extracted filterpapers and sample containers (for the rock powder) were used there is no reason to suppose any regular contamination during laboratory treatment.

Accumulation and migration

Before any interpretation of the differences between the two types of extract is made we should know whether a significant oil accumulation and/or migration has occurred in the sections studied. The following survey of the petrographic and organic geochemical characters of the sections addresses this issue.

The mud-supported texture of the limestone is incompatible with high permeability due to its low porosity. No evidence of significant fracturing was seen in either the macroscopic description or the electric and neutron–neutron logs.

The fact that the major part of the extract from the limestone samples was obtained after crushing suggests no significant oil accumulation. Also, the homogeneous yellow or dull brown fluorescence of the limestone matrix makes it probable that the extract is indigenous to the rock. We believe that these petrographic and organic geochemical data exclude a significant oil accumulation in the limestone.

If oil migration had occurred from the marls we would expect it to have been more efficient in the thin beds (Vyshemirsky *et al.*, 1971). However, the extract to C_{org} ratios of the thin beds and of the thick calcareous marl underlying the limestone section are similar (average values are 88 mg g^{-1} and 78 mg g^{-1} respectively). We believe, therefore, that no significant oil migration has occurred in the marls.

Open and closed pore extracts

The question arises as to whether the time of extraction (40 hours) is sufficient. To check this point, two supplementary samples (a limestone and a marl) were extracted as described above, but with their yields successively weighed after 8, 16, 24, 32, 40, 56, 72, 96 and 136 h of extraction. The extraction was repeated after crushing and the yields were weighed after 16, 32 and 80 h. The results are plotted in Fig. 4. The extraction data for the two supplementary samples are summarized in Table 4. The differences for these samples between the two types of extract are similar to those found earlier for the 26 samples.

We have calculated the quantity of extractable organic matter obtainable from fully exhaustive extraction of a non-crushed sample using the data for the extraction yield with time. This assessment has been made using an estimated value for the total amount of extractable matter, calculating the best fit curve with a Hewlett-Packard 97 computer using an exponential curve fitting program (Standard Pac Hewlett-Packard 97). The initial value of extractable matter was then

Table 4

Data for supplementary samples. Upper value to left: crushed extracts. Lower values to right: non-crushed extracts

Depth (m)	HCl-insoluble residue (%)	Total extract (%)	Crushed to non-crushed ratio	Saturates (%)	(%)	Aromatics (%)	(%)	Resins (%)	(%)	Asphaltenes (%)	(%)
663.5	14	0.187	5.20	10.0	16.0	20.0	15.0	39.0	45.0	31.0	22.0
674.0	24	0.117	0.59	20.0	31.0	5.9	17.0	51.0	43.0	21.0	9.5

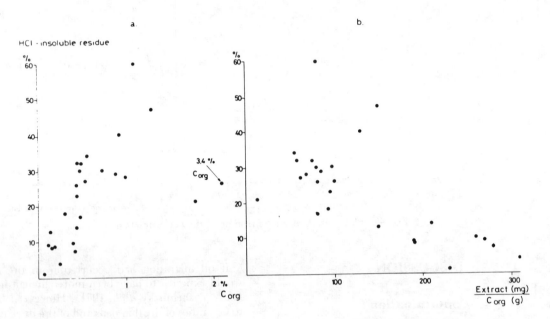

Fig. 5. Plots of C_{org} contents (a) and extract/C_{org} ratios (b) v. HCl-insoluble residues.

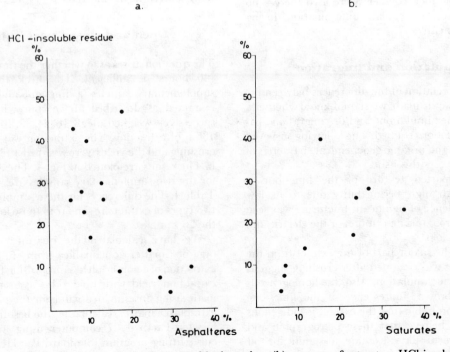

Fig. 6. Plots of the asphaltene (a) and saturated hydrocarbon (b) contents of extracts v. HCl-insoluble residues.

lowered and the calculation was repeated. In this way r^2 (the coefficient of determination) values were increased. When r^2 had reached 1.00 from 0.99 the calculation was stopped and the penultimate value was taken as the accurate one. The same procedure was followed for the second extraction (crushed samples).

Extractable components are mobilized more efficiently by Soxhlet-extraction than by the mechanism that operates under geological conditions. Hence the greater part of the crushed extract, which is the predominant one for the limestone samples, was actually in the closed pores (Fig. 4).

If the extensive extraction procedure above had been followed for all 26 samples the crushed to non-crushed ratios (more non-crushed and less crushed extracts) would have been lower than the values actually obtained. Nevertheless the systematic differences between the ratios for limestones and for marls would have been remained.

The relationship between organic geochemical parameters and lithology

In general terms the C_{org} content increases and the extract to C_{org} ratio decreases with increasing HCl-insoluble residue (Fig. 5). For 9 samples the composition of the total extracts (non-crushed + crushed) could be calculated. From these data, the asphaltene content is seen to decrease and the saturate content to increase with increasing HCl-insoluble residue (Fig. 6).

The positive correlation between C_{org} and HCl-insoluble residues is well-known. Changes in the quantity and quality of extracts are usually discussed as functions of C_{org}, but we have found better correlation with the HCl-insoluble residues (Table 5).

The higher extract to C_{org} ratio found for the more carbonate-rich samples cannot be taken as a result of oil accumulation (see above). The difference between the asphaltene contents of the total extracts for the two rock types is too high to be explained as a function of their different adsorptive capacities. It is presumed here that the organic matter of the more carbonate-rich samples contained more material derived from plankton, but underwent stronger diagenetic alteration and

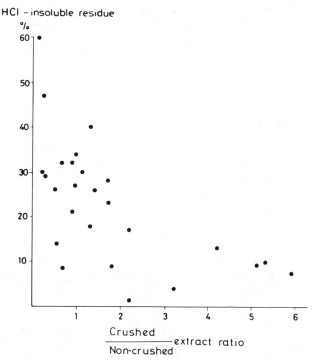

Fig. 7. Plots of crushed extract/non-crushed extract ratios *v.* HCl-insoluble residues.

sulphurization than that of the less carbonate-rich samples (Neruchev *et al.*, 1974).

The crushed to non-crushed extract ratios generally decrease with increasing HCl-insoluble residue (Fig. 7). Since both significant oil accumulation and migration are improbable, the movement of part of the hydrocarbons and NSO-compounds generated from the kerogen into the open pores seems likely. This process occurred more efficiently in the marly rocks. The relationship between the intensity of hydrocarbon redistribution and the carbonate content is said by Beletzkaya *et al.* (1976) to be a general phenomenon. Indeed the redistributed components could be partly trapped by the carbonate formed during catagenesis. Such a phenomenon must have occurred in the section studied since no weakening of the yellow fluorescence of the fracture-filling carbonate matter was observed after the first extraction for the great majority of the samples.

Table 5

Comparison of the dependence of selected organic geochemical parameters on the C_{org} content and the HCl-insoluble residue

Parameter	r^2 (coefficient of determination)		Type of curve[a]
	v. C_{org}	*v.* HCl-insoluble residue	
Extract $\overline{C_{org}}$	0.14	0.42	Linear
$\dfrac{\text{Crushed}}{\text{Non-crushed}}$	0.20	0.55	Exponential
Asphaltene content of the total extract	0.27	0.51	Logarithmic
CH content of the total extract	0.43	0.68	Logarithmic
$\dfrac{\text{CH}}{C_{org}}$	0.16	0.44	Logarithmic

[a] For these calculations the curve fitting programs of the Standard Pac Hewlett–Packard 97 were used. The types of curve given are those that show the highest r^2 values.

Table 6
Summary of observed differences between crushed and non-crushed extracts

	Crushed extract	Non-crushed extract
Degree of condensation of aromatics	>	
$\dfrac{\text{Aromatic C=C}}{\text{Methylene}}$	>	
$\dfrac{\text{Carbonyl}}{\text{Methylene}}$	>	
Ester	presence	absence
$\dfrac{\text{Hydrocarbons}}{\text{NSO-compounds}}$	<	
Saturates (%)	<	
Asphaltenes (%)	>	
$\dfrac{\text{Saturates}}{\text{Aromatics}}$	<	

Differences between the two types of extract

The differences between the crushed and non-crushed extracts are summarized in Table 6. Most of these are also found in comparisons of oil–source rock extracts. As the crushed extracts, particularly for the marls, generally also contain matter from the open pores (Fig. 4) the values for the differences between the two types of extract are not fully representative of the extractable organic matter present in the open and closed pores.

CONCLUSIONS

1. In the section studied, which includes marls and limestones, a significant part of the hydrocarbons and NSO-compounds generated during catagenesis have accumulated in the open pores.
2. The redistribution of components generated by catagenesis is more efficient in the marls.
3. The open pores are enriched in less polar and lower molecular weight components. The marls were found to be at the point of oil migration although no significant primary migration had occurred.
4. This case history is not general, however, it serves to focus attention on the fact that primary migration from carbonates can be hindered not only by the lack of appropriate compaction but also by the relatively low rate of accumulation of hydrocarbons in their open pores.

Acknowledgements

The authors express their thanks to I. Fabók and B. Szabó for their analytical assistance. Valuable information from many of the staff of the Geological Survey of Hungary is also much appreciated. Finally, we thank R. Pelet and the anonymous reviewers for several helpful comments.

REFERENCES

Baker, D. R. (1962) Organic geochemistry of Cherokee Group in southeastern Kansas and northeastern Oklahoma. *Am. Ass. Petrol. Geol. Bull.*, **46**, 1621–1642.

Beletzkaya, S. N. *et al.* (1976) Changes in distribution of hydrocarbons in the pore system of sedimentary rocks during recrystallization of carbonates and burial. (In Russian). In *Study of Organic Matter*. Ed. by Vassoevich, N. B. and Timofeiev, P. P. Nauka, Moscow. pp. 155–162.

Connan, J. and Cassou, A. M. (1980) Properties of gases and petroleum liquids derived from terrestrial kerogen at various maturation levels. *Geochim. Cosmochim. Acta* **44**, 1–23.

Hunt, J. M. (1962) Distribution of hydrocarbons in sedimentary rocks. *Geochim. Cosmochim. Acta* **22**, 37–49.

Hunt, J. M. (1979) *Petroleum Geochemistry and Geology*. W. H. Freeman and Co.

Neruchev, S. G. *et al.* (1974) A new classification of the diagenetic and catagenetic alteration of planktonogenic (sapropelic) dispersed organic matter. (In Russian). In *Study of Organic Matter*. Ed. by Vassoevich, N. B. Nauka, Moscow. pp. 81–106.

Vyshemirsky, V. S., Kontorovich, A. E. and Trofimuk, A. A. (1971) *Migration of the Dispersed Bitumens*. (In Russian.) Nauka, Moscow.

Young, A. and McIver, R. D. (1977) Distribution of hydrocarbons between oils and associated fine-grained sedimentary rocks. Physical chemistry applied to petroleum geochemistry. Pt. 2. *Am. Ass. Petrol. Geol. Bull.* **61**, 1401–1436.

Environmental Organic Geochemistry

Advances in Organic Geochemistry 1981, pp. 185–197
© *John Wiley & Sons Limited, 1983*

Fatty Acids, Wax Esters, Triacylglycerols and Alkyldiacylglycerols Associated with Particles Collected in Sediment Traps in the Peru Upwelling

S. G. Wakeham, J. W. Farrington and J. K. Volkman

Chemistry Department, Woods Hole Oceanographic Institution, Woods Hole, Massachusetts 02543, USA

Marine particulate matter samples were collected in free-drifting sediment traps in the Peru upwelling region to assess the vertical flux and organic composition of lipids associated with particles sinking out of the euphotic zone. Fatty acids of total hexane-soluble lipid, wax esters, triacylglycerols and alkyldiacylglycerols were determined in a set of four sediment traps deployed at 14 m and at 52 m during a diel cycle. Fluxes of specific organic compound classes show much greater variations than for bulk particulate organic carbon (POC). Total fatty acids accounted for about 2% of the daytime POC flux, but up to 10% of the nocturnal POC flux. The maximum fatty acid flux was measured in the 14 m night trap. The composition of the fatty acids was indicative of a mixed phytoplankton/zooplankton source. The flux of particulate 16:0 calculated to be sinking across 52 m based on sediment trap data is 20-fold greater than the estimated accumulation rate in the sediments, indicating that a large portion of this fatty acid is altered either in the water column below 52 m or at the sediment/water interface. Wax esters, triacylglycerols, and alkyldiacylglycerols all contain esterified fatty acids, but show flux and compositional trends different from total fatty acids, as well as from each other. Wax ester fluxes into the night 14 m trap were nearly 25 times greater than fluxes into the other three traps, and can be attributed in part to entrapment of live euphausiids in the shallower night trap. Triacylglycerols were about an order of magnitude more abundant in the night traps compared to the day traps. The dominant source of triacylglycerols into the day traps probably is phytodetritus. However, it appears that different zooplankton communities, one active above 14 m and one between 14 and 52 m, are significant triacylglycerol sources to the two night traps. Alkyldiacylglycerols, most likely containing a phytanyl ether moiety, were only found in the 14 m trap at night. The close correspondence between wax esters and alkyldiacylglycerols suggests a related source.

INTRODUCTION

Organic geochemical studies of marine particulate matter have a direct bearing on understanding the carbon cycle in the oceans. Sinking particles provide a means of energy transfer in the form of photosynthetically-fixed carbon from the euphotic zone to deeper ocean environments. Biochemical changes involving organic matter sinking through the water column can influence the organic and inorganic chemical composition of seawater and sediments.

Large particles (e.g. > 32 μm) such as fecal pellets, aggregates of fecal matter, and marine snow (macroscopic aggregates) may comprise only a small portion of the total particulate matter in the oceans, but may account for most of the vertical mass flux (McCave, 1975; Honjo, 1980). Sediment trap experiments provide a direct assessment of the large particle flux and its composition (e.g. Honjo, 1980; Brewer *et al.*, 1980; Deuser *et al.*, 1981; Wakeham *et al.*, 1980; Prahl and Carpenter, 1979; Tanoue and Handa, 1980; Crisp *et al.*, 1979; Knauer *et al.*, 1979; De Baar *et al.*, 1983; Gagosian

et al., 1983a). Large particles have sinking rates of tens to hundreds of metres per day (Honjo and Roman, 1978; Small *et al.*, 1979), resulting in transit through a 5000 m water column in weeks compared to hundreds of years for smaller (< 32 μm) particles.

Despite relatively fast sinking rates, Wakeham *et al.* (1980) have shown that alterations in the composition of lipids are apparent when comparing sediment trap samples from 389, 988, 3755 and 5068 m in the equatorial Atlantic. This implies that biological and/or chemical processes are acting on the rapidly sinking particles to change organic matter composition and probably also are important to the biogeochemistry of other chemicals associated with these same particulates. We have undertaken studies in the upwelling areas off the coasts of Peru and California to further elucidate the relationships between the organic matter composition of large particles and biological processes in the water column, including biosynthesis in the euphotic zone. We are also investigating the relationship between the composition of organic matter in large particles deposited at the sediment/water interface and the organic matter which becomes buried in the sediments as geological deposits (e.g. see Volkman *et al.*, 1983; Repeta and Gagosian, 1983; Gagosian *et al.*, 1983b).

We report here measurements for fatty acid of total hexane-soluble lipid, wax esters, triacylglycerols and alkyldiacylglycerols in particulate matter collected in day/night pairs of free-drifting sediment traps deployed in the Peru upwelling region. Our objectives were: (i) to examine the downward flux and composition of these important biochemicals out of the euphotic zone and into deeper water; (ii) to determine the temporal and spatial variations in flux and composition; (iii) to investigate the relationship between biological processes in the upper part of the water column to the formation of sinking particles; and (iv) to investigate the relation between particle flux and accumulation in the underlying sediments.

This investigation is part of a coordinated effort to understand better the biogeochemistry of organic matter in the Peru coastal area and includes studies of hydrocarbons, fatty alcohols, sterols, steroid ketones, long chain ketones, carotenoids, and amino acids in source organisms, large and small particulate matter, and sediments (e.g. Henrichs, 1980; Staresinic, 1983; Lee and Cronin, 1982; Volkman *et al.*, 1983; Repeta and Gagosian, 1983; Gagosian *et al.*, 1983a,b). Highly productive upwelling areas, such as those off the coast of Namibia (Southwest Africa), Peru, and Chile, are important areas for organic geochemical studies because they couple high biological productivity in surface waters with accumulation of large amounts of organic matter in the sediments (Price and Calvert, 1973; Bremner, 1974, 1975; Boon *et al.*, 1975, 1977; Morris and Calvert, 1977; Gagosian and Farrington, 1978).

METHODS

Sampling

Free-drifting sediment traps (FSTs) were deployed off the Peruvian coast near the Coastal Upwelling Ecosystems Analysis 'C' transect at about 15 °S (Fig. 1) during February–March, 1978 on R/V *Knorr* Cruise 73/2. The water column depth at the sampling location discussed here was 400 m. The FSTs consisted of a pair of 41 cm diameter cylinders (0.26 m² total collecting area) as described in detail by Staresinic (1978; 1983); the rationale of using free-drifting traps as opposed to moored trap arrays has been discussed by Staresinic *et al.* (1978). Two identical arrays of FSTs were deployed simultaneously, one at the base of the euphotic zone (14 m) and one at the bottom of the seasonal thermocline at about 52 m. To assess the diel fluctuation in particulate flux and composition, a pair of traps were set during the day (FST 9 at 14 m, FST 8 at 52 m) and a second pair at night (FST 10 at 14 m, FST 11 at 52 m). Mean drift trajectories for these traps are shown in Fig. 1. Traps were recovered after 8–12 h deployments so no poisons were used to inhibit bacterial spoilage.

In all, 18 sets of FSTs were deployed for organic geochemical studies in the active upwelling; two additional traps were deployed 50 km offshore out of the upwelling zone. Four sets of day/night–shallow/deep trap samples were collected. We report here only one set of four traps, so interpretations will require confirmations from analysis of other FSTs. In addition, a series of sediment cores were collected during the cruise, and results for some lipid class analyses in the sediments are

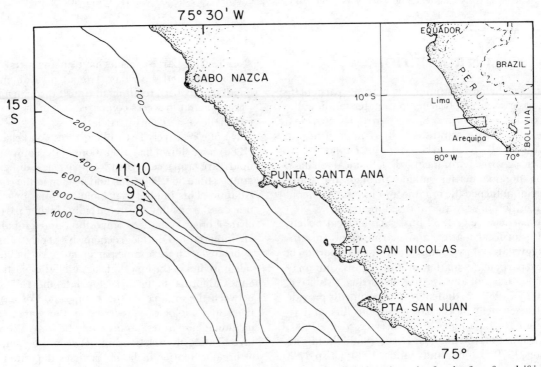

Fig. 1. Location of sediment trap deployment in the Peru upwelling showing drift trajectories for the four free-drifting traps.

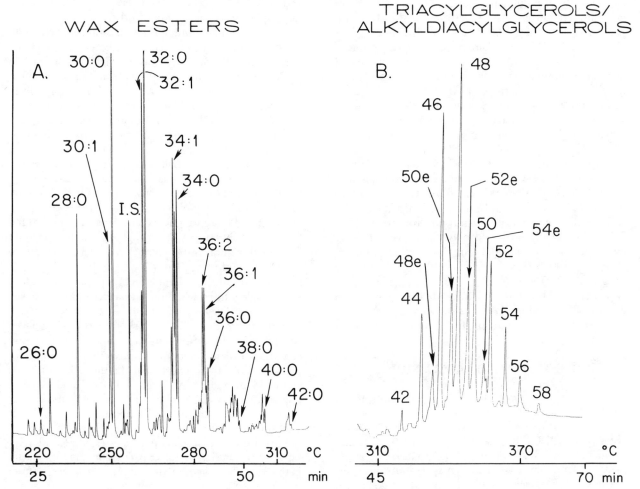

PERU FLOATING SEDIMENT TRAP 10

WAX ESTERS

TRIACYLGLYCEROLS/ ALKYLDIACYLGLYCEROLS

Fig. 2. Glass capillary gas chromatograms of intact wax esters (A), and intact triacylglycerols and alkyldiacylglycerols (B). Numbers with wax ester peaks refer to carbon chain length :number of double bonds; numbers for triacylglycerol peaks refer only to carbon number; alkyldiacylglycerols are designated by 'e'.

reported by Volkman *et al.* (1983). Amino acid data for FSTs and sediments have been described elsewhere by Lee and Cronin (1982) and Henrichs (1980), respectively, and Gagosian *et al.* (1983a,b) report FST sterol data.

Analysis

Following recovery of the FSTs, the collected particulate matter was split by a plankton splitter and an aliquot (38%) was filtered on to precombusted glass fibre filters. The filters were immediately freeze-dried and stored frozen until extraction in the shore-based laboratory. The particulates and filters were exhaustively Soxhlet-extracted with toluene/methanol (1:1) and the lipids thus extracted partitioned into hexane. An aliquot of the hexane-soluble lipids (25%) was saponified with methanolic KOH, methylated with BF_3–MeOH, and the fatty acid methyl esters purified by silica gel adsorption chromatography (Merck silica gel 60, 5% deactivated with water). A second aliquot of the lipids (50%) was fractionated into constituent lipid class compounds by silica gel chromatography. Wax esters were eluted with

50% toluene in hexane and triacylglycerols and alkyldiacylglycerols were eluted by 10% ethyl acetate in hexane. Aliquots of the wax ester and triacylglycerols/alkyldiacylglycerols fractions were subsequently saponified and analysed for constituent fatty acids and fatty alcohols.

Fractions were analysed by glass capillary gas chromatography on a Carlo Erba FTV Model 4160 gas chromatograph equipped with an on-column injector and a flame ionization detector. Compounds were separated on a 25 m × 0.3 mm i.d. silylated column coated with SE-52 (Grob, 1980). Fatty acid methyl esters were analysed with a hydrogen carrier gas flow of 0.8 kg/cm² and a linear temperature programme of 100–320 °C at 3°/min. Intact wax esters were analysed with hydrogen carrier at 1.5 kg/cm² and a programme of 180–360° at 2°/min. Intact triacylglycerols and alkyldiacylglycerols were analysed with hydrogen carrier at 2.0 kg/cm² and a programme of 150–370° at 3.5°/min. The FID temperature was set at 350 °C. Quantification of GC peaks was obtained by electronic measurement of peak heights and areas using a Columbia Scientific Instruments Supergrator 3 and by comparison with internal and external standards.

Structural information was obtained by co-injection experiments with authentic standards and by capillary gas chromatography/mass spectrometry. Electron impact mass spectra of fatty acid methyl esters were obtained using a Varian Aerograph 1400 gas chromatograph equipped with a 20 m × 0.3 mm i.d. SE–52 capillary column and interfaced with a Finnigan 1015C quadrupole mass spectrometer. Methane chemical ionization spectra of intact wax esters, and electron impact spectra of intact triacylglycerols and alkyldiacylglycerols were obtained using a Finnigan 9500 GC and a Finnigan 3200 quadrupole mass spectrometer; both the GC and MS were modified for high temperature work as described by Wakeham and Frew (1983). Wax esters were separated on a SE–52 column (20 m × 0.3 mm i.d.) using helium carrier at 1.3 kg/cm² and a temperature programme from 180–360° at 3°/min; triacylglycerols and alkyldiacylglycerols were analysed on a 15 m × 0.3 mm i.d. SE–30 capillary column with helium carrier at 0.75 kg/cm² and programmed from 250–370° at 4°/min. The glass capillary GC/MS interface was silylated and maintained at 370–380 °C. Mass spectral data were acquired and processed using a Finnigan Incos Model 2300 data system.

RESULTS AND DISCUSSION

The Peru coastal area is one of the world's major upwelling systems. Primary productivity rates of 2–4 g C/m² day, and sometimes exceeding 10 g C/m² day (Staresinic, 1978, 1983; Gagosian et al., 1980; Zuta and Guillen, 1970; Ryther et al., 1971; Gagosian et al., 1983a), have until recently supported an immense anchoveta (Engraoulis ringens) population, making the region the largest single fishery in the world. The high overall productivity produces organic-rich (3–5% organic carbon, up to 9.5%; Henrichs, 1980) diatomaceous sediments where depleted oxygen levels in bottom waters enhance preservation of organic matter. Sulphate reduction can occur in this oxygen minimum zone, at depths of 100 to 500 m (Dugdale et al., 1977), and in places the sediment is covered by a Thioploca-like sulphur bacteria mat (Gallardo, 1978).

The dry mass flux and bulk composition of particulate matter collected in free-drifting sediment traps in the area of active upwelling was reported by Staresinic (1978, 1983). The flux of particulate matter was about 3 g/m² 12 h (range 2.9–4.6 g/m² 12 h) and varied little with sample depth or time of collection, similar to the data shown in Table 1 for the four samples (FSTs 8–11) considered here. Organic carbon comprised about 5–10% of the particulate matter. The mean flux of particulate organic carbon (POC) across the base of the euphotic zone (14 m) was about 275 mg C/m² 12 h; roughly 12% of the primary production. Fluxes across 50 m were roughly half of these values. Mean POC fluxes during the day and night were comparable (∼200 mg C/m² 12 h) but the 14 m samples at night generally contained significantly more POC than the 50 m samples at night (e.g. Table 1). In addition, Staresinic has pointed out that diatoms were especially abundant in the shallow traps, while anchoveta faecal pellets packed with diatom frustules in various stages of destruction accounted for a significant portion of the particulates collected at 50 m, especially at night. Night traps also contained greater amounts of phytodetritus and zooplankton molts and carcasses than did the day traps. Some of the 14 m night traps (e.g. FST 10) contained live euphausiids. Zooplankton faecal pellets were also present in the traps, but their contribution to the POC flux is unknown.

Bulk POC measurements suggest spatial and temporal variations in the flux of particulate organic matter in the upper 50 m of the water column. However, a closer examination of the specific composition of this organic matter is more revealing. Total hexane-soluble lipid fluxes, for example, were similar in the two-day samples (13–15 mg/m² 12 h), and lipids accounted for only about 0.5% of the total particulate flux. At night, lipid fluxes were 2–5 times greater (24 and 76 mg/m² 12 h) than the day-time fluxes and lipids made up 1–2% of the

Table 1
Bulk organic geochemical flux data for Peru FSTs 8–11

	Day		Night	
	FST 9 (14 m)	FST 8 (52 m)	FST 10 (14 m)	FST 11 (52 m)
Dry mass flux[a] (g/m².12 h)	2.93	2.92	3.34[b]	2.48
POC flux[a] (mg/m².12 h)	164	140	313[b]	131
Lipids flux (mg/m².12 h)	13.3	14.9	76.1	24.4
Lipid flux/POC flux	0.08	0.11	0.24	0.19
Total fatty acid flux (μg/m².12 h)	3100	2600	24 500	14 000
Total fatty acid flux/POC flux	0.02	0.02	0.08	0.10
Total wax ester flux (μg/m².12 h)	41	80	1150	18
Wax ester flux/POC flux	0.0003	0.0006	0.004	0.0001
Total triacylglycerol flux (μg/m².12 h)	36	160	600	870
Triacylglycerol flux/POC flux	0.0002	0.001	0.002	0.007
Total alkyldiacylglycerol flux (μg/m².12 h)	n.d.[c]	n.d.	200	n.d.
Alkyldiacylglycerol flux/POC flux	—	—	0.0006	—

[a] Staresinic (1983).
[b] Live euphausiids removed before mass and POC measurements.
[c] Not detected.

particulates. Thus not only was transport of lipid greater at night than during the day, but the particulate matter collected in the night traps was relatively more lipid-rich than material caught during the day, with by far the most lipid being in the 14 m night sample.

Fatty acids of total hexane-soluble lipids

Fatty acids released by saponification of total hexane-soluble lipid accounted for 0.1% of the particulate matter in the day time FSTs (Table 1), about 2% of the POC, and 17–23% of the lipid. In contrast, fatty acids in the nocturnal traps comprised 0.6–0.7% of the particulates, 8–10% of the POC, and 32–58% of the lipids. Fatty acid fluxes at night were 5–10 times the daytime fluxes (Tables 1 and 2), and there were significant compositional differences between the day/night pairs, although the day and the night 14 m/52 m pairs were quite similar in terms of relative fatty acid composition (Table 2). Fatty acids in all four trap samples were relatively simple mixtures. In the two-day traps, the dominant fatty acids were straight-chained and saturated: 16:0, 14:0, and 18:0 (in order of decreasing relative abundance). The 16:0 acid alone accounted for almost 55% of the total fatty acid content. Monounsaturated 16:1, 18:1Δ9 (oleic acid), and 18:1Δ11 (cis-vaccenic acid) were present at lower amounts. Polyunsaturated fatty acids, particularly 20:5 and 22:6, branched 15:0 and 17:0 acids, and acids of chain length $> C_{20}$ were present at low levels. In contrast, the pair of night traps contained relatively more 16:1, where 16:1

was only slightly less abundant than 16:0, and 18:1, with both 18:1 isomers being more abundant than 18:0. 20:5 and 22:6 were present as 1–3% of the total acids.

The fatty acid distributions found in all four FSTs are indicative of a mixed phytoplankton and zooplankton source. Analysis of the major diatom species (the pennate *Thalassionema nitzchioides* and the centric *Thalassiosira eccentrica*) which Staresinic (1983) found in the traps for fatty acid content of total lipids are not available in the literature and we intend to analyse phytoplankton samples collected during a recent cruise to the Peru upwelling. However, a variety of other marine diatoms have been examined for fatty acids (Ackman *et al.*, 1964, 1968; Kates and Volcani, 1966; Opute, 1974; Fisher and Schwarzenbach, 1978). The principal fatty acids of diatoms are 14:0, 16:0, 16:1Δ9, 20:4 and 20:5. C_{22} acids are often minor components, while C_{18} fatty acids are usually trace components. Inputs of significant amounts of diatom-derived fatty acids to the FSTs correlates with the observations of Staresinic (1978, 1983) on the importance of diatoms to the FST particulate matter. Diatom fluxes to the two night traps apparently were an order of magnitude greater than to the day traps; some 20% of the POC flux into FST 10 is estimated to be diatom-related (Staresinic, personal communication).

One mechanism for transporting intact or only partially degraded diatoms, and hence organic matter, to the sediment traps, as well as to the benthos, may be anchoveta faecal pellets, which were conspicuous in the FSTs (Staresinic *et al.*, 1982). Fragments of anchoveta faecal matter accounted for up to 17% of the POC flux to some of the 50 m FSTs (1.7%, 2.4%, 4.7% and 17.4% for FSTs 9, 8, 10, and 11, respectively). *T. nitzchioides* fragments could account for 62% of the anchoveta pellet fragment POC. Diatom fatty acids, either unaltered or partially degraded, could also be transported to the sediment traps by zooplankton faecal pellets. There are no data available for the impact of zooplankton fecal pellets on the POC flux into the FSTs. However, Volkman *et al.* (1980a) have shown that fecal pellets of the copepod *Calanus helgolandicus*, fed in the laboratory on unialgal diets, contain fatty acids which generally resemble the algal food.

Zooplankton, while also containing abundant C_{16}, C_{20}, and C_{22} acids, have been found to produce major amounts of C_{18} fatty acids but comparatively little C_{14} (Lee, 1974; Culkin and Morris, 1969; Morris, 1971). In some cases, 18:1 (usually oleic acid [18:1Δ9]) is the most abundant fatty acid present. The dominant zooplankton in the Peru upwelling during the sampling period was *Euphausia mucronata* (its fatty acid composition is unknown at present) and euphausiid molts were present in the night traps. Some live euphausiids were found in FST 10 upon recovery, but none were in FST 11. *E. mucronata* migrates from daytime depths of about 300 m to within 15 m of the surface to feed at night (Mauchlin and Fisher, 1969). Zooplankton tows through the upper 15 m of the water column caught these euphausiids only at night (Staresinic, 1978). Lasker (1964, 1966) has shown in laboratory studies that euphausiids often molt at night.

A bacterial contribution to the fatty acids in the FSTs

Table 2
Total fatty acid fluxes for Peru FSTs 8–11

Carbon number	Day		Night	
	FST 9 (14 m)	FST 8 (52 m)	FST 10 (14 m)	FST 11 (52 m)
	(μg/m^2.h)			
12:0	—[a]	—	8.1	—
14:0	43	29	220	79
i 15:0	1.5	—	7.4	—
a 15:0	0.6	—	1.6	—
15:0	3.7	1.4	14	—
16:1	17	25	410	260
16:0	150	120	660	320
i 17:0	—	—	11	—
a 17:0	—	—	6.3	—
17:0	internal standard			
18:1Δ9	9.2	11	280	320
18:1Δ11	16.0	8.1	170	80
18:0	24	20	61	49
19:0	internal standard			
20:5	—	—	20	16
20:1	—	0.6	90	7.8
20:0	1.0	0.4	34	2.7
22:6	—	—	16	31
22:1	—	—	3.4	14
22:0	0.7	0.4	1.4	0.9
24:0	0.5	0.4	0.3	0.7
Total fatty acid flux				
(μg/m^2.h)	260	220	2040	1200
(μg/m^2.12 h)	3090	2600	24 500	14 100

[a] At or below detection limit.

is possible but difficult to assess. The relatively high concentrations of 18:1Δ11 may be a product of bacterial synthesis, as this $C_{18:1}$ isomer is abundant in several aerobic and anaerobic heterotrophs and in bacterial species isolated from a marine sediment (Perry et al., 1979; Volkman et al., 1980b). However, 18:1Δ11 has also been reported in other marine organisms including plankton (Perry, 1977), eucaryotic algae (Johns et al., 1977), molluscs (Ackman and Hooper, 1973; Perry, 1977) and fish (Ackman et al., 1967) when analyses were of sufficient resolution to separate it from the 18:1Δ9 isomer. The value of 18:1Δ11 as a bacterial marker may be its higher relative concentration in bacteria than in other organisms (Perry et al., 1979). Two of the FSTs also contained detectable levels of branched 15:0 and 17:0 fatty acids. These compounds are often also used as indicators of bacterial sources as they were relatively common in the bacteria examined by Perry et al. (1979), in *Desulfovibrio desulfuricans* (Boon et al., 1978), and in a number of *Bacillus* species studied by Kaneda (1967). (Kaneda presented no data on 18:1 fatty acids.) Fatty acids of 20 strains of marine Gram-negative bacteria (Oliver and Colwell, 1973) contained low levels of branched C_{15} and C_{17} fatty acids; 18:1 was often the major acid, but the isomer distribution was not specified. However, like 18:1Δ11, the branched C_{15} and C_{17} acids are also present in small amounts in marine organisms. Information on the microbial populations in the Peru upwelling at the time of our sampling is not known.

If the relative abundances of 18:1Δ11 and the presence of the branched acids were due to a bacterial source, then two interesting questions are raised. Were these bacteria normal populations in the water column in the highly productive upwelling area where there were large amounts of organic matter available? If so, then the presence of bacterial fatty acids in the sediment traps would represent an input of compounds from the naturally occurring bacterial communities. On the other hand, the sediment traps were deployed without poisons, based on the assumption that a 6–12 h deployment would be short enough to limit bacterial activity in the traps. Did the bacterial markers come from microbial activity taking place in the trap, where the effect of concentrating organic matter in the trap itself could well enhance microbial growth? In this case microbial reworking of organic matter in the traps could well alter the composition of this organic material. Answers to both questions are needed in order to allow proper interpretation of sediment trap results and will require further experiments.

An interesting comparison is the downward fatty acid flux measured in the FSTs versus an estimated flux of fatty acids accumulating in the sediments calculated from sediment data. Considering 16:0, which in the FSTs probably is primarily of planktonic origin, for the two 52 m traps (Table 2), the range of downward fluxes is 1400 to 3800 $\mu g/m^2$ 12 h (mean 2600 $\mu g/m^2$ 12 h). In a sediment core taken about 15 km closer to the shore than the FSTs and in 90 m of water, Volkman et al. (unpublished data) found a surface sediment (0–1 cm) concentration for 16:0 of 25 $\mu g/g$ dry sediment. For a nearby core, Henrichs (1980) reported a ^{210}Pb-derived sedimentation

rate of 1.1 cm/yr and a water content of about 80% for the upper 1 cm. A range of water contents for surface sediments from 70–90% has been reported (Henrichs, 1980) for a variety of surface sediments in the Peru region. Assuming a water content of 80% and a wet sediment density of 1.2 gm/cm^3, we calculate an accumulation rate for 16:0 in the surface sediment layer of 90 $\mu g/m^2$ 12 h, subject to a potential error of ±50%. Thus the estimated flux of particulate 16:0 passing across 52 m in the water column is some 20 times greater than the estimated rate of accumulation in the surface sediment. A similar calculation for 24:0, which is usually attributed to terrestrial higher plants, yields 5–8 $\mu g/m^2$ 12 h at the 52 m FSTs compared to about 5 $\mu g/m^2$ 12 h accumulating in the sediment (using a measured concentration of 1.3 $\mu g/g$ dry weight 24:0 in the 0–1 cm interval).

These calculations are preliminary and will need further verification from future measurements in additional FSTs and sediment cores, as well as resolving uncertainties in the water content of the sediment. It should also be pointed out that FST data reflect processes occurring over 6–12 h deployment periods whereas the sediment results are integrated over a year, and temporal variations in organic matter production both in the water column and in the sediments cannot be evaluated at present. Nevertheless, the differences between fluxes for the two compounds from FST and sediment analyses are revealing. For 16:0, the elevated FST flux relative to the sediment accumulation strongly suggests that a very large portion of the 16:0 produced in the euphotic zone and associated with particles sinking below 52 m is degraded either in the water column below 52 m and/or at the sediment/water interface. In fact, the 20-fold difference in FST versus sediment flux values should be considered as a minimum difference, since *in situ* microbial biosynthesis of 16:0 within the sediment is likely. An additional source of 16:0 would mean that the amount of the fatty acid reaching the sediment from above is lower than its concentration in the sediment would indicate.

The apparent agreement between FST-derived and sediment-derived fluxes for 24:0 is possibly fortuitous. Two sources of terrestrial 24:0 are possible: (1) Aeolian transport and subsequent deposition on the sea surface, and (2) fluvial inputs of material during periods of high rainfall followed by longshore transport of suspended particulate matter. At present we cannot quantify either process. A dual source for the organic matter in the sediments would also account for the observations that particulates in the FSTs have many compositional differences compared with the surface sediments, some of which cannot be attributed to diagenetic alterations alone. The organic composition of surface sediments is the result of a dynamic balance between inputs and diagenesis of organic matter, and both processes must be considered together to gain a true understanding of the relative importances of each process. One additional comment is needed. The fatty acid analyses we report are only for solvent-extractable 'free' compounds. Measurements of the 'bound' fatty acids may result in an increase of the fatty acid content of the sediment by a factor of 2–3 (Farrington et al., 1977) or more, which may affect flux comparisons. On the other hand, the concept of physically distinct compartments containing different portions of organic matter with differing availabilities to the biota needs further investigation, as pointed out by Prahl and Carpenter (1979) and Volkman *et al.* (1983).

Wax esters and triacylglycerols

Wax esters over the carbon chain-length range of C_{26}–C_{42} were present in the FSTs, although all compounds could not be detected in each of the four traps (Table 3). The most abundant chain lengths were C_{30}, C_{32}, and C_{34}. For chain lengths of C_{32} and less, the saturated esters were generally more abundant than the unsaturated esters, while for C_{34} and longer chains, the unsaturated wax esters were prevalent. The complexity of the wax ester distribution in the FSTs is illustrated in Fig. 2(a) showing a glass capillary gas chromatogram of intact wax esters from FST 10.

Fluxes of wax esters to the FSTs were quite variable. The two daytime traps collected comparable amounts of wax esters (41 and 80 $\mu g/m^2$ 12 h total wax esters in FST 9 and FST 8, respectively). Whether the flux difference

for the two depths is significant is unknown. The composition of the wax esters in the day traps was similar, with 34:1 and 32:0 as the major components. In contrast the night traps had a 60-fold difference in wax ester flux, the 14 m trap (FST 10) clearly collecting most of the wax ester flux at night. Such a large wax ester flux was not indicated by either total lipid or total fatty acid data. At night, the dominant wax esters were 30:0, 34:1/34:2, and 32:1/32:0. Preliminary indications are that the day versus night difference in wax ester composition may reflect the presence of copepods in the daytime traps versus euphausiids at night, but again further analyses are required.

The fatty alcohol/fatty acid combinations comprising the wax esters in the FSTs have been determined by GC/MS (see Wakeham and Frew (1982) for procedures), but detailed results are beyond the scope of the present discussion. For example, the 30:0 esters in FST 10 are made up of 16:0/14:0 (51%), 14:0/16:0 (44%), 18:0/12:0 (4%), and 18:0/12:0 (1%) alcohol/acid combinations. The 32:0 esters are 16:0/16:0 (81%), 14:0/18:0 (11%), 18:0/14:0 (7%), and 12:0/20:0 (1%). This means that the 16:0/14:0, 14:0/16:0, and 16:0/16:0 wax esters account for 4.6%, 4.0%, and 8.0% of the total wax ester content of the FST 10 sample. Without presenting the complete set of GC/MS data, suffice it to say that the major fatty alcohols and fatty acids in the FST wax esters are 16:0, 14:0, 18:0, 16:1, and 18:1, in agreement with data on fatty alcohols and acids released by saponification (e.g. Fig. 3).

Distributions of triacylglycerols in the FSTs are given in Table 4 and show total carbon chain ranging from C_{42}–C_{60} (carbon number is the sum of acyl carbons). Figure 4 illustrates the triacylglycerol (and alkyldiacylglycerol; see below) pattern of FST 10 obtained by GC. The C_{48} triacylglycerol was the major component in FSTs 9, 8, and 10, but C_{52} dominated FST 11. Broadening of the GC peaks compared to single-component reference standards indicates that each triacylglycerol peak was actually composed of a complex mixture of compounds having the same overall carbon number but varying degrees of unsaturation and saturation. For instance, GC/MS analysis of the C_{48} triacylglycerol of FST 10 showed that the principal fatty acid components were 14:0, 16:0, 16:1, 16:2, 18:0, and 18:1, several combinations of which would give a total of 48 carbon atoms.

Fatty acid chain length distributions obtained by saponification of the triacylglycerol fractions helps to explain the differences in triacylglycerol distributions between FSTs 9, 8, and 10, and FST 11. It should be pointed out that fatty acid composition of FST 10 includes a small contribution from alkyldiacylglycerols. Mean fatty acid abundances (taking unsaturated, saturated, and polyunsaturated acids of equal carbon number together for the sake of this discussion) for FSTs 9, 8, and 10 were C_{14} 4%; C_{16} 36%; C_{18} 32%; C_{20} 10%; C_{22} 10%; and C_{24} 2% (e.g. Fig. 3(c)). For FST 11, the corresponding abundances were: C_{14} 1%; C_{16} 17%; C_{18} 53%; C_{20} 11%; C_{22} 12%; and C_{24} 2%. Therefore, in FSTs 9, 8, and 10, there is relatively more C_{16} and less C_{18} compared to FST 11, so there is a shift to higher total carbon numbers for the triacylglycerols in FST 11.

Table 3
Wax ester fluxes for Peru FSTs 8–11

	Day		Night	
Carbon number	FST 9 (14 m)	FST 8 (52 m)	FST 10 (14 m)	FST 11 (52 m)
	($\mu g/m^2$.h)			
26:0	0.05	—	0.32	—
27:0	0.01	—	0.13	—
28:1	—	—	0.31	—
28:0	0.08	0.29	3.2	0.06
29:0	0.02	0.02	0.57	0.02
30:1	0.12	0.24	3.9	—
30:0	0.16	0.37	8.7	0.11
31:1	0.05	0.11	0.53	—
31:0	internal standard			
32:1	0.19	0.41	—	—
32:1	0.13	0.53	6.8	0.15
32:0	0.67	0.57	9.5	0.18
33:1	—	0.15	1.0	—
33:0	0.05	0.06	0.91	0.02
34:2	—	—	9.7	0.24
34:1	0.83	2.5	3.3	0.08
34:0	0.10	0.20	3.7	0.14
35:1	—	0.10	—	—
35:0	0.05	0.02	0.73	0.02
36:2	—	—	3.7	0.17
36:1	0.30	0.58	3.8	0.12
36:0	0.08	0.03	1.3	0.04
37:0	0.05	0.02	—	—
38:2	—	0.11	2.4	—
38:1	0.14	0.10	2.6	—
38:0	0.07	0.4	0.61	—
39:0	0.02	0.02	0.34	—
40:1	0.10	0.14	1.1	0.12
40:0	0.03	—	0.29	0.06
42:1	0.05	0.03	0.60	—
42:0	0.02	0.02	0.17	—
Total wax ester flux				
($\mu g/m^2$.h)	3.4	6.7	96	1.5
($\mu g/m^2$.12 h)	41	80	1150	18

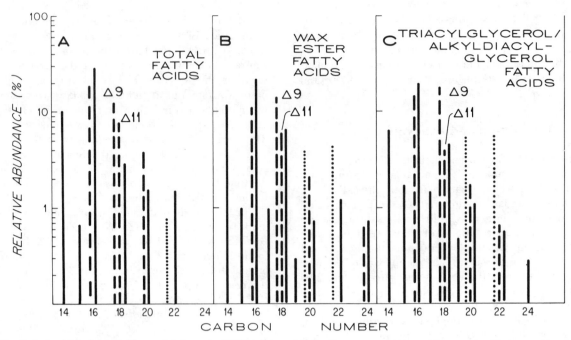

Fig. 3. Relative abundances of fatty acids from the FST 10 (14 m night) sediment trap: (A) total fatty acids; (B) fatty acids released by saponification of the wax esters; (C) fatty acids released by saponification of the triacylglycerols and alkyldiacylglycerols. Solid lines (———) represent saturated fatty acids, dashed lines (– – –) monounsaturated acids, and dotted lines (······) polyunsaturated (20:5 and 22:6) acids

Table 4

Triacylglycerol and alkyldiacylglycerol fluxes for Peru FSTs 8–11

Total carbon number[a]	Day		Night	
	FST 9 (14 m)	FST 8 (52 m)	FST 10 (14 m)	FST 11 (52 m)
	(μg/m².h)			
42	0.1	0.2	0.7	—
43	0.03	—	—	—
44	0.3	1.1	3.7	1.7
45	0.03	0.3	—	—
48e[a]	—	—	3.2	—
46	0.6	3.1	10.1	3.5
47	0.05	0.4	—	0.1
50e	—	—	5.9	—
48	0.7	3.9	12.7	6.1
49	0.05	0.4	—	0.2
52e	—	—	6.2	—
50	0.3	1.6	8.3	9.3
51	—	—	—	0.6
53e	—	—	1.0	—
52	0.4	1.3	6.6	21.9
53	—	—	—	0.6
54	0.4	0.9	4.6	12.9
55	—	—	—	—
56	—	—	1.7	7.6
57	—	—	—	—
58	—	—	1.2	3.4
60	—	—	—	2.8
Total triacylglycerol flux				
(μg/m².h)	3.0	13	50	72
(μg/m².12 h)	36	160	600	870
Total alkyldiacylglycerol flux				
(μg/m².h)	—	—	16	—
(μg/m².12 h)	—	—	200	—

[a] Alkyldiacylglycerol.

The composition of fatty acids in the wax esters and in the triacylglycerols of FST 10 was obtained by saponification and is compared to the fatty acids of total lipid for FST 10 in Fig. 3. Generally the fatty acids in each fraction are similar, the major compounds being 16:0, 16:1, 18:1, 14:0, and 18:0. However, subtle differences exist. The 18:1 isomers account for about 25% of the fatty acid content in each fraction, but the 18:0 acid represents about 3% of the total fatty acids, 7% of the wax esters, and 5% of the triacylglycerols. Thus the total fatty acid pool seems to be depleted in 18:0 relative to the other acid-containing fractions. Furthermore, the ratio of 18:1Δ9 to 18:1Δ11 varies in the three fractions: 1.7 in total fatty acids, 2.3 in wax esters, 4.6 in triacylglycerols. The triacylglycerols are enriched in 18:1Δ9 compared to the other fractions. In fact, 18:1Δ9 in the triacylglycerol fraction is only slightly less abundant than 16:0. Perhaps more significant is the fact that polyunsaturated fatty acids 20:5 and 22:6 would appear to be relative minor components of the total fatty acid pool, each representing <1% of the total acid content. But in the wax esters and triacylglycerols 20:5 and 22:6 were present as 4–6% of the acids. In neither case are these amounts of polyunsaturated fatty acids particularly high, even though they are essential fatty acids in marine organisms.

The data in Tables 1 and 4 shows that the fluxes and composition of triacylglycerols in the day traps were significantly less than and different from the compounds in the night traps, and that fluxes into the 14 m traps were lower than into the 52 m traps. This trend is very different from the patterns for total fatty acid and wax ester fluxes described above, and again clearly points out that investigations of different organic compound classes can lead to different, but hopefully complementary, sets of interpretations.

Wax esters and triacylglycerols account for a major portion of the neutral lipid in most living organisms (Kolattukudy, 1976). Triacylglycerols are the primary metabolic energy reserve lipid in terrestrial animals and in most phytoplankton (Sargent, 1976). In marine animals, however, triacylglycerols are not the only, or even the most abundant, reserve lipid. Many species of zooplankton elaborate wax esters for energy storage in response to living in environments characterized by short periods of food abundance followed by long periods of food shortage (Nevenzel, 1970; Sargent et al., 1981). Other zooplankton preferentially biosynthesize triacylglycerols and may contain little or no wax ester (Lee et al., 1971a, b; Sargent and Falk-Petersen, 1981, among others. Zooplanktoniverous fish efficiently convert dietary wax esters to triacylglycerols in the fishes' intestinal mucosae (Bauermeister and Sargent, 1979; Sargent et al., 1979).

The abundance of wax esters in FST 10 can be explained in terms of a significant input of wax ester-containing zooplankton lipids into FST 10. A sample of 'mixed' zooplankton taken by a net tow from 15 m-surface at the time of FST deployment was rich in C_{30}, C_{32}, and C_{34} wax esters. Staresinic (1983) pointed out that FST 10 contained intact (some living) euphausiids, although FST 11 (as well as FST 10) contained euphausiid molts. The wax ester content of euphausiids is variable. *E. superba* contains only traces of wax esters but abundant triacylglycerols (Clarke, 1980; Bottino, 1975; Raymont et al., 1971), while *E. crystallorophias* is rich in wax esters (Bottino, 1975). Sargent and Falk-Petersen (1981) report that the Arctic krill *Meganyctiphanes norvegica* and *Thysanoessa raschi* contained primarily triacylglycerols but *T. inermis* was rich in wax esters. The wax ester content of *E. mucronata* in the Peru upwelling is unknown, but in light of finding both intact organisms and the highest wax ester concentrations in FST 10 strongly suggests a connection. It is interesting to note that the euphausiid molts were apparently not major contributors of wax esters to the FSTs since both FST 10 and 11 contained the molts but only FST 10 had the elevated wax ester fluxes. The wax ester content of zooplankton faecal pellets off Peru is unknown at present.

The inclusion of live zooplankters in FST 10 may have occurred for two reasons. The organisms, which rise to the surface at night to feed (Mauchlin and Fisher, 1969), could have fallen or swum into the trap in search of food and been unable to escape. Alternatively, the euphausiids may have become entrapped in the sediment trap just before the trap was recovered in early morning at a time when the zooplankton were beginning their descent to daytime depths. While we cannot distinguish between these two mechanisms, the problem of collecting live organisms (are they 'sinking particles'?) in sediment traps needs to be resolved since it may introduce significant errors in sinking particle flux and composition measurements. Errors could be in either direction depending on whether the trapping of zooplankton artificially increases the measured flux, or whether the zooplankton descend below the trap depth with full guts, resulting in an underestimate of the particle flux. All of the night-time 14 m sediment traps in Peru appear to contain very high wax ester contents which may be due to incorporation of intact zooplankton in the trap samples.

The low wax ester fluxes into FSTs 9, 8, and 11 are in agreement with the generally held notion that phytoplankton, the dominant source of organic matter in these traps, are not significant producers of wax esters when grown under normal environmental conditions. We have analysed several laboratory-grown species of phytoplankton relevant to the Peru upwelling (*Thalassiosira sp.*, *Chaetoceros debilis*, *Skeletonema costatum*, *Asterionella japonica*, *Emiliania huxleyi*, *Gonyaulax sp.*) and found traces of wax esters. However, these results must be viewed with caution, since the composition of planktonic organisms in the upwelling zone changes drastically from year to year, and indeed from week to week. The major phytoplankton species in the water column at the time of the sediment trap deployment (*Thalassionema nitzchioides* and *Thalassiosira eccentrica*) have not yet been analysed by us, either as laboratory or as field samples. Furthermore, there is some evidence that phytoplankton may synthesize wax esters when grown under abnormal conditions (Antia et al., 1974; Hilenski et al., 1976). It would be tempting to speculate on whether the high nutrient levels and growth rates in the Peru upwelling area constitute 'normal' environmental conditions.

If the $181\Delta11$ and branched C_{15} and C_{17} fatty acids in the FSTs are an indication of bacterial lipids, then a microbial source for wax esters must also be considered. Weete (1976) has reported that fungi do not contain wax esters, but bacteria do (Bryn et al., 1977; Russell, 1978; Russell and Volkman, 1980). Bacterial wax esters generally are C_{32}, C_{34}, and C_{36} and contain relatively high proportions of mono- and di-unsaturated moieties.

Triacylglycerols in contrast to wax esters, are biosynthesized both by phytoplankton, and by zooplankton species not producing large amounts of wax esters. Fatty acids of phytoplankton triacylglycerols are mainly C_{14} and C_{16}, with little C_{18}, leading to a triacyglycerol distribution which is sharply skewed toward shorter chain-lengths. On the other hand, zooplankton triacylglycerols generally contain relatively more C_{18} acids which results in a more symmetrical triacylglycerol distribution. Our analyses of intact triacylglycerol in phytoplankton and zooplankton samples have tended to support this distinction (Wakeham, unpublished data), but more analyses are needed.

In the case of the FSTs, determining the triacylglycerol sources is difficult. Staresinic (1978, 1983) has stressed the phytodetritus was a major contributor of particulate matter to the traps. Indeed the triacylglycerol distribution in the day traps is indicative of a phytoplankton input. The difference in the triacylglycerol flux at 14 m and 52 m is difficult to explain as it goes against the general observation (Staresinic, 1982) that less POC reached the 52 m trap than the 14 m trap. But there is no reason why triacylglycerol fluxes need to mirror POC fluxes (indeed, the total fatty acid and wax ester discussions above have already pointed this out).

The situation at night is more complicated. Phytoplankton cells were an order of magnitude more abundant at night than in the day traps, in part because phytoplankton cells were incorporated into anchoveta faecal pellets which were collected in the traps at night (Staresinic et al., 1983). Thus, the input of phytoplankton triacylglycerols to the night traps should also be higher. But the compound distribution at night does not resemble the day-time distribution which we attribute to phytoplankton (i.e. the daytime pattern is skewed while the night-time pattern is more symmetrical due to greater amounts of C_{18} fatty acids). On the other hand, the night traps also contained live euphausiids (FST 10) and euphausiid molts (FST 10 and 11). Our zooplankton sample contained triacylglycerols having a smooth homologous distribution peaking at C_{51}, similar to the composition of FST 10.

However, triacylglycerols in FSTs 10 and 11 were quite different compositionally, FST 10 peaking at C_{48} and FST 11 peaking at C_{52}. One explanation for the triacylglycerol distributions in the night-time traps is that there are different zooplankton sources contributing to the two traps. One group of zooplankters would be active above 14 m and would contribute particulate material to the 14 m trap while the other group would be active below 14 m and contribute material primarily to the 52 m trap. An alternative explanation is that anchovy faecal pellets, which are especially abundant in FST 11 (perhaps 17% of the POC; Staresinic, et al., 1983) contain the triacylglycerol distribution found in this trap. Recent evidence from our laboratory, however, has shown that the anchovy faecal pellets may be comprised primarily of intact phytoplankton cells, and that the anchovy faecal pellet triacylglycerols are essentially phytoplankton triacylglycerols (and contain little wax ester). We favour a mixed zooplankton source, although conclusive evidence can only come from zooplankton tows taken in the depth intervals above both sediment traps at the time the traps are deployed. The triacylglycerol data also show the material reaching the night-time 52 m sediment trap is not merely a fraction of particulate organic matter produced in the upper 15 m of the water column but rather is of a distinctly different source.

Alkyldiacylglycerols

The triacylglycerol fraction of FST 10 contained, in addition to triacylglycerols, significant amounts of a homologous series of alkyldiacylglycerols (Fig. 2(b) and Table 4). These compounds were not detected in FSTs 9, 8, or 11. Analysis of the ethers by GC/MS showed that the acyl groups were predominantly 14:0, 16:0, and 18:0, and that the alkyl moiety was 20:0. Retention times for the alkyldiacylglycerols were approximately two-carbons early, indicating that the alkyl moiety is branched. We therefore concluded that these components were phytanyl diacylglycerols.

Alkyldiacylglycerols have been reported in a variety of marine organisms, especially squaloid sharks (Malins and Varanasi, 1972; Hallgren et al., 1978). Alkyl- and alkenyl-diacylglycerols are the dominant forms, although 2-methoxy-substituted compounds are known. The alkyl moiety, most often C_{14}, C_{16}, or C_{18}, is usually located at the 1-position of the glycerol molecule, with the 2- and 3-positions esterified to fatty acids. Compositional similarities between alkyldiacylglycerols and wax esters suggest closely related biochemical roles (Sargent, 1976). In fact, both compound classes are biosynthesized from the same lipid precursors (Sargent, 1976) and both have similar distributions in the marine environment (Sargent, 1976; Wakeham, 1982).

Only in FST 10 were alkyldiacylglycerols abundant, and only in this sediment trap were wax esters present in high concentrations. This observation supports the close biochemical relationship for these two different compound classes. The mixed zooplankton sample which we analysed also contained the same series of phytanyl ethers. Whether the alkyldiacylglycerols are components of the euphausiids in FST 10 is not known. Nevertheless a zooplankton source of these compounds into FST 10 is indicated. Further insight into the biogeochemical significance of the alkyldiacylglycerols should be forthcoming in the future.

CONCLUSIONS

The downward flux and molecular composition of fatty acids and fatty acid esters in the form of wax esters, tri-acylglycerols, and alkyldiacylglycerols show significant variations in the upper part of the water column in the Peru upwelling depending on the depth and time of sampling. These fluctuations are much greater than bulk POC measurements would indicate, thus showing that it is necessary to examine a variety of lipid compound classes in order to understand the dynamics of the system. In general the flux of fatty acids and their esters are greater at night than in the day, but details of the day/night and 14 m/52 m variations and thus in the processes controlling the distributions of these biochemicals are much more complicated. This is especially evident when the distributions are suggestive of differing source functions, even at the same time but at different depths.

In determining fatty acids of total lipid, we are able to account for 2–4% of the total POC flux in the upper 50 m of the water column during the day versus 8–10% of the nocturnal POC flux. Of the total lipid, fatty acids made up for about 20% of the particulate-associated lipids during the day compared with 32–58% of the lipids at night. Thus total fatty acids are relatively minor components of the bulk organic matter but rather important components of the lipids, especially at night. For comparison, amino acids comprise 20–30% of the POC flux (Lee and Cronin, 1982) while free sterols represent some 0.4% of the daytime POC flux and ~2% of the night-time POC flux (Gagosian et al., 1983a).

However, the three fatty acid ester fractions we have examined do not account for much of the total fatty acid. For example, in FST 10, wax esters contribute an estimated 2% to the total fatty acids, triacylglycerols about 1%, and the alkyldiacylglycerols about 1%. Clearly we have not yet analysed the dominant fatty acid containing components in the extractable lipids, which could include free fatty acids, mono- and di-acylglycerols, and a wide variety of polar lipids.

Many studies in the Peru upwelling have pointed out how dynamic the ecosystem actually is; the greatly fluctuating anchoveta fishery is perhaps the most visible manifestation of this dynamicism. Our sediment trap data certainly agree, even to the extent that different organic compound classes follow different patterns of source and transport. Short-term deployments of sediment traps offer a chance to examine changes in organic matter composition and flux on a short time scale, but the interpretation of the data is complex. Clearly more than one set of day/night — 14 m/52 m trap samples will be necessary to understand fully the sources and transport of particulate organic matter in the Peru upwelling. Analyses of additional FST sample, sediments, and source organisms are currently underway in our laboratory. On the other hand, long term deployments of sediment traps, while providing an integrated look at particle flux and composition, have difficulties due to unknown effects of microbial activity in the traps during deployment. Much more work is needed to determine how best to sample and preserve labile organic matter in sediment traps.

The results and interpretations presented here can only be considered as an initial glimpse of the organic geochemistry of the Peru upwelling area. Verification will await further measurements and integration of data for a number of organic compound classes (e.g. amino acids, ketones, hydrocarbons, sterols, etc.) since we have shown here that investigating only one or two classes of compounds may result in an incomplete, or even distorted, picture. Nevertheless, we are beginning to understand the complex relationship between lipid biogeochemistry of sediment trap particulate matter, the lipid biogeochemistry of the underlying sediments, and the biological and geochemical processes active in the water column and benthic ecosystems of diverse oceanic regimes.

Acknowledgements

We thank Dr Nick Staresinic and Dr Robert B. Gagosian for many useful discussions throughout the course of this research. Dr Nelson M. Frew was helpful in obtaining mass spectra; Ms Gale Nigrelli and Mr Joaquim Livramento helped in sample analysis. This work was funded by the Office of Naval Research Contract N00014–79–C–0071, National Science Foundation Grants OCE 77–26084 and OCE 80–18436 and a WHOI Postdoctoral Scholar Fellowship to J.K.V. Woods Hole Oceanographic Institution Contribution No. 5057.

REFERENCES

Ackman, R. G., Jangaard, P. M., Hoyle, R. J. and Brockerhoff, H. (1964) The origin of marine fatty acids. I. Analysis of the fatty acids produced by the diatom *Skeletonema costatum*. *J. Fish. Res. Board Can.* **21**, 747–756.

Ackman, R. G., Sipos, J. C. and Jangaard, P. M. (1967) A quantitation problem in the open tubular gas chromatography of fatty acid esters from cod liver lipids. *Lipids* **2**, 251–257.

Ackman, R. G., Tocher, C. S. and McLachlan, J. M. (1968) Marine phytoplankter fatty acids. *J. Fish. Res. Board Can.* **25**, 1603–1620.

Ackman, R. G. and Hooper, S. N. (1973) Non-methylene-interrupted fatty acids in lipids of shallow water marine invertebrates. A comparison of two molluscs (*Littorina littorea* and *Lumatin triseriata*) with the sand shrimp (*Changon septemspinosus*). *Comp. Biochem. Physiol. B.* **46**, 153–165.

Antia, N. J., Lee, R. F., Nevenzel, J. C. and Cheng, Y. Y. (1974) Wax ester production by the marine cryptomonad *Chroomonas salina* grown heterotrophically on glycerol. *J. Protozool.* **21**, 768–771.

Bauermeister, A. and Sargent, J. R. (1979) Wax esters: major metabolites in the marine environment. *Trends in Biochemical Sciences* **4**, 209–211.

Boon, J. J., De Leeuw, J. W. and Schenck, P. A. (1975) Organic geochemistry of Walvis Bay diatomaceous ooze — I. Occurrence and significance of fatty acids. *Geochim. Cosmochim. Acta* **39**, 1559–1565.

Boon, J. J., De Lange, F., Schuyl, P. J. W., De Leeuw, J. W. and Schenck, P. A. (1977) Organic geochemistry of Walvis Bay diatomaceous ooze — II. Occurrence and significance of hydroxy fatty acids. In *Advances in Organic Geochemistry, 1975*, ed. by Campos, R. and Goni, J. Enadimsa, Madrid, pp. 255–273.

Boon, J. J., Liefkens, W., Rijpstra, W. I. C., Baar, M. and De Leeuw, J. W. (1978) Fatty acids of *Desulfovibrio desulfuricans* as marker molecules in sedimentary environments. In *Environmental Biogeochemistry and Geomicrobiology* ed. by Krumbein, W. E. Ann Arbor Science Publishers.

Bottino, N. R. (1975) Lipid composition of two species of antarctic krill: *Euphasia superba* and *E. crystallorophais*. *Comp. Biochem. Physiol. B* **50**, 479–484.

Bremner, M. (1974) Texture and composition of surficial continental margin sediments between Kunene River and Sylvia Hill, S.W.A. Technical Report No. 6, Joint Geological Survey/University of Capetown, Marine Geology Program, Department of Geology, University of Capetown, Capetown, R.S.A. VII, pp. 39–43.

Bremner, M. (1975) Mineralogy and distribution of clay minerals on the southwest African continental shelf and adjacent Hinterland. Technical Report No. 7, Joint Geological Survey/University of Capetown, Marine Geology Program, Department of Geology, University of Capetown, Capetown, R.S.A. IX, pp. 46–55.

Brewer, P. G., Nozaki, Y., Spencer, D. W. and Fleer, A. P. (1980) Sediment trap experiments in the deep North Atlantic: isotopic and elemental fluxes. *J. Mar. Res.* **38**, 703–728.

Bryn, K., Jantzen, E. and Bovre, K. (1977) Occurrence and patterns of waxes in Neisseriaceae. *J. Gen. Microbiol.* **102**, 33–43.

Clarke, A. (1980) The biochemical composition of *Euphausia superba* Dana from South Georgia. *J. Exp. Mar. Biol. Ecol.* **43**, 221–236.

Crisp, T. P., Brenner, S., Venkatesan, M. I., Ruth, E. and Kaplan, I. R. (1979) Organic chemical characterization of sediment trap particulates from San Nicholas, Santa Barbara, Santa Monica, and San Pedro Basins, California. *Geochim. Cosmochim. Acta* **43**, 1791–1801.

Culkin, F. and Morris, R. J. (1969) The fatty acids of some marine crustaceans. *Deep-Sea Res.* **16**, 109–116.

De Baar, H., Farrington, J. W. and Wakeham, S. G. (1983) Vertical fluxes of fatty acids in the North Atlantic Ocean. Submitted to *J. Mar. Res.*

Deuser, W. G., Ross, E. H. and Anderson, R. F. (1981) Seasonality in the supply of sediment to the deep Sargasso Sea and implications for the rapid transfer of matter to the deep ocean. *Geochim. Cosmochim. Acta* **28**, 495–505.

Dugdale, R. C., Goering, J. J., Barber, R. T., Smith, R. L. and Packard, T. T. (1977) Denitrification and hydrogen sulfide in the Peru upwelling region during 1976. *Deep-Sea Res.* **24**, 601–608.

Farrington, J. W., Henrichs, S. M. and Anderson, R. (1977)

Fatty acids and Pb-210 geochronology of a sediment core from Buzzards Bay, Massachusetts. *Geochim. Cosmochim. Acta* **41**, 289–296.

Fisher, N. S. and Schwarzenbach, R. P. (1978) Fatty acid dynamics in *Thalassiosira pseudonana* (Bacillariophyceae): Implications for physiological ecology. *J. Phycol.* **14**, 143–150.

Gagosian, R. B. and Farrington, J. W. (1978) Sterenes in surface sediments from the southwest African shelf and slope. *Geochim. Cosmochim. Acta* **42**, 1091–1101.

Gagosian, R. B., Loder, T., Nigrelli, G., Mlodzinska, M., Love, J. and Kogelshatz, J. (1980) Hydrographic and nutrient data from R/V *Knorr* Cruise 73, Leg 2 — February to March, 1978 — off the coast of Peru. W.H.O.I. Tech. Rpt. 80–1, 77 pp.

Gagosian, R. B., Nigrelli, G. E. and Volkman, J. K. (1983a) Vertical transport and transformation of biogenic organic compounds from a sediment trap experiment off the coast of Peru. In *NATO Advanced Research Institute on Coastal Upwelling and its Sediment Record*, ed. by Suess, E. and Thiede, J. Plenum Press, New York. In press.

Gagosian, R. B., Volkman, J. K. and Nigrelli, G. E. (1983b) The use of sediment traps to determine sterol sources in coastal sediments off Peru. In *Advances in Organic Geochemistry, 1981*, ed. by Bjorøy, M. John Wiley & Sons, London. This volume.

Gallardo, V. (1978) Large benthic microbial communities in sulphide biota under Peru–Chile subsurface countercurrent. *Nature (London)* **268**, 331–332.

Grob, K. (1980) Persilylation of glass capillary columns. Part 4: Discussion of parameters. *J. H. R. C. & C. C.* **3**, 493–496 (and references cited therein).

Hallgren, B., Stallberg, G. and Boeryd, B. (1978). Occurrence, synthesis, and biological effects of substituted glycerol ethers. *Prog. Chem. Fats Other Lipids* **16**, 45–58.

Henrichs, S. M. (1980) Biogeochemistry of amino acids in interstitial waters of marine sediments. Ph.D. Thesis, W.H.O.I./M.I.T. Joint Program in Oceanography, W.H.O.I. Technical Report 80–39, 253 pp.

Hilenski, L. L., Walne, P. L. and Snyder, F. (1976) Aliphatic chains of esterified lipids in isolated eyespots of *Euglena gracilis* var. *bacillaris*. *Plant Physiol.* **57**, 645–646.

Honjo, S. and Roman, M. R. (1978) Marine Copepod fecal pellets: production, preservation, and sedimentation. *J. Mar. Res.* **36**, 45–57.

Honjo, S. (1980) Material fluxes and modes of sedimentation in the mesopelagic and bathypelagic zones. *J. Mar. Res.* **38**, 53–97.

Johns, R. B., Perry, G. J. and Jackson, K. S. (1977) Contribution of bacterial lipids to recent marine sediments. *Est. Coast Mar. Sci.* **5**, 521–529.

Kaneda, T. (1967) Fatty acids in the genus *Bacillus*. I. Iso- and anteiso-fatty acids as characteristic constituents of lipids in 10 species. *J. Bacteriol.* **93**, 894–903.

Kates, M. and Volcani, B. E. (1966) Lipid components of diatoms. *Biochem. Biophys. Acta* **116**, 264–278.

Knauer, G. A., Martin, J. H. and Bruland, K. W. (1979) Fluxes of particulate carbon, nitrogen, and phosphorus in the upper water column of the northeast Pacific. *Deep Sea Res.* **26**, 97–108.

Kolattukudy, P. E. (1976) *Chemistry and Biochemistry of Natural Waxes*. Elsevier, New York.

Lasker, R. (1964) Molting frequency of a deep sea crustacean, *Euphausia pacifica*. *Nature (London)* **203**, 96.

Lasker, R. (1966) Feeding, growth, respiration and carbon utilization of euphausiid crustacean. *J. Fish. Res. Board Can.* **23**, 1291–1317.

Lee, C. and Cronin, C. (1982) The vertical flux of particulate organic nitrogen in the sea: decomposition of amino acids in the Peru upwelling area and the equatorial Atlantic. *J. Mar. Res.* In press.

Lee, R. F., Nevenzel, J. C. and Paffenhoffer, G.-A. (1971a) Importance of wax esters and other lipids in the marine food chain: phytoplankton and copepods. *Mar. Biol.* **9**, 99–108.

Lee, R. F., Hirota, J. and Barnett, A. M. (1971b) Distribution and importance of wax esters in marine copepods and other zooplankton. *Deep Sea Res.* **18**, 1147–1165.

Lee, R. F. (1974) Lipids of zooplankton from Bute Inlet, British Columbia. *J. Fish. Res. Board Can.* **31**, 1577–1582.

Malins, D. C. and Varanasi, U. (1972) The ether bond in marine lipids. In *Ether Lipids*, ed. by Snyder, F. Academic Press, New York, pp. 297–311.

Mauchline, J. and Fisher, L. R. (1969) The biology of euphausiids. *Adv. Mar. Biol.* **7**, 1–454.

McCave, I. N. (1975) Vertical flux of particles in the ocean. *Deep Sea Res.* **22**, 491–502.

Morris, R. J. (1971) Variations in the fatty acid composition of oceanic euphausiids. *Deep Sea Res.* **18**, 525–529.

Morris, R. J. (1972) The occurrence of wax esters in crustaceans from the northeast Atlantic Ocean. *Mar. Biol.* **16**, 102–107.

Morris, R. J. and Calvert, S. E. (1977) Geochemical studies of organic-rich sediments from the Namibian Shelf — I. The organic fractions. *Deep Sea Res.* (Deacon Volume).

Nevenzel, J. C. (1970) Occurrence, function, and biosynthesis of wax esters in marine organisms. *Lipids* **5**, 308–319.

Oliver, J. D. and Colwell, R. R. (1973) Extractable lipids of Gram negative marine bacteria: fatty acid composition. *Int. J. Syst. Bacteriol.* **23**, 442–458.

Opute, F. I. (1974) Lipid and fatty acid composition of diatoms. *J. Exp. Biol.* **25**, 823–835.

Perry, G. J. (1977) Lipids in the Marine Environment. Ph.D. Thesis, University of Melbourne.

Perry, G. J., Volkman, J. K., Johns, R. B. and Bavor, H. J. Jr. (1979) Fatty acids of bacterial origin in contemporary marine sediments. *Geochim. Cosmochim. Acta* **43**, 1715–1725.

Prahl, F. G. and Carpenter, R. (1979) The role of zooplankton fecal pellets in the sedimentation of polycyclic aromatic hydrocarbons in Dabob Bay, Washington. *Geochim. Cosmochim. Acta* **43**, 1959–1972.

Price, N. B. and Calvert, S. E. (1973) The geochemistry of iodine in oxidized and reduced recent marine sediments. *Geochim. Cosmochim. Acta* **37**, 2149–2158.

Repeta, D. and Gagosian, R. B. (1983) Carotenoid transformations in the oceanic water column. In *Advances in Organic Geochemistry, 1981*, ed. by Bjorøy, M. John Wiley & Sons, London. This volume.

Raymont, J. E. G., Srinivasagam, R. T. and Raymont, K. K. B. (1971) Biochemical studies on marine zooplankton, IX. The biochemical composition of *Euphausia superba*. *J. Mar. Biol. Ass. U.K.* **51**, 581–588.

Russell, N. J. (1978) The differential effect of growth temperature on the phospholipid and neutral fatty acid composition of *Micrococcus cryophilus*. *FEMS Microbiol. Lett.* **4**, 335–338.

Russell, N. J. and Volkman, J. K. (1980) The effect of growth temperature on wax ester composition in the psychrophilic bacterium *Micrococcus cryphilus* ATCC 15174. *J. Gen. Microbiol.* **118**, 131–141.

Ryther, J. H., Menzel, D. W., Hulburt, E. M., Lorenzen, C. J. and Corwin, N. (1971) The production and utilization of organic matter in the Peru coastal current. *Inv. Pesq.* **35**, 43–59.

Sargent, J. R. (1976) The structure, metabolism and function of lipids in marine organisms. In *Biochemical and Biophysical Perspectives in Marine Biology*, Vol. 3, ed. by Malins, D. C. and Sargent, J. R. Academic Press, New York, pp. 149–212.

Sargent, J. R., McIntosh, R., Bauermeister, A. and Blaxter, J. H. S. (1979) Assimilation of the wax esters of marine zooplankton by herring (*Clupea harengus*) and rainbow trout (*Salmo gairdnerii*). *Mar. Biol.* **51**, 203–207.

Sargent, J. R. and Falk-Petersen, S. (1981) Ecological investigations on the zooplankton community in Balsfjorden, Northern Norway: lipids and fatty acids in *Meganyctiphanes norvegica*, *Thysanoessa raschi*, and *T. inermis* during midwinter. *Mar. Biol.* **62**, 131–137.

Sargent, J. R., Gatten, R. R. and Henderson, R. J. (1981) Marine wax esters. *Pure Appl. Chem.* **53**, 867–871.

Small, L. F., Fowler, S. W., Unlu, M. Y. (1979) Sinking rates of natural copepod fecal pellets. *Mar. Biol.* **51**, 233–241.

Staresinic, N. (1978) The vertical flux of particulate organic matter in the Peru upwelling as measured with a free-drifting sediment trap. Ph.D. Thesis, W.H.O.I./M.I.T. Joint Program in Biological Oceanography, 255 pp.

Staresinic, N., Rowe, G. T., Shaughnessy, D. and Williams, A. J. III (1978) Measurement of the vertical flux of particulate organic matter with a free-drifting sediment trap. *Limnol. Oceanogr.* **23**, 559–563.

Staresinic, N. (1983) Downward flux of bulk particulate organic matter in the Peru coastal upwelling. *J. Mar. Res.* In press.

Staresinic, N., Farrington, J. W., Gagosian, R. B., Clifford, C. H. and Hulburt, E. M. (1983) Downward transport of particulate matter in the Peru coastal upwelling: Role of the anchoveta, *Engraulis ringens*. In *NATO Advanced Research Institute on Coastal Upwelling and its Sediment Record*, ed. by Suess, E. and Thiede, J. Plenum Press, New York. In press.

Tanoue, E. and Handa, N. (1980) Vertical transport of organic materials in the northern North Pacific as determined by sediment trap experiment. Part 1. Fatty acid composition. *J. Oceanogr. Soc. Jpn* **36**, 231–245.

Volkman, J. K., Corner, E. D. S. and Eglinton, G. (1980a) Transformations of biolipids in the marine food web and in underlying bottom sediments. In *Colloques Internationaux du C.N.R.S. No. 293. Biogeochimie de la matiere organique a l'interface eau sediment marin*, pp. 185–197.

Volkman, J. K., Johns, R. B., Gillan, F. T., Perry, G. J. and Bavor, H. J. Jr. (1980b) Microbial lipids of an intertidal sediment – I. Fatty acids and hydrocarbons. *Geochim. Cosmochim. Acta* **44**, 1133–1143.

Volkman, J. K., Farrington, J. W., Gagosian, R. B. and Wakeham, S. G. (1983) Lipid composition of surface sediments and bacterial mats from the Peru upwelling region. In *Advances in Organic Geochemistry, 1981*, ed. by Bjorøy, M. John Wiley & Sons, London. This volume.

Wakeham, S. G., Farrington, J. W., Gagosian, R. B., Lee, C., De Baar, H., Nigrelli, G. E., Tripp, B. W., Smith, S. O. and Frew, N. M. (1980) Fluxes of organic matter from sediment traps in the equatorial Atlantic Ocean. *Nature* **286**, 798–800.

Wakeham, S. G. and Frew, N. M. (1982) High temperature glass capillary gas chromatography/mass spectrometry of wax esters, steryl esters, and triacylglycerols. *Lipids*. In Press.

Wakeham, S. G. (1982) Sources and fates of organic matter from a sediment trap experiment in the equatorial north Atlantic: wax esters, steryl esters, triacylglycerols and alkyldiacylglycerols. *Geochim. Cosmochim. Acta*. In press.

Weete, J. D. (1976) Algal and fungal waxes. In *Chemistry and Biochemistry of Natural Waxes*, ed. by Kolattukudy, P. E. Elsevier, New York, pp. 350–418.

Zuta, S. and Guillen, O. (1970) Oceanographia de las aguas costeras del Peru. *Bol. Inst. Mar Peru* **2**, 157–324.

Advances in Organic Geochemistry 1981, pp. 198–206
© *John Wiley & Sons Limited, 1983*

Monounsaturated Fatty Acids as Specific Bacterial Markers in Marine Sediments

F. T. Gillan,* R. B. Johns, T. V. Verheyen and P. D. Nichols

Department of Organic Chemistry, University of Melbourne, Grattan Street, Parkville, Victoria 3052, Australia

R. J. Esdaile

Division of Materials Science, C.S.I.R.O., Grattan Street, Parkville, Victoria 3052, Australia

H. J. Bavor

Department of Microbiology, University of Melbourne, Australia

The monounsaturated fatty acids present in a range of marine bacterial isolates and in a selection of diverse marine sediments have been analysed in detail. SIM GC–MS analysis of the trimethylsilyl ethers of the dihydroxy acids (produced by OsO_4 oxidation of the fatty acids) confirmed the identifications of many unusual bacterial acids. Among other results, one bacterial isolate was shown to produce predominantly $\Delta10$-unsaturated acids dominated by Z-$\Delta10$-16:1 and Z-$\Delta10$-i 16:1, while another biosynthesized a range of *cis*- and *trans*- straight-chain monoenoic acids with an overall *trans/cis* ratio of *ca*. 1.0. The major acids in this latter case were *cis*- and *trans*- vaccenic acid (Z-$\Delta11$-18:1 and E-$\Delta11$-18:1 respectively). Both of these results are unexpected. The monounsaturated fatty acid distributions observed for five marine sediments suggest a bacterial contribution to the acids of between 10% and 80 + %. The results support the use of specific monounsaturated acids as bacterial markers. The chain length and substitution pattern of these marker fatty acids are reported in detail. In addition, isomer ratios provide a convenient means of assessing relative bacterial distributions. The presence of large amounts of straight chain *trans*-acids in one isolate supports a proposed direct bacterial origin for these acids in marine sediments.

INTRODUCTION

In a previous paper (Gillan *et al.*, 1981) we demonstrated that osmium tetroxide oxidation, trimethylsilyl ether formation and subsequent GC/MS analysis could provide a facile, accurate approach to the determination of the positional isomer distribution of the monoenoic fatty acids in bacteria. A range of unusual acids were characterized (e.g. E-i16:1Δ5 and E-a17:1Δ5 (where E designates *trans* stereochemistry) as major isomers). Most of these acids have not previously been identified in sediments (see, for example, Boon *et al.*, 1978) and Matsuda and Koyama, 1977). It was thus of interest to analyse a range of marine sediments for their monoenoic acids in order to demonstrate the presence of these, and other, specifically bacteria-derived acids.

Studies of the adenylate energy charges in marine sediments (Christensen and Devol, 1980) are consistent with the bacterial population being in a physiologically depressed state: the energy charge of sedimentary populations is close to that observed in late stationary

phase laboratory cultures. Previous studies have also indicated that the majority of the bacteria in the sediments we have studied were facultative aerobes, even in strongly anoxic muds (Perry *et al.*, 1979; Volkman *et al.*, 1980). This suggests that growth of these bacteria is microaerophilic. Since acetate is commonly the major soluble organic carbon source in marine sediments (Belyaev *et al.*, 1980), cultures grown microaerophilically to stationary phase on acetate as carbon source should best mimic the sedimentary conditions. Growth was, however, observed to be more rapid with glucose as carbon source: minimal alteration of the fatty acid distribution, compared to growth on acetate, was observed (Gillan, Bavor and Johns, unpublished results). However, this approach has its limitations since it is well known that culture conditions can significantly affect lipid composition, and so the fatty acids produced in culture may differ from those produced by the same organism in a sediment.

Whilst the relative abundances of acids biosynthesized by the sedimentary bacteria will probably differ from those of the same bacteria in culture, the enzyme-determined positions of unsaturation and chain-branching are not expected to be altered: analyses of

---

* Present address: Australian Institute of Marine Science, P.M.B. No. 3, Townsville M.S.O., Queensland 4810, Australia.

cultured bacteria permit assessment of which acids can be derived from *in situ* bacterial populations, but do not necessarily allow a precise determination of the relative proportions of such acids.

In order to establish a broader basis from which to assess the probable isomer distribution derived from *in situ* bacteria, a further eight bacterial cultures have been examined. The cultures were grown on glucose to stationary phase and then harvested. It was of interest to discover whether it were possible to determine an approximate algal/bacterial contribution to the monoenoic acids of the sediments from these data. These contributions would include a proportion of fatty acids derived from lysed cells and also of acids derived by reworking of the lipids from such lysed cells.

The accuracy of this approach is limited since the lipid composition of a sediment which contains a complex mixture of microorganisms and detritus, is clearly not a simple summation of the lipids of the individual components since interaction between them — i.e. reworking — must occur. This restricts the validity of using data from individual pure cultures to quantitate fatty acid contributions to a sediment.

METHODS

Bacterial cultures

Seven of the bacteria (LIAB 1, LIAB 2, LIAB 4, LIAB 6, LIAB 8, LIAB 13 and LIAB 16) studied were facultative aerobic, Gram negative rods isolated from the Low Isles (North Queensland) sediment. The remaining culture *Cellulomonas uda* was a marine bacterium being studied at the University of Melbourne. All the bacteria were grown on modified Zobell's 2216E medium as described previously (Perry *et al.*, 1979), and were harvested in stationary phase growth. The cultures were unshaken to approximate microaerophilic growth conditions.

Sediment samples

Two mangrove-associated sediments, one tropical (Low Isles, North Queensland), and the other temperate (Port Franklin, Victoria), a sandy intertidal sediment (Old Yanakie Beach, Corner Inlet, Victoria), an algal mat ooze (Laguna Figueroa, Baja, California) and a deep oceanic basin sediment (Santa Catalina Basin, California; depth = 1297 m) were examined.

All the sediment samples studied were of the sediment–water interface (collected by careful scraping: depth *ca.* 0–2 mm) except the Santa Catalina Basin sediment which was a core section (depth *ca.* 5–20 mm), and the Laguna Figueroa sediment which was of the 'ooze' from beneath a surface cyanobacterial mat.

Extraction procedures

The bacterial cultures were extracted as described previously (Gillan *et al.*, 1981).

The total solvent-extractable fatty acids of the sediments were isolated by extraction with chloroform/methanol, saponification and methylation. In order to avoid the possibility of *cis/trans* isomerization, the samples were not fractionated by thin-layer argentation chromatography (TLC) (e.g. into saturated acids, monoenoic acids... (Perry *et al.*, 1979)). Instead, the total fatty acid mixture was examined by capillary GC on both non-polar (SCOT SE30, 50 m × 0.5 mm, SGE Australia) and polar (WCOT SIL-47-CNP, 45 m × 0.2 mm, Chromalytic Technology) columns (Gillan *et al.*, 1981). The fatty acids were quantified on the assumption of equal FID mass response. In order to confirm positions of unsaturation, the total fatty acid methyl ester sample was oxidized with osmium tetroxide. The resultant monocarboxylic acid, dihydroxy acid and polyhydroxy acid methyl ester mixture was reacted with bistrimethylsilylacetamide to produce a trimethylsilyl ether mixture. This was examined by gas chromatography/mass spectrometry (GC/MS) and by non-polar column GC.

GC/MS procedures

GC/MS analyses were performed on a HP 5995A system (Hewlett–Packard) fitted with an open split interface (SGE Australia) between the capillary column and the mass spectrometer. Separation of the trimethylsilyl ethers was achieved using a SE30 vitreous silica WCOT column (50 m × 0.2 mm, SGE Australia) programmed from 180 to 280° at 3° min^{-1}. The GC/MS system was operated in SIM (Selected Ion Monitoring) mode. Other MS details are as follows: electron energy, 70 V; electron multiplier, 2400 V; SIM window size, 0.50 a.m.u.; ion masses: 88, 101, 159, 173, 187, 201, 203, 215, 217, 229, 231, 243, 245, 257, 259, 271, 273, 287, 301, 315; dwell times, 50 mS each. The inbuilt smoothing program was not used during output of the data. Peak areas were integrated by hand and compared with GC analyses. In general, quantitation of co-eluting components was based on the intensity of the ω fragment as this was not influenced as strongly by possible further fragmentation (the Δ fragment can easily lose .OCH$_3$). However, isotope peaks from the —.OCH$_3$ fragmentation of the Δ fragment resulted in weak extraneous peaks in the ω profile: these were generally resolvable (by GC) from the 'authentic' ω peaks. The ion set used in this study made it possible to fully identify the double bond positional isomers of the monoenoic acids, however, the positions of branching of the branched-chain monoenoic acids were based only on the GC characteristics of the monounsaturated acids on polar and non-polar capillary GC columns.

RESULTS AND DISCUSSION

Bacterial analyses

The chain-length distributions for the bacterial monoenoic acids are listed in Table 1. Five of the cultures are characterized by an abundance of straight-chain monoenoic acids: the monoenoic acids constituting 31.3 to 82.7% of the total acids. The other

Table 1

Abundance[a] and chain-length distributions of the bacterial monoenoic acids

Chemotype	cis/trans		Vaccenic acid		$\Delta7/\Delta9$	Branched acid		
Isolate	LIAB 1	LIAB 8	LIAB 2	LIAB 13	LIAB 4	LIAB 6	LIAB 16	C.u.[b]
Chain distribution								
i15	—[e]	—	—	—	—	⎱ 3.6	—	2.1
a15	—	—	—	—	—	⎰	—	32.0
i16	—	—	—	—	—	20.1	19.2	11.4
i17	—	—	—	—	—	⎱ 47.3	⎱ 24.2	2.0
a17	—	—	—	—	—	⎰	⎰	2.0
14	0.8	2.3	—	—	1.7	1.0	1.5	4.0
15	0.6	—	—	—	—	—	—	6.0
16	15.0	39.5	2.4	6.9	68.7	23.0	49.8	28.7
17	5.8	0.1	—	—	2.2	—	—	—
18	78.5	57.9	97.6	93.1	27.4	4.8	4.1	13.6
20	—	0.4	—	—	—	—	—	—
Abundances[c]								
%E	48.6	48.5	—	—	4.3	—	—	—
%br	—	—	—	—	—	71.0	43.4	47.5
%Δ	—	—	32.9	—	—	—	—	—
% total monoenoic[d]	82.7	59.9	35.1	52.9	31.3	2.5	6.8	3.5

[a] Data are uncorrected for GC/MS response
[b] C.u. = Cellulomonas uda.
[c] Percentage of monoenoic acids with the specific structural feature E = trans; br = branched; Δ = cyclopropyl
[d] Percencentage of the total cellular acids that are monounsaturated
[e] Not detected

Table 2

Positional isomer distributions of the monoenoic acids from eight bacterial cultures

Chemotype	cis/trans		Vaccenic acid		$\Delta7/\Delta9$	Branched acid		
Isolate	LIAB 1	LIAB 8	LIAB 2	LIAB 13	LIAB 4	LIAB 6	LIAB 16	C.u.[a]
Isomer								
Z-Δ3	—[b]	—	—	—	0.2	—	—	—
E-Δ4	—	0.1	—	—	—	—	—	—
Z-Δ4	—	T[c]	—	—	—	2.4	3.7	27.1
E-Δ5	0.2	0.1	—	—	—	—	—	—
Z-Δ5	2.2	1.2	3.1	1.9	3.3	3.8	4.6	11.2
E-Δ6	0.3	0.1	—	—	—	—	—	—
Z-Δ6	0.3	0.1	0.9	3.9	1.7	5.0	1.8	25.5
E-Δ7	0.2	1.1	—	—	0.9	—	—	—
Z-Δ7	0.8	1.4	—	—	27.8	0.7	—	—
E-Δ8	0.2	—	—	—	—	—	—	—
Z-Δ8	0.2	—	—	—	0.3	3.5	—	6.7
E-Δ9	8.1	17.7	—	—	3.4	—	—	—
Z-Δ9	7.6	17.6	2.8	8.5	49.5	6.1	3.3	17.5
E-Δ10	0.6	0.3	—	—	—	—	—	—
Z-Δ10	1.0	0.4	—	—	0.4	66.8	71.4	5.2
E-Δ11	35.8	25.8	—	—	—	—	—	—
Z-Δ11	35.7	26.6	79.9	76.2	8.1	4.3	9.3	4.8
E-Δ12	0.1	0.3	—	—	—	—	—	—
Z-Δ12	0.2	0.4	—	—	—	7.2	3.9	1.8
E-Δ13	3.1	3.0	—	—	—	—	—	—
Z-Δ13	4.0	4.0	13.3	9.5	4.4	4.4	0.8	—

[a] C.u. = Cellulomonas uda.
[b] Not detected.
[c] T = trace (<0.1%).

three isolates yielded only small amounts of monoenoic acids (2.5 to 6.8%) and contained branched-chain acids (43.4 to 71%). All eight isolates can thus be considered 'typical' bacteria with respect to chain structure and degree of unsaturation (see Gillan and Johns, 1981).

The straight-chain monoenoic acid producers can be subdivided into three groups on the bases of chain-length, geometry and positions of unsaturation (see Table 2). LIAB 1 and LIAB 8 form one group characterized by a 1 : 1 *cis* : *trans* ratio with 16 : 1Δ9 and 18:1Δ11 as the predominant isomers. The presence of E- and Z-14:1Δ7 in LIAB 8 indicates that a series of chain elongations from a shorter-chain unsaturated precursor is the probable biosynthetic pathway. The pathway is thus probably similar to the anaerobic pathway: the only difference being the production of both *cis* and *trans* acids. LIAB 2 and LIAB 13 belong to a second group of straight-chain producers (the presence of cyclopropyl acids in LIAB 2 is not, for the purpose of this discussion, considered taxonomically significant). Both bacteria produce *cis* vaccenic acid (Z-18:1Δ11) as their major monoenoic acid. Z-16:1Δ9 and Z-18:1Δ13 are also present, but at a much lower abundance. The remaining straight-chain producer (LIAB 4) synthesizes a suite of monoenoic acids dominated by Z-16:1Δ7, Z-16:1Δ9 and Z-18:1Δ9. The two 16:1 isomers are present at similar abundances. Its monoenoic acid composition is thus very similar to that of certain cyanobacteria (Gillan, Wetherbee and Johns, unpublished results). The three proposed bacterial chemotypes are distinct in

that they require different enzyme systems for the biosynthesis of the observed acids: it is probable that they represent true chemosynthetic divisions of bacteria. In terms of sedimentary input, one can envisage at least these three bacterial straight-chain monoenoic acid sources. Many further detailed analyses of such bacteria will be necessary to accurately define the compositional means for bacteria in each of these groups. It seems probable that further groups of straight-chain monoenoic acid producing bacteria exist. The average compositions for each of the three groups proposed will be employed as a first approximation in the analysis of the sediment data (see below).

The branched-chain producers biosynthesize only traces of monoenoic acids (mean of the three isolates: 4.3%): unless the biomass of the branched-chain producers is much greater than that of the straight-chain monoenoic acid producing bacteria, the abundance of the sedimentary branched-chain monoenoic acids will be relatively small. As we have previously indicated (Gillan and Johns, 1981), certain atypical bacteria produce large amounts of branched-chain monoenoic acids. Such bacteria will probably contribute a large proportion of the branched-chain monoenoic acids observed in sediments. The three isolates analysed in this study are thus relatively unimportant in terms of the input of branched-chain monoenoic acids to marine sediments; however, these monoenoic acids may have much greater significance taxonomically.

The branched-chain producers, LIAB 6 and LIAB 16

Table 3
Monoenoic acids identified in bacteria[a]

	Branched-chain acids								Straight-chain acids					
Structure	i15	a15	i16	i17	a17	i18	i19	a19	14	15	16	17	18	20
Isomers														
Z:														
Δ3											+			
Δ4	+		+++	+					+	++	++			
Δ5		++	++	++	++				+		++		++	
Δ6	+	+	+	+	+				++	++	+++	+	+	
Δ7	00	0	0	+	+				+		+++		+	
Δ8	++	++	++								+	+	++	
Δ9	×××	++	××	000	000	×			+		+++	+	+++	
Δ10	+	++	+++	+++	+++					+	+++	+	+	
Δ11			++	×		0	0	0			++	++	+++	
Δ12			++		++							+	+	
Δ13													+++	+
E:														
Δ4											+			
Δ5			×××	××	×××				+		×××		+	
Δ6											+		+	
Δ7									+		+		+	
Δ8											+		+	
Δ9									+		+++	+	+	
Δ10										+	+	+	+	
Δ11											+	++	+++	
Δ12												+	+	
Δ13												++		+

[a] Data from this report: + = present, + + = present at > 2% in at least one isolate, + + + = present at > 10% in at least one isolate. Data from Gillan *et al.* (1981): × = present, × × = present at > 2% etc. Data from Boon *et al.* (1978): 0 = present, 00 = present at > 2%, etc. (in each, % refers to % of monoenoic acids).

biosynthesize predominantly Z-Δ10 monoenoic acids. The Δ10 acids are the major isomers of the i16:1, 16:1 and br17:1 acids. The Δ8 isomer is predominant in the br15:1 acids (LIAB 6), Δ6 acids are observed for 14:1, i16:1, 16:1, br17:1 and 18:1, and Δ4 acids for i16:1 and 16:1. It is reasonable to propose that a Δ4 desaturase and a chain elongase active for monoenoic acids are present. Further work will be necessary to define the pathway of biosynthesis of these acids. In contrast to this Z-Δ10 predominance, *C. uda*, the third branched-chain producer, biosynthesizes predominantly Z-Δ4 monoenoic acids with Z-Δ6 acids also being abundant. The most abundant monoenoic acids in *C. uda* are Z-a15:1Δ4 and Z-16:1Δ6. As in the cases of LIAB 6 and LIAB 16, Δ4-desaturation and subsequent chain elongation could explain most of the observed distribution of monoenoic acids in *C. uda*. The observed differences in the isomer distributions of these three isolates could, in part, be the result of differences in the chain-length specificity of the enzymes involved. Neither the reported composition of *Desulfovibrio desulfuricans* (Boon *et al.*, 1977) nor the analyses of two marine bacteria reported previously (Gillan *et al.*, 1981) match the isomer distributions observed here. It is evident that branched-chain producing bacteria biosynthesize a diverse range of monoenoic acids. Since other organisms produce, at most, only traces of branched acids, all of the branched-chain monoenoic acids observed in sediments can be considered to be derived from *in situ* bacteria and/or the cellular debris from lysed bacterial cells (Gillan and Johns, 1981). No further subdivision of the branched-chain monoenoic acid producers into chemotypes will be attempted.

This and two previous studies (Boon *et al.*, 1977; Gillan *et al.*, 1981) have resulted in the identification of approximately 100 different monoenoic acids in bacteria. The identified acids are mapped in Table 3.

Sediment analyses

Analyses of sediment from two of these environments (Old Yanakie Beach, Corner Inlet (CI) and the Low Isles (LI)) have been reported previously (Perry *et al.*, 1979; Volkman *et al.*, 1980). In both reports, tentative positional isomer identifications were assigned on the basis of GC retention characteristics. In this study, many of the previous tentative identifications have been confirmed by GC/MS of the OsO$_4$ oxidation products and additional isomers have been characterized.

Tables 4 and 5 list the determined chain-length and positional isomer distributions for the monoenoic acids in the five sediments. Table 6 lists the monoenoic acids observed and provides an approximate assessment of their abundance. 126 monoenoic acids were detected. These included all of the previously identified bacterial acids (Table 3) except 14 branched-chain isomers and three straight-chain *trans* acids. All of the major branched-chain isomers produced by the 'atypical' high-branched, high-monoenoic acid producers (*D. desulfuricans* (Boon *et al.*, 1978) and LIAB 3 (Gillan *et al.*, 1981)) were detected in the sediments. Indeed, of the acids produced by these two bacteria, only Z-i19:1Δ11 and Z-a19:1Δ11 (both very minor components in *D.*

Table 4

Abundance[a] and chain-length distributions of the sedimentary monoenoic acids

| | Sediment[b] | | | | |
	LI	PF	CI	LF	SCB
Chain distribution					
i15	0.3	0.2	—[d]	—	—
a15	0.1	T	—	—	—
i16	0.1	0.2	0.5	5.8	—
i17	0.3	0.1	—	0.6	1.2
a17	T[d]	0.2	—	0.5	1.0
i18	0.8	0.1	—	1.9	—
i19	1.7	0.2	—	2.9	—
a19	1.2	0.1	—	1.8	—
14	0.8	0.4	1.3	0.4	1.4
15	1.1	1.4	0.9	0.6	2.1
16	37.9	74.8	89.5	20.2	60.1
17	4.1	2.9	0.9	5.3	5.6
18	50.4	19.4	6.9	56.6	28.7
19	0.3	—	—	3.3	—
20	0.8	—	—	0.3	—
Abundances[c]					
% E	9.9	2.6	2.0	19.2	2.9
% br	4.5	1.1	0.5	13.5	2.2

[a] Data are uncorrected for GC/MS response.
[b] LI: Low Isles, PF: Port Franklin, CI: Corner Inlet, LF: Laguna Figueroa, SCB: Santa Catalina Basin.
[c] As per Table 1.
[d] $T < 0.05\%$; — not detected.

Table 5

Positional isomer distribution of the sedimentary monoenoic acids

| | Sediment | | | | |
	LI	PF	CI	LF	SCB
Isomer					
E-Δ3	0.6	0.6	0.5	0.1	—
Z-Δ3	0.4	0.4	0.1	0.2	—
E-Δ4	0.1	—[a]	—	T[a]	—
Z-Δ4	0.8	0.3	—	1.1	—
E-Δ5	0.3	0.2	0.1	0.3	—
Z-Δ5	3.0	2.9	5.2	2.5	2.5
E-Δ6	0.1	—	—	0.4	—
Z-Δ6	0.7	0.6	0.7	1.4	3.1
E-Δ7	0.2	—	—	1.6	—
Z-Δ7	1.7	1.3	1.5	7.1	5.5
E-Δ8	0.1	T	—	0.6	—
Z-Δ8	0.4	0.6	0.3	1.5	1.0
E-Δ9	2.9	1.1	1.1	6.8	1.9
Z-Δ9	38.4	68.7	83.4	23.0	56.6
E-Δ10	0.2	T	—	1.4	—
Z-Δ10	0.7	0.3	0.5	4.3	—
E-Δ11	4.7	0.6	0.3	7.1	1.0
Z-Δ11	36.4	20.4	5.6	29.6	26.4
E-Δ12	0.1	—	—	0.4	—
Z-Δ12	0.3	0.5	0.1	2.7	—
E-Δ13	0.5	0.1	—	0.6	—
Z-Δ13	7.0	1.4	0.7	7.5	2.1
E-Δ15	T	—	—	—	—
Z-Δ15	T	—	—	—	—

[a] As per Table 4.

Table 6
Monoenoic acids identified in the sediment s[a]

Structure	Branched-chain acids								Straight-chain acids						
	i15	a15	i16	i17	a17	i18	i19	a19	14	15	16	17	18	19	20
Isomers															
Z:															
Δ3									+		+				
Δ4	+	+	++						+	+	+				
Δ5	+		+	+	+				+ +	+	+ + +	+	+ +		
Δ6			+	+ .	+				+	+	+ + +	+	+		
Δ7	+	+	+	+	+				+ +	+	+ + +	+ +	+ +		
Δ8		+	+	+					+	+	+	+	+ +		
Δ9	+	+	+ +	+ +	+ +	+ +			+	+ + +	+ + + +	+ + +	+ + + +	+	+
Δ10			+	+	+		+ +	+ +		+ +	+ +	+	+	+ +	
Δ11			+ +	+		+ +					+ + +	+ + +	+ + + +	+	+
Δ12						+						+ +	+ +	+	
Δ13						+	+ + +	+ +					+ + +	+ +	+
Δ15															+
E:															
Δ3										+ +					
Δ4										+					
Δ5									+	+	+		+		
Δ6			+							+	+		+		
Δ7			+						+	+	+ +	+	+		
Δ8									+	+	+	+	+ +		
Δ9			+							+	+ + +	+	+ + +	+	
Δ10											+		+ +		
Δ11			+		+						+	+	+ + +	+	+
Δ12												+	+		
Δ13													+ +		+
Δ15															+

[a] + = present (detection limit Ca. 0.01%); + + = >0.5% in at least one sediment; + + + = >2.0% in at least one sediment; + + + + = >8.0% in at least one sediment.

desulfuricans) were not identified in the sediments. Many of the monoenoic acids produced by the 'low-monoenoic' acid producers were not detected.

The very high abundances of C_{16} and Δ9 acids in the Port Franklin (PF), Santa Catalina Basin (SCB) and CI sediments are in contrast to the much lower abundances observed for the Laguna Figueroa (LF) and LI sediments (Tables 4 and 5). Since eukaryotic algae biosynthesize predominantly Z-16:1Δ9 in their monoenoic acids, the sediments with high abundances of this acid probably have major eukaryotic algal inputs. This has previously been proposed for the CI sediment on the basis of polyunsaturated fatty acid (Volkman *et al.*, 1980) and pigment (Gillan and Johns, 1980) abundances. The presence of E-16:1Δ3 in this sediment has been used by Volkman *et al.* (1980) to confirm the proposed algal input. E-16:1Δ3 was the only E-Δ3 acid detected in the sediments. In all cases it was more abundant than the corresponding *cis* isomer. It has not been found in bacteria (Table 3), though the *cis* isomer has been identified in one isolate. E-16:1Δ3 is abundant (*ca.* 0.6% of total monoenoic acids) in the LI, PF and CI sediments, of low abundance in the LF sediment and below detection in the SCB sediment (the level of detection in this last instance was 0.5%). It is possible that eukaryotic algae are a major input to this latter sediment. It will be necessary to use other, more abundant acids to characterize the algal input. The only

conclusion that can be drawn from the E-16:1Δ3 abundances is that the eukaryotic algal input to the LF sediment is relatively minor.

C_{18} and Δ11 acids, and *trans* acids are more abundant in the LI and LF sediments than in the other sediments. Vaccenic acid (Z-18:1Δ11) and *trans* acids have been proposed as bacterial markers in the earlier study on the LI sediment (Perry *et al.*, 1979). A high abundance of these acids is thus indicative of a relatively high abundance of vaccenic acid and *trans* acid producing bacteria. Before any quantitative assessment of the relative contributions from the various bacterial chemotypes and algae to the sedimentary monoenoic acids can be attempted, the mean compositions of each chemosynthetic group must be defined. Table 7(a) lists the mean compositions (for five selected acids and a structural group of acids) of the bacterial groups suggested previously in this report, an algal enrichment culture from the Corner Inlet sediment (reported by Volkman *et al.*, 1980), and a higher plant analysis (the mangrove, *Avicennia marina*, which is associated with both the LI and PF sediments (Wannigama *et al.*, 1981)). Analyses of the five sediments are also reported (Table 7(b)). The five acids were selected on the basis that they were the predominant acids in each of the chemotypes. It is to be stressed that the calculated mean compositions are, at best, approximations of the actual mean compositions of the chemotypes. Any additional inputs

Table 7
Mean compositions[a] of the sedimentary input chemotypes[b] and of the marine sediments

(a)	Bacterial chemotype					Eukaryotic algae	Higher plants
	cis/trans	Δ7/Δ9	Vaccenic acid	Branched acid			
Z-16:1Δ7	0.4	25.6	0.0	0.0		0.0	0.7
Z-16:1Δ9	11.3	29.9	2.3	2.4		90.1	8.6
Z-18:1Δ9	1.1	18.4	3.4	4.7		4.7	75.1
E-18:1Δ11	28.9	0.0	0.0	0.0		0.0	0.0
Z-18:1Δ11	28.3	2.0	78.1	0.4		1.7	2.7
Σ branched acids[c]	0.0	0.0	0.0	54.0		0.0	0.0
(b) Marine sediments	LI	PF	CI	LF	SCB		
Z-16:1Δ7	0.46	0.58	1.1	4.3	3.5		
Z-16:1Δ9	27.2	62.7	79.9	8.4	43.2		
Z-18:1Δ9	8.1	3.4	2.4	11.8	7.0		
E-18:1Δ11	4.0	0.25	0.32	5.7	1.0		
Z-18:1Δ11	30.9	13.4	3.2	24.5	17.0		
Σ branched acids	4.5	1.1	0.48	13.5	2.2		

[a] % of total monoenoic acids.
[b] See text for explanation.
[c] Summation of identified branched-chain monoenoic acids.

not belonging to one or the other of the chemosynthetic groups defined here will be evident in the summation of the determined abundances of the chemotypes: the chemotypes will be unable to explain 100% of the monoenoic acids observed in the sediments. Since there are six data points for each sediment (the abundance of each component) and there are six unknowns (the abundance of each input chemotype), the data can be reduced to a unique solution. Figure 1 portrays the

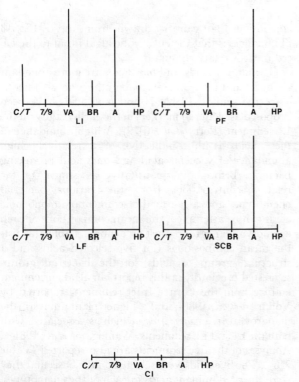

Fig. 1. Chemotype distributions of the marine sediments. C/T cis/trans, 7/9: Δ7/Δ9, VA: Vaccenic acid, BR: Branched acid, A: Eukaryotic algae, HP: Higher plant. The distributions are scaled to the most abundant chemotype.

calculated chemotype distribution for each sediment. Three slightly negative data points are evident (e.g. HP for the CI sediment). This is probably largely due to errors in the proposed input compositions.

All of the sediments other than the LP sediment exhibit quite high eukaryotic algal contributions to the sedimentary monoenoic acids as expected on the basis of E-16:1Δ3 abundances (see previous discussion). The bacterial contribution exceeds the algal contribution in only two sediments: LF and LI. In the former case (LF) bacteria (including cyanobacteria) contribute at least 84% of the monoenoic acids. In contrast, in the CI sediment the bacterial contribution is approximately 8%.

The algal input to the monoenoic acids is most evident in the CI sediment where the eukaryotic algal contribution was found to be 87%. Approximately 10% (± 5%) of the monoenoic acid distribution is unexplained by the six inputs. This possibly reflects errors in the mean compositions of the various chemotypes. Both the LF and the SCB sediments contain appreciable amounts of the Δ7/Δ9 chemotype. Since the 'algal mat ooze' analysed for Laguna Figueroa underlies a predominantly cyanobacterial mat, the high abundance of the Δ7/Δ9 chemotype is probably indicative of a cyanobacterial contribution to the lipids of this sediment. Insufficient data are available on the inputs to the SCB sediment to permit the assessment of the significance of this chemotype in this sediment. The LI and LF sediments are characterized by a relatively high abundance of trans acid producing bacteria. The very low abundance of this chemotype in the PF and CI sediments may reflect the lower environmental temperature: it is conceivable that the trans acid bacteria proliferate only in hotter regions. It is equally possible that environmental factors including E_h and/or pH will affect the distribution of these bacteria in sediments. Further studies of sedimentary trans acids will be necessary before any causal relationships can be established.

Many of the acids identified in the bacteria are not present to any significant extent in other organisms which are likely to contribute to the sediments, e.g. only bacteria have been noted to produce iso- and anteiso-branched acids as major cellular fatty acids, although a few fungi and fungi imperfecti, and the cyanobacterium *Anacystis nidulans* have been reported to produce small amounts of branched-chain acids. The branched-chain acids thus derive predominantly from bacteria; the acids likely to be contributed predominantly or exclusively by bacteria have been discussed by Perry *et al.* (1979). Clearly, since the acids are distinctly bacterial in origin, the results are generally applicable. Indeed, a less detailed approach using fatty acids as indicators of bacterial populations has been successfully employed in other microbial ecology studies, e.g. Bobbie *et al.* (1981).

Variations in the relative contributions to the monoenoic acids by the four bacterial chemotypes are evident in Fig. 1. Vaccenic acid producing bacteria are relatively abundant in the LI, PF and SCB sediments, the branched-chain monoenoic acid producers dominate the LF sediment profile, and for the CI sediment, the $\Delta 7/\Delta 9$ producers are the major bacterial chemotype contributing to the monoenoic acids. It is thus possible that this type of analysis could provide a 'fingerprint' of the bacterial community structure. On this basis, analysis of, for example, a sedimentary depth profile, could provide a very informative assessment of the bacterial population distributions. However, it is to be noted that conversion factors (% monoenoic acid: dry wt.) for each of the chemotypes would need to be determined before biomass assessments could be made.

SUMMARY

Analyses of eight bacterial isolates for their monoenoic acids has led to the characterization of at least four bacterial chemotypes. The first grouping was of bacteria which synthesize both *cis* and *trans* acids in approximately equal quantities. Variation in the relative abundance of this group of bacteria due to various environmental factors could fully explain the variations in *trans* monoenoic acid abundances in sediments that have been reported by various authors (Boon *et al.*, 1978; Van Vleet and Quinn, 1976, 1979). The other three chemotypes are characterized by the presence of both Z-16:1Δ7 and Z-16:1Δ9 as major acids, the predominance of vaccenic acid in the monoenoic acid distribution, and the synthesis of large amounts of branched-chain acids respectively.

Five sediments were analysed and a total of 126 monoenoic acids were identified. The acids observed in the sediments included nearly all of those previously identified in marine bacteria. The Laguna Figueroa sediment was found to contain relatively high abundances of vaccenic acid and *trans* acids. This was taken to indicate a dominant bacterial input to the monoenoic acids of this sediment. In contrast, the Corner Inlet sediment yielded predominantly Z-16:1Δ9 in its monoenoic acids. This indicated a major input from eukaryotic algae. More refined analyses of the sedimentary monoenoic acid distributions using

estimated bacterial and algal chemotype compositions were performed. The resultant chemotype profiles for each sediment demonstrated an eukaryotic algal contribution to the sedimentary monoenoic acids of between 0% (Laguna Figueroa) and 87% (Corner Inlet) and a bacterial (sum of four chemotypes) contribution of between 8% (Corner Inlet) and 84% (Laguna Figueroa). The bacterial chemotype distributions for each sediment were distinctive.

The technique developed in this paper can potentially provide an estimate of both bacterial and algal biomasses in marine sediments. It has the added advantage (over other approaches to biomass determination) of providing a distributional index for the *in situ* bacterial population.

Acknowledgements

The authors wish to thank Professor G. P. Wanningama (University of Paradeniya, Sri Lanka) for providing extracts of the Port Franklin sediment, Professor Ken Smith of Scripps Institute of Oceanography for the Santa Catalina core, and Dr Nils Holm (SIO) and Professor L. Margulis (Boston University) for facilitating collection of the Laguna Figueroa sample. F.T.G. and P.D.N. acknowledge financial assistance from a CPG Award and a Melbourne University P.G. Award respectively. The secretarial staff at the Australian Institute of Marine Science are thanked for their help in the preparation of this paper.

REFERENCES

Belyaev, S. S., Lein, A. Yu. and Ivanov, M. V. (1980) Role of methane-producing and sulfate-reducing bacteria in the destruction of organic matter. In *Biogeochemistry of Ancient and Modern Environments*, ed. by Trudinger, P. A. and Walter, M. R. Australian Academy of Science, Canberra, pp. 235–242.

Bobbie, R. J., Nickels, J. S., Smith, G. A., Fazio, S. D., Findlay, R. H., Davis, W. M. and White, D. C. (1981) Effect of light on biomass and community structure of estuarine detrital microbiota *Appl. Environ., Microbiol.* **42**, 150–158.

Boon, J. J., De Leeuw, J. W., Van Der Hoek, G. J. and Vosjan, J. H. (1977) Significance and taxonomic value of iso and anteiso monoenoic fatty acids and branched β-hydroxy acids in *Desulfovibrio desulfuricans*. *J. Bacteriol.* **129**, 1182–1192.

Boon, J. J., De Leeuw, J. W. and Burlingame, A. L. (1978) Organic geochemistry of Walvis Bay diatomaceous ooze — III. Structural analysis of the monoenoic and polycyclic fatty acids. *Geochim. Cosmochim. Acta* **42**, 631–644.

Christensen, J. P. and Devol, A. H. (1980) Adenosine triphosphate and adenylate energy charge in marine sediments. *Mar. Biol.* **56**, 175–182.

Gillan, F. T. and Johns, R. B. (1980) Input and early diagenesis of chlorophyll in a temperate intertidal sediment. *Mar. Chem.* **9**, 243–253.

Gillan, F. T. and Johns, R. B. (1981) Chemical markers for marine bacteria. In *Monograph on Biological Markers*, ed. by Johns, R. B. (in preparation).

Gillan, F. T., Verheyen, T. V., Johns, R. B., Volkman, J. K.

and Bavor, H. J. (1981) Trans-monounsaturated acids in a marine bacterial isolate. *Appl. Environ. Microbiol.* **41**, 849–856.

Matsuda, H. and Koyama, T. (1977) Positional isomer composition of monounsaturated acids from a lacustrine sediment. *Geochim. Cosmochim. Acta* **41**, 341–345.

Perry, G. J., Volkman, J. K., Johns, R. B. and Bavor, H. J. (1979) Fatty acids of bacterial origin in contemporary marine sediments. *Geochim. Cosmochim. Acta* **43**, 1715–1725.

Van Vleet, E. S. and Quinn, J. G. (1976) Characterisation of monounsaturated fatty acids from an estuarine sediment. *Nature* **262**, 126–128.

Van Vleet, E. S. and Quinn, J. G. (1979) Early diagenesis of fatty acids and isoprenoid alcohols in estuarine and coastal sediments. *Geochim. Cosmochim. Acta* **43**, 289–303.

Volkman, J. K., Johns, R. B., Gillan, F. T., Perry, G. J. and Bavor, H. J. (1980) Microbial lipids of an intertidal sediment — I. Fatty acids and hydrocarbons. *Geochim. Cosmochim. Acta* **44**, 1133–1143.

Wannigama, G. P., Volkman, J. K., Gillan, F. T., Nichols, P. D. and Johns, R. B. (1981) A comparison of lipid components of the fresh and dead leaves and pneumatophores of the mangrove *Avicennia marina. Phytochemistry* **20**, 659–666.

Advances in Organic Geochemistry 1981, pp. 207–227
© *John Wiley & Sons Limited, 1983*

Organic Geochemical Studies of Solar Lake
Laminated Cyanobacterial Mats

J. J. Boon,* H. Hines and A. L. Burlingame

Biomedical and Environmental Mass Spectrometry Resource, School of Pharmacy, University of California, San Francisco, California, USA

J. Klok, W. I. C. Rijpstra and J. W. DE Leeuw

Delft University of Technology, Department of Chemistry and Chemical Engineering, Organic Geochemistry Unit, De Vries van Heystplantsoen 2, 2628 RZ Delft, The Netherlands

K. E. Edmunds and G. Eglinton

Organic Geochemistry Unit, School of Chemistry, University of Bristol, Bristol BS8 1TS, UK

The very regular sequence of laminated cyanobacterial mats (thickness about 80 cm) present in Solar lake was studied to determine the fate of cyanobacterial organic matter over a time span of 2400 years. Data were obtained about morphology, total organic carbon, total carbohydrate, pyrolysis characteristics, carbohydrate components, hydrocarbons, ketones, fatty acids, alcohols, sterols, carotenoids, hopanetetrols, ethers and ester cleavage products of residual fractions using microscopy, Curie point pyrolysis instruments (PyMS and PyGC), chromatographic techniques (HPLC, TLC, GLC) and mass spectrometric methods. Organic matter morphology, monitored by microscopy, changes rapidly with depth to a residual fraction which consists mainly of empty sheath tubes.

The chemical composition of the 0–3 mm layer of the top mat is close to the composition of laboratory cultures of cyanobacteria. Lipids and carbohydrates are the abundant storage products of photosynthetic overproduction. Glucose reaches a concentration of 78 mg/g dry sediment in the 0–0.5 mm layer. The only hopane type compounds in the 0–3 mm layer are two hopane tetrols. The 10–20 mm layer has been subjected to several years of heterotrophic bacterial decomposition processes. Total organic carbon, total carbohydrate, extractable lipids and carotenoids have diminished in concentration by several orders of magnitude. Abundant carbonate is deposited. Fatty acids with iso, anteiso and cyclopropane structures appear. A number of hopanoic acids were identified with $17\beta(H),21\beta(H)$-bishomohopanoic acid as the major component. The $\Delta^5/5\alpha(H)$ ratio of the sterol fraction changes to low values due to sterol reduction processes. The hydrocarbon fraction consists of top mat hydrocarbons and a relatively large amount of Δ^2-sterenes and steradienes. The oldest mat consists mainly of empty sheath tubes. Its olive–green colour is not caused by morphologically discernible cyanobacterial cell remains. Pyrolysis data point to a carbohydrate fraction which generates furan compounds on analysis and to unknown fractions which generate phenols, olefins and aromatic hydrocarbons. Phenols are also found as ether cleavage products. Two hopane tetrols were tentatively identified. The major tetrol of the top mat has disappeared. A number of hopane type triterpenoid hydrocarbons, fatty acids and alcohols are present as decomposition products of the tetrols. The hydrocarbon fraction consist mainly of Δ^2-sterenes and steradienes. No top mat hydrocarbons remain and most of the top mat fatty acids have disappeared. The mixture consists triterpenoid acids, straight chain acids ranging from C_{20} to C_{30}, n-$C_{18:0}$ and n-$C_{16:0}$. Sterols have increased in intensity compared to the sterol fraction of 10–20 mm. The 24-ethyl cholesterol is the major component. Major carotenoids are α-carotene, echinone and zeaxanthin. In all fractions analysed, unknowns were observed with potential as marker molecules. In general, most marker molecules of the top mat living community have been transformed or are completely degraded after 2400 years of burial.

INTRODUCTION

Reconstruction of the ancient stromatolite environment by its chemical fossils is the rationale for our organic geochemical study of present day algal and bacterial

* Author to whom correspondence should be addressed.
Present address: FOM-Institute Kruislaan 407, Amsterdam, The Netherlands.

environments. We wanted to investigate the closest available analogues to the (cyano) bacterial ecosystems of the Precambrian era in order to be able to deduce environmental parameters from organic compounds. Recent stromatolitic sediments are formed by growth and metabolic activity of cyanobacterial (blue–green algae), but none of the environments where stromatolitic sediment is presently formed are exactly like those of the past (Hoffman, 1975). Nevertheless, their study provides us with an observational framework within which stromatolites and their paleoenvironment can be understood (Awramik *et al.*, 1978).

Cyanobacterial mats in Baja California (Mexico), Abu Dhabi, Shark Bay (Australia) and Baffin Bay (Texas) have been investigated for certain lipid classes (Parker and Leo, 1965; Cardoso *et al.*, 1973, 1976; Huang and Meinschein, 1978; Philp *et al.*, 1978a) for carotenoids (Tibbetts *et al.*, 1978; Watts *et al.*, 1977), and for kerogen (Philp *et al.*, 1978b; Brown *et al.*, 1980; Philp, 1981). These studies not only showed that chemical fossils do exist as remains of the photosynthetic communities, but also pointed to the vulnerability of some compound classes to bacterial attack and degradation. None of these sediments were investigated in sufficient detail, however, to understand the sequence of events leading to the altered molecular 'signatures' of the original cyanobacterial ecosystem, nor do we know this signature for subrecent stromatolites. Therefore, new studies were desirable, designed to determine the fate of a benthic cyanobacterial ecosystem exposed to various decomposition processes after burial over an extensive period of time. The sediments present in Solar lake (Sinai) appeared to be the most suitable for this purpose.

In the hypersaline, mesothermal Solar lake (Sinai), a continuous sequence of laminated cyanobacterial mats is present with a thickness of about one meter (Krumbein *et al.*, 1977). The accumulation of these sediments began 2400 years b.p. and still continues (Krumbein and Cohen, 1974). Stable hydrographic conditions throughout the depositional history is the main reason that the present-day environmental conditions prevailing in the photosynthetic communities at the benthic surface resemble those when microbial mat accumulation began (Cohen *et al.*, 1977). This opens up the possibility of evaluating the molecular stratigraphy of these sediments in terms of processes of degradation, transformation, de novo synthesis and preservation because the living generation in the top mat is underlaid by the debris of similar previous generations now undergoing bacterial degradation. In lower layers, active carbonate precipitation interferes with the biological transformation processes and presumably imposes more chemically oriented transformation or even preservation processes.

Initially we have chosen to analyse top mat layers (0–3 mm, 3–10 mm, 10–20 mm) and several sediment sections lower in the core. The samples were studied by ordinary transmitted light and epifluorescence microscopy. Major lines of biogeochemical change were determined by bulk parameters such as total organic carbon, carbohydrate, lipid and carotenoid content and pyrolysis characteristics of the samples. Detailed analysis of lipids, carotenoids and carbohydrate components provided information on the molecular marker level.

The results of the molecular profiling show rapid transformation in organic matter composition in the top mats which are metabolically the most active. The chemical composition of the oldest layers will serve as a basis for comparison with geologically older cyanobacterial mats.

EXPERIMENTAL

Site description and sampling

Samples were taken from the shallow benthic cyanobacterial mats present in Solar lake, a small (140 × 50 m) lake, situated 18 km south of Eilat (Israel) on the coast of Sinai (Cohen *et al.*, 1977). The mats were dark green in colour. Water cover was about 70 cm at the time of sampling (November 1980). The sampling site was situated about halfway along the eastern shore and about one metre in front of the slope in the deep part of the lake. Laminated mats are found at this location to a depth of 80 cm (Krumbein *et al.*, 1977).

Six cores were taken using perspex tubes (1.2 m long, 5 cm i.d.). The cores were transported intact to the Netherlands and, within 36 h of arrival, the sediments were divided into sections 3 cm thick. The temperature during transport was considerably lower than the *in situ* sediment temperature of 40 °C. Top mat sections were collected separately close to the core sampling sites. A slice of top mat was divided into 0–3, 3–10 and 10–20 mm layers. These sections were packed and immediately cooled on dry ice; all samples were kept deep frozen until analysis.

Microscopy

Sediment samples were studied in filtered Solar lake water by transmitted light, phase contrast and epifluorescence microscopy using a Zeiss Photomicroscope II. Fluorescence of algae was studied by excitation at 365 nm and emitted light was filtered by a 420 nm colour splitter and a 481 nm long pass filter.

Organic carbon

Organic carbon was determined by the method of Menzel and Vaccaro (1964) using a 'glass ampoule purging and sealing unit' and 'total carbon system' of Oceanography International Corp., Texas, USA. Aliquots of dried homogenized sediment were weighed in precleaned glass ampoules, digested with phosphoric acid, purged with nitrogen and mixed with a standard amount of $K_2S_2O_8$. The glass ampoules were sealed and autoclaved. After oxidation of the organic carbon, the CO_2 in the instrument was measured using IR detection. Samples were analysed in triplicate. Sucrose was used for calibration.

Carbonate determination

Carbonate was determined by acid digestion with HCl and gravimetric analysis of evolved CO_2 following the method of Pieters (1948).

Total carbohydrates

Dried homogenized sediment was hydrolysed in 1.0 N paratoluene sulphonic acid in sealed glass ampoules. The hydrolysate was passed over a Dowex-X8 cation exchange column. Neutral and acidic carbohydrates were quantified by spectrophotometry using the Cu–biscinchoninate complex (Mopper, 1977). Samples were analysed in triplicate and analytical precision was within 3%. Glucose was used for calibration.

Pyrolysis methods

About 1 mg of dried homogenized sediment was suspended in 1 ml methanol. Ferromagnetic sample wires (Curie temperature of wires was 510 °C) were coated with 10 μl of this suspension and inserted in glass tubes. The samples were pyrolysed using Curie point pyrolysis in an instrument described by Meuzelaar *et al.* (1977). The pyrolysis mass spectra were factor analysed according to the methods developed by Windig *et al.* (1980). Pyrolysis gas–liquid chromatography was carried out on microgram size samples using Curie point pyrolysis in an instrument set-up described by Van der Meent *et al.* (1980). The gas chromatograph, equipped with a cryogenic unit, was programmed from -25 °C to 275 °C at a rate of 3 °C/min. A 50 m (0.5 mm i.d., 1.2 μ film thickness) glass capillary column coated with CP-sil^{tm}5 (Chrompack, Middelburg) was used for the separation. Helium was used as carrier gas.

Carbohydrate component analysis

About 0.5 g of the freeze-dried sediment samples was used for hydrolysis of carbohydrate polymers. Carbonate was digested by 0.5 N H_2SO_4 prior to the hydrolysis and the pH of the hydrolysis medium was adjusted. Hydrolysis was performed in sealed glass tubes over a period of 80 h at 100 °C. The hydrolysate was neutralized with $BaCO_3$ and *m*-inositol was added as internal standard. Reduction with $NaBH_4$, derivatization of the obtained alditols and subsequent analysis by GLC and GC/MS were performed as described previously (Klok *et al.*, 1981).

Lipid analysis

Each freeze-dried sediment sample (average weight used, 15 g) was extracted sequentially with methanol, methanol–dichloromethane and dichloromethane using ultrasonication. On pooling of these extracts, inorganic salts precipitated. The precipitate was removed by centrifugation. The supernatant was evaporated to a small volume and taken up in methanol–dichloromethane (1:1). This solution was centrifuged once more and an aliquot was taken to dryness to determine the weight of the extracted lipids. An amount of the extract was saponified in 1 N methanolic KOH (96%) under reflux for 1 h. After cooling, the solution was acidified and extracted with dichloromethane. The dichloromethane extract was washed with methanol–H_2O (1:1) and dried over anhydrous Na_2SO_4. The extract was taken to dryness under nitrogen and taken up in acetone, centrifuged and evaporated once more. The extract was weighed and taken up in dichloromethane. A weighed amount of extract was applied to a preparative TLC plate (Kieselgel 60,

Merck) and separated into hydrocarbon, ketone, fatty acid, alcohol and sterol fractions by elution according to the method of Skipski *et al.* (1965). Rhodamine 6G solution in ethanol (0.05%) aided in the detection of the fractions. Each fraction was weighted after extraction, centrifugation and evaporation. Fatty acid, alcohol and sterol fractions were derivatized by diazomethane. Alcohol and sterol fractions were subsequently silylated using BSA in ethyl acetate.

Gas–liquid chromatography of each fraction was performed on a Carlo Erba 4160 with the 'on-column injector' using a 30 m glass capillary column (I.D. 0.25 mm coated with CPSil5. The oven temperature was programmed from 150–330 °C at a rate of 4 °C/min. Helium was used as carrier gas. GCMS was performed under similar conditions with a Varian 3700 on line with the MAT44. Mass spectra were obtained at 80 eV.

Carotenoid analysis

Exposure to air and light was minimized throughout and, where possible, operations were carried out under nitrogen. All fractions were stored in the dark at -20 °C. The wet sediment samples were extracted by ultrasonication with hexane–isopropanol (1:1) and toluene–methanol (1:1). Extracts were combined. Dry weight of sediment was determined after extraction. Each sediment extract was saponified under mild conditions (aqueous KOH/ethanol, room temperature, 24 h, dark, nitrogen) and the neutral fractions analysed by HPLC and spectrophotometry. HPLC conditions were: 5 μm Spherisorb (Phase Separations Ltd.) in a 25 cm $\times$ 0.46 cm (i.d.) stainless steel column using a gradient of acetone in hexane (1–80%) over 35 min with a 1.8 ml/min flow rate. The HPLC was a Spectra Physics SP 8100 HPLC system coupled to a LDS 1202 UV/VIS detector, set at 451 nm. Electronic absorption spectra were recorded on a Perkin–Elmer UV/VIS spectrophotometer using acetone or ethanol as solvent. Spectra were recorded from 300–600 nm at a scan speed of 120 nm/min (1.5 nm slit width). Quantitation was obtained from the absorbance at λ_{max} by using literature data (Davies, 1976) for $E_{1cm}^{1\%}$. For unknown carotenoids and for total carotenoid content, an average value of 250 for $E_{1cm}^{1\%}$ was used. The extract of the top mat 0–3 mm layer and the bottom layer of core SL 4 were separated by preparative TLC on silicagel G using ethyl acetate–dichloromethane (1:4) as developer. Fractions obtained were further purified by TLC eluted with mixtures of acetone (25–50%) in hexane. Polar carotenoids were derivatized to the corresponding acetates. The fractions were analysed by HPLC, UV/VIS, as described, and by mass spectrometry.

For mass spectrometry, an AEI MS-30 was used, coupled to an INCOS data system. Operating conditions were: ionization energy, 70 eV (electron impact mode); source temperature, 160 °C; scan time 5 s over 35–600 a.m.u. or 8 s over 35–800 a.m.u. Fractions were analysed by direct probe with temperature of the probe controlled manually. Carotenoids were observed in the temperature range of 260–280 °C.

Bacteriohopanetetrols

Polyhydroxybacteriohopane fractions were obtained from a top mat chunk of 0–5 mm depth and from a deep algal mat section at 56.8–62 cm by silica gel TLC of the lipid extracts after saponification with hexane–diethylether (3:2, v/v) and subsequent isolation of the most polar fraction ($R_f = 0$). These fractions were acetylated with acetic acid anhydride in pyridine. The tetrol acetates were obtained by silica gel TLC using hexane–diethyl ether (3:2, v/v) as eluant. The purified acetate fractions were subjected to GLC using on-column injection and a 20 m glass capillary column coated with CP-Sil-5 for separation. Temperature was programmed from 50° to 320 °C. Helium was used as the carrier gas.

The mass spectrometric analysis was carried out on the AEI MS 30 mentioned in the carotenoid section, using the same conditions.

Residue analysis

Four samples were prepared for SMEAH analysis according to the method of Brown et al. (1980). Samples from two very similar cores (SL 2 and SL 5) were combined. Sections 5–85 mm (A), 185–258 mm (C), 258–388 mm (D) and 528–648 mm (F) were chosen for analysis. The sediments were freeze-dried and extracted sequentially with methanol, methanol–dichloromethane and dichloromethane. Saponifications were performed using the method described by Farrington and Quinn (1971). Extracts obtained after acidification of the benzene, methanol, water, KOH solution were analysed (without further separation) after derivatization to prepare methyl esters and silyl ethers for GC and GC/MS. The residue remaining after saponification was suspended in water, neutralized with 6 N HCl to pH 7 and extracted again with water, methanol, methanol–chloroform (1:1) and chloroform. The residue remaining was dried in a vacuum oven at 41 °C for 3–5 days. Five gram portions of these residues were subjected to the SMEAH reduction described by Brown et al. (1980).

Gas chromatographic analyses were performed on a Varian 3700 gas chromatograph equipped with a Grob-type splitless injector, a WCOT OV–1 fused silica column (25 m × 0.16 mm) and an FID detector. Helium was used as the carrier gas with a flow of approximately 2 ml/min. The oven was temperature-programmed from 70° to 330 °C at 5 °C/min with a 3 min initial delay and a 3 min hold at the final temperature. A 30 s split time was used.

High resolution GC/low resolution mass spectrometry (HRGC/LRMS) was performed on a modified Hitachi M–52 mass spectrometer equipped with a Grob-type spitless injector, and a 20 m × 0.325 mm WCOT OV–1 glass capillary column. Saponification products were analysed by temperature-programming the GC oven from 120° to 310 °C/min with an initial delay of 2.5 min. SMEAH reduction products were analysed using a temperature programme of 90° to 310 °C at 5 °C/min and an initial delay of 4 min. A 30 s split time was used for both types of analyses. Spectra were obtained using an electron energy of 70 eV and a scan time of 2.2 s/decade. Data were processed and recorded by a Xerox Sigma 7 data system on-line to the mass spectrometer.

THE BENTHIC CYANOBACTERIAL MATS

Descriptions of the hydrochemistry and biogeochemistry of Solar lake and its sediments can be found in the papers of Cohen, Krumbein and Jörgensen. The carbonate mineralogy of the lake sediments has been studied by Friedman et al. (1973).

We saw a small saline lake about 150 m wide, surrounded by steep bare rocks on three sides and a gravel bar which separated the lake from the sea. One Salicornia, a halophyte, was observed to grow on a mixture of rock debris and salt. The mats in shallow water were very disturbed by footprints, but the mats in deeper water were undisturbed. The disturbed mats may dry out during spring and summer; the undisturbed mats remain permanently water covered.

The cyanobacterial mats at the sampling site are exposed to an annual variation in light intensity, salinity, temperature and pH as a result of annula variation in the equilibrium between evaporation from the lake and seepage of water through the gravel bar. Consequently the surface mats are exposed to a varying water cover with a salinity ranging from 40‰ (winter) to about 180‰ (summer) and temperatures ranging from 16° to 27 °C. Temperature and salinity are occasionally higher if the cyanobacterial mats are exposed to water from below the thermocline with temperatures up to 55 °C and salinities up to 180‰ S.

The annual variation in physiocochemical parameters is accompanied by a biological cycle. During winter, Microcoleus chtonoplastes (a filamentous cyanobacterium (LPP2)) is dominant; in spring and early summer, red and olive-green rod-shaped unicellular cyanobacteria, Achromatium-like organisms, the diatom Nitszchia thermalis and some colourless sulphur bacteria overgrow the Microcoleus lawns; in late summer and early autumn, Aphanothece (a green rod-shaped unicellular cyanobacterium) blooms on the surface (Krumbein and Cohen, 1977). The annual variation in microbial species is reflected in the characteristic green (winter) and greyish green or yellow (summer) lamination in the sediments. The summer laminations are also characterized by relatively large amounts of airborne rock debris.

Core description

The recovered cores consisted of 68 cm of laminated elastic olive-green sediment. The top 19 cm was black as a result of ferrous sulphide precipitates. Exposure of the top 19 cm to air for about 10 h resulted in the loss of the black colour and revealed similar greenish laminated sediments. At several depths, tiny clay layers (0.1–0.2 mm thick) occurred and these were useful for the stratigraphic correlation of the cores taken. Laminae below 35 cm were characterized by coarse carbonate particles (oncolites).

Occasionally borings of Bledius larvae (4 mm i.d.) were present at depths from 10–25 cm (fresh) and 50–55

Table 1

Macroscopic characteristics seen in laminated cyanobacterial mat cores from Solar lake.

0 – 3 mm	dark green tufted cyanobacterial mat with bleached lower layer
3–200 mm	black coloured elastic sediments (green, laminated upon exposure to air)
85 mm	grey clay layer (0.2 mm thick)
175 mm	clay layer (0.1 mm thick)
200–230 mm	zone with thick (1–2 mm) carbonate layers and *Bledius* borings
265–295 mm	zone with well developed fine laminations
295–415 mm	laminated green elastic sediment with increased amounts of carbonate particles in lower layers
415–475 mm	loosely bound sediment with abundant carbonate pellets, bored by *Bledius*
475–658 mm	laminated green elastic sediments with abundant carbonate pellets
628 mm	clay layer (0.2 mm thick)
below 658 mm	grey gypsum sands

cm (old). Table 1 summarizes the macroscopic characteristics seen in the cores.

Samples for preliminary analysis were chosen from the black sulphide zone (115–145 mm), the zone of well developed laminations (265–295 mm), a zone of laminated sediment with oncolites (385–415 mm) and the oldest laminated sediments (625–655 mm). The phenomena in the top mats were studied in the dry ice-frozen samples taken from 0–3 mm, 3–10 mm and 10–20 mm depth.

Microscopic observations

The upper millimeter of the algal mat consisted of a lawn of green *Microcoleus* ($\phi 5 \mu$) in twisted bundles of 5–10 filaments, surrounded by a very thin external sheath. These cyanobacteria showed the red fluorescence indicative of intact chlorophyll. Bordeaux-red blue fluorescent 1 μ filaments (*Chloroflexus?*) were relatively abundant in more shaded areas of the top mat. Occasionally colonies of light-green rod-shaped cyanobacteria of the genus *Aphanothece* (2 μ long) embedded in slime were observed. Just below this layer at about 3 mm depth, the sediment consisted of a translucent substance with abundant rock fragments, filaments of *Microcoleus* (red fluorescence), strongly red fluorescent *Aphanothece* colonies, but also partially lysed *Microcoleus* trichomes. Occasionally nematodes and filaments of the colourless sulphur bacteria *Beggiatoa*, filled with sulphur droplets, were seen. Several millimeters lower, we saw green *Microcoleus*, generally 2 red fluorescent filaments, in thick sheath, abundant blue fluorescent 1 μ filaments, blue fluorescent cysts ($\phi 15 \mu$) and many empty sheaths. Only rarely were remains of red photosynthetic bacteria observed. Below 10 mm the amount of red fluorescent filaments drops significantly, while blue fluorescent filaments remain. From 10–25 mm, occasionally red fluorescent unicellular cyanobacteria were seen between rock debris, carbonate particles and empty sheath. While the sheath remains, the cells inside lyse completely and no visible structure remains, or a shrinking and browning process takes place leaving series of cell remains within the sheath material.

At 115–145 mm the organic remains consisted of colourless strongly intertwined tubuli (about 9 μ wide), sometimes filled with cell remains oriented lengthwise. These remains showed a vague red fluorescence. Also

blue fluorescent cysts were seen. At 265–285 mm we saw an intimately mixed mass of rock fragments, carbonate particles, pyrite (?) framboids and colourless tubuli (sheath remains). Blue fluorescent cysts were often encountered. Very rarely we saw cell remains in the sheath. At 625–658 mm, the sediment consisted of rock fragments, carbonate and colourless sheath remains (empty flattened tubes of about 7 μ), which were much less tightly packed than in the upper layers.

Age estimation

The relatively dense *Microcoleus* layer can be used as winter indicator. Estimated ages for the top mat layers are:

0–3 mm layer: one-year cycle, winter 1979–winter 1980

3–10 mm layer: three-year cycles, winter 1976–winter 1979

10–20 mm layer: six-year cycles, winter 1970–winter 1976.

The layer at 660 mm has been shown to be 2400 years old using ^{14}C-dating of its organic matter (Krumbein and Cohen, 1974).

ORGANIC GEOCHEMISTRY OF THE BENTHIC MATS

Bulk parameters

Results on some organic bulk parameters in the sediments are presented in Table 2. It is evident that organic carbon, carbohydrate, lipid and carotenoid content decrease with depth. The organic carbon content has decreased by a factor of 2 in layer 3–10 mm compared to 0–3 mm. Below this layer, the organic carbon content is approximately constant. A more detailed sampling programme may reveal some anomalies in lower layers. The rapid drop in organic carbon and in organic nitrogen were also observed in earlier years (Krumbein *et al.*, 1977). The decrease was thought to be the result of autolysis of cyanobacterial organic matter and microbial degradation processes.

A considerable portion of the organic matter in the sediments consisted of carbohydrates. The contents found are probably underestimated because a loss of

Table 2

Organic bulk parameters measured in Solar lake cyanobacterial mat sediments (expressed on dry weight basis)

Depth (mm)	org. C (mg/gram)	CaCO₃ (%)	Lipid extract (mg/gram)	Carbohydrates[a] (mg/gram)	Carotenoids (μg/gram)
0–3	97	1.9	30.6	134	847
3–10	46	6.6	10.9	41	155
10–20	34	25.6	6.8	19	32
115–145	27	15.0	4.4	30	n.d.
265–295	29	6.9	n.d.[b]	15	35
385–415	34	28.3	n.d.	16	n.d.
628–658	30	32.0	2.8	18	40

[a] Expressed as hexose units using glucose standard solution.
[b] n.d. = not determined.

carbohydrate during hydrolysis is to be expected. In the 0–3 mm layer at least 50% of the organic C was in the form of carbohydrate carbon. In lower layers this value decreased to about 20%. These high carbohydrate abundances in all the sediments strongly suggest that a considerable portion of the sheath material is of carbohydrate nature. The decrease in extractable lipids and carotenoids points to a rapid metabolism of these organic matter fractions, which often contain many biological marker molecules (Eglinton, 1973).

Calcium carbonate increases with depth, but particularly so in the top mat layer where organic matter is strongly decreasing. Earlier, Krumbein and co-workers (1977) suggested that carbonate precipitation is mainly the result of microbial degradation, which increases bicarbonate concentrations in pore water, in the aphotic zone. Calculations of Jörgensen and Cohen (1977) indicate there is also a need for dissolved organic carbon diffusing downward from the photic zone to account for all the carbonate carbon in lower layers. No data are presently available on organic C content of the pore water, but this carbon is included in our total organic C measurements. Lower sediment sections show high amounts of carbonates in accordance with the macroscopic observations (Table 1). The relatively low value of 26 cm, unaccompanied by an increase in organic carbon, must point to another solid phase in this interval.

Pyrolysis characteristics of the organic matter

Microgram quantities of sediment were investigated by pyrolysis mass spectrometry and pyrolysis gas liquid chromatography using the Curie point pyrolysis technique (Meuzelaar *et al.*, 1977).

The pyrolysis mass spectrometric results were factor analysed to determine correlated variations of mass peaks in the spectra of the sediments. Figure 1 shows factor spectra of the first factor, which describes 50% of the intersample variability. Factor scores are shown in Fig. 2.

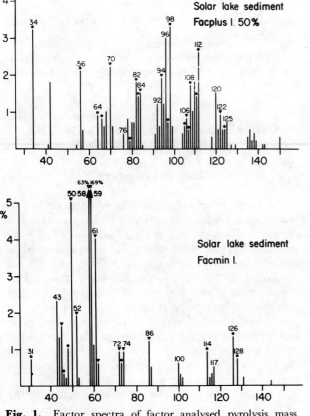

Fig. 1. Factor spectra of factor analysed pyrolysis mass spectra of selected Solar lake cyanobacterial mats.

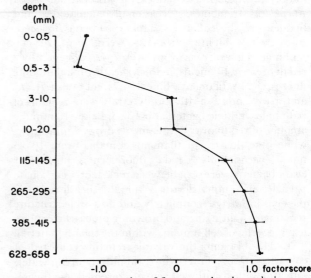

Fig. 2. Factor score plot of factor analysed pyrolysis mass spectra of selected Solar lake cyanobacterial mats.

This result and the pyrolysis mass spectra indicate that the composition of 0–0.5 mm and 0.5–3 mm is similar, these layers may be considered as one unit. A large compositional difference exists between the 0–3 mm top layer and the lower layers at 3–10 and 10–20 mm. The differences between the 10–20 mm layer and lower layers in the core are more gradual.

The patterns in the mass peaks of the pyrolysis mass spectra are interpretable in terms of chemical substances (Haverkamp et al., 1980; Boon et al., 1979; Boon et al., 1981). Mass peaks in the 0–3 mm layer (Fig. 3(a)) indicate the presence of choline containing complex lipid from m/z 50, 52, 58, 59, 61; carbohydrate polymers from m/z 32, 43, 55, 72, 74, 82, 85, 86, 96, 98, 100, 102, 110, 112, 114, 126, 128; proteinaceous substances from m/z 34, 48, 67, 81, 92, 94, 106, 108, 117, 131; and N-acetyl amino-sugar polymer (presumably in the form of the cyanobacterial cell wall polymer peptidoglycan (Boon et al., 1981) from m/z 71, 73, 81, 83, 95, 97, 109, 111, 123, 125, 137, 139.

The pyrolysis mass spectrum of the 0–3 mm layer (Fig.

3(a)) is largely in accordance with pyrolysis mass spectra of cyanobacteria (Boon, unpublished results), except for the relatively intense m/z 96, 100 and the very intense m/z 50, 52, 58, 59, 61.

The mass spectrum of the 3–10 mm layer (Fig. 3(b)) shows the decrease in the lipid mass peaks m/z 50, 52, 58, 59, 61 and the increase in m/z 96. The facmin spectrum (Fig. 1) demonstrates a decrease in m/z 72, 74, 86, 100, 114, 126, 128, indicators of a hexose polymer (Meuzelaar et al., 1982), presumably cyanophycean starch. The decrease of the latter peaks is more evident in the mass spectrum of the 10–20 mm layer (not shown). This phenomenon is confirmed by the carbohydrate analyses. Protein mass peaks and murein mass peaks have slightly increased intensities.

A salient feature in the mass spectra of the deeper sediment layers is a series m/z 68, 82, 96, 110, which is prominent in pyrolysis mass spectra of cyanobacterial sediments from other environments as well (unpublished results). The mass peaks represent the molecular ions from furan, methyl furan, furfuraldehyde and methyl furfuraldehyde (see also PyGC section), pyrolysis products of carbohydrate polymers (Shafizadeh and Lai, 1972). These peaks are thought to be characteristic of the carbohydrate fraction of the sheath material in the core.

The deepest layer, 628–658 mm (Fig. 3(c)), shows the pyrolysis characteristics of proteins, procaryotic cell wall material and sheath material. A series m/z 56, 70, 84, 98, 112, presumably olefins, becomes rather prominent in lower layers, but the chemical origin of these pyrolysis products is unknown. A special feature in the Py–MS of this layer is m/z 120 of unknown significance.

The mass range of the pyrolysis mass spectrometer is limited and precludes the detection of larger molecules. Separation of the pyrolysates of the sediment layers by capillary gas liquid chromatograph not only showed the presence of fatty acids in the pyrolysate, but also confirmed most of the tentatively identified mass peaks in the pyrolysis mass spectra. The Py–GC traces of 0–0.5 mm and 3–10 mm are shown in Fig. 4. Peak numbers in these traces correspond with identifications in Table 3. The identifications were confirmed by Py–GC/MS (Boon et al. in preparation). The most intense peaks in the 0–0.5 mm trace are found in the very low temperature area — i.e., ethane, propane, chloromethane, acetic aldehyde and butene — and in the high temperature area with the n-$C_{16:0}$ fatty acid as the most intense pyrolysis product. Comparison of the two GC traces in Fig. 4 immediately demonstrates the large difference in composition of these two layers in the top mat. Intensity changes of peaks can conveniently be expressed relative to peaks 31 (furfuraldehyde) and 39 (methyl furfuraldehyde), with equal intensity in both traces. Quite a number of peaks have disappeared in the trace of the 3–10 mm and lower layers (not shown), e.g., peak numbers 4, 8, 9, 10, 15, 16, 23, 27, 28, 43, 49, 51, 53, 62, 64 and 71.

The fatty acids (peaks 65, 70, 73, 77, 79, 80, 81) and peak 8, trimethylamine from the pyrolysed choline containing lipid, are pyrolysis products of lipids. The distribution of the fatty acids is similar to the fatty acid distribution found after saponification of the lipid extract of the layers. Peaks 67 and 68 represent the

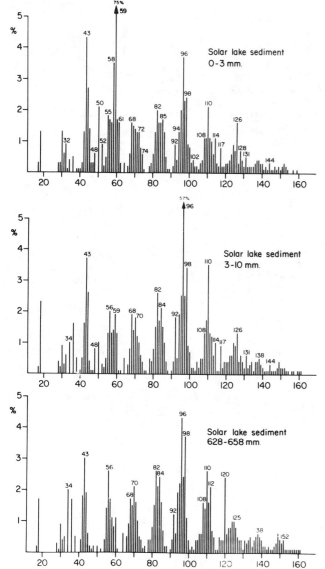

Fig. 3. Pyrolysis mass spectra of some Solar lake cyanobacterial mat sections.

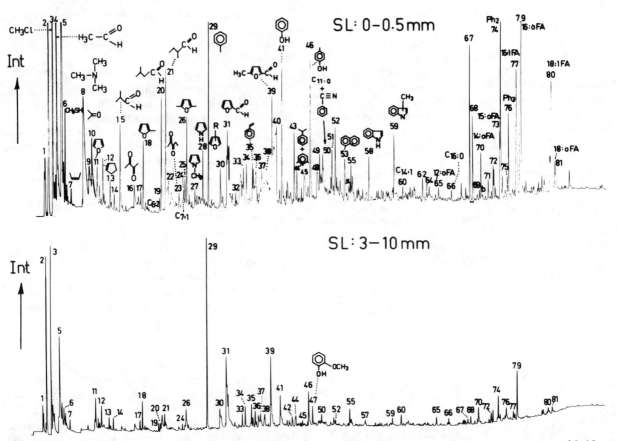

Fig. 4. Pyrolysis cryogenic capillary gas liquid chromatogram of Solar lake cyanobacterial top mat layers 0–0.5 mm and 3–10 mm. Numbers refer to identified peaks listed in Table 3.

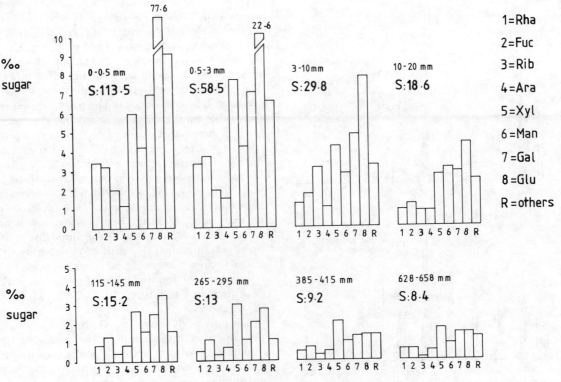

Fig. 5. Carbohydrate component distribution in selected Solar lake cyanobacterial mats. The S:value is the sum total of the neutral sugars in the hydrolysates of each layer.

Table 3

Pyrolysis products in pyrolysis gas liquid chromatograms of Solar lake sediments

1. methane, ethane, ethene	42. 1,2,4-trimethylbenzene
2. propane, propene	43. decane, unknown
3. chloromethane	44. 2-methylethylbenzene, trimethylbenzene
4. acetaldehyde	45. *o*-cresol, acetophenone
5. 1-butene, 2-methyl-1-propene	46. *p*-cresol
6. methanethiol	47. 2-methoxy-phenol
7. *cis*-2-butene	48. unknown in 0–3 mm
8. trimethylamine	49. undecene
9. 2-methylbutane	50. 2-phenyl-ethane
10. acetone	51. dimethylphenol
11. furan	52. unknown
12. cyclopenten	53. naphthalene
13. 2-methyl-2-butene	54. parahydroxy-styrene
14. cyclopentadiene	55. dodecene
15. 2-methylpropanal	56. unknown in 265–295 mm
16. 2,3-butandione	57. unknown in 265–295 mm
17. 1-hexene	58. indole
18. 2-methylfuran	59. methylindole
19. hexadiene, hexatriene	60. tetradecene
20. 3-methylbutanal, hexatriene	61. unknown in 265–295 mm
21. 2-methylbutanal, benzene	62. unknown in 0–3 mm
22. acetic acid, unknown	63. unknown in 265–295 mm
23. 2,3-pentadione	64. pentadecane
24. heptene	65. dodecanoic acid
25. unknown	66. hexadecane
26. 2,5 dimethylfuran	67. heptadecene
27. *N*-methylpyrrole	68. heptadecane
28. pyrrole	69. prist-1-ene
29. toluene	70. tetradecanoic acid. b. pris-2-ene
30. furan with unknown side chain ($M^+ = 96$)	71. unknown
31. 2-furfuraldehyde	72. octadecane
32. methylpyrrole	73. pentadecanoic acid
33. ethylbenzene	74. phytadiene
34. 1,4-dimethylbenzene, 1,3-dimethylbenzene	75. phytene
35. styrene	76. phytadiene
36. furan derivative ($M^+ = 110$)	77. hexadecenoic acid
37. nonane	78. unknown in 265–295 mm
38. unknown	79. hexadecanoic acid
39. methyl-furfuraldehyde	80. octadecenoic acid
40. benzaldehyde	81. octadecanoic acid
41. phenol	

hydrocarbon n-$C_{17:0}$ and $C_{17:1}$ which are presumably distilled off the pyrolysis sample wire during rapid temperature rise. Both hydrocarbons are prominent components in the hydrocarbon fraction in the 0–3 mm layer (see below). The phytadienes are known pyrolysis products of the phytol moiety of chlorophyll (Van der Meent *et al.*, 1980b).

It is clear from a comparison of the traces that all these pyrolysis products decrease in intensity relative to peaks 31 and 39, going from the top 0.5 mm to lower layers. This demonstrates a rapid decrease in lipid material and chlorophyll a, which is confirmed by the other measurements (Krumbein *et al.*, 1977).

The observed furan derivatives furan (11), methylfuran (18), dimethylfuran (26), furan with unknown side chain (30), furfuraldehyde (31) and methylfurfuraldehyde (39), together with the aldehydes (peaks 4, 15, 20 and 21) and diketones (nr. 16 and 23) are characteristic for pyrolysed carbohydrates (Shafizadeh and Lai, 1972; Martin *et al.*, 1979). The aldehydes and diketones disappear in layers below 3 mm depth, but the furans remain and are prominent features in the Py–GC

traces. These furan derivatives are also marked pyrolysis products of the oldest algal mat layer which almost entirely consists of sheath material from cyanobacteria.

The phenols (41, 46), toluene (29), pyrroles (27, 28, 32), methanethiol (6), several short chain olefins, benzene derivatives, nitriles, indole and methylindole are pyrolysis products of proteins (Medley *et al.*, 1975). Most of these peaks decrease in lower layers relative to peaks 31 and 39. These pyrolysis products in the older sediments are probably not generated from cytoplasmic protein or peptide fractions but rather from condensed humified cell remains which are sometimes seen with the light microscope.

The organic matter in top layers consists primarily of labile lipid, polysaccharide and protein. The deeper sediment layers are generally characterized by furan derivatives from cyanobacterial sheath, olefins, aromatic hydrocarbons and phenols from humified cells, a small amount of fatty acids present in Ca-salts (?) or bound to the humic fraction and phytadienes. The presence of phytadienes in even the deepest layers points to trapped chlorophylls or pheophytins, which may well explain the persistence of the green laminations all over the core.

MOLECULAR MARKERS IN BENTHIC CYANOBACTERIAL MATS

Carbohydrates

The neutral reducing sugar fraction of the sediments consists of eight major components and a number of minor components pooled under R (others). The major components identified are the deoxy-sugars (rhamnose and fucose), the pentoses (arabinose, ribose and xylose) and the hexoses (mannose, galactose and glucose). The minor components, posted in R, are methylated sugars which are still under investigation for complete structural elucidation. Figure 5 shows the concentration of the neutral sugars expressed in mg of sugar component per gram dry sediment. The sum total (S:) in each section demonstrates that a rapid quantitative change occurs in the top layers and a slower decrease below 2 cm depth. Comparison with the total carbohydrate values obtained spectrophotometrically (Table 2) shows that most of the carbohydrates in the upper centimetres of the core are present as neutral sugars, but in lower layers other sugar components must be present. The spectrophotometric measurement includes uronic acids.

The sugar composition changes drastically with depth. In the upper few millimetres, glucose is the predominant monomer, presumably as a homopolymer in the form of cyanophycean starch, a storage carbohydrate. Biodegradation of the glucose (polymer) takes place immediately below the 0.5 mm level and continues to the 10 mm level. Below this depth the glucose content remains almost constant with depth. Except for glucose, no major variations in sugar component concentration occur in the sediment layers. Ribose is relatively abundant in the 3–10 mm layer. This pentose is a component of many metabolically significant molecules such as RNA, ATP, $NADH_2$ and NADPH. We consider it to be a marker for the increased catabolic activity by the microbial community in the 3–10 mm layer. In the deepest layer only trace amounts of ribose are present.

Mannose, galactose, glucose, rhamnose, fucose and xylose have all been found as components in the outer cell wall of cyanobacteria (Drews, 1973). Xylose increases with depth relative to the other sugar components. The sugar spectrum of the 628–658 mm layer shown in Fig. 5 is probably a close approximation to the sugar composition of the sheath material because the microscopic observations show that this layer consists

almost entirely of empty sheaths. If xylose is present in the form of xylans of more than 3 units, the pyrolysis data can be understood better, because furan-derivatives are easily formed from such polymers (Ohnishi et al., 1977). The R-fraction in Fig. 5 accounts for 10% of all neutral sugars throughout the core. Even in the top mat, their concentration is considerable. The compounds represent methylated sugars presumably from lipopolysaccharides of cyanobacteria (Schmidt et al., 1980) or other microorganisms (Sutherland, 1977).

Lipid markers

Table 4 presents the weight of the extractable lipids and of each lipid class isolated from the extracts, expressed in μg/mg organic carbon. Hydrocarbon, ketone, fatty acid, alcohol and sterol fractions were obtained from all extracts, except for the one from 628–658 mm, in which no ketone fraction was detected.

The sum of the weight of the isolated lipid classes is given under header Σ. About 80% of the lipids of the 0–3 mm layer is present in the classes isolated. In lower layers this figure is about 50% showing that a larger amount of extractable lipid is more polar. This discrepancy will be the subject of further studies.

A relatively large amount of the lipid extract of the 0–3 mm layer consists of fatty acids, which decrease in concentration by a factor of 5 in lower layers. The rapid decrease in fatty acids was already obvious from the pyrolysis gas chromatography results.

Hydrocarbons from about 10% of the lipid extract in all layers. Only the weight of the sterol fraction rises with depth. As will be shown, the composition of the isolated lipid classes varies with depth. A comparison of fraction weights must take this into account.

The inventory of lipids is still in a survey stage. We will present here the results of the analysis of the 0–3 mm, 10–20 mm and 628–658 mm layers which represent: the living photosynthetic community, the microbial ecosystem after about 10 years of darkness and heterotrophic activity and the oldest laminated algal mat present in the core. More details about other layers to complete the profile will be published in the future. Identification of compounds is based on mass spectra and relative retention times. Several assigned peaks are tentative and await coinjection with standard compounds, which will have to be synthesized.

0–3 mm layer — the photosynthetic community

Gas–liquid chromatograms of hydrocarbons, fatty acids and sterol fractions isolated from this layer are shown in

Table 4

Weight of the extractable lipid fraction and isolated lipid classes from Solar lake sediments, expressed in μg/mg organic C

Depth (mm)	Extractable lipids	Hydrocarbons	Fatty acids	Ketones	Alcohols	Sterols	Σ
0–3	316	35	147	24	30	17	273
3–10	237	24	24	19	27	14	108
10–20	200	18	18	11	25	12	84
115–135	163	15	17	8	19	12	71
628–658	93	9	7	—	10	12	38

Figs 6(a), 7(a) and 8(a), respectively. Peak identifications based on mass spectral evidence, are given in Tables 5, 6 and 7.

Hydrocarbons. The hydrocarbon mixture consists of hydrocarbons ranging from nC_{15} to nC_{21} with $nC_{17:1}$ as the major peak to squalene. Several monounsaturated and diunsaturated compounds, phytene and 8-methylhexadecane were identified. The mass spectrum of the 8-methylhexadecane showed a parent peak at m/z 240 ($C_{17}H_{36}$) and fragment ions at m/z 126 (C_9H_{18}) and m/z 140 ($C_{10}H_{20}$, indicative of a 8-methyl group (Thomson *et al.*, 1981). Scanning over this peak did not reveal other positional isomers.

A number of mainly planktonic cyanobacteria have been analysed for hydrocarbons (Winters *et al.*, 1969;

Han *et al.*, 1968; Gelpi *et al.*, 1970; Paoletti *et al.*, 1976). A predominant C_{17} alkane and/or alkene is generally found. The hydrocarbon mixtures range from $C_{15}-C_{21}$ and in some species monomethyl alkanes are characteristic features. Han (1968) reported an equimolar mixture of 7-methyl and 8-methylheptadecane in *Nostoc*, which were also found in considerable quantity in *Lyngbya aestuarii* by Gelpi *et al.* (1970). We have no evidence for the presence of this compound in this layer nor for the triterpenehop-22 (29)ene. Squalene has been found in cyanobacteria (Gelpi *et al.*, 1970; Paoletti *et al.*, 1976) and is considered to be the precursor for steroids and triterpenoids in these organisms. No phytene has been reported in cyanobacteria.

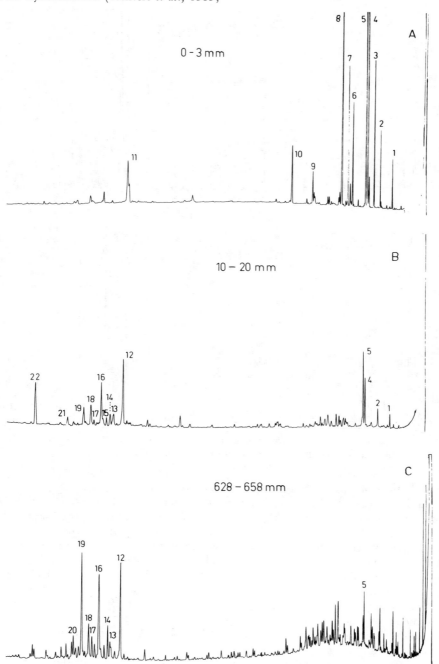

Fig. 6. Hydrocarbons in Solar lake cyanobacterial mats from 0–3 mm. (A) 10–20 mm; (B) and 628–658 mm (C). Numbers in the gas liquid chromatograms refer to identified compounds listed in Table 5.

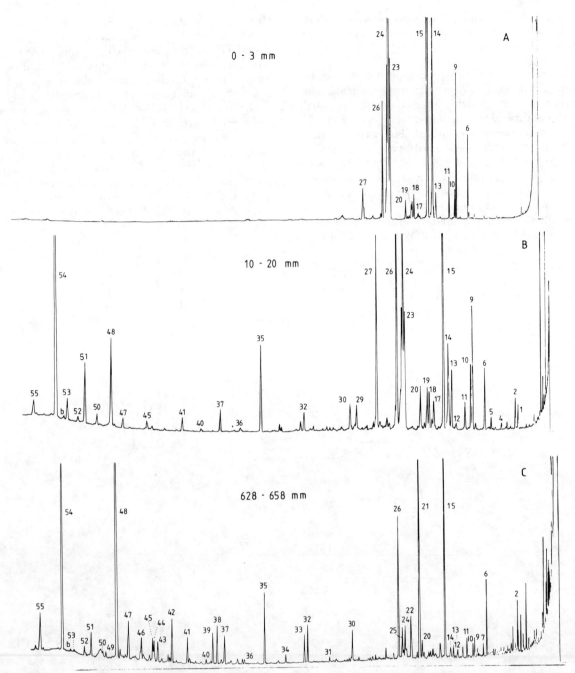

Fig. 7. Fatty acids in Solar lake cyanobacterial mats from 0–3 mm (A), 10–20 mm (B) and 628–658 mm (C). Numbers in the gas liquid chromatograms refer to identified compounds listed in Table 6.

Fatty acids. The fatty acid mixture present in section 0–3 mm consists of n-$C_{16:0}$ and n-$C_{18:1}$ as major components with minor amounts of n-$C_{14:0}$, iso-$C_{15:0}$, n-$C_{16:1}$ and n-$C_{18:0}$. No evidence was found for the presence of $n C_{18:3}$. Trace amounts were present of anteiso $C_{15:0}$, n-$C_{15:0}$, iso-$C_{16:0}$, 10-methyl-$C_{17:0}$, iso-$C_{17:0}$, anteiso-$C_{17:0}$, n-$C_{17:0}$ and Δ-$C_{19:0}$. Identification of these compounds by mass spectrometry and relative retention times presented no difficulties. The assignment of peak 27 as cyclopropane $C_{19:0}$ (lactobacillic acid) is still tentative although it coinjects with the standard compound.

Of all cyanobacteria studied for their fatty acids, only *Oscillatoria* and *Lyngbya* are ecologically and morphologically closest to the *Microcoleus* in Solar Lake mats. The fatty acids of these filamentous cyanobacteria (Kenyon *et al.*, 1972) are n-$C_{16:0}$, n-$C_{16:1}$, n-$C_{18:1}$, n-$C_{18:2}$ and sometimes n-$C_{18:3}(\alpha)$. The relative amounts of these compounds depends on the species studied and on environmental (culture) conditions. The major fatty acids of the 0–3 mm layer are typically cyanobacterial. The n-$C_{18:1}$ is the major acid in the top mat. The trace fatty acids show the bacterial characteristics of iso and anteiso branching, 10-methylation and cyclopropane group (Cranwell, 1973).

Sterols. All compounds in the sterol fraction, listed in Table 7, could be identified using reference mass spectra (Knights, 1967) or standard compounds. Only partial chromatograms are shown in Fig. 8. Several 24-desmethyl, 24-methyl and 24-ethyl sterols were

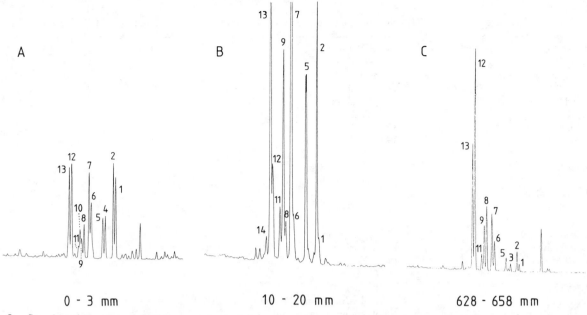

Fig. 8. Sterols and stanols in Solar lake cyanobacterial mats from 0–3 mm (A), 10–20 mm (B) and 628–658 mm (C). Numbers in the partial gas liquid chromatograms refer to identified compounds listed in Table 7.

identified with double bonds at Δ^5 or Δ^7 and/or in the side chain at Δ^{22}.

Corresponding $5\alpha(H)$ stanols and stenols were found for the sterols identified. The mass spectra of these compounds were compared with standards. Stanols and sterols are not unusual for cyanobacteria (Nes and McKean, 1977) although their occurrence is still disputed (Albrecht, personal communication). Diatoms, which occur in the mats mainly in spring and summer but which are rapidly decomposed upon burial, may contribute steroids as well. Diatoms isolated from the summer mats did not contain stanols however (Boon and Rijpstra, unpublished results). The proportion of steroids with a saturated nucleus is fairly high for a living microbial community. We point, however, to observations of Ballantine *et al.* (1979) who demonstrated light quality and age of several eucaryotic microorganisms (except diatoms) tends to increase the proportion of saturated steroids in their sterol composition. Similar processes may play a role in the

Table 5
Hydrocarbons identified in Solar lake sediment section 0–3 mm, 10–20 mm, 628–658 mm

1. pentadecane	13. 24-methyl-5α(H)-cholest-2,22-diene
2. hexadecane	
3. 8-methyl-hexadecane	14. 14-methyl-5α(H)-cholest-2-ene (tentative)
4. heptadecene	15. 17β(H)-trisnorhopane
5. heptadecane	16. 24-methyl-5α(H)-cholest-2-ene
6. octadecene	17. 24-ethyl-5α(H)-cholest-2,22-diene
7. octadecane	
8. phytene	18. 24-methylcholesta-3,5-diene
9. eicosene	19. 24-ethyl-5α(H)-cholest-2-ene
10. heneicosadiene	20. hop-17(21)-ene
11. squalene	21. unknown triterpene (m/z 177, 189, 191, 395, 410)
12. 5α(H)-cholest-2-	22. hop-22(29)-ene

cyanobacteria. Nishimura and Koyama have demonstrated the occurrence of $5\alpha(H)$ stanols in *Microcystis*, a planktonic cyanobacterium. Gaskell and Eglinton (1973) have shown that stanols can be formed from sterols extracellularly in lake sediment, presumably by bacterially mediated hydrogenation. This may play a role in this top layer as well.

10–20 mm layer — the heterotrophic zone

The gas liquid chromatograms of hydrocarbon, fatty acid and sterol fractions are shown in Figs 6(B), 7(B) and 8(B) respectively. Assigned peaks are numbered and listed in Tables 5, 6 and 7. Mass spectral evidence and relative retention time were used in the identifications.

Hydrocarbons. The hydrocarbon fraction in this layer consists of a number of straight short chain alkanes and alkenes, steroid and triterpenoid hydrocarbons. The heptadecane is the major alkane in this layer, and is of equal intensity to $5\alpha(H)$-cholest-2-ene (peak 12) which indicates a large difference with the hydrocarbons of the 0–3 mm layer. The sterenes and steradienes identified were compared with mass spectra of standards (Brassell, 1980). The $5\alpha(H)$-Δ^2, Δ^{22}-steradienes showed m/z 149, 215 (small), 255, 257, 269, 284, M^+–54 (small), M^+– 15 and M^+ (molecular ion). The 24-methyl-cholestra-3,5-diene showed the characteristic ions m/z 382 (M^+), 367 (M^+–15), 274, 261, 255, 213, 247, 145. Peak 14 was tentatively identified as 14-methyl-5α(H)-cholest-2-ene. Its mass spectrum is shown in Fig. 9. The molecular ion at m/z 384 points to a C_{28} sterene. The m/z 330 (loss of 54 amu) can be rationalized as a retro-Diels Alder of a Δ^2 double bond in the A-ring. The pattern of m/z 217, 229 and 244 is similar to the 203, 215, 230 pattern encountered in 5α(H)-cholest-2-ene but 14 amu higher, which points to an extra methyl group in the B, C, D ring system because the loss of 54 amu argues against a 4-

Table 6
Assigned fatty acids in GC traces of Solar lake sediment section 0–3 mm, 10–20 mm and 628–658 mm

1. *n*-12:1
2. *n*-12:0
3. *i*-13:0
4. *n*-13:0
5. *i*-14:0
6. *n*-14:0
7. unknown
8. ispr. 16:0
9. *i*-15:0
10. *ai*-15:0
11. *n*-15:0
12. isorp. 17:0
13. *i*-16:0
14. *n*-16:1
15. *n*-16:0
16. unknown
17. 10.Me–16:0
18. *i*-17:0
19. *ai*-17:0 + Δ-17:0 (?)
20. *n*-17:0
21. *unknown* (base peak 109)
22. unknown (base peak 109)
23. *n*-18:2
24. *n*-18:1 (two isomers) + isopr. 20:0
25. unknown (base peak 123)
26. *n*-18:0
27. Δ19:0
28. *n*-19:0

29. *n*-20:1
30. *n*-20:0
31. *n*-21:0
32. *n*-22:0
33. phthalate
34. *n*-23:0
35. *n*-24:0
36. *n*-25:0
37. *n*-26:0
38. unknown (m/z 177, 258)
39. unknown (m/z 135, 136, 137, 191, 195, 340, 402)
40. *n*-27:0
41. *n*-28:0
42. C_{28} stenol?
43. cycloartanol
44. unknown
45. *n*-30:0
46. C_{29} stenol?
47. hopanol
48. 22-hydroxy-homohopanol (m/z 191, 221, 409, 442)
49. unknown triterpenoid
50. bishomohopenoic acid (m/z 191, 206, 207, 208, 231, 261, 367, 467, 482)
51. 17α(H), 21β(H)-bishomohopanoic acid
52. 17β(H),21β(H)-homohopanoic acid
53. bishomohopenoic acid (m/z 119, 189, 263, 367, 482)
53.[b] 17α(H),21β(H)-3-methyl-bishomohopanoic acid (m/z 191, 205, 263, 498)
54. 17β(H),21β(H)-bishomohopanoic acid
55. 17β(H),21β(H)-3-methyl-bishomohopanoic acid (m/z 191, 205, 263, 383, 483, 498)

methyl group. We propose a 14-methyl group for biosynthetic reasons. Preparation of the standard and coinjection will prove the validity of this proposal. Several triterpenes and triterpadienes were observed but only a few could be compared with mass spectra of known compounds (Wardroper, 1979). All assigned triterpenes have hopanoid skeletons.

The organic matter in this layer has been subject to several years of heterotrophic activity by microorganisms under both aerobic (in the upper millimetre) and anaerobic (in deeper layers) conditions. The decrease in straight chain and branched alkanes is quite evident. This trend is even more striking in lower layers where a 'hump' develops in this region. The phenomenon of preferential decomposition of straight chain alkanes is known from oil decomposition (Connan *et al.*, 1980). Steroid and triterpenoid skeletons usually remain under such conditions.

The origin of the Δ²-sterenes and steradienes is most probably by dehydration of their corresponding stanols and stenols. The distribution of the sterols, stanols and the steroid hydrocarbons is such that some preference for transformation of the 24-desmethyl isomer is suggested. The hopenes are formed by bacterial degradation of the cell wall component bacteriohopanetetrol (Ourisson *et al.*, 1979). Although many hopanoic compounds have

Table 7
Identified sterols and stanols in Solar lake sediment sections 0–3 mm, 10–20 mm and 628–658 mm

Peak no.	Identity
1	cholesterol
	5α(H)-cholestanol
3	Δ5, 24(25)-cholestadienol
4	24-methyl-Δ5, 22-cholestadienol
5	24-methyl-Δ22-5α(H)-cholestenol
6	24-methyl-cholesterol
7	24-methyl-5α(H)-cholestanol
8	24-ethyl-Δ5, 22-cholestadienol
9	24-ethyl-Δ22-5α(H)-cholestenol
10	24-methyl-Δ7, 22-cholestadienol
11	24-methyl-Δ7-cholestenol
12	24-ethyl-cholesterol
13	24-ethyl-5α(H)-cholestanol
14	24-ethyl-Δ7-cholestenol

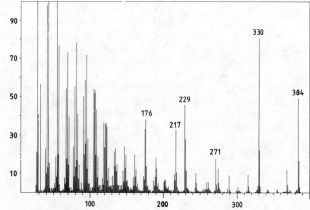

Fig. 9. Mass spectrum of a methyl sterene, which occurs in the hydrocarbon fractions of the 10–20 mm, and 628–658 mm layer (compound 14 in Fig. 6(B) and (C)). The tentative identification is a 14 methyl-5α(H)-cholest-2-ene.

been identified up till now (Wardroper, 1979; Rohmer *et al.*, 1980) no complete rationalization or decomposition scheme has been put forward for microbial transformation of the hopanetetrols. The hop-22(29)-ene has been found as a secondary metabolite in some cyanobacteria (Gelpi *et al.*, 1970).

Fatty acids. The fatty acid distribution of this layer (Fig. 7(B), Table 6) shows that major changes have occurred. The n-$C_{16:0}$ is now the dominant component, together with the $17\beta(H)$, $21\beta(H)$-homohopanoic acid (peak 54). The n-$C_{18:1}$ is less abundant compared to the trace of section 0–3 mm, but n-$C_{18:0}$ and the Δ-$C_{19:0}$ have increased in intensity. The number of minor and trace components have increased significantly. Iso and anteiso compounds, the 10-methyl hexadecanoic acid and the cyclopropane acids ($C_{19:0}$ and $C_{17:0}$?), all point to specific bacterial contributions.

Most of the normal C_{18} and C_{16} saturated and unsaturated fatty acids may be of bacterial origin as well, representing a completely new set of fatty acids compared to section 0–3 mm. Novel to this layer is the fatty acid series from C_{20} to C_{30} with C_{24} as major component, and a selection of hopane-type triterpenoid acids. The very long chain fatty acids have been encountered before in another algal sediment, i.e., a diatomaceous ooze from offshore Walvis Bay (Boon *et al.*, 1978) which is strongly influenced by microbial decomposition. Yeasts were proposed as possible source organisms. An *in situ* origin for these acids is also proposed for the Solar Lake sediments. The presence of β-hydroxy C_{24} fatty acid in the residues after extraction (see below) is an argument in favour of this view.

Quite a collection of triterpenoid acids has been found in this layer and lower layers of the Solar Lake core. The $17\beta(H)$, $21\beta(H)$-bishomohopanoic acid is the major triterpenoid acid. Its $17\alpha(H)$ isomer was detected in small amounts (peak 51).

Several homologous hopanoic acids ranging from C_{30} to C_{34} were identified from their mass spectra (Van Dorsselaer, 1974; Boon *et al.*, 1978). Two monounsaturated bishomohopanoic acids (peaks 50 and 53) were observed. The mass spectra of both compounds show m/z 367 which indicates one double bond in the pentacyclic structure. The m/z 119, 189 and 263 in the mass spectra of peak 53 points to an unsaturation in ring A or B. A compound with a similar spectrum has been described from Walvis Bay sediments (Boon *et al.*, 1978). The other compound shows a mass spectrum with m/z 191 and 261, pointing to a double bond in C or D ring. Two methyl-bishomohopanoic acids (peaks 53b and 55) were observed with mass spectra showing m/z 205, 263, 483 and 498.

Assuming an origin from 3-methylhopanetetrol (Rhomer and Ourisson, 1976), we have proposed a 3-methyl position for the extra methyl group on the pentacyclic system. The presence of a $17\beta(H)$ (major component) and a $17\alpha(H)$ (minor component) was found from relative retention time and the ratio of the m/z 205 to m/z 263 in the mass spectra, in accordance with the criteria used for the 3-desmethyl hopanoic acids. Quite a number of hopane type derivatives are now considered to be derived from bacteriohopanetetrol

by microbial transformation (Rohmer *et al.*, 1980). Comparison of the fatty acids of the 10–20 mm layer with those of the 0–3 mm layer demonstrates that triterpenoid fatty acids become major components of the fatty acid mixture over the short time period of about ten years.

Sterols. The same sterols and stanols were found in this layer as in the top mat 0–3 mm layer, but the $\Delta^5/5\alpha(H)$ ratio has changed from 1 to 0.1. The predominance of the stanols points to a relatively rapid conversion of Δ^5-sterols to $5\alpha(H)$ stanols by bacteria present in the decomposing mats. Such a transformation process has probably already occurred in the 0–3 mm layer, since a $\Delta^5/5\alpha(H)$ ratio of about 1 is very unusual for living organisms. No 5β-stanols were detected.

628–658 mm layer — the oldest cyanobacterial mats

The gas liquid chromatograms of hydrocarbon, fatty acid and sterol fractions are shown in Figs. 6(C), 7(C) and 8(C), respectively. Assigned peaks are listed in Tables 5, 6 and 7.

Hydrocarbons. The hydrocarbon fraction in this layer consists of a partially resolved mixture of short chain hydrocarbons, which shows a slight hump, and a mixture of steroid and triterpenoid hydrocarbons.

The number of unknown triterpenoid compounds increased with respect to the analytical results of the 10–20 mm layer. The $5\alpha(H)$-Δ^2-sterenes have increased in intensity, especially the 24-ethyl-cholest-2-ene. The hop-22(29)-ene decreased in intensity and a double peak shows up at its elution position. These compounds are not yet identified. Two thousand years of burial have not greatly influenced the steroid hydrocarbon composition of this layer, although the relative amounts of the major Δ^2-sterenes have changed, which seems to be connected with the stanol composition (see below).

Many more triterpenoid compounds were observed, but could not yet be identified. This indicates that triterpenoid diagenesis continues with time and leads to a more complex mixture than that present after only a few years of decomposition.

Fatty acids. The composition of the fatty acid mixture of this layer showed some important changes with respect to the 10–20 mm layer. First, as a consequence of TLC separation, we saw several cyclic alcohols (peaks 21, 22, 25), cycloartanol (peaks 43 and 66), some stenols (peaks 42 and 46) and some hopanols (peaks 47 and 48), which obviously have larger Rf values on TLC than the other alcohols. Peak 48 was present in all ester fractions analysed so far, usually a major peak. High resolution mass spectrometry revealed the elemental composition $C_{31}H_{54}O$ of the molecular ion at m/z 442. The fragmentation pattern and the strong loss of water (m/z 424), is indicative of a homohopanol. However, its mass spectrum differs from that of homohopan-31-ol (58); m/z 221 is much more abundant than m/z 203 (m/z 221–H_2O). This pentacyclic alcohol is tentatively assigned as homohopan-22-opl. The compound has been isolated for further structural analysis.

Major methyl esters were $nC_{14:0}$, $nC_{16:0}$, $nC_{18:0}$, $nC_{24:0}$ and $17\beta(H)21\beta(H)$-bishomohopanoic acid. The n-$C_{16:1}$ and n-$C_{18:1}$ as well as iso, anteiso and 10-methyl acids were detectable but only as small peaks. No indication was found for the presence of Δ-$C_{19:0}$. All the triterpenoid acids described for the 10–20 mm were also present in this layer.

The fatty acids smaller than C_{20} changed in their relative distribution with time. Unsaturated fatty acids are liable to decomposition and/or incorporation into the residual fraction by reactions with the double bond. This phenomenon has been observed in many recent sediments and was first described for the cyanobacterial mats of Baffin Bay (Texas) (Parker and Leo, 1965). The lower abundance of the specific bacterial marker fatty acids in this sediment layer may indicate that these acids are indicators of the actual living microbial population, which is much lower in this layer than in the 10–20 mm layer (Krumbein et al., 1977). These compounds apparently do not have a survival potential and are not to be expected in older cyanobacterial sediments.

The fatty acids longer than C_{20} and the triterpenoid acids do not seem to be affected by time-dependent processes. The triterpenoid acids and other compounds derived from bacteriohopane-tetrols are now generally accepted as markers for procaryotes (Rohmer et al., 1980). They are formed from the cyanobacterial organic matter by microbial transformation processes. Therefore, they are markers for the original presence of procaryotes in the sediment as well as markers for as yet unknown transformation processes carried out by sedimentary bacteria on triterpenoid tetrols.

Sterols. The qualitative composition of the sterol, stanol mixture (Fig. 8) has not changed much in comparison to the mixture in the 0–3 mm and 10–20 mm layers. Relative abundances of each component have changed markedly with time. The 24-ethylcholesterol has become the major component and is more abundant than its corresponding stanol. A relative increase of the C_{27} and C_{28} sterols is apparent from Fig. 8(C). The $\Delta^5/5\alpha(H)$ has significantly increased in this mat compared to the mats of the 10–20 mm layer.

No $5\beta(H)$ stanols were detected in this layer, although the transformation of Δ^5-sterols into $5\beta(H)$-stanols can be expected in the anaerobic parts of a sediment. It appears that $5\alpha(H)$-stanols are gradually removed as time goes by. Interestingly, while $5\alpha(H)$-stanols disappear in the sterol fraction, corresponding Δ^2-sterenes show up in the hydrocarbon fraction. We conclude that the reduction of Δ^5-sterols to $5\alpha(H)$-stanols only takes place in the upper centimetres of the core, while the transformation of $5\alpha(H)$-stanols to Δ^2-$5\alpha(H)$-sterenes occurs deeper in the sediments. Studies of other sediment layers are in progress to provide more detail for the steroid transformation pathways.

Alcohol and ketone fractions

No data are shown about the composition of the ketone and alcohol fraction. In all samples investigated, the ketone fraction consists of hexahydrofarnesylacetone (a

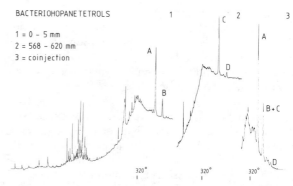

Fig. 10. Partial gas chromatograms of hopanetetrol fractions isolated from Solar lake cyanobacterial mats from 0–5 mm and from 568–620 mm depth. Partial gas chromatogram 3 is the result of the coinjected hopanetetrol fractions of both layers.

degradation product of phytol), cycloartanone and several structurally related compounds.

The alcohol fractions are rather complex. The major peak in all fractions examined so far is phytol, the side chain of chlorophyll and pheophytin. Most fractions showed straight chain saturated alcohols ranging from C_{14} to C_{26}. Diplopterol, cycloartanol and several cycloartanol structural isomers were found in all the layers examined. Further work is in progress.

Bacteriohopanetetrols

Bacteriohopanetetrols were observed during analysis of acetylated carotenoids by direct probe mass spectrometry. The direct probe spectrum of the bottom mat fraction showed mass peaks at 714, 712, 710, 493, 369 and 191, indicative of a bacteriohopanetetra-acetate and some unsaturated isomers (Förster et al., 1973).

Gas–liquid chromatographic analysis of the appropriate fractions from the top mat (0–5 mm) and the oldest algal mats revealed two components (Fig. 10). The minor component from the top mat coinjected with the major component of the bottom mat with a bacteriohopanetetrol recently isolated from surface sediments of Rostherne Mere (unpublished results). Final identification awaits GCMS analysis and coinjection with standards. The finding of more than one tetrol in the sediments is not unusual since Föster and co-workers (1973) found four tetrols in *Acetobacter xylinum*: two monounsaturated ones (C_{35} and C_{36}) and two saturated ones (C_{35} and C_{36}). The presence of hopanetetrols in the top mat of Solar lake sediment is to be expected considering their occurrence in several cyanobacteria (Ourisson et al., 1971). Their presence in the bottom mat after 2400 years of exposure to diagenesis processes is remarkable in view of the wealth of decomposition products derived from these compounds. It raises the question of how these tetrols are protected from degradation.

Carotenoids

Table 8 summarizes the identified carotenoids isolated from the top mat 0–3 mm layer, their concentrations and their inferred origin. The major carotenoids in the top

Table 8

Carotenoids identified by UV/VIS spectrophotometry and direct probe (EI) mass spectrometry in Solar lake top mat 0–3 mm layer

Carotenoid	Concentration (ppm)[a]	Inferred origin
β-Carotene	31	
Echinone	26.5	cyanobacteria
Rhodopin	} 3	purple photosynthetic bacteria
Dehydrorhodpin		
Canthaxantin	1.5	cyanobacteria
Hydroxyechinone	2.5	cyanobacteria
Zeaxanthin	24	cyanobacteria
Myxoxanthophyll	6.5	cyanobacteria
2 polar carotenoids	23	

[a] μg of carotenoid/gram dry extracted weight of sediment.

mat are β-carotene, echinone and zeaxanthin. All these compounds have been shown to occur in cyanobacteria (Hertzberg et al., 1971). The carotenoids β-carotene, echinone, zeaxanthin, isozeaxanthin and myxoxanthophyll were identified by MS and UV/VIS in the saponified top mat extract. This carotenoid is unique for cyanobacteria. Two, as yet unidentified, carotenoids slower on TLC than myxoxanthophyll, had a concentration of 23 ppm. Both compounds did not survive direct probe MS analysis. They will be analysed further after derivation. No diatom nor dinoflagellate carotenoids were detected. The only carotenoids indicative for purple photosynthetic bacteria were rhodopin and dehydrorhodopin. Several carotenoids found to be present in other microbial mats (Tibbetts et al., 1978; Watts et al., 1977) (i.e. tetrahydro-spirilloxanthin (from photosynthetic sulphur bacteria), spheroidenone (non-S-photosynthesizers), spirilloxanthin (purple photosynthetic bacteria) and okenone (purple photosynthetic sulphur bacteria)) could not be detected. The Baja California mats are much richer in red photosynthetic bacteria (Margulis and Stolz, personal communication) than the predominantly green Solar lake mat which consists almost exclusively of cyanobacteria.

The absolute amount of extractable carotenoids shows a rapid decrease with depth (see Table 2), but the distribution of the carotenoids judged from comparison of HPLC traces does not change much with depth (Fig. 11(A) and 11(B)).

The presence of β-carotene (15 ppm), echinone (3 ppm) and zeaxanthin (5 ppm) in the 628–658 mm layer was confirmed by mass spectrometry and UV/VIS spectrophotometry. However, the mass spectrum of the 'β-carotene' TLC band was unusual, containing m/z 536, 538 and 548 which suggests that apart from β-carotene (parent peak m/z 536), a dihydrocarotene (m/z 538) and a dodecahydro (6 double bonds reduced) carotene (m/z 548) are also present. The ion at m/z 538 may be the parent peak of some other carotenoid, e.g., β-zeacarotene, α-zeacarotene, 1,2-dihydrolycopene or neurosporene, which are biosynthetic precursors of α- and β-carotenes (Goodwin, 1971). They normally do not accumulate in organisms except when the dehydrogenation sequence is blocked (Weedon, 1971). The α- and β-carotenes and the above mentioned precursors are known to coelute on silicagel TLC and silica HPLC (Davies, 1976). No m/z 538 nor 548 was observed in mass spectrum of the β-carotene isolated from the top mat sample, which suggests that partial hydrogenation in fact occurred after burial during the biogeochemical diagenesis period.

Several pigments isolated by TLC remained unidentified although reasonably good mass spectra were obtained. One fraction with a characteristic m/z 576 (M..?) in its mass spectrum coincided with canthaxanthin (M.. at 564) on HPLC and showed a UV/VIS spectrum with a λ_{max} at 420 mm. Another fraction with mass peaks at m/z 568, 570 and 572 and a λ_{max} at 420 mm, could consist of hydrogenated zeaxanthins (M.. at 568). During this analysis the earlier mentioned bacteriohopane tetrol-tetracetate was detected in one of the most polar TLC fractions.

Diagenetic transformation products of carotenoids are not easy to identify. Small amounts of partially hydrogenated carotenoids may escape attention because they lose their spectrophotometric properties. Despite these problems, evidence for partial hydrogenated carotenoids was obtained from the extract of the bottom mat of the Solar Lake core. Preservation of carotenoids is not uncommon. Carotenoids have been found in sediments of more than 10⁶ years old (Tibbetts, 1980). We are not aware of reports about partially hydrogenated carotenoids, but some compounds with a fully hydrogenated alicyclic chain have been reported (Murphy et al., 1969; Schaefle et al., 1977).

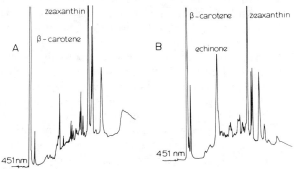

Fig. 11. HPLC traces of carotenoids isolated from Solar lake cyanobacterial mats from a depth of 0–2 mm (A) and 628–658 mm (B).

Residue analysis

Larger sediment sections were used for analysis of the residue after extraction with solvents. Saponification was used to liberate biomolecules from the 'protokerogen' matrix through ester cleavage. Table 9 summarizes yields of extractable material after saponification and yields of chloroform extracts after SMEAH (sodium bis-2-methoxy-ethoxy aluminium hydride). The SMEAH treatment is capable of attacking ether, amide and ester linkages (Brown *et al.*, 1980). The initial saponification reduces the ester linkages which permits SMEAH to attack the non-ester reducible bonds. The compounds detected in the extracts after saponification are listed in Table 10.

The extracts were directly analysed after derivatization by GCMS. Phytol is the dominant component in all the gas liquid chromatograms. It is liberated from chlorophyll or pheophytin, which was found to persist up to the deepest layer (Krumbein *et al.*, 1977). Phytol is a major compound in the alcohol fraction, as mentioned previously. The presence of phytol in the residues may indicate an incomplete liberation of solvent extractables and/or a trapping of chlorophyll or pheophytins in organic complexes by

Table 9

Product yields from saponification and SMEAH treatments of Solar lake protokerogen

Core section	Treatment	Yield
SLA 5–85 mm	Saponification	591.1 mg (2.1%)
	SMEAH[a]	17.7 mg (0.4%)
SLC 185–258 mm	Saponification	109.8 mg (0.4%)
	SMEAH[a]	13.3 mg (0.3%)
SLD 258–388 mm	Saponification	528.0 mg (1.8%)
	SMEAH[a]	1.5 mg (0.04%)
SLF 528–648 mm	Saponification	137.0 mg (0.5%)
	SMEAH[a]	4.0 mg (0.1%)

[a] Yields for $CHCl_3$ extract only.

Table 10

Identified compounds (HRGC/LRMS) in extractable lipids after saponification of pre-extracted Solar lake sediments

Fatty acids
$nC_{12:0}$, $nC_{14:0}$, $nC_{15:0}$, $nC16:0$, $nC_{17:0}$, $nC_{18:0}$, $nC_{18:1}$, $nC_{20:0}$, $nC_{22:0}$, $nC_{24:0}$, $nC_{26:0}$
iso $C_{15:0}$, iso $C_{16:0}$, iso $C_{17:0}$, iso $C_{18:0}$
anteisco $C_{15:0}$, anteiso $C_{17:0}$
phytanic acid; Δ-$C_{19:0}$ (lactobacillic acid)

β-hydroxy fatty acids
$nC_{10:0}$, $nC_{12:0}$, $nC_{14:0}$, $nC_{16:1}$, $nC_{16:0}$, $nC_{18:0}$, $nC_{20:0}$, $nC_{24:0}$

Alcohols
phytol
$nC_{14:0}$, $nC_{16:0}$, $nC_{18:0}$

Ketones
hexahydrofarnesylaceton

covalent bonds, leaving the phytol side chain unharmed.

Major fatty acids are n-$C_{16:0}$ and n-$C_{18:0}$. The n-$C_{18:1}$ is a major peak in SL-A (5–85 mm), which is in accordance with the findings in the extractable fatty acids. The β-hydroxy fatty acids are medium intensity peaks in all the sections analysed with chain lengths of 14, 16 and 18 carbon atoms. A β-hydroxy $C_{24:0}$ fatty acid was detected in SL-D (258–388 mm). The β-hydroxy fatty acid composition of lipopolysaccharide from unicellular cyanobacteria (Schmidt *et al.*, 1980) consists of C_{14} and C_{16} compounds with small amounts of iso and anteiso β-hydroxy C_{15} fatty acids. The sedimentary β-hydroxy fatty acids may have the same origin. Saponification must have released these compounds from the insoluble bacterial and cyanobacterial residues.

Other minor compounds observed were a $nC_{16:0}$ alcohol in SF-L and hexahydrofarnesylacetone, which may well be a degradation product of phytol produced during the saponification procedure (de Leeuw *et al.*, 1974). The principal products of SMEAH reduction which have been identified are lactic acid, phenol, cresol, xylenol and cyclohexenol. The lactic acid may have been released from muramic acid in peptidoglycan, a cell wall polymer of cyanobacteria (Drews, 1973). The origin of phenol, cresol and xylenol is unknown. The same compounds are released by pyrolysis, and were thought to be generated from aromatic amino acids (see above). The SMEAH results suggest that they may be present as such in combination with insoluble residues (perhaps the sheaths).

IMPACT OF BIOGEOCHEMICAL TRANSFORMATION ON A CYANOBACTERIAL ECOSYSTEM: SUMMARY

In summary, a cross-section through the results of these initial investigations of the Solar lake sediment should concentrate on the central theme: What molecular markers are left over after a period of 2400 years of decomposition of cyanobacterial organic matter?

The microscopy, organic carbon content, the carbonate content, the pyrolysis results, the carbohydrate and lipid markers point to rapid changes in the 0–20 mm section. The environmental conditions at the cyanobacterial mat–water interface continuously lead to new development of cyanobacterial matter which overgrows the previous flora. Once in the dark, autolysis, starvation and subsequently cell lysis of the photosynthetic community sets in. The morphological characteristics present in the living communities of the top millimetres of the sediment are attacked and degraded. Cell content dissolves and apparently resistant structures from outside the cell walls of the cyanobacteria remain behind as a bulk materials. These sheaths are likely traps for lysed cyanobacteria, bacterial remains and inorganic particles. They may act as an absorbant. Carbonate formation becomes substantial in the 10–20 mm layer of the top mat. This lithification process leads to inclusion of organic matter and hence the preservation of molecular fossils. Sheaths have been shown to play a role in the carbonate crystallization process (Gebelein and Hoffman, 1973).

The rapid changes in the top mat layers were monitored on the polymer level by pyrolysis mass spectrometry and pyrolysis gas chromatography. Carbohydrate polymers decrease in abundance in the top 10 mm, which is corroborated by a rapid decrease in glucose content. This carbohydrate monomer is presumably present as cyanophycean starch, a storage polysaccharide of cyanobacteria. Another feature is a rapid decrease in complex lipid material which is confirmed by a decrease in fatty acid content of the top mat layers. Also organic carbon content decreases rapidly from 10% to about 3% in deeper layers. In the 3–10 mm layer of the top mat and also in lower layers, a fraction of structural carbohydrates survives the heterotrophic processes. The characteristic pyrolysis products of this organic matter are furans, phenols and toluene. Ether cleavage by SMEAH indicates that the phenols are present, as such, covalently bound as ethers.

Morphologically this organic matter is mainly empty sheath tubes. Neutral sugars of these fractions consist of deoxysugars, pentoses and hexoses. Xylose, especially in the lower layers, is the most important monomer. Presence of uronic acids cannot be excluded because a significant carbohydrate fraction, as determined by spectrophotometry, is absent from our analyses. Moreover, an acidic polysaccharide, thought to be a polyuronide, was isolated recently from a cyanobacterial mat from Mururoa (Disnar and Trichet, 1981). Many photosynthetic community marker molecules do not survive the heterotrophic decomposition stage. Most hydrocarbons and fatty acids of the 0–3 mm layer are mineralized.

The 10–20 mm layer is characterized by the appearance of steroid and triterpenoid hydrocarbons and fatty acids. The $\Delta^5/5\alpha(H)$ ratio in the sterol fraction becomes very small, which indicates a rapid generation of $5\alpha(H)$ stanols by reduction of sterols. This process has been observed in several other cyanobacterial ecosystems as well by Cardoso *et al.* (1976), but has not yet been proved by radiolabelling experiments (Edmunds *et al.*, 1980).

The composition of the 10–20 mm layer serves as a starting point for comparison of the top mat with the bottom mats. Bacteriohopanetetrols were found to be present in the bottom mat, despite the extensive series of presumed decomposition products of this cyanobacterial cell wall marker in the hydrocarbon, fatty acid and alcohol fraction. Carotenoids also survive, although the absolute amount decreases strongly. The β-carotene, echinone and zeaxanthine carotenoids were identified. Some evidence for possible reduction of double bonds was found. Sterols, when compared to stanols, increased in abundance by the transformation of $5\alpha(H)$ stanols into Δ^2-sterenes which are present in the hydrocarbon fraction as major components. The C_{2g} sterol becomes a major sterol component for unknown reasons. The original hydrocarbon composition, as seen in the top mats, is completely lost. The same is observed for fatty acids. The n-$C_{18:1}$ fatty acid, the major compound in the top mat (0–3 mm), a minor component in the bottom mat fatty acid mixture. The $17\beta(H)$, $21\beta(H)$-bishomohopanoic acid has become the major compound.

The composition of the bulk of the bottom mat is similar to the composition of the 10–20 mm layer. Sheath material is morphologically the dominant organic material. Pyrolysis–mass spectrometry and pyrolysis–gas liquid chromatography of this material indicates that furans, phenols and toluene are the dominant compounds. Neutral sugars are basically the same as in the 10–20 mm layer. Phytadienes in the Py-Gc trace point to the survival of chlorophyll or pheophytins. The lipid fraction of the bottom mat contains many transformation markers. The Solar lake sediment profile appears to be a good natural model system for study of the transformation of sterols and hopanetetrols. So far no evidence exists which points towards other sources of organic matter, but the direct conversion of solar energy by photosynthesis at the benthic interface. Transformation of sterols and hopane tetrols is thought to be caused by microbial and perhaps also abiological diagenetic processes in the sediments. Understanding the significance of the various degradation products of these precursors in terms of pathways and transformation mechanisms will provide new diagenetic markers.

Quite a number of new compounds especially in the sterol, and alcohol and the ketone fractions have been observed. Some tentatively identified compounds have been mentioned. Since a number of these new compounds are thought to be very specific marker molecules, further work is in progress to establish their structures. Elucidation of the structure of the bulk material i.e. sheath, will help understand why this organic matter is so resistant. It has considerable potential as a chemical fossil, because even in the oldest stromatolite (the Bulawayan stromatolite of 2.8×10^9 years b.p.) indications for its presence are found in the furans produced upon pyrolysis (Nagy *et al.*, 1977).

Acknowledgements

The authors gratefully acknowledge the advice given by Drs W. E. Krumbein (University of Oldenburg, SFR) and Y. Cohen (Marine Biological Laboratory, Eilat) during preparation of the field work and sampling. Dr Y. Cohen actively assisted in the selection of sample sites and was out host in the Marine Biological Laboratory. We thank Dr J. Haverkamp for the use of the pyrolysis mass spectrometry facility in the FOM Institute for Atomic and Molecular Physics in Amsterdam; the skillful technical assistance of Mrs B. Brand, A. Tom, S. Lewis, E. Nieberg-van-Velsen, A. Gowar. Mr A. Kok, J. Heteman, T. Viets are gratefully mentioned. Drs P. Marriott, K. McNeil and P. Gashini (University of Bristol) assisted in direct probe mass spectrometry. J.J.B. acknowledges the Netherlands Institute for Sea Research (N10Z, Texel) for their hospitality and for the use of the facilities. K.E. was supported by a SERC studentship. The project is supported by NASA Grant NGL–05–003–003.

REFERENCES

Awramik, S. M., Gebelein, C. D. and Cloud, P. (1978) Biogeologic relationships of ancient stromatolites and modern analogs. In *Environmental Biogeochemistry and Geomicrobiology*, ed. by. Krumbein W. E. Ann Arbor Science Publishers, Ann Arbor, Michigan, pp. 165–179.

Ballantine, J. A., Lavis, A. and Morris, R. J. (1979) Sterols of phytoplankton — effects of illuminations and growth stage. *Phytochemistry* **18**, 1459–1466.

Boon, J. J. and Haverkamp, J. (1979) Pyrolysis mass spectrometry of a benthic marine ecosystem — the influence of *Arenicola marina* on the organic matter cycle. *Neth. J. Sea Res.* **13**, 457–478.

Boon, J. J., de Boer, W. R., Kruyssen, F. J. and Wouters, J. T. M. (1981) Pyrolysis mass spectrometry of whole cells, cell walls and isolated cell wall polymers of *Bacillus subtilis* var. *niger* WM. *J. Gen. Microbiol.* **122**, 119–127.

Brassell, S. C. (1980) The lipids of deep sea sediments: their origin and fate in the Japan Trench. Ph.D. Thesis, University of Britsol.

Brown, S., Baillie, T. A. and Burlingame, A. L. (1980) Analytical approaches to the investigation of kerogen structure by mass spectrometric techniques. In *Advances in Organic Geochemistry 1979*, ed. by Douglas, A. G. and Maxwell, J. R. Pergamon Press, Oxford, pp. 475–484.

Cardoso, J. N., Watts, C. D., Maxwell, J. R., Goodfellow, R., Eglinton, G. and Golubic, S. (1973) A biogeochemical study of the Abu Dhabi algal mats: A simplified ecosystem. *Chem. Geol.* **23**, 273–291.

Cardoso, J. N., Brooks, P. W., Eglinton, G., Goodfellow, R., Maxwell, J. R. and Philp, R. P. (1978) Lipids of recently deposited algal mats at Laguna Mormona, Baja California. In *Environmental Biogeochemistry I*, ed. by Nriagu, J. O. Ann Arbor Science Publishers, Ann Arbor, Michigan, pp. 149–174.

Cohen, Y., Krumbein, W. E., Goldberg, M. and Shilo, M. (1977) Solar Lake (Sinai). I. Physical and chemical limnology. *Limnol. Oceanogr.* **22**, 597–609.

Connan, J., Restle, A. and Albrecht, P. (1980) Biodegradation of crude oil in the Aquitaine basin. In *Advances in Organic Geochemistry, 1979*, ed. by Douglas, A. G. and Maxwell, J. R. Pergamon Press, Oxford, pp. 1–19.

Cranwell, P. A. (1973) Branched-chain and cyclopropanoid acids in a recent sediment. *Chem. Geol.* **11**, 307–313.

Davies, B. H. (1976) Carotenoids. In *Chemistry and Biochemistry of Plant Pigments*, ed. by Goodwin, T. W. Academic Press, New York, pp. 38–165.

Disnar, J.-R. and Trichet, J. (1981) Etude expérimentale de la fixation de métaux par un matériau sédimentaire actuel d'origine algaire — I. Isolement, purification et caractérisation de la matière organique. *Geochim. Cosmochim. Acta* **45**, 353–363.

van Dorsselaer, A. (1974) Triterpènes de sediments. Thèse à l'Université Louis Pasteur, Strasbourg, France.

Drews, G. (1973) Fine structure and chemical composition of the cell envelopes. In *The Biology of Blue–Green Algae*, ed. by Carr, N. G. and Whitton, B. A. Botanical monographs 9, Blackwell Scientific Publishing, Oxford, pp. 99–117.

Edmunds, K. L. H., Brassell, S. C. and Eglinton, G. (1980) The short term diagenetic fate of 5α(H)-cholestan-3β-ol: *in situ* radiolabelled incubations in algal mats. In *Advances in Organic Geochemistry 1979*, ed. by Douglas A. G. and Maxwell, J. R. Pergamon Press, Oxford, pp. 427–434.

Eglinton, G. (1973) Chemical fossils: a combined organic geochemical and environmental approach. *Pure Appl. Chem.* **34**, 611–632.

Enzell, C. R., Francis, G. W. and Liaaen-Jensen, S. (1969) Mass spectrometric studies of carotenoids-2. A survey of fragmentation reactions. *Acta Chem. Scand.* **23**, 727–750.

Farrington, J. W. and Quinn, J. G. (1971) Comparison of sampling and extraction techniques for fatty acids in recent sediments. *Geochim. Cosmochim. Acta* **35**, 735–742.

Föster, H. J., Biemann, K., Haigh, W. G., Tattrie, N. H. and Colvin, J. R. (1973) The structure of novel C_{35} pentacyclic terpenes from *Acetobacter xylinum*. *Biochem. J.* **135**, 133–143.

Friedman, G. M., Amiel, A. J., Braun, M. and Miller, D. S. (1973) Generation of carbonate particles and laminites in algal mats — example from sea — marginal hypersaline pool, gulf of Aqaba, Red Sea. *AAPG Bull.* **57**, 541–557.

Gaskell, S. J. and Eglinton, G. (1973) Rapid hydrogenation of sterols in a contemporary lacustrine sediment. *Nature (London)* **254**, 209–211.

Gebelein, C. D. and Hoffman, P. (1973) Algal origin of dolomite laminations in stromatolite limestone. *J. Sediment. Petrol.* **43**, 603–613.

Gelpi, E., Schneider, H., Mann, J. and Oro, J. (1970) Hydrocarbons of geochemical significance in microscopic algae. *Phytochemistry* **9**, 603–612.

Goodwin, T. W. (1971) Biosynthesis. In *Carotenoids*, ed. by Isler, O. Birkhauser Verlag, Basel, pp. 577–636.

Han, J., McCarthy, E. D., Calvin, M. and Benn, M. H. (1968) Hydrocarbon constituents of the blue–green algae. *Nostoc muscorum, Anacystic nidulans, Phormidium luridum* and *Chlorogloea fritschii*. *J. Chem. Soc. C* 2785–2791.

Haverkamp, J., Meuzelaar, H. L. C., Beuvery, E. C., Boonekamp, P. and Tiesjema, R. H. (1980) Characterization of *Neisseria meningitidis* capsular polysaccharides containing sialic acids by pyrolysis mass spectrometry. *Anal. Biochem.* **104**, 407–418.

Hertzberg, S., Liaaen-Jensen, S., Siegelman, H. W. (1971) The carotenoids of blue–green algae. *Phytochemistry* **10**, 3121–3127.

Hoffman, P. (1975) Recent and ancient algal stromatolites: seventy years of pedagogic cross-pollination. In *Evolving Concepts in Sedimentology*, ed. by Ginsburg, R. N. University Press, Baltimore, pp. 178–191.

Huang, W. Y. and Meinschein, W. G. (1978) Sterols in sediments from Baffin Bay, Texas. *Geochim. Cosmochim. Acta* **42**, 1391–1397.

Jörgensen, B. B. and Cohen, Y. (1977) Solar Lake (Sinai) 5: The sulphur cycle of the benthic cyanobacterial mats. *Limnol. Oceanogr.* **22**, 657–666.

Jörgensen, B. B., Revsbech, N. P., Blackburn, T. H. and Cohen, Y. (1979) Diurnal cycle of oxygen and sulphide microgradients and microbial photosynthesis in a cyanobacterial mat sediment. *Appl. Environ, Microbiol.* **38**, 46–58.

Kenyon, C. N., Rippka, R. and Stanier, R. Y. (1972) Fatty acid composition and physiological properties of some filamentous blue–green algae. *Arch. Mikrobiol.* **83**, 216–236.

Klok, J., Nieberg-van Velzen, E. H., de Leeuw, J. W. and Schenck, P. A. (1981) Capillary gas chromatographic separation of monosaccharides as their alditol acetates. *J. Chromatogr.* **207**, 273–275.

Knights, B. A. (1967) The identification of plant sterols using combined GLC/mass spectrometry. *J. Gas Chromatogr.* **5**, 273–282.

Krumbein, W. E. and Cohen, Y. (1974) Biogene, klastische und evaporitische Sedimentation in einem mesothermen monomiktischen ufernahen See (Golf von Aqaba). *Geol. Rundsch.* **63**, 1035–1065.

Krumbein, W. E. and Cohen, Y. (1977) Primary production, mat formation and lithification: contribution of oxygenic and facultative anoxygenic cyanobacteria. In *Fossil Algae*, ed. by Flügel, E. Springer-Verlag, New York, pp. 37–56.

Krumbein, W. E., Cohen, Y. and Shilo, M. (1977) Solar Lake (Sinai) 4: Stromatolitic cyanobacterial mats. *Limnol. Oceanogr.* **22**, 635–657.

Krumbein, W. E. (1978) Algal mats and their lithification. In *Environmental Biogeochemistry and Geomicrobiology*, ed. by Krumbein, W. E. Ann Arbor Science Publishers, Ann

Arbor, Michigan, pp. 209–225.

Leeuw, J. W. de, Correia, V. A. and Schenck, P. A. (1974) On the decomposition of phytol under simulated geological conditions and in the top layer of natural sediments. In *Advances in Organic Geochemistry, 1973* ed. by Tissot, B. and Bienner, F. Editions Technip., Paris, pp. 993–1005.

Martin, F., Saiz-Jimenez, C. and Cert, A. (1979) Pyrolysis–gas chromatography–mass spectrometry of soil humic fractions I: the low boiling point compounds. *Soil Sci. Soc. Am.* **41**, 1114–1118.

Medley, E. E., Simmonds, P. G. and Manatt, S. L. (1975) A pyrolysis gas chromatography–mass spectrometry study of the Actinomycete *Streptomyces Longisporoflavus. Biomed. Mass Spectrom.* **2**, 261–265.

Menzel, D. W. and Vaccaro, R. F. (1964) The measurement of dissolved and particulate carbon in seawater. *Limnol. Oceanogr.* **9**, 138–142.

Meuzelaar, H. L. C., Kristemaker, P. G., Eshuis, W. and Boerboom, H. A. J. (1977) Automated pyrolysis mass spectrometry: application to the differentiation of microorganisms. In *Advances in Mass Spectrometry* Vol. 7B, ed. by Daly, N. R. Heyden, London, pp. 1452–1456.

Meuzelaar, H. L. C., Haverkamp, J. and Hileman, F. D. (1982) *Curiepoint pyrolysis mass spectrometry of recent and fossil biomaterials*, Compendium and atlas. Elsevier, Amsterdam (In press).

Mopper, K. (1977) Sugars and uronic acids in sediment and water from the Black Sea and North Sea with emphasis on analytical techniques. *Marine Chemistry* **5**, 585–603.

Murphy, Sr. M., McCormick, A. and Eglinton, G. (1969) Perhydro-β-carotene in the Green River shale. *Science* **157**, 1040.

Nagy, B., Nagy, L. A., Zumberge, J. E., Sklarew, D. S. and Anderson, P. (1977). Indications of a biological and biochemical evolutionary trend during the Archean and early Proterozoic. *Precambrian Research* **5**, 109–120.

Nes, W. R. and McKean, M. L. (1977) *Biochemistry of Steroids and other Isopentenoids.* University Park Press, Baltimore.

Nishimura, M. and Koyama, T. (1977) The occurrence of stanols in various living organisms and the behavior of sterols in contemporary sediments. *Geochim. Cosmochim. Acta* **41**, 379–387.

Ohnishi, A., Kato, K. and Takagi, E. (1977) Pyrolytic formation of 3-hydroxy-2-penteno-1,5-lactone from xylan, xylan-oligosaccharides and methylxylopyranosides. *Carbohydrate Res.* **58**, 387–395.

Ourisson, G., Albrecht, P. and Rohmer, M. (1979) The hopanoids. Paleochemistry and biochemistry of a group of natural products. *Pure Appl. Chem.* **51**, 709–729.

Paoletti, C., Pushparaj, B., Florenzano, G., Capella, P. and Lercker, G. (1976) Unsaponifiable matter of green and blue–green algal lipids as a factor of biochemical differentiation of their biomass: I. Total unsaponifiable and hydrocarbon fraction. *Lipids* **11**, 258–265.

Parker, P. and Leo, R. F. (1965) Fatty acids in blue–green algal mat communities. *Science* **184**, 372–379.

Philp, R. P., Brown, S., Calvin, M., Brassel, S. and Eglinton, G. (1978) Hydrocarbon and fatty acid distributions in recently deposited algal mats at Laguna Guerrero, Baja California. In *Environmental Biogeochemistry and Geomicrobiology*, ed. by Krumbein, W. E. Ann Arbor Science Publishers, Michigan, pp. 255–270.

Philp, R. P., Calvin, M., Brown, S. and Yang, E. (1978b) Organic geochemical studies of kerogen precursors in recently deposited algal mats and oozes. *Chem. Geol.* **22**, 207–231.

Philp, R. P. (1981) Comparative organic geochemical studies of recent algal mats and sediments of algal origin. In *Biogeochemistry of Ancient and Modern Environments* ed. by Trudinger, P. A. and Walter, M. R. Springer-Verlag, New York, pp. 173–185.

Pieters, (1948) Notes on analytical procedures. I. Determination of carbon dioxide. *Anal. Chim. Acta* **2**, 263–269.

Rohmer, M. and Ourisson, G. (1976) Méthyl-hopanes d'*Acetobacter xylinum* et d'*Acetobacter rancens*: une nouvelle famille de composés triterpéniques. *Tetrahedron Lett.* **40**, 3641–3644.

Rohmer, M., Dastillung, M. and Ourisson, G. (1980) Hopanoids from C_{30}–C_{35} in recent muds. *Naturwissenschaften* **67**, 456–458.

Schaefle, J., Ludwig, G., Albrecht, P. and Ourisson, G. (1977) Hydrocarbures aromatiques d'origine geologique II. Nouveaux carotenoides aromatiques fossiles. *Tetrahedron Lett.* **41**, 3673–3676.

Schmidt, W., Drews, G., Weckesser, J., Fromme, I. and Borowiak, D. (1980) Characterisation of the lipopolysaccharides from eight strains of the cyanobacterium *Synechococcus. Arch. Mikrobiol.* **127**, 209–215.

Shafizadeh, F. and Lai, Y. F. (1972) Thermal degradation of 1,6-anhydro-β-D-glucopyranose. *J. Org. Chem.* **27**, 278–284.

Skipski, V. P., Smolowne, A. F., Sullivan, R. C. and Barclay, M. (1965) Separation of lipid classes by thin layer chromatography. *Biochim. Biophys. Acta* **106**, 386–396.

Sutherland, I. (1977) Surface carbohydrates of procaryotic cells. Academic Press.

Thomson, M. J., Glancey, B. M., Robbins, W. E., Logfren, C. S., Dutkey, S. R., Kochansky, J., Vandermeer, R. K. and Glover, A. R. (1981) Major hydrocarbons of the post-pharyngeal glands of mated queens of the red imported fire ant *Solenopis invicta. Lipids* **16**, 485–594.

Tibbetts, P. J. C., Maxwell, J. R. and Golubic, S. (1978) Algal mat and ooze from Laguna Mormona. In *Environmental Biogeochemistry and Geomicrobiology*, ed. by Krumbein, W. E. Ann Arbor Science Publishers, Michigan, pp. 271–284.

Tibbetts, P. J. C. (1980) The origin of the carotenoids of some quaternary Pliocene sediments. Ph.D. Thesis, University of Bristol.

Van der Meent, D., Brown, S. C., Philp, R. P. and Simoneit, B. R. T. (1980a) Pyrilysis — high resolution gas chromatography and pyrolysis gas chromatography mass spectrometry of kerogens and kerogens precursors. *Geochim. Cosmochim. Acta* **44**, 999–1013.

Van der Meent, D., Leeuw, J. W. de and Schenck, P. A. (1980b) Origin of unsaturated isoprenoid hydrocarbons in pyrolysates of suspended matter and surface sediments. In *Advances of Organic Geochemistry, 1979*, ed. by Douglas, A. G. and Maxwell, J. R. Pergamon Press, Oxford, pp. 469–475.

Wardroper, A. M. K. (1979) Aspects of the geochemistry of polycyclic isoprenoids. Ph.D. Thesis, University of Britsol.

Watts, C. D., Maxwell, J. R. and Kjøsen, H. (1977) The potential of carotenoids as environmental indicators. In *Advances in Organic Geochemistry, 1975*, ed. by Campos, R. and Goni, J. Enadimsa, Madrid, pp. 391–413.

Weedon, B. C. L. (1971) Occurrence. In *Carotenoids*, ed. by Isler, O. Birkhauser-Verlag, Basel, pp. 30–59.

Windig, W., Kistemaker, P. G., Haverkamp, J. and Meuzelaar, H. L. C. (1980) Factor analysis of the influence of changes in experimental conditions in pyrolysis mass spectrometry. *J. Anal. Appl. Pyrol.* **2**, 7–18.

Winters, K., Parker, P. L. and van Baalen, C. (1969) Hydrocarbons of blue–green algae: geochemical significance. *Science* **163**, 467–468.

Advances in Organic Geochemistry 1981, pp. 228–240
© *John Wiley & Sons Limited, 1983*

Lipid Composition of Coastal Marine Sediments from the Peru Upwelling Region

J. K. Volkman,* J. W. Farrington, R. B. Gagosian and S. G. Wakeham

Department of Chemistry, Woods Hole Oceanographic Institution, Woods Hole, Massachusetts 02543, USA

The compositions of several lipid classes extracted from coastal sediments from the upwelling area at 15° S off Peru have been studied using capillary gas chromatography–mass spectrometry. Many of the sedimentary lipids originate from autochthonous sources in the water column as shown by comparison with the lipid composition of large particles trapped by free-drifting sediment traps deployed in the same area. A major mechanism by which many of these labile compounds reach the sea floor appears to be by incorporation into fast sinking anchoveta and zooplankton fecal pellets. Detailed compositional data are presented for the hydrocarbon and acyclic ketone fractions. The hydrocarbons in the surface sediments show a predominance of branched acyclic C_{25} polyunsaturated alkenes of presumed planktonic origin with smaller concentrations of long-chain n-alkanes. The latter show little odd-carbon predominance in offshore sediments in contrast to inshore sediments where a contribution from higher plants can be recognized. The ketone fractions contain significant amounts of very long-chain unsaturated C_{37}–C_{39} ketones which may originate from the marine alga *Emiliania huxleyi*. These compounds are also abundant in the sediment trap particulate material. Small amounts of C_{23}–C_{35} n-alkan-2-ones are present in those sediments containing n-alkanes of higher-plant origin but not in sediments further offshore. The data support earlier suggestions that these compounds may be indirect markers for terrigenous organic matter but sources in addition to *in situ* oxidation of n-alkanes are required to explain the distributions observed. The C_{18} isoprenoid ketone 6,10,14-trimethylpentadecan-2-one is abundant in both surface and subsurface sediments and presumably arises from degradation of phytol. Its concentration is also high in the sediment traps implying a rapid formation in the water column.

INTRODUCTION

Studies of the lipid composition of Recent sediments representing a range of depositional environments have led to an appreciation of the importance of early diagenesis in determining the organic compounds likely to be incorporated into the sedimentary record. In marine and lacustrine sediments the relationship between the organic compounds in the sediment and those produced in the overlying water column has been difficult to assess, both quantitatively and qualitatively. Interpretations have relied on extrapolations from analyses of marine organisms, either cultured or isolated from the environment, and analyses of filtered, slow sinking, small particulate matter. These data have rarely been sufficiently comprehensive to enable firm conclusions to be made and it is not clear in most cases whether the major transformation reactions and metabolism of these compounds occurs before or after deposition.

Many recent studies have demonstrated that fast sinking large particles, such as fecal pellets, are important in the transport of organic matter to the sea

floor (see Honjo, 1980; Honjo and Roman, 1978; Knauer *et al.*, 1979; Prahl and Carpenter, 1979; Prahl *et al.*, 1980; Wakeham *et al.*, 1980 for leading references), but few data are available concerning the transport of specific marker compounds. Prahl and Carpenter (1979) have calculated that zooplankton fecal pellets could account for *ca.* 100% of the flux of polycyclic aromatic hydrocarbons in Dabob Bay, Washington. Wakeham *et al.* (1980) have shown that large particles caught by moored traps deployed in the equatorial Atlantic Ocean contain significant concentrations of a variety of labile lipids, many of which have been found in marine sediments.

In 1978, 20 free-drifting sediment traps (FSTs) and 9 moored traps (MSTs) were deployed in the Peru coastal zone at 15° S (Staresinic, 1980; Gagosian *et al.*, 1980) to investigate the biogeochemical processes associated with this upwelling area. Samples of seawater, large particles, phytoplankton, zooplankton and underlying sediments were obtained to make a detailed and comprehensive comparison of the lipid composition of each major stage of the organic carbon cycle in this upwelling ecosystem. Details of the biogeochemistry of amino acids in the sediments (Henrichs, 1980; Henrichs *et al.*, 1982) and sediment traps (Lee and Cronin, 1982) have been presented. Initial results of some of the sediment trap

* Present address: CSIRO Marine Laboratories, Division of Oceanography, P.O. Box 21, Cronulla, N.S.W., 2230, Australia.

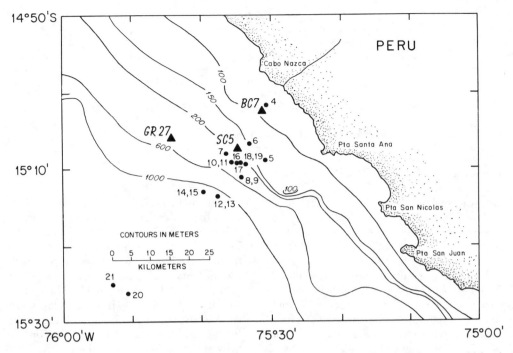

Fig. 1. Locations of the free-drifting sediment traps deployed during cruise 73–2 of R/V *Knorr* in February and March, 1978, with sites (SC5, GR27 and BC7) where sediment samples discussed in this paper were collected.

lipid data are reported in this volume by Gagosian *et al.* (1982a), Repeta and Gagosian (1982), Wakeham *et al.* (1982) and elsewhere, Gagosian *et al.* (1982b).

The Peru coastal zone offers several advantages for organic geochemical studies. The area is characterized by high primary productivity, sometimes exceeding 10 gC/m².day (Ryther *et al.*, 1971; Gagosian *et al.*, 1980), as a result of consistent upwelling in the coastal system (Zuta *et al.*, 1978). Organic compounds are biosynthesized in large quantities during phytoplankton (mainly diatom) blooms and as much as 19% of the organic carbon from primary productivity is rapidly transported below the euphotic layer (Staresinic, 1978) via large particles consisting of anchoveta and zooplankton fecal pellets, euphausiid molts and other material. Considerable amounts of data are now available concerning the biology and nutrient chemistry of the area, in addition to hydrographic data (Ryther *et al.*, 1971; Staresinic, 1980; Gagosian *et al.*, 1981). The coast and hinterland are sparsely vegetated and river flow into this area is infrequent, suggesting that the input of terrigenous organic matter would be minor.

Within the upwelling area, high sedimentation rates of 1.1–1.2 cm/yr in this area have been calculated from Pb-210 data (Henrichs, 1980). Sediment organic carbon values generally range from less than 3% to more than 5% in this area (Rosato *et al.*, 1975), with values up to 9.5% recorded (Henrichs, 1980). Remineralization of organic carbon leads to an oxygen minimum zone which impinges on the continental slope at depths between 100 and 500 m (Wyrtki, 1967). Within this area, large microbial communities dominated by filamentous *Thioploca* bacteria are widespread, producing dense spongy mats at the sediment surface (Gallardo, 1977). Thus, chemosynthesis by bacteria must be considered as an additional source of organic matter in the bottom sediments.

In this paper we present compositional data for hydrocarbon and acyclic ketone fractions of three surface sediments and a box core taken close to shore (Fig. 1). Hydrocarbons were chosen since these should indicate any significant contribution of terrigenous organic matter to the coastal zone as well as information on autochthonous sources and the possibility of fossil fuel contamination. The ketone fractions were specifically examined for *n*-alkan-2-ones to test the hypothesis that these compounds are formed from *n*-alkanes by *in situ* microbial activity (Brassell *et al.*, 1980). Also, we hoped to determine whether recently discovered very long-chain $C_{37} - C_{39}$ unsaturated ketones, perhaps indicative of an input from the alga *Emiliania huxleyi* (Volkman *et al.*, 1980a–c), were present in these sediments. Although both of these lipid classes have been studied extensively, definitive interpretations of some aspects of their biogeochemistry are not yet possible.

EXPERIMENTAL

Samples

Sediment and sediment trap samples were collected during February and March, 1978 on Cruise 73–2 of R/V *Knorr*. The locations of these samples are shown in Fig. 1. A detailed account of the bulk composition of the free-drifting sediment trap particulate matter has been given by Staresinic (1980, 1982) and Staresinic *et al.* (1982). These traps were deployed at 14 m (the base of the euphotic zone) and 52 m, both at night and during the day, for 8 to 12 h. No bacteriocide was added since the deployment times were short. Hydrographic data obtained during this sampling period have been presented by Gagosian *et al.* (1980).

Table 1

Water column depths and locations of sites where sediment samples were taken

Sediment sample	Date sampled	Type of sample	Location	Water column depth
SC5	6 March 1978	Soutar core 0–1 cm	15°07.1′S, 75°35.1′W	175 m
GR27	7 March 1978	Grab sample 0–2 cm	15°05.7′S, 75°43.9′W	268 m
BC7	4 March 1978	MK III Box Core[a] 0–30 cm	15°02.2′S, 75°30.9′W	85 m

[a] Sandia Hessler (Oceanic Instruments, San Diego, CA).

Table 1 lists the sediment samples discussed here together with data for locations, water depths and time of sampling. Sediment samples were obtained using a Soutar box corer (0.1 m² × 1 m), a Sandia-Hessler Type Mark III box corer (0.25 m² × 30 cm) and a grab sampler (Table 1). Three surface sediment samples (SC5, GR27 and BC7(0–1)), all diatomaceous oozes, were extracted to study any changes of lipid concentration and composition with increasing distance from the shore and with increasing water column depth. A box core (BC7) from close inshore (*ca.* 7 km) was sectioned into 0–1, 2–3, 4–5, 8–9 and 16–19 cm intervals to study any changes of lipid composition with increasing sediment depth. The sedimentation rate near this site is *ca.* 1.1 cm/yr (Henrichs, 1980) so the core sections studied represent less than 20 years of sediment accumulation. Each of the sediments are located in the oxygen minimum zone (<0.1 ml/l sea water) which eliminates benthic fauna or restricts it to a few benthic metazoans such as polychaete worms. Small populations of benthic fauna may develop at the inshore BC7 site due to seasonal changes in the oxygen content of the overlying waters. Filaments of *Thioploca* bacteria (Gallardo, 1977) were conspicuous in each of the surface sediments and were found to a depth of at least 10 cm in the box core. Examination of the near-shore core sections by microscopy revealed an abundance of siliceous diatom tests, the major species being identified as *Thalassionema nitzschioides* and *Thalassiosira eccentrica* (Staresinic, 1982), and some sand grains. Few calcareous species were present and little CO_2 was evolved on addition of HCl to the sediment. Much of the organic matter consisted of amorphous, degraded material of indeterminable origin.

A small sample of *Thioploca*, hand-picked from dredge sediments obtained off Chile (Gallardo, 1977), was kindly donated by Dr Victor Gallardo. This sample was not originally intended for organic geochemical study and was stored in formalin. Total lipids were extracted with toluene–methanol using sonication at 20 °C. Subsequent work-up was the same as for the sediment samples. Since the sample was hand-picked, a small proportion of animal tissue was probably still present which may account for the identification of cholesterol as the major component (>90%) of the sterol fraction.

Extraction

Portions of surface samples SC5 and GR27 (15 g and 14.8 g wet weight respectively) were extracted with toluene–methanol (1:1 v/v; 40 ml) in 50 ml screw cap centrifuge tubes by heating in boiling water for 10 min. After centrifugation, the total lipids were partitioned into hexane (3 × 15 ml) and transferred to a separatory funnel. Methanol (2 × 10 ml) was added and water soluble material removed by partitioning into a saturated NaCl solution (20 ml). This extraction method would not have extracted the sediment lipids completely, but it was used to obtain preliminary data for the lipid fractions. Although the concentration data are only semi-quantitative the relative amounts within any given fraction should accurately represent those occurring in the sediment.

Portions of the BC7 samples (30–50 g wet weight) were transferred to a pre-extracted Soxhlet thimble to which was added an internal standard consisting of C_{19} *n*-alkanol (13 μg), C_{19} *n*-alkan-2-one (13 μg) and C_{22} *n*-alkane (15 μg). Each sediment was successively Soxhlet extracted with toluene–methanol mixtures (1:1 v/v, 300 ml, 23 h; 3:1 v/v, 2 × 280 ml, 2 × 23 h). The extracts were combined, reduced to 200 ml using a rotary evaporator at 18 °C, transferred to a separatory funnel with saturated NaCl solution (10 ml) and partitioned into hexane–toluene (4 × 50 ml). The combined extracts were reduced to near-dryness on a rotary evaporator and transferred to a 3 ml vial with ethyl acetate. Hexane alone dissolved only a small fraction of the total extracted lipids.

Column chromatography

The total solvent extractable lipids were partially purified on a Cu/Al_2O_3 column consisting of a 4 cm layer of 5% deactivated alumina over a 1 cm bed of copper filings activated by immersion in 3N HCl for 30 min. Total lipids were eluted with hexane and ethyl acetate mixtures (100 ml). Polar material was eluted with methanol and stored for future examination. A 30% aliquot of total lipids was then separated into lipid classes using a 0.9 cm diameter bulb column packed to a depth of 22 cm with silica gel (70–230 mesh) deactivated with 5% (by weight) of distilled water. Fourteen fractions were collected by elution with hexane, toluene and ethyl acetate mixtures. Fraction I eluted with 25 ml of hexane, contained the total hydrocarbon fraction. *n*-Alkan-2-ones, C_{37} and C_{38} unsaturated methyl ketones, and the C_{18} isoprenoid ketone occurred in fraction VI which was eluted with 20 ml of 10% ethyl acetate in hexane. Unsaturated C_{38} and C_{39} ethyl ketones were eluted from the column in fraction V using 20 ml of 5% ethyl acetate

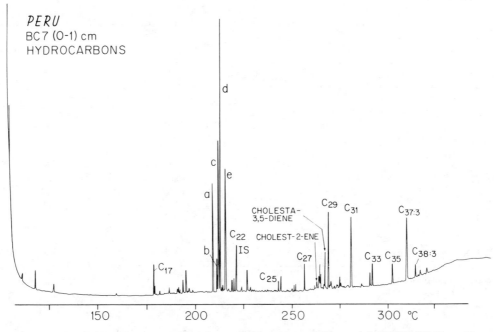

Fig. 2. Gas chromatogram of total hydrocarbons in BC7 surface sediment; 20 m × 0.30 mm i.d. WCOT SE-52 capillary column programmed from 80 to 330 °C at 4 °C/min.

in hexane, but these compounds were not studied in detail.

Gas chromatography (GC) and gas chromatography–mass spectrometry (GC–MS)

Compounds were tentatively identified using high resolution capillary gas chromatography (GC) from both retention time measurements and coinjection with authentic standards. A 20 m × 0.32 mm i.d. pyrex WCOT column coated with SE–52 and deactivated by persilylation (Grob, 1980), mounted in a Carlo Erba FTV 2150 gas chromatograph, was used for most analyses. The sample was injected splitless at room temperature with helium at 1.5–2 ml/min as the carrier gas and injector and detector temperatures of 350 °C. A temperature programme of 80 to 330 °C at 4 °C/min was usually used (Fig. 2.). Additional data were obtained using a similar column mounted in a Carlo Erba FTV 4160 gas chromatograph using on-column injection (Grob and Grob, 1978). This was particularly useful for the analysis of the C_{37}–C_{39} unsaturated ketones since some discrimination against these less volatile long-chain compounds occurred using the flash vaporization injector, even when operated at 350 °C (cf. Grob, 1979). Retention time data for the branched alkenes were also obtained using a 15 m × 0.3 mm i.d. WCOT column coated with PG–1540 (Carbowax) programmed from 70 to 220 °C at 3 °C/min. Helium at 2 ml/min was used as the carrier gas.

Electron impact mass spectra were obtained from a Finnigan 1015C quadrupole mass spectrometer coupled to a ' Varian Aerograph 1400 gas chromatograph modified for capillary operation. A 25 m × 0.3 mm i.d. SE–52 WCOT capillary column was used with He at 8 psi as the carrier gas. The mass spectrometer was

scanned linearly from 40 to 550 or 600 amu in 1 s intervals. Data acquisition used a Finnigan INCOS 2300 data system.

Contamination

Stringent precautions were taken to minimize contamination. A full procedural blank was carried out by spiking the Soxhlet thimble, in the absence of sediment, with the internal standard mixture and carrying out the extraction and separation procedures through to the gas chromatography stage. Fraction I contained very minor amounts of long-chain C_{18}–C_{33} n-alkanes but these were each less than 0.05% of the n-C_{22} standard and thus would not be significant contaminants of the hydrocarbon fraction. Small amounts of phthalate esters ($<20\%$ of C_{19} ketone standard) were found in some of the ketone fractions but these were readily recognized. Recoveries of the internal standards were 85–95%.

RESULTS AND DISCUSSION

Hydrocarbons

The hydrocarbon fractions of each sediment sample consisted of n-alkanes (n-C_{20} to n-C_{35}) and n-alkenes (n-$C_{37:3}$ and n-$C_{38:3}$) together with small amounts of sterenes and unidentified components. Partially characterized branched acyclic C_{25} alkenes were abundant in each of the surface samples, but their concentration rapidly decreased with depth. A gas chromatogram of the total hydrocarbons of the 0–1 cm sediment section from BC7 is shown in Fig. 2. n-Alkanes with less than 20 carbon atoms, pristane and phytane were only trace constituents of the sediments.

Table 2
Concentrations (ppm dry wt.) and Kovat's indices of alkenes in Peru BC7 sediment sections

| | | Kovat's index | | | Concentration (ppm) | | | | |
	Alkene[a]	SE–52	SP–2100[b]	PG–1540	cm 0–1	2–3	4–5	8–9	16–19
a	25:3	2044	2044	2077	4.0	1.7	0.45	0.36	0.19
b	?	2072	—	2089	1.2	0.71	0.25	0.07	0.13
c	25:4	2082	2078	2147	5.5	1.8	0.42	0.44	0.18
d	25:3′	2092	2090	2131	10.1	3.2	1.0	0.66	0.41
e	25:4′	2129	2124	2210	4.4	1.5	0.35	0.64	0.45
f	?	2170	—	—	0.34	0.13	TR	0.05	TR
g	?	2183	—	—	0.44	0.63	0.07	0.81	0.44
h	?	2188	—	2140	0.57	0.82	0.34	0.57	0.49
Sum of a–h					26.6	10.5	2.9	3.6	2.3
	37:3	3652	—	—	2.0	0.24	0.03	0.13	0.08
	38:3	3754	—	—	0.39	0.03	TR	TR	TR

[a] Letters refer to peaks labelled in Fig. 2.
[b] Data from Barrick *et al.* (1980).
TR: <0.02 ppm.

Telkova *et al.* (1976) have analysed the top 10 cm of several terrigenous clays and silts from the Peruvian shelf and slope. They found C_{20}–C_{33} *n*-alkanes with odd/even ratios of 1.14 for a shelf station and 1.53 and 1.69 for two slope stations. The latter ratios were interpreted as an input of lipids from the continent but the authors did not speculate as to the reason for the small predominance of odd carbon chain-lengths. The distribution of alkanes in their slope station is very similar to that of the SC5 sediment (Fig. 4).

(a) Alkenes. The three surface samples contained high concentrations of compounds which eluted between *n*-C_{20} and *n*-C_{22} on an apolar SE–52 capillary column (peaks a–g, Fig. 2) and between *n*-C_{20} and *n*-C_{23} on a polar PG-1540 (carbowax) column. Kovat's indices and concentration data are presented in Table 2. The shift in Kovat's indices between the two columns indicates the presence of unsaturation in these hydrocarbons. Peaks a–g disappeared from the gas chromatogram, and one major and one minor product were produced after mild catalytic hydrogenation confirming unsaturation. The major alkane co-eluted with *n*-C_{21} on the SE–52 column but eluted before *n*-C_{21} on the PG–1540 column indicating a branched structure.

EI mass spectra of a–g were typical of long chain alkenes but molecular ions were only observed for alkenes a, c and d. The mass spectrum of d was identical with that presented by Barrick *et al.* (1980) for a multibranched $C_{25:3}$ alkene which occurs in surface sediments of Puget Sound, Washington. Kovat's indices on SE–52 for a, c, d and e are close to those determined by Barrick *et al.* (1980) using an SP–2100 column for $C_{25:3}$, $C_{25:4}$, $C_{25:3}$ and $C_{25:4}$ alkenes (Table 2). Moreover, the EI mass spectrum they presented for the C_{25} alkane produced from hydrogenation of these alkenes is the same as that obtained in our study, from which we conclude that the same alkenes occur in sediments from Peru and Puget Sound. The full structures of these alkenes have yet to be determined, but it is clear from their very low Kovat's indices that they are highly branched. Further speculation on the structures of these alkenes is presented by Barrick and Hedges (1981).

Barrick *et al.* (1980) suggest that these four alkenes are structurally identical except for the occurrence of *cis* and *trans* isomers about one double bond and the presence of an additional double bond at a remote site in the branched $C_{25:4}$ alkenes. Our data agree with this assessment with the possible exception of the occurrence of *cis–trans* isomers about a single double bond. The large difference in Kovat's indices between the two trienes (a and d) is much greater than found for *cis–trans* pairs of other unsaturated compounds, such as Δ^9 and Δ^{11} methyloctadecenoate, chromatographed on SE–52.

An additional minor branched alkane was found in the hydrogenation products which eluted just after *n*-C_{21} on SE–52 (Kovat's index 2106). The EI mass spectrum was very similar to that of a bicyclic C_{25} alkane (MW 348) produced from hydrogenation of a C_{25} diene isolated from Buzzards Bay, Massachusetts surface sediments (Farrington *et al.*, 1977). Several cyclic C_{25} dienes have been isolated from surface marine sediments (Farrington *et al.*, 1977; Boehm and Quinn, 1978; Prahl *et al.*, 1980; Barrick and Hedges, 1981), but as yet full structural identifications have not been achieved.

The distributions of these acyclic C_{25} alkenes (a, c, d and e) in the Peru sediments are remarkably similar to those found in surface sediments of Puget Sound, Washington (Barrick *et al.*, 1980). Prahl *et al.* (1980) also report the occurrence of a compound, apparently identical to compound 'd', in surface sediments from Dabob Bay, Washington. Inspection of the gas chromatogram presented by Prahl *et al.* (1980) suggests that compounds a, c and e were also present in a distribution very like that of the Peru sediments (Fig. 2). These similarities imply a common biosynthesis, or transformation of the same precursor(s) and hence the probability of a common origin from the same, or related, organism(s).

Our identification of these same alkenes in some of the sediment traps deployed off Peru implies that they

Table 3

Concentrations and selected ratios for *n*-alkanes and *n*-alkan-2-ones in BC7 sediments

Compound	depth (cm)	Concentrations (ppm dry wt.)				
		0–1	2–3	4–5	8–9	16–19
n-Alkanes						
Total C_{20}–C_{35} (i)		7.6	6.8	6.6	12.5	8.9
Higher plant alkanes (ii)		6.9	6.5	6.3	12.2	8.9
'Marine' alkanes (iii)		0.7	0.3	0.3	0.3	0.0[a]
% 'Marine' alkanes		8.7	4.7	3.9	2.4	0.0
n-Alkan-2-ones						
Total C_{20}–C_{35} (iv)		0.24	0.34	0.64	0.82	0.63
O/E[b] *n*-Alkanes (v)		7.3	8.6	8.9	9.6	10.8
O/E[b] *n*-Alkan-2-ones (vi)		3.6	4.3	4.2	4.4	4.2
Ketones/Alkanes (iv/i)		0.032	0.050	0.097	0.066	0.071
Ketones/Plant alkanes (iv/ii)		0.035	0.052	0.101	0.067	0.071
O/E Ketones/O/E Alkanes (vi/v)		0.49	0.50	0.47	0.46	0.39

[a] Assumed to be zero, see text.
[b] O/E: Total odd carbon chain-lengths/total even carbon chain-lengths for C_{20}–C_{35}.

originate from an autochthonous source in the water column. These traps contain large amounts of fecal matter, primarily from zooplankton, together with anchoveta fecal pellets, zooplankton molts and phytodetritus. It has not been possible to analyse each of these sources separately, so a definitive statement as to the origin of these unusual alkenes is not yet possible. Also, there are no reports of the occurrence of these alkenes in biological systems with which to compare these data.

Since a large proportion of the lipids in these surface sediments are directly related to phytoplankton origin, it is conceivable that the alkenes also originate from phytoplankton; possibly from diatoms which predominate in this area. This is consistent with the wide geographical occurrence of these alkenes. Recently, during Cruise 108, leg 3 of R/V *Atlantis* II, several samples of the diatom blooms in this area were obtained, which we intend to analyse to test this hypothesis.

Prahl *et al.* (1980) identified a compound (designated I 2090), presumed to be identical to compound d, in sediment traps deployed in Dabob Bay. These traps, like those from Peru, contained mainly zooplankton fecal pellets. These authors did not detect branched acyclic C_{25} alkenes in mixed plankton samples which contained large amounts of zooplankton such as *Calanus*. Since there are no reports of these alkenes in the many studies of zooplankton hydrocarbons, and since we were unable to detect them in a mixed zooplankton haul from Peru, we suggest that the occurrence of these alkenes in the traps reflects their origin from the zooplankton food, i.e. phytoplankton. Laboratory studies show that a small proportion (probably <10%) of dietary lipids are excreted by copepods (Volkman *et al.*, 1980a) and that the amounts are likely to be higher when food is abundant, as in a bloom, due to superfluous feeding. Microscopic examination of the fecal pellets isolated from the Peru sediment traps indicated the presence of abundant diatom cells, principally *Thalassionema nitzschioides* and *Thalassiosira eccentrica*, many of which were still intact (Staresinic, 1982). Remains of these

diatoms are abundant in the sediments. A phytoplankton origin is thus consistent with the available data but more studies of the lipid composition of marine organisms are obviously required.

The distribution of the branched acyclic C_{25} alkenes was very similar in each of the surface sediments and in each case they were the predominant hydrocarbons present. However, in the inshore box core samples (BC7) a marked decrease in concentration with depth was found such that at 4–5 cm their concentration had decreased by an order of magnitude (Table 2). This contrasts with the long-chain *n*-alkanes which showed a slight increase with depth (Table 3). Clearly, these two compounds classes have different sources and/or a very different diagenetic history in the sediment.

This decrease in concentration of the C_{25} alkenes could be due to a major change in the abundance of the contributing source organism(s), but this seems unlikely from the biological descriptions of this area. More likely, the compounds are rapidly degraded in the surface sediment. Barrick *et al.* (1980) also noted an approximately exponential decrease of these compounds in Puget Sound sediments which they ascribed to *in situ* chemical degradation. Farrington *et al.* (1977) noted similar depth profiles in sediments from Buzzards Bay, Massachusetts. In the Peru sediments microbial degradation is also likely to be important in view of the high bacterial biomass present. However, no data are available concerning the ability of the *Thioploca* community to utilize long-chain organic compounds for heterotrophic growth. Hydrogenation does not seem to be a significant transformation pathway but at this stage we have no information as to any other mechanisms by which these compounds are degraded or what products are formed. One possibility is that they are rapidly and irreversibly bound to accreting polymeric material *via* cross-linking reactions involving the double bonds.

Two very long-chain alkenes were present in the gas chromatograms of each hydrocarbon extract (Fig. 2). These identified as $C_{37:3}$ and $C_{38:3}$ *n*-alkenes from the similarity of their EI mass spectra and retention

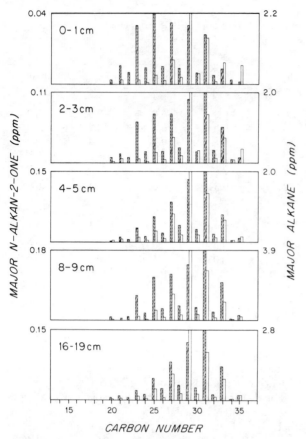

Fig. 3. Histograms of *n*-alkane (open bars) and *n*-alkan-2
-one (hatched bars) distributions in BC7 depth profile.

times with data presented by de Leeuw *et al.* (1980) and
Volkman *et al.* (1980b, c). These alkenes were converted
to *n*-C$_{37}$ and *n*-C$_{38}$ alkanes on mild hydrogenation,
supporting the proposed structures. These alkenes have
been isolated from the marine alga *Emiliania huxleyi*
(Volkman *et al.*, 1980a–c, 1981a) but there are no reports
of their occurrence in other organisms, although few
have been studied. They are widely distributed in
marine sediments to which *E. huxleyi* is likely to be a
significant contributor (Volkman *et al.*, 1980b).

(b) *n*-**Alkanes**. *n*-Alkanes were abundant (7–12
ppm) in each of the sediments analysed (Table 3). In the
BC7 sediments these ranged from C$_{20}$ to C$_{35}$ and showed
a strong predominance of odd carbon chain-lengths
(Fig. 3), with *n*-C$_{29}$ the major homologue. Similar
distributions have been found in many lacustrine and
marine sediments, and without exception these have
been attributed to an input of higher plant lipids since
such alkane distributions are typical of the epicuticular
waxes of land plants.

The concentrations of C$_{20}$–C$_{35}$ *n*-alkanes was fairly
constant in the top 5 cm of the box core and then
increased 2 fold at 8–9 cm. In the deepest section
analysed, 16–19 cm, the concentration was intermediate
between these values (Table 3). Since the distributions of
homologues in each section are very similar (Fig. 3), this
must imply that the amount of higher plant lipids
deposited in this environment has fluctuated over the
last two decades or that the rate of sediment

accumulation has changed. Large fluctuations in
sediment accumulation are not consistent with either
Pb-210 dating of cores in this area (Henrichs, 1980) or
the absence of large lithological changes in the BC7 core.
However, minor changes in sediment accumulation
could account for some of the observed concentration
changes.

In offshore GR27 and SC5 surface sediments the *n*-
alkanes had the same carbon number range, but
exhibited little predominance of odd or even carbon
chain-lengths (Table 3). Fossil fuel products often show
such distributions (e.g. Farrington, 1980), but no other
evidence indicative of fossil fuel input, such as an
unresolved complex mixture (UCM), steranes, hopanes,
or aromatic hydrocarbons could be detected in these
sediments.

From data presented in Table 3, it can be seen that the
relative proportion of odd carbon chain-lengths (O/E
ratio) increases slightly with increasing sediment depth
in the BC7 core to a maximum value of 10.8 at 16–19 cm.
One explanation for these results is that the C$_{20}$–C$_{35}$
alkanes have at least two sources. The major one, from
higher plants, which has an odd–even predominance of
ca. 10.8, is typified by the distribution in BC7(16–19).
Superimposed on this is a distribution that shows no
predominance of odd carbon chain-lengths which is
typified by the distributions in GR27 and SC5 surface
sediments. If one takes the distributions in BC7(16–19)
and SC5 as end-members typical of the two source terms,
then it is possible to calculate the proportion of each term
which, when added together, will generate the observed
odd–even predominance in the BC7 alkane
distributions. Data calculated in this way are presented
in Table 3. These suggest that *ca.* 91% of the C$_{20}$–C$_{35}$ *n*-
alkanes in BC7(0–1) are derived from higher plants,
and this proportion increases with depth. Of the offshore samples, SC5 contains almost no higher plant
alkanes but a small contribution can be discerned in
GR27 (Fig. 4).

If we assume that there are at least two sources of C$_{20}$–
C$_{35}$ *n*-alkanes, what is the origin of those distributions in
SC5 and GR27 which show no predominance of odd
carbon chain-lengths? Laboratory contamination might
yield such a distribution but this can be ruled out on the

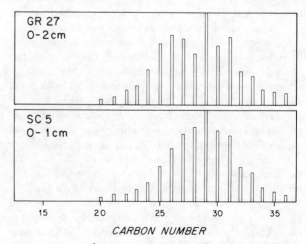

Fig. 4. Histograms of *n*-alkane distributions in off-shore SC5
and GR27 surface sediments.

basis of extensive blank experiments. Moreover, each of the BC7 samples were treated in the same way and it is highly unlikely that such a systematic trend in odd–even predominance would be observed. Petroleum or crude oil contamination of the coastal environment is possible since there is some tanker traffic through this general area. However, the hydrocarbon distributions from such sources should show a pronounced unresolved complex mixture (UCM) of branched/cyclic alkanes and none could be observed in the hydrocarbon fractions from these sediments. It is difficult to conceive of a process by which branched and cyclic alkanes, which form the UCM, are removed in preference to *n*-alkanes, and this would contradict the numerous studies of crude oil degradation which have been carried out. The absence of steranes and triterpanes characteristic of a mature hydrocarbon source also suggests that a fossil fuel source is unlikely, although the possibility that a highly paraffinic oil might be involved cannot be entirely discounted.

We suggest that these alkanes may have a biogenic ('marine') origin. Several studies have indicated that some phytoplankton species biosynthesize long-chain alkanes showing no predominance of odd carbon chain-lengths (Blumer *et al.*, 1971; Volkman *et al.*, 1980d), but few data are available and this is still subject to debate (Murray *et al.*, 1977). Most of the FST samples contained significant quantities of C_{20}–C_{35} *n*-alkanes which showed no odd–even predominance but, with the exception of FST 5, one or more UCMs were also present in the gas chromatograms. It is commonly assumed that these two features have a common origin from fossil fuel products, but this need not always be the case. However, in the absence of data on the possible occurrence of such alkane distributions in phytoplankton species found in Peru coastal waters, no definitive assignment of these alkanes to an algal origin is possible at this stage.

Another source of *n*-alkanes is from the bacterial population of the sediment. In this environment, large bacterial communities, dominated by a filamentous *Thioploca* species, are found at the surface and these could account for the high concentrations of the C_{20}–C_{35} *n*-alkanes found there. Filaments of *Thioploca* are found to a depth of *ca.* 10 cm but rarely below this, which is consistent with the lower concentration of these alkanes found in the box core samples to 9 cm, and apparent absence from the 16–19 cm section. A direct test of this hypothesis has not been feasible since it has not been possible to grow *Thioploca* in laboratory cultures. However, a small hand-picked sample of the natural *Thioploca* community growing off Chile at 36° S (Gallardo, 1977) did contain C_{20}–C_{35} alkanes which showed no odd-predominance. The major homologue in this case was *n*-C_{25} and not *n*-C_{29} and since the sample was not taken specifically for organic geochemical analysis this result needs further confirmation.

There are several reports of the occurrence of long-chain *n*-alkanes in bacteria and some distributions show no odd–even predominance (Albro and Dittmer, 1967; Davis, 1968; Calvin, 1969), but the amount of data available is limited. Of geochemical interest is the occurrence of C_{24}–C_{35} *n*-alkanes in the ubiquitous anaerobic sulphate-reducing bacterium *Desulfovibrio*

desulfuricans (Davis, 1968). These show no odd–even predominance and, like the GR27 and SC5 sediment samples, the major homologue is *n*-C_{29}. The results of Johnson and Calder (1973) also suggest that bacteria may be a source of such *n*-alkane distributions in sediments. They showed that surface salt marsh sediments exhibited a high predominance of odd carbon chain-lengths, typical of dormant *Spartina*, maximizing at *n*-C_{29} as in the Peru samples. However, by 15 cm this distribution was replaced by one showing almost no predominance of odd carbon chain-lengths. Johnson and Calder (1973) suggest that these changes are brought about by *in situ* microbial activity rapidly breaking down the higher plant alkanes with resynthesis of a distribution lacking odd-predominance. Implicit in this interpretation is that the sedimentary bacteria biosynthesize long-chain *n*-alkanes, which show little or no predominance of odd carbon chain-lengths.

In summary, we think that biogenic sources within the Peru coastal environment, perhaps bacteria or phytoplankton, are the most likely sources of C_{20} to C_{35} *n*-alkane distributions which show no odd carbon predominance. If this is true of other environments, then we may need to reinterpret the origin of *n*-alkane distributions in other recent sediments and seawater particulate material which show little or no predominance of odd carbon chain-lengths.

Acyclic ketones

(a) 6,10,14-Trimethylpentadecan-2-one (6,10,14-TMPD-2-one).

The C_{18} ketone was a major component of the cyclic ketone fraction isolated from each sediment. Its concentration in the BC7 sediment was greatest at the surface (0.92 ppm), decreased by a factor of 3 at 4–5 cm depth (Table 4) and then showed a small increase in the two deeper sections. This ketone has been suggested to be a marker for oxic conditions during sedimentation (Ikan *et al.*, 1973) since it is formed from phytol, the side-chain of chlorophyll *a*, by oxidative pathways. However, other studies have shown that microbial degradation of phytol also yields 6,10,14-TMPD-2-one (Brooks and Maxwell, 1974; Brooks *et al.*, 1978; Ertel, 1978). The ketone is abundant in all of the

Table 4

Concentrations of C_{37} and C_{38} unsaturated methyl ketones and C_{18} isoprenoid ketone in BC7 sediments

Compound	Depth (cm)	0–1	2–3	4–5	8–9	16–19
		\multicolumn{5}{c}{Concentrations (ppm dry wt.)}				
6,10,14-Trimethylpenta-decan-2-one		0.92	0.77	0.30	0.43	0.35
Methyl ketones						
37:3		2.1	0.92	0.76	1.0	0.55
37:2		0.64	1.1	1.5	2.4	0.90
38:3		0.60	0.24	0.24	0.34	0.19
38:2		0.14	0.24	0.32	0.51	0.18
Total		3.5	2.5	2.8	4.3	1.8
Ratio $C_{37:3}/C_{37:2}$		3.3	0.84	0.51	0.42	0.61
Ratio $C_{38:3}/C_{38:2}$		4.3	1.0	0.75	0.67	1.0
Ratio C_{37}/C_{38}		3.7	4.2	4.0	4.0	3.9

FST samples suggesting that large particles in the water column are a contributing source of the isoprenoid ketone in the sediments. The ketone may also be formed in sediment by microbial degradation of phytol or by oxidative pathways since the surface sediment layer is periodically exposed to oxic conditions. One interpretation of the concentration changes with depth is that there is net degradation of 6,10,14-TMPD-2-one in the upper 5 cm of the sediment but below this depth there is a small net production from phytol or phytol derivative. However, an indeterminable amount of the variation may reflect changes in the flux of 6,10,14-TMPD-2-one from the water column.

(b) *n*-**Alkan-2-ones**. Small amounts of *n*-alkan-2-ones (methyl ketones) ranging from C_{20} to C_{35} were detected in each of the BC7 samples. The quantitation of these compounds was complicated by the co-elution of other compounds so a mass fragmentogram of the sum of m/z 58, 59 and 71 was used to define the distribution. The base peak of these spectra changes from m/z 58 to m/z 59 with increasing chain-length so neither ion adequately represents the entire distribution. Histograms of these distributions are shown in Fig. 3 and concentration data are presented in Table 3.

n-Alkan-2-ones are common constituents of both marine and lacustrine sediments, but their origin is still the subject of speculation; in general, *in situ* microbial production from either *n*-alkanoic acids or *n*-alkanes has been proposed (e.g. Morrison and Bick, 1966; Cranwell, 1977; Simoneit *et al.*, 1979). *n*-Alkanes have been considered to be the more likely substrate on the basis of similarities in the distributions of the two compound classes (Brassell *et al.*, 1980; Volkman *et al.*, 1981b) but this remains unproven. Often the two distributions do not show the same predominance of odd carbon chain-lengths and the major homologue in many cases is not the same (Cranwell, 1977; Volkman *et al.*, 1981b). Most authors concur that such *n*-alkan-2-one distributions are indirect markers of a higher plant input (Simoneit *et al.*, 1979).

In marine and lacustrine sediments at least two other sources must be considered. The first is that *n*-alkan-2-ones are not diagenetic products but represent the direct input of natural products. These ketones were not thought to be present in plant lipids (Morrison and Bick, 1967), but the recent identification of n-C_{26} to n-C_{31} methyl ketones, with n-C_{29} predominating, in the seed pods of *Brassica napus* (Richter and Krain, 1981) suggests that this assumption is incorrect. Second, the input of soil and its associated organic matter can be a major contributor of lipids to lacustrine and coastal marine sediments (Cranwell, 1977). Significant concentrations of *n*-alkan-2-ones have been detected in a garden soil (Morrison and Bick, 1966, 1967) and this has been assumed to be a common feature of soil lipids. The *n*-alkan-2-ones found in sediments could thus originate from soil transported to the site of deposition. Such distributions would be subject to extensive microbial reworking in the soil and to the effects of weathering and degradation during transportation and thus may bear little resemblance to the *n*-alkane distributions found in the same sediment.

If *in situ* oxidation of *n*-alkanes was the major source of *n*-alkan-2-ones one might expect that the ketone/alkane ratio would increase with depth until microbial activity ceases. In the upper 5 cm of BC7 this is indeed the case (Table 3); there is a 3-fold increase by 5 cm. However, at 8–9 cm the concentration of *n*-alkanes is double that in the overlying sediment sections whereas the ketone concentration is only slightly enhanced producing a decrease in the ratio. The concentration of *n*-alkan-2-ones at 16–19 cm is actually lower than at 8–9 cm. These changes can be explained if one assumes that degradation of *n*-alkan-2-ones becomes important below 5 cm. Although there is no direct evidence for this, it is perhaps not unreasonable since *n*-alkan-2-ones are more labile chemicals than *n*-alkanes.

However, it is difficult to reconcile the hypothesis of *in situ* oxidation with the chain-length distributions and odd–even predominance of the two lipid classes. Moreover, *n*-alkan-2-ols which would be intermediates in the conversion of alkanes to *n*-alkan-2-ones, could not be detected. In the BC7 sediment sections the *n*-alkan-2-one distributions do not closely resemble the distributions of *n*-alkanes. In the surface (0–1) cm section the predominant *n*-alkan-2-one is n-C_{25}, but in each of the underlying sections n-C_{31} is the major homologue. In contrast, each of the *n*-alkane distributions show a predominance of n-C_{29}. The enhanced abundance of C_{20}–C_{25} *n*-alkan-2-ones is particularly noteworthy and contrasts with the low relative abundance of the corresponding *n*-alkanes. This disparity might be explained by assuming a marked chain-length specificity of the enzyme system(s) involved, but such a dramatic effect is not typical of biochemical systems. Even if one assumes this to be true, the predominance of the C_{31} *n*-alkan-2-one in the subsurface layers would require a substantial removal of shorter-chain ketones with increasing depth and time of burial.

In situ oxidation also fails to account for the different odd–even predominances of the alkanes and ketones. Odd-carbon *n*-alkan-2-ones are 3.6 to 4.4 times more abundant than even-carbon components, but the odd carbon chain-length predominance of the *n*-alkanes is approximately 2-fold greater than this (Table 3). It is difficult to envisage how a direct product–precursor relationship could change the odd–even predominance so markedly. Moreover, if *in situ* oxidation was a major source of *n*-alkan-2-ones one might expect that the odd predominance of the ketones would approach that of the hydrocarbons with increasing sediment depth but the reverse trend is seen (Table 3). Also, *n*-alkan-2-ones were not detectable in the off-shore GR27 and SC5 surface sediments, despite the higher abundances of C_{20}–C_{35} *n*-alkanes in these sediments. At least in these sediments, *in situ* oxidation of alkanes to alkan-2-ones does not seem to be occurring. C_{20}–C_{35} *n*-alkan-2-ones are apparently not formed on fast sinking particulate matter since several samples of sediment trap material (FSTs 6, 10 and 11) were analysed for *n*-alkan-2-ones but in each case none were detected.

The major source of the *n*-alkan-2-one distributions in these coastal sediments does not seem to be from *in situ* production; we cannot rule out the possibility that this process occurs, but the rate must be very slow. It seems likely that these compounds are formed by another pathway or they are derived from another source. β-Oxidation and decarboxylation of fatty acids has been suggested (Arpino *et al.*, 1972) but in the surface Peru sediments C_{20}–C_{32} fatty acids are present in very low abundance (authors' unpublished data) and are unlikely substrates for the production of *n*-alkan-2-ones. The major C_{20}–C_{32} fatty acid is 24:0; oxidation and decarboxylation would yield the C_{23} *n*-alkan-2-one and not the predominance of C_{25} and C_{31} found in the sediments.

We suggest that these distributions of *n*-alkan-2-ones are most probably derived from an allochthonous source, such as soil, which has been transported to the coastal zone either by land run-off or atmospheric transport. *n*-Alkan-2-ones are present in significant concentrations (0.021% of TOC) in soil (Morrison and Bick, 1966, 1967) and in sediments which receive substantial inputs of soil organic matter (Cranwell, 1977). Only one set of data is available to compare with our data, but it is noteworthy that the soil distribution showed the same predominance of odd carbon chain-lengths as found in the Peru sediments (4.1 cf. 3.6–4.4, Table 3). Such low values are possibly indicative of extensive microbial reworking since the odd predominance of ketones isolated from a peat was very much higher (10.9; data from Morrison and Bick, 1967). Thus, the suggestion that C_{20}–C_{35} *n*-alkan-2-one distributions are indicative of *in situ* bacterial activity in sediments (Brassell *et al.*, 1980) may not be true in many cases.

(c) C_{37} – C_{39} Unsaturated Ketones.

Very long-chain di- and triunsaturated C_{37} and C_{38} methyl ketones and C_{38} and C_{39} ethyl ketones were major components of the ketone fractions isolated from each of the sediments. Concentration data for the methyl ketones in the BC7 samples are shown in Table 4. Ethyl ketones were less abundant and detailed data for these compounds were not obtained.

In the surface BC7(0–1) cm sediment, 37:3 and 38:3 methyl ketones greatly predominated over the corresponding diunsaturated compounds (Table 4). This distribution is very similar to that found in the marine coccolithophore *Emiliania huxleyi* (Volkman *et al.*, 1980a–c, 1981a). The co-occurrence in these sediments of other unusual lipids biosynthesized by *E. huxleyi*, viz. $C_{37:3}$ and $C_{38:3}$ *n*-alkenes and a $C_{36:2}$ *n*-alkenoic acid (authors' unpublished data), suggest that *E. huxleyi* is the source of these unusual lipids in the sediment. To date, there are no reports of these compounds in other organisms (Volkman *et al.*, 1981a) but few studies have used gas chromatographic columns which would have allowed them to be detected. Thus, the assignment of these unusual lipids to an input from *E. huxleyi* is still equivocal at this stage.

E. huxleyi is ubiquitous in the oceans and its presence (recorded as *Coccolithus huxleyi*) in the Peru upwelling area is well documented (Ryther *et al.*, 1971), although its distribution is very patchy. Ryther *et al.* (1971) studied a number of stations in this area and found concentrations of *E. huxleyi* ranging from 0 to 35 cells/ml. Often *E. huxleyi* was the 3rd to 6th most abundant species

Table 5

Fluxes of C_{37} and C_{38} unsaturated methyl ketones in free-drifting sediment traps 8 to 11

	Flux ($\mu g/m^2$. 12 h)	
	Day	Night
	FST 9	FST 10
14 m	0.6	6.4
	FST 8	FST 11
52 m	1.7	2.5

identified but its concentration ranged only from 0 to 12% of total cell numbers.

This patchy distribution is reflected in order of magnitude differences in the concentrations of ketones found in the sediment traps. Data for FSTs 8, 9, 10 and 11 (Table 5) show a 10-fold difference in flux between day and night for traps deployed at 14 m. However, the flux through 52 m was only 50% greater at night than during the day. Preliminary calculations suggest that these fluxes are amongst the highest recorded during the deployment period, but systematic variations between day/night and different depth deployments are not apparent in the data. These changes probably reflect variations in phytoplankton abundances or variations associated with herbivores grazing on phytoplankton (Staresinic, 1982; Staresinic *et al.*, 1982).

From the ketone concentrations in the surface sediment, we have calculated that this is equivalent to an accumulation rate of 7.8 $\mu g/m^2$ 12 h. In this calculation we have assumed a sedimentation rate of 1.1 cm/yr, based on Pb–210 data for nearby cores (Henrichs, 1980), a sediment water content of 80% and a wet sediment density of 1.2 g/cm^3. Errors in these assumptions could introduce an error of at most $\pm 50\%$. The calculated accumulation rate is three times larger than the maximum flux measured through 52 m but comparable to the value calculated for FST 10 (Table 5). Given the uncertainties of the calculations, the large temporal and spatial variations influxes, and the problem of comparing sediment trap data which integrates the flux over 8 to 12 h and a surface sediment sample which integrates over one year, the agreement is surprisingly good. By comparison, a similar calculation of the flux of total 16:0 fatty acid (Wakeham *et al.*, 1982) indicated a sediment accumulation rate which was at least 20 times less than the flux through 52 m.

These calculations suggest that these very long-chain ketones are relatively resistant to degradation and thus their concentration in the sediment is an approximate measure of the input flux. This is consistent with feeding experiments which show that these long-chain ketones are not measurably assimilated by a copepod, *Calanus helgolandicus*. The occurrence of these compounds in 6 million year old sediments from the Japan Trench illustrates the survival of these compounds in the sediment record (Volkman *et al.*, 1980b). However, some evidence suggestive of degradation is the marked decrease in the ratios of triunsaturated to diunsaturated ketones with sediment depth (Table 4). Some proportion of these changes is due to processes occurring in the water column since in some of the sediment trap particulate material (e.g. FSTs 8, 9 and 10) the 37:2 ketone was slightly more abundant than the 37:3 ketone. At present we have no information concerning what products might be formed by such degradation. Much of the organic matter in the sediment traps is associated with fecal pellets so this change in ratio may be effected by grazer organisms such as anchoveta, copepods and euphausiids. In some sedimentary environments, such as anoxic Unit 1 sediments in the Black Sea, the ratio of 37:3 to 37:2 methyl ketones is very similar to that in *E. huxleyi* suggesting that little degradation has occurred. It may be that this ratio contains information as to the redox conditions of the depositional environment or processes occurring in the water column, but more data are required to test this.

SUMMARY AND CONCLUSIONS

The data presented in this paper illustrate the variety of sources contributing lipids to sediments in an area of coastal upwelling off Peru. Since the marine productivity in this area is very high and land plant and animal life is sparse on the coast, one would expect to see a high proportion of lipids attributable to phytoplankton in the sediment, but the hydrocarbon and ketone fractions do not reflect this. This is not surprising since the main primary producers, diatoms, do not biosynthesize large amounts of ketones or hydrocarbons, except the alkene n-$C_{21:6}$ which is rapidly degraded. The branched C_{25} acyclic alkenes may reflect this high productivity but the origin of these alkenes is still uncertain. One phytoplankter, *Emiliania huxleyi* could be the source of the C_{37}–C_{39} alkenes and unsaturated ketones, but this alga is ubiquitous in the oceans and the presence of these compounds does not necessarily imply high productivity. Other biological marker compounds, such as sterols, fatty acids and carotenoids (Gagosian *et al.*, 1982a,b; Repeta and Gagosian, 1982; Wakeham *et al.*, 1982), which are biosynthesized in large amounts by phytoplankton, are probably better markers of high productivity areas.

These lipid fractions do show an unexpectedly large contribution of higher plant lipids to the inshore BC7 sediments which is confirmed by the presence of C_{20}–C_{30} fatty acids and alcohols, C_{38}–C_{54} saturated alkyl esters and 24-ethylcholest-5-en-3β-ol (authors' unpublished data). This lipid signature is barely detectable in the offshore SC5 and GR27 surface sediments.

The lipid data suggest a rapid turnover of the more labile, unsaturated compounds in the surface sediment layers. Since most of these are from autochthonous sources, such as phytoplankton, those lipids from higher plants become relatively more important with depth. As a consequence, it is difficult to distinguish the hydrocarbon composition of the 16–19 cm section from that found in lake sediment. The reasons for the greater stability of these plant lipids is not known; either it is due to the absence of unsaturation and long chain-length or due to their physical association in the sediment which limits microbial degradation.

The role of the *Thioploca*-dominated microbial population in these sediments as a source of lipids or as an agent for their degradation is not clear. Bacteria may be the source of the C_{20}–C_{35} n-alkane distributions which show no predominance of odd or even carbon chain-lengths. It is worth emphasizing that, despite the great number of hydrocarbon studies which have been carried out, no conclusive statement as to the origin of most of the hydrocarbons in the offshore sediments can be made at this time. We also suggest that the n-alkan-2-ones derive from allochthonous sources and not from *in situ* oxidation of n-alkanes. The use of these compounds as biological markers for *in situ* microbial activity would thus seem to be inadvisable. Clearly, even for these well studied compound classes there are major gaps in our knowledge.

Acknowledgements

We thank Dr Victor Gallardo and Dr Nick Staresinic for very useful discussions and Dr Nelson Frew for obtaining mass spectra. This work was funded by Grants OCE 79–08665, OCE 77–26084 and OCE 80–18436 from the National Science Foundation, Grant N00014–79–C–0071 from the Office of Naval Research and a W.H.O.I. Postdoctoral Scholar award to J.K.V., Woods Hole Oceanographic Institution Contribution No. 5079.

REFERENCES

Albro, P. W. and Dittmer, J. C. (1970) Bacterial hydrocarbons: occurrence, structure and metabolism. *Lipids* **5**, 320–325.

Arpino, P., Albrecht, P. and Ourisson, G. (1970) Séries homologues aliphatiques dans un sédiment éocène d'origine lacustre. *C.R. Acad. Sci., Sér D* **270**, 1760–1763.

Barrick, R. C., Hedges, J. I. and Peterson, M. L. (1980) Hydrocarbon geochemistry of the Puget Sound region. I. Sedimentary acyclic hydrocarbons. *Geochim. Cosmochim. Acta* **44**, 1349–1362.

Barrick, R. C. and Hedges, J. I. (1981) Hydrocarbon geochemistry of the Puget Sound region. II. Sedimentary diterpenoid, steroid and triterpenoid hydrocarbons. *Geochim. Cosmochim. Acta* **45**, 381–392.

Blumer, M., Guillard, R. R. L. and Chase, T. (1971) Hydrocarbons of marine phytoplankton. *Mar. Biol.* **8**, 183–189.

Boehm, P. D. and Quinn, J. G. (1978) Benthic hydrocarbons of Rhode Island Sound. *Estuarine Coastal Mar. Sci.* **6**, 471–498.

Brassell, S. C., Comet, P. A., Eglinton, G., Isaacson, P. J., McEvoy, J., Maxwell, J. R., Thomson, I. D., Tibbetts, P. J. C. and Volkman, J. K. (1980) The origin and fate of lipids in the Japan Trench. In *Advances in Organic Geochemistry, 1979*, ed. by Douglas, A. G. and Maxwell, J. R. Pergamon Press, pp. 375–392.

Brooks, P. W. and Maxwell, J. R. (1974) Early stage fate of phytol in a recently deposited lacustrine sediment. In *Advances in Organic Geochemistry, 1973*, ed. by Tissot, B. and Bienner, F. Editions Technip, Paris, pp. 977–991.

Brooks, P. W., Maxwell, J. R. and Patience, R. L. (1978) Stereochemical relationships between phytol and phytanic acid, dihydrophytol and C_{18} ketone in Recent sediments. *Geochim. Cosmochim. Acta* **42**, 1175–1180.

Calvin, M. (1969) *Chemical Evolution*. Oxford University Press.

Cranwell, P. A. (1976) Decomposition of aquatic biota and

sediment formation: organic compounds in detritus resulting from microbial attack on the alga *Ceratium hirundinella. Freshwater Biol.* **6**, 41–48.

Cranwell, P. A. (1977) Organic geochemistry of Cam Loch (Sutherland) sediments. *Chem. Geol.* **20**, 205–221.

Davis, J. B. (1968) Paraffinic hydrocarbons in the sulfate-reducing bacterium *Desulfovibrio desulfuricans. Chem. Geol.* **3**, 155–160.

De Leeuw, J. W., v. d. Meer, F. W. and Rijpstra, W. I. C. (1980) On the occurrence and structural identification of long-chain unsaturated ketones and hydrocarbons in recent and subrecent sediments. In *Advances in Organic Geochemistry, 1979*, ed. by Douglas, A. G. and Maxwell, J. R. Pergamon Press, Oxford, pp. 211–217.

Ertel, J. R. (1978) The fate of phytol in the sea surface microlayer. M.Sc. Thesis, the Florida State University, College of Arts and Sciences. 36 pp.

Farrington, J. W., Frew, N. M., Gschwend, P. M. and Tripp, B. W. (1977) Hydrocarbons in cores of Northwestern Atlantic coastal and continental margin sediments. *Estuarine Coastal Mar. Sci.* **5**, 793–808.

Farrington, J. W. (1980) An overview of the biogeochemistry of fossil fuel hydrocarbons in the marine environment. *Advances in Chemistry Series, No. 185. Petroleum in the marine environment.* American Chemical Society, pp. 1–22.

Gagosian, R. B., Loder, T., Nigrelli, G., Mlodzinska, Z., Love, J. and Kogelschatz, J. (1980) Hydrographic and nutrient data from R/V *Knorr* cruise 73, leg 2 — February to March, 1978 — off the coast of Peru. Technical Report WHOI–80–1. Woods Hole Oceanographic Institution.

Gagosian, R. B., Volkman, J. K. and Nigrelli, G. E. (1982a) The use of sediment traps to determine sterol sources in coastal sediments off Peru. In *Advances in Organic Geochemistry, 1981*, ed. by Bjorøy, M. This volume.

Gagosian, R. B., Nigrelli, G. E. and Volkman, J. K. (1982b) Vertical transport and transformation of biogenic organic compounds from a sediment trap experiment off the coast of Peru. NATO Advanced Research Institute on Coastal Upwelling and its Sediment Record, ed. by Suess, E. and Thiede, J. Plenum Press, New York (in press).

Gallardo, V. (1977) Large benthic microbial communities in sulphide biota under Peru–Chile subsurface countercurrent. *Nature (London)* **268**, 331–332.

Grob, K. and Grob, K. Jr. (1978) On-column injection onto glass capillary columns. *J. Chromatogr.* **151**, 311–320.

Grob, K. Jr. (1979) Evaluation of injection techniques for triglycerides in capillary gas chromatography. *J. Chromatogr.* **178**, 387–392.

Grob, K. (1980) Persilylation of glass capillary columns. Part 4: Discussion of parameters. *J. High Resol. Chromatogr. and Chromatogr. Commun.* **4**, 493–496.

Henrichs, S. M. (1980) Biogeochemistry of dissolved free amino acids in marine sediments. Ph.D. Thesis. Massachusetts Institute of Technology/Woods Hole Oceanographic Institution. WHOI–80–39.

Henrichs, S. M., Farrington, J. W. and Lee, C. (1982) Peru upwelling region sediments near 15° S — II. Dissolved free and total hydrolyzable amino acids. *Limnol. Oceanogr.* (submitted for publication).

Honjo, S. and Roman, M. R. (1978) Marine copepod fecal pellets: production, preservation and sedimentation. *J. Mar. Res.* **36**, 45–57.

Honjo, S. (1980) Material fluxes and modes of sedimentation in the mesopelagic and bathypelagic zones. *J. Mar. Res.* **38**, 53–97.

Ikan, R., Baedecker, M. J. and Kaplan, I. R. (1973) C_{18}-isoprenoid ketone in Recent marine sediments. *Nature (London)* **244**, 154–155.

Johnson, R. W. and Calder, J. A. (1973) Early diagenesis of fatty acids and hydrocarbons in a salt marsh environment. *Geochim. Cosmochim. Acta* **37**, 1943–1955.

Knauer, G. A., Martin, J. H. and Bruland, K. W. (1979) Fluxes of particulate carbon, nitrogen and phosphorus in the upper water column of the northeast Pacific. *Deep Sea Res.* **26A**, 97–108.

Lee, C. and Cronin, C. (1982) The vertical flux of particulate organic nitrogen in the sea: decomposition of amino acids in the Peru upwelling area and the equatorial Atlantic. *J. Mar. Res.* **40**, 227–251.

Morrison, R. I. and Bick, W. (1966) Long-chain methyl ketones in soils. *Chem. Ind.* pp. 596–597.

Morrison, R. I. and Bick, W. (1967) The wax fraction of soils: separation and determination of some components. *J. Sci. Food Agric.* **18**, 351–355.

Murray, J., Thomson, A. B., Stagg, A., Hardy, R., Whittle, K. J. and Mackie, P. R. (1977) On the origin of hydrocarbons in marine organisms. *Rapp. P.V. Réun. Cons. Int. Explor Mer* **171**, 84–90.

Prahl, F. G. and Carpenter, R. (1971) The role of zooplankton fecal pellets in the sedimentation of polycyclic aromatic hydrocarbons in Dabob Bay, Washington. *Geochim. Cosmochim. Acta* **43**, 1959–1972.

Prahl, F. G., Bennett, J. T. and Carpenter, R. (1980) The early diagenesis of aliphatic hydrocarbons and organic matter in sedimentary particulates from Dabob Bay, Washington. *Geochim. Cosmochim. Acta* **44**, 1967–1976.

Repeta, D. and Gagosian, R. B. (1982) Carotenoid transformation products in the upwelled waters off the Peruvian coast. In *Advances in Organic Geochemistry, 1981*, ed. by Bjorøy, M. This volume.

Richter, I. and Krain, H. (1981) Cuticular lipid constituents of cabbage seedpod weevils and host plant oviposition sites as potential pheromones. *Lipids* **15**, 580–586.

Rosato, V. J., Kulm, L. D. and Derks, P. S. (1975) Surface sediments of the Nazca plate. *Pacific Sci.* **29**, 117–130.

Ryther, J. H., Menzel, D. W., Hulbert, E. M., Lorenzen, C. J. and Corwin, N. (1971) The production and utilization of organic matter in the Peru coastal current. *Invest. Pesq.* **35**, 43–59.

Simoneit, B. R. T., Mazurek, M. A., Brenner, S., Crisp, P. T. and Kaplan, I. R. (1979) Organic geochemistry of recent sediments from Guaymas Basin, Gulf of California. *Deep Sea Res.* **26A**, 879–891.

Staresinic, N. (1980) The vertical flux of particulate organic matter in the Peru coastal upwelling as measured with a free-drifting sediment trap. Ph.D. Thesis. Massachusetts Institute of Technology/Woods Hole Oceanographic Institution. WHOI–80–4.

Staresinic, N. (1982) Downward flux of bulk particulate organic matter in the Peru coastal upwelling. *J. Mar. Res.* (in press).

Staresinic, N., Farrington, J. W., Gagosian, R. B., Clifford, C. H. and Hulburt, E. M. (1982) Downward transport of particulate matter in the Peru coastal upwelling: role of the anchoveta, *Engraulis ringens*. NATO Advanced Research Institute on Coastal Upwelling and its Sediment Record, ed. by Suess, E. and Thiede, J. Plenum Press, New York (in press).

Telkova, M. S., Rodionova, K. F., Shlyakhov, A. F. and Dyuzhikova, T. N. (1976) Normal and isoprene hydrocarbons in the modern oceanic and marine sediments. *Geochem. Int.* **13**, 84–90.

Volkman, J. K., Corner, E. D. S. and Eglinton, G. (1980a) Transformations of biolipids in the marine food web and in underlying bottom sediments. In *Colloques Internationaux du C.N.R.S. No. 293. Biogéochimie de la matière organique à l'interface eau sédiment marin*, pp. 185–197.

Volkman, J. K., Eglinton, G., Corner, E. D. S. and Sargent, J.

R. (1980b) Novel unsaturated straight-chain C_{37}–C_{39} methyl and ethyl ketones in marine sediments and a coccolithophore *Emiliania huxleyi*. In *Advances in Organic Geochemistry, 1979*, ed by Douglas, A. G. and Maxwell, J. R. Pergamon Press, Oxford, pp. 219–227.

Volkman, J. K., Eglinton, G., Corner, E. D. S. and Forsberg, T. E. V. (1980c) Long-chain alkenes and alkenones in the marine coccolithophorid *Emiliania huxleyi*. *Phytochemistry* **19**, 2619–2622.

Volkman, J. K., Johns, R. B., Gillan, F. T., Perry, G. J. and Bavor, H. J. Jr. (1980d) Microbial lipids of an intertidal sediment. I. Fatty acids and hydrocarbons. *Geochim. Cosmochim. Acta* **44**, 1133–1143.

Volkman, J. K., Smith, D. J., Eglinton, G., Forsberg, T. E. V. and Corner, E. D. S. (1981a) Sterol and fatty acid composition of four marine Haptophycean algae. *J. Mar. Biol. Assoc. U.K.* **61**, 509–527.

Volkman, J. K., Gillan, F. T., Johns, R. B. and Eglinton, G.

(1981b) Sources of neutral lipids in a temperate intertidal sediment. *Geochim. Cosmochim. Acta* **45**, 1817–1828.

Wakeham, S. G., Farrington, J. W., Gagosian, R. B., Lee, C., De Baar, H., Nigrelli, G., Tripp, B. W., Smith, S. O. and Frew, N. M. (1980) Organic matter fluxes from sediment traps in the Equatorial Atlantic Ocean. *Nature (London)* **286**, 798–800.

Wakeham, S. G., Farrington, J. W. and Volkman, J. K. (1982) Fatty acids, wax esters, triglycerides and glyceryl ethers associated with particles collected in sediment traps in the Peru upwelling. In *Advances in Organic Geochemistry, 1981*, ed. by Bjorøy, M. This volume.

Wyrtki, K. (1963) The horizontal and vertical field of motion in the Peru Current. *Bulletin, Scripps Institution of Oceanography* **8**, 313–345.

Zuta, S., Rivera, T. and Bustamante, A. (1980) Hydrological aspects of the main upwelling areas off Peru. In *Upwelling Ecosystems*, ed. by Boze, R. and Tomczak, M. Springer–Verlag, Heidelberg, pp. 235–260.

Advances in Organic Geochemistry 1981, pp. 241–250
© *John Wiley & Sons Limited, 1983*

Preservation and Alteration of Present-Day Sedimentary Organic Matter

R. Pelet

Institut Francais du Pétrole, Avenue de Bois-Préan, 92500 Rueil-Malmaison, France

Extensive chemical measurements have been obtained during the four Orgon cruises on present-day and recent sedimentary organic matter. These show definite variations in the compositions of fractions: biochemicals, hydrocarbons, fatty acids, humic and fulvic acids and stable residues. The large background of geological and biological studies performed on Orgon samples permits these organic geochemical variations to be viewed in their sedimentological context. The most significant factor for these variations in the composition of the organic matter is its biological origin, which extends beyond the classical distinction between terrestrial and marine sources: important differences exist within planktonic organic matter depending on the dominant organisms in the region under study. Apart from these origin-induced differences, orderly variations remain which can be traced to predepositional alteration. Such alteration can take place for terrestrial organic matter first on the continent, by biological and/or chemical agents, then in the oceanic water column, and its intensity will therefore depend both on the climate, and on the binding of the organic matter with its mineral matrix; for marine organic matter, the alteration, mainly biological, can occur only in the oceanic waters. It is clear that a reduced mean oxygen content of oceanic water leads to an overall reduced rate of consumption of the sedimenting organic matter. The sedimentary, early-diagenetic alteration is difficult to evaluate, and anyway is one to two orders of magnitude quantitatively less intense than that occurring prior to deposition. One consequence is that the redox status of the water column is certainly more important for preservation of organic matter than the redox status of the sediment, which merely reflects the organic influx in the sediment. If an important supply of organic matter is a prerequisite for good preservation, the rate of preservation of this supply will always be high in environments with restricted circulation, whereas it can vary in open sea environments, depending more on regional than on local factors.

INTRODUCTION

In 1974 the 'Orgon' group was constituted by various French industrial and scientific organizations. With its loose and rather informal structure, this group was devoted to what can be termed the sedimentology of organic matter in present day oceans, namely organic geochemistry in its geographic–geologic context, with special emphasis on microbiological processes. Four cruises were conducted in widely different regions (Fig. 1; the Norwegian Sea in 1974, the Cariaco trench and the Western Atlantic Ocean offshore the Amazon River in 1975, the Eastern Atlantic Ocean offshore Mauretania and Senegal in 1976 and the Oman Sea and the Gulf of Aden in 1978) resulting in a number of basic data and studies published in the four volumes of the Orgon proceedings (Orgon I, 1977; Orgon II, 1978; Orgon III, 1979; Orgon IV, 1981) and in a number of papers grouped in the four cruise reports (Orgon 1, 1975, Orgon 2, 1977; Orgon 3, 1979; Orgon 4, 1980). In this paper the reader is referred to these proceedings and cruise reports for general details and for all pertinent data concerning the cruises themselves, the coring techniques, the retrieval and storage of the samples, and

the analytical techniques. The special value of the Orgon programme, compared to most other organic geochemical studies of oceanic cores arises from the number and variety of scope of disciplines involved in the examination of each core. This enables the organic geochemical interpretations to be considered in comparison with data from other disciplines, and inconsistencies eliminated.

For the various Orgon samples, all of the fractions of sedimentary organic matter usually distinguished (lipids, humic and fulvic acids, hydrolysable fraction, stable residue) have been analysed in various detail and in a fairly systematic manner, depending on the cruise, the cores etc . . . For consistency, and in order to include the greatest possible number of samples, this paper focuses on humic acids and stable residues, which together amount to 50—70% of the total organic carbon (Fig. 2). However, for each parameter, different numbers of samples have been analysed. To cite extremes, there are 213 elemental analyses of humic acids, but only 6 stable residues of terrestrial origin whose proportion of the total organic matter has been measured and for which elemental analyses are available. Moreover, it must be remembered that stable residues and humic acids are independent entities

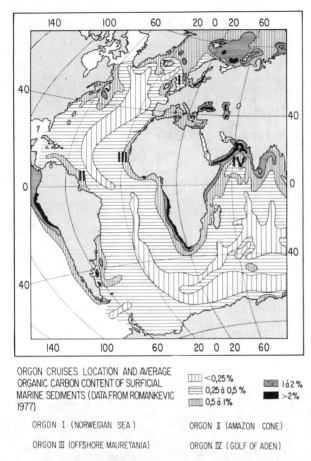

ORGON CRUISES LOCATION AND AVERAGE
ORGANIC CARBON CONTENT OF SURFICIAL
MARINE SEDIMENTS (DATA FROM ROMANKEVIC
1977)

<0,25 %
0,25 à 0,5 %
0,5 à 1%
1à2%
>2%

ORGON I (NORWEGIAN SEA)

ORGON III (OFFSHORE MAURETANIA)

ORGON II (AMAZON CONE)

ORGON IV (GOLF OF ADEN)

Fig. 1. Geographic locations of Orgon cruises.

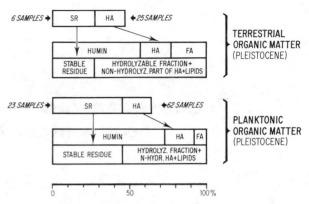

Fig. 2. Average fractional composition of terrestrial and planktonic organic matter.

(stable residues do not include any portion of humic acids, and vice versa) and are not obtained from the same isolation scheme, humic acids being hydrolysable (Fig. 2). The data used in this paper are to be found in the respective Orgon volumes, especially in papers by Debyser *et al.* (1977, 1978, 1979, 1981); when other sources of data are used, they are stated.

VARIATIONS IN THE COMPOSITION OF THE SEDIMENTARY ORGANIC MATTER

Fractional compositional variations

After lipid extraction (with chloroform) two types of fractionation are performed:

(a) Cold, alkaline solution (here NaOH + Na pyrophosphate) is used to recover humic and fulvic acids; the remainder of the organic matter, which is not separated from the mineral matrix, is termed 'humin'.

(b) Following acid hydrolysis (boiling HCl 6 N) of the humin, destruction of the mineral matrix by HF/HCl gives the stable residue, which should not be confused with the humin.

I shall not comment further on the lipids, which are a minor constituent (from 0.1 to 5% of total organic carbon) the size of which does not show obvious trends depending on the biological origin. Although the

detailed composition of some lipid fractions (*n*-alkanes, *n*-alkenes, cyclanes, cyclenes, isoprenoids, fatty acids etc.) may show some relation with biological factors, it is a huge subject that will not be dealt with here.

If we now consider the results of the two different fractionations described above some regularities appear (Fig. 2). The most clearcut concerns the fulvic acids and the stable residues: terrestrial organic matter, on average, contains double the quantity of fulvic acids but only half the amount of stable residue of planktonic organic matter. In addition to the average values shown in Fig. 2, the values of the fulvic acid contents of individual samples (Fig. 3) cluster about the average values, whereas those for the stable residue contents are more dispersed. In Fig. 3 it can be seen that the samples with the smallest stable residues for planktonic organic matter come from Orgon III, where a small continental supply is always present and mainly from two cores, KL 10 and KL 11. This point will be discussed in detail hereafter, but it is an indication that consideration of factors other than the origin of the organic matter can explain the observed dispersion of some parameters.

Elemental compositional variations

In the previous section no trend is apparent in the content of humic acids. The elemental composition of humic acids and stable residues (elemental analysis of fulvic acids was performed only for Orgon IV samples so that they cannot be used in this comparison) is given in Fig. 4, using the same points as in Fig. 3, with the exception of those from Orgon III. A clear differentiation between products of terrestrial and of planktonic origin can be seen. More precisely, marine materials are richer in hydrogen and nitrogen (elements which, incidentally, are generally related in the organic matter of recent sediments), and terrestrial humic acids are richer in oxygen (as are humic acids from soils, see e.g. Huc and Durand, 1974; see also Kalle, 1966). Compared to average estimates for the composition of living, marine or terrestrial organic matter (Fig. 4, see Appendix for the construction of the representative points) humic acids contain less hydrogen and, for marine ones only, also less nitrogen. Even though the estimate for the composition of terrestrial organic matter is not very reliable (see Appendix), the difference in the

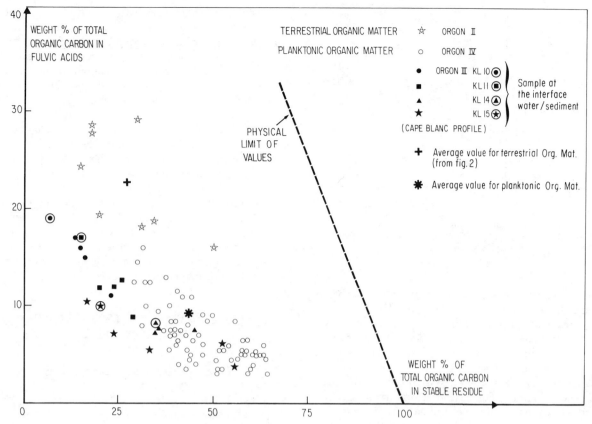

Fig. 3. Stable residue versus fulvic acid contents for Orgon II, III and IV samples.

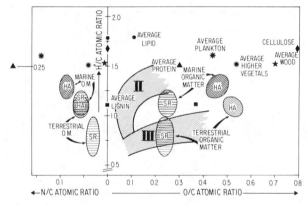

Fig. 4. Average chemical composition of humic acids, and stable residues of marine and terrestrial organic matter, compared to the average chemical composition of some biopolymers.

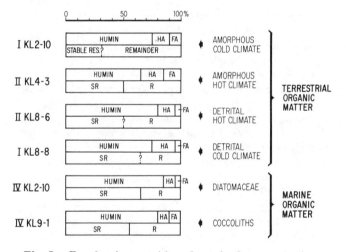

Fig. 5. Fractional composition of samples from contrasting environments.

nitrogen values is too great to be a simple artefact. It certainly corresponds to a fundamental difference in humic acid formation processes — perhaps amino aromatic condensation products of terrestrial origin are more stable than amino sugars condensation products of marine origin; this is a reasonable guess, but no more. Compared to humic acids the N/C ratios of the stable residues are lower, whereas the differences in O/C ratios of samples from marine and terrestrial origins have virtually disappeared although the differences in their H/C ratios remain. These observations can be tentatively explained as a disappearance of all the labile

functional oxygen-containing groups (acidic and alcoholic).

Discussion

Clearly, the distinction between terrestrial and planktonic organic matter is only general. It is not possible, however, to introduce any more precise environmental distinction with statistically based conclusions, given the small number of samples available within each precise category and appropriate analyses.

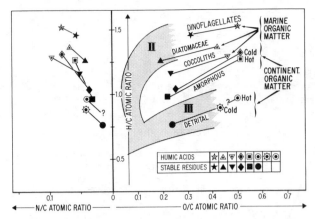

Fig. 6. Chemical composition of humic acids and stable residues from the samples of Fig. 5, plus a sample from the Black Sea (cf. text).

As a consequence the following points which are based on individual samples, are not definitive. Figure 5 shows the variations in the fractional composition of six selected samples that differ in certain environmental factors. The differences between the two marine samples cannot be considered, for they may be a consequence of diagenesis, since the diatomaceous sample is older than the coccolithic one. For terrestrial organic matter, no trend related to the influence of climate is apparent. The amorphous organic matter, however, is richer in fulvic acids and poorer in stable residue than the detrital one; and comparing this observation with the above the detrital fraction of terrestrial organic matter appears more 'planktonic' than the amorphous one, which is rather paradoxical. If, however, the elemental analyses of the same samples are considered (Fig. 6) this last paradox disappears, since the detrital fraction is leaner in hydrogen than the amorphous one, and consequently farther from 'planktonic' organic matter. Again the distinction between hot and cold climates shows no systematic trend. In contrast, the difference between the diatomaceous and organic matter is now significant, with the older sample richer in hydrogen than the younger one, contrary to the general trend of diagenesis (Huc, 1980). An additional point (from the Black Sea, cf. Pelet and Debyser, 1977) for another type of plankton (dinoflagellates) has been added in Fig. 6. This point extends the range of the compositional variations of marine organic matter and clearly demonstrates the possibility that planktonic organic matter can vary between limits as dispersed as those for continental organic matter. It can be seen that, to some extent, coccolithic material differs from the general correlation between H/C and N/C.

Conclusion

As predicted, definite variations in the composition of sedimentary organic matter related to its origin have been observed. In addition, three novel aspects have been recognized:

(i)   From the background of Orgon studies, it has been possible to ascertain the origin of the organic

material under examination, and to interpret the corresponding variations in composition.

(ii) It appears that, independent of mixing or diagenetic processes, planktonic matter can exhibit large variations in composition, resulting from the thriving of specific planktonic forms under specific environmental conditions. In other words, a typical 'equilibrium' mixture representing a world ocean phytoplanktonic background does not occur anywhere.

(iii) The examination of Fig. 6 shows clearly that the area of the Van Krevelen diagram between organic matter types II and III, as defined by Tissot *et al.* (1971), Albrecht *et al.* (1976), and summarized by Durand (1980) is covered by varieties of marine (closer to type II) then terrestrial (closer to type III) organic matter. Such variations are again independent of any mixing effects or diagenetic processes.

ALTERATION IN THE MARINE ENVIRONMENT

The Cape Blanc and Sukra alteration profiles

It has been noted above that samples from Orgon III KL 10 and KL 11 cores fall within a zone entirely

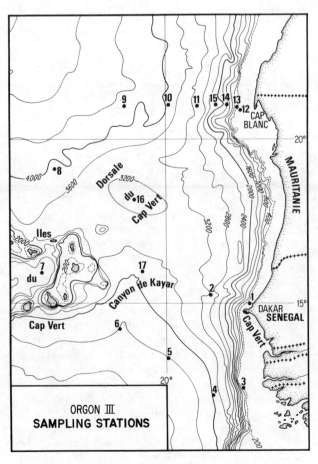

Fig. 7. Geographic setting of Orgon III cruise.

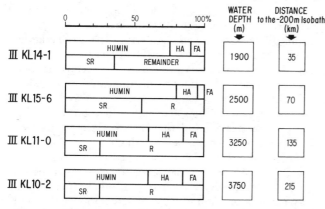

Fig. 8. Fractional composition of four samples along the Cape Blanc profile. (Sample ages 14–1: *ca* 12 000 a; 15–6: *ca* 20 00 a; 11–0: *ca* 8000 a; 10–2: 20 000 a. Closer age spacings are not possible due to the unavailability of stable residues for appropriate samples.)

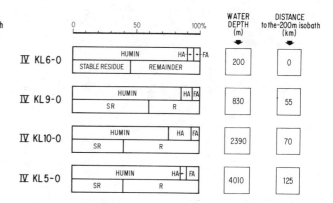

Fig. 10. Fractional composition of four samples along the Sukra profile.

distinct from that of planktonic Orgon IV samples and Orgon III KL 15 and KL 14 cores (Fig. 3). Consequently, all Orgon III data were omitted in Fig. 4, awaiting the present discussion. If we now consider the geographic setting of the Orgon III locations (Fig. 7), it is apparent that the profile KL 14–15–11–10 in that order, forms a relative alteration profile. Indeed, the major source of organic matter in this region is the seasonal planktonic bloom due to the upwelling which occurs between KL 14 and the shore, in shallow waters, and consequently the distance and duration of the transportation of organic matter to deeper and deeper

waters increases as one goes from KL 14 to KL 10, with the latter lying at the edge of the abyssal plain. Some orderly variation is apparent in Fig. 3, but the samples represented differ in age and, consequently, probably differ in diagenetic status and perhaps in paleoenvironmental conditions of deposition. To avoid these problems, comparisons can be made between samples of closely related ages, which are shown for the fractional composition and for elemental composition in Fig. 8 and Fig. 11, respectively. The success of this approach led us to produce this type of plot elsewhere when possible, although the only other suitable sample suite is that of the Orgon IV Sukra profile (see Fig. 9) for Orgon IV locations). Comparing Figs 8 and 10, the transportation distances are much shorter for the Sukra

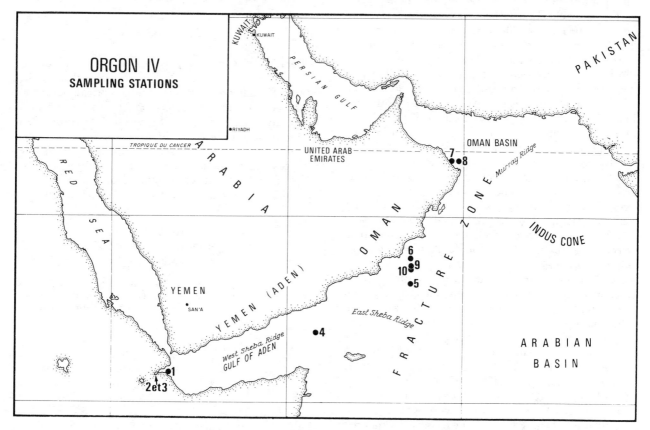

Fig. 9. Geographic setting of Orgon IV cruise.

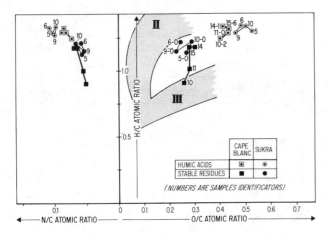

Fig. 11. Chemical composition of humic acids and stable residues from the samples of Figs. 8 and 10.

profile than for Cape Blanc, and result in a smaller effect, if any, on their compositions (Figs 10 and 11). This result is also to be expected from consideration of the low oxygen content of the water of the Gulf of Aden compared to the Atlantic Ocean (see under, Daumas *et al.* 1979 and Garleno *et al.*, 1980).

Discussion

The variations in composition observed due to marine transportation and subsequent, essentially biological, oxidation are real and occur in the direction expected (loss of hydrogen and nitrogen), but are relatively unimportant. On the Sukra profile alone, such variations would not have been suspected, and it is only for the Cape Blanc profile, with distances of more than 250 km with smooth slopes (i.e. long transportation times) that they became evident. The reason for this observation is clear; only a differential effect is observed. The organic matter sedimented even very close to the areas of production has already suffered important biological degradation, and the extent of this marine alteration of sedimentary organic matter can be inferred for its planktonic component by consideration of Fig. 4: the discrepancy between the point representing 'average plankton' and the zones for humic acids and stable residues of marine organic matter gives an idea of this presedimentary alteration, and shows that it is in fact very important. In addition only qualitative variations have been considered, which are the reflection of a selective destruction of the more labile fractions of the organic matter. For the Cape Blanc profile, as a first approximation, it may be assumed that the mineral fraction of the sediments remains unchanged for all cores. Hence, only the organic matter suffers alteration. The average organic carbon content of the cores therefore provides an indication of the quantitative alteration. These values are KL 14 = 1.61%, KL 15 = 1.98%, KL 11 = 0.98%, KL 10 = 0.54% for Orgon III and for Sukra (Orgon IV) KL 6 = 0.95%, KL 9 = 2.55%, KL 10 = 1.79%, KL 5 = 0.97%. Over two-thirds of the organic matter have been lost between KL 14–15 and KL 10 or KL 9 and KL 5 — but we also know that this differential alteration is small relative to the total, which

consumes 98–99% of the total primary production (extreme estimations 91–99%, the first one being rather unlikely, see e.g. Garrels and Perry, 1974; Romankevic, 1977; Muller and Suess, 1979, this last work refines previous global preservation rates by the consideration of interesting correlations with sedimentation rates, but in a rather dogmatic manner). Finally, due to the lack of pertinent data, nothing has been said about terrestrial organic matter. Considering the discrepancy between the point representing 'average higher plants' and the zones for the terrestrial humic acids and stable residues (Fig. 4) it can be seen that presedimentary alteration is qualitatively as severe for this type of organic matter as it is for that of planktonic origin. There is some indication that the bulk of this alteration takes place during subaerial weathering and transportation, but more data is needed to go further.

Another unsolved problem is the qualitative and quantitative effect of benthic consumption of organic matter. The data to hand are insufficient to make firm conclusions: none exist for qualitative effects, and quantitative values are doubtful since they assume that environmental conditions remained completely constant during the deposition of the samples considered. Such effects are, however, of a different order of magnitude from those of presedimentary alteration. The most significant decrease in the organic carbon content is in the 0–22 cm zone (a reasonable depth for benthic activity) of core KR 7 from Orgon IV, which has a high content of microbes and among the highest meiofauna content. Table 1 shows that the effect is at most a one-third reduction, which makes it almost negligible compared to presedimentary alteration.

Conclusion

Alteration of sedimentary planktonic organic matter in the marine environment has been observed from the study of its differential effects on cores taken at increasing distance from the primary production zone. From a qualitative point of view, although such alteration can have important effects, the differences in the origin of the organic matter always remain apparent from the composition of the samples. Thus, the effects of post-depositional alteration on the composition of the sedimentary organic matter are either slight or

Table 1
Orgon IV KR 7 Core

Depth in the core (cm)	Organic carbon content (weight %)	Number of meiofauna individuals (in 10 cm²)	Microbial content of the core (10³ cells/ml)
0–2	5.52	548	79
2–4	5.20	164	29
10–12	4.80	n.d. (usually 0)	2
20–22	4.00	n.d. (usually 0)	4

Basic data from Sautriot (1981), Romano and Dinet (1981), Bensoussan *et al.* (1980).

dependent on the origin of the organic matter. This latter assumption seems probable, especially when the quantitative effects of the presedimentary alteration are considered. However, from the above, these quantitative effects cannot be explained simply from local sedimentary conditions. Indeed the question of the quantitative preservation of the organic matter must be considered in more general terms.

OVERALL PRESERVATION OF SEDIMENTARY ORGANIC MATTER

General

The expression 'preservation of sedimentary organic matter' is fraught with ambiguity, since it is often taken to be equivalent to 'presence of high contents of sedimentary organic matter'. Conceptually one can imagine an environment where an initial low input of organic matter could result in a low content of sedimentary organic matter, but with a very high preservation rate. In fact, we have no quantitative basis for preservation processes *sensu stricto*, hence the question remains entirely theoretical, and following general usage, we shall consider conditions favourable or unfavourable to high accumulations of organic matter.

A distinction must be made between concentrations and quantities accumulated, with the latter related to the former by the rate of sedimentation. Such distinction is useful in that it separates environments with negligible detrital continental supply, with low sedimentation rates and where high concentrations may result in low accumulated quantities of organic matter, from detrital environments with high sedimentation rates, and where low concentrations may result in high accumulated quantities of organic matter.

Discussion

We have seen above that, in quantitative terms, the destruction of organic matter in the water column before sedimentation is, by far, the most important alteration process. In general, 1–2% of the formerly-living organic matter escapes biological recycling. With such a system, the greatest initial organic supply does not produce the highest escape from the cycle *a priori*. This hypothesis is nevertheless the simplest, and it can be seen (Table 2) that high concentrations and accumulated quantities are, as a rule, present only in zones with a high supply of organic matter, a fact further corroborated by the data of Muller and Suess (1979). Another consequence of the relative importance of pre- and post-depositional alterations is that the redox status of the water column is a more important factor than the redox status of the sediment. This can be seen in Table 2, where the oxygen

Table 2

Sampling location				Water characteristics							Surficial sediment characteristics			
				Oxygen content (ppm)			Redox potential mV (H₂ electrode)					Organic carbon		
Name	Organic supply	Geo-graphic setting	Depth (m)	In the water column	At the sediment/ water interface		Inter-face	−15 cm layer	Type of environ-ment	Specific gravity[a] g/cm³	Rate of sedimen-tation cm/10³.a	Content weight %	Accumu-lation mg/cm².a
Orgon II St. 22	Low	Shelf	23	—	6.5 (over saturated)		+265	+210	Oxidized	1.48	<40[b]	0.58	<0.34
Orgon II St. 8	Low	Abyssal plain	4300	n.d.	8.8 (100% saturated)		+320	+395	Oxidized	1.37	⩽5	0.44	⩽0.03
Orgon IV St. 6	High	Shelf	200	3.84 (88% Sat.)	0.80 (13% Sat.)		+220	−210	Reduced	1.57	⩾15[c]	1.32	⩾0.31
Orgon IV St. 9	High	Oxygen minimum zone	830	2.32 (53% Sat.)	1.40 (21% Sat.)		+180	−150	Reduced	1.47	<15[d]	6.88	<1.52
Orgon III St. 10	Medium	Abyssal plain	3750	n.d.	7.36 (90% Sat.)		+220	+200	Oxidized	1.29	~5	0.50	~0.03
Orgon II St. 1	Medium	Barred basin (trench)	1350	<0.80 (below 300 m)	0.80 (15% Sat.)		−120	−150	Anoxic	1.26	>75	2.53	>2.39

Basic data from: Daumas *et al.* (1977), Moyes *et al.* (1978), Daumas *et al.* (1979), Moyes *et al.* (1979), Garlenc *et al.* (1980), Moyes *et al.* (1981).
[a] Calculated by averaging the water contents of the measured layers in KR cores.
[b] By analogy with KS 20 and 21.
[c] Very rough estimation.
[d] Recalculated.
n.d.: not determined.

Table 3
Description of the environments samples at the various Orgon stations

Cruise	Station number	Holocene	Pleistocene
Orgon I	1, 2, 3, 4, 5, 6, 7, 15	Norwegian Channel, sediment trap on the shelf. Mineral and organic supply mainly from the continent, especially the British Isles, deposited by suspension processes. Cold climate, very high sedimentation rates.	*Idem*, when encountered (stations 6, 7, 15)
	8, 9, 10, 11, 12, 13, 14	Continental slope. Mineral and organic matter mainly from the continent, deposited by turbidity currents. Often no sedimentation in the holocene. Cold climate.	Glacial sedimentation ('tillites' for stations 8 and 9). Turbidites for stations 11, 12 and 14. Not encountered at station 10.
Orgon II	1	Cariaco trench. Barred basin of tectonic origin, sediment trap in the shelf. Bottom waters anoxic. Mineral supply mainly of continental origin (Orinoco River sediments) deposited by turbidity currents. Organic supply mainly of marine origin, microbial component noticeable. High sedimentation rate.	*Idem*. Glacial stages correspond to non-anoxic periods.
	2, 3, 4, 5	Continental slope between Orinoco and Amazon rivers zones of influence. Mineral and organic matter essentially from resedimentation of Amazon River sediments. Moderate sedimentation rate.	*Idem*. Rate of sedimentation more important.
	9, 20, 21, 22	Shelf. Mineral and organic matter essentially of continental origin, both very fine grained. Very high sedimentation rate.	Not encountered.
	10, 12, 13, 14, 15, 16, 17, 18, 19	Amazon cone. As above, with lower sedimentation rates.	Deltaic deposits, essentially fine grained clays and silts with plant debris. High sedimentation rates.
	6, 7, 8, 11	Abyssal plain. As above, with low sedimentation rates.	As above, but with coarser deposits.
Orgon III	8, 9, 10, 11, 12, 13, 14, 15, 16	Shelf, continental slope and abyssal plain offshore desertic land. Mineral matter mainly organogenic, organic matter essentially marine planktonic. Upwelling on the shelf: sedimentation rates high on slope, low on shelf and abyssal plain.	*Idem*.
	1, 2, 3, 4, 5, 6, 17	Shelf, continental slope and abyssal plain offshore forested, humid land. Many coastal rivers. Mineral and organic matter mostly continental. No upwelling, sedimentation rates as above.	*Idem*. with higher sedimentation rates during interglacial stages.
Orgon IV	2, 3	Ghubbet el Kharab. Lagoon. Continental (volcanic) mineral matter, planktonic organic matter. High sedimentation rate.	Organogenic diatomites in zone 5 (below 30 000 a BP)
	1, 4, 5, 6, 9, 10	Shelf, continental slope and abyssal plain offshore desertic land. As Orgon III stations 8 to 16, but with an upwelling more vigorous and extended, and consequently an organogenic character more intense. High organic content. Low mean oxygen content in the waters.	Organic content lower than in Holocene.
	7, 8	As above, but with a mineral continental supply more important. Upwelling more diffuse.	*Idem*.

content of the water column (oceanic oxygen concentration) shows a better correlation with organic accumulation than the oxygen content of the water at the sediment/ocean interface (local oxygen concentration). The latter concentration is greatly influenced by in-sediment processes (benthic consumption), which determine the redox status of the sediment. Indeed, environments with a low supply of organic matter always appear to be oxidizing (or more precisely, oxidized) and those with a high supply of organic matter appear to be more or less reducing (or more precisely reduced) depending on the effective supply at the location of sedimentation, on the benthic activity and finally on the redox status of the water column (Table 2).

Conclusion

The conditions favourable to a high concentration and accumulation of sedimentary organic matter are quite simple: the prerequisite is a high initial supply of organic matter, minimum predepositional alteration (biological recycling in the water column), then minimum postdepositional alteration (benthic consumption, resedimentation). A high supply of organic matter may be found in areas of high phytoplanktonic productivity, for instance upwelling regions, and of high continental matter supply (large deltas). Predepositional alteration is minimal when the oxygen content of the water column is zero (anoxic basins) and varies according to this parameter. Post-depositional alteration reaches a minimum when benthic activity is prevented (anoxic basins, regions with very high sedimentation rates).

CONCLUSIONS

We have observed compositional differences between organic matter of different origin, not only when terrestrial versus marine organic matter is considered, but also within these categories themselves. When considering marine planktonic matter, it seems that the regional dominance of a given biological species can result in deposits of organic matter with largely different properties. It happens that type II and III organic matter are the upper and lower compositional limits for marine and terrestrial organic material, respectively. If most terrestrial samples correspond to type III (see e.g. Durand, 1980), it appears that the dispersion of marine samples below the type II curve may be solely due to differences in their original material, without any consideration of mixing processes, which must be confirmed if invoked.

It has been shown that preservation of organic matter in the sedimentary record is much more dependent on regional oceanic conditions than on local environmental parameters. The two most important factors, a high organic supply and a minimum predepositional alteration, are determined on a regional basis. Benthic consumption, which is local, does not appear to be an important factor. The redox status of the sediment is a consequence, and not a cause, of the organic richness,

which has been shown directly. It is also a necessary consequence of the previous considerations. In contrast, the oxygen content of the water column is a highly significant factor, since it directly determines the intensity of predepositional alteration of organic matter. It is in this respect that anoxic basins are highly favourable to the concentration and accumulation of organic matter.

A final indirect proof of the dominant role of regional factors is given by the consideration of the organic matter content of all Orgon samples. Despite individual differences that are sometimes large, sensible regional groupings can be distinguished. The sediments of the Amazon cone lean in organic carbon or the medium values of sediments offshore West Africa, with oxygen saturated waters, are opposed to the sediment rich in organic matter from the Gulf of Aden or Cariaco Trench, with oxygen depleted waters. For planktonic marine organic matter at least, the key to the understanding of organic sedimentology essentially lies in the hands of oceanographers.

APPENDIX

It is difficult to find reliable estimates in the literature for the elemental composition of living matter. We have constructed our representative points beginning by phytoplanktonic matter as follows:

(1) The estimates of Milner (1953) in Foree and McCarty (1970) for average compositions of proteins ($C_{3.96}H_{6.12}O_{1.26}$ N) and lipids ($C_{18}H_{32}O_2$) of phytoplankton appear quite reasonable and are retained as basic data; we shall take $C_6(H_2O)_5$ as the estimate for polysaccharides composition.

(2) The estimate of Redfield *et al.* (1965) for the N/C ratio of phytoplankton (15.5:108) seems generally accepted (see e.g. Romankevic, 1977 or Mosetti, 1964). We shall assume that only proteins, polysaccharides and lipids make up phytoplanktonic matter, and take a proportion of 9% (dry weight) of lipids, which appears to be reasonable (see e.g. Degens and Matheja, 1968).

(3) These assumptions give $C_{6.97}H_{11.22}O_{3.10}$ N as the average formula for phytoplankton, hence its atomic ratios are H/C = 1.61, O/C = 0.44, N/C = 0.14 and the final proportions: proteins 55% (weight %), polysaccharides 36%, lipids 9%. This is the same result as that of Romankevic (1977), who does not give the basis of his calculation explicitly.

For terrestrial organic matter, the calculation is less simple. It is possible to obtain a reasonable estimate for lignin composition, from Freudenberg and Markin (1964) in Grusnikov and Elkin (1973), namely $CH_{1.10}O_{0.28}$, as well as an estimate of the average lignin content of terrestrial vegetation (20%). It is also possible to find (see e.g. Van Krevelen, 1961) estimates for average wood composition, but the only general and reliable estimates we know of are in Waksman (1938), which have rather large ranges of values, due to the very different composition of the different parts of higher plants. It is noteworthy that the terrestrial organic material submitted to transportation to sedimentary basins is not equivalent to the living biomass *in situ*: deciduous trees, for instance, lose their leaves each year, but their trunk and main branches only once; in view of this consideration, we shall now consider Waksman's estimate with the highest protein content, which corresponds to deciduous parts of plants. Finally, we shall take the following composition: proteins 15%, lipids 8%, lignin 20% and consequently polysaccharides 57%, which results in the ratios H/C = 1.52, O/C = 0.53, N/C = 0.04. Certain points however must be stressed: (i) this estimation is far less reliable than that for phytoplankton, (ii) it gives a composition very different from the phytoplankton composition, which can be explained by the fact that phytoplankters are almost entirely reproductive cells, whereas terrestrial plants have developed secondary specialized tissues, enriched in lignin and polysaccharides, the weight of which greatly outweighs that of reproductive cells, which are nitrogen-rich, (iii) the N/C value obtained appears very low, markedly lower than the N/C content of terrestrial humic acids. However, it seems unrealistic to raise the protein content above the 15% used here. Moreover, such an increase in proteins balanced by a decrease in polysaccharides would lead to a low O/C ratio, which also appears unrealistic compared, for instance, with the general estimations of Degens and Matheja (1968).

REFERENCES

Orgon proceedings.

Géochimie organique des sédiments marins profonds. *Orgon I — Mer de Norvège*, Editions du CNRS Paris 1977, 296 pp. *Orgon II — Atlantique Nord-Est, Brésil*, Editions du CNRS, Paris 1978, 390 pp. *Orgon III — Mauritanie, Sénégal, Iles du Cap-Vert*, Editions du CNRS, Paris 1979, 441 pp. *Orgon IV — Golfe d'Aden, Mer d'Oman*, Editions du CNRS, Paris, 1981, 547 pp.

Orgon cruises reports.

La Géochimie organique des sédiments marins profonds. Généralités et résultats obtenus à la mer. Mission Orgon 1, 1974 (Mer de Norvège), 1975. Revue IFP, XXIX, 1, pp. 17–211. Mission Orgon 2, 1975 (Bassin de Cariaco et cône de l'Amazone) (1977) Revue IFP, XXXII, 5, pp. 675–701. Mission Orgon 3, 1976 (Mauritanie, Sénégal, Iles du Cap-Vert) (1979) Revue IFP, XXXIV, 6, pp. 847–908. Mission Orgon 4, 1978 (Golfe d'Aden, Mer d'Oman) (1980). Revue IFP, XXXV, 5, pp. 773–810.

Other references

Albrecht, P., Vandenbroucke, M. and Mandengue, M. (1976) Geochemical studies of the organic matter from the Douala basin. *Geochim. Cosmochim. Acta* **40**, p. 791.
Bensoussan, M., Marty, D. and Bonnefont, J. L. (1980) *Orgon 4 Cruise Report*, pp. 804–809.
Daumas, R., Laborde, P. and Romano, J. C. (1975) *Orgon 1 Cruise Report*, pp. 199–203.
Daumas, R., Laborde, P., Romano, J. C. and Sautriot, D. (1977) *Orgon 2 Cruise Report*, pp. 691–702.
Daumas, R., Laborde, P., Romano, J. C. and Sautriot, D. (1979) *Orgon III Proceedings*, pp. 67–94.
Degens, E. T. and Matheja, J. (1968) Origin, development and diagenesis of biogeochemical compounds. *J. Br. Interplanet. Soc.* **21**, pp. 52–59.
Debyser, Y. and Gadel, F. (1977) *Orgon I Proceedings*, pp. 247–268.
Debyser, Y., Gadel, F., Leblond, C. and Martinez, M. J. (1978) *Orgon II Proceedings*, pp. 339–354.
Debyser, Y. and Gadel, F. (1979) *Orgon III Proceedings*, pp. 375–404.
Debyser, Y. and Gadel, F. (1981) *Orgon IV Proceedings*, pp. 447–482.
Durand, B. (1980) Elemental analyses of kerogens. In *Kerogen*, ed. by Durand, B. Editions Technip, Paris, pp. 113–142.
Foree, E. G. and McCarty, P. L. (1970) Anaerobic decomposition of algae. *Environ. Sci. Technol.* **4**, 842–849.
Garlenc, S., Laborde, P., Romano, J. C., Sautriot, D. and Souza-Lima, Y. (1980) *Orgon 4 Cruise Report*, pp. 788–803.
Garrels, R. M. and Perry, E. A. Jr. (1974) Cycling of carbon, sulfur and oxygen through geologic time. In *The Sea*, vol. 5, Marine Chemistry. John Wiley and Sons, New York, pp. 303–336.
Grusnikov, O. P. and Elkin, V. V. (1973) Achievements and problems in lignin chemistry. *Nauka*, Moscow, publishers, p. 6 (in Russian).
Huc, A. Y. and Durand, B. (1974) Etude des acides humiques et de l'humine de sédiments récents. In *Advances in Organic Geochemistry, 1973*. Editions Technip, Paris, pp. 53–72.
Hay, A. Y. (1980) Origin and formation of organic matter in recent sediments and its relation to kerogen. In *Kerogen*, ed. by Durand, B. Editions Technip, Paris, pp. 445–474.
Kalle, K. (1966) The problem of the Gelbstoff in the sea. *Oceanogr. Mar. Biol. Ann. Rev.* **4**, 91–104.
Mosetti, F. (1964) Oceanografia, *Del Bianco*, Udine, publishers, p. 349.
Moyes, J., Gayet, J., Pujol, C. and Pujos-Lamy, A. (1977) *Orgon I Proceedings*, pp. 81–138.
Moyes, J., Gayet, J., Poutiers, J., Pujol, C. and Pujos-Lamy, A. (1978) *Orgon II Proceedings*, pp. 105–156.
Moyes, J., Duplantier, F., Duprat, J., Faugeres, J. C., Pujol, C., Pujos-Lamy, A. and Tastet, J. P. (1979) *Orgon III Proceedings*, pp. 121–214.
Moyes, J., Duprat, J., Faugeres, J. C., Gonthier, E. and Pujol, C. (1981) *Orgon IV Proceedings*, pp. 189–264.
Muller, P. J. and Suess, E. (1979) Productivity, sedimentation rate and sedimentary organic matter in the oceans. *Deep Sea Res.* **26A**, 1347–1362.
Pelet, R. and Debyser, Y. (1977) Organic geochemistry of Black Sea cores. *Geochim. Cosmochim. Acta* **41**, pp. 1575–1586.
Redfield, A. C., Ketchum, B. H. and Richards, F. A. (1965) The influence of organisms on the composition of sea water. In *The Sea*, Vol. 2, pp. 26–77. ed. by Hill, M. N. Interscience publishers, New York.
Romankevic, E. A. (1977) Geochemistry of the organic matter in the ocean. *Nauka*, Moscow, publishers, pp. 124, 144 (in Russian).
Romano, J. C. and Dinet, A. (1981) *Orgon IV Proceedings*, pp. 158–180.
Sautriot, D. (1981) *Orgon IV Proceedings*, pp. 133–157.
Tissot, B., Califet-Debyser, Y., Deroo, G. and Oudin, J. L. (1971) Origin and evolution of hydrocarbons in early Toarcian shales. *AAPG Bull.* **55**, pp. 2177–2193.
Van Krevelen, D. W. '1961) *Coal*. Elsevier, New York, p. 117.
Waksman, S. A. (1938) *Humus*. The Williams and Wilkins Company, Baltimore, p. 95.

Advances in Organic Geochemistry 1981, pp. 251–258
© *John Wiley & Sons Limited, 1983*

Analysis and Budget of Biogeochemical Markers in Dissolved, Small and Large Size Suspended Matter in the Ocean

A. Saliot, C. André, A. Février, M. Goutx and M. J. Tissier

Laboratoire de Physique et Chimie Marines de l'Université Pierre et Marie Curie, ERA CNRS, Tour 24, 4 Place Jussieu, 75230 PARIS Cedex 05, France

The budget of organic matter between the sea water surface and sediments has been determined by examining the distributions of biogeochemical marker compounds in surface (200–0 m) and deep water layers (below 1000 m) in three fractions: dissolved matter, small size particles and large size particles. Samples have been collected in the Arabian Sea at sites of high organic productivity and in the Mediterranean Sea at a site of low and high productivity successively in autumn and spring. A BRES large volume bottle has been used to collect small particles ($> 1\,\mu$m) and the water was extracted to obtain the dissolved organic matter. Vertical and horizontal net tows have provided large size particles ($> 50\,\mu$m). The nature (phytoplankton and zooplankton species and faecal pellets) and particle distribution have been examined by microscopy. Saturated acyclic hydrocarbons and saturated and unsaturated *n*-fatty acids have been identified and quantitated by GC and computerized GC/MS. The absolute concentrations of the saturated hydrocarbons vary in the range 20–1000 ng l^{-1} for the dissolved and small particulate fractions, whereas the concentrations of the large particles vary in the range 0.002–0.2 ng l^{-1}. The concentrations of the fatty acids vary in the range 100–1500 ng l^{-1} for the dissolved and small particulate fractions, 5–250 ng l^{-1} for the large size particles. Comparison of *n*-alkane and isoprenoid alkane distribution patterns yields further information on the nature of the large particles and their content in living organisms; over a regular distribution between *n*-C21 to *n*-C35 common to the three fractions, pristane is largely predominant. Deep large particles have a composition close to the surficial plankton. Saturated and unsaturated *n*-fatty acid distribution patterns confirm that the deep large size particles have been recently biosynthesized. These large size particles carry specific compounds not encountered in the dissolved matter and small particle size fractions, which may play an essential function in the food supply for organisms living at depth. Interactions can exist between the lipid pools, as shown by the transport by large size particles of lipid distributions originating from surficial bioaccumulation of dissolved organics (e.g. retene, a polynuclear aromatic compound of terrigenous origin, was found in both the dissolved matter and the large particles in the Arabian Sea). The relationship between the particulate fractions ($> 1\,\mu$m; 50–230 μm and $> 230\,\mu$m) is discussed from results obtained in Villefranche using different large size particle samplers. Our results show that the study of organic sedimentation throughout the water column should involve not only the analysis of dissolved matter and small particles, which represent an important background mass, but also, the measurement of the vertical flux of large size particles.

INTRODUCTION

Although large size particles ($> 50\ \mu$m) are very dispersed in sea water, representing only a small part of the total organic matter of the ocean, they play an important role in biological and, for their non-living fraction, sedimentation processes.

These large size particles are complex and various and include living and dead organisms, faecal pellets and mixed mineral-organic aggregates. Due to this complex nature, they are involved in many processes. They are closely associated with the development of vegetal and animal life, at the moment of their formation, particularly with zooplankton activity. Different interactions between living organisms and the organic matter associated with the dissolved and small size particulate fractions may occur at any depth.

The non-living part of these particles is responsible for more than 90% of the vertical flux of organic matter from the productive surficial ocean to the bottom sediments. This has been demonstrated by analysing the biological and chemical nature of $> 50\ \mu$m particles collected using high volume *in situ* filtration systems (Bishop *et al.*, 1977, 1978, 1980), sediment traps (Honjo, 1978, 1980) or deep vertical plankton net tows (Boussuge *et al.*, 1981; Saliot *et al.*, 1982).

Large size particles are dispersed in an important background mass of organic and mineral compounds, dissolved or associated with small size particles. In order to evaluate possible interactions between the three pools,

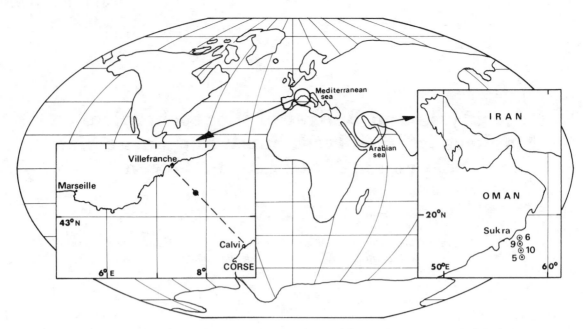

Fig. 1. Location of sampling sites.

dissolved organic matter, organic matter associated with small size particles and organic matter associated with large size particles, we have undertaken a systematic study of the budget of organic matter in these three pools for both the surficial (0–200 m) and the deep ocean (below 1000 m). Interaction processes have been considered by analysing established biogeochemical markers such as *n*- and isoprenoid alkanes and *n*-fatty acids (Wakeham *et al.*, 1980).

We have chosen two sites representative of marine autochtonous sedimentation. The Arabian Sea sampled during Orgon 4 cruise, November 1978; Moyes *et al.*, 1981; Boussuge *et al.*, 1981) is characterized by a high superficial productivity, a low oxygen content of sea water and low terrigenous inputs. The other site is a station in the North Mediterranean Sea, sampled in October 1979 when the phytoplankton activity was low and thus provides a reference station for non-productive marine area. The same site was sampled in spring, May 1980, when the plankton activity was high.

EXPERIMENTAL

Samples

Samples were obtained at various sites in the Arabian and Mediterranean seas (Fig. 1). The first samples were collected in the north–western Indian ocean during the **Orgon 4 cruise, in November 1978**. Two stations, St. 10 (17°26′60 N; 57°30′50 E; 2390 m depth) and St. 5 (16°45′90 N; 57°30′70 E; 4010 m depth) of the Sukra leg have been selected as representative of organic deep sedimentation, characterized by high surficial productivity (Ryther and Menzel, 1965), low oxygen content of sea water (Daumas *et al.*, 1981) and low terrigenous inputs (limited in this area to aeolian contributions from the north of India and the African continent, Goldberg and Griffin, 1970).

On the other hand, a station was chosen in the Ligurian Sea, ~20 nautical miles of Villefranche (43°21′00 N; 7°43′00 E; 2200 m depth) during the autumn, October 1979 and the Spring, May 1980, periods of low and high primary productivity (Gostan, 1968). Two other different characteristics distinguish the Ligurian Sea; a high oxygenation of deep waters and noticeable terrigenous inputs by several rivers.

Particulate samples were collected using conventional or BRES large volume sea water bottles, plankton nets and a sediment trap. Sea water was collected using an all metallic 130 l or 220 l sampler except for the autumnal cruise in Villefranche where a 30 l Niskin bottle rinsed several times with distilled water was used. Water (30 or 100 l) was filtered through a pre-extracted Whatman GF/C glass fibre filter. The suspended material collected onto the filter (>1 μm) was denoted 'small size particles'. The sampling of surficial planktonic material was achieved from 200 m to the surface using vertical tows of plankton nets, carefully rinsed, equipped with a stainless steel collector. The wide mesh was 50 μm. In May 1980 a free-drifting sediment trap (Staresinic *et al.*, 1978) was deployed for 8 h at 50 m depth. In deep layers, the probability of efficiently collecting representatively large particles using large volume bottles is low, due to their dispersion in the water column (Sheldon *et al.*, 1972). Their sampling was achieved using vertical tows of nets (wide mesh: 50 μm) by pulling the net at 0.5 m sec^{-1} from 2000 to 1000 m for station 10, 3800 to 2000 m for Station 5, 2000 to 1000 m for Villefranche, and then closing the net. The resulting material, surface and deep, was divided by filtration of the collector content through a 150 (Orgon) or 230 μm (Villefranche) membrane into two fractions denoted 50–150 or 50–230 μm and >150 or >230 μm.

Methods

Dissolved lipids were extracted by liquid–liquid

extraction of filtered sea water with chloroform (× 2) at pH 8 and a third time at pH 2 (Goutx and Saliot, 1980). The organic extracts were dessicated over $CaCl_2$ and evaporated at a reduced temperature ($t < 40$ °C).

Particulate samples were extracted with benzene–methanol 1:1 for 24 h in a soxhlet apparatus.

All the extracts were saponified for 2 h with a solution of 2N KOH in 1:1 methanol–benzene. After extracting the unsaponifiable matter with ether, the free fatty acids were released by 6N HCl and extracted with ether. The acid extract was then methylated by a solution of 14% BF_3 in methanol, before analysis. The unsaponifiable fraction was separated by adsorption chromatography on a microcolumn filled with 2/3 Davison silica gel, 100–200 mesh, impregnated with 1% $AgNO_3$, and 1/3 Merck alumina 80, 2% deactivated with distilled water and by elution with a series of solvents of increasing polarity. The analysis of the two first fractions (hexane and hexane–benzene), composed essentially of saturated and aromatic hydrocarbons is reported here.

The molecular composition of the compound classes was determined by capillary gas liquid chromatography on a Girdel 3000 gas chromatograph, and by computerized capillary gas liquid chromatography/mass spectrometry on a LKB 2170–2130/LKB 9000 S instrument with PDP 11 E 10 data system. The analytical procedure is given in detail in Boussuge *et al.* (1979) and Tissier (1981).

RESULTS AND DISCUSSION

Budget of *n*-alkanes, isoprenoid alkanes and *n*-fatty acids

The budget of *n*-alkanes and isoprenoid alkanes in the three pools, dissolved matter, small size particles and large size particles for the surficial ocean (0–200 m) and for the deep layer (below 1000 m) is expressed in absolute concentrations in ng l^{-1} of sea water in Table 1. The percentage of hydrocarbons in the three pools is shown in Fig. 2. For the two sites (Arabian and Mediterranean seas) large size particles account for only a small part of the total dissolved and suspended matter in the surface samples (0.5% for St. 5, 5% for St. 10). This feature is further enhanced in the deep layers where, for instance, the percentage of hydrocarbons in the large size particles is even lower (0.004% for St. 5, 0.006% for St. 10 and 0.002% for Villefranche).

The budget of fatty acids in the three pools is given in Table 2. Considering the partition of fatty acids in surface samples (Fig. 3), as for hydrocarbons, the most important fractions are those that are dissolved or associated with small size particles. The importance of fatty acid concentrations associated with large size particles in deep layers is highly variable; it is very low for St. 5 (0.3%) but higher for St. 10 (6%). There are great discrepancies between marker concentrations associated with large size particles in deep layers. These are explained by the fact that the biological species distributions are very different. St. 5 contains less than 6% of living organisms. Contrarily St. 10 is characterized by a large abundance of copepods (see Table 3).

Table 1

Budget of *n*-alkanes and isoprenoid alkanes in the three organic matter pools, dissolved matter, small size particles and large size particles. Total concentrations are expressed in ng per litre of sea water.

Superficial layer (0–200 m)	Organic matter pools			
	Dissolved matter	Small size particles	Large size particles 50–150 μm	> 150 μm
Arabian Sea				
Station 10	81.9	14.0	0.39	4.0
Station 5	30.8	37.4	0.16	0.08
Mediterranean Sea			50–230 μm	> 230 μm
Villefranche	nd[a]	nd	0.21	0.02

Deep layer (1000–2000 m)				
Arabian Sea			> 50 μm	
Station 10	53.3	28.1	0.005	
Station 5	25.0	25.2	0.002	
Mediterranean Sea				
Villefranche	206	1050	0.021	

[a] nd = non-determined.

It is known that copepods are rich in glycerides (Lee *et al.*, 1971; Sargent *et al.*, 1977), which could explain the relative enrichment of the large size particles in the total fatty acid pool — 6% for St. 10 —.

When deep large size particles do not contain living organisms, their organic content, evaluated through biogeochemical markers, accounts for only a few per cent (2.5% for St. 5) of surface large size particles content, escaping the degradation and mineralization processes.

Biological marker distributions

We will first examine the normal and isoprenoid alkane and fatty acid distribution patterns for St. 10 of the Orgon 4 cruise, selected because it represents a productive marine environment (Figs 4 and 5).

Figure 4 shows evidence of the specificity of large size particles with an important biological imprint. The major alkanes present are *n*-C15 and *n*-C17 + pristane both for the surficial and the deep material. This biogenic imprint cannot only be related to the presence of living copepods because the predominance of pristane over all hydrocarbons has been noted in deep large size particles collected at deeper layers devoid of living organisms as in St. 5 and others (Boussuge *et al.*, 1981; Saliot *et al.*, 1982).

In contrast this predominance of *n*-C17 + pristane is less pronounced in the surface small size particles and absent in the deep small size particles. This may reflect (i) no interchange between the two pools (small and large size particles) and (ii) no relationship between surface and deep small size particles. This latter is to be

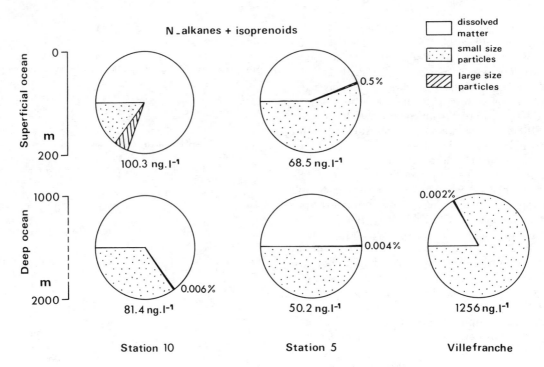

Fig. 2. Budget of *n*-alkanes and isoprenoid alkanes in dissolved matter, small and large size particles in surficial and deep ocean. Total hydrocarbon concentrations, from Table 1, are mentioned in ng l^{-1}.

Table 2

Budget of fatty acids in the three organic matter pools, dissolved matter, small size particles and large size particles for two stations in the Arabian Sea. Total concentrations are expressed in ng per litre of sea water

	Organic matter pools		
Superficial layer (0–200 m)	Dissolved matter	Small size particles	Large size particles > 50 µm
Station 10	1510	1260	248
Station 5	780	310	146
Deep layer (1000–2000 m)			
Station 10	1200	110	92.5
Station 5	1220	430	5.3

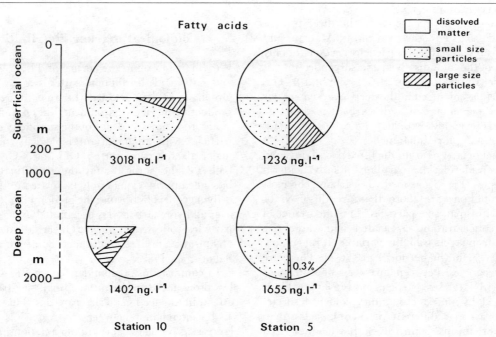

Fig. 3. Budget of *n*-fatty acids in dissolved matter, small and large size particles in surficial and deep ocean. Total *n*-fatty acid concentrations, from Table 2, are mentioned in ng l^{-1}.

Table 3

Distribution of biological large size (> 50 μm) particles collected at Stations 5 and 10 in the Arabian Sea, using deep net tows. The specific composition is expressed in percentage of each biological class abundance in respect to total species. The approximate size of particles is given either as an equivalent diameter Φ or by the length L and width l in μm

Sampling depth Biological species < 2 mm	Approximate size	Station 5 3800–2000 m	Station 10 2000–1000 m
		Specific composition (%)	
Centrate diatoms			
coscinodisceae	$\Phi = 50\text{--}80 \ \mu m$	10	20
rhizosoleniae	$\Phi = 50\text{--}80 \ \mu m$	10	
Radiolaria	$\Phi = 200 \ \mu m$	29	10
Tintinnids		10	10
Nauplii	$\Phi = 50 \ \mu m$	⎧ —	
Copepodits	$L = 200 \ \mu m; \ l = 50 \ \mu m$	⎩	
Copepods			
< 1 mm	$L = 500 \ \mu m; \ t = 50 \ \mu m$		10
> 1 mm			30
Faecal pellets	$\Phi = 300\text{--}500 \ \mu m$	35	20
Biological species > 2 mm			
Appendicularia		0.3	0.3
Chaetognatha		0.4	0.1

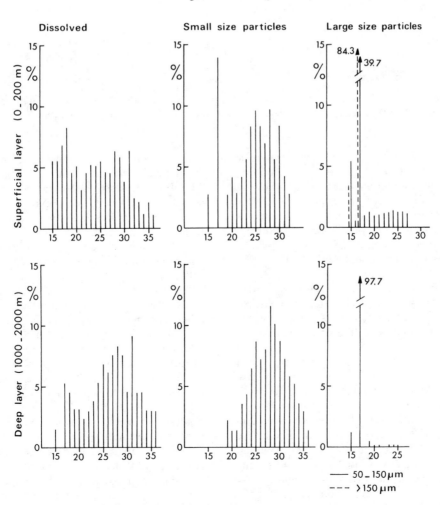

Fig. 4. Distribution patterns of *n*-alkanes and isoprenoid alkanes for the dissolved matter, small size and large size particles in the surficial and deep ocean (Arabian Sea, Station 10).

Organic matter pools

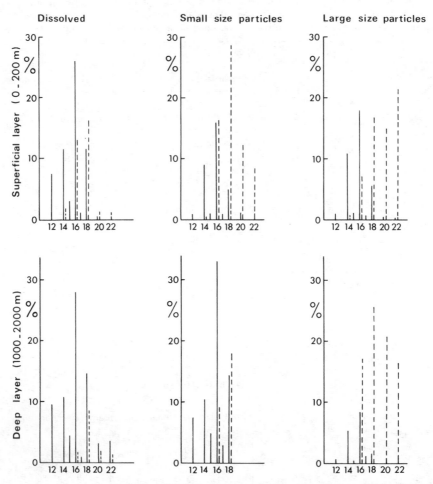

Fig. 5. Distribution patterns of *n*-fatty acids for the dissolved matter, small size and large size particles in the surficial and the deep ocean (Arabian Sea, Station 10). Solid line = saturated acids. Dashed line = unsaturated acids.

expected, as we know that small size particles can be generated in another water mass and they are often present in the water column for long periods, allowing ample time for transformations to occur.

The *n*-alkane distribution of the dissolved fraction is regular, with no single compound predominating, a distribution which is very common in non-productive, non-polluted areas (Goutx and Saliot, 1980; Saliot, 1981).

The fatty acid distributions (Fig. 5) confirm several of the preceding remarks. The importance of biological unsaturated fatty acids (C16, C18, C20 and C22) in the large size particles emphasizes the recent planktonic origin and the extent of preservation of this material even for the deep particles. The same predominance of unsaturated fatty acids is noted even for deep large size particles collected at St. 5, devoid of significant amounts of living organisms; in small size particles the biological planktonic imprint, shown by the importance of unsaturated C20 and C22 compounds in the surface layer, disappears with depth, leading to a distribution characterized with the unsaturated C16 acid and the unsaturated C18 acids as the major compounds.

Of note is the unusual relative abundance, for the deep dissolved matter, of the two unsaturated C20 and

C22 components, whose presence could not only be explained by an interchange with large size particles. The observation of these compounds in the bottom water could be related to an input from sediments and interstitial water which has been shown to be enriched in C20 and C22 unsaturated fatty acids (Boussuge *et al.*, 1981) and a good extent of preservation due to quasi-anoxic conditions of the water column (Daumas *et al.*, 1981).

To evaluate possible relationships between the three pools of organic matter collected, we have observed other geochemical markers in naturally occurring aromatic hydrocarbon series. The polycyclic aromatic hydrocarbon retene, a terrigenous marker, has been identified in the surface dissolved pool at St. 10, in the planktonic material and also in deep large size particles collected between 2000 and 1000 m (Tissier, 1981; Boussuge *et al.*, 1981); surprisingly it was not found in small size particles. This suggests a bioaccumulation process from the dissolved organic matter.

We have analysed in detail the large size particles collected in Villefranche focusing on interaction processes between particulate fractions. Fig. 6 shows *n*-alkane distribution patterns for the deep Villefranche samples (October 1979). Deep large size particles have

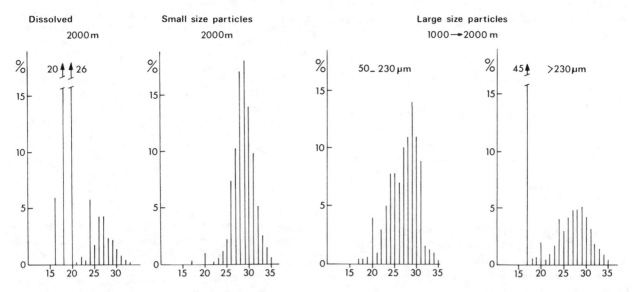

Fig. 6. Distribution patterns of *n*-alkanes and isoprenoid alkanes for the dissolved matter, small size and large size particles in the deep ocean (Mediterranean Sea, Villefranche, Autumn 1979, period of low planktonic productivity).

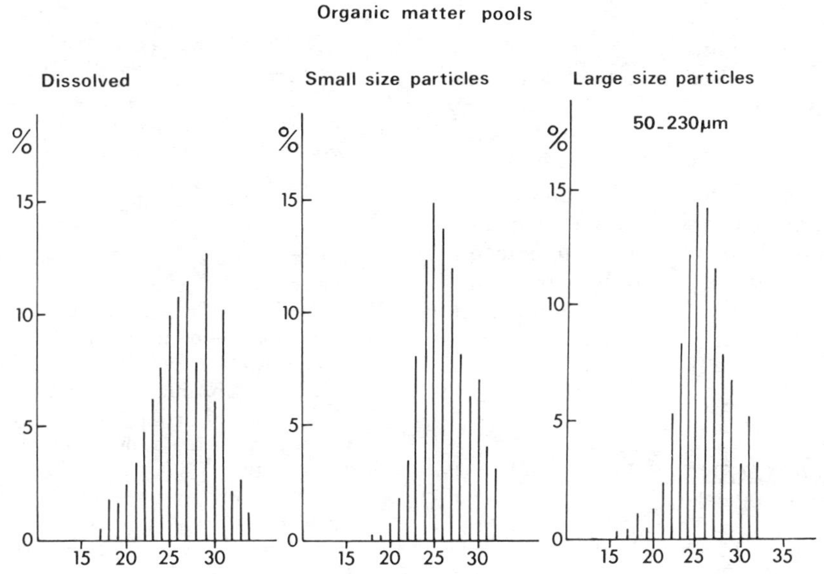

Fig. 7. Distribution patterns of *n*-alkanes and isoprenoid alkanes for the dissolved matter, small size and large size particles collected using a free-drifting sediment trap in the surficial ocean (Mediterranean Sea, Villefranche, Spring 1980, period of high planktonic productivity).

been separated into two fractions 50–230 μm and > 230 μm which contains large organisms such as copepods and large size faecal pellets and aggregates. The > 230 μm fraction is characterized, as expected, by the predominance of pristane (45% of total hydrocarbons; *n*-C17 is present as trace amounts). This marker occurs in unusually high concentrations (1–3% of the body lipid) in different zooplankton (Blumer *et al.*, 1963). Contrarily the 50–230 μm fraction shows a regular *n*-alkane distribution between *n*-C22 and *n*-C35, maximizing at *n*-C29, as for the small size particulate fraction. This could suggest a relationship between the two particulate pools through compaction. The dissolved pool is not concerned by a parallel interaction process. It is

characterized by an even carbon numbered *n*-alkane predominance (*n*-C16, *n*-C18 and *n*-C20) which could be interpreted as a bacterial imprint (Goutx and Saliot, 1980).

Sedimenting large size particles have been collected using a free-drifting sediment trap (50 m) at the same station, but during a period of high planktonic productivity. The analysis of hydrocarbons confirms that large size material (50–230 μm) could result from the aggregation of small size particles, probably stimulated by biological processes. Effectively Fig. 7 shows that the *n*-alkane distribution patterns of small size particles and sedimenting material are similar, maximizing at *n*-C25. There is no interchange between the particulate and dissolved pools. The dissolved pool is marked by terrestrial inputs indicated by the predominance of odd carbon numbered *n*-alkanes in the range *n*-C27–*n*-C33.

CONCLUSIONS

This study shows that large size particles are characterized by a remarkable specificity in chemical nature with respect to small size particles and the pool of dissolved organic matter which constitute an important background mass. The high relative abundance of pristane and unsaturated fatty acids in large size particles collected in areas of both high and low productivity is evidence that large size particles are essentially composed of both living organisms and recent biological material. This latter material, which rapidly settles, carries other contributions due to interactions with the other pools, dissolved matter and small size particles.

First, the identification of retene in surface dissolved matter and in large size particles (St. 10, Arabian Sea) confirms the role of large size particles in the interchange between surficial dissolved organic matter and the sediment initiated by bioaccumulation in surface waters.

The other interaction is observed between small and large size particles and could be explained by bioaggregation.

In conclusion, our results show that a study of organic sedimentation throughout the water column should involve the analysis of total dissolved and particulate organic matter pools, because of the specific interactions between large size particles and dissolved organic matter and small size particles which represent the important background mass.

REFERENCES

Bishop, J. K. B., Edmond, J. M., Ketten, D. R., Bacon, M. P. and Silker, W. B. (1977) The chemistry, biology, and vertical flux of particulate matter from the upper 400 m of the equatorial Atlantic Ocean. *Deep Sea Res.* **24**, 511–548.

Bishop, J. K. B., Ketten, D. R. and Edmond, J. M. (1978) The chemistry, biology and vertical flux of particulate matter from the upper 400 m of the Cape Basin in the southeast Atlantic Ocean. *Deep Sea Res.* **25**, 1121–1161.

Bishop, J. K. B., Collier, R. W., Ketten, D. R. and Edmond, J. M. (1980) The chemistry, biology and vertical flux of particulate matter from the upper 1500 m of the Panama Basin. *Deep Sea Res.* **27A**, 615–640.

Blumer, M., Mullin, M. M. and Thomas, D. W. (1963) Pristane in zooplankton. *Science* **140**, 974.

Boussuge, C., Goutx, M., Saliot, A. and Tissier, M. J. (1979) Acides gras et hydrocarbures aux interfaces eau de mer-sédiment et eau interstitielle-sédiment en Atlantique tropical est. In *Géochemie organique des sédiments marins profonds, Orgon III. Mauritanie, Sénégal, Iles du Cap Vert*, ed. by Arnould, M. and Pelet, R. Editions du CNRS, Paris, pp. 303–352.

Boussuge, C., Goutx, M., Tissier, M. J., Tusseau, D. and

Saliot, A. (1981) Sédimentation organique en mer d'Arabie: biologie et transfert de lipides entre zone euphotique et interface océan-sédiment. In *Géochimie organique des sédiments marins profonds. Orgon IV. Golfe d'Aden, Mer d'Oman*. Editions du CNRS, Paris, pp. 415–445.

Daumas, R., Laborde, P., Romano, J. C. and Sautriot, D. (1981) Hydrologie et particules en suspension en mer d'Arabie. In *Géochimie organique des sédiments marins profonds. Orgon IV. Golfe d'Aden, Mer d'Oman*. Editions du CNRS, Paris, pp. 71–94.

Goldberg, E. D. and Griffin, J. J. (1970) The sediments of the northern Indian Ocean. *Deep Sea Res.* **17**, 513–537.

Gostan, J. (1968) Contribution à l'étude hydrologique du bassin liguro-provençal entre la riviera et la corse: distribution et variations saisonnières de la température, de la salinité, de l'oxygène et des phosphates minéraux dissous dans les masses d'eau superficielles, intermédiaires et profondes. Doct. Etat. Université de Paris.

Goutx, M. and Saliot, A. (1980) Relationship between dissolved and particulate fatty acids and hydrocarbons, chlorophyll *a* and zooplankton biomass in Villefranche Bay, Mediterranean Sea. *Mar. Chem.* **8**, 299–318.

Honjo, S. (1978) Sedimentation of materials in the Sargasso Sea at a 5367 m deep station. *J. Mar. Res.* **36**, 469–492.

Honjo, S. (1980) Material fluxes and modes of sedimentation in the mesopelagic and bathypelagic zones. *J. Mar. Res.* **38**, 53–97.

Lee, R. F., Nevenzel, J. C. and Paffenhöfer, G. A. (1971) Importance of wax esters and other lipids in the marine food chain: phytoplankton and copepods. *Mar. Biol.* **9**, 99–108.

McCave, I. N. (1975) Vertical flux of particles in the ocean *Deep Sea Res.* **22**, 491–502.

Moyes, J., Duprat, J., Faugeres, J. C., Gonthier, E. and Pujol, C. (1981) Etude stratigraphique et sédimentologique. In *Géochimie organique des sédiments marins profonds. Orgon IV. Golfe d'Aden, Mer d'Oman*. Editions du CNRS, Paris, pp. 189–263.

Ryther, J. H. and Menzel, D. W. (1965) On the production, composition and distribution of organic matter in the western Arabian Sea. *Deep Sea Res.* **12**, 199–209.

Saliot, A. (1981) Natural hydrocarbons in sea water. In *Marine Organic Chemistry*, ed. by Duursma, E. K. and Dawson, R. Elsevier, Amsterdam, pp. 327–374.

Saliot, A., Goutx, M., Février, A., Tusseau, D. and Andrié, C. (1982) Organic sedimentation in the water column in the Arabian Sea: relationship between the lipid composition of small and large size, surface and deep particles. *Mar. Chem.* **11**, 257–278.

Sargent, J. R., Gatten, R. R. and McIntosh, R. (1977) Wax esters in the marine environment — their occurrence, formation, transformation and ultimate fates. *Mar. Chem.* **5**, 573–584.

Sheldon, R. W., Prakash, A. and Sutcliffe, W. H. (1972) The size distribution of particles in the ocean. *Limnol. Oceanogr.* **17**, 327–340.

Staresinic, N., Rowe, G. T., Shaughnessey, D. and Williams III, A. J. (1978) Measurement of the vertical flux of particulate organic matter with a free-drifting sediment trap. *Limnol. Oceanogr.* **23**, 559–563.

Tissier, M. J. (1981) Les hydrocarbures aromatiques polycycliques dans l'environnement marin. Distribution, origine et transfert. Doct. Etat. Université Pierre et Marie Curie, Paris.

Wakeham, S. G., Farrington, J. W., Gagosian, R. B., Lee, C., deBaar, H., Nigrelli, G. E., Tripp, B. W., Smith, S. O. and Frew, N. M. (1980) Organic matter fluxes from sediment traps in the equatorial Atlantic ocean. *Nature (London)* **286**, 798–800.

Advances in Organic Geochemistry 1981, pp. 259–267
© *John Wiley & Sons Limited, 1983*

The Organic Matter in Upwelling Environments: West Africa (Mauritania) (or 'Cap Blanc') and South Arabia (Sukra) Continental Margins

Y. Debyser

Institut Francais du Pétrole

L. Jocteur Monrozier

Centre Pédologique de Nancy

D. Sautriot and R. Daumas

Station Marine D'Endoume

A comparative study of organic matter (particles and sediments) from two upwelling areas is presented. These areas are located on tropical desertic stable margins: off Mauritania (West Africa) and Sukra (South Arabia). The largest part of the organic supply comes from primary production and the organic matter from the two zones show some similar general features characteristic of marine origin: (a) a high abundance of phaeopigments in the particles above the sediment and in the surficial sediments; (b) high amounts of organic nitrogenous compounds and aliphatic character of kerogens. In the Sukra margin, upwelling is much more widespread, the waters are less oxygenated, slope morphology is dominated by traps and the kerogens have geochemical characteristics different from those of Mauritania: (a) the quantity of organic matter accumulated is higher, even in the abyssal plain; (b) stable insoluble residue is the major fraction of the kerogen; (c) the largest part of the nitrogen is non-extractable; (d) hydrogen index (as determined by Rock-Eval pyrolysis) is higher. In the two areas, evolution follows the same path: lateral evolution down to the abyssal plain, revealed by an increase in small oxygenated organic molecules (fulvic acids, hydrolyzable compounds) consequently, this evolution is more important when the waters are rich in dissolved oxygen; evolution with the depth in the core, marked by an increasing insolubilization of buried organic matter.

INTRODUCTION

The existence of marine areas receiving essentially autochthonous organic matter (OM), is of the utmost interest when studying the early diagenesis of OM in deep marine environments, whose sediments are the precursors of oil source beds. Areas of waters rich in nutrients (i.e. upwellings) are good models for such a study. These areas, often located on the edge of desert regions (Occidental Sahara, Namibian desert, Arabian desert) are essentially supplied by autochthonous OM and terrestrial OM of Aeolian origin does not represent an important contribution (Simoneit, 1978; Caratini *et al.*, 1981).

Two upwelling areas located on tropical desertic stable margins have been studied:

(1) Cap Blanc, Mauritania (North–west Africa) bordering on the Sahara (Fig. 1) characterized by primary production (Shemainda *et al.*, 1975; Hartmann *et al.*, 1976) lasting almost all year, restricted to the shelf, its external border and a regular slope cut by shallow channels, grading smoothly to a continental rise (Moyes *et al.*, 1979);

(2) the North of the Indian Ocean (Sukra) bordering on the Arabian peninsula (Fig. 2) where resurgences are much more widespread and show seasonal variations (Ryther *et al.*, 1966; Kuz'menko, 1968). The Sukra margin which falls abruptly to the abyssal plain, is cut by a series of parallel faults resulting in the continental slope being divided into a series of transverse troughs. Dissolved oxygen contents, in Mauritanian water near the sea-bed, are higher than in the Arabian Sea (Table 1) (Daumas *et al.*, 1979, 1981).

In each area, the qualitative and quantitative evolution of OM is compared in samples collected from the continental shelf to the abyssal plain. Coring and

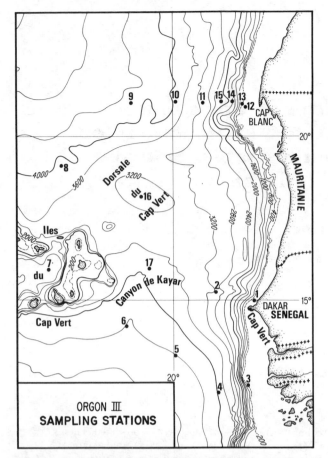

Fig. 1. Geographical locations of sampling stations for the Orgon III cruise off N.W. Africa.

analytical techniques are fully described in the reports of the Orgon III and IV cruises (CEPM, CNEXO, 1979 and 1981).

This present study is concerned with the two following problems:

(1) The distribution of labile biogenic compounds in particles above the sediment and in the surficial sediment.

(2) The geochemistry of kerogens in the sediments, with a special emphasis on nitrogenous compounds.

RESULTS AND DISCUSSION

1. Distribution of carbon and nitrogen of some biogenic compounds, in the near-sediment particles and in the surficial sediments

The annual primary productivity is more important in the Mauritanian Sea than in the Arabian one: Mauritania: 250 g $C \cdot m^{-2} y^{-1}$ (Shemainda *et al.*, 1975); Arabian sea: 120 g $C \cdot m^{-2} y^{-1}$ (Kuz'menko, 1968), but the organic carbon and nitrogen contents of the particles sampled near the sea-bed (between 10 and 5 meters above the sediment) do not show the influence of the upwelling and are similar to those found in other oceanic areas at equivalent depths (Table 1) (Daumas *et al.*, 1977, 1978). The influence of the upwelling is reflected in the phaeopigment contents. They reach their

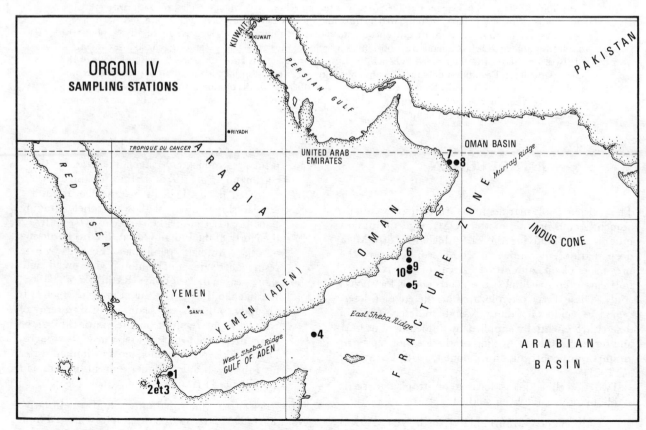

Fig. 2. Geographical locations of sampling stations for the Orgon IV cruise in South Arabian Sea.

Table 1

Composition of near bottom (5–10 m) particulate organic matter from selected stations of the Orgon III (Cap Blanc) and Orgon IV (Sukra) cruises. C soluble carbohydrates = Soluble carbohydrates $\mu g\, l^{-1}/2.5$; N primary amines = primary amines $\mu M\, l^{-1} \times 14$

	Stations (see Figs. 1 and 2)	Water depths (m)	Dissolved oxygen (ppm)	Carbon ($\mu g\, l^{-1}$)	Nitrogen ($g\, l^{-1}$)	Phaeo-pigments ($g\, l^{-1}$)	Soluble carbo-hydrates ($\mu g\, l^{-1}$) (glucose equivalents)	Primary amines ($10^{-2}\, \mu M\, l^{-1}$) (norleucine equivalents)	$\dfrac{C}{N}$	C Soluble carbo-hydrates $\dfrac{}{N\ \text{Primary amines}}$	Phaeo-pigments $\times$ 100 $\dfrac{}{\text{organic C}}$
Mauritania	13	900	3.4	43	5.6	107	23.4	0.31	7.68	215	2.49
	14	1900	7.3	38	5.4	20	14.6	0	7.04	—	0.53
	15	2500	7.4	27	5.0	11	10.0	0.16	5.40	178	0.41
	11	3250	7.5	48	6.1	5	43.2	0.86	7.87	143	0.10
	10	3750	7.4	43	6.7	3	65.0	0.42	7.3	442	0.07
Arabian Sea	6	200	0.8	61.8	4.1	52	15.5	0.62	15.1	71	0.84
	9	830	1.4	41.9	3.5	55	14.8	1.85	12.0	23	1.31
	10	2390	3.8	97.6	11.6	44	23.2	4.29	8.4	15	0.45
	5	4010	5.3	33.6	2.7	42	10.5	2.06	12.4	14	1.25

Table 2

Organic matter composition of surficial sediments from selected stations of the Orgon III (Cap Blanc) and Orgon IV (Sukra) cruises

Depth (cm)	Carbon (%)	Nitrogen (%)	Phaeopigments $\mu g\, g^{-1}$	Soluble carbohydrates $\mu g\, l^{-1}$ (glucose equivalents)	Primary amines $\mu M\, g^{-1}$ (norleucine equivalents)	$\dfrac{C}{N}$	C Soluble carbohydrates $\dfrac{}{N\ \text{Primary amines}}$	Phaeopigments $\times$ 100 $\dfrac{}{\text{Org. C.}}$
Station 13 (900 m) slope								
0.2	1.30	0.14	38.5	429	2.8	9.29	27.36	2.96
10.12	1.35	0.13	24.5	311	1.8	10.38	30.85	1.81
20.22	1.10	0.11	18.5	194	1.2	10.00	28.87	1.68
Station 14 (1900 m) slope								
0.2	2.27	0.39	29.5	1078	5.8	5.82	33.19	1.30
10.12	1.72	0.25	11.2	659	3.5	6.88	33.62	0.65
20.22	—	—	—	—	—	—	—	—
Station 15 (2500 m) rise								
0.2	1.89	0.20	16.5	1178	4.0	9.45	52.59	0.87
10.12	1.81	0.18	18.3	837	3.4	10.06	43.96	1.01
20.22	1.79	0.17	18.3	787	2.8	10.53	50.19	1.02
Station 11 (3250 m) AB								
0.2	0.74	0.10	2.3	334	3.0	7.40	19.88	0.31
10.12	0.78	0.10	3.0	461	2.8	7.80	29.40	0.38
20.22	0.69	0.08	2.5	412	1.9	8.63	38.72	0.36
Station 10 (3750 m) AB								
0.2	0.53	0.05	0.8	108	1.1	10.60	17.53	0.15
10.12	0.37	0.05	0.4	83	0.9	7.40	16.47	0.11
20.22	0.68	0.04	0.4	89	0.5	17.00	31.79	0.06
Station 6 (200 m) SH								
0.2	1.32	0.20	35.8	668	7.6	6.60	15.70	2.71
10.12	1.02	0.15	19.2	301	3.3	6.80	16.29	1.88
20.22	1.00	0.10	18.0	113	1.3	10.00	15.52	1.80
Station 9 (830 m) slope								
0.2	6.88	0.96	117.5	2094	41.6	7.17	8.99	1.71
10.12	5.88	0.86	84.9	1239	13.9	6.84	15.92	1.44
20.22	6.48	0.80	69.1	1154	10.0	8.10	20.61	1.07
Station 10 (2390 m) slope								
0.2	2.70	0.36	31.6	1061	12.4	7.50	15.28	1.17
10.12	2.84	0.32	22.2	804	7.1	.88	20.22	0.78
20.22	2.94	0.34	19.1	614	8.5	.65	12.90	0.65
Station 5 (4010 m) AB								
0.2	2.06	0.32	22.3	1038	16.1	6.44	11.51	1.08
10.12	1.64	0.23	11.7	708	.7	7.13	16.42	0.71
20.22	1.16	0.17	7.9	494	2.9	6.82	30.42	0.68

Table 3

Data relating to C. soluble carbohydrates/N. primary amines ratio in near bottom particulate and surficial sediments from selected stations of the Orgon III (Cap Blanc) and Orgon IV (Sukra) cruises

| | C Soluble carbohydrates/N Primary amines | | | | | | | | |
| | off Mauritania | | | | | Arabian Sea | | | |
Stations (see Figs. 1 and 2)	13	14	15	11	10	6	9	10	5
Particulate organic matter	215	—	178	143	442	71	23	15	14
Surficial sediment	27	33	53	20	18	16	9	15	12

maximum on the continental slope and decrease towards the ocean sea only in the case of Mauritanian area (Table 1). The values are high compared to the phaeopigment contents of particulate OM sampled at equivalent depths in other deep sea areas, (usually less than 10 ng l^{-1}; Saijo, 1969). The quantity of OM contained in the near bed particles is identical in the two areas, but some differences appear in the labile compounds (phaeopigments, primary amines); higher amounts are noted in the Arabian sea continental slope (Table 1).

In the surficial sediments, a comparison of the data in the two areas (Table 2) shows that at equivalent water

depths, organic C and N are more abundant in the Arabian sea sediments than in Mauritanian ones; the nitrogen fractions exhibit better conservation in the surficial sediments of the Arabian sea than in those off Mauritania (Suess and Muller, 1980). This observation is probably related to the relative oxygen deficiency of the waters in the north of the Indian Ocean which ensures protection of the particulate matter during sedimentation. In both cases, the highest contents of OM were found on the continental slope (Table 2).

Some discrepancy appears between OM fixed on the particles and OM in the sediment of the 0–2 cm layer, principally in the labile fractions (Table 3). The ratio C (soluble carbohydrates)/$[N]$ (primary amines), is generally higher in the particles than in the surficial sediments, indicating a difference between these two materials; the decrease of this ratio could be related to the presence in the sediment of abundant fauna (Suess and Muller, 1980). Nevertheless, the estimation of the meiofauna (Romano and Dinet, 1981) and of the bacterial populations (Bensoussan *et al.*, 1981) which is not particularly important, does not confirm this hypothesis. If we consider that primary amines are more labile biochemical components than soluble carbohydrates, then another explanation, that of Bishop and Edmond (1976), could be that the OM fixed on surficial sediments is more recently deposited than that on the near-bed particles.

2. The kerogen* in the sediments

2.1 Organic contents (Figs 3 and 4). The Holocene sediments contain a high organic carbon content, particularly in the Sukra transect: 6% at Station 9, which is the highest value noticed during 'Orgon cruises'. Organic matter is less abundant in the Mauritanian samples (maximum 2%). The Pleistocene era was characterized, particularly in Sukra sediments, by a higher sedimentation rate than in Holocene time. Sediments contain a coarser material, which was deposited by gravity flow (Moyes *et al.*, 1979, 1981) (mud flows and turbidites) partly controlled by contour currents. So organic matter is submitted to oxygenation during transportation and consequently the amounts are lower in the Pleistocene sediments than in the Holocene ones. On both margins during the Holocene era organic carbon contents decrease from the shelf to the abyssal plain, particularly off Mauritania. Off Arabia, the fact that primary production is more widespread, the water less oxygenated and transportation of organic matter to the abyssal plain shorter, due to the morphology of the slope (Moyes *et al.*, 1981), all result in a better preservation of organic matter.

2.2 Chemical fractionation of the organic matter. *Carbon distribution.* Two distinctive characteristics have been identified: (a) the amounts of the acid-soluble fraction, of humic compounds and of hydrolyzed humine fraction are higher in Mauritanian

* Kerogen is that part of organic matter insoluble in organic solvents, which, in recent sediments, is partly extractable by acid or basic aqueous solutions.

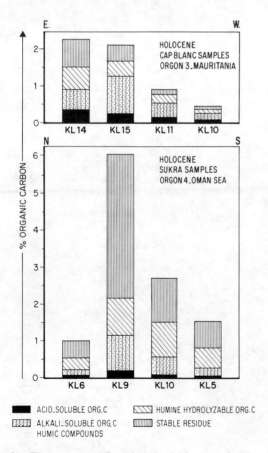

Fig. 3. The organic carbon data for the kerogen fractions of Holocene sediments from the Orgon III and IV cruises.

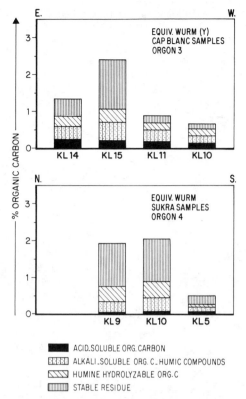

Fig. 4. The organic carbon data for the different kerogen fractions of Pleistocene sediments (equivalent to Würm) from the Orgon III and IV cruises.

kerogens than in the Arabian Sea (Figs 3 and 4) (Table 4). So the stable residue (insoluble part of the organic matter) represents the major fraction in the Arabian Sea kerogens whereas it is considerably lower in the Cap Blanc area; (b) the total acid hydrolyzable fraction (Fig. 5) increases from the shelf to the abyssal plain, especially in the Mauritanian sediments.

As the two areas are essentially supplied by the same type of organic matter (marine microplankton, mainly composed of oceanic pelagic species, Caratini *et al.*, 1979, 1981), it appears that the extractability differences may be due to the hydrological setting and more particularly to the oxygenation conditions. These characteristics are moreover strengthened for abyssal sediments, where organic matter has been submitted to longer transportation times: then, in the oxygenated environment, condensation of kerogen is affected and fulvic acids, i.e. the small acid molecules, are much more abundant (Table 4) (Brown *et al.*, 1971; Pelet, 1979). This is the case in the Cap Blanc area, especially in the abyssal plain: as this phenomenon has already been observed in previous studies (Orgon cruises: Debyser and Gadel, 1977, 1979, 1981; Debyser *et al.*, 1978), it seems not to depend on the origin and the structure of organic matter.

Nitrogen distribution. The total amount of nitrogen in sediments depends on the origin of the deposited OM: sediments containing OM from terrestrial origin, generally have a high C/N ratio (> 10); lower values are

Table 4

Data relating to the distribution of carbon and nitrogen in different organic fractions isolated from selected sediments of the Orgon III (Cap Blanc) and Orgon IV (Sukra) cruises

Samples (See Figs. 1 and 2)	Sediments			Humic compounds (F: Fulvic and H: Humic) C% tot. org. C–N% tot. N					Hydro-lyzable carbon	Stable residue
	$C\%$	$N\%$	C/N	C_F	N_F	C_H	N_H	C_F/C_H	% Tot. org. C	
Cap Blanc										
Station 14										
0.0 m	2.28	0.22	10.3	8.3	8.3	17.6	14.3	0.47	50	35
3.0 m	1.28	0.10	12.8	7.8	9.5	21.9	12.8	0.36	45	36
Station 15										
0.0 m	2.08	0.23	9.0	10.1	14.2	38.8	27.6	0.26	50	20
6.0 m	2.42	0.23	10.5	4.1	6.4	17.4	21.8	0.24	35	56
Station 11										
0.0 m	0.91	0.10	5.1	16.5	28.4	23.1	10.1	0.71	67	15
5.0 m	0.84	0.07	12.0	11.9	16.6	23.8	20.5	0.50	48	24
Station 10										
0.0 m	0.43	0.04	10.7	18.7	36.4	23.2	8.1	0.80	79	7
3.0 m	0.63	0.05	12.7	11.1	23.9	22.2	37.3	0.50	62	23
Sukra										
Station 6										
0.0 m	0.95	0.094	10.0	6.5	3.2	4.0	8	1.62	53	45
Station 9										
0.0 m	6.05	0.668	9.0	6.5	7.2	10.5	10.8	0.62	24	58
4.0 m	1.98	0.176	11.2	5.0	5.0	9.0	.9	0.56	23	63
Station 10										
0.0 m	2.66	0.310	8.5	6.0	6.1	16.5	15.8	0.36	41	40
3.0 m	2.01	0.169	11.9	5.0		13.0		0.38	23	59
Station 5										
0.0 m	1.52	0.130	11.6	4.0	13.8	9.0	5.4	0.44	53	41
1.0 m	0.48	0.065	7.3	8.5	7.7	18.5	12.3	0.46	46	49

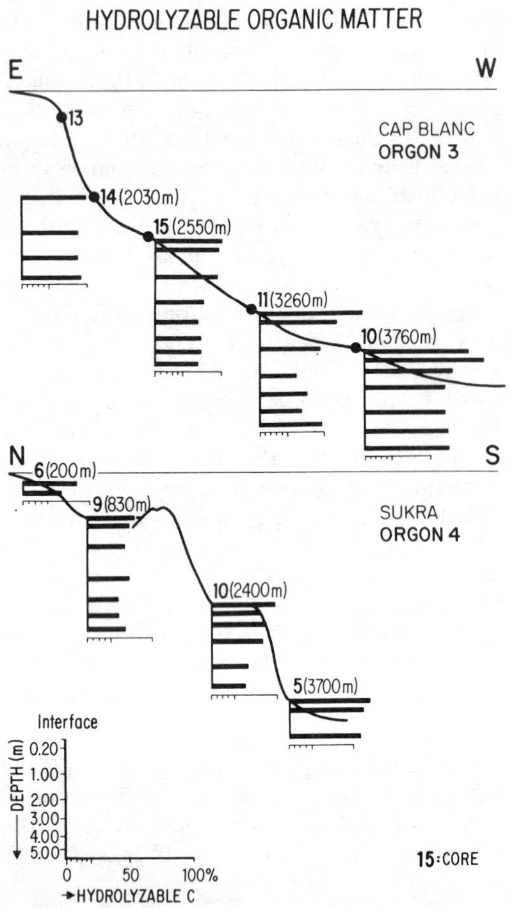

HYDROLYZABLE ORGANIC MATTER

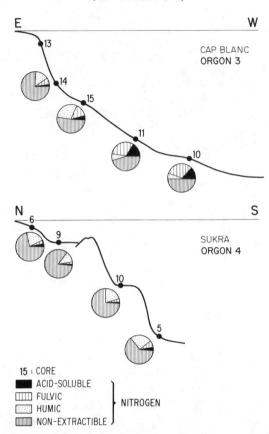

Fig. 5. Hydrolyzable organic matter in sediments from selected stations of the Orgon III and IV cruises.

Fig. 6. The distribution of nitrogen in kerogen fractions from the surface sediments from the Orgon III and IV cruises.

observed in marine autochthonous OM, rich in proteinaceous components (Huc, 1980): this is generally found in upwelling areas (Vinogradov, 1953). In the sediments studied here, C/N ratio shows variation from 5 to more than 10 (Table 2). These observations can be attributed to:

(1) *Sedimentation rate*: according to Hartmann *et al.* (1976), a high sedimentation rate contributes to a better preservation of nitrogen. This is supported by our analysis: the Sukra margin having a higher sedimentation rate than Mauritanian one, shows lower C/N ratio than the latter; in the upper rise of the Cap Blanc margin, the lowest C/N ratio coincides with the highest sedimentation rate (site 14) (Moyes *et al.*, 1979);

(2) *Mineralogical composition of the sediment*: in Cap Blanc margin, the high carbonate content of the abyssal sediments (60% $CaCO_3$ at the maximum water depth versus 30 to 40% in the other areas) (Debyser *et al.*, 1979) coincides with an unusual high C/N value (Table 2) (Jocteur Monrozier and Jeanson, 1979): Rittenberg *et al.* (1963) observed that C/N ratio usually decreases in surficial abyssal sediments, probably due to the fact that, in deep waters, sediments contain more clay than carbonates. Thus, sedimentation rate and nature of the mineral constituents influence the nitrogen content of the sedimentary OM.

Extractability of nitrogen humic compounds may vary according to the nature and depositional conditions of OM.

(1) In the biomass, the cytoplasmic components (proteins, RNA, amino acids) and the fluid constituent part, contain high amounts of alkali-soluble nitrogen, whereas the supporting material (cells walls, organic skeletons, muscles, chitinous tests and fibrous proteins) are less soluble in dilute cold alkali (Lehninger, 1972). Thus, in aquatic environments which favour biological activity, nitrogen extractability may prevail over the carbon one. Our analysis show that in the Mauritanian margin, in the surficial sediments, extractability of organic nitrogen (Fig. 6) is higher than in the Sukra samples, except for the upper rise (sample 6) which was submitted to high biological activity (Romano and Dinet, 1981;

(2) When biomass detritus settles in an environment depleted in oxygen, mineralization and biological anabolism are lowered (Demaison and Moore, 1980): humic genesis prevails, the amounts of extractable carbon and nitrogen tend to be similar and low due to the humification processes and deoxygenation of organic matter (Jocteur Monrozier, 1981): a comparison between carbon and nitrogen extractability (Table 4) shows that the humification processes prevail in samples from

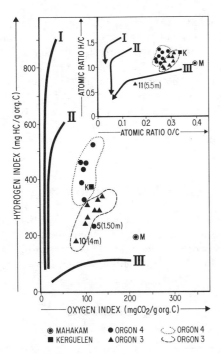

Fig. 7. Plots of H/C against O/C and hydrogen index against oxygen index for stable residues of sediments from Orgon III and IV cruises.

Sukra margin (except for sample 6) and in site 14 from Cap Blanc which have been submitted to more reducing conditions (Daumas *et al.*, 1979). It appears that nitrogen extractability increases when oxygenation increases, as does carbon extractability; but it increases faster than the carbon extractability, if biological activity prevails (Cap Blanc 15, 11, 10) and when humification processes have been prominent (Sukra 9, 10, 5).

2.3 Elemental analysis — hydrogen index. In the two areas, the kerogens present a similar aliphaticity (Fig. 7, Table 5) expressed by the H/C atomic ratio. This aliphaticity is not as high as should be expected for autochthonous organic matter (Brown *et al.*, 1972) as compared to Kerguelen kerogen, for example (Debyser *et al.*, 1978), OM of which comes essentially from microalgae (Table 5). Pelet (1981) shows that planktonic species by their own specific chemical characters, may have an influence on the aliphaticity of kerogen. The conditions of preservation governed by the environment may also interfere: the kerogens of the deepest sediments cored in the abyssal plain off Mauritania and Arabia (Stations 10 and 5) have low *H/C* ratios Table 5, Fig. 7) close to one of kerogens from terrestrial origin, cored in Mahakam delta in Indonesia (Boudou, 1981).

Table 5

Elemental analysis data for humic acids and corresponding stable residues from selected sediments of the Orgon III (Cap Blanc) and Orgon IV (Sukra) cruises

Samples (see Figs. 1 and 2)	Humic acids				Stable residues			
	H/C	O/C	N/C	S/C	H/C	O/C	N/C	% pyrite
Station 14								
1.0 m	1.34	0.42	0.083	0.017	1.20	0.28	0.065	35.9
3.0 m	1.29	0.41	0.073	0.017	1.07	0.25	0.045	43.00
Station 15								
0.0 m	1.36	0.44	0.086	0.011	1.21	0.29	0.059	11.3
6.0 m	1.32	0.44	0.087	0.024	1.20	0.30	0.068	28.2
Station 11								
0.0 m	1.32	0.44	0.083	0.007	1.22	0.28	0.052	0.7
3.0 m	1.34	0.41	0.081	0.017	1.24	0.32	0.067	41.7
Station 10								
1.5 m	1.26	0.42	0.076	0.007	1.14	0.31	0.058	17.0
4.0 m	1.20	0.51	0.063	0.010	0.88	0.27	0.038	26.2
Sukra								
Station 6								
0.0 m	1.35	0.49	0.107	0.015	1.23	0.25	0.060	1.36
Station 9								
0.0 m	1.29	0.46	0.099	0.011	1.16	0.23	0.054	3.58
4.5 m	1.09	0.42	0.070	0.025	1.10	0.25	0.054	16.41
Station 10								
0.0 m	1.35	0.50	0.096	0.014	1.23	0.29	0.061	1.56
2.5 m	1.32	0.46	0.085	0.030	1.19	0.25	0.047	12.64
Station 5								
0.0 m	1.32	0.53	0.100	0.011	1.15	0.27	0.058	0.60
1.0 m	1.32	0.48	0.079	0.012	1.03	0.25	0.045	25.22
Mahakam: terrestrial origin	1.00	0.67	0.059	0.011	1.05	0.43	0.016	11.08
Kerguelen	1.41	0.54	0.11	0.035	1.33	0.35	0.061	28.31

In the Holocene Cap Blanc transect, the organic matter of the lower part of the continental rise sediments (Stations 11 and 10) has less aliphatic character than the shelf sediments (Table 5). Only transportation can explain this difference for a kind of organic marine material which is so fragile and sensitive to degradation processes (Degens *et al.*, 1963). In Station 10 (in the abyssal plain), Caratini *et al.* (1979) noticed by optical examination of the stable residues a fairly high participation of allochthonous material which, in fact, had been concentrated. In the south Arabian margin, where the transportation is reduced due to the slope morphology and where the primary production spreads far offshore, this phenomenon is less obvious.

The N/C ratios of stable residues* are high (Table 5) relative to the values generally obtained on residues of OM from terrestrial origin (Mahakam deltaic sediments in Indonesia: Boudou, 1981) (Table 5), or evolved in an oxic environment (Debyser and Gadel, 1977, 1979). This characterizes marine autochthonous organic matter, rich in carbohydrates and proteins. The petroleum potential of stable residues, evaluated by 'Rock Eval pyrolysis' (Espitalié *et al.*, 1977; Herbin and Deroo, 1979; Debyser and Gadel, 1981) is clearly higher in all Sukra samples (Fig. 7) than in Mauritanian residues. Conseequently, kerogen structures of the south Arabian margin and Cap Blanc areas are probably different, even if the initial organic matter and its elementary composition are quite identical.

CONCLUSIONS

In both areas, the organic matter is mostly of planktonic origin and has typical geochemical characteristics of marine originated material: namely, significant abundance of phaeopigments in the particles and surficial sediments, high amounts of nitrogen compounds and aliphatic rich kerogens. The conditions of preservation and stabilization are good, as seen by fairly high amounts of organic matter and a generally low content of hydrolyzable fraction. Depositional conditions are different in the two margins (water oxygenation, morphology of the slope, sedimentary transportation). They affect some features of the organic matter: in the Sukra transect, where waters were poorly oxygenated and transportation time reduced, the kerogen is better stabilized than in the Cap Blanc area: the amounts of humic compounds are lowered, the stable residue is the major fraction of the kerogen; nitrogenous organic compounds are less extractable, hydrogen index evaluated by Rock Eval pyrolysis is higher.

In the two areas, evolution follows the same path: a lateral evolution, down to the abyssal plain with increasing amounts of small oxygenated organic molecules (fulvic acids, hydrolyzable compounds). This evolution is more important when the waters are rich in dissolved oxygen (Mauritania); an evolution with depth in the core, expressed by an increasing insolubilization of buried organic matter.

---

* Stable residue is the insoluble part of humine (after mineral fraction has been destroyed) (Debyser and Gadel, 1979).

To conclude, it appears that in upwelling areas, where the origin of the organic matter deposited is similar, its quantity and its structure is directly related to depositional conditions. These relations are nevertheless complicated and moreover different environmental conditions could result in the same gross chemical composition of the sedimentary organic matter. So any interpretation of ancient sediments, only based on organic criteria, seems at this standpoint of knowledge risky.

Acknowledgements

We thank Dr J. C. Faugères and J. Poutiers (Institut Géologique du Bassin d'Aquitaine) and Dr F. Gadel (Centre sédimentologique de Perpignan). We are grateful for their comments and preliminary reports.

REFERENCES

Bensoussan, M., Bianchi, A., Bonnefont, J. L., Boudabous, A., Marty, D. and Sonier, L. (1981) Les communautés bactériennes des eaux et des sédiments profonds du golfe d'Aden et de la mer d'Oman. I. Distribution. In *Géochimie organique des sédiments marins profonds. Orgon IV. Golfe d'Aden, mer d'Oman*, Editions CNRS, Paris, pp. 13–22.

Bishop, J. K. B. and Edmond, J. M. (1976) A new large volume filtration system for the sampling of oceanic particulate matter. *J. Mar. Res.* **24**, 181–199.

Boudou, J. P. (1981) Diagénèse organique de sédiments deltaïques (delta de la Mahakam, Indonésie). Thèse Doctorat Es-Sciences, Orléans.

Brown, F. S., Baedecker, M. J., Nissenbaum, A. and Kaplan, I. R. (1972) Early diagenesis in reducing fjord of Saanich Inlet. British Columbia. III — Changes in organic constituents of sediments. *Geochim. Cosmochim. Acta* **36**, 1185–1203.

Caratini, C., Bellet, J. and Tissot, C. (1979) Etude microscopique de la matière organique: palynologie et palynofaciès. In *Géochimie organique des sédiments marins profonds. Orgon III. Mauritanie, Senegal, Isles du Cap Vert*. Editions CNRS, Paris, pp. 215–226.

Caratini, C., Bellet, J. and Tissot, C. (1981) Etude microscopique de la matière organique: palynologie et palynofaciès. In *Géochimie organique des sédiments marins profonds. Orgon IV. Golfe d'Aden, mer d'Oman*. Editions CNRS, Paris, pp. 265–308.

CEPM-CNEXO (1979) *Géochemie organique des sédiments marins profonds. Orgon III. Mauritanie, Sénégal, Iles du Cap Vert*. Editions CNRS, Paris, 441 pp.

CEPM-CNEXO (1981) *Géochimie organique des sédiments marins profonds. Orgon IV, Golfe d'Aden, mer d'Oman*. Editions CNRS, Paris, 547 pp.

Daumas, R., Laborde, P., Romano, J. C. and Sautriot, D. (1977) Minéralisation de la matière organique dans les sédiments marins récents. In *Géochimie organique des sédiments marins profonds. Orgon I. Mer de Norvège*. Editions CNRS, Paris, pp. 32–56.

Daumas, R., Laborde, P., Paul, R., Romano, J. C. and Sautriot, D. (1978) Les mécanismes de transformation de la matière organique en Atlantique intertropical. Etude de la minéralisation et de la diagénèse dans les sédiments superficiels. In *Géochimie organique des sédiments marins profonds. Orgon II. Atlantique, Nord-Est Brésil*. Editions CNRS, Paris, pp. 44–83.

Daumas, R., Laborde, P., Romano, J. C. and Sautriot, D. (1979) Distribution et évolution des constituants biochimiques de la matière organique dans les sédiments: relations avec la composition des eaux interstitielles. In *Géochimie organique des sédiments marins profonds. Orgon III. Mauritanie, Sénégal, Iles du Cap Vert.* Editions CNRS, Paris, pp. 67–92.

Daumas, R., Laborde, P., Romano, J. C. and Sautriot, D. (1981) Hydrologie et particules en suspension en mer d'Arabie. In *Géochimie organique des sédiments marins profonds. Orgon IV. Golfe d'Aden, mer d'Oman.* Editions CNRS, Paris, pp. 71–94.

Debyser, Y. and Gadel, F. (1977) Etude géochimique des composés humiques et des kérogènes. In *Géochimie organique des sédiments marins profonds. Orgon I. Mer de Norvège.* Editions CNRS, Paris, pp. 247–268.

Debyser, Y. and Gadel, F. (1979) Géochimie des kérogènes dans les sédiments. In *Géochimie organique des sédiments marins profonds. Orgon III. Mauritanie, Sénégal, Iles du Cap Vert.* Editions CNRS, Paris, pp. 375–404.

Debyser, Y. and Gadel, F. (1981) Géochimie des kérogènes dans les sédiments. In *Géochimie organique des sédiments marins profonds. Orgon IV. Golfe d'Aden, mer d'Oman.* Editions CNRS, Paris, pp. 447–482.

Debyser, Y., Gadel, F., Leblond, C. and Martinez, M. J. (1978) Etude des composés humiques des kérogènes et de la fraction hydrolysable dans les sédiments. In *Géochimie organique des sédiments marins profonds Orgon II. Atlantique, Nord-Est Brésil.* Editions CNRS, Paris, pp. 339–454.

Degens, E. T., Emery, K. O. and Reuter, J. H. (1963) Organic material in recent and ancient sediments: part 3. Biochemical compounds in San Diego through- California. In *Neue Jahrbuch für geologie und paleölontologie,* pp. 231–248.

Demaison, G. J. and Moore, G. T. (1980) Anoxic environments and oil source bed genesis. *Org. Geochem.* **2**, 2–31.

Espitalié, J., Laporte, J. L., Madec, M., Marquis, F., Leplat, P., Paulet, J. and Boutefeu, A. (1977) Méthode rapide de caractérisation des roches mères, de leur potentiel pétrolier et de leur degré d'évolution. *Rev. Inst. Fr. Pétrol.* **32**, 23–42.

Hartman, M., Muller, P. J., Suess, E. and Van der Weijden (1976) Chemistry of last quaternary sediment and their interstitial water from the N.W. African continent margin. *Meteor Vorstung Ergebnisse Reihe,* **24**, 1–67.

Herbin, J. P. and Deroo, G. (1979) Sédimentation de rift. Géochimie organique dans les forages DSDP de la mer Rouge et du golfe d'Aden. Publ. interne I.F.P., ref. 23597.

Huc, A. Y. (1980) Origin and formation of organic matter in recent sediments and its relation to kerogen. In *Kerogen,* ed. by Durand, B. Editions Technip, Paris, pp. 445–474.

Jocteur Monrozier, L. and Jeanson, P. (1979) L'azote organique et ammoniacal — Combinaisons et stabilité chimique. In *Géochimie organique des sédiments marins profonds. Orgon III. Mauritanie, Sénégal, Iles du Cap Vert.* Editions CNRS, Paris, pp. 405–422.

Jocteur Monrozier, L. (1981) Les composés humiques à l'interface océan sédiment. *Oxeanis* **7**, 309–325.

Kuz'menko, L. V. (1968) Primary production in the Arabian sea in the summer monsoon period. *Oceanology* **8**, 367–370.

Lehninger, A. L. (1972) *Biochemistry. The Molecular Basis of Cell Structure and Function.* 6th ed. Worth Publishers Inc. New York, 833 pp.

Moyes, J., Duplantier, F., Duprat, J., Faugeres, J. C., Pujol, C., Pugos Lamy, A. and Tastet, J. P. (1979) Etude stratigraphique et sédimentologique. In *Géochimie organique des sédiments marins profonds. Orgon III. Mauritanie, Sénégal, Iles du Cap Vert.* Editions CNRS, Paris, pp. 121–213.

Moyes, J., Duprat, J., Faugeres, J. C., Gonthier, E. and Pujol, C. (1981) Etude stratigraphique et sédimentologique. In *Géochimie organique des sédiments marins profonds. Orgon IV. Golfe d'Aden, mer d'OOman.* Editions CNRS, Paris, pp. 164–189.

Pelet, R. (1979) Géochimie organique des sédiments marins profonds au large de la Mauritanie et du Sénégal: vue d'ensemble. In *Géochimie organique des sédiments marins profonds. Orgon III. Mauritanie, Sénégal, Isles du Cap Vert.* Editions CNRS, Paris, pp. 425–441.

Pelet, R. (1981) Preservation and alteration of sedimentary organic matter (in this volume).

Rittenberg, F. C., Emery, K. O., Sobfthulserann, Degens, E. T., Fay, R. C., Reuter, J. H., Grady, J. R., Richardson, S. H. and Bray, E. E. (1963) Biochemistry of sediment in experimental Mohole. *J. Sediment Petrol.* **33**, 140–172.

Romano, J. C. and Dinet, A. (1981) Relations entre l'abondance du meiobenthos et de la biomasse des sédiments superficiels estimée par la mesure des adenosines 5′ phosphate (ATP, ADP, AMP). *Géochimie organique des sédiments marins profonds. Orgon IV, Golfe d'Aden, mer d'Oman.* Editions CNRS, Paris, pp. 159–180.

Ryther, J. H., Hall, J. R. and Pease, A. K. (1966) Primary organic production in relation to the chemistry and hydrography of the Western Indian Ocean. *Limnol. Oceanogr.* **11**, 371–380.

Saijo, Y. (1969) Chlorophyll pigments in the deep sea. *B. Jap. Soc. Fish. Oceanogr.* Special Issue, Nov. 1969, 179–182.

Schemainda, K., Nehring, D. and Schulz, (1975) Ozeanogische Untersuchungen zum Produksionspotential der nordwest-africanischen wesserauftriebsregion 1970–1973. *Geodatische und Geophysikalische Veroffentlichungen* **IV**, 85.

Simoneit, B. R. T. (1978) The organic chemistry of marine sediments. In *Chemical Oceanography,* Vol. 7, 2nd ed., ed. by Riley, J. P. and Chester, R. Academic Press, London, New York, San Francisco, pp. 234–311.

Suess, E. and Muller, P. (1980) Productivity, sedimentation rate and sedimentary organic matter in the oceans. II. Elemental fractionation. Colloque *Biogéochimie de la matière organique à l'interface eau-sédiment marin,* Marseille, 1979. Editions CNRS, Paris.

Vinogradov, A. P. (1953) The elementary chemical composition of marine organisms. Sears Foundation for Marine Research. Mémoire no. 2. Yale University (translated from Russian), 647 pp.

Advances in Organic Geochemistry 1981, pp. 268–278
© *John Wiley & Sons Limited, 1983*

Pyrolytic and Naturally Occurring Polycyclic Aromatic Hydrocarbons in the Marine Environment

M. J. Tissier and A. Saliot

Laboratoire de Physique et Chimie Marines de l'Université Pierre et Marie Curie, ERA CNRS, Tour 24, 4 Place Jussieu, 75230 PARIS Cedex 05, France

The nature of the polycyclic aromatic hydrocarbon fraction (PAH) has been investigated in surficial and deep oceanic waters, plankton, faecal pellets, deep recent sediments and interstitial waters collected during the four Orgon cruises in the Norwegian Sea, western and eastern intertropical Atlantic Ocean and Arabian Sea. Qualitative and quantitative analyses have been performed by spectrofluorimetry, gas chromatography (GC) and computerized GC/mass spectrometry. Total pyrolytic-like PAH concentrations are very low, ranging from 5 to 50 ng l^{-1} in surficial waters, from 1 to 18 ng l^{-1} in deep waters, from 0.3 to 16 000 ng l^{-1} in interstitial waters and from 0.1 to 2800 ng g^{-1} in deep recent sediments. This survey leads to the following conclusions: (a) A distribution of pyrolytic type PAH is always found in sediments and fine suspended particulate matter even off very little industrialized or desert areas, because of marine currents and aeolian inputs. In these samples phenanthrene predominates over fluoranthene, pyrene and chrysene. (b) The distributions of pyrolytic-like PAH encountered in the dissolved fraction of marine water are different, characterized by the predominance of pyrene and fluoranthene. These distributions can be explained by the physicochemical fractionations occurring at the air/sea interface between vapour, liquid and solid phases. (c) Bioaccumulation enriches the PAH content through the marine food web and results in their incorporation in the sedimentary column, partly via the interstitial water. (d) Naturally occurring PAH (perylene and terpene derivatives) are found in the water column especially in the dissolved fraction. They reflect terrestrial inputs. Combined biological, dynamical, physicochemical and topographical factors can explain the unexpected presence of aromatic terrestrial markers in sediments from typically marine sedimentation areas and can control the distribution and the importance of the two PAH classes, pyrolytic-like and naturally occurring, in the marine environment.

INTRODUCTION

The anthropogenic polycyclic aromatic hydrocarbons (PAH) are now well documented in recent coastal marine and freshwater sediments, especially near highly industrialized areas (Youngblood and Blumer, 1975; Giger and Schaffner, 1977; Laflamme and Hites, 1978; Neff, 1979; Wakeham *et al.*, 1980a). Several origins have been clearly demonstrated: pyrolysis, combustion and petroleum products.

But diagenetic processes also produce a mixture of PAH derived from polycyclic biogenic precursors originating from bacterial lipids, terrestrial higher plant terpenoids and unknown precursors. Perylene and retene related compounds, among the most abundant PAH, are known as short term diagenetic products (Simoneit, 1977a, b; Laflamme and Hites, 1978). The precursors of perylene remain unknown. The first general studies of higher plant triterpenoid and bacterial lipid derived PAH in sediments were carried out by Spyckerelle (1975) and Spyckerelle *et al.* (1977). A bacterial origin was ascribed for the aromatization and degradation of the precursors. Subsequently, Tissier and

Spyckerelle (1977), Tissier and Dastillung (1978), Laflamme and Hites (1979), Boussuge *et al.* (1979), Wakeham *et al.* (1980b) and Riolo *et al.* (1981) examined recent lacustrine and marine sediments for these naturally derived PAH.

The Orgon programme permitted the investigation of both classes of PAH, pollutants and naturally derived, in a wide variety of deep marine sediments from Skagerrak and the Norwegian Sea (Orgon I cruise), Cariaco trench and the Amazon river delta (Orgon II cruise), off the Cape Verde islands and the Senegalese and Mauritanian coasts (Orgon III cruise) and from the Arabian Sea (Orgon IV cruise). Sedimentological, stratigraphical, palynological, bacteriological, biochemical and geochemical data are compiled in the four Orgon reports (Pelet, 1977; Combaz and Pelet, 1978; Arnould and Pelet, 1979; Pelet, 1981).

The analysis of sediment samples was accompanied by the examination of the PAH content of interstitial waters and the water column. Dissolved material and particles, collected by filtration, were separately analysed from the surface microlayer to the bottom waters in the North-eastern tropical Atlantic Ocean. In the Arabian Sea,

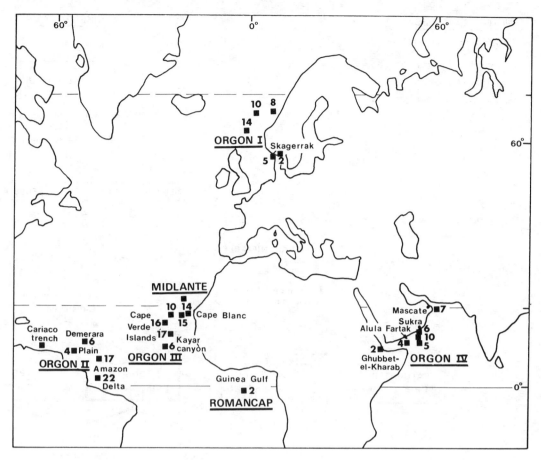

Fig. 1. Location of sampling stations.

plankton and large size particles were also collected by tows of nets.

This study of PAH in the marine environment has been complimented by analyses of aerosols (gaseous and particulate fractions) collected off the Cape Verde islands and in the Gulf of Guinea (Midlante and Romancap cruises, Marty *et al.*, 1979; Marty, 1981) and by the study of the effect of diagenesis on PAH distributions in some coals (Tissier, 1981).

This paper is a synthesis of our observations on the distribution, origin and selected transfer mechanisms of PAH in the marine environment.

EXPERIMENTS

Samples

The sampling locations for the four Orgon cruises on the R/V *Jean Charcot* are shown in Fig. 1: Orgon I in the Norwegian Sea (August 1974); Orgon II in the Amazon river delta, the Demerara plain and the anoxic Cariaco trench (October 1975); Orgon III off the Senegalese and Mauritanian coasts and off the Cape Verde islands (October 1976); Orgon IV in the productive Arabian Sea (November 1978).

Sediments were obtained with short and long Reineck corers and were of late Quaternary age (up to 100 000 years). Sea water was collected using an all metallic 130 l bottle equipped with an ultrasonic pinger, at *ca.* 5 m

above the sediment and at 50 m depth. Interstitial water (from 1 to 2.5 l) was obtained by pressing at 4 kg cm^{-2} *ca.* 6 Kg of sediment over a Millipore 0.45 μm membrane in an all-metallic press. Water (100 l) was filtered through a pre-extracted 1 μm GF/C fibreglass Whatman filter. The suspended material collected on the filter (>1 μm) was denoted 'small size particles'. The sampling of surficial planktonic material was achieved from 200 m to the surface using vertical tows of carefully rinsed plankton nets (50 μm wide mesh). In deep layers, the probability of efficiently collecting representatively large particles (>50 μm) using large volume bottles is low, due to their dispersion in the water column (Sheldon *et al.*, 1972). Their sampling was achieved using vertical tows of nets (50 μm wide mesh) from a 100 m above the sea floor to 1000 or 2000 m. The large size material, surface and deep, was filtered through a 150 μm membrane providing two fractions denoted 50–150 μm and >150 μm.

Analyses

The extraction and isolation procedure have been described (Dastillung and Corbet, 1978; Boussuge *et al.*, 1979). The analytical flow diagram is given in Fig. 2.

Gas chromatographic analysis was performed on a Girdel 3000 gas chromatograph with flame ionization detector. Two columns were used: (i) packed stainless steel (4 m × 2.2 mm i.d.; 1% Dexsil 300 on Gas Chrom Q 80–100 mesh; temperature programmed from 100 to 300

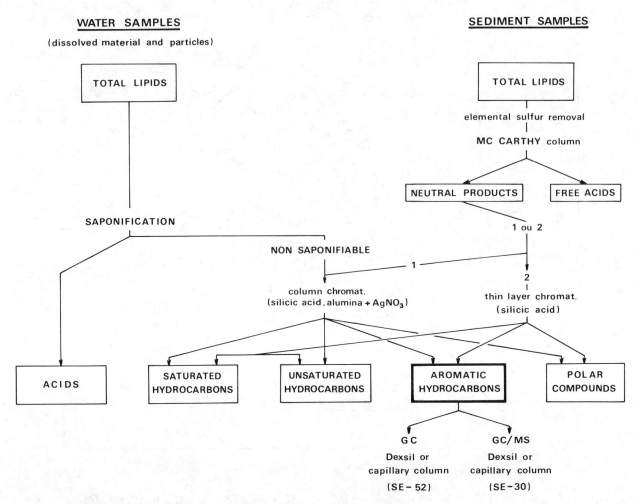

Fig. 2. Analytical flow diagram.

°C at a rate of 4 °C min^{-1}, carrier gas: helium, 25 ml min^{-1}) and (ii) glass capillary (25 m × 0.4 mm i.d.; SE 52; temperature programmed from 100 to 250 °C at a rate of 3 °C min^{-1}; carrier gas: helium, 2 ml min^{-1}) Concentrations were obtained by comparison of sample peak areas with those of known amounts of standards (dioctyl phthalate, phenanthrene, fluoranthene, chrysene, benzo[a] pyrene and perylene) run under the same analytical conditions.

Gas chromatographic/mass spectrometric identification and quantitation of individual PAH were carried out on a LKB 9000 S apparatus coupled with digital equipment PDP 11 E 10 computer. Gas chromatographic conditions were: (i) glass capillary (50 m × 0.2 mm i.d., SE 30); temperature programmed from 150 to 300 °C at a rate of 4 °C min^{-1}; carrier gas: helium, 2 ml min^{-1} (Orgon I and IV) and (ii) packed glass column (4 m × 2.2 mm i.d., 1% Dexsil 300 on Gas Chrom Q); carrier gas: helium, 22 ml min^{-1} (Orgon II and III). The molecular weights of the examined parent PAH and their alkylated homologues ranged from 178 (phenanthrene and anthracene) to 300 (coronene).

The quantitation of individual compounds was performed using in each water, suspended particulate matter and sediment sample, dioctyl phthalate (DOP), a common environmental contaminant, as internal standard, in the following manner. Knowing the absolute concentration of DOP from GC analysis, the ratio between individual PAH and DOP concentrations was determined by computerized GC/MS, which allowed the absolute concentration of PAH to be determined. There was a good agreement (better than 10%) between GC and GC/MS responses for the main components that were measured using standards (DOP, phenanthrene, fluoranthene, chrysene, benzo[a] pyrene and perylene).

For Orgon I sediment samples, the precise quantitation of fluoranthene, benzo-1,2 pyrene, benzo-3,4 pyrene, benzo-8,9 fluoranthene and perylene was achieved by spectrofluorimetry using a Bearn type Jobin-Yvon apparatus (Tissier and Spyckerelle, 1977).

For phenanthrenic and chrysenic triterpene derivatives, the quantitation was obtained by quasi-linear Shpolsk'ii spectrofluorimetry with the use of synthetic molecules or known mixtures as references (Ewald, 1978) and also by gas chromatography by comparison with the parent structures, e.g. phenanthrene and chrysene.

Precision and detection limits

The global error on the absolute concentrations was determined by analysing several times a mixture of standards in the same conditions as for water or sediment samples. Owing to the extraction, isolation, purification

Table 1

Total pyrolytic-like PAH concentrations (ng l^{-1}) in surficial waters for dissolved and particulate material

Marine area	Station and collection depth	Dissolved material	Particles $>1 \mu m$	Particles $>50 \mu m$ collected between 200 m and the surface
Orgon III Cape Verde islands	16 (50 m)	5	0.2	
Orgon IV Arabian Sea	10 (50 m) 4 (50 m)	12	3.6	0.02 3.10 .[a]
Romancap Gulf of Guinea	2 (0.4 mm) (0.2 m)	35.2 6	15 9	

and evaporation steps a maximum value of 60% is to be expected. Reported PAH concentrations have not been corrected.

Great care was taken to avoid contamination during sampling and laboratory analysis. Blanks of distilled solvents, extracts of KOH, filters, silicic acid were found to contain small amounts of teflon derivatives, which were removed during liquid chromatography, and PAH, which were negligible compared with sample concentrations. The absolute concentration detectable by GC/MS is 0.1 ng for individual PAH, which leads to a wide range of detection limits depending on the weight or the volume of the sample. The detection limits for individual PAH are: 3×10^{-3} ng l^{-1} for sea water collected with the 100 l bottle, 10^{-5} ng l^{-1} for surficial

plankton obtained by filtering *ca.* 30 000 l of sea water with plankton nets, 10^{-6} ng l^{-1} for deep particles obtained by filtering 150 000 to 750 000 l of sea water with special nets and 5×10^{-2} ng g^{-1} for sediments.

RESULTS AND DISCUSSION

Because of the large quantity of information obtained on the various cruises, only selected data is presented in this paper.

Pyrolytic-like PAH

In the group of pyrolytic-like PAH, the following major compounds and their lakylated homologues were selected for quantitation: phenanthrene (+anthracene), fluoranthene, pyrne, chrysene (+triphenylene and benzo (a) anthracene), bnezofluoranthenes, benzopyrenes and perylene. When the relative percentage of perylene exceeded 10% of total pyrolytic-like PAH, this compound is considered to have arisen from a diagenetic process.

Total pyrolytic-like PAH concentrations. The total pyrolytic-like PAH concentrations range from 5 to 50 ng l^{-1} in surficial waters (Table 1) and from 1 to 18 ng l^{-1} in deep waters (Table 2). PAH are essentially found in the dissolved fraction (passing through a 1 μm filter). Very small amounts are found in the planktonic material sampled between 200 m and the surface.

For the dissolved material, PAH represent from q to 13% of total non-aromatic hydrocarbons.

Table 2

Total pyrolytic-like PAH concentrations (ng l^{-1}) in overlying and interstitial waters at the sea–sediment interface. The enrichment factor (EF) is defined as the concentration of a particular lipid class in interstitial waters compared to the overlying waters (dissolved fraction)

Marine area	Station	Compounds	Overlying water		Surficial interstitial water (0–0.4 m)	EF
			Dissolved material	Particles $>1 \mu m$		
Orgon II Demerara Plain	6	PAH	4	3	150	38
		HC	114*		3180*	28
		FA	200		730	4
Orgon III Cape Blanc transect	14	PAH	17	1	900	53
		HC	860		13620	16
		FA	460		10700	23
	15	PAH	17	1	16260	956
		HC	130		5850	45
		FA	980		9190	9
	10[a]	PAH	16	0.2	7280	455
		HC	1570		58000	37
		FA	1360		46980	35
Orgon IV Alula Fartak trench	4	PAH	4	0.02	~0	0
		HC	165		12260	74
		FA	5920		18200	3
Sukra transect	10	PAH	1	0.1	40	40
		HC	162		780	5
		FA	1310		11000	8

PAH: pyrolytic-like aromatic hydrocarbons; HC: non-aromatic hydrocarbons (*only *n*-alkanes); FA: fatty acids.
[a] Sediments characterized by exceptional bacteriological level (Bensoussan *et al.*, 1979)

Table 3
Perylene and total pyrolytic-like PAH content (including perylene) of marine sediments

Marine area	Station	Depth (m)	Org. Carbon (%)	PAH (ng g^{-1})	Perylene (ng g^{-1})	Perylene/O.C. (ng g^{-1})(g g^{-1})
Orgon I						
Skagerrak	2	0.0	1.89		2[a]	100
		0.5	1.76	567	16	900
		0.75	1.66	593	46	2800
		2.25	1.39	166	9	600
		2.75	1.45	166	11	800
		3.0	1.45		0.02[a]	1
	5	0.0	1.90		0.2[a]	10
		4.0	1.07		10[a]	900
Norwegian Sea	8	0.0	0.40		0.7[a]	200
		0.5	0.56		0.06[a]	10
		1.0	0.30	18	2	700
		3.5	0.39		89[a]	22 900
	10	0.0	1.01		0.7[a]	70
		1.0	0.85	290	22	2600
		6.0	0.81		0.07[a]	10
	14	0.0	0.40		0.6[a]	200
		8.0	0.41	250	7	1800
		8.5	0.44		18[a]	4100
Orgon II						
Cariaco trength	1	0.0	3.02	110	54	1800
		0.5–1.5	3.05	40	35	1200
		5.5	3.20	190	172	5400
Demerara Plain	4	0.0–2.0	0.61	15	4	700
Orgon III						
Cape Blanc transect	14	0.0–0.5	1.79	10	0.5	30
		2.5–3.0	1.51	15	0.4	30
	10	0.0	0.43	3	0.03	7
		4.0	0.49	3	0.03	6
Kayar canyon	17	0.0	0.57	0.1	0.002	0.3
		2.0	1.01	0.1	0.01	1
	6	0.0	0.35	0.1	0.001	0.3
		0.5–1.5	1.24	3	2	160
		2.0–3.0	1.15	4	0.4	30
Orgon IV						
Ghubbet el Kharab	2	0.0	1.76	140	0	0
		4.0	2.80	1	0	0
Alula Fartak trench	4	0.0	2.67	2800	232	8700
		2.0	2.48	340	35	1400
Sukra transect	6	0.0	0.95	160	0	0
	10	0.0	2.66	70	0	0
		1.0	1.62	2	0	0
		3.0	2.01	0.3	0	0
Mascate transect	7	0.0	4.20	20	0	0
		5.5	1.48	10	6	400

[a] Quantitation by spectrofluorimetry.

The total pyrolytic-like PAH concentrations range from trace to high values, e.g. 16 260 ng l^{-1} in interstitial waters (Table 2). The high values obtained for the eastern Atlantic (Stations 10 and 15) could be explained by intense bioaccumulation of PAH by microorganisms (see below).

The total pyrolytic-like PAH concentrations in the recent sediments range from 0.1 to 2800 ng g^{-1} (Table 3). All water and sediment samples have very low total pyrolytic-like PAH concentrations compared with those reported in the literature for coastal marine or lacustrine polluted locations (Laflamme and Hites, 1978; Neff, 1979; Wakeham et al., 1979; 1980a).

Origin of pyrolytic-like PAH. The low contents of pyrolytic-like PAH, which have been detected, represent the present background in marine environments far from industrialized areas and off deserts. It is difficult to determine the origin of these components. The distribution of these PAH in sediments (e.g. Fig. 4) is very similar to those observed in lignite, coal and wood ashes (Tissier, 1981). The relative importance of alkylated homologues can sometimes differentiate between the various sources. For instance, coal can contain higher abundances of certain alkylated compounds (Tissier, 1981). However, the similarity of the alkylated homologues in wood ashes, diagenetized

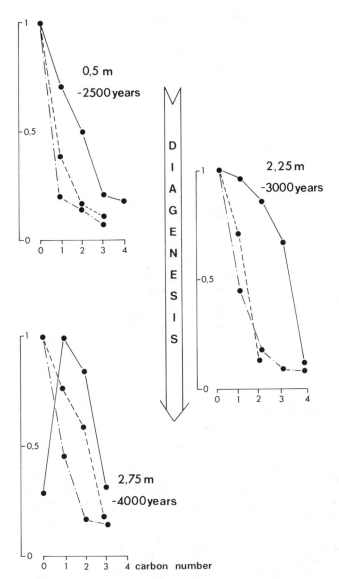

Fig. 3. Alkylated homologues distributions (normalized to the most abundant compound) for different depths in the sediment cores in Station 2, Skagerrak, Orgon I cruise: phenanthrene and anthracene series (———), fluoranthene and pyrene series (–––), chrysene, triphenylene and benz(a)anthracene series (–·–·–).

material such as lignite, and the sediments and particulate matter (>1 μm) (Tissier, 1981) prevents a clear determination of the source of PAH in these marine environments. An additional complication is that diagenesis over a time period of only a few thousand years can rapidly enhance the amount of alkylated homologues (see Fig. 3). The distributions probably arise partly from natural and anthropogenic combustion and partly from diagenesis.

Pyrolytic-like PAH distributions. In the Atlantic Ocean, a similar distribution of pyrolytic-like PAH is observed in the small size suspended particles (>1 μm) and sediments, where phenanthrene is the major PAH (Fig. 4). On the contrary, a very different distribution is encountered in the dissolved material since pyrene and fluoranthene predominate (Fig. 4).

The difference between the PAH distributions in the dissolved fraction and the sediments or particles can be explained in terms of physicochemical fractionation process. The original study of the air–sea interface off the Cape Verde islands and in the Gulf of Guinea has shown the migration of components, having a vapour pressure greater than 10^{-5} mmHg, from the subsurface waters (0–50 m) to the microlayer (400 μm thickness) (Marty *et al.*, 1978; Marty, 1981). Then these compounds, concentrated in the surface microlayer, evaporate into the atmosphere (Marty, 1981; Tissier, 1981). Vapour pressure rapidly decreases with increasing aromatic ring number: for example the vapour pressure of phenanthrene is 6.8×10^{-4} mmHg; in comparison the vapour pressure of pyrene is three orders of magnitude lower. The preferential extraction of the most volatile compounds into the water surface followed by the evaporation into the atmosphere, consistent with the models of Junge (1977) and Marty (1981), explains the depletion of phenanthrene, both relative and absolute, and the dominance of the compounds of molecular weights ranging from 202 to 228 in the subsurface layer and consequently in all the water column.

Biological processes and pyrolytic-like PAH. Table 4 illustrates a larger enrichment of pyrolytic-like PAH through the biological chain in surficial waters (50 m), compared to the enrichment observed for the less biological labile compounds such as non-aromatic hydrocarbons and *n*-fatty acids. In Table 4, the enrichment is defined as the ratio of absolute concentrations of pyrolytic-like PAH in the two particulate fractions 50–150 μm and >150 μm. The largest fraction is essentially composed of zooplankton among which many species are known as particle grazers and opportunistic particle feeders (Poulet, 1978). This enrichment occurs without selection of any individual PAH; effectively the PAH distributions of 50–150 μm and >150 μm fractions are close to those of small size particles, with phenanthrene as the dominant component (Tissier, 1981).

A study of large size particles collected in the deep ocean (below 1000 m) was undertaken in order to evaluate the vertical transfer of organic matter between the surface ocean and the sediments. Table 5 shows that the pyrolytic-like PAH are not excreted in faecal pellets but probably remain in association with the lipids of the organisms, since the particles (>50 μm) collected at Station 4 in the Arabian Sea between 1000 and 4700 m, consisting essentially of faecal pellets, are practically devoided of PAH. Nevertheless, we cannot rule out direct biosynthesis of marine precursors of an aeolian input of atmospheric dusts containing these terrestrial markers.

Table 2 demonstrates another biological process resulting in PAH accumulation. This occurs at the ocean–sediment interface. The enrichment observed in surface interstitial waters versus the overlying waters is generally higher for PAH in comparison to non-aromatic hydrocarbons, sterols and fatty acids, particularly where an abundant microorganic crop has been detected by bacteriological strains quantification (st. 10 off Cape Blanc) (Bensoussan *et al.*, 1979) or shown

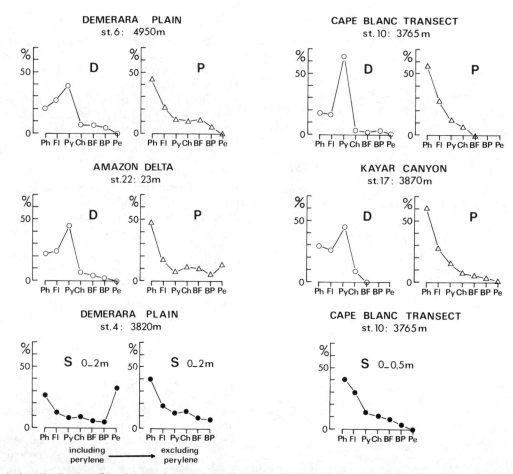

Fig. 4. Relative distribution (%) of the major pyrolytic-like parent PAH in deep water and sediment samples collected in the Eastern and Western intertropical Atlantic Ocean. D = dissolved material; P = suspended particulate matter, retained on a 1 μm filter; S = sediment (and depth in core). Ph = phenanthrene + anthracene; Fl = fluoranthene; Py = pyrene; Ch = chrysene (+ triphenylene and benz(a)anthracene); BF = benzofluoranthenes; BP = benzopyrenes; Pe = perylene.

Table 4

Orgon IV, Arabian Sea, Station 10. Fatty acids, non-aromatic hydrocarbons and total pyrolytic-like PAH concentrations (ng l^{-1}) in the dissolved and small size particles collected at 50 m depth and in the two sizes of planktonic material 50–150 μm and > 150 μm, collected with a > 50 μm mesh plankton net between 200 m and the surface

| | Dissolved matter | Particles > 1 μm | Planktonic material | | Enrichment factor[a] |
			50–150 μm	> 150 μm	
Fatty acids	1510	1260	50	198	4
Non-aromatic hydrocarbons	130	140	0.6	4	7
Pyrolytic-like PAH	12	3.6	5.10^{-5}	2.10^{-2}	400

[a] The enrichment factor is defined as the ratio of lipid concentrations in > 150 μm versus 50–150 μm particles.

Table 5

Orgon IV, Arabian Sea. Total pyrolytic-like PAH concentrations in large size particles collected with a 50 μm net in deep water

Station	Sampling depth	Biological characteristics of large size particles (% of predominant species[a])	Pyrolytic-like PAH concentrations (ng l^{-1})
Orgon IV Arabian Sea			
10	from 2000 to 1000 m	Copepods: 40 Facal pellets: 20	5.10^{-3}
5	from 3800 to 2000 m	Faecal pellets: 35 Radiolarian: 29	1.10^{-3}
4	from 4700 to 1000 m	Faecal pellets: 60 (absence of living organisms)	$<10^{-6}$

[a] From Boussuge *et al.* (1981).

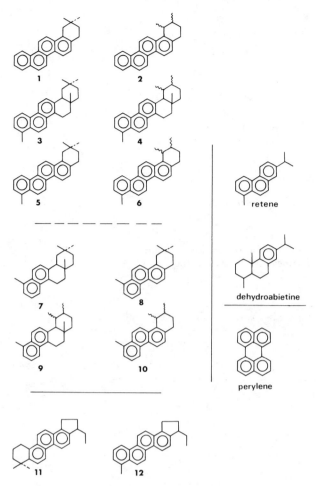

Fig. 5. Biogenic PAH found in water and sediment samples.

by the quantitation of biological markers (st. 15 off Cape Blanc) (Boussuge *et al.*, 1979). This phenomenon may illustrate another way PAH (or other poorly metabolized substances) can be incorporated into the sedimentary column, i.e. via the interstitial water.

Naturally occurring PAH

Several naturally occurring derived structures have been detected in the marine environment, in water, particles and sediments. Figure 5 shows the structures of biogenic PAH, i.e. short term diagenetic products, including perylene encountered during this study.

Naturally occurring PAH in water and particles. The following structures have been detected:

(i) Retene and dehydroabietine in large size particles collected from 2000 to 1000 m, st. 10 and from 3800 to 2000 m, st. 5, in the Arabian Sea.
(ii) The hopanoid triterpene (diploptene) in the Arabian Sea, associated with large and small size particles collected below 1000 m. Hopane derived PAH (e.g. Structures **11, 12**, Fig. 5) have not been found in the sediments collected at the same stations, st. 4 and 5. This algal and bacterial marker occurred with stanols and heavy even

carbon numbered *n*-alkanes (C_{20}–C_{30}) attributed to bacterial activity (Dembicki *et al.*, 1976; Goutx and Saliot, 1980; Saliot *et al.*, 1982a and b).

(iii) Higher plant triaromatic derivatives (structures **3** and **4**, Fig. 5), in the dissolved and colloidal material (passing through a 1 μm filter) in surface waters collected at 0.2 m in the Gulf of Guinea.

(iv) Perylene in the dissolved fraction in many water samples. This compound has been quantitatively determined for the first time in open marine waters and for different fractions, i.e. dissolved, associated with small size particles (> 1 μm) and associated with large size particles (> 50 μm) (Table 6). The concentrations are generally very low. Earlier, the occurrence of perylene (3.05 ng l^{-1}) had been reported in the lagoon water of the Clipperton atoll (Niaussat and Auger, 1970).

With the exception of diploptene, which has been detected in small size particles, the terrigenous markers such as retene, dehydroabietin, perylene were found in the dissolved and colloidal fraction and not in the small size particles. The same finding was established for other terrigenous markers such as heavy odd carbon numbered *n*-alkanes, heavy even carbon numbered *n*-fatty acids, C_{29} sterols (Boussuge *et al.*, 1981). These observations confirm the preferential dissolved state of continental markers in the water column when they are encountered far from their emission sources, i.e. several hundred km (Boussuge *et al.*, 1981; Barbier *et al.*, 1981).

Naturally occurring PAH in sediments. Several quantitative estimates of biogenic components are presented in Table 7. These compounds are often the major components of the PAH fraction in sediments: for example, in the sediments from the Sukra transect in the Arabian Sea, the tetra-aromatic hopane derivative (Structure **12** in Fig. 5) is the predominant compound while perylene predominates in the Cariaco trench.

Aromatic derivatives of higher plant triterpenoids are always encountered in sediments which have received a detrital terrestrial input (Norwegian Sea; western tropical Atlantic, Kayar canyon; eastern Atlantic, Amazon river delta). They are present in highly aromatized forms (four and to a lesser extent, three aromatic rings for the pentacyclic structures and three aromatic rings for the bacterially degraded tetracyclic forms (Tissier, 1981). Among each form, the β-amyrin skeleton (e.g. structures **1, 3, 5**, in Fig. 5) is the most abundant.

Hopanes and hopenes are ubiquitous compounds in the sedimentary column (Ourisson *et al.*, 1979). Table 7 confirms that aromatization in the hopane series drastically varies from a location to location, probably in connection with the microbial activity of sediments (Ourisson *et al.*, 1979). Thus, in the Arabian Sea sediments, aromatic hopanic derivatives (e.g. structure **12**) may be the predominant PAH such as in st. 2, 6 and 10 or may be completely absent such as in st. 4 and 7. In the deep sediments, all the PAH derived from triterpenoids show the same trend: they disappear with burial (e.g. Table 7).

The finding of perylene in some deep sediments in the

Table 6
Perylene concentrations expressed in ng l^{-1}, in open sea water.

Marine area	Station	Sampling design	Fraction analysed	Concentration (ng l^{-1})
Orgon II				
Amazon river delta	22	20 m	particles > 1 μm	0.3
Orgon III				
Cape Blanc	14	1960 m	dissolved matter	0.2
Kayar canyon	6	4400 m	dissolved matter	1.10^{-2}
			particles > 1 μm	5.10^{-3}
	17	3800 m	particles > 1 μm	2.10^{-2}
Orgon IV				
Sukra transect	10	from 2000 to 1000 m	particles > 50 μm	2.10^{-4}
	5	from 3800 to 2000 m	particles > 50 μm	1.10^{-5}
Midlante				
North of the Cape Verde islands		0.2 m	dissolved and particulate fractions (mean for different stations)	1.5

Table 7
Identification and quantitative determination of some biogenic PAH in sediments (ng g^{-1})

Marine area	Station	Sediment depth (m)	Structures[a]											
			1	2	3	4	5	6	7	8	9	10	11	12
Orgon I														
Skagerrak	2	0.5	−	−	+	−	25	10	+	+	+	10	−	−
		2.25	−	−	−	−	5	1	+	+	+	3	−	−
Norwegian Sea	8	1.0	−	−	+	−	+	−	+	+	+	−	−	+
	10	1.0	−	−	−	−	+	−	+	+	+	−	−	−
Orgon II														
Cariaco trench	1	0.0	−	−	+	+	40	20	−	+	+	+	+	10
		5.5	−	−	+	+	−	−	−	−	−	−	−	+
Amazon river delta	12	0–0.5	−	−	nd	nd	+	+	−	−	−	−	−	+
	17	0–0.5	+	−	−	+	+	+	−	+	+	+	−	+
Orgon III														
Kayar canyon	6	0.0	−	−	−	−	−	−	−	−	−	−	−	−
		0.5–1.5	+	+	+	+	+	+	−	+	+	+	−	−
Orgon IV														
Ghubbet el Kharab	2	0.0	−	−	−	−	−	−	−	−	−	−	−	160
		4.0	−	−	−	−	−	−	−	−	−	−	−	5
Alula Fartak trench	4	0.0	−	−	−	−	−	−	−	−	−	−	−	−
Mascaste transect	7	0.0	−	−	−	−	−	−	−	−	−	−	−	−
Sukra transect	6	0.0	−	−	−	−	−	−	−	−	−	−	+	70
	10	0.0	−	−	−	−	−	−	−	−	−	−	147	200
		1.0–3.0	−	−	−	−	−	−	−	−	−	−	−	−

[a]   Structure numbers refer to Fig. 5.
+ = identification; − = absence (the detection limit is around 5.10^{-2} ng g^{-1}); nd = non-determined.

Arabian Sea (8700 ng g^{-1}) for st. 4, Table 3, far from obvious terrestrial sources may be related to the presence of perylene in the water column, especially in large size rapidly sinking particles (Table 6). The perylene content of st. 4 sediments is significant and compares with the data for a Namibian shelf sediment (Walvis Bay) (Wakeham *et al.*, 1979), another typically marine sedimentary area.

The other Arabian Sea sites receive an equivalent organic contribution deposited in comparable reducing conditions. These reducing conditions are supposed to favour the conservation of perylene precursors and the generation of perylene (Aizenshtat, 1973). Nevertheless these sediments do not contain perylene, except st. 7 (off Mascate, Table 3), which has a local riverborne terrigenous source.

We conclude from these observations that these chemical markers, which are especially resistant to physicochemical degradation processes, are widespread in surface waters due to dispersal by marine currents. Several conditions favour a biological extraction from sea water and a concentration of non-metabolized compounds such as PAH, allowing them to settle rapidly via large size particles. The specific sedimentation conditions are highly biological activity such as in upwelling areas with a fast chemical turnover, reducing conditions in the water column and still bottom waters such as in trenches.

CONCLUSIONS

The collection of large samples (volume and weight) and the use of GC and GC/MS techniques have facilitated the detection and quantitation of PAH throughout the marine environment, in sea water (dissolved fraction, small and large size particles), deep recent sediments and interstitial waters.

The low contents of pyrolytic-like PAH which have been detected represent the actual background in marine environments far from industrialized areas and off deserts.

The pyrolytic-like PAH originate partly from natural and anthropogenic combustion processes and partly from diagenesis.

The sytematic depletion of phenanthrene observed in the dissolved fraction in the water column and not in the suspended material can be explained by a loss occurring at the sea–air interface, related to evaporation of compounds with high vapour pressures.

Bioaccumulation of PAH, which are biologically resistant structures compared to the easily metabolized fatty acids, has been observed, both in the surficial ocean and at the ocean–sediment interface.

PAH accumulation in interstitial water correlates well with microbiological activity, which is only of local importance in deep marine sediments. But for coastal areas where microbiological and benthic activity is intense, this phenomenon is consequently a route for the incorporation of these compounds and other pollutants to the sedimentary column via the interstitial water.

The biogenic PAH are often the major compounds in deep marine sediments. However, they have been detected only in a few water samples.

The presence of perylene in sea water far from terrestrial sources and the occurrence of biological extraction and concentration processes in the euphotic layer suggest an explanation for the perylene occurrence in sediments of typically marine sedimentation areas.

Acknowledgements

We are grateful to Dr P. Albrecht (University L. Pasteur, Strasbourg), for the GC/MS analyses.

This study was supported by the CEGMA (Comité d'Etudes de Géochimie Marine).

REFERENCES

Aizenshtat, Z. (1973) Perylene and its geochemical significance. *Geochim. Cosmochim. Acta* **37**, 559–567.

Arnould, M. and Pelet, R. (1979) *Géochimie organique des sédiments marins profonds. ORGON III. Mauritanie, Sénégal, Iles du Cap Vert.* Centre National de la Recherche Scientifique, Paris.

Barbier, M., Tusseau, D., Marty, J. C. and Saliot, A. (1981) Sterols in aerosols, surface microlayer and subsurface water in the North–Eastern Tropical Atlantic. *Oceanol. Acta* **4**, 77–84.

Bensoussan, M., Bianchi, A., Bianchi, M., Boudabous, A., Marty, D., Roussos, S. and Lizarraga-Partida, M. L. (1979) Bactériologie des eaux et des sédiments profonds en Atlantique intertropical est. I — Distribution et structure des populations bactériennes. In *Géochimie organique des sédiments marins profonds. ORGON III. Mauritanie, Sénégal, Iles du Cap Vert*, ed. by Arnould, M. and Pelet, R. Centre National de la Recherche Scientifique, Paris, pp. 13–25.

Boussuge, C., Goutx, M., Saliot, A. and Tissier, M. J. (1979) Acides gras et hydrocarbures aux interfaces eau de mer-sédiment et eau interstitielle-sédiment en Atlantique tropical est. In *Géochimie organique des sédiments marins profonds. ORGON III. Mauritanie, Sénégal, Iles du Cap Vert*, ed. by Arnould, M. and Pelet, R. Centre National de la Recherche Scientifique, Paris, pp. 303–352.

Boussuge, C., Goutx, M., Tissier, M. J., Tusseau, D. and Saliot, A. (1981) Sédimentation organique en mer d'Arabie: biologie et transfert de lipides entre zone euphotique et interface océan-sédiment. In *Géochimie organique des sédiments marins profonds. ORGON IV. Golfe d'Aden, Mer d'Oman.* Centre National de la Recherche Scientifique, Paris, pp. 415–445.

Combaz, A. and Pelet, R. (1978) *Géochimie organique des sédiments marins profonds. ORGON II. Atlantique-N-E Brésil.* Centre National de la Recherche Scientifique, Paris.

Dastillung, M. and Corbet, B. (1978) La géochimie organique des sédiments marins profonds I. — Hydrocarbures saturés et insaturés des sédiments. In *Géochimie organique des sédiments marins profonds. ORGON II. Atlantique-N-E, Brésil*, ed. by Combaz, A. and Pelet, R. Centre National de la Recherche Scientifique, Paris, pp. 293–323.

Dembicki, H., Meinschein, W. G. and Hattin, D. F. (1976) Possible ecological significance of the predominance of even-carbon number C_{20}–C_{30} n-alkanes. *Geochim. Cosmochim. Acta* **40**, 203–208.

Ewald, M. (1978) Inventaire et dynamique des lipides à l'interface eau de mer-sédiment VI. Application de la spectrofluorimétrie à la caractérisation et au dosage des hydrocarbures aromatiques polycycliques des sédiments marins. In *Géochimie organique des sédiments marins profonds. ORGON II. Atlantique-N-E, Brésil*, ed. by Combaz, A. and Pelet, R. Centre National de la Recherche Scientifique, Paris, pp. 285–292.

Giger, W. and Schaffner, C. (1977) Aliphatic, olefinic and aromatic hydrocarbons in recent sediments of a highly eutrophic lake. In *Advances in Organic Geochemistry 1975*, ed. by Campos, R. and Goni, J. Enadisma, Madrid, pp. 375–390.

Goutx, M. and Saliot, A. (1980) Relationship between dissolved and particulate fatty acids and hydrocarbons, chlorophyll *a* and zooplankton biomass in Villefranche Bay, Mediterranean Sea. *Mar. Chem.* **8**, 299–318.

Junge, C. E. (1977) Basic considerations about trace constituents in the atmosphere as related to the fate of global pollutants. In *Fate of pollutants in the air and water environments* (ed. by Suffet, I. H. Vol. 8. John Wiley and Sons, Inc. pp. 7–25.

Laflamme, R. E. and Hites, R. A. (1978) The global distribution of polycyclic aromatic hydrocarbons in recent sediments. *Geochim. Cosmochim. Acta* **42**, 289–303.

Laflamme, R. E. and Hites, R. A. (1979) Tetra- and pentacyclic, naturally occurring, aromatic hydrocarbons in recent sediments. *Geochim. Cosmochim. Adta* **43**, 1687–1691.

Marty, J. C. (1981) Chimie de l'interface air-mer: L'accumulation des lipides dans la microcouche, leur éjection et leur évaporation dans l'atmosphère. Thèse Doctorat d'Etat, Univ. P. et M. Curie, Paris.

Marty, J. C., Saliot, A. and Tissier, M. J. (1978) Inventaire, répartition et origine des hydrocarbures aliphatiques et polyaromatiques dans l'eau de mer, la microcouche de surface et les aérosols marins en Atlantique Tropical Est. *C.R. Acad. Sci. Ser. D* **286**, 833–836.

Marty, J. C., Saliot, A., Buat-Menard, P., Chesselet, R. and Hunter, K. A. (1979) Relationship between the lipid compositions of marine aerosols, the sea surface microlayer and subsurface water. *J. Geophys. Res.* **84**, 5707–5716.

Niaussat, P. and Auger, C. (1970) Mise en évidence et répartition du benzo-3,4-pyrène et du pérylène chez différents organismes de la biocénose lagunaire de Clipperton. *C.R. Acad. Sci. Ser. D* **270**, 2702–2705.

Neff, J. M. (1979) *Polycyclic Aromatic Hydrocarbons in the Aquatic Environment. Sources, Fates and Biological Effects.* Applied Science, London.

Ourisson, G., Albrecht, P. and Rohmer, M. (1979) The hopanoids. Paleochemistry and biochemistry of a group of natural products. *Pure Appl. Chem.* **51**, 709–729.

Pelet, R. (1977) Géochimie organique des sédiments marins profonds de la mer de Norvège: Vue d'ensemble. In *Géochimie organique des sédiments marins profonds. ORGON I. Mer de Norvège.* Centre National de la Recherche Scientifique, Paris, pp. 281–296.

Pelet, R. (1981) Géochimie organique des sédiments marins profonds du Golfe d'Aden et de la mer d'Oman: Vue d'ensemble. In *Géochimie organique des sédiments marins profonds. ORGON VI. Golfe d'Aden. Mer d'Oman.* Centre National de la Recherche Scientifique, Paris, pp. 529–547.

Poulet, S. A. (1978) Comparison between five coexisting species of marine copepods feeding on naturally occurring particulate matter. *Limnol. Oceanogr.* **23**, 1126–1143.

Riolo, J., Corbet, B., Albrechet, P., Tissier, M. J., Boussuge, C. and Saliot, A. (1981) Hydrocarbures et acides des sédiments et des eaxu interstitielles. In *Géochimie organique des sédiments marins profonds. ORGON IV. Golfe d'Aden. Mer d'Oman.* Centre National de la Recherche Scientifique, Paris, pp. 483–501.

Saliot, A., Andrié, C., Février, A., Goutx, M. and Tissier, M. J. (1982a) Analysis and budget of biogeochemical markers in dissolved, small and large size suspended matter in the ocean. In press, in *Advances in Organic Geochemistry 1981.*

Saliot, A., Goutx, M., Février, A., Tusseau, D. and Andrié, C. (1982b) Organic sedimentation in the water column in the Arabian Sea: relationship between the lipid composition of small and large size, surface and deep particles. *Mar. Chem.*

11, 257–278.

Sheldon, R. W., Prakash, A. and Sutcliffe, W. H. (1972) The size distribution of particles in the ocean. *Limnol. Oceanogr.* **17**, 327–340.

Simoneit, B. R. T. (1977a) Organic matter in eolian dusts over the Atlantic Ocean. *Mar. Chem.* **5**, 443–464.

Simoneit, B. R. T. (1977b) Diterpenoid compounds and other lipids in deep sea sediments and their geochemical significance. *Geochim. Cosmochim. Acta* **41**, 463–476.

Spyckerelle, C. (1975) Constituants lipidiques de sédiments. Thèse Doctorat d'Etat. Univ. L. Pasteur, Strasbourg.

Spyckerelle, C., Greiner, A. C., Albrecht, P. and Ourisson, G. (1977) Aromatic hydrocarbons from geological sources III. A tetrahydrochrysene derived from triterpenes in recent and old sediments: 3,3,7-trimethyl-tetrahydrochrysene. *J. Chem. Res.* (M), 1977, 3746–3777; (S), 1977, 303–331.

Tissier, M. J. (1981) Les hydrocarbures aromatiques polycycliques dans l'environnement marin. Distribution, origine et transfert. Thèse Doctorat d'Etat. Univ. P. et M. Curie, Paris.

Tissier, M. J. and Spyckerelle, C. (1977) Hydrocarbures polyaromatiques des sédiments. In *Géochimie organique des sédiments marins profonds. ORGON I. Mer de Norvège.* Centre National de la Recherche Scientifique, Paris, pp. 229–236.

Tissier, M. J. and Dastillung, M. (1978) Inventaire et dynamique des lipides à l'interface eau de mer-sédiment. V. Hydrocarbures polyaromatiques de sédiments, de l'eau de mer et de l'eau interstitielle. In *Géochimie organique des sédiments marins profonds. ORGON II. Atlantique-N-E Brésil*, ed. by Combaz, A. and Pelet, R. Centre National de la Recherche Scientifique, Paris, pp. 275–283.

Wakeham, S. G., Schaffner, C., Giger, W., Boon, J. J. and de Leeuw, J. W. (1979) Perylene in sediments from the Namibian shelf. *Geochim. Cosmochim. Acta* **43**, 1141–1144.

Wakeham, S. G., Schaffner, C. and Giger, W. (1980a) Polycyclic aromatic hydrocarbons in recent lake sediments: I. Compounds having anthropogenic origins. *Geochim. Cosmochim. Acta* **44**, 403–413.

Wakeham, S. G., Schaffner, C. and Giger, W. (1980b) Polycyclic aromatic hydrocarbons in recent lake sediments: II. Compounds derived from biogenic precursors during early diagenesis. *Geochim. Cosmochim. Acta* **44**, 415–429.

Youngblood, W. W. and Blumer, M. (1975) Polycyclic aromatic hydrocarbons in the environment: homologous series in soils and recent marine sediments. *Geochim. Cosmochim. Acta* **39**, 1303–1314.

Advances in Organic Geochemistry 1981, pp. 279–288
© *John Wiley & Sons Limited, 1983*

The Geochemical Sulphur Enrichment of Recent Organic Matter by Polysulfides in the Solar-Lake

Z. Aizenshtat and A. Stoler

Energy Research Center, Organic Chemistry, The Hebrew University of Jerusalem, Israel

Y. Cohen

Marine Biology Laboratory, Elat, the Hebrew University of Jerusalem, Israel

H. Nielsen

Geochemistry, The University of Göttingen, FRG

The Solar Lake is a marine hypersaline stratified heliothermal heated water body located on the Sinai Coast of the Gulf of Aqaba. The lake is a good model for a recent sulphuritum exhibiting very high microbial activity which is recorded in over 1 m thick undisturbed stromatolitic microbial mat. Due to the extensive microbial sulphur cycle and limitation of free iron, the lower stratified water column and the sediments are rich in polysulphides. The model for enrichment of organically bonded sulphur in sediments was studied in correlation to the high microbial production of both HS^- and S^0 and low availability of iron. The existence of high ammonia concentration with pH ~8.0 in the interstitial water stabilizes the polysulphide pool. The study of the various sulphur species revealed enrichment of the organically bonded sulphur along the sedimentary column from 1.4% to 8.2% at 80–87 cm depth. Concomitantly, this sulphur fraction is enriched in ^{32}S from $\delta^{34}S$–12☉ to -26 ± 1☉ for the protokerogen. This finding together with the data presented support the sulphur–H_2S–polysulphide role in the secondary sulphur enrichment of organic matter in reduced sediments even at the early stages of diagenesis.

INTRODUCTION

The sulphur cycle is very complex because of the many redox changes through which the sulphur atom can transform. In Fig. 1 we have attempted to summarize the two major parts of the sulphur cycle: (a) the biologically controlled pathway and (b) the chemical-physical pathway. Much attention was devoted to the biologically controlled pathway, dissimilatory and assimilatory. But, only lately evidence was brought as to the possible model for the chemically controlled secondary enrichment of sulphur bonded organically in sediments (Dinur *et al.*, 1980).

The Solar Lake is a stratified hypersaline, heliothermal heated water body situated on the coast of Sinai of the Gulf of Aqaba. The lake (140×70 m with maximal depth of 5.5 m) is separated from the sea by a 60 m terrestrial barrier, it is strongly stratified for nine to eleven months per year (Cohen *et al.*, 1977a, b). The Solar Lake microorganisms activities engulf most of pathway (a) in Fig. 1 (Jørgensen *et al.*, 1979a, b; Padan and Cohen, 1980). It can therefore, be considered as a highly productive biological 'transformer' that processes large amounts of sulphur through the various paths of

the cycle (Fig. 1). The microbial geochemistry of the Solar Lake sulphur cycle was studied in the water column (Jørgensen *et al.*, 1979a) and in the four types of stromatolitic cyanobacterial mats (Jørgensen *et al.*, 1979b; Cohen *et al.*, 1980). During stratification the hypolimnion of the lake shows a steady pool of 150 μ mol/l polysulphides which is in equilibrium with both elemental sulphur and sulphide. Elemental sulphur production is mainly due to anoxygenic photosynthesis by cyanobacteria (Cohen *et al.*, 1975) and shows a marked diurnal cycle picking up in the late afternoon and disappearing towards morning due to the reduction of the photosynthetically produced elemental sulphur by endogenous respiration of cyanobacteria at night (Oren and Shilo, 1979). Ferrous sulphides comprise a minute fraction within the sediments and no framboidal structures were detected by scanning electron microscopy. The major source of iron is clay particles of terrestrial origin which are brought to the lake by desert floods. This supply is limited because of the arid environment exhibiting a mean annual rainfall of only 10 mm. Therefore, the following conditions exist in the Solar Lake: (i) hypersalinity, (ii) high microbial activity as a result of high primary production, (iii) exceptionally

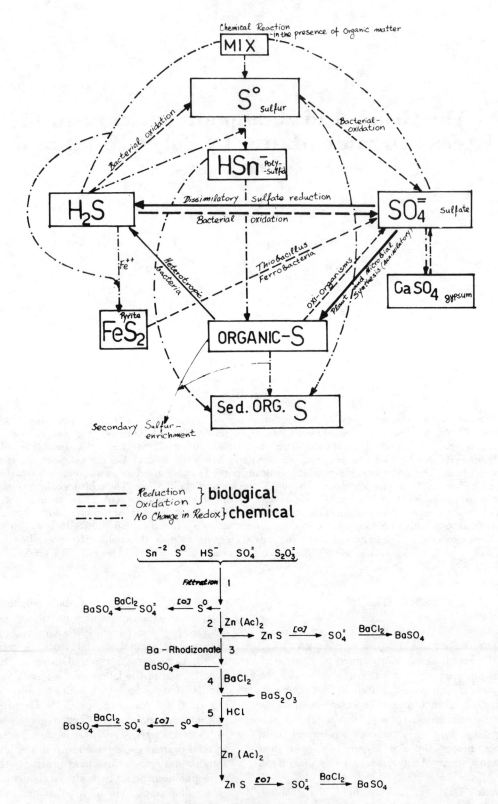

Fig. 1. The sulphur cycle, including the biologically controlled pathways and the chemical-physical pathways. Introducing the secondary sulphur enrichment.

rapid microbial sulphur transformation, (iv) low availability of iron, (v) somewhat elevated temperatures, (vi) anoxic sediment, (vii) organically rich sediment, (viii) very low terrestrial contribution and (ix) high H/C values for the organic matter (Cohen *et al.*, 1980). To some extent these conditions resemble the proposed environment of deposition for the bituminous chalks of the Maastrichtian-Campanian Ghareb Formation (Dinur *et al.*, 1980). Many of the deposits of organically rich sediments are also enriched in organically bonded sulphur and this sulphur is in most cases isotopically lighter by about 15‰ than the sea sulphate at the time of its deposition. In general this phenomenon is also true for sulphur in petroleum indicating that the assimilatory process is not the only source for the organically bonded sulphur. The study of the sulphur cycle in a geochemically young sedimentation basin which was dated back to 2000 years can give us insight into the biogeochemical processes while still occurring. Furthermore, the sulphur cycle of the Solar Lake and other sulphurita bodies with similar biota can illuminate the onset of the evolution of oxygenated atmosphere.

EXPERIMENTS

Separation of the various sulphur species in the water column

The schematic separation of the various sulphur species is described by Cohen *et al.* (1980). Sampling of the water column in the Solar Lake is somewhat 'tricky' since the physical and chemical limnology changes diurnally and seasonally and therefore sampling was based on previous knowledge presented by Jørgensen *et al.* (1979a, b).

Sediment sampling (cores)

Two cores were taken for the present study; one from the east bank of the Lake was marked SLA–I through VII. The second core was taken at the deepest part of the lake and was marked SLA–VIII and IX. Coring was done with polyethylene pipe (10 cm diameter) gravimetrically introduced down to 1 m depth. Both cores were sealed and deep-frozen cuttings of the cores were taken from the frozen core and the section kept under argon at > − 20 °C until analysed. SLA–I: The upper part of the core (covered with thin sulphur film which was removed mechanically). SLA–II: The first 5 cm section, green in colour and well laminated. SLA–III: The 5–10 cm section very similar to section II. SLA–IV: The 80–87 cm section with yellow–green colour much richer in carbonates with the laminated mats. SLA–V: The bottom part 87–94 cm yellowish, contains quite high amounts of gypsum, but still contains pigments. SLA–VI: The mid-section 30–45 cm laminated and SLA–VII: the 45–80 cm section similar in physical appearance. The middle zone sections were selected for extensive separation of protokerogen and other groups of compounds. The core from the bottom of the lake was divided into two major sections SLA–VIII and SLA–IX. This was done since the bottom material is muddy, very well mixed with no stratification at all and its lower section is highly enriched with CaSO$_4$ (Krumbein *et al.*, 1977).

Sediment treatment

It is impossible to schematically describe the chemical separation in a flow diagram because the various sections exhibited different problems. However, in general the interstitial waters were separated by centrifugation after the mats were destroyed by high speed blending. The sulphate was then precipitated as BaSO$_4$. The sediment

was then separated into two batches (i) treated with HCl and dried for elemental analysis and (ii) treated with NaOH and then HCl for possible humic matter which were not detected in any of the many samples studied. In all acid and basic treatments the water filtrates were coloured indicating pigments and other organic matter in solution. The 'bitumen' was extracted with benzene/methanol mixture (3:7 v/v) twice; first in a high-speed blender at room temperature and the second with reflux for 12 h. In some cases the extraction was conducted on the total wet sample to avoid loss of extractables during acid or base treatment, three extractions, in such cases, were performed: (i) total sample, (ii) residue after HCl treatment (carbonate removal), (iii) protokerogen (after HF/HCl treatment). The elemental analysis and isolation of sulphur was carried out on all samples. The analysis of the various compounds in the extractable fractions (i), (ii), (iii) was conducted as described by Aizenshtat *et al.* (1973).

A special problem was caused by the very high gypsum concentration in the lower part of both cores as its removal for better analysis of the protokerogen required large quantities of water. A better solution is presented in Fig. 2, utilizing the fact that the organic matter is non-soluble and floats. The 'putty' formed on the sintered glass is treated as previously described.

In some samples with very high sulphur (elemental mixed with the organic matter) content, the separation of elemental sulphur was by sublimation under vacuum. This sulphur was then oxidized to sulphate and for $\delta^{34}S$ analysis was precipitated as BaSO$_4$.

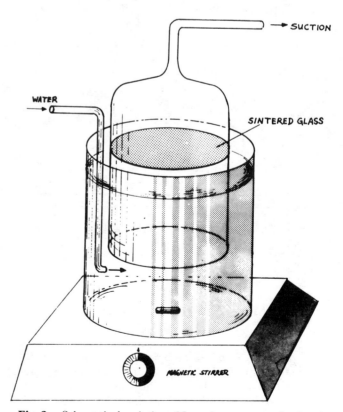

Fig. 2. Schematic description of floatation apparatus for the separation of organic matter concentrates from large gypsum crystals.

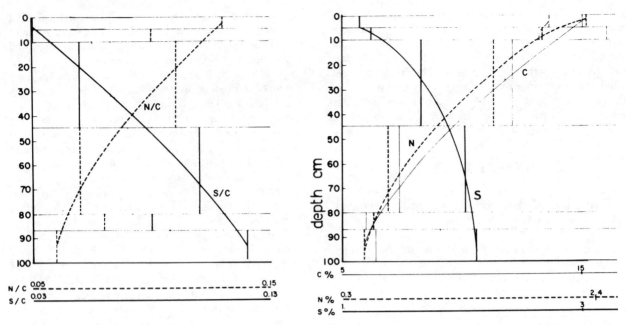

Fig. 3. Graphic presentation of elemental analyses results on total sediment and the calculated atomic ratios changes with depth (cm), (upper core).

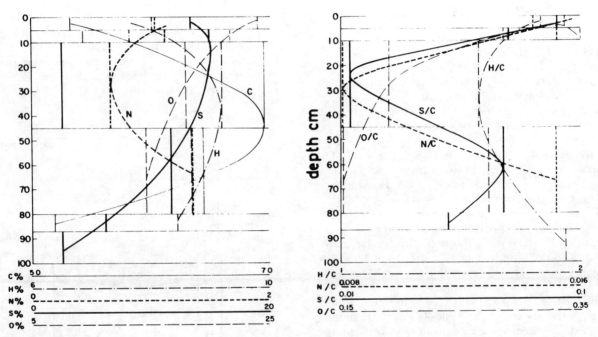

Fig. 4. Graphic presentation of elemental analyses changes with depth (cm) for extractables (I) and the calculated atomic ratios (upper core).

Mass spectra analysis of $\delta^{34}S$

Preparation of samples was mostly in the form of $BaSO_4$. The $CaSO_4$ from the bottom was analysed directly and two samples of CdS from the water column were compared with oxidized form. The extractables and protokerogens were treated by the Eshka method to give $BaSO_4$ as the end product (Furman, 1962). The mass spectra analyses were conducted by Dr Nielsen

(Gottingen University FRG) as described by Nielsen (1978) with $\pm 0.2\%_{00}$ experimental error.

Reaction of sulphur with organic matter

In principle the experimental method used for the enrichment of humics and protokerogens with sulphur is similar to that described by Dinur *et al.* (1980). However, in the discussion we mention reactions of polysulphides with organic matter, these 'simulations'

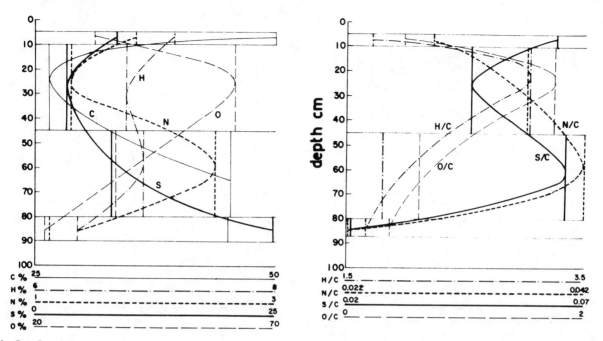

Fig. 5. Graphic presentation of elemental analyses and calculated atomic ratios for extractables (II) after carbonate removal (HCl treatment), (upper core).

will be discussed in another paper (reaction temperature > 65 °C).

RESULTS AND DISCUSSION

The two cores studied were analysed with the intention of following major chemical changes on total sediment and isolated fractions. The results presented in Fig. 3 derive from the elemental analysis of several samples at each section. It is evident from Fig. 3 that in the total sediment the concentrations of carbon (C org) and nitrogen decrease from 15–6% and 2.3–0.5% respectively while the sulphur is increasing from 1.1–2.1% as also demonstrated by the atomic ratios S/C. Oxygen was determined by difference and therefore the analytical error is much larger, hydrogen analysis on total sediment samples is definitely influenced by organically bonded hydrogen (therefore not presented in Fig. 3). The decrease in nitrogen is 5-fold while sulphur concentration is doubled.

The extractables (in benzene/methanol, see experiments) were analysed, the elemental analysis and the atomic ratios are presented in Fig. 4. The overall picture is quite similar for the first extract (room temperature) and reflux. However, the first extract is always somewhat richer in carbon and hydrogen containing compounds. The concentration of sulphur in these extracts decreases with depth, but we will show that this is due to less 'free' elemental sulphur which is easily extractable in benzene. The extracts exhibit lower O/C which may indicate that the high oxygen containing molecules are hydrophyllic. The extract (II) after carbonate removal with HCl shows again the similarity in N/C and S/C ratio (Fig. 5). These ratios tend to decrease and increase simultaneously, this may result from amino acids hydrolysed by the HCl treatment. These extractables (II) are exceptionally

enriched in elemental sulphur (up to 24.8% of the extract). This sulphur can be isolated by sublimation and we believe that the acid treatment breaks the polysulphides stability releasing H_2S and enriching the residual sediment with elemental sulphur. The extracts after removal of the silicates (HF/HCl 3:1) are shown in Fig. 6.

The first extracts were studied for hydrocarbon pigments and special attention was devoted to the lack of perylene (Aizenshtat, 1973). Some of these results were previously discussed (Cohen *et al.*, 1980). Since we wish to concentrate on the sulphur cycle we will just note the very high carotenoid concentration at the top 10 cm of the core and the existence of chlorophyll a and bacteriochlorophyll a.

The protokerogen isolated from the upper core was analysed and the results are presented in Fig. 7. The distribution of elements is quite similar to the analysis of the total sediment. There is a marked enrichment in sulphur with depth. This sulphur is not pyritic as shown in X-ray analysis and by the absence of Fe after combustion it is not elemental, so therefore, has to be considered as organically bonded into the protokerogen's structure. The atomic ratios indicate S/C and H/C increasing with depth (Fig. 8) while N/C decreases.

The bottom core was less extensively studied, in general it is richer in inorganic constituents especially gypsum, carbonates and some silicates. The organic carbon content is between 6.7–4.4%. The amount of elemental sulphur and organically bonded sulphur is similar to the average at the upper core. However, if no mistake is due to residual $CaSO_4$ it seems that somewhat elevated temperatures at the bottom of < 65 °C further enhanced the enrichment of sulphur in the organic matter. A better comparison can be derived from the extractables which exhibit normal nitrogen concentrations (1.4–2.4%) while containing up to 20%

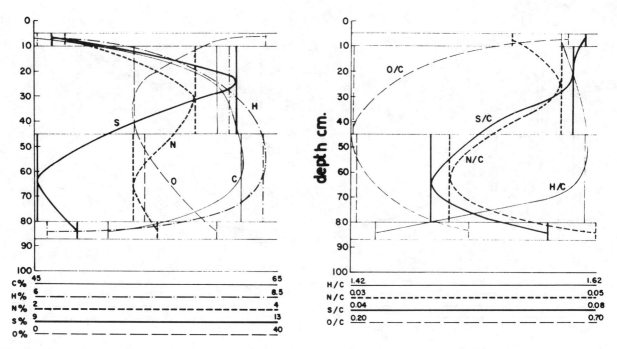

Fig. 6. Graphic presentation of elemental analyses and calculated atomic ratios for extractables (III) after silicates removal (HF:HCl treatment), (upper core).

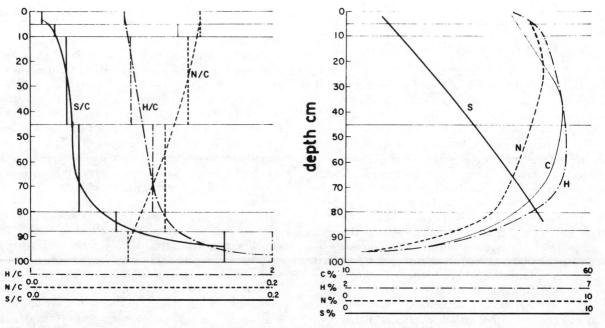

Fig. 7. Graphic presentation of protokerogen isolated elemental analyses and atomic ratios (calculated), changes with depth (cm) upper core.

elemental sulphur. The extraction after acidification shows even higher sulphur concentration of up to 43.5%. This extracted high sulphur was also marked after floatation and could be the result of oxidation of the polysulphides and sulphides by atmospheric oxygen.

The relative abundance of the various sulphur species in the water column is well documented in previous works (cf. Cohen *et al.*, 1980). Samples for $\delta^{34}S$ measurements were prepared from the oxygenated zone, interface (H_2S–O_2) chemocline layer, anoxic (H_2S–poly-S) section, sediment water interface and interstitial

waters at various depths. A sulphate sample from the open sea, Gulf of Aqaba, east of the barrier, was taken on the same day for comparison. The results of the $\delta^{34}S$ mass spectra analyses are presented in Table 1 which includes interstitial water samples, protokerogen isolated elemental sulphur and extractables. The general section in Table 1 shows the values of $\delta^{34}S$ for the water column, open sea and $CaSO_4$ taken at the bottom core (SLA–X). The $+20.7\%$ value for the sea sample and $+20.5$–$+21.0\%$ values for the sulphate in the Solar Lake water body indicate quite rapid transport which erases almost

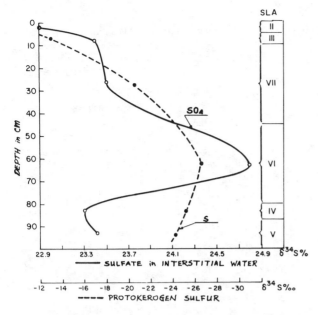

Fig. 8. Changes in $\delta^{34}S$ values with depth (cm), sections marked SLA–I through V (see experimental section) for interstitial water sulphate and protokerogen organically bonded sulphur.

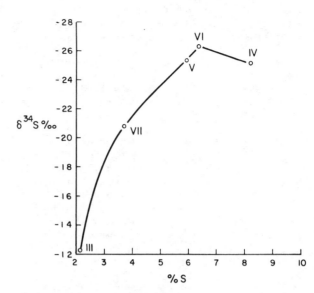

Fig. 9. $\delta^{34}S$ values plotted versus per cent sulphur for isolated protokerogen samples of the upper core.

completely the biological effect. The interstitial waters range in their $\delta^{34}S$ values between 22.9 up to $+24.8\%$ for the sulphate, the highest value is obtained for the middle section of the sediment core (45–80 cm, SLA–VI). It is interesting to note that interstitial waters at the bottom core are lighter isotopically ranging from $+20.9$–21.3%.

The changes in $\delta^{34}S$ as a function of depth in the upper core are presented in Fig. 8, the same values for the protokerogen are plotted against the protokerogen sulphur concentration in Fig. 9.

The protokerogen of the bottom core exhibits $\delta^{34}S$ values of $+9.3$ and $+15.5\%$. These results must be considered with the fact that these samples contained 'high ash' and could have been contaminated by sulphate ($+22.2\%$) from $CaSO_4$. However, the extractable organic matter from the top section SLA–I through III and the bottom core SLA–IX and X are within the same range of -12 to -14%, whereas the elemental sulphur (depending on the method of isolation) gave $\delta^{34}S$ values of -14 up to -21.9%. The H_2S sampled from the lake gave regardless of the

Table 1

$\delta^{34}S$ results for various sulphur species of Solar Lake, water column, interstitial waters and organically bonded.

Sample	Interstitial water ($SO_4^=$)	Protokerogen organic S $\delta^{34}S$ ‰	Other sulphur species $\delta^{34}S$ ‰
SLA–II (0–5 cm)	$+22.9$	—	Extractables, sulphur -12.0; -14.0
SLA–III (5–10 cm)	$+23.4$	-13.1; -12.2	Extractables -12.2; -13.1
SLA–VII (10–45 cm)	$+23.5$	-20.8	
SLA–VI (45–80 cm)	$+24.8$	-26.3; -26.3	Sublimted sulphur from protokerogen Isolation -20.6
SLA–IV (80–87 cm)	$+23.3$	-25.2	
SLA–V (87–89 cm)	$+23.4$	-25.4; -24.1	
SLA–IX (0–30 cm)	$+20.9$	$+10.2$; $+9.9$	Bottom core extractables -12.9
SLA–VIII (30–60 cm)	$+21.3$	$+15.5$; $+15.5$	(1) Sublimed sulphur, after HCl as extracted -21.9
			(2) In extractables -14.0
Algae from bottom core (top) SLA–X			extractables -12.6
Gulf Sea water			sulphate $+20.7$ (water)
Solar Lake (oxic)			sulphate $+20.9$ (water)
Solar Lake (anoxic)			sulphate $+20.1$; $+21.0$ (water)
Solar Lake (3.5 m)			sulphate $+20.9$ (water)
Solar Lake (3.5 m)			H_2S -16.3 (water)
Solar Lake (3.5 m)			H_2S (removal of S^0) -16.3 (water)
$CaSO_4$ (bottom core)			$CaSO_4$ $+22.2$ (solid)

$\delta^{34}S$ C.D.T. $\pm0.1\%$

Table 2

Analytical results of sulphur enrichment experiments (at 175 °C) with elemental sulphur (AR-sublimed).

Sample protokerogen	Reaction conditions	C[a]	H%[a]	N%[a]	S%[a]	Per cent of enrichment in S
SLA–II	Starting protokerogen	46.0	5.4	7.6	1.4	
	Ampoule 175 °C	44.3	4.7	—	1.3	
	Ampoule 175 °C with S°	43.7	5.4	6.5	13.0	992
SLAIII[b]	Starting protokerogen	44.7	6.0	7.65	2.2	
	Ampoule 175 °C				6.1	(?)
	Ampoule 175 °C with S°	15.5	1.8	1.77	9.34	65 (only S change taken)
SLA–IV	Starting protokerogen	43.0	5.5	5.9	8.2	
	Ampoule 175 °C	42.2	5.4	5.9	4.6	
	Ampoule 175 °C with S°	40.4	5.9	5.4	14.7	315
SLA–V	Starting protokerogen	13.5	2.3	1.3	.0	(high ash sample)
	Ampoule 175 °C	13.4	2.2	1.5	2.7	
	Ampoule 175 °C with S°	15.9	2.2	1.6	8.6	333
SLA–VI	Starting protokerogen	51.5	6.5	7.0	6.4	
	Ampoule 175 °C	47.4	6.0	5.8	6.0	
	Ampoule 175 °C with S°	42.0	4.8	5.9	15.9	269
SLA–VII	Starting protokerogen	52.9	6.3	8.0	3.9	
	Ampoule 175 °C	52.0	6.4	7.7	2.9	
	Ampoule 175 °C with S°	48.0	5.5	7.1	9.9	338
SLA–X	Starting protokerogen	29.6	4.2	5.1	1.0	(algae from bottom)
	Ampoule 175 °C	22.4	3.2	—	—	
	Ampoule 175 °C with S°	—	—	—	6.9	671

[a] C, H, N analyses $+0.3\%$ S $\pm0.5\%$.
[b] Sample SLA–III results show an unexplained 30% C change.

position of sampling (in the anoxic zone) values of ca. $-16.0\%_{oo} \pm 0.2\%_{oo}$.

Two sets of experiments of thermal enrichment of the protokerogen were conducted at 175 °C with elemental sulphur and at 65 °C with polysulphide solution. The results of the sulphur enrichment at 175 °C are listed in Table 2. Similar enrichment was obtained by polysulphides, but since the protokerogen is very sensitive to basic hydrolysis ($NH_4S_x^-$ solution used $> pH 9$) these changes must be studied further. In all the experiments (7 samples) presented in Table 2 a marked sulphur enrichment is recorded from 65% up to 99.2%. However, it is important to note the instability of the already organically bonded sulphur in the blank samples heated to 175 °C without sulphur. The tests were conducted in sealed ampoules (Dinur et al., 1980). When these ampoules were opened large amounts of H_2S escaped. In all samples the elemental analysis shows decrease in carbon and negligible changes in hydrogen. The maximum sulphur content after sulphur enrichment is 15.9% and the highest ratio (in per cent) of enrichment is on protokerogens with original low sulphur content.

Despite the very active biologically controlled sulphate reduction in the Solar Lake the $\delta^{34}S_{(SO_4^{2})}$ values are almost identical as compared with the neighbouring sea water ($+20.9$ and $+20.6\%_{oo}$ respectively). This may serve as supporting evidence for the rapid seepage of sea water into the Solar Lake and the relatively short residence time of the water as calculated by Aharon et al. (1978) using salt water balance calculations. Nevertheless, the sulphate along the whole water body is somewhat isotopically heavy (by $0.3\%_{oo}$) due to the extensive microbial sulphur cycle in the lake. The sulphate concentration becomes even higher in the interstitial water, but it seems from the isotopic measurements (Fig. 8) that diffusion occurs at both ends of the cores on top from the water sediment interface and the bottom (1 m) with the seepage coming through the barrier. The only section where the sulphate reduction is faster than the re-equilibration is at the mid-section (45–80 cm). This fast diffusion is marked also in the bottom core (samples SLA–IX and X) where the pore water show $+20.9 – +21.3$ through the whole core. This could stem from one or all three causes: (i) slower microbial activity (in comparison with the upper core), (ii) better mixing, no lamination, (iii) depth of burial and higher hydrostatic pressure allowing faster diffusion.

In order to keep the stratification of the lake the seepage of the Red Sea water must be mainly through the upper part of the barrier to keep the density gradient. This density gradient forms a barrier for diffusion of atmospheric oxygen and allows the formation of an anoxic condition below it. This may control the oxic–non-oxic zone and determine the metalimnion.

In the present work all of the H_2S samples analysed isotopically for $\delta^{34}S$ gave values of $-16.0 \pm 0.2\%_{oo}$ whereas the elemental sulphur was lighter up to $-21.0 \pm 2.0\%_{oo}$. This may be a result of the photosynthetic oxidation of H_2S to S° by cyanobacteria (Cohen et al., 1975) with possible isotopic fractionation enriching the elemental sulphur in ^{32}S while the sulphur in H_2S is kept heavier. This phenomenon is quite important in the understanding of the sulphur cycle in the Solar Lake especially the possible introduction of the light (^{32}S enriched) sulphur to the sedimentary organic matter.

The elemental analysis of total sediment after removal of carbonates shows the same trends, but somewhat diluted, as the protokerogen. We are interested in this discussion in the decrease in N/C and increase in S/C with depth (Figs 3 and 7). A more complex picture is revealed in the various extractions (Figs 4, 5 and 6). It seems to us that the sulphur concentration depends more on the available elemental sulphur to organic solvents extraction than the concentration of the organically bonded sulphur. Since we are studying a very young sediment each stage of the chemical treatment may cause chemical changes in the extractables, e.g. the S/C in Fig. 4 has almost the reverse trend with depth if compared with extract III (Fig. 6). The protokerogen being somewhat more stable chemically shows trends that we can correlate to $\delta^{34}S$ changes.

It is surprising that even the top sediment (0–5 cm) is already influenced by the dissimilatory reduced sulphur. At first we thought that the -10 to $-14\%_0$ values of the $\delta^{34}S$ measured at the 5–10 cm section (SLA–III) derive from the same mechanism proposed by Dinur *et al.* (1980) for the oil shales: chemical reaction between sulphate and hydrogen sulphide to give elemental sulphur which can then react with the organic matter. However, the isolation of elemental sulphur at the same section with $\delta^{34}S-20.0\%_0$ proved this mechanism as non-valid in this case.

While the studied samples of extractable sulphur stay within the range of $\delta^{34}S-14\%_0 \pm 2\%_0$, the protokerogen is enriched in ^{32}S isotope with the increase of sulphur concentration. We hesitate to introduce the idea that the polysulphide pool enriches the protokerogen with sulphur lighter than that of the pool. However, the value of $-26.3\%_0$ measured twice in different samples (45–80 cm section SLA–VI) and -25.2, -25.4 and $-24.1\%_0$ recorded for the lower section protokerogens could not be the result of a methodological error.

We have proposed for the reaction of sulphur introduction into organic matter by polysulphides the free radical mechanism. The immediate products may not be stable and stabilize via elimination of sulphur and recombination of the R–Sn·. So far no information is available on any isotopic effect that such reactions may have. We have recorded changes in sulphur concentration upon 175 °C heating of the protokerogen (elimination) and recombination with enrichment in excess sulphur, S° tends to form free radicals at 175 °C. Polysulphides exist even at low temperature in the free radical form (in equilibrium).

In order to support this hypothesis we sublimed sulphur from the sample SLA–VI and twice measured $\delta^{34}S$ with the value of $-20.6\%_0$ while the isolated sulphur from the protokerogen exhibited $-26.3\%_0$.

CONCLUSIONS

The Solar Lake sulphur cycle was studied as an example of sulphurita bodies. It is evident that with the lack of sufficient available iron for the formation of pyrite the polysulphides pool reacts with young organic matter introducing via secondary chemically controlled reactions dissimilatory ^{32}S enriched sulphur.

The destruction of amino acids increases the NH_3 concentration in the interstitial waters and in turn stabilizes the polysulphides pool formed. No evidence was found for organic matter derived from terrestrial sources, therefore, all changes could be attributed to the system studied.

The protokerogen is enriched with depth in sulphur simultaneously showing lighter $\delta^{34}S$ values. The value of $-26.3\%_0$ is the highest ^{32}S enriched sulphur organically bonded recorded so far. The increase in S/C and the decrease in N/C with depth supports our previously expressed model that organically bonded sulphur is introduced, into fossil organic matter by secondary reaction, at least in sulphur-rich organic deposits.

Acknowledgements

This research was supported by KFA–Jülich (FR Germany) through the NCRD–Israel and partially by grants from the Ministry of Technology and Sciences at Niedersachen to Zeev Aizenshtat and Yehuda Cohen.

REFERENCES

Aharon, P., Kolodny, Y. and Sass, E. (1977) Recent hot brine dolomitization in the Solar Lake, Gulf of Elat; isotopic, chemical and mineralogical study. *J. Geol.* **85**, 27–48.

Aizenshtat, Z. (1973) Perylene and its geochemical significance. *Geochim. Cosmochim. Acta* **37**, 559–567.

Aizenshtat, Z., Baedecker, M. J. and Kaplan, I. R. (1973) Distribution and diagenesis or organic compounds in JOIDES sediments from Gulf of Mexico and Western Atlantic. *Geochim. Cosmochim. Acta* **37**, 1887–1898.

Cohen, Y., Jørgensen, B. B., Padan, E. and Shilo, M. (1975) Sulfide dependent anoxygenic photosynthesis in the cyanobacterium *Oscillatoria limnetica. Nature (London)* **257**, 489–492.

Cohen, Y., Krumbein, W. E., Goldberg, M. and Shilo, M. (1977a) Solar Lake (Sinai). 1. Physical and chemical limnology. *Limnol. Oceanogr.* **22**, 597–608.

Cohen, Y., Krumbein, W. E. and Shilo, M. (1977b) Solar Lake (Sinai). 2. Distribution of photosynthetic microorganisms and primary production. *Limnol. Oceanogr.* **22**, 609–620.

Cohen, Y., Aizenshtat, Z., Stoler, A. and Jørgensen, B. B. (1980) The microbial geochemistry of Solar Lake Sinai. In *Environmental Biogeochemistry of Ancient and Recent Sediments*, ed. by Trudinger, P. A. and Walter, M. Aust. Acad. Sci., Canberra, pp. 167–172.

Dinur, D., Spiro, B. and Aizenshtat, Z. (1980) The distribution and isotopic composition of sulfur in organic-rich sedimentary rocks. *Chem. Geol.* **31**, 37–51.

Furman, N. H. (1962) Eshka method in *Standard Method of Chemical Analysis*, Vol. 1: The elements, 6th edition, Van Nostrand, Princeton N.J., pp. 1006–1007.

Jørgensen, B. B., Kuenen, J. G. and Cohen, Y. (1979a). Microbial transformations of sulfur compounds in a stratified lake (Solar Lake, Sinai). *Limnol. Oceanogr.* **24**, 799–822.

Jørgensen, B. B., Revsbeck, N. P., Blackburn, T. H. and Cohen, Y. (1979b) Diurnal cycle of oxygen and sulfide microgradients and microbial photosynthesis in an organic sediment. *Appl. Environ, Microbiol.* **38**, 48–65.

Krumbein, W. E., Cohen, Y. and Shilo, M. (1977) Solar Lake (Sinai) 4. Stromatolitic cyanobacterial mats. *Limnol. Oceanogr.* **22**, 635–606.

Nielsen, H. (1978) Sulfur (16-B Section). Isotopes in nature. *Handbook of Geochemistry Vol. II/5.* Springer-Verlag Berlin, Heidelberg, New York.

Oren, A. and Shilo, M. (1979) Anaerobic heterotrophic dark metabolism in the cyanobacterium *Oscillatoria limnetica:*

sulfur respiration and lactate fermentation. *Arch. Microbiol.*
122, 77–84.

Padan, E. and Cohen, Y. (1980) Anoxygenic photosynthesis.

In *The Biology of Cyanobacteria*, ed. by Carr, N. G. and
Whitton, B. A. Blackwell Scientific Publications, Oxford
(in press).

Advances in Organic Geochemistry 1981, pp. 289–298
© *John Wiley & Sons Limited, 1983*

Oxic and Anoxic Diagenesis of Diterpenes in Lacustrine Sediments

M. A. Barnes and W. C. Barnes

Department of Geological Sciences, University of British Columbia, 6339 Stores Road, Vancouver, British Columbia V6T 2B4, Canada

Powell Lake, located on the west coast of Canada, is a former fjord which became separated from the open sea about 12 000 years ago by post-glacial isostatic rebound. The lake is divided into basins by shallow sills. South Basin, with a total depth of 360 m, has an anoxic monimolimnion of relict sea water below 150 m. West Basin is oxygenated throughout its 305 m depth. It is dimictic, and its sediments show a sharp redox boundary at 3 cm. Both basins share common higher plant, mainly coniferous, and planktic sources. The interlinked basins provide a unique means of identifying the effects of oxic and anoxic depositional environments on lipid diagenesis. Hydrocarbons from cores from both basins were analysed by computerized on-line GC–MS and quantified using GLC(FID). A significant depletion occurs in hydrocarbons isolated from above and below the redox boundary in West Basin relative to those isolated from South Basin. The distribution of branched hydrocarbons, perylene, pentacyclic triterpenes (M^+ 410) and β,β-C_{31} hopane relative to normal saturated hydrocarbons is unaffected by depositional environment. Major differences in distribution with depositional environment occur in the diterpenes related to abietic acid. Anoxic South Basin sediments contain the entire series of partially to fully aromatized diterpenes. Retene, which comprises 15% of the total hydrocarbons from South Basin, occurs in trace amounts in West Basin. Sediments from above and below the redox boundary in West Basin contain zero, trace or small amounts of the mono-, di- and tri-aromatic diterpenes. The chemocline in South Basin affects the rates of seston sedimentation; settling organic matter is exposed to a series of oxic, low-oxygen and anoxic chemical and microbiological systems. Differences in diterpene distribution in the two basins sharing the same organic precursors provide a measure of the effects of oxic and anoxic diagenetic environments on the structure and aromaticity of terpene hydrocarbons.

INTRODUCTION

Powell Lake is a deep fjord lake on the southwest coast of British Columbia, Canada. The lake was formerly a fjord, much like other fjords along the coast. The sill at the mouth of this fjord was sufficiently shallow, however, that post-glacial isostatic rebound caused the sill to rise above sea level about 12 000 years ago, separating the fjord from the sea and trapping seawater in the lake basin. The lake is located in a humid, temperate maritime climatic region and has a surface elevation of 56 m above sea level. Roads are present only at the southern end of the lake, where it borders the town of Powell River. A major pulp mill is present in the town, only 1.5 km from the southern tip of the lake, but at an elevation less than 10 m above sea level. No water-borne pollutants enter the lake from this source; airborne pollutants may reach the lake, particularly during the winter when southerly winds are common, but are unlikely to contain diterpenes because of high stack temperatures. Timber cutting has taken place for several decades near the north end of the lake, with the log booms being floated to the south end of the lake for transport to the mill, contributing bark and wood fragments to the lake sediment.

Powell Lake is divided into a series of basins, each with a flat floor and steep walls, separated from one another by sills (Fig. 1). South and East Basins are separated from the remainder of the lake by especially shallow sills, and are meromictic, with dense, saline monimolimnions which are permanently anoxic. The other basins are dimictic and, because of their great depths, have hypolimnions which are oxygenated throughout the year. The great depth of the lake and the differing oxygen contents of the bottom waters of the various basins make Powell Lake uniquely useful for organic geochemical studies. South and West Basins were chosen as representative of the two environments; in addition, they have similar planktic and terrestrial sources of organic matter.

South Basin has a maximum depth of 360 m. Between 100 m and 300 m, the salinity of the water increases exponentially, reaching a maximum of 16.5 permil (Fig. 2). Dissolved oxygen content decreases to zero at 160 m; dissolved sulphide increases below this depth, reaching a maximum of 89 mg l^{-1} at the bottom of the basin (Williams *et al.*, 1961). During the summer, the water temperature reaches a minimum between 100 and 120 m, increasing below this depth to a maximum of 9.4 °C at the bottom. East Basin, separated from South Basin

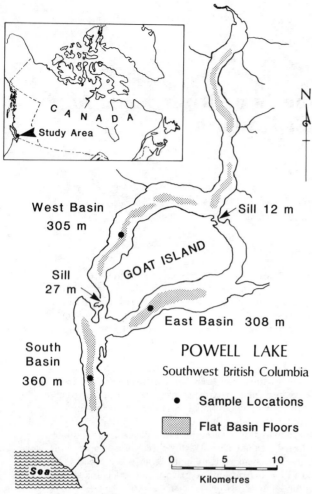

Fig. 1. Location map. Sill depths are measured from mean lake level. Area labelled 'Sea' in the lower left corner is the Strait of Georgia, located between Vancouver Island and the mainland of British Columbia. Map adapted from Mathews (1962).

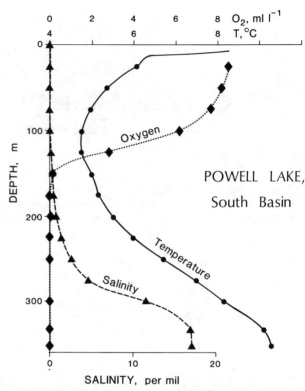

Fig. 2. Temperature, salinity and dissolved oxygen profiles for the South Basin of Powell Lake. Data from Williams *et al.* (1961).

only by a deep sill, shows similar values for temperature, salinity, dissolved oxygen and dissolved sulphide with depth.

Although a major river enters the head of Powell Lake (Fig. 1), both East and South Basins are sufficiently remote from the delta of this river that little inorganic sediment reaches them from this source. Only very small streams enter either basin, and the steep walls of the lake cause any sediment entering the basins from these streams to be carried directly into deep water. Both basins are geographically and geologically similar. South Basin has a surface area of 28.8 km² and a drainage basin area of 87.5 km²; West Basin has a surface area of 22.3 km² and a drainage basin of 89.6 km². Both basins are underlain principally by plutonic igneous rocks, mainly granodiorite and quartz diorite, with lesser amounts of diorite. Small roof pendants and screens of greenstone, volcanic breccia and minor argillite and limestone belong to the Lower Cretaceous Gambier Group. Scattered patches of glacial and glaciofluvial sediments, derived from these bedrock types, occur in the drainage basins of both South and West Basins.

An inventory of forest resources in the drainage basin of Powell Lake, taken in 1978, showed the following

POWELL LAKE PLANKTON

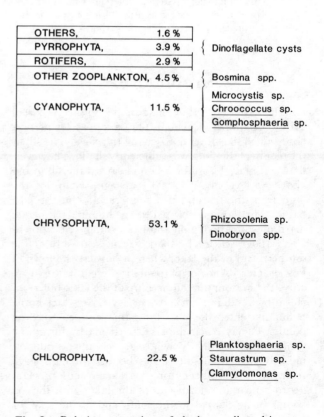

Fig. 3. Relative proportions of plankton collected in a tow taken 6 July 1975.

proportions of mature trees in accessible areas. Conifers are principally *Tsuga heterophylla* and *Abies* spp. (37.8% and 24.3% respectively). *Thuja plicata* (16.4%), *Pseudotsuga menziesii* (13.6%) and *Chamaecyparis nootkatensis* (7.1%) are moderately abundant. Pines, spruce and alder are less abundant (J. B. Mountain, oral communication, 1981), but as the survey covered only accessible mature trees, alders in particular are under-represented, as they occur mainly as immature trees and in less accessible areas. Red alder pollen is the most abundant deciduous tree pollen, comprising 8 to 20% of the total pollen in South Basin sediments (S. J. Pocock, written communication, 1974). Plankton were collected from both South and West Basins by towing a 100 μm net at a depth of approximately 2 m, and were analysed by Styan (1976), who found no significant difference between the plankton populations of the two basins. The composition by phylum and representative genera for South Basin are shown in Fig. 3. The plankton were collected in early July, 1975. The proportions of phyla would, of course, be different at other times of the year, but the species present would not change. At the time of sampling Powell Lake algae were dominated by *Rhizosolenia* sp., a thin-walled, fragile diatom, and *Dinobryon* sp., a flagellate unicellular Chrysophyte, which together comprised about half of the total algae present. Subdominant genera included *Planktosphaeria*, *Staurastrum* and *Clamydomonas*, all of which are Chlorophytes characteristic of oligotrophic waters. However, several of the minor genera, such as the diatoms *Asterionella* and *Melosira*, the Chlorophytes *Ankistrodesmus*, *Cosmarium* and *Scenedesmus*, and the Cyanophyte *Microcystis*, are indicative of mesotrophic to eutrophic waters (Hutchinson, 1957; Wetzel, 1975). Using a number of the indices proposed by Nygaard (1949), Powell Lake can be identified as a productive lake. Nutrient and major elements in the lake waters are presently being studied by T. Pedersen, Department of Oceanography, University of British Columbia. Water and sediment properties are given in Table 1.

METHODS

Pfleger cores 2.5 cm in diameter were collected from the sites in South and West Basins shown in Fig. 1. Both sites are in the deepest parts of the basins. South Basin cores were 80 cm long, but only 40 cm cores were obtained from West Basin. In order to obtain sufficient material for analysis, the entire South Basin core was treated as a single bulk sample. Three cores from West Basin were divided into 0–5 cm and 5–30 cm fractions, and the respective fractions for the three cores combined. Because of the rapid exsolution of gases, the cores were sectioned immediately upon being brought to the surface, with the sections being stored in precleaned glass bottles with screw caps lined with cleaned aluminium foil. Samples were stored at 0 °C until the end of the day, when they were transferred to a freezer at −20 °C. They were kept at this temperature until they were extracted.

After thawing, the wet sediment samples were acidified to pH 2 with distilled HCl and allowed to equilibrate for 12 h. Fragments, mainly needles and bark, greater than 0.5 mm were removed by wet sieving. The samples were then centrifuged to remove excess water and extracted 5 times under nitrogen by 15 minute sonications with 1:1 benzene–methanol. Water soluble hydrocarbons were extracted from the aqueous centrifugate and combined with the sediment extracts. The combined extracts were neutralized to pH 7 and their volume reduced with a rotary evaporator to remove remaining water and methanol. The benzene–methanol ratio was adjusted to 1:1 and KOH added to a concentration of 0.5 M. The extracts were then sealed in glass ampoules under nitrogen and hydrolyzed at 92 °C for 12 h. The neutral fraction from the hydrolysis was partitioned into anhydrous diethyl ether, dried with anhydrous $MgSO_4$, evaporated and dissolved in heptane. The hydrocarbons were separated from the neutral fraction by column chromatography on silica gel (5% H_2O) with 5 column volumes of heptane. Total

Table 1

Water and sediment properties for the South and West Basins of Powell Lake

Parameter	South Basin	West Basin
Water depth	360 m	305 m
Bottom water		
Colour[a]	yellow (2.5Y 8/4)	colourless
Temperature	9.5 °C	6 °C
pH	6.8	6.2
Chlorinity	9 permil	0 permil
Character	effervescent, strong H_2S odour	non-effervescent, odourless
Oxygen content of water	oxic from 0 to 175 m, anoxic below 175 m	oxic from 0 to 305 m
Sediment		
Colour	olive black (5Y 2/2)	light grey (N7) 0–5 cm dark olive grey (5Y 3/2) >5 cm
Infauna	none	polychaetes
Character	sapropelic diatom ooze conifer needles and desmid cells green	sapropelic diatom ooze conifer needles brown

[a] Colour numbers after Munsell Color (1975).

extractable hydrocarbons were determined by evaporating 10 to 50 μl aliquots and weighing the residues on a Cahn electrobalance. The hydrocarbon extracts were then sealed in glass capillaries and stored at $-20\,°C$ prior to analysis. Hydrocarbon extracts of 10 to 20 g subsamples of three South Basin cores gave 338 ± 30 μg total hydrocarbons per gram dry sediment. The bulk extract of 120 g of South Basin sediment was 35% less efficient, however, yielding only 219 $\mu g\ g^{-1}$ total hydrocarbons. For the 0–5 cm West Basin sample, 71 μg g^{-1} total hydrocarbons were obtained from a 20.6 g sample; from 5–30 cm, 98 $\mu g\ g^{-1}$ were obtained from 73.6 g of dry sediment. Total hydrocarbons represented 9.7%, 4.5% and 5.6% of the neutral fractions extracted from the South Basin, the 0–5 cm West Basin and the 5–30 cm West Basin samples, respectively. The total hydrocarbons from South Basin were fractionated by thin-layer chromatography on 10% $AgNO_3/SiO_2$; saturated hydrocarbons (46%), diterpenes, retene and triterpenes (30%), retene (10%) and perylene with other hydrocarbons (22%) were recovered in four fractions. The saturated hydrocarbons were adducted with 0.5 nm molecular sieve.

All solvents were redistilled with glass fractionating columns from reagent grade materials. Water was distilled, run through Millipore Milli-Q resin beds and redistilled in glass. Blanks were run on all solvents and on the silica gel used in the column chromatography. Small amounts of dioctyl phthalate were observed.

Hexadecane was added to all hydrocarbon samples as an internal standard. Three analytical systems were used. Mass spectra were obtained for South Basin total hydrocarbons and thin-layer chromatography fractions using a 1% OV-17 capillary column on a Varian 204 GC coupled directly to a Dupont 21-492-1 double-focusing MS with a Dupont 21-094B data system. Subsequent work on both South and West Basin samples was done on 3% Dexsil 300 (2 m × 2 mm i.d. glass) using a Hewlett–Packard 5754 GC and a Varian 1440 GC (injector 300 °C; separator 300 °C; line 300 °C; oven 100 to 300 °C; 4 °C min^{-1}) coupled to a single-focusing Varian MAT 111 MS with a Varian data system. Similar amounts of total hydrocarbon were used for standards and samples in GLC (~20 μg) and GC/MS analyses (~100 μg). Mixtures of standard hydrocarbons containing hexadecane were run at the beginning and end of each working day to monitor detector response. Hexadecane

added as an internal standard was used to quantify the individual hydrocarbons using GLC(FID). Where peak overlap occurred [III (19:4) and IV (19:6) with I (fichtelite)] (Table 3), the GLC peak area was apportioned on the basis of the proportion of diterpene ions relative to the total ion area for the GC/MS analysis. Values in Table 3 were normalized to a constant total hydrocarbon sample size and adjusted for the difference in total extractable hydrocarbons per gram dry sediment for the three samples. Diterpenes matched published spectra for fichtelite (Douglas and Grantham, 1974), tetrahydroretene, simonellite (Wakeham et al., 1980b), dehydroabietin, retene, methyl dehydroabietate (Simoneit, 1977), and dehydroabietane (Simoneit, 1975). Other hydrocarbons were identified by comparison of their mass spectra with published spectra for octahydrochrysenes (Spyckerelle et al., 1977; Laflamme and Hites, 1979; Wakeham et al., 1980b), fernene and arborene (Nishimoto et al., 1968) and diploptene (Bird et al., 1971). Samples for elemental analysis and to determine the dry sediment weight were taken after acidification but prior to solvent extraction. Elemental analyses were done on samples dried at 105 °C by Canadian Microanalytical Services, Vancouver, using a Carlo Erba C–H–N analyser. Duplicate samples from South Basin varied 0.46 % (C), 0.23% (H) and 2.35% (N). Total sulphur was determined as barium sulphate after burning with oxygen at 1200 °C, and showed a variation of 2.49%.

RESULTS AND DISCUSSION

South Basin sediments (Table 1) are olive-black diatomaceous oozes which consist of about 70% sapropel and 25% diatom frustules. Conifer needles and desmids with intact chloroplasts retain their green colour to the base of the 80 cm cores. Upon being brought to the surface core samples expand rapidly with the exsolution of H_2S and CH_4. Carbon and sulphur analyses (Table 2) show a parallel distribution with depth, with maxima of 16:21% C and 8.05% S at 10–20 cm and minima of 9.49% C and 3.01% S at 60–70 cm (Fig. 4). The permanently anoxic saline monimolimnion below 160 m in the water column contributes to the formation of a sink for both carbon and sulphur. The absence of

Table 2

Elemental analyses of South and West Basin sediments. Carbon is entirely organic; no carbonate carbon is present. Sulphur values are total sulphur

South Basin					West Basin				
Depth	C	H	N	S	Depth	C	H	N	S
0–10 cm	15.14	2.22	0.85	7.85	–5 cm	4.63	0.66	0.36	0.84
10–20 cm	16.21	2.14	0.96	8.05	5–20 cm	9.32	1.53	0.42	0.75
20–30 cm	13.37	2.02	0.76	6.91	20–35 cm	9.93	1.50	0.52	0.77
30–40 cm	13.53	2.01	0.75	7.31	35–46 cm	12.77	1.84	0.68	0.82
40–50 cm	12.68	1.94	0.90	7.15					
50–60 cm	11.87	1.99	0.82	6.53					
60–70 cm	9.49	1.70	0.72	3.01					
70–80 cm	10.54	1.90	0.74	6.07					

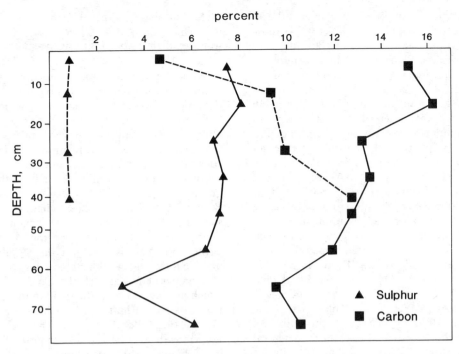

Fig. 4. Carbon and sulphur analyses for South (solid line) and West Basin (dashed line) cores. Values are in per cent dry weight of sediment.

Table 3
Diterpenes in Powell Lake sediments

Compound	West Basin[a] 0–5 cm	West Basin[a] 5–30 cm	South Basin[a] 0–80 cm
I Fichtelite (M$^+$ 262)[c]	63	479	439
II 19:4 (M$^+$ 260)[b]	234 ng g^{-1}	1416 ng g^{-1}	294 ng g^{-1}
III 19:4 (M$^+$ 260)[b,c]	0	47	35
IV 19:6 (M$^+$ 256)[c,d]	0	0	84
V Dehydroabietin (M$^+$ 256)	7	102	774
VI Tetrahydroretene (M$^+$ 238)	0	43	3362
VII Retene (M$^+$ 234)	4	131	33 374
VIII 20:4 (M$^+$ 274)	16	157	415
IX Dehydroabietane (M$^+$ 270)	35	362	865
20:5 (M$^+$ 272)[e]	0	(+)	(+)
X Simonellite (M$^+$ 252)	3	33	1572
Total diterpenes, ng g^{-1}	362	2770	41 214
Total RH, μg g^{-1} [f]	71	98	219
Diterpenes as % Tot. RH	0.51%	2.83%	18.82%
Retene as % diterpenes	1.10%	4.73%	81.0%

[a] ng g^{-1} dry sediment weight, based on GLC(FID) response relative to hexadecane used as an internal standard.

[b] 19:4 (II, 4 isomers) elute on GLC before 19:4 (III, 3 isomers).

[c] Where peak overlap occurred for I, III and IV, the GLC peak area was apportioned on the basis of the proportions of the diterpene ions relative to the total ion area for the GC/MS sample.

[d] Dehydroabietin analogue.

[e] On the basis of the molecular ion (272) and the relative areas for 229 (M$^+$–43), normalized to a constant GC/MS sample weight and adjusted for the extractable hydrocarbons per gram dry sediment, West Basin and South Basin sediments contain approximately equal amounts ($\sim$50 ng g^{-1}) of an abietadiene.

[f] Total extractable hydrocarbons as μg g^{-1} dry sediment.

sulphate in the bottom water (Williams *et al.*, 1961) and the large total sulphur content in the sediment suggest that both terrestrial plants and the initial sulphate of the trapped sea-water are required to account for the present sulphur contents of water and sediments. As reducing conditions appear to have persisted at least over the approximately 200 years represented by the cores, variations in carbon content probably reflect

fluctuations in lake productivity rather than changes in the depositional or diagenetic environments.

West Basin sediments are sapropelic diatom oozes which are dark olive grey except for the upper 5 cm, which are light grey (Table 1). The colour change probably represents a change from oxic to anoxic conditions in the sediment. The upper 2 cm of the sediment contain tube-forming polychaete worms.

Conifer needle fragments are brown throughout the 40 cm cores from the basin. West Basin sediments, like those of South Basin, lack visible stratification. Bottom water samples were colourless, odourless and did not effervesce when brought to the surface. Organic carbon contents in West Basin sediments increase with depth from a surface minimum of 4.63% to a maximum of 12.77% at 35–46 cm, a value similar to that observed at the same depth in South Basin. Sulphur contents are constant with depth, at ∼0.8%. Low sulphur values indicate that relict seawater was probably not trapped in West Basin during the time represented by the cores. As both West and South Basins share common sources of organic matter, differences in the trends for carbon and sulphur probably reflect differences in depositional environment.

Acyclic hydrocarbons in South and West Basin sediments range from C_{17} to C_{35}, with maxima at 6-methyl hexadecane and n-C_{27}. Total extractable hydrocarbons increase from 70 μg g^{-1} to 98 μg g^{-1}, on a dry sediment basis, for samples taken above and below the redox boundary in West Basin. Total extractable hydrocarbons are 219 μg g^{-1} in South Basin (Table 3). The amount of hydrocarbons relative to the total neutral fraction increases from 4.5% to 5.6% to 9.7% in the three samples. All samples show a strong odd-carbon

preference for the normal hydrocarbons (C_{18} to C_{35}) which increases from 4.12 to 5.11 to 6.55 with the change from oxidizing to progressively more reducing environments.

While aerobic depositional environments showed a significant decrease in extractable total hydrocarbons, the proportions of the various classes of branched, cyclic and aromatic hydrocarbons relative to the saturated aliphatic hydrocarbons were similar in all three sediment samples. Hydrocarbon distributions are consistent with derivation from multiple sources. 6-Methyl hexadecane, which contains a mid-chain methyl group, is characteristic of blue–green algae (Barnes and Barnes, 1978) and has been identified in *Chroococcus* species (Bird and Lynch, 1974), which are present in Powell Lake (Styan, 1976). Other hydrocarbons in South and West Basins, and their probable sources, include the following: long chain normal hydrocarbons from higher plant waxes (Kolattukudy, 1975); perylene, which may be either a reduction product of higher plant pigments (Aizenshtat, 1973) or have a planktic source (Wakeham *et al.*, 1979); arborene and fernene (four isomers with M$^+$410 and a base peak of 243), derived from higher plants (Ourisson *et al.*, 1979); β,β-homohopane, from bacteria, and diploptene, derived

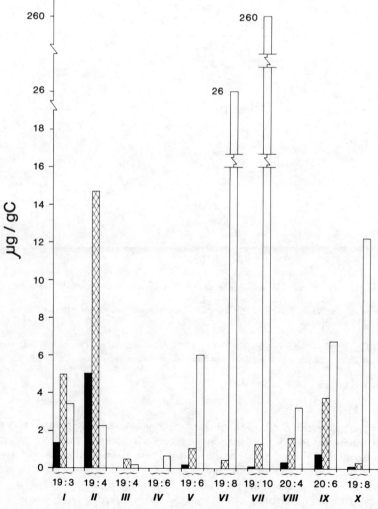

Fig. 5. Powell Lake sediment diterpenes expressed as μg g^{-1} organic carbon. Solid bar represents West Basin sediments above the redox boundary; hatched bar West Basin sediments below the redox boundary; and open bar South Basin sediments.

both from blue green algae and bacteria (Ourisson *et al.*, 1979); octahydrochrysenes (3 isomers with M⁺ 292), the products of photochemically or microbially mediated alteration (Corbet *et al.*, 1980) of β-amyrin-type triterpenes (Laflamme and Hites, 1979; Wakeham *et al.*, 1980b). A photosynthetic anaerobe has been reported as a source of fern-9(11)-ene and hop-22(29)-ene (Howard, 1980); however, it is a less likely source as the top of the anoxic layer in South Basin is well below the photic zone. Similar distributions of these compounds (relative to the normal hydrocarbons in the same sample) from oxic and anoxic depositional and diagenetic environments may occur because: (1) both basins share common sources of organic matter; (2) these hydrocarbons form in the upper freshwater layer shared by both basins as products of photochemical or aerobic microbial processes; or (3) they are protected from the effects of an oxic depositional environment through rapid sedimentation in zooplankton fecal pellets (Prahl and Carpenter, 1979). No zooplankton fecal pellets have been recognized in Powell Lake sediments but carapaces of *Bosmina* and rotifers are abundant.

Major differences in hydrocarbon distribution with depositional environment in Powell Lake sediments occur mainly in the diterpenes related to conifer-derived abietic acid. Diterpenes are summarized in Table 3, as ng g⁻¹ dry sediment. As the organic carbon content of the anoxic South Basin sediments is about three times that of West Basin sediments above the redox boundary, diterpenes are also plotted as μg g⁻¹ carbon on Fig. 5. Anoxic South Basin sediments contain dehydroabietic acid, abietatetraenoic acid and the entire series of partially to fully aromatized phenanthrenes (Fig. 6). Dehydroabietin, tetrahydroretene and retene are mono-, di- and tri-aromatic diterpenes which have lost the

original C₄-carboxyl of abietic acid. Abietene, abietadiene, dehydroabietane and simonellite are unsaturated and aromatic diterpenes which have retained the original C₄-carboxyl as a reduced methyl group. The order of relative abundance is retene > > tetrahydroretene > simonellite > dehydroabietane ~ dehydroabietin > fichtelite. Retene, the most abundant hydrocarbon in South Basin, comprises 15% of the total hydrocarbons. In addition, South Basin sediments contain small amounts of other diterpenes: 19:4 (4 isomers), 19:4 (3 isomers), 19:6, an analogue of dehydroabietin, 20:4 and 20:5. Mass spectra have characteristic ions for the loss of methyl and propyl groups. Fragmentation patterns for the 19:4 and 20:4 isomers are not distinguishable from those for the corresponding tetracyclics. The mass spectrum for the dehydroabietin analogue is very similar to that for dehydroabietin; however, the ratio of the 256/213 ions (1.4) is substantially smaller than the value of 4 reported for the corresponding 19-norabieta-8,11,13-triene (Simoneit, 1977).

Sediments from aerobic West Basin, from above and below the redox boundary (Table 3) contain zero, trace or small amounts of mono-, di- and tri-aromatic analogs which are abundant in South Basin sediments. Diterpene concentrations for sediments above the redox boundary are 100 times less than for South Basin sediments; retene is 8000 times smaller and tetrahydroretene is absent. Values for diterpenes from sediments below the redox boundary are 2 to 250 times less than the corresponding values from South Basin. The West Basin reduced sediments do contain tetrahydroretene; relative to the surface sediments, they show a 10 to 30 times increase in aromatic diterpenes (Table 3) and a 4 to 10 times enrichment at constant

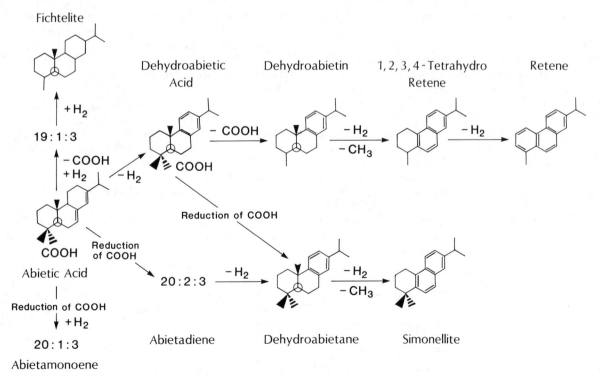

Fig. 6. Schematic relationships of diterpene acids and hydrocarbons.

organic carbon (Fig. 5). In marked contrast to South Basin sediments, the most abundant diterpenes in surface and reduced sediments in West Basin are the 19:4 diterpenes.

Diterpenes related in structure to abietic acid have recently been reported in soils (Laflamme and Hites, 1978), lake sediments (Tan and Heit, 1981; Wakeham *et al.*, 1980a, 1980b), marine sediments (Simoneit, 1977; Simoneit and Mazurek, 1979a, 1979b; Barrick and Hedges, 1981), fossil resins (Douglas and Grantham, 1974), in Kraft pulp mill effluents (Rogers *et al.*, 1979) and as pollutants in lake sediments (Brownlee *et al.*, 1977) and marine sediments (Yamaoka, 1979) arising from Kraft pulp mill effluents.

Aromatic diterpene concentrations in West Basin sediments parallel those reported for other lakes, whereas that of South Basin shows considerable enrichment. Reducing sediments from West Basin contain aromatic diterpenes in amounts similar to those reported for two Adirondack lakes (Tan and Heit, 1981); retene is one-sixth the maximum value reported for Lake Washington (Wakeham *et al.*, 1980b). While retene is the dominant diterpene in these lakes, dehydroabietane, fichtelite and 19:4 diterpenes are dominant in West Basin. Relative to the Adirondack lakes, South Basin sediments contain 10 to 56 times the amounts of the partially aromatized diterpenes and 115 times more retene; South Basin sediments contain 40 times the retene reported for Lake Washington (Wakeham *et al.*, 1980b). Retene in Lake Washington shows an increase from the sediment surface to a maximum at 6 to 9 cm, followed by a decrease with greater depth. Our work on the change in diterpene content with depth in West Basin is still incomplete; however, it appears to follow the Lake Washington pattern. The two Adirondack lakes (Tan and Heit, 1981) have a more complex pattern — high surface diterpene values which first decrease with depth, then increase to maxima and finally decrease with greater depth.

Diterpene acids with the abietane skeleton, including abietic, dehydroabietic, palustric and neoabietic acids, are widely distributed in conifers which are present in the Powell Lake drainage basin, including *Pinus* species (Norin and Winell, 1972a; Sinclair and Dymond, 1973; Conner *et al.*, 1980a, 1980b), *Pseudotsuga menziesii* (Rogers *et al.*, 1979; Foster *et al.*, 1980) and *Picea* species (Norin and Winell, 1972b; Conner *et al.*, 1980c). Abietane hydrocarbons are less commonly reported. Dehydroabietane and abietadienes have been found in *Pinus* (Vlad *et al.*, 1975), *Abies* (Ribo *et al.*, 1974, 1977) and *Pseudotsuga menziesii* (Rogers *et al.*, 1979). Alcohols with similar structures have been reported in pines (Schmidt and Pentegova, 1977; Conner and Rowe, 1977) and spruce (Norin and Winell, 1972b); corresponding aldehydes have been found mainly in pines (Norin and Winell, 1972a; Zinkel and Conner, 1973).

While fichtelite and aromatic diterpene hydrocarbons have been isolated from lake sediments, from soils associated with conifers, and from lake and marine sediments exposed to Kraft pulp mill effluents, dehydroabietane is the only diterpene hydrocarbon reported from conifers and from Kraft pulp mill effluents (Rogers *et al.*, 1979). *In situ* formation via microbial alteration of diterpenes related to abietic acid has been suggested as a source of these hydrocarbons in soils, peats and sediments (Maxwell *et al.*, 1971; Simoneit, 1977; Laflamme and Hites, 1978; Wakeham *et al.*, 1980a, 1980b). Their occurrence in fossil resins (Douglas and Grantham, 1974), and their absence in neutrals associated with decaying spruce wood infected with fungi (Ekman, 1979), suggest a combination of aerobic and anaerobic processes may contribute to their formation in soils and lake sediments. Half-lives of 6 weeks to 21 years have been estimated for the loss of dehydroabietic acid from the water column and sediments of Lake Superior affected by Kraft pulp mill effluents (Brownlee *et al.*, 1977). Reports of oxidized resin acids include: 7-ketodehydroabietic acid in lake water (Brownlee and Strachan, 1977); 7-hydroxydehydroabietic acid, 7-ketodehydroabietic acid and 7-keto-15-hydroxydehydroabietic acid in Douglas fir (Rogers and Mahood, 1981). Kieslich (1976) and Rogers (1983) reviewed the oxidation of diterpene acids by bacteria and fungi. Hydroxyl groups (at $C_{1,2,3,5,7}$) are introduced into the A and B rings with retention of the C_4-carboxyl group (Ekman, 1979; Kutney *et al.*, 1981); keto and hydroxyl functions are introduced at C_3 and C_7 with both retention and loss of the C_4-carboxyl group (Ekman, 1979; Biellmann, 1973a, 1973b).

Lower concentrations of aromatic diterpene hydrocarbons in West Basin sediments may reflect oxidation of precursor diterpene acids to more polar products which are not isolated in the neutral hydrocarbon fraction. The major enrichment in aromatic diterpene hydrocarbons in South Basin sediments, which accumulate beneath a 200 m anoxic water column, and the significant enrichment in West Basin reducing sediments relative to those above the redox boundary, suggest reducing environments are a major factor in the preservation of aromatic diterpenes and probably contribute to their *in situ* formation. The permanent chemocline in the water column of South Basin permits a series of oxic, microaerophilic and anoxic chemical and microbial systems which, in turn, may oxidize, hydroxylate, dehydrate, aromatize and reduce precursor diterpene acids to form the aromatic diterpene hydrocarbons observed in the sediments.

Acknowledgements

This project has benefited from the assistance of many individuals. F. S. Abbott made available his GC–MS data system in the Department of Pharmaceutical Sciences at the University of British Columbia, and R. Burton taught us how to use it. R. P. Philp made available a GC–MS data system in the Department of Chemistry, University of California at Berkeley, S. J. Pocock analysed the palynomorphs from a South Basin core. W. H. Mathews and T. F. Pedersen provided information on the physical and chemical limnology of the lake and applied rational reins to some of our wilder speculations. R. L. Chase, W. H. Mathews and J. W.

Murray provided financial support to one of us (M.A.B.). The work on which this paper is based has been supported by the Natural Sciences and Engineering Research Council of Canada through grants A–0032, A–1107, A–3542 and A–7027, and by grants from Esso Resources Canada and Gulf Canada Resources. Finally, we sincerely appreciate the financial support of the European Organic Geochemistry Committee, without which we would not have been able to attend the conference.

REFERENCES

Aizenshtat, A. (1973) Perylene and its geochemical significance. *Geochim. Cosmochim. Acta* **37**, 559–567.

Barnes, M. A. and Barnes, W. C. (1978) Organic compounds in lake sediments. In *Lakes: Chemistry, Geology, Physics*, ed. by Lerman, A. Springer-Verlag, Heidelberg, pp. 127–152.

Barrick, R. C. and Hedges, J. I. (1981) Hydrocarbon geochemistry of the Puget Sound region — II. Sedimentary diterpenoid, steroid and triterpenoid hydrocarbons. *Geochim. Cosmochim. Acta* **45**, 381–392.

Biellmann, J. F., Branlant, G., Gero-Robert, M. and Poiret, M. (1973a) Degradation bacterienne de l'acide dehydroabietique par *Flavobacterium resinovorum*. *Tetrahedron* **29**, 1227–1236.

Biellman, J. F., Branlant, G., Gero-Robert, M. and Poiret, M. (1973b) Degradation bacterienne de l'acide dehydroabietique par un *Pseudomonas* et une *Alcaligenes*. *Tetrahedron* **29**, 1237–1241.

Bird, C. W. and Lynch, J. M. (1974) Formation of hydrocarbons by micro-organisms. *Chem. Soc. Rev.* **3**, 309–328.

Bird, C. W., Lynch, J. M., Pirt, F. J., Reid, W. W., Brooks, C. J. W. and Middleditch, B. S. (1971) The identification of hop-22(29)-ene in prokaryotic organisms. *Tetrahedron Lett.* 1971, pp. 3189–3190.

Brownlee, B., Fox, M. E., Strachan, W. M. J. and Joshi, S. R. (1977) Distribution of dehydroabietic acid in sediments adjacent to a Kraft pulp and paper mill. *J. Fish. Res. Board Canada* **34**, 838–843.

Brownlee, B. G. and Strachan, W. M. J. (1977) Distribution of some organic compounds in the receiving waters of a kraft pulp and paper mill. *J. Fish. Res. Board Can.* **34**, 830–837.

Conner, A. H. and Rowe, J. W. (1977) New neutral diterpenes from southern pine tall oil. *Phytochemistry* **11**, 1777–1781.

Conner, A. H., Diehl, M. A. and Rowe, J. W. (1980a) Tall oil precursors and turpentine in jack and eastern white pine. *Wood Sci.* **12**, 194–200.

Conner, A. H., Diehl, M. A. and Rowe, J. W. (1980b) Tall oil precursors in three western pines: pondersoa, lodgepole and limber pine. *Wood Sci.* **12**, 183–191.

Conner, A. H., Diehl, M. A. and Rowe, J. W. (1980c) Tall oil precursors and turpentine in black and white spruce. *Wood Sci.* **13**, 111–116.

Corbet, B., Albrecht, P. and Ourisson, G. (1980) Photochemical or photomimetic fossil triterpenoids in sediments and petroleum. *J. Am. Chem. Soc.* **102**, 1171–1173.

Douglas, A. G. and Grantham, P. J. (1974) Fingerprint gas chromatography in the analysis of some native bitumens, asphalts and related substances. In *Advances in Organic Geochemistry, 1973* (ed. by Tissot, B. and Bienner, F. Editions Technip, Paris, pp. 261–276.

Ekman, R. and Sjoholm, R. (1979) Hydroxylation of dehydroabietic acid by *Fomes annosus*. *Acta Chem. Scand.* **B33**, 76–78.

Ekman, R. and von Weissenberg, K. (1979) Sapwood extractives in Norway spruce inoculated with *Fomes annosus*. *Acta Acad. Abo., Ser.* **B39**, 1–8.

Foster, D. O., Zinkel, D. F. and Conner, A. H. (1980) Tall oil precursors of Douglas fir. *TAPPI* **63**, 103–105.

Howard, D. L. (1980) Polycyclic triterpenes of the anaerobic photosynthetic bacterium *Rhodomicrobium vannielii*. *Diss. Abstr.* **41**, B1205.

Hutchinson, G. E. (1957) *A Treatise on Limnology. I. Geography, Physics and Chemistry*. Wiley, New York, 1015 pp.

Kieslich, K. (1976) *Microbial Transformations of Non-steroid Cyclic Compounds*. John Wiley, New York, pp. 77–80.

Kolattukudy, P. E. (1975) Biochemistry of cutin, suberin and waxes, the lipid barriers on plants. In *Recent Advances in the Chemistry and Biochemistry of Plant Lipids* ed. by Galliard, T. and Mercer, E. I. Academic Press, London, pp. 203–246.

Kutney, J. P., Singh, M., Hewitt, G. M., Salisbury, P. J., Worth, B. R., Servizi, J. A., Martens, D. W. and Gordon, R. W. (1981) Studies related to biological detoxification of Kraft pulp mill effluent. I. The biodegradation of dehydroabietic acid with *Mortierella isabellina*. *Can. J. Chem.* **59**, 2334–2341.

Laflamme, R. E. and Hites, R. A. (1978) The global distribution of polycyclic aromatic hydrocarbons in recent sediments. *Geochim. Cosmochim. Acta* **42**, 289–303.

Laflamme, R. E. and Hites, R. A. (1979) Tetra- and pentacyclic, naturally-occurring aromatic hydrocarbons in Recent sediments. *Geochim. Cosmochim. Acta* **43**, 687–691.

Mathews, W. H. (1962) Bathymetry of Powell Lake, British Columbia, Manuscript Rept. 13, Inst. Oceanography, Univ. British Columbia, Vancouver, Canada.

Maxwell, J. R., Pillinger, C. T. and Eglinton, G. (1971) Organic geochemistry. *Quart. Rev.* **25**, 571–628.

Munsell Color (1975) Munsell soil color charts. Macbeth Division, Kollmorgen Corporation.

Nishimoto, K., Ito, M., Natori, S. and Ohmoto, T. (1968) The structures of arundoin, cylindrin and fernenol: triterpenoids of fernane and arborane groups of *Imperata cylindrica* var. *Koenigii*. *Tetrahedron* **24**, 735–752.

Norin, T. and Winell, B. (1972a) Extractives from the bark of Scots pine, *Pinus sylvetris*. *Acta Chem. Scand.* **26**, 2297–2304.

Norin, T. and Winell, B. (1972b) Extractives from the bark of common spruce, *Picea abies*. *Acta Chem. Scand.* **26**, 2289–2296.

Nygaard, G. (1949) Hydrobiological studies on some Danish ponds and lakes. Part II. The quotient hypothesis and some new or little known phytoplankton organisms. *K. Dan. Vidensk. Selsk. Biol. Skr.* **7**, 293 pp.

Ourisson, G., Albrecht, P. and Rohmer, M. (1979) The hopanoids: paleobiochemistry of a group of natural products. *Pure Appl. Chem.* **51**, 709–729.

Prahl, F. G. and Carpenter, R. (1979) The role of zooplankton fecal pellets in the sedimentation of polycyclic aromatic hydrocarbons in Dabob Bay, Washington. *Geochim. Cosmochim. Acta* **43**, 1959–1972.

Ribo, J. M., Mitja, M. R. and Ramentol, J. (1974) Diterpenoids in *Abies alba*. *Phytochemistry* **13**, 1614.

Ribo, J. M., Raventos, J. U. and Serra, A. M. (1977) Hydrocarbons in two *Abies* species. *Phytochemistry* **16**, 767.

Rogers, I. H. (1983) Biological interactions. In *Naval Stores: Production, Chemistry and Utilization*, ed. by Campbell, D., Soltes, E. and Zinkel, D. Pulp Chemicals Association, New York, in press.

Rogers, I. H. and Mahood, H. W. (1981) Oxidized resin acids in Douglas fir wood extractives. In *Advances in Identification and Analysis of Organic Pollutants in Water*, ed. by Keith, L. H. Ann Arbor Science Publishers, Ann Arbor, Michigan, pp. 1097–1113.

Rogers, I., Mahood, H., Servizi, J. and Gordon, R. (1979)

Identifying extractives toxic to aquatic life. *Pulp Pap. Can.* **80**, T286–T290.

Shmidt, E. N. and Pentegova, V. A. (1977) Diterpenoids from *Picea koraiensis, Picae glehnii* and *Picea excelsa* resins. *Khim. Prir. Soedin.* 1977(5), 653–657.

Simoneit, B. R. T. (1975) Sources of organic matter in oceanic sediments. Ph.D. Thesis, University of Bristol.

Simoneit, B. R. T. (1977) Diterpenoid compounds and other lipids in deep-sea sediments and their geochemical significance. *Geochim. Cosmochim. Acta* **41**, 463–476.

Simoneit, B. R. T. and Mazurek, M. A. (1979a) Search for eolian lipids in the Pleistocene off Cape Bojador and lipid geochemistry of a Cretaceous mudstone, DSDP/IPOD Leg 47A. *Init. Repts. Deep-Sea Drilling Project* **47A**, 541–545.

Simoneit, B. R. T. and Mazurek, M. A. (1979b) Lipid geochemistry of Cretaceous sediments from Vigo Seamount, DSDP/IPOD Leg 47B. *Init. Repts. Deep-Sea Drilling Project* **47B**, 565–570.

Sinclair, G. D. and Dymond, D. K. (1973) Distribution and composition of extractives in jack pine trees. *Can. J. For. Res.* **3**, 516–521.

Spyckerelle, C., Greiner, A. C., Albrecht, P. and Ourisson, G. (1977) Aromatic hydrocarbons from geological sources. Part IV. An octahydrochrysene derived from triterpenes, in oil shale: 3,3,7,12a-tetramethyl-1,2,3,4,4a,11,12,12a-octahydrochrysene. *J. Chem. Res. (S)*, 1977, 332–333; *(M)*, 1977, 3801–3828.

Styan, W. B. (1976) Plankton and early fatty acid diagenesis in a fjord lake, British Columbia. Unpubl. B.Sc. thesis, Univ. British Columbia, 55 pp.

Tan, Y. L. and Heit, M. (1981) Biogenic and abiogenic polynuclear aromatic hydrocarbons in sediments from two remote Adirondack lakes. *Geochim. Cosmochim. Acta* **45**, 2267–2279.

Vlad, P. F., Russo, A. G. and Koltsa, M. N. (1975) Diterpene hydrocarbons from *Pinus pallasiana* oleoresin. *Khim. Prir. Soedin.* **11**, 257–258.

Wakeham, S. G., Schaffner, C., Giger, W., Boon, J. J. and De Leeuw, J. W. (1979) Perylene in sediments from the Namibian Shelf. *Geochim. Cosmochim. Acta* **43**, 1141–1144.

Wakeham, S. G., Schaffner, C. and Giger, W. (1980a) Diagenetic polycyclic aromatic hydrocarbons in Recent sediments: Structural information obtained by high performance liquid chromatography. In *Advances in Organic Geochemistry, 1979* ed. by Douglas, A. G. and Maxwell, J. R. Pergamon Press, Oxford, pp. 353–363.

Wakeham, S. G., Schaffner, C. and Giger, W. (1980b) Polycyclic aromatic hydrocarbons in Recent lake sediments — II. Compounds derived from biogenic precursors during early diagenesis. *Geochim. Cosmochim. Acta* **44**, 415–429.

Wetzel, R. G. (1975) *Limnology*. Saunders, Philadelphia, 743 pp.

Williams, P. M., Mathews, W. H. and Pickard, G. L. (1961) A lake in British Columbia containing old sea-water. *Nature (London)* **191**, 830–832.

Yamaoka, Y. (1979) Identification of terpenoid compounds in the sediment of Hiro Bay by gas chromatography–mass spectrometry. *Agric. Biol. Chem.* **43**, 1143–1144.

Zinkel, D. F. and Conner, A. H. (1973) Diterpenes of *Pinus quadrifolia*. *Phytochemistry* **12**, 938–939.

Advances in Organic Geochemistry 1981, pp. 299–308
© John Wiley & Sons Limited, 1983

Alkyl Esters in Recent Sediments of Two Productive Lakes

P. A. Cranwell

Freshwater Biological Association, The Ferry House, Ambleside, Cumbria LA22 0LP, UK

Alkyl esters isolated from recent sediments of two productive lakes consisted mainly of C_{24}–C_{36} saturated constituents, among which iso- and anteiso-branched esters were almost as abundant as straight-chain esters. The similarity in molecular composition of corresponding branched-chain esters from the two sites, determined by gas chromatography-mass spectrometry, and the structures of these esters, together suggest that they originate from the microbial populations associated with decomposition of organic matter in productive lakes. The presence of *cis*- and *trans*-monoenoic esters in the sediments is also reported. Straight-chain saturated C_{38}–C_{50} esters, present in two sediment sections from Crose Mere but only in the oldest sediment from Upton Broad, showed a predominance of homologues with an even chain length, characteristic of a higher-plant origin. In these sediments the bimodal chain-length distribution of saturated esters suggests that the esters are characteristic of discrete source organisms and are not products of resynthesis.

INTRODUCTION

The solvent-extractable lipids (geolipids) occurring in recent aquatic sediments have been used as biological markers for the source organisms which contributed organic matter to the sediment (Eglinton *et al.*, 1979). Long-chain alkyl esters (wax esters) occur widely in living organisms (Kolattukudy, 1976) and show variation in chain length, degree of unsaturation and extent of branching. These features have potential value for distinguishing sedimentary input derived from different sources, thus the alkyl esters of higher plants consist almost entirely of even carbon number straight-chain saturated esters in the C_{32}–C_{64} region (Tulloch, 1976), although the range is often smaller. The chain lengths of wax esters in marine organisms, however, lie in the range C_{26}–C_{42}, and unsaturated alkyl and acyl moieties occur widely (Sargent *et al.*, 1981).

Mass spectrometric determination of the specific alcohol–acid combinations present in an isomeric mixture of saturated straight-chain esters (Aasen *et al.*, 1971) gives additional detail about ester composition and may aid identification of the origin of sedimentary alkyl esters. Detailed compositional data of long-chain esters isolated from sediments have been reported for three sites. A marine diatomaceous sediment contained C_{32}–C_{44} saturated esters (Boon and de Leeuw, 1979), a chain length range consistent with several sources, including zooplankton, although the absence of unsaturation is not typical of zooplankton. C_{28}–C_{32} wax esters detected in an algal mat and sediment of a high altitude Andean lake (Simoneit *et al.*, 1980) were attributed to microbial input. Saturated C_{32}–C_{52} alkyl esters showing a predominance of constituents having an

even carbon number, characteristic of higher plant waxes, were identified in recent sediments of an oligotrophic Scottish loch (Cranwell and Volkman, 1981). Differences in molecular composition occur between esters of the same chain length isolated from these sites.

Branched-chain esters have been reported in a variety of organisms (Wheeler and Holmlund, 1975). Among these the freshwater ciliate *Tetrahymena pyriformis* was the only feasible source of such esters in aquatic sediments, however the only branched-chain esters previously reported in aquatic sediments appear to be esters of phytanic acid (Boon and de Leeuw, 1979).

Analysis of recent sediments from two eutrophic freshwater lakes has shown the presence of alkyl esters in the C_{24}–C_{36} range, including abundant saturated branched-chain constituents and minor unsaturated esters which are now reported. In some horizons C_{38}–C_{50} esters showing even carbon predominance, as previously found in Loch Clair (Cranwell and Volkman, 1981), were also present.

EXPERIMENTAL

Sites

The Norfolk Broads, East Anglia, were formed by flooding of peat excavations around the 14th and 15th centuries. Upton Broad (area, 0.5 km², max. depth 1.4 m; grid reference TG 389134), in the valley of, but not connected with the River Bure, is surrounded by drained grazing marsh and extensive alder woodland which has developed over lacustrine sediments. The broad contains abundant submerged macrophytes and there are no tidal fluctuations or other regular water movement. The sediment, obtained with a pneumatic corer (Mackereth, 1969), consisted of soft organic and calcareous deposits about 75 cm thick, overlying wood peat. The uppermost 15 cm was stained green, below which was a pale buff zone, gradually darkening with increasing depth, while the underlying peat was dark brown. A similar core, dated using ^{210}Pb (Moss *et al.*, 1979), shows an acceleration in deposition rate since 1935 when an increase in trophic status occurred. The sections analysed were 0–6 cm, from the uppermost green deposits, 20–30 cm, deposited about 1920–1950, and 55–65 cm, from the earliest lacustrine stage prior to 1600 AD.

Crose Mere (area, 0.15 km²; max. depth 9.2 m) is a productive lake of the Shropshire–Cheshire plain (grid ref. SJ 430305), fed mainly by the sub-surface flow of groundwater from a catchment (area 2.1 km²) consisting of pasture and arable land. The seasonal phytoplankton succession and physical limnology have been studied (Reynolds 1973a, b). The surficial sediments are uncompacted, flocculent and calcareous. Alkyl esters were isolated from the 0–12 cm and 40–60 cm sections: major lipid classes in three sections from the uppermost 40 cm of this profile have been reported (Cranwell, 1977, 1978, 1980).

Extraction and isolation of esters

Sediment sections were stored at −20° prior to analysis. Wet sediment was extracted three times with chloroform–methanol (1:2) at room temperature, followed by extraction with chloroform, first at room temperature, then under reflux (Soxhlet). The crude lipids, obtained from the combined extracts, were purified by repeated extraction with boiling heptane to give, on evaporation of the solvent, the solvent-extractable lipids. The neutral portion was separated by column chromatography into three fractions of increasing polarity (Cranwell, 1978). The intermediate fraction was separated by thin-layer chromatography (TLC) (Skipski *et al.*, 1965) and alkyl esters were isolated from a band having the mobility of authentic hexadecyl octadecanoate. Saturated and unsaturated esters were separated by TLC on silica gel containing 10% silver nitrate, developing with hexane–diethyl ether (9:1) to give five bands. Aliquots of these sub-fractions were saponified and the alcohols and fatty acids were separately isolated by standard methods (Cranwell and Volkman, 1981).

Gas chromatography and mass spectrometry

Mixtures of alkyl esters up to C_{36} were analysed by gas chromatography (GC) using a vitreous silica column (25 m × 0.25 mm i.d.) coated with SE–30, temperature programmed from 180° to 275° at 3°/min using hydrogen carrier gas and flame ionization detection. In a typical GC trace (Fig. 1), each peak consists of a number of esters differing in alkyl and acyl groups but having the same overall carbon number and branching pattern (except for some minor constituents described later). Saponification products were similarly analysed, using 120° as the initial temperature; alcohols were derivatized as trimethylsilyl ethers and fatty acids as methyl esters. Unsaturated saponification products were analysed on a glass column (25 m × 0.35 mm i.d.) coated with SP 1000. Ester fractions containing C_{24}–C_{50} constituents were analysed on a 15 m × 0.35 mm i.d.

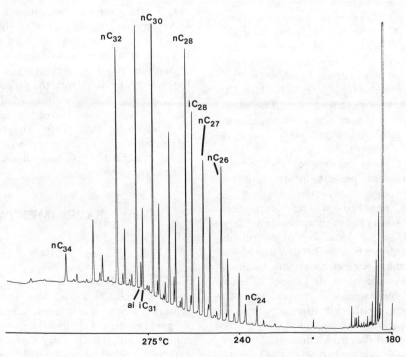

Fig. 1. Gas chromatogram of saturated alkyl esters from Upton Broad sediment (0–6 cm). Conditions: Vitreous silica capillary column (25 m × 0.25 mm i.d.) coated with SE–30, temperature programmed 180–275°/3°/min., using hydrogen as carrier gas at 0.5 kPa inlet pressure and flame ionization detector. (Peak identification: n = normal, i = iso-, ai = anteiso branching.)

Table 1

Abundance of saturated and unsaturated alkyl esters in lacustrine sediments.

Source	Depth (cm)	Organic carbon (%)	Yield[a]	Abundance[b] Saturated	Abundance[b] Unsaturated	C₂₄–C₃₆ Normal	C₂₄–C₃₆ Branched	≥C₃₈
Upton Broad	0–6	14.2	8.8	4900	1220	66	34	—
Upton Broad	20–30	8.3	18.8	7280	900	55	45	—
Upton Broad	55–65	10.0	3.3	450	50	70	12	18
Crose Mere	0–12	10.8	3.0	1200	210	33	53	14
Cross Mere	40–60	9.5	0.6	210	10	40	38	22
Loch Clair	0–10	8.7	0.01	1100	—	2	—	98

(Chain length distribution[c], C₂₄–C₃₆)

[a] Weight of alkyl esters as percentage of neutral extractable lipids.
[b] Expressed as parts C per 10⁶ parts organic carbon in sediment, assuming carbon content of 80% in alkyl esters.
[c] As percentage of saturated esters.

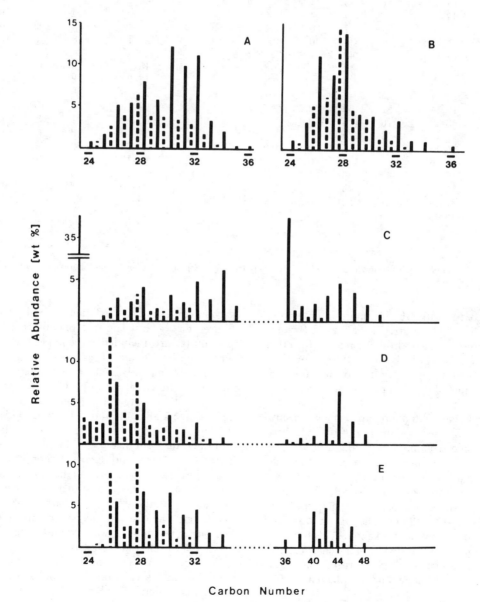

Fig. 2. Percentage composition of saturated esters from Upton Broad (A, B and C, in order of increasing depth) and Crose Mere (D and E, in order of increasing depth) sediments. Solid lines depict straight-chain compounds, dotted lines depict the combined abundance of iso- and anteiso- singly-branched esters having the carbon number of the higher adjacent normal homologue. Esters in which both alkyl and acyl groups are branched have been omitted.

Table 2

Molecular composition of straight-chain saturated alkyl esters in sediments from Upton Broad and Cross Mere.

Chain length	Alcohol–Acid	% of chain length[a]		% of total esters[a]		Chain length	Alcohol–Acid	% of chain length[a]		% of total esters[a]	
24	14–10	70		0.8		32	16–16	67	(52)	2.4	(2.1)
	15–9	23		0.3			17–15	14	(29)	0.5	(1.2)
	13–11	7		0.1			15–17	9	(4)	0.3	(0.2)
25	15–10	60		2.0			18–14	8	(14)	0.3	(0.6)
	14–11	21		0.7		33	17–16	55	(65)	0.6	(1.1)
	16–9	17		0.6			16–17	33	(28)	0.4	(0.5)
26	16–10	56	(82)	6.2	(4.5)		18–15	10	(6)	0.1	(0.1)
	15–11	29	(6)	3.3	(0.3)	34	18–16	49	(58)	0.4	(0.9)
	14–12	15	(12)	1.7	(0.6)		16–18	27	(18)	0.2	(0.3)
27	16–11	44	(42)	4.0	(1.1)		17–17	23	(24)	0.2	(0.4)
	15–12	41	(36)	3.7	(0.9)	36	18–18	97		35.9	
	17–10	11	(20)	1.0	(0.5)	38	20–18	32	(8)	0.6	(0.1)
	14–13	4		0.4			18–20	28		0.5	
28	16–12	76	(77)	10.6	(5.3)		22–16	27	(92)	0.5	(1.4)
	15–13	11	(5)	1.5	(0.3)		24–14	5		0.1	
	17–11	8	(7)	1.1	(0.4)		16–22	5		0.1	
	18–10	3	(7)	0.4	(0.4)	40	24–16	43	(22)	0.8	(0.9)
	14–14	2	(4)	0.3	(0.2)		22–18	18	(16)	0.3	(0.7)
29	16–13	42	(49)	1.8	(2.1)		20–20	16	(57)	0.3	(2.4)
	17–12	39	(42)	1.6	(1.8)		18–22	10	(5)	0.2	(0.2)
	15–14	13	(8)	0.5	(0.3)		16–24	8		0.1	
	18–11	5	(tr)	0.2	(tr)	42	26–16	36	(20)	1.0	(1.0)
30	16–14	51	(56)	2.1	(3.9)		22–20	33	(67)	0.9	(3.2)
	18–12	20	(10)	0.8	(0.7)		20–22	21	(9)	0.5	(0.5)
	17–13	13	(29)	0.5	(2.0)		24–18	10	(3)	0.3	(0.1)
	15–15	10	(3)	0.4	(0.2)	44	22–22	42	(80)	1.9	(5.8)
	14–16	6	(2)	0.3	(0.1)		26–18	29	(20)	1.3	(1.5)
31	16–15	47	(36)	1.1	(1.4)		28–16	16		0.7	
	15–16	26	(5)	0.6	(0.2)		24–20	12		0.6	
	17–14	21	(50)	0.5	(1.9)	46	24–22	52		1.7	
	18–13	5	(9)	0.1	(0.4)		22–24	29		1.0	
							23–23	12		0.4	
							26–20	7		0.2	

[a] C_{24}–C_{34} esters isolated from Upton Broad 20–30 cm, C_{36}–C_{46} esters isolated from Upton Broad 55–65 cm. Figures in parentheses refer to Cross Mere (40–60 cm). tr = trace.

glass column coated with SE–30, programming from 180–345°/3°/min. Quantitative analyses of alkyl esters were obtained using a 'dropping needle' injection system (Cranwell and Volkman, 1981) and an Infotronics 304 computing integrator to measure peak area; the reproducibility of duplicate determinations was ±4%.

Computerized gas chromatography–mass spectrometry (C–GC–MS) used a Finnigan 9610 GC, fitted with a vitreous silica column (25 m × 0.2 mm i.d.), for esters up to C_{36}, or a 10 m × 0.32 mm i.d. column for fractions containing esters up to C_{50}. The GC was coupled to a Finnigan 4000 quadrupole filter mass spectrometer. Mass spectral data were acquired and edited using an INCOS 2300 data system. Iso- and anteiso-branched alkanols and alkanoic acids obtained by saponification were identified from the characteristic fragmentation of the methyl ethers (Karlsson et al., 1973) and methyl esters (Ryhage and Stenhagen, 1960), respectively.

RESULTS

The abundance of saturated and unsaturated esters, the proportion of branched chain esters and the organic

carbon content of the sediments are given in Table 1; figures for Loch Clair, an oligotrophic site studied previously, are included for comparison. Alkyl esters were the major neutral free lipid component in Upton Broad 0–6 cm and 20–30 cm sediments, whereas in surficial sediment from Loch Clair the abundance of esters, relative to organic carbon, was much lower than that of free n-alkanols and n-alkanoic acids (Cranwell, 1981). The distribution of the saturated esters in shown in histogram form in Fig. 2. The bimodal distributions in the Crose Mere and deepest Upton Broad sediments show the greater complexity of the short-chain esters, the absence of branched constituents among the higher homologues and the high even carbon predominance of the latter. The distribution pattern above C_{37} in these sediments resembles that previously reported in Loch Clair (Cranwell and Volkman, 1981).

The molecular composition of co-eluting saturated straight-chain esters from Upton Broad and Crose Mere (40–60 cm), determined from the relative intensities of the $RCO_2H_2^+$ ions in average mass spectra obtained from each GC peak, is given in Table 2, using the short-hand notation of Aasen et al. (1971) in which the alcohol precedes the acid. A more exact treatment would take

Table 3

Molecular composition of branched chain saturated alkyl esters from Upton Broad 20–30 cm.

Chain length	Branch[a]	Alcohol–Acid	Percent of GC peak	Percent total esters	Chain length	Branch[a]	Alcohol–Acid	Percent of GC peak	Percent total esters
25	i,n —	15–10	77	0.6	29	ai,n	16–13	59	0.5
	ai,n	16–9	15	0.1			17–12	34	0.3
		14–11	7	0.05			18–11	3	0.03
26	i,i	16–10	96	0.3	30	i,i	16–14	59	0.6
		14–12	3	0.01			18–12	39	0.4
26	i,n	16–10	76	3.9	30	i,n —	16–14	51	1.9
		14–12	19	1.0		ai,n	18–12	36	1.4
27	i,n	15–12	48	2.8			17–13	7	0.3
		16–11	40	2.4	31	i,ai †	14–17	39	0.15
		17–10	9	0.5		n,10Me	16–15	37	0.15
27	ai,n	16–11	52	0.2			17–14	16	0.06
		17–10	25	0.1	31	i,n	16–15	39	0.4
		15–12	15	0.07			17–14	26	0.3
28	i,i	16–12	97	2.0			15–16	23	0.2
28	i,n	16–12	92	13.0			18–13	10	0.1
		15–13	3	0.35	31	ai,n	16–15	67	0.3
		14–14	2	0.25			17–14	15	0.06
29	i,i	16–13	82	0.2			15–16	9	0.04
		17–12	11	0.03			18–13	9	0.04
		15–14	7	0.02	32	i,i	16–16	76	0.2
29	i,ai	16–13	50	0.1			18–14	23	0.06
		17–12	49	0.1	32	n,10Me	15–17	98	0.5
29	i,n	17–12	47	1.9	32	i,n	16–16	77	0.9
		16–13	36	1.4			18–14	11	0.1
		15–14	12	0.5			17–15	8	0.1
		18–11	5	0.2	33	n,10Me	16–17	99	0.9
					33	i,n	16–17	62	0.3
							17–16	34	0.15

[a] i = iso-branching, ai = anteiso-branching, 10 Me = 10-methyl substituent, n = straight-chain. Designations can apply to alkyl or acyl moiety, subject to restrictions imposed by composition of saponification products; 10-methylhexadecanoic acid was only mid-chain branched constituent. †not fully resolved; — mass spectra averaged over both components.

into account the intensities of other ions (Aasen et al., 1971) but in spectra obtained from the quadrupole mass spectrometer these were of low intensity (5–10% of $RCO_2H_2^+$) and would not significantly alter the calculated proportions. Average mass spectra were used since mass fragmentography of the $RCO_2H_2^+$ ions showed that the ester constituents of each GC peak eluted at slightly different retention times.

The molecular composition of branched-chain esters (Table 3) was calculated by assuming, in the absence of authentic reference compounds, that the intensity of the $RCO_2H_2^+$ ions reflects the abundance of the corresponding ester species whether the alkyl or acyl chain is branched. The site of branching in compounds eluting between the straight-chain homologues was tentatively assigned from their equivalent chain length (ECL) values. Ackman (1972) showed that monomethyl substitution in the iso position of fatty acid methyl esters gave an increment in the ECL of 0.62, anteiso branching gave an increment of 0.71, both figures referring to a non-polar GC phase; similar values are obtained for branched alcohols. Analyses of the alcohols and acids released on saponification (Table 4) confirm the branching pattern deduced from ECL values and also show that the minor constituents must contain iso or anteiso branching in both alkyl and acyl moieties, consistent with ECL values calculated by assuming

additivity of increments for each substituent. The branched-chain esters in Crose Mere (40–60 cm), for which molecular compositions are not reported, closely resembled the corresponding products in Upton Broad sediment in alcohol–acid pairing.

Features of the mass spectra may enable the type of branching in the alcohol moiety to be determined, by analogy with the spectra of other branched-chain lipids. The m/e 56 to m/e 57 ion intensity ratio is higher (0.38 to 0.48) in esters having ECL values characteristic of one iso-branch than in the straight-chain esters (0.24–0.30 for $nC_{24}–nC_{42}$). Esters with ECL values indicating that both alkyl and acyl groups are iso-branched showed an even higher ratio (ca. 0.72). Correspondingly, esters with ECL values characteristic of anteiso branching show an enhanced m/e 70:57 peak ratio (0.39–0.46) compared with straight-chain isomers (0.25–0.30). Methyl ethers of long-chain iso and anteiso branched alkanols give mass spectra showing strong diagnostic fragment ions at m/e 56 and 70, respectively (Karlsson et al., 1973). These strong fragment ions do not occur in mass spectra of iso- and anteiso-branched fatty acid methyl esters (Ryhage and Stenhagen, 1960), thus, by analogy, it is suggested that branching in the alcohol group produces the enhanced m/e 56,70 fragment ions observed in mass spectra of branched-chain esters. The low m/e 56:57 and 70:57 ratios in the C_{32} and C_{33} esters assigned n and 10-

Table 4

Composition of alkanols and alkanoic acids obtained by saponification of saturated esters from Upton Broad 20–30 cm sediment. (See footnote to Table 3 for explanation of symbols.)

Compound	Percentage composition	
	Alkanols	Alkanoic acids
$n\text{-}C_9$	—	0.7
$i\text{-}C_{10}$	—	2.7
$n\text{-}C_{10}$	—	10.5
$i\text{-}C_{11}$	—	0.7
$ai\text{-}C_{11}$	—	0.2
$n\text{-}C_{11}$	—	10.7
$i\text{-}C_{12}$	—	16.6
$n\text{-}C_{12}$	—	25.8
$i\text{-}C_{13}$	—	1.3
$ai\text{-}C_{13}$	—	1.3
$n\text{-}C_{13}$	0.6	5.7
$i\text{-}C_{14}$	0.6	3.3
$n\text{-}C_{14}$	7.1	4.7
$i\text{-}C_{15}$	1.4	0.5
$ai\text{-}C_{15}$	0.3	0.8
$n\text{-}C_{15}$	18.9	2.6
$i\text{-}C_{16}$	14.6	0.8
$n\text{-}C_{16}$	40.5	5.8
$10Me\text{-}C_{16}$	—	2.1
$i\text{-}C_{17}$	0.9	0.2
$ai\text{-}C_{17}$	0.7	0.2
$n\text{-}C_{17}$	8.1	1.1
$i\text{-}C_{18}$	2.2	—
$n\text{-}C_{18}$	4.1	1.0
$n\text{-}C_{20}$	—	0.1

Me branching in the respective alkyl and acyl chains (Table 3), from the incremental ECL value (0.38) and presence of 10-methylhexadecanoic acid after saponification, confirm the absence of esters containing iso- and anteiso- or di-anteiso-branching. These esters would show incremental ECL values of 0.33 and 0.42, respectively, and may not be resolved from the mid-chain singly-branched ester. The analogous C_{31} ester consists of the $n14$–10-Me16 alcohol–acid pairing mixed with iso/anteiso di-branched esters, using the same criteria.

The chain-length range, TLC mobility, saponification products and the inferred structural characteristics of the unsaturated esters from Upton Broad (20–30 cm) are shown in Table 5. Two monoenoic and two dienoic ester fractions were obtained. As the TLC mobility of an authentic *cis*-monoenoic ester corresponded to the slower-running monoenoic ester fraction, the faster-running component was believed to be *trans*-unsaturated (Morris, 1966). Saponification of the total esters from Upton Broad (0–6 cm), followed by argentation TLC of the fatty acid methyl esters, showed the presence of *trans*-unsaturated acids on the basis of their co-chromatography with authentic *trans*-18:1ω9. Authentic *trans*-unsaturated alcohols were not available for TLC comparison with the neutral saponification product which was resolved into saturated and total unsaturated alcohols only, hence the stereochemistry of the alkyl group is unknown.

GC–MS analysis of the least polar monoenoid ester fraction gave the molecular composition shown in Table

Table 5

Analysis of unsaturated esters from Upton Broad 20–30 cm sediment.

TLC band[a] R_f	GLC			Saponification products[b]		Ester structures[c]
	Chain length	Major peak	Other features	Acids	Alcohols	
0.55–0.65	C_{30}–C_{36}	C_{34}	branched compounds, nC_{odd}	n.d.	n.d.	Saturated–*trans*-monoene
0.43–0.52	C_{30}–C_{36}	C_{32}	branched compounds, nC_{odd}	n.d.	n.d.	Saturated–*cis*-monoene
0.30–0.40	C_{28}–C_{36}	C_{34}	C_{even} dominant	n16:1ω7,ω9; n18:1ω7,ω9; n14:1; n14:0–18:0. 80% monoenes	16:1(2), 18:1(2), phytol, n14–18:0 75% monoenes	Monoene–monoene (*trans–cis* or *trans–trans*?)
0.18–0.28	C_{32}–C_{38}	C_{34}	C_{even} dominant	n16:1ω7,ω9; n18:1ω7,ω9; n14,15,17:1; n12,14–16:0. 85% monoenes	n14,16,18:1(2); n16:0 87% monoenes	Monoene–monoene (*cis–cis*?)

[a] Silica gel containing 10% silver nitrate, developed with hexane–ether (9:1). Saturated esters, R_f 0.72–0.85; authentic 16:0–18: *cis* 1ω9, R_f 0.45–0.50.

[b] Percentage of monoenes based on GLC peak area. Site of unsaturation given, where authentic material available for co-elution study. Number of unsaturated alcohol isomers in parentheses. n.d.-not determined.

[c] Alkyl-acyl pairing; where alkyl and acyl chains differ in saturation or stereochemistry, the assignments given are interchangeable. Saponification of total esters from Upton 0–6 cm sediment, followed by argentation TLC of fatty acid methyl esters, showed presence of *trans* 16:1 and 18:1 acids, by comparison of TLC mobility with authentic compounds.

Table 6

Molecular composition of *trans*-monoenoic alkyl esters isolated from Upton Broad 20–30 cm sediment.

Chain length[a]	Alcohol–Acid	Per cent GC peak	Per cent of total esters
br30	16:0–14:1	61	0.7
	14:0–16:1	39	0.4
n30	14:0–16:1	72	2.7
	16:0–14:1	15	0.6
	16:1–14:0	13	0.5
br31	NA		1.9
n31	15:0–16:1	92	4.2
	16:1–15:0	8	0.4
br32	16:0–16:1	95	7.3
	14:0–18:1	3	0.2
	16:1–16:0	2	0.2
n32	16:0–16:1	65	9.0
	14:0–18:1	16	2.2
	16:1–16:0	13	1.8
	18:1–14:0	5	0.7
br33	NA		3.5
n33	15:0–18:1	78	8.0
	17:0–16:1	16	1.6
	18:1–15:0	6	0.6
br34	16:0–18:1	95	11.9
	18:0–16:1	5	0.6
n34	16:0–18:1	87	21.4
	18:1–16:0	5	1.2
	18:0–16:1	4	1.0
	16:1–18:0	3	0.7
br35	NA		2.8
n35	17:0–18:1	92	5.2
	18:0–17:1	8	0.4
n36	NA		3.8

[a] br = branched chain, n = straight chain. NA = not analysed. In absence of saponification data, no assignment of branching to alkyl or acyl chain is possible.

6, calculated as described by Spencer (1979). Intense peaks in unsaturated esters occur at $(RCO-1)^+$ and RCO^+ if the acid moiety is unsaturated and at $(R^1-1)^+$ if the alcohol is unsaturated (Spencer, 1979; Vajdi *et al.*, 1981); ions due to the saturated moiety are much less abundant. Combinations of two odd-chain moieties to give an even chain monoenoid ester cannot be estimated because of coincident diagnostic ions. A moderately intense ion at $(RCO-43)^+$, coincident with the $(RCO-1)^+$ ion of the unsaturated acyl moiety with three fewer carbon atoms, could make quantitative results inaccurate, however weaker ions associated with the saturated group suggest that chain lengths of the major unsaturated alkyl and acyl moieties within an ester cluster only differ by two carbon atoms (Table 6).

Some resolution is observed in the GC trace of peaks corresponding to straight-chain esters in all four unsaturated ester fractions. The identification of at least two series of both *cis* and *trans* monoenoic acids on saponification suggests that partial resolution of ω7 and ω9 unsaturated esters occurs, as reported by Russell and Volkman (1980).

Esters which are mono-unsaturated in both alkyl and acyl moieties were major constituents of the dienoic esters, based on saponification studies (Table 5). The presence of small amounts of saturated compounds in the saponification products may indicate that minor unassigned GC peaks in these products were di-unsaturated.

DISCUSSION

Upton Broad and Crose Mere are eutrophic lakes having an anoxic hypolimnion during the summer months. Organic matter, especially labile compounds such as unsaturated lipids and chlorophyll pigments, is well preserved under these anoxic conditions which result from intense activity by decomposer organisms in the water column and at the sediment surface. Sedimentary geolipids widely used as biological markers of sedimentary source materials include *n*-alkanes, *n*-alkanoic acids, *n*-alkanols and sterols (stenols + stanols). In the three homologous series of free lipids compounds below C_{20} have been attributed to autochthonous input, while higher homologues are characteristic of allochthonous input derived from higher-plant sources (Cranwell, 1978). Recently, preferential diagenesis of lower homologues has been observed in sediments (Cranwell, 1981 and references therein) although compounds below C_{20} have been found in 10 000-year-old sediments and are believed to provide a qualitative record of autochthonous input (Giger *et al.*, 1980). Among the sterols the $C_{29}\Delta^5$-stenol and related 5α-stanol have been regarded as indicators of terrestrial input (Huang and Meinschein, 1976).

In Upton Broad surficial sediment the bimodal distributions of free *n*-alkanes and *n*-alkanols, in which C_{17} and C_{16}, respectively, are dominant, the distribution of *n*-alkanoic acids, in which C_{16} is dominant with very small input of homologues above C_{18}, the small proportion (20%) of C_{29} sterols, all indicate a dominance of autochthonous sources of sedimentary organic matter, consistent with the high contemporary trophic status.

The intermediate section (20–30 cm) showed a slight predominance of C_{24} over C_{16} in the *n*-alkanols, a more marked dominance of C_{29} over C_{17} in the *n*-alkanes and an increasing proportion of C_{22}–C_{30} *n*-alkanoic acids, although C_{16} remained dominant. These changes, compared to the surficial sediment, may be attributed to selective diagenesis of lower homologues as the C_{29} sterol content is similar to that of the surface sediment, but shows an increase in the 5α-stanol:Δ^5 stenol ratio, characteristic of sterol diagenesis under anoxic conditions (Gaskell and Eglinton, 1975). The low input of terrestrial origin in these two sections is consistent with the absence of alkyl esters having more than 36 carbon atoms.

Essentially unimodal distributions of free *n*-alkanes and *n*-alkanols, maximizing at C_{29} and C_{26}, respectively, occurred in Upton Broad (55–65 cm). Among the *n*-alkanoic acids the abundance of C_{26} exceeded that of C_{16} while the C_{29} sterol component was 40% of the total. These features indicate that input from terrestrial detritus was higher than in the upper horizons, consistent with the presence of C_{38}–C_{50} esters, however the abundance of the C_{16} acid (8% of the total) and the C_{27} sterol component (15% of the total) suggest a much higher autochthonous input than in Loch Clair sediment of similar age, *ca*. 400 years, which contained negligible amounts of esters below C_{38} (Cranwell, 1981).

In Crose Mere sediment (0–12 cm) the C_{17} alkane and C_{16} alkanoic acid are less dominant, relative to higher homologues, than in the corresponding lipid classes isolated from Upton Broad (0–6 cm). These observations suggest a greater present-day input from higher-plant sources than in Upton Broad, consistent with the presence of C_{38}–C_{48} alkyl esters. The older sediment from Crose Mere shows the same changes as the Upton Broad profile, the C_{27} alkane and C_{26} alkanoic acid becoming dominant, possibly due to diagenesis of lower homologues, since the combined abundance of the $C_{29}\Delta^5$-stenol and related 5α-stanol (30% of total sterols) is similar to that of the surface sediment.

The molecular compositions of the C_{38}, C_{40} and C_{42} esters from the two sites show differences in their respective dominant constituent (Table 2). In the deepest Upton Broad sediment, these alkyl esters show the same dominant constituent as those in Loch Clair (Cranwell and Volkman, 1981), a feature possibly reflecting inwash of peat shortly after formation of the Broad, since peat was also the dominant source of Loch Clair sediment. Pollen analysis of the sediment profile of Crose Mere (Beales, 1976) shows that peaty soils have never occurred within the drainage basin. At higher molecular weights similarities between Upton Broad and Crose Mere reappear, thus C_{44}, the most abundant chain length above C_{37}, has 22–22 as the dominant constituent at both sites, whereas this molecular species was only a minor C_{44} constituent in Loch Clair sediment. The high abundance of the C_{36} ester, consisting of 18–18 almost entirely, in Upton Broad (55–65 cm) may result from input from a specific source, as adjacent homologues consist of several molecular species.

The dominant feature of the saturated ester distributions in these sediments is the complexity of the C_{24}–C_{34} region (Fig. 1). The straight-chain esters show a low predominance of homologues having an even number of carbon atoms, while branched chain components account for almost 50% of the total esters in some sections (Table 1). The similarity in chain-length distribution and in molecular composition of these shorter-chain esters from the two different sites (Table 2) suggests input from a group of source organisms common to both lakes. The abundance of anaerobic micro-organisms in surficial sediments of productive lakes (Jones *et al.*, 1979) may constitute a source of this suite of esters. The presence of iso- and anteiso-branching in the alkyl and acyl moieties provides circumstantial evidence of a bacterial origin since this branching pattern occurs widely in bacterial lipids (Shorland, 1962; Kaneda, 1977). Mid-chain branching, as in the 10-methyl C_{16} acid obtained on saponification, also occurs in micro-organisms (Ballio and Barcelona, 1971).

The occurrence of wax esters in bacteria has been reviewed (Albro, 1976); simple mono-esters, rarely found, mainly contained C_{16} and C_{18} straight-chain acids. More recent studies, noted by Russell and Volkman (1980), found only straight-chain mainly even-carbon homologues, maximizing in abundance between C_{30} and C_{36}. Among other possible sources, the wax esters of few algal species have been studied (Weete,

1976): none contained branched-chain compounds. Unidentified branched-chain C_{16}–C_{19} alcohols and C_{15}–C_{21} fatty acids were abundant in the saponification products of wax esters from the ciliated protozoan, *Tetrahymena pyriformis*, grown on a chemically-defined medium (Wheeler and Holmlund, 1975). Dense populations of ciliated protozoa occur in organic-rich freshwater environments (Webb, 1961), feeding on bacteria. Natural and cultured populations may differ in lipid composition; long-chain alkyl esters have not been reported in the former.

Additional evidence of a microbial origin for the C_{24}–C_{28} straight-chain and branched-chain saturated esters identified in lacustrine sediments is the isolation by Quirk (1978) of ^{14}C-labelled wax esters having this chain-length range (2 GLC peaks per carbon number) from the incubation of ^{14}C-acetate in a fen peat. The structure of the esters was not defined but the molecular composition was studied. The major constituent of each presumed n-C_{26}–C_{28} ester (the later eluting peaks at these carbon values) in the peat was the same as that of the corresponding peak from these sediments (Table 2). The molecular composition of the earlier-eluting, presumably branched-chain, C_{25}–C_{27} esters from the peat agrees well with averaged values obtained for the corresponding iso- and anteiso-monobranched esters from Upton Broad (Table 3).

Selective diagenesis of the shorter-chain esters in the Crose Mere profile is suggested to explain the absence of components below C_{26} and the reduced abundance, relative to n-C_{28}, of other esters below n-C_{28} in the lower sediment (Fig. 2). The relative abundance of each branched-chain and isomeric straight-chain ester is little changed in the two sediments, suggesting similar initial distributions of these lower molecular weight esters.

In certain organisms, a random combination of the constituent fatty alcohols and fatty acids gives an ester composition and molecular distribution close to that actually found, but in other organisms this is not so (Russell and Volkman, 1980, and references therein). In microbiologically-active sediments, resynthesis of wax esters from the pool of lipids has been postulated (de Leeuw *et al.*, 1977). The presence of two distinct distribution patterns of saturated esters, differing in chain-length range, carbon preference index and branching, as in the surficial sediment from Crose Mere, suggests that here the esters do represent original input rather than products of resynthesis.

Unsaturated alkyl esters occur in marine animals and were first recognized from the unsaturated alcohols and acids liberated by saponification. Surface slicks rich in esters, produced naturally and occasionally washed ashore, consisted of 20:1–14:0, 22:1–14:0 and 20:1–16:0 esters, indicative of a calanoid copepod source (Sargent *et al.*, 1981); the 20:1 and 22:1 alcohols have also been detected in wax esters of a marine sediment (Sargent *et al.*, 1977). A wider range of mono- and dienoic esters was identified to whale oil by analysis of the alkoxy–acyl combinations using GC–MS (Spencer, 1979).

In the freshwater environment, wind-blown foam accumulating on the shore of an Andean lake was shown to contain 15:0–9:1 and 15:0–11:1 alkyl esters attributed to aquatic micro-organisms (Simoneit *et al.*,

1980). Esters of phytenic acid appear to be the only unsaturated esters previously identified in a lacustrine sediment (de Leeuw *et al.*, 1977).

Mono- and di-unsaturated esters occur in a number of bacterial groups (Russell and Volkman, 1980 and references therein); more highly-unsaturated esters have recently been detected in bacterial lipids by CI–MS (Christopher *et al.*, 1980). *Cis* Δ^9 and *cis* Δ^{11} monoenoic esters and dienoic esters having combinations of these positional isomers within the alkyl and acyl moieties were detected by Russell and Volkman (1980). *Trans*-monoenoic acids have been found in a marine bacterial isolate (Gillan *et al.*, 1981) and marine sediment (Perry *et al.*, 1979), suggesting that these acids and the esters containing them are biological markers of bacterial input. In general, bacterial wax esters contain all of the fatty acids occurring in bacterial lipids (Albro, 1976). Another acidic constituent more abundant in bacteria than in other organisms is *cis*-vaccenic acid (18:1ω7). The more-polar di-unsaturated esters giving *cis*-18:1ω7 on saponification may, therefore, also be of bacterial origin.

CONCLUSIONS

Sediments from two productive lakes contain the following series of long-chain esters, differing in structure and degree of unsaturation:

(1) Straight-chain saturated C_{24}–C_{50} esters in which the short-chain homologues (up to C_{34}) show a low predominance of even chain length members. Esters above C_{36} show a dominance of even-carbon homologues, consistent with a higher-plant origin.

(2) C_{24}–C_{33} esters containing an iso- or anteiso-branch in either the alkyl or acyl chain, with minor products branched in both chains. These esters are postulated to be of bacterial origin, based on their branching pattern and the isolation of radiolabelled similar esters from incorporation of ¹⁴C-labelled acetate in peat.

(3) Monounsaturated C_{30}–C_{36} esters with *trans*- or *cis*-stereochemistry, the former suggested to be of bacterial origin.

(4) Two series of esters in which both alkyl and acyl groups are monounsaturated.

The molecular composition of the shorter-chain saturated esters shows a close similarity between corresponding constituents from the two sites; differences between the C_{38}, C_{40} and C_{42} esters possibly result from differences in terrestrial source material.

The bimodal distribution of saturated esters, seen in some of the sediments, is attributed to direct input of esters from aquatic micro-organisms and from higher-plant detritus.

Acknowledgements

I thank Dr D. Livingstone and Mr P. V. Allen for providing the Upton Broad sediment core and Dr C. S. Reynolds and Mr M. C. Thompson for assistance in obtaining the sediment from Crose Mere. I thank Professor G. Eglinton and Dr J. R. Maxwell (Bristol University) for use of GC–MS facilities provided by grants GR3/2951 and GR3/3758 from the Natural Environment Research Council, and Mrs A. P. Gowar for assistance in processing GC–MS data.

REFERENCES

Aasen, A. J., Hofstetter, H. H., Iyengar, B. T. R. and Holman, R. T. (1971) Identification and analysis of wax esters by mass spectrometry. *Lipids* **6**, 502–507.

Ackman, R. G. (1972) Influence of methyl substituent position on retention times in the GLC of higher monomethyl-branched fatty acid esters and hydrocarbons. *J. Chromatogr. Sci.* **10**, 243–246.

Albro, P. W. (1976) Bacterial waxes. In *Chemistry and Biochemistry of Natural Waxes*, ed. by Kolattukudy, P. E. Elsevier, Amsterdam, pp. 419–445.

Ballio, A. and Barcellona, S. (1971) Identification of 10-methyl branched fatty acids in *Microbispora parva* by combined gas chromatography–mass spectrometry. *Gazz. Chim. Ital.* **101**, 635–636.

Beales, P. W. (1976) Palaeolimnological studies of a Shropshire mere. Ph.D. Thesis, University of Cambridge, UK.

Boon, J. J. and de Leeuw, J. W. (1979) The analysis of wax esters, very long mid-chain ketones and sterol ethers isolated from Walvis Bay diatomaceous ooze. *Mar. Chem.* **7**, 117–132.

Christopher, R. K., Duffield, A. M. and Ralph, B. J. (1980) Identification of some neutral lipids of *Thiobacillus thioparus* using gas chromatography-chemical ionization mass spectrometry. *Aust. J. Biol. Sci.* **33**, 737–741.

Cranwell, P. A. (1977) Organic compounds as indicators of allochthonous and autochthonous input to lake sediments. In *Interactions between Sediments and Fresh Water 1976*, ed. by Golterman, H. L. Junk and Pudoc, The Hague and Wageningen, pp. 133–140.

Cranwell, P. A. (1978) Extractable and bound lipid components in a freshwater sediment. *Geochim. Cosmochim. Acta* **42**, 1523–1532.

Cranwell, P. A. (1980) Branched/cyclic alkanols in lacustrine sediments (Great Britain): recognition of *iso-* and *anteiso-*branching and stereochemical analysis of homologous alkan-2-ols. *Chem. Geol.* **30**, 15–26.

Cranwell, P. A. (1981) Diagenesis of free and bound lipids in terrestrial detritus deposited in a lacustrine sediment. *Org. Geochem.* **3**, 79–89.

Cranwell, P. A. and Volkman, J. K. (1981) Alkyl and steryl esters in a recent lacustrine sediment. *Chem. Geol.* **32**, 29–43.

De Leeuw, J. W., Rijpstra, W. I. C., Boon, J. J., de Lange, F. and Schenck, P. A. (1977) The relationship between lipids from *Fontinalis antipyretica*, its detritus and the underlying sediment: the fate of waxesters and sterolesters. In *Interactions between Sediments and Freshwater 1976*, ed. by Golterman, H. L. Junk and Pudoc, The Hague and Wageningen, pp. 141–147.

Eglinton, G., HajIbrahim, S. K., Maxwell, J. R., Quirke, J. M. E., Shaw, G. J., Volkman, J. K. and Wardroper, A. M. K. (1979) Lipids of aquatic sediments, Recent and ancient. *Philos. Trans. R. Soc. London Ser. A.* **293**, 69–91.

Gaskell, S. J. and Eglinton, G. (1975) Rapid hydrogenation of sterols in a contemporary lacustrine sediment. *Nature (London)* **254**, 209–211.

Giger, W., Schaffner, C. and Wakeham, S. G. (1980) Aliphatic and olefinic hydrocarbons in recent sediments of Greifensee, Switzerland. *Geochim. Cosmochim. Acta* **44**, 119–129.

Gillan, F. T., Johns, R. B., Verheyen, T. V., Volkman, J. K. and Bavor, H. J. (1981) *trans*-Monounsaturated acids in a marine bacterial isolate. *Appl. Environ. Microbiol.* **41**, 849–856.

Huang, W.-Y. and Meinschein, W. G. (1976) Sterols as source indicators of organic materials in sediments. *Geochim. Cosmochim. Acta* **40**, 323–330.

Jones, J. G., Orlandi, M. J. L. G. and Simon, B. M. (1979) A microbiological study of sediments from the Cumbrian lakes. *J. Gen. Microbiol.* **115**, 37–48.

Kaneda, T. (1977) Fatty acids of the genus *Bacillus*: an example of branched-chain preference. *Bacteriol. Rev.* **41**, 391–418.

Karlsson, K. A., Samuelsson, B. E. and Steen, G. O. (1973) Improved identification of monomethyl paraffin chain branching (close to the methyl end) of long-chain compounds by gas chromatography and mass spectrometry. *Chem. Phys. Lipids* **11**, 17–38.

Kolattukudy, P. E. (Ed.) (1976) *Chemistry and Biochemistry of Natural Waxes*. Elsevier, Amsterdam, 459 pp.

Mackereth, F. J. H. (1969) A short core sampler for sub-aqueous deposits. *Limnol. Oceanogr.* **14**, 145–151.

Morris, L. J. (1966) Separations of lipids by silver ion chromatography. *J. Lipid Res.* **7**, 717–732.

Moss, B., Forrest, D. E. and Phillips, G. (1979) Eutrophication and palaeolimnology of two small mediaeval man-made lakes. *Arch. Hydrobiol.* **85**, 409–425.

Perry, G. J., Volkman, J. K., Johns, R. B. and Bavor, H. J. (1979) Fatty acids of bacterial origin in contemporary marine sediments. *Geochim. Cosmochim. Acta* **43**, 1715–1725.

Quirk, M. M. (1978) Lipids of peat and lake environments. Ph.D. Thesis, University of Bristol, UK.

Reynolds, C. S. (1973a) The phytoplankton of Crose Mere, Shropshire. *Br. Phycol. J.* **8**, 153–162.

Reynolds, C. S. (1973b) Growth and buoyancy of *Microcystis aeruginosa* Kütz. emend. Elenkin in a shallow eutrophic lake. *Proc. R. Soc. London Ser. B* **184**, 29–50.

Russell, N. J. and Volkman, J. K. (1980) The effect of growth temperature on wax ester composition in the psychrophilic bacterium *Micrococcus cryophilus* ATCC 15174. *J. Gen. Microbiol.* **118**, 131–141.

Ryhage, R. and Stenhagen, E. (1960) Mass spectrometric studies IV. Esters of monomethyl-substituted long chain carboxylic acids. *Ark. Kemi* **15**, 291–304.

Sargent, J. R., Gatten, R. R. and McIntosh, R. (1977) Wax esters in the marine environment — their occurrence, formation, transformation and ultimate fates. *Mar. Chem.* **5**, 573–584.

Sargent, J. R., Gatten, R. R. and Henderson, R. J. (1981) Marine wax esters. *Pure Appl. Chem.* **53**, 867–871.

Shorland, F. B. (1962) The comparative aspects of fatty acid distribution and occurrence. In *Comparative Biochemistry*, Vol. 3A, ed. by Florkin, M. and Mason, H. S. Academic Press, New York, pp. 1–92.

Simoneit, B. R. T., Halpern, H. I. and Didyk, B. M. (1980) Lipid productivity of a high Andean Lake. In *Biogeochemistry of Ancient and Modern Environments*, ed. by Trudinger, P. A., Walter, M. R. and Ralph, B. J. Australian Academy of Science, Canberra, pp. 201–210.

Skipski, V. P., Smolowe, A. F., Sullivan, R. C. and Barclay, M. (1965) Separation of lipid classes by thin-layer chromatography. *Biochim. Biophys. Acta* **106**, 386–396.

Spencer, G. F. (1979) Alkoxy-acyl combinations in the wax esters from winterized sperm whale oil by gas chromatography–mass spectrometry. *J. Am. Oil Chem. Soc.* **56**, 642–646.

Tulloch, A. P. (1976) Chemistry of waxes of higher plants. In *Chemistry and Biochemistry of Natural Waxes*, ed. by Kolattukudy, P. E. Elsevier, Amsterdam, pp. 235–287.

Vajdi, M., Nawar, W. W. and Merritt, C. (1981) GC/MS analysis of some long chain esters, ketones and propanediol diesters. *J. Am. Oil Chem. Soc.* **58**, 106–110.

Webb, M. G. (1961) The effects of thermal stratification on the distribution of benthic protozoa in Esthwaite Water. *J. Anim. Ecol.* **30**, 137–151.

Weete, J. D. (1976) Algal and fungal waxes. In *Chemistry and Biochemistry of Natural Waxes*, ed. by Kolattukudy, P. E. Elsevier, Amsterdam, pp. 349–418.

Wheeler, M. A. and Holmlund, C. E. (1975) Identification of wax esters in *Tetrahymena pyriformis*. *Lipids* **10**, 260–262.

Advances in Organic Geochemistry 1981, pp. 309–316
© *John Wiley & Sons Limited, 1983*

Comparison of Lipid Compositions in Marine and Lacustrine Sediments

M. J. Leenheer

Cities Service Company, Energy Resources Group, Exploration and Production Research, Box 3908, Tulsa, Oklahoma 74102, USA

P. A. Meyers

Department of Atmospheric and Oceanic Science, The University of Michigan, 2455 Hayward Avenue, Ann Arbor, Michigan 48109, USA

Fatty acids, sterols, fatty alcohols, and alkanes in lacustrine and marine sediment cores have been examined in order to compare differences in the source history and subsequent diagentic processes which have occurred in these different environments. Lacustrine core samples representing large lake environments, obtained from Lake Michigan and Lake Huron, record the most recent 1000 years of sediment deposition. Sediment samples from a small lake environment were obtained from Heart Lake in the Adirondacks and record the last 500 years of this lake's history. Marine samples include cores from a coastal environment — the Wilkinson Basin in the Gulf of Maine — and from an open ocean environment — the Bermuda Rise. Results indicate that different processes are important in the different environments. In the Great Lakes, post-depositional alteration processes, such as preferential degradation of the lipids derived from aquatic sources over those derived from terrigenous sources and preferential removal of unsaturated over saturated components or reduction of double bonds, appear to be important. The Heart Lake sediment core has the greatest amount of terrigenous lipids which are well-preserved due to the high sedimentation rate. In sediments from the Gulf of Maine, as in those from the Great Lakes, reduction processes of preferential removal of unsaturated lipid components appears to be important. Also, conversion of the lipid material from an unbound to a bound form is occurring at this location. In the Bermuda Rise core post-depositional changes appear to be masked by source input related changes or episodic events. Thus, the variations in the character of the lipid material downcore observed among the four environments reflect changes in source inputs, differences in sedimentation rates, and variations in the amount and types of other post-depositional processes which are active at these locations.

INTRODUCTION

Organic matter in subaqueous sediments represents the residue of a variety of aquatic and terrigenous biological inputs which have experienced degradation and alteration during transport and deposition and after burial. Local environments determine the relative importance of different sources of organic matter, so that the organic contents of different places may be dissimilar. Furthermore, changes in local conditions over time as well as post-depositional alterations may be reflected in depth profiles of the organic character of sediments.

Geolipid compositions have been widely employed in geographical and temporal comparisons of subaqueous sediments. Brooks *et al.* (1976, 1977) studied fatty acid and hydrocarbon distributions in modern sediments from three English lakes and from three coastal marine locations. Meyers and Takeuchi (1979) used the same approach to compare 10 sedimentary environments in Lake Huron. Organic matter inputs over long periods of depositional history have been characterized by distri-

butions of fatty acids, alkanes, and sterols in sediments of Mono Lake (Reed, 1977) and Cam Loch (Cranwell, 1977). Sterols appear to be particularly useful source indicators and have been studied in estuarine sediments (Huang and Meinschein, 1976, 1978) and in sediments from a number of marine areas (Lee *et al.*, 1979, 1980). These reports show that geolipid distributions in marine and lacustrine sediments differ with depth and location and reflect both differences in the type and amount of organic matter preserved, and also, variations in the post-depositional alterations which are occurring.

As part of our continuing study of organic matter in the North American Great Lakes, we wished to make a direct comparison of the sediment contents of these large lakes with those of smaller lakes and with those of marine areas. To carry out this comparison, we decided to investigate four classes of geolipids–fatty acids, hydrocarbons, sterols, and alcohols — in each of our sediment samples. This report summarizes the findings of our analyses of aqueous sediment cores from five locations.

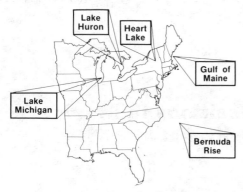

Fig. 1. Locations of sediment cores.

EXPERIMENTAL

Sampling

Sediment cores were obtained from three lacustrine and two marine locations (Fig. 1).

(1) Lake Huron is the second largest of the North American Great Lakes and is oligotrophic. A core from station 18 in 65 m of water in the southeastern part of this lake was obtained. This location is described by Bourbonniere (1979). A sedimentation rate of 0.10 cm/year is estimated by ^{210}Pb and ^{14}C geochronology. Total organic carbon (TOC) values range from 1.7 to 3.0 per cent.

(2) Lake Michigan is the third largest of the Great Lakes. It is oligotrophic like Lake Huron and its organic matter inputs should also be similar. Station 27 in 68 m of water in southern Lake Michigan yielded a 95 cm core for which the sedimentation rate is estimated to be 0.034 to 0.22 cm/year according to ^{137}Cs and ^{14}C dating (Leenheer, 1981). TOC values range from 1.4 to 2.6 per cent.

(3) Heart Lake is a small lake (11 ha) situated within an unpopulated watershed forested with hardwood trees. The lake is considered oligotrophic, although it has experienced productivity fluctuations over its post-glacial history. The core site was near the centre of the lake in 14 m of water, its greatest depth. Sedimentation rate is estimated to be 0.24 to 0.55 cm/year. TOC values ranging from 24 to 30 percent were found in this core.

(4) The Gulf of Maine location was in 250 m of water in the Wilkinson Basin. These coastal marine sediments were highly bioturbated by benthic fauna. Sedimentation rates were estimated to be 0.048 to 0.180 cm/year for this location (Repeta, unpublished manuscript); TOC values were approximately 2 percent.

(5) Deep ocean sediments were obtained from a site located in 4970 m of water on the northern Bermuda Rise in the Atlantic Ocean. They are described in more detail by Leenheer (1981). ^{14}C dating gave a sedimentation range of 0.012 to 0.74 cm/year; TOC values ranged from 0.6 to 1.2 per cent.

Cores were stored in frozen sections or under refrigeration from the time of collection until analysis.

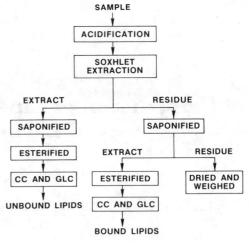

Fig. 2. Sediment extraction scheme.

Sediments from these locations consist of silt-clay biogenic and clastic materials. No major lithologic changes were found in any of the five cores.

Analytical methods

The extraction scheme (Fig. 2) was adapted from that used by Lee *et al.* (1977). After acid treatment to remove carbonates, the sediment samples were Soxhlet-extracted for 48 h with a mixture of toluene/methanol to produce the unbound extract. The residual sediment was then saponified to release lipids more tightly bound within the sediment matrix. This extract was designated the bound extract. Both extracts were esterified and then separated by column chromatography into three fractions which contained the hydrocarbons, fatty acids (as methyl esters), and sterols and alcohols. Trimethylsilyl (TMS) derivatives of the sterol-alcohol fraction were made. All fractions were analyzed by gas chromatography using a 20 m glass capillary column (0.32 mm i.d.) coated with SE–54. Selected samples were also analyzed by combined gas chromatography/mass spectrometry.

RESULTS AND DISCUSSIONS

The definitions of unbound and bound extracts are quite procedure dependent and thus, the initial treatment with acid may have released some bound lipids by hydrolyzing ester linkages. However, the unbound/ bound fractionations of the lipids in this study are similar to the fractionations which others have obtained both with and without initial acid washes (Lee *et al.*, 1977; Nishimura, 1977; Cranwell, 1981). Hence, the affect of the acid wash appears to be minimal.

The TOC values and sedimentation rates differed significantly in the five cores under study. These differences are responsible, in part, for the amount of lipid material preserved in the sediment. The large sedimentation rates which characterize the Heart Lake core result in significant preservation of the lipid material at this location. Likewise, the low sedimentation rates of the Bermuda Rise sample allow little preservation of lipid material; thus, more processes can act upon the

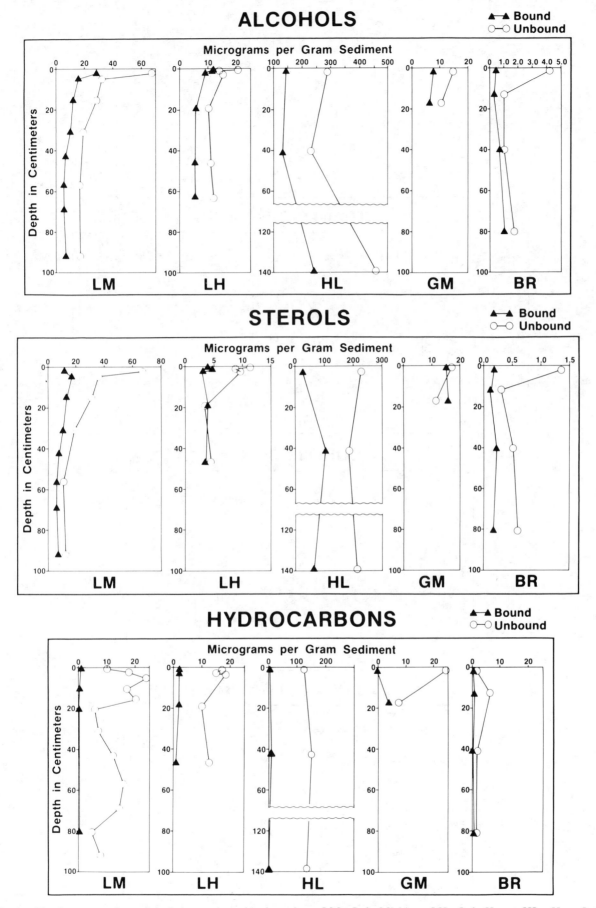

Fig. 3. Total concentrations of alcohols, sterols, and hydrocarbons. LM = Lake Michigan, LH = Lake Huron, HL = Heart Lake, GM = Gulf of Maine, BR = Bermuda Rise.

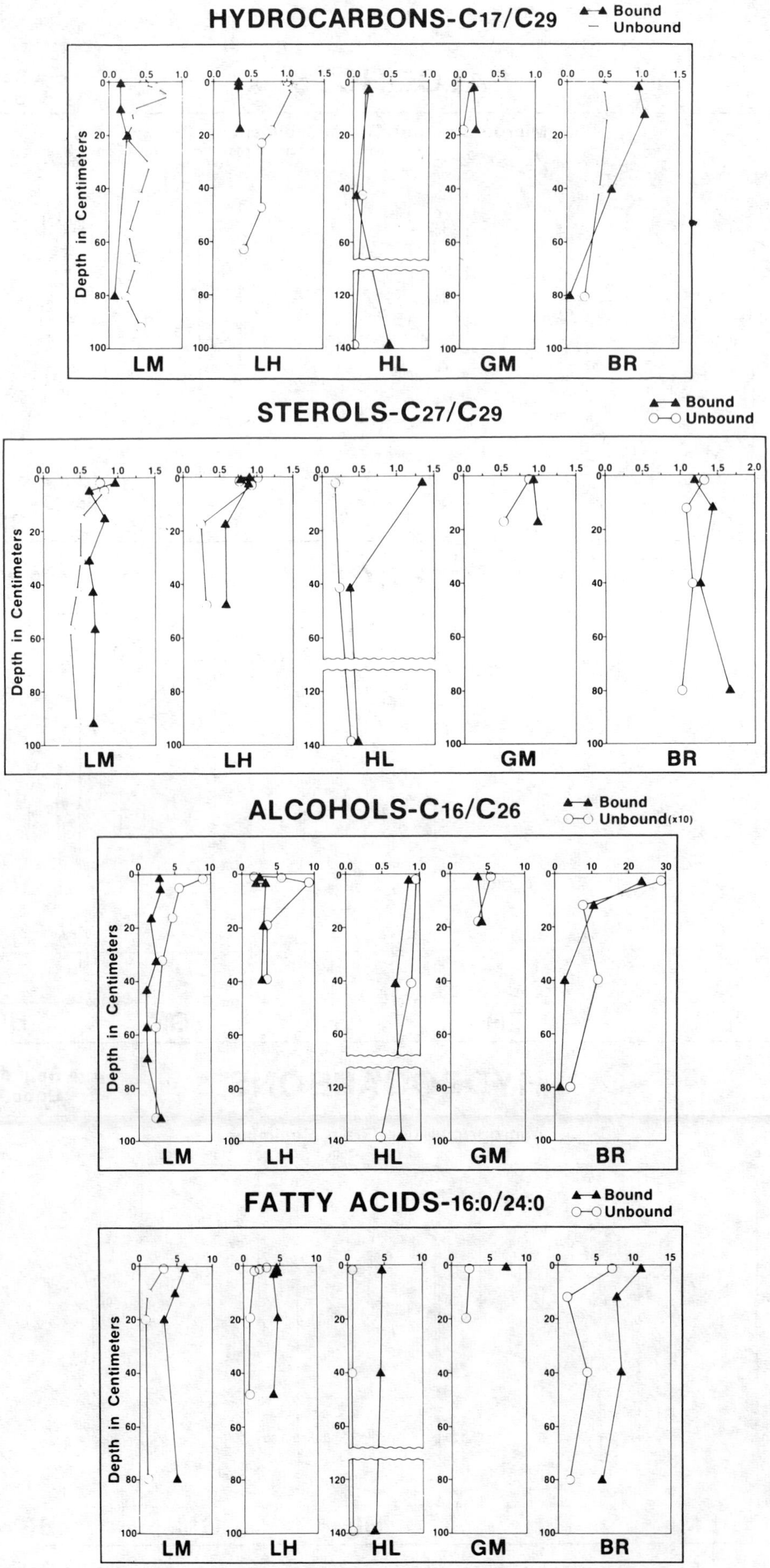

Fig. 4. Possible aquatic/terrigenous indicators represented by ratios of short chain to long chain components of fatty acids, alcohols, sterols and hydrocarbons. Location key is the same as that of Fig. 3.

lipids before burial in the sediment. The Great Lakes and Gulf of Maine sediments have intermediate TOC and sedimentation rates, resulting in greater preservation of lipid material than occurs in the Bermuda Rise sediments.

The results will be presented in terms of three different parameters for the sake of comparison and brevity. Further details are presented by Leenheer (1981). The three parameters illustrate the similarities and differences between the five cores analysed. Total concentrations describe variations in the absolute amounts of lipids found in the different environments. Possible aquatic/terrigenous indicators compare ratios of short chain, characteristically aquatic, components to long chain components which are characteristically derived from higher plants, terrigenous sources. Alteration indicators illustrate cases in which hydrogenation or preferential microbial degradation of the unsaturated components may represent post-depositional alterations.

Total concentrations

Total concentration profiles for hydrocarbons, alcohols, and sterols are shown in Fig. 3. Generally, the unbound lipid concentrations are larger than the bound lipid concentrations in all of the cores analysed. The absolute concentrations in units of $\mu g/g$ sediment, however, vary significantly from core to core with Heart Lake $\gg$ Lake Michigan = Lake Huron = Gulf of Maine > Bermuda Rise sediment concentrations. These concentration variations agree well with the differences apparent from total organic carbon values.

Absolute lipid concentrations in units of mg/g carbon reveal that similar concentrations exist for the lacustrine samples and the Gulf of Maine core with Bermuda Rise sediments still having lower concentrations (Leenheer, 1981). This suggests that the lipid content of the organic material in Heart Lake core is similar to that present in the Great Lakes and the Gulf of Maine while the Bermuda Rise core contains more inextractable organic matter, probably resulting from more weathering before deposition of the open ocean station.

The unbound lipids of the Great Lake cores have similar downcore profiles displaying large decreases in concentrations in the top 20 cm followed by slower decreases below that depth. The initial large decreases in lipid concentration probably represent destructive degradation resulting from microbial activity. These decreases are not as well defined in the hydrocarbon profiles in agreement with Cranwell's (1981) observation that hydrocarbon are less reactive than sterols and alcohols. The bound lipids display only small decreases downcore and, thus, are not as reactive as the unbound extracts. Furthermore, no significant unbound to bound conversion is apparent, which agrees with results obtained by Nishimura (1977) in the lacustrine environment.

Alcohol concentration variations in Heart Lake downcore data indicate a large increase in concentration at the bottom of the core. This probably indicates a change in source input composition or, alternatively, increased preservation due to a sedimentation rate change. A similar increase is also evident in the fatty acid total

concentration data but not in the sterol and hydrocarbon concentration data. An increased sedimentation rate which would preserve the more labile fatty acids and alcohols at depth could account for the increases in their concentrations without corresponding increases in the less reactive sterol and hydrocarbon components.

Gulf of Maine concentration profiles show the downcore decrease in the unbound extract accompanied by an increase in the bound extract concentrations suggesting an unbound to bound conversion which was also observed by Lee *et al.* (1977, 1979) in coastal marine sediments. In all lipid classes, the percent bound increases downcore while the hydrocarbon and sterol bound concentrations also show an absolute increase.

The Bermuda Rise has a decrease in the unbound alcohol and sterol concentrations in the top 15 cm followed by a slight increase in concentrations below that depth (Fig. 3). The bound lipid concentrations vary little with depth. While the decrease in the unbound surficial concentrations may represent microbial degradation, these concentrations are considerably smaller than those present in the other cores and, thus, given the low sedimentation rates at this station, these variations probably result from large scale processes such as turbidity flows and microbial degradation while the lipids were in surficial sediments rather than small scale post-depositional alterations.

Possible aquatic/terrigenous indicators

Several studies have discussed the use of C_{16}–C_{18} lipid components as indicators of aquatic inputs and longer chain components as indicators of higher plants or components contributed from land detritus (Huang and Meinschein, 1979; Nishimura and Koyama, 1977; Lee *et al.*, 1979; Cranwell, 1978; Gearing *et al.*, 1976). For comparison of the different sedimentary environments represented by the five lakes, ratios of possible aquatic/terrigenous inputs are plotted downcore (Fig. 4). Comparison of the surficial values of the aquatic/terrigenous ratios gives the relative amount of aquatic versus terrigenous input to the sediments. The largest ratios for all lipid classes are found in the Bermuda Rise core which are consistent with the location of this core farthest from shore. However, a significant amount of long chain material was still present at this location and is thought to originate from the Canadian Maritime Province by distal turbidite flows (Laine, 1978; Tucholke *et al.*, 1977). The Great Lakes cores and the Gulf of Maine core have similar intermediate ratios, while Heart Lake generally has the lowest ratios, which reflect the largest terrigenous input.

In most lipid classes the unbound extract contains significantly more long chain components than the bound extract. However, C_{17}/C_{29} profiles vary from core to core. Thus, the unbound extract has a more terrigenous character while the bound extract, containing more short chain material, can be characterized as more aquatic.

The downcore profiles of the fatty acid ratios are surprisingly constant for Lake Michigan and Lake Huron. While fatty acid concentrations in the Great

ALTERATION INDICATORS

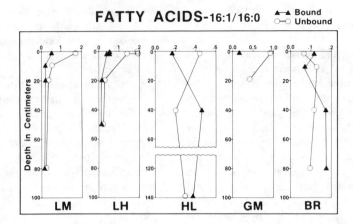

FATTY ACIDS-16:1/16:0

△—△ Bound
○—○ Unbound

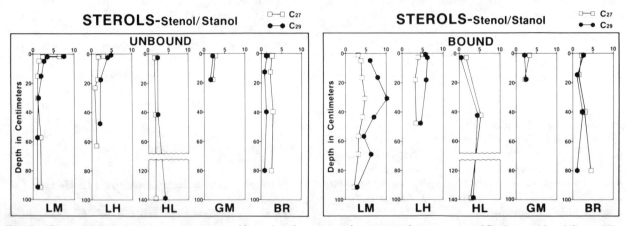

STEROLS-Stenol/Stanol

□—□ C₂₇
●—● C₂₉

UNBOUND

STEROLS-Stenol/Stanol

□—□ C₂₇
●—● C₂₉

BOUND

Fig. 5. Potential alteration processes represented by ratios of unsaturated to saturated components of C_{16} fatty acid and C_{27} and C_{29} sterols. Location key is the same as that of Fig. 3.

Lakes decrease five-fold downcore, the 16:0/24:0 ratios decrease only slightly. Thus, it appears that 16:0 and 24:0 degrade at similar rates downcore. Downcore trends in the fatty acid ratio in Heart Lake and the Gulf of Maine are also relatively constant.

The alcohol, sterol, and hydrocarbon ratios of Lake Huron and Lake Michigan show similar trends downcore. In the unbound extracts, the ratios decrease more rapidly in the surficial sediments suggesting preferential degradation of shorter chain components over longer chain. Such decreases are largest for the alcohol ratios, intermediate for the sterols, and smallest for the alkanes. These variations in rates of decrease demonstrate the relative reactivity of these compound classes and agree with the results obtained by Cranwell (1981). The ratios of the bound extracts remain relatively constant or display a slight decrease downcore. Thus, lipid material of the bound extract appears to be less reactive than that present in the unbound extract.

In Heart Lake, the aquatic/terrigenous ratios do not display a general decrease downcore, but rather vary for the different lipid classes. This indicates that source changes and/or sedimentation rate changes are probably more important in determining the amount of lipid preservation downcore rather than post-depositional alteration processes.

The Gulf of Maine core shows decreases in the unbound lipid ratios downcore accompanied by small

increases in the bound lipid ratios. These demonstrate that the character of the unbound and bound extracts is changing downcore and suggests that unbound to bound conversion is occurring at this location.

The various lipid ratios for the Bermuda Rise sediment core show trends which vary for the different lipids. Since the absolute concentrations are quite small, some of this variation could be due to the small concentration changes which would be magnified in the ratios. As the ratios do not show consistent patterns, they are probably related to large scale processes which would result in source changes at this location rather than post-depositional alterations.

Alteration indicators

Fatty acid and sterol alteration processes discussed here involve the possible hydrogenation of double bonds along with preferential degradation of the unsaturated compounds (Fig. 5) as evidenced by decreases in selected ratios of unsaturated to saturated components. The decreases in the alteration ratios of the unbound extracts of the Great Lakes cores suggests that preferential degradation and/or hydrogenation occurs more rapidly in the top 20 cm of sediment than in the underlying sediment. The more rapid decrease of the C_{27} stenol/stanol ratio in the surficial sediments over the C_{29} ratio suggests that the C_{27} sterols are more labile than the C_{29} sterols, which agrees with the findings of Nishimura (1978). The bound lipid extracts in the Great Lakes cores also show a decrease in the fatty acid ratios downcore. The sterol data for the bound fractions of these cores, however, do not show similar decreases, indicating that they are probably more resistant to reduction and/or degradation than the fatty acids.

The preferential removal of unsaturated components or the reduction of double bonds discussed for the Great Lakes is not as evident in the other sample locations. The Heart Lake core is characterized by small alteration indicator ratios indicating that only small amounts of the unsaturated components are present in the surface sediment. Downcore variations in the Heart Lake ratios probably represent source related changes rather than alteration processes. As in the Great Lakes cores, a decrease is seen in the alteration indicator ratios of the Gulf of Maine cores for the unbound lipids suggesting that reduction or preferential degradation of the unsaturated components is occurring. The surface values of the Gulf of Maine are smaller than those of the Great Lakes cores and probably result from the severe bioturbation occurring in the Gulf of Maine which dilute the surface ratios with more reduced sterols and fatty acids. Similar to the Heart Lake core, the Bermuda Rise core contains only small amounts of the unsaturated components and, thus, any variations in the ratios are probably source-related rather than process-related.

CONCLUSIONS

Comparison of the absolute concentrations of lipids present in the five cores reveal that those in Heart Lake $\gg$ Lake Michigan = Lake Huron = Gulf of Maine $>$ Bermuda Rise. Similarly, the terrigenous character of these sedimentary environments is largest for Heart Lake, intermediate for the Great Lakes and the Gulf of Maine, and smallest for the Bermuda Rise core. Comparison of lipid compositions present in sediment cores taken from different marine and lacustrine environments reveals differences in source history and post-depositional alteration processes which have occurred.

In the Great Lakes, where the cores appear to be homogeneous, several alteration processes seem to be active after deposition. These include destructive degradation, preferential degradation of aquatic over terrigenous lipids, and preferential removal of unsaturated over saturated components or reduction of double bonds. These downcore changes probably represent alteration changes rather than changes in input since greater alteration was observed for the more reactive lipid components.

In contrast, Heart Lake, a small oligotrophic lake, is characterized by high total organic carbon input and high sedimentation rates which cause preservation of lipid material regardless of chain length or amount of saturation. Downcore changes, in this case, probably represent source changes or sedimentation rate changes.

The Gulf of Maine sediments, representing a coastal marine environment, are severely bioturbated and little change was expected over the 20 cm core. However,

some preferential removal of unsaturated over saturated components or reduction of double bonds does appear to occur and, unlike the Great Lakes, the conversion from unbound to bound forms is also postulated. This latter conversion could be related to the character of the input organic matter.

The open ocean station, located on the Bermuda Rise, has lower organic carbon and lower sedimentation rates than the other locations. The deposited lipid material is quite weathered as evidenced by the small alteration indicator ratios. Downcore variations probably represent source-related changes or episodic events rather than post-depositional alterations.

Acknowledgements

We would like to thank J. W. Farrington, Woods Hole Oceanographic Institution, and D. R. Whitehead, Indiana University, for providing some of the sediment samples, and C. Sutton and J. Zumberge, Cities Service Research Laboratory, for helpful comments and suggestions. Financial support from the geochemical section of the National Science Foundation and from the Petroleum Research Fund, administered by the American Chemical Society, is gratefully acknowledged. Special thanks to K. D. Flessland and O. E. Kawka for technical analyses; M. Draughon for typing the manuscript; and J. Sommers for drafting the figures.

REFERENCES

Bourbonniere, R. A. (1979) Geochemistry of humic matter in Holocene Great Lakes sediments. Ph.D. dissertation. University of Michigan.

Brooks, P. W., Eglinton, G., Gaskell, S. H., McHugh, D. J., Maxwell, J. R. and Philp, R. P. (1976) Lipids of recent sediments, part I: Straight-chain hydrocarbons and carboxylic acids of some temperate lacustrine and sub-tropical lagoonal/tidal flat sediments. *Chem. Geol.* **18**, 21–38.

Brooks, P. W., Eglinton, G., Gaskell, S. J., McHugh, D. J., Maxwell, J. R. and Philp, R. P. (1977) Lipids of recent sediments, part II. Branched and cyclic alkanes and alkanoic acids of some temperate lacustrine and sub-tropical lagoonal/tidal flat sediments. *Chem. Geol.* **20**, 189–204.

Cranwell, P. A. (1977) Organic Geochemistry of Cam Loch (Sutherland) sediments. *Chem. Geol.* **230**, 205–221.

Cranwell, P. A. (1978) Extractable and bound lipid components in a freshwater sediment. *Geochim. Cosmochim. Acta* **42**, 1523–1532.

Cranwell, P. A. (1981) Diagenesis of free and bound lipids in terrestrial detritus deposited in a lacustrine sediment. *Org. Geochem.* **3**, 79–89.

Gearing, P., Gearing, J. N., Lytle, T. F. and Lytle, J. S. (1976) Hydrocarbons in 60 northeast Gulf of Mexico shelf sediments: A preliminary survey. *Geochim. Cosmochim. Acta* **40**, 1005–1017.

Huang, W. Y. and Meinschein, W. G. (1976) Sterols as source indicators of organic materials in sediments. *Geochim. Cosmochim. Acta* **40**, 323–330.

Huang, W. Y. and Meinschein, W. G. (1978) Sterols in sediments from Baffin Bay, Texas. *Geochim. Cosmochim. Acta* **42**, 1391–1396.

Huang, W. Y. and Meinschein, W. G. (1979) Sterols as ecological indicators. *Geochim. Cosmochim. Acta* **43**, 739–745.

Laine, E. P. (1978) Geological effects of the Gulf Stream system in the North American basin. Ph.D. dissertation. Massachusetts Institute of Technology/Woods Hole Oceanographic Institution Joint Program in Oceanography.

Lee, C., Farrington, J. W. and Gagosian, R. B. (1979) Sterol geochemistry of sediments from the Western North Atlantic Ocean and adjacent coastal areas. *Geochim. Cosmochim. Acta* **43**, 35–46.

Lee, C., Gagosian, R. B. and Farrington, J. W. (1977) Sterol diagenesis in recent sediments from Buzzards Bay, Massachusetts. *Geochim. Cosmochin Acta* **41**, 985–992.

Lee, C., Gagosian, R. B. and Farrington, J. W. (1980) Geochemistry of sterols in sediments from Black Sea and the southwest African shelf and slope. *Org. Geochem.* **2**, 103–113.

Leenheer, M. J. (1981) Use of lipids as indicators of diagenetic and source-related changes in Holocene sediments. Ph.D. dissertation. University of Michigan.

Meyers, P. A. and Takeuchi, N. (1979) Fatty acids and hydrocarbons in surficial sediments of Lake Huron. *Org. Geochem.* **1**, 127–138.

Nishimura, N. (1977) The geochemical significance in early sedimentation of geolipids obtained by saponification of lacustrine sediments. *Geochim. Cosmochim. Acta* **41**, 1817–1823.

Nishimura, M. and Koyama, T. (1977) The occurrence of stanols in various living organisms and the behavior of sterols in contemporary sediments. *Geochim. Cosmochim. Acta* **41**, 379–385.

Nishimura, M. (1978) Geochemical characteristics of the high reduction zone of stenols in Suwa sediments and the environmental factors controlling the conversion of stenols into stanols. *Geochim. Cosmochim. Acta* **42**, 349–357.

Reed, W. E. (1977) Biogeochemistry of Mono Lake, California. *Geochim. Cosmochim. Acta* **41**, 1231–1245.

Tucholke, B. E., Vogt, P., McCave, I. N., Murdmaa, I. O., Rothe, P., Houghton, R. L., Galehouse, J., Kaneps, A., McNulty, C., Okada, H., Kendrick, J. and Demurs, K. (1977) *Initial Reports of the Deep Sea Drilling Project*, 43, US Government Printing Office, Washington, D.C.

Advances in Organic Geochemistry 1981, pp. 317–322
© *John Wiley & Sons Limited, 1983*

Incorporation of Plant Lipids into Recent Sediments

A. Février, D. Tusseau and A. Saliot

Laboratoire de Physique et Chimie Marines de l'Université Pierre et Marie Curie, ERA CNRS, Tour 24, 4 place Jussieu, 75230 Paris Cedex 05, France

F. Gadel

Laboratoire de Sédimentologie Marine de l'Université de Perpignan, ERA CNRS, avenue de Villeneuve, 66 Perpignan, France

During early diagenesis, sedimentary organic matter becomes progressively altered by biological and physicochemical processes. However, several studies have shown that this organic matter often consists of two fractions — a solvent extractable (SE) fraction and a component closely associated with the organo-mineral matrix and commonly termed the bound (B) fraction. In this study, the role of the SE and B lipids in sedimentary processes has been monitored over several months by examining the sterols, fatty acids and n-alkanes of a green alga (*Ulva lactuca*), a sea-grass (*Zostera marina*), and the underlying sediment in a Mediterranean lagoon. The SE and B lipid fractions change independently with time in both the plants and the sediment. In the plant material, for instance, microbial degradation appears to have a pronounced effect on the distribution and concentrations of B lipids but this is not apparent in the SE fraction. In the surficial sediment, inputs from the alga and from various other contributors can be discerned. The SE lipid pool also contains compounds ascribable to short term inputs of terrestrial vegetal material or benthic contributions. The incorporation of plant lipids into the sediment occurs through a highly pronounced microbial step and essentially into the bound fraction of the sediment. This study shows that certain essential features of organic sedimentation are associated with the bound fraction and that this fraction contains evidence of many of the processes occurring in the sediments and in the water column.

INTRODUCTION

Biological cycles are the major processes involved in the production and degradation of organic matter in aquatic environments. Only a few per cent of the primary productivity escapes from degradation occurring in the water column (Degens and Mopper, 1976) and at the sea–sediment interface material sedimenting from the water column is further degraded. The incorporation of compounds issued from superficial primary productivity into sediments has been estimated to be in the range 0.1–0.01% (Welte, 1970). The ultimate step of the incorporation of organic substances into sediments is still not completely understood.

Two different approaches have been used to study the latter processes. First, standard compounds (usually radiolabelled) have been introduced into natural sediments and their temporal fate investigated (Gaskell *et al.*, 1976; de Leeuw *et al.*, 1977; Cahet and Cadel, 1979). Secondly, the decomposition of algal mats, a process known to result in sediment formation, has been studied (Schultz and Quinn, 1973; Harrison and Mann, 1975a, b; Cardoso *et al.*, 1976; Cranwell, 1976a, b; Lee *et al.*, 1980). In both types of experiments, the importance

of microbial activity in sediment formation processes has been underlined.

During early diagenesis, recent organic matter becomes progressively changed by biological and physicochemical reactions. As a consequence, only the resistant fraction of initially biosynthesized matter accumulates in the sediments whilst the non-resistant fraction is consumed and altered by microscopic and macroscopic benthic organisms. These two fractions could be considered separately during the analysis of plants and sediments. The non-resistant fraction is easily extractable, whilst the resistant fraction is closely associated with the organo-mineral matrix and necessitates a more rigorous extraction procedure rarely used in routine studies (Van Vleet and Quinn, 1979; Février, 1981).

This paper deals with a study of the role of the two different matter pools: solvent extractable (SE) and bound (or closely associated to complex organic substances and minerals) fraction (B), in sedimentary processes. Two problems have been examined using lipid markers. Considering the fate of plant mats and background natural inputs to the sediment, what is the fate of lipid markers according to their initial association with other chemical species? What is the role of

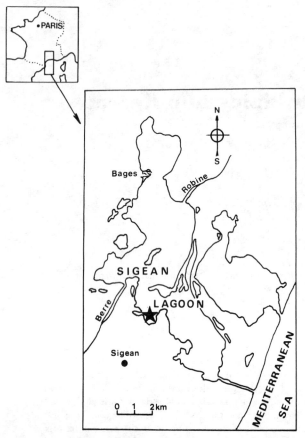

Fig. 1. Experimental site (★) for algal mat incorporation into sediments of Sigean lagoon.

microorganisms in the evolution of lipids in the plants during their decay and in the sediment after incorporation?

METHODS

Two independent experiments have been conducted in a Mediterranean natural lagoonal environment (Fig. 1). Two plant mats, a green alga *Ulva lactuca* and the eelgrass *Zostera marina*, have been maintained 5 m apart by nets close to the sediment. The surface sediment and the decaying plant material were each sampled at the beginning of the experiments in May 1977 and again three times during the following months in July, November and December 1977.

The sediments were sieved (500 μm). The fraction <500 μm and the plant material were immediately freeze dried and stored ($t < 30$ °C) prior to extraction. Solvent extractable lipids (SE) were obtained using chloroform in a soxhlet apparatus (2 × 24 h, the solvent being changed). The lipid extract, after removal of elemental sulphur on a copper column, was saponified; SE fatty acids and unsaponifiable compounds such as hydrocarbons and sterols were isolated by ether extraction.

The second step was conducted, following the method described by Farrington and Quinn (1971), leading for unconsolidated and vegetal material to a lipid fraction equivalent to kerogen-bound lipids from ancient

sediments. The soxhlet residue was saponified for 4 h (250 ml KOH/MeOH 0.5 N per 100 g of dry material). Bound lipids (B) were obtained by ether extraction. After acidification by HCl 6 N, B fatty acids were obtained by ether extraction.

SE and B acids were methylated (BF$_3$ 14% in methanol) and analysed by gas liquid chromatography (GC) using a Girdel 3000 gas chromatograph with flame ionization detector.

Two columns were used: (1) stainless steel, 4 m long, 2.2 mm internal diameter (i.d.) packed with 1% Dexsil 300 on gas chrom Q 80–100 mesh; temperature programmed from 120 to 320 °C at a rate of 6 °C min^{-1}; carrier gas: helium at a flow of 30 ml min^{-1}; (2) glass, 30 m long, 0.25 mm i.d., coated with Carbowax PEG 20M; temperature programmed from 70 to 190 °C at a rate of 2 °C min^{-1}; carrier gas: helium at a flow of 2 ml min^{-1}.

SE and B alkanes and sterols were separated by adsorption chromatography on a microcolumn filled with 2/3 Davison SiO$_2$ 100–200 mesh and 1/3 alumina Merck 80 and by elution with a series of solvents of increasing polarity. Alkanes were analysed by GC using a Girdel 3000 gas chromatograph with a stainless steel column, 30 m long, 0.25 mm i.d., coated with SE 52; temperature programmed from 120 to 270 °C at a rate of 3 °C min^{-1}; carrier gas: helium at a flow of 2 ml min^{-1}.

Sterols after derivatization as acetates (acetic anhydride–pyridine, 2:3; 24 h) were purified by thin layer chromatography on SiO$_2$ and analysed by GC and GC/mass spectrometry. This GC/MS was performed using a Girdel 3000/Nermag R 10 10/sidar computer unit. The glass column used was 40 m long, 0.35 mm i.d., coated with SE 52; temperature programmed from 230 to 270 °C at a rate of 0.2 °C min^{-1}; carrier gas: helium at a flow of 2 ml min^{-1}.

RESULTS AND DISCUSSION

Evolution of the two lipid pools (SE and B) in the algal mat

The concentrations of SE and B lipids in the alga *Ulva lactuca* are given in Table 1.

SE fatty acids and *n*-alkanes represent only a minor part (5.3 and 11.1%) of the respective total analysable lipids (SE + B), of the fresh alga. The result of two

Table 1

Solvent extractable (SE) and bound (B) sterols, *n*-alkanes and fatty acids concentrations in the alga *Ulva lactuca* mat, in μg g^{-1}, at the initial algal deposition time (May) and two months later (July)

		May	July
Sterols	SE	5.2	7.9
	B	2.2	4.1
N-alkanes	SE	0.9	2.1
	B	7.0	0.6
Fatty acids	SE	22.9	65.0
	B	412.0	531.0

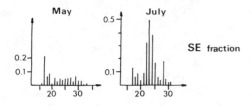

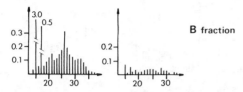

Fig. 2. *N*-alkane distributions (absolute concentrations in μg g .^{1} of dry sediment versus carbon number) for the solvent extractable (SE) and bound (B) fractions of the algal mat *Ulva lactuca* at the initial deposition time (May) and two months later.

months of degradation is an enhancement of the SE fractions, slight for the fatty acids (from 5.3 to 10.9%), highly pronounced for *n*-alkanes (from 11.1 to 77.5%). Contrarily the SE/SE + B sterol ratio is practically constant during the experiment (from 70.3 to 65.8%). The constancy of this ratio for sterols is probably related to their importance as membrane constituents since they are universally encountered in microorganisms, vegetals and animals. Following this hypothesis, it appears that *n*-alkanes and fatty acids are more indicative of active processes such as bacterial degradation, fresh biosynthetic inputs by associated fauna and epiphytes and leaching and loss of *Ulva* fragments.

The observation of marker patterns, for example *n*-alkanes (Fig. 2), confirms the differences in chemical composition and amounts of the two SE and B pools. At the beginning of the experiment, a very small quantity of *n*-alkanes is solvent extractable (0.9 μg g^{-1}), with *n*-C_{17} as predominant compound, although 7.0 μg g^{-1} are present as bound lipids with two major compounds, *n*-C_{15} and *n*-C_{17}. Two months later, the greater proportion of *n*-alkanes is associated with the SE fraction although the total *n*-alkane concentrations are less than for the fresh alga. In the SE fraction of the decayed alga at this

time, a remarkable *n*-alkane distribution is observed, maximizing at *n*-C_{23}, which cannot be related to the initial distribution of *n*-alkanes in the B fraction which maximized at *n*-C_{26}. This may be due to the development of protozoans (Harrison and Mann, 1975a) or epiphytes (Volkman *et al.*, 1980).

The role of such microorganisms during the plant decay can be observed through the variation in concentrations of other microbial markers such as *anteiso* C_{15} and C_{17} fatty acids, monounsaturated C_{16} and C_{18} fatty acids and stanols. The first two criteria have been used for the alga as shown in Fig. 3.

An increase of microbial marker concentrations is observed between the two steps of the plant decay; this increase is considerably higher in the bound fraction, a consequence of the complex structure of bacterial cell-wall materials, as shown by Philp and Calvin (1976).

Is there a direct incorporation of algal material into the sediment, for both the SE and B pools? What is the role of microorganisms in this transfer? To answer these questions, we have observed the two SE and B markers in the surficial sediment.

Pathways of organic matter transfer to the sediment

General data relative to the sediment for the period May–November 1977 are given in Table 2.

Although the organic carbon content of the surficial sediment does not show any marked evolution, each matter pool shows great variation, a general tendency being an increase of the free fraction (SE) between May and July, followed by a decrease between July and November. The bound fraction is characterized by a regular increase during the experiment, except for the *n*-alkanes.

The two different SE and B marker pools are indeed influenced by very different processes; the free lipid pool by natural organic matter inputs of the lagoon, the bound by the direct and indirect (through microbial action) incorporation by the algal mat.

Evolution of the SE lipid pool. SE *n*-alkane distribution patterns for the sediment are given in Fig. 4. Of note is the superposition over an initial poor background of *n*-alkanes in the range C_{15}–C_{30} of another

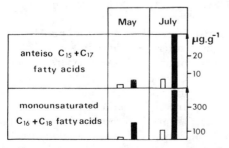

Fig. 3. Evolution of microbial marker concentrations (C_{15} + C_{17} *anteiso* fatty acids and C_{16} + C_{18} monounsaturated fatty acids) in the algal mat. Data are presented in μg g^{-1} of dry sediment both for the SE (□) and B (■) pools.

Table 2

Evolution of organic carbon content (in % of dry sediment) and sterols, fatty acids, *n*-alkanes concentrations (in μg g^{-1} of dry sediment) for surficial sediment located under an *Ulva lactuca* algal mat, between May and November 1977

		May	July	November
Organic carbon %		2.23	2.30	2.26
Sterols	SE	5.4	15.6	9.7
	B	0.9	1.4	2.0
Fatty acids	SE	16.6	30.1	17.5
	B	23.5	28.1	35.3
N-alkanes	SE	0.5	2.1	1.4
	B	0.1	0.7	0.1

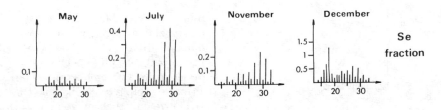

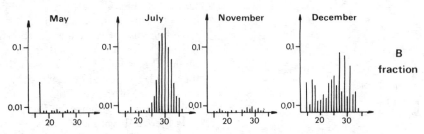

Fig. 4. SE and B *n*-alkane distributions (absolute concentrations in μg g^{-1} of dry sediment versus carbon number) for surficial sediment located under an *Ulva lactuca* mat between May, initial deposition time, and December 1977.

Table 3

Percentage composition of SE and B sterols from Sigean sediment samples, during the algal mat *Ulva lactuca* experiment period (*less than 0.1%)

	SE sterols			B sterols		
	May	July	November	May	July	November
24-norcholestadienol	0.3	—	0.6	0.9	0.5	0.9
22-*cis* dehydrocholesterol	—*	0.7	—	—	0.2	0.4
22-*trans* dehydrocholesterol	5.3	1.7	2.7	3.0	4.0	5.5
Cholesterol	37.9	11.9	21.5	19.9	14.2	13.7
Cholestanol	—	1.1	2.2	4.3	5.1	2.4
Brassicasterol and/or crinosterol	5.1	3.9	6.1	5.0	5.0	6.5
22-*trans* dehydrocholestanol	3.5	2.9	3.3	4.6	2.9	3.3
24-methylene cholesterol	3.5	3.4	5.4	6.2	10.6	9.7
Campesterol and/or dihydrobrassicasterol	7.4	4.6	5.3	7.7	7.3	8.0
Stigmasterol and/or poriferasterol	10.8	27.3	16.8	18.1	18.0	17.9
β-Sitostanol	—	3.7	2.0	6.0	4.4	4.3
β-Sitosterol	26.2	36.2	31.7	20.3	25.1	23.6
Avenasterol	—	2.6	2.4	—	3.2	3.8
Total sterol concentrations (μg g^{-1} of dry sediment)	5.4	15.6	9.7	0.9	1.9	2.1

contribution in the range C_{21}–C_{33}, marked by a strong odd carbon predominance. This terrestrial input which is not related to *Ulva* is important in July (2.1 μg g^{-1} of *n*-alkanes) and remains visible until December.

This incorporation in the sediment of an external terrigenous input in July is also clearly demonstrated by the presence of even carbon fatty acids in the range C_{22}–C_{30} and C_{29} sterols, stigmasterol and β-sitosterol (Table 3).

The direct incorporation of algal material into the sediment in the SE lipids cannot be distinguished through *n*-alkane or fatty acid distributions in the range $<C_{20}$, because they are ubiquitous in plants and sediments, both marine and terrigenous. Nevertheless, this incorporation can be shown by using more specific compounds such as avenasterol. This sterol is present in the original *Ulva* (3% of the SE sterols; 17.3% of the B

sterols). This compound was identified in the sediment just under the algal mat in July and November (Table 3). Sediment collected a few metres from the algal mat did not contain any trace of avenasterol.

Evolution of the B lipid pool. B *n*-alkane distribution patterns are given in Fig. 4. The initial B *n*-alkane content of the sediment is extremely low (0.1 μg g^{-1}). In July, this content increases to reach a value of 0.7 μg g^{-1}; this unexpected regular *n*-alkane distribution maximizing at *n*-C_{30}, also encountered under the *Zostera marina* mat, suggests an original input, not related to either the algal material or terrestrial inputs observed in the SE fraction. Although we cannot definitely rule out pollution of the sediment lagoon, the more probable explanation is to be found in an input through benthic organisms or transported particulates.

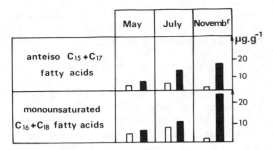

Fig. 5. Evolution of microbial marker concentrations (C_{15} + C_{17} *anteiso* fatty acids and C_{16} + C_{18} monounsaturated fatty acids) in the surficial sediment located under an *Ulva lactuca* mat between May, initial deposition time, and November 1977. Data are presented in $\mu g\ g^{-1}$ of dry sediment, for both the SE (□) and B (■) pools.

In November and in a more pronounced manner in December, a new *n*-alkane distribution pattern is observed characterized by a slight odd carbon predominance. This distribution is the same as in the July SE fraction, suggesting a possible transfer between the two pools in a period of the order of several months.

Although the concentrations of sterols increase from May ($0.9\ \mu g\ g^{-1}$) to November ($20\ \mu g\ g^{-1}$), no significant differences in their relative distribution were observed. This common distribution, different from the SE fraction (Table 3) is marked by the predominance of the β-sitosterol (around 23%), stigmasterol (around 18%) and cholesterol (around 15%). Of note is the relatively higher proportion of stanols in the B fraction (around 13%) than in the SE one (around 7%).

The direct incorporation of algal material into the sediment as determined by the presence of avenasterol (absent in May, up to 76 ng g^{-1} in November) was also observed in the B fraction.

The significant transfer between the algal mat and the sediment is essentially effected by microbially transformed products. This is apparent from the data shown in Fig. 5, where absolute B specific microbial markers concentrations show an increase during the experiment. This increase parallels that observed for B algal material (Fig. 3). This phenomenon corresponds to an indirect sedimentation process which is not an input of the alga itself, but of products synthesized by microorganisms degrading the alga.

CONCLUSION

During this study of the incorporation of plant lipids into a recent sediment, we have observed a parallel evolution of the two SE and B lipid marker pools, both for the alga and the surficial sediment. A schematic representation of the processes identified and involved in this experiment is presented in Fig. 6.

The first observation is that the SE and B lipid fractions change independently with time in both alga and sediment. It has been shown previously in quite similar experiments by Schultz and Quinn (1973) and Cranwell (1976a, b) that fresh algal material is rapidly degraded in natural environments through microbial action. The action of microorganisms appears to affect the bound compounds greatly but not the SE fraction.

Concerning the evolution of surficial sediments, different inputs are observed both from algal material and the various contributions of the lagoon. The analysis of fatty acids and common sterols does not allow one to identify specific inputs due to the occurrence of these markers in various marine and terrestrial sources and due to the high background levels in the sediment at the beginning of the experiment. Nevertheless, more specific compounds such as avenasterol, odd carbon number *n*-alkanes in the range C_{21}–C_{33}, and *anteiso* C_{15} and C_{17} fatty acids allow the observation of particular processes; e.g. from the avenasterol, a direct incorporation from the algal mat both in the SE and B fractions; from the *n*-alkanes, an important terrestrial input in July essentially in the SE fraction; from *anteiso* fatty acids, the evaluation of bacterial activity.

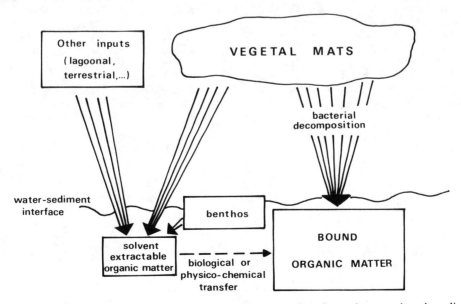

Fig. 6. Synthetic scheme of the different processes involved in the incorporation of organic matter into the sediment in a lagoonal model.

The incorporation of algal mat material is effected not directly as a fresh material but through microbial metabolism and into the bound fraction. Contrarily, the SE lipid pool is indicative of different inputs such as external temporary terrestrial, vegetal or benthic contributions. There is a transfer between the two pools in the order of several months, suggested by the similarity of the SE July and B November and December *n*-alkane patterns.

From these experiments, it is established that the incorporation of plant lipid into a sediment occurs through a highly pronounced microbial step and essentially into an organic complex bound fraction, which has not yet been systematically analysed. These two results described in detail through the *Ulva lactuca* experiment are also confirmed by the incorporation simulation using the marine eelgrass *Zostera marina*. The study of SE markers provides information on short-term changes initiated by seasonal or punctuated inputs. Much information in organic sedimentation is associated with the bound compounds, which provide evidence of many of the processes occurring in sediments and in the water column.

Acknowledgement

We wish to thank the E.N.S.P.M., Institut Francais du Pétrole, for financial support for one of us (A.F.).

REFERENCES

Cahet, G. and Gadel, F. (1979) Addition de molécules organiques simples marquées, à des eaux et des sédiments profonds des côtes Nord-ouest africaines. Observations biologiques et géochimiques. In *Géochimie organique des sédiments marins profonds – ORGON III — Mauritanie, Sénégal, iles du Cap Vert*, ed. by Arnould, M. and Pelet, R. Editions CNRS, Paris, pp. 45–65.

Cardoso, J., Brooks, P. W., Eglinton, G., Goodfellow, R., Maxwell, J. R. and Philp, R. P. (1976) Lipids in recently-deposited algal mats at laguna Mormona, Baja California. In *Environmental Biogeochemistry*, ed. by Nriagu, J. O. Ann Arbor Science Publishers, Ann Arbor, Michigan, pp. 149–174.

Cranwell, P. A. (1976a) Decomposition of aquatic biota and sediment formation: organic compounds in detritus resulting from microbial attack on the algal *Ceratium Hirundinella*. *Freshwater Biol.* **6**, 41–48.

Cranwell, P. A. (1976b) Decomposition of aquatic biota and sediment formation: lipid components of two blue–green algal species and of detritus resulting from microbial attack. *Freshwater Biol.* **6**, 481–488.

Degens, E. T. and Mopper, K. (1976) Factors controlling the distribution and early diagenesis of organic matter in marine sediments. In *Chemical Oceanography*, ed. by Riley, J. P. and Chester, R. Academic Press, London, pp. 60–114.

Farrington, J. W. and Quinn, J. G. (1971) Comparison of sampling and extraction techniques for fatty acids in recent sediments. *Geochim. Cosmochim. Acta* **35**, 735–741.

Février, A. (1981) Les matières organiques à structure complexe des eaux de mer et des sédiments. Interactions avec les traceurs géochimiques. Thèse Doct. Etat. Université P. et M. Curie, Paris, 130 pp.

Gaskell, S. J., Rhead, M. M., Brooks, P. W. and Eglinton, G. (1976) Diagenesis of oleic acid in an estuarine sediment. *Chem. Geol.* **17**, 319–324.

Harrison, P. G. and Mann, K. H. (1975a) Detritus formation from eelgrass (*Zostera marina* L.): the relative effects of fragmentation, leaching and decay. *Limnol. Oceanogr.* **20**, 924–934.

Harrison, P. G. and Mann, K. H. (1975b) Chemical changes during the seasonal cycle of growth and decay in eelgrass (*Zostera marina*) on the Atlantic coast of Canada. *J. Fish. Res. Board Can.* **32**, 615–621.

Lee, C., Howarth, R. W. and Howes, B. L. (1980) Sterols in decomposing *Spartina alterniflora* and the use of ergosterol in estimating the contribution of fungi to detrital nitrogen. *Limnol. Oceanogr.* **25**, 290–303.

de Leeuw, J. W., Simoneit, B. R., Boon, J. J., Rijpstra, W. I. C., de Lange, F., van der Leeden, J. C. W., Correia, V. A., Burlingame, A. L. and Schenck, P. A. (1977) Phytol derived compounds in the geosphere. In *Advances in Organic Geochemistry 1975*, ed. by Campos, R. and Goni, J. Enadimsa, Madrid, pp. 61–79.

Philp, R. P. and Calvin, M. (1976) Possible origin for insoluble organic (kerogen) debris in sediments from insoluble cell-wall materials of algae and bacteria. *Nature (London)* **262**, 134–136.

Schultz, D. M. and Quinn, J. G. (1973) Fatty acid composition of organic detritus from *Spartina alterniflora*. *Estuarine coastal Mar. Sci.* **1**, 177–190.

Van Vleet, E. S. and Quinn, J. G. (1979) Early diagenesis of fatty acids and isoprenoid alcohols in estuarine and coastal sediments. *Geochim. Cosmochim. Acta* **43**, 289–303.

Volkman, J. K., Johns, R. B., Gillan, F. T., Perry, G. J. and Bavor, H. J. Jr. (1980) Microbial lipids of an intertidal sediment. I. Fatty acids and hydrocarbons. *Geochim. Cosmochim. Acta* **44**, 1133–1143.

Welte, D. H. (1970) Organischer Kohlenstoff und die Entwicklung der Photosynthese auf der Erde. *Naturwissenschaften* **57**, 17–23.

Advances in Organic Geochemistry 1981, pp. 323–327
© John Wiley & Sons Limited, 1983

Distribution of Organic Matter in Grain-size Fractions of some Recent Sediments

L. Jocteur Monrozier, M. Benijoly, P. Pillon, F. Andreux and B. Souchier

Centre de Pédologie Biologique, C.N.R.S., B.P. 54501 Vandoeuvre-les-Nancy Cedex, France

R. Pelet

Institut Français du Pétrole, Avenue de Bois-Préau, 92500 Rueil-Malmaison, France

Mechanical dispersion in distilled water was used to separate particle size subfractions from four recent marine deposits. Six classes were obtained (> 100 μm, 100–50 μm, 50–5 μm, 5–0.5 μm, 0.5–0.1 μm and <0.1 μm) and the corresponding organic matter studied. Generally organic carbon content reached the highest values in the finest size fractions (<0.5 μm); but in coarse deposits, which result from fast sedimentation processes, sands (> 50 μm) and silts (50–5 μm) also contained substantial quantities of organic matter with characteristic C/N ratios. Yield and nature of humic compounds and their stability towards acid hydrolysis may also yield information regarding the geochemical processes occurring in the environment. High rates of extractable humic compounds, nitrogen-rich proteinaceous components and divergence among fractions appear to be associated with marine organic material and oxidizing conditions. Low rates of extraction, more 'humic' nitrogen and similarity of the particles of different size may be related to reducing environments. Finally, clay organic associations (especially 5–0.5 μm and 0.5–0.1 μm classes) differ noticeably when they derive from continental aerated processes compared with aquatic or surface deposit processes.

INTRODUCTION

The distribution and content of the organic matter of sediments may be related to particle size. For example, high amounts of organic carbon are often associated with the finest-grained sediments (Bordovskiy, 1965).

This is usually attributed to the association of argillaceous sediments with deposition under anoxic conditions when the organic material is well preserved or with the stabilization of organic compounds on colloidal surfaces. However, fine particulate matter with high organic carbon content does not appear to provide the majority of the organic matter found in sediments since the nature and abundance of material in the water column often does not correlate with that of the settled material (Saliot and Tissier, 1977; Suess and Muller, 1979). Indeed, coarse particles (as vegetal remains, pellets or flocculated colloids) may carry the major part of the organic matter to sediments (Eppley and Peterson, 1979).

The complexity and heterogeneity of the organic matter (commonly sediments contain materials from various origins) require fractionation in order that detailed studies can be made. The techniques used should permit separation of organic or organo-mineral colloidal phases from the other, somewhat inert, materials.

In order to understand better the structure of organic sedimentary components, we have obtained subfractions of a number of recent sediments based on grain-size and attempted to correlate the results with the nature and/or stability of the organic matter. Physical separations of

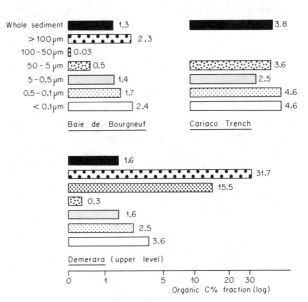

Fig. 1. Organic carbon distribution in grain-sized particles from typical recent marine sediments.

this kind may also be used to study stable aggregates or coacervates of various organo-mineral particles. However, because in our experiments the particle size distribution was obtained by physical dispersion in distilled water (as described below), the method does not relate to the sedimentation processes occurring in seawater.

METHODS

Samples

All the samples were recent marine sediments from four sites:

Baie de Bourgneuf (47°1′30″ N–2°1′ W). This sample was taken from the surficial oxygenated deposit of coastal diatoms muds under shallow water (1 m), with no noticeably terrestrial organic matter supply (Gouleau, 1975).

Cariaco Trench (10°31′ N–64°39′ W). This site represents a typical euxenic environment. Deposits are silty carbonate muds with planktonic and benthic forams associated with detritic components (Moyes *et al.*, 1978). Water depth: 1378 m.

Skagerrak (57°44′4″ N–7°53′9″ E). At this site, benthic foram muds with numerous pellets show significant variations in detritic supply (Moyes *et al.*, 1977). Two samples were studied from the same core at different depths: 100 cm and 520 cm. Water depth: 440 m.

Demerara (7°34′6″ N–47°50′9″ W). The samples are abyssal deposits from the Amazon deep sea fan (sands and silts with vegetal remains). Pelagic muds become more abundant at the top of the core in the upper sample (50 cm). Detritic components are most prominent in the deeper one (350 cm) (Moyes *et al.*, 1978). Water depth: 4300 m.

Fractionation

Freeze-dried sediments, or equivalent humid material (10 g) was placed in a centrifuge bottle with distilled water (200 ml) and five agate marbles, and rolled for one night (Bruckert *et al.*, 1979). Upon standing the particles flocculated immediately. The mixture was centrifuged and the settled residue resuspended in an additional aliquot of distilled water (200 ml). Centrifugation and dispersion was repeated until the suspension remained stable for more than 2 h.

The dispersions were passed through 100 μ and 50 μ mesh sieves and the smaller particles ($<50 \mu$) allowed to settle. The colloidal phase ($<5 \mu$) was pumped off until turbidity had disappeared and silts alone remained in the settling vessels. Final fractionation of the colloidal phase (in distilled water) was achieved by ultracentrifugation. This yielded three additional subfractions ($<0.1 \mu$; 0.1–0.5 μ and 0.5–5 μ).

In total, this physical fractionation therefore yielded six fractions, viz: $>100 \mu$ (coarse sands), 100–50 μ (fine sands), 50–5 μ (silts), 5–0.5 μ coarse clays), 0.5–0.1 μ (medium clays) and $<0.1 \mu$ (fine clays). Unstable macroaggregates such as fecal pellets are not preserved under the conditions employed.

Techniques

C and N determinations. For the whole sample and the organo-mineral fractions, *organic* carbon was measured by combustion in a Carmograph 8 (Wösthoff) after decarbonatation with HCl 6 N; for the same, *nitrogen* determinations were performed on C–H–N analyser (Carlo Erba) by the Dumas method.

All elemental analyses of humic acids (C, H, N, O) were also performed on the C–H–N analyser.

Humic components. Aliquots of each subfraction were decarbonated by addition of HCl 6 N, then HCl 0.01 N until the solution reached pH 2. After centrifugation and washing, the residue was resuspended in alkaline solution ($Na_2P_4O_7$ 1%, NaOH 0.1 N) and extraction performed according to Kononova techniques (Kononova and Bel'chikova, 1960). Fulvic and humic acids were separated at pH 2, and the flocculated humic acids were solubilized by NaOH 0.1 N, then dialysed and decationized on Dowex 50 H^+ before freeze-drying.

Infrared spectra. 0.4 mg of freeze-dried humic acid were crushed with 400 mg of oven-dried KBr. The powder was vitrified under high pression (10 T) and the disc put on an IR Beckman spectrometer.

Acid hydrolysis. Step hydrolysis with HCl 3 N was used (Janel *et al.*, 1978). Hydrolysable carbon was measured on a TCM Analyser (Carlo Erba) and nitrogen by the Kjoeldahl method.

RESULTS

Weight distribution of particles and organic matter

The weight, organic carbon and nitrogen content of the sample fractions are given in Table 1. In all cases the sediments contained low amounts ($<10\%$ by weight) of coarse material ($>50 \mu$). Except for the detrital abyssal deposits, clays formed the major part of the sediments, but the proportions of the different clay-size particles varied significantly even at the same sampling location. For example, at Skaggerak, the deeper sample contained three times more fine clays ($<0.1 \mu$) than the upper sample, although both contained the same total amount of clays (Table 1).

As expected, the various grain-size particles contain somewhat different proportions of organic matter. In some samples, the total organic content of the lighter weight fraction (sand) is particularly significant. For instance, the sandy fraction of the Demerara abyssal plain sediments contains 8% of the total organic carbon

Table 1

Weight distribution for carbon and nitrogen content of particles, in relation to grain size in some recent marine sediments

Samples	Water depth (m)	Sediment depth (cm)	>100 μ			100–50 μ			50–5 μ			5–0.5 μ			0.5–0.1 μ			<0.1 μ		
			W[a]	C[a]	N[a]	W	C	N	W	C	N	W	C	N	W	C	N	W	C	N
1	<1	0–20	0.7	1.7	nd	4.3	1.7	nd	28.8	10.7	7.0	21.3	22.0	20.0	26.4	31.6	46.5	18.5	32.3	26.5
2	440	100	0.1	nd	nd	0.1	nd	nd	21.5	5.8	3.0	19.0	14.6	13.0	36.8	49.5	48.0	22.5	27.6	30.0
3	440	520	0.1	nd	nd	0.1	nd	nd	21.2	6.0	3.2	38.6	29.5	21.4	31.7	50.2	48.6	8.3	10.9	15.6
4	1366	50	0.2	nd	nd	0.7	nd	nd	25.3	24.0	24.0	23.8	16.0	17.0	40.3	48.0	49.0	9.6	12.0	10.0
5	4300	50	0.4	8.0	4.0	0.3	3.0	2.0	46.5	9.0	13.0	17.0	16.5	17.0	28.8	43.5	39.0	7.0	15.0	18.0
6	4300	350	4.9	44.0	22.0	3.8	6.0	4.0	57.3	17.5	14.0	8.0	5.0	8.5	15.0	10.0	19.0	11.0	15.0	28.5

1. Baie de Bourgneuf (French Atlantic coast): coastal diatoms muds.
2. Skagerrak (southern Norwegian coast): benthic foram muds.
3. Skagerrak: id.
4. Cariaco Trench (Caribbean Sea): various bioclastic and detrital materials.
5. Demerara abyssal plain (West Atlantic): detrital sands and silts of Amazon deep sea fan.
6. Demerara abyssal plain: id.

[a] W = Weight of particles of defined size % total weight of sediment; C = Organic carbon % total organic carbon of the whole sediment; N = Nitrogen % total nitrogen of the whole sediment.
nd = not determined.

Table 2

C/N ratios of different particles classes

Sampling location		Particles C/N					
		100–50 μ	50–5 μ	5–0.5 μ	0.5–0.1 μ	<0.1 μ	Whole sediments
1	0–20	4	7	4	8	5	
2	50		8	7	8	9	8
3	50	20.5	8	4	13	11	12
4	300	21.5	18	9	7.5	8	14
5	100		12	8	7	6	7
6	520		10	9	7	5	7

1. Baie de Bourgneuf; 2. Cariaco Trench; 3. Demerara (50 cm depth); 4. Demerara (350 cm depth); 5. Skagerrak (100 cm depth); 6. Skagerrak (520 cm depth).

of the sediment although it only represents 0.4% of the total weight of the sediment. In general, the organic carbon content of the silt-size fractions is more diluted by mineral phases (though the anoxic, organic-rich deposits, of the Cariaco Trench are an exception).

Carbon/nitrogen ratios

In the upper levels of sediments changes in C/N ratios do not seem to be related to particle size. However, decreasing values occur with decreasing particle size in the deeper samples (Table 2). Moreover, in the coarser particles (sands and, partly, silts), which contain fragments of terrestrial biodetritus, C/N ratios reach higher values ($\simeq 20$) than in marine bioclasts of 'autochtonous' sediments (4–8). Obviously, the nature of the organic matter differs within each sample according to particle size even in those samples where the grain size distributions have been artificially created by ball-mill crushing.

Humic compounds

The extractability of humic compounds from sediments by alkaline liquids varies depending on the environmental conditions under which the sediments are deposited. This is particularly evident where surficial sediments are oxidizing. For instance the Demerara abyssal plain samples (oxic) yielded high amounts of extractable humic matter whereas the Cariaco Trench samples (which are deposited under anoxic conditions) yielded only small amounts of humic compounds (Fig. 2). Significant differences also appear in the fractions of differing particle size. The fine clays ($<0.1\ \mu$) and silty fractions (5–$50\ \mu$) are characterized by higher amounts of extractable humic substances whilst the medium and coarse clay size particles contain lower amounts (Fig. 2). Therefore the latter may be regarded as having more stable clay–organic associations. Ratios between carbon of fulvic acids and carbon of humic acids increase with decreasing particle size, and the nitrogen content of the fulvic acids show the same trend, i.e. the finest grain-size fractions of most of the sediments have more nitrogen-

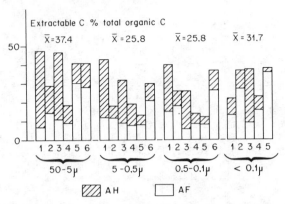

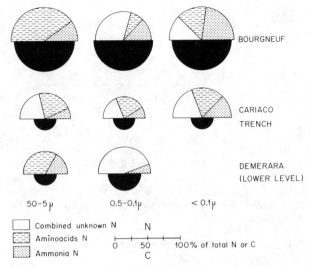

Fig. 2. Humic matter extractability from sized particles. 1. Baie de Bourgneuf; 2. Skagerrak (upper level); 3. Skagerrak (lower level); 4. Cariaco Trench; 5. Demerara abyssal plain (upper level); 6. Demerara abyssal plain (lower level). AH = humic acid carbon; AF = fulvic acid carbon.

Fig. 4. Hydrolysable organic matter of particles from some recent marine sediments. Upper parts of graphs represent hydrolysable nitrogen and its distribution. Lower part represents hydrolysable organic carbon. The diameter of the half-circle is related to percent of hydrolysable matter, nitrogen or carbon.

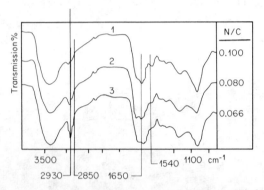

Fig. 3. Infrared spectra and atomic N/C of humic acids from Cariaco Trench surficial sample. 1. 50–5 μm subfraction; 2. 5–0.5 μm subfraction; 3. 0.5–0.1 μm subfraction.

containing polar compounds than the coarser grain sizes. Anoxic samples are distinguished from others by a greater homogeneity among the size fractions; however even in this case, the nature of the humic acids differs noticeably in different grain-size classes. The aliphatic character of the humic acids (as measured by the C→H stretch in the infrared spectrum at 2930 and 2850 cm^{-1}; Fig. 3) reaches its maximum in the fine particles, but proteinaceous matter (as indicated by the N/C values and peptide binding) appears more abundant in the coarser ones.

Stability of organic matter

Chemical degradation by hydrolytic procedures generally results in higher yields of hydrolysable nitrogen (as a percentage of the total nitrogen content) than of hydrolysable carbon. For instance the hydrolysable nitrogen of the sediments examined generally exceeded 50% of the total nitrogen and in some cases (e.g. Bourgneuf, Fig. 4) reached 100%. Hydrolysable carbon values on the other hand, were markedly lower except for well-oxygenated surficial muds (Bourgneuf).

When different particle classes are compared, amounts of hydrolysable matter exhibit no particular

trends with decreasing size, but two groups of sediments can be distinguished. In some samples, such as Bourgneuf and Cariaco Trench, hydrolysis of all particle sizes gave nearly identical yields of carbon and nitrogen. In other cases, one or two fractions, generally the medium coarse (0.5–0.1 μ) or the finest clays (<0.1 μ) were more hydrolysable (Fig. 4). Since the silt fraction corresponds to marine biomass remains, the grain-size fractionation allows the separation of labile hydrolysable marine bioclasts (upper abyssal silts) in which hydrolysable carbon and nitrogen reach 100%, from stable continental plant fragments (hydrolysable carbon ≃ 30%).

Hydrolysability of organic matter and yields of fulvic acid show the same trends in the fine clays; small polar molecules available for acid dissolution are more abundant in this fraction of the sediment.

These results indicate that chemical degradation of organic matter by hydrolysis is not a reliable process when applied to whole unfractionated sediments. The amount and nature of hydrolysable compounds may vary according to the size of the particles with which they are associated. For example, amino acids were the major nitrogen-containing compounds in the 50–5 μ fraction of most of the sediments examined (excepting the anoxic sediments), whereas condensation products such as melanins or melanoidins, appear in medium and coarse clays originating from continental, perhaps pedogenetic, organo-mineral associations (Bourgneuf, Demerara).

CONCLUSIONS

Physical fractionation of sediments yields classes of different particle sizes even after attempted homogenization by ball-mill crushing. The nature of the organic matter associated with each grain-size class may yield information regarding the geochemical processes occurring in the environment. Higher yields of humic compounds, nitrogen-rich proteinaceous compounds and divergence among fractions appear to be associated with marine organic material and oxidizing conditions; low rate of extraction, more 'humic' nitrogen and similarity of the particles of different size may be related to reducing environments. Finally, clay–organic associations differ noticeably when they derive from continental aerated processes compared with aquatic or surface deposit processes.

REFERENCES

Bordovskiy, O. K. (1965) Accumulation and transformation of organic substances in marine sediments. *Mar. Geol.* **3**, 1, 114.

Bruckert, S., Andreux, A., Correa, A., Ambouta, S. and Souchier, B. (1979) Fractionnement des agrégats appliqué à l'analyse des complexes organo-minéraux des sols. *Note Technique no. 22.* Centre de Pédologie Biologique, C.N.R.S., Vandoeuvre, France.

Eppley, R. and Peterson, B. J. (1979) Particulate organic matter flux and planktonic new production in the deep ocean. *Nature* **282**, 677–680.

Gouleau, D. (1975) *Les premiers stades de la sédimentation sur les vasières littorales atlantiques. Rôle de l'émersion.* Thèse Doct. Etat, Univ. de Nantes, pp. 241.

Janel, Ph., Jocteur Monrozier, L. and Toutain, F. (1978) Caractérisation de l'azote des litières et des sols par hydrolyse acide. *Soil Biol. Biochem.* **11**, 141–146.

Kononova, M. M. and Bel'chikova, N. P. (1960) A study of soil humus substances by fractionation. *Pochvovedeniye* **11** (1).

Moyes, J., Gayet, J., Pujol, C. and Pujos-Lamy, A. (1977) Etude stratigraphique et sédimentologique. In *Geochimie Organique des Sediments marins profonds. Orgon II. Atlantique, Nord-Est Brésil,* 105–156. Editions C.N.R.S.

Saliot, A. and Tissier, M. (1977) Interface Eau-Sédiment: acides gras et hydrocarbures dissous et particulaires dans l'eau de mer. In *Géochimie organique des sédiments marins profonds. Orgon I, Mer de Norvège.* Editions CNRS, Paris, pp. 197–208.

Suess, E. and Muller, P. J. (1979) Productivity, sedimentation rate and sedimentary organic matter in the oceans. II. Elemental fractionation. In *Biogéochimie de la matière organique à l'interface Eau-Sédiment marin.* Coll. Intern. CNRS, 293, pp. 17–26.

Advances in Organic Geochemistry 1981, pp. 328–335
© *John Wiley & Sons Limited, 1983*

Preliminary Data on the Origin and Diagenesis of the Organic Matter in the Phosphate Basin of Gafsa (Tunisia)

H. Belayouni and J. Trichet

Laboratoire de Géologie Appliquée, ERA 601, Université d'Orléans, 45046 Orleans-Cédex, France

The core S.R. 15 drilled in the Gafsa Basin (Tunisia) provides a model of alternatively richly and poorly phosphatized strata. The poorly phosphatized samples are shales, marls, cherts or limestones. Palynological studies have shown that the organic matter contained in all the strata, phosphorus rich or not, had the same planktonic origin. Thermal Rock-Eval analysis shows that the organic matter associated with the different strata belongs to one of the three following types: (1) the organic matter associated with shales has a high hydrogen index (HI) and a low oxygen index (OI), (2) the organic matter present in limestones has a lower HI and a larger OI than shales, (3) in phosphatized beds, HI is similar to HI of shales and OI is similar to OI of limestones. Such a separation of the points representative of samples in a HI/OI diagram cannot result from a 'matrix effect' during pyrolysis. It is interpreted as the result of the differential oxidation undergone by the same organic matter in three different physicochemical environments. Redox potential has been reducing during shale sedimentation, oxidizing during limestone sedimentation and intermediate during phosphatogenesis. The geochemical study of the humic acids extracted from these sediments shows that the phosphatized samples were particular rich in such compounds (40 < humic acids carbon < 80% of TOC). The chemical composition of these acids in all the strata (shales, phosphates, limestones) confirms the homogeneity and the marine origin of their organic matter. The conditions leading to the synthesis of humic acids appear to be also favourable for phosphatogenesis during diagenesis.

INTRODUCTION

Several authors have already emphasized the importance of studying the organic content of phosphatized sediments for understanding phosphatogenesis (Murray and Renard, 1891; Blackwelder, 1916; Strakhov, 1937; McKelvey *et al.*, 1953; Brongersma-Sanders, 1957; Emery, 1963; Sheldon, 1964; McKelvey, 1967; Baturin *et al.*, 1972; Slansky and Fauconnier, 1973).

Some recent studies have proposed criteria for determining the origin and the degree of evolution of the organic matter associated with phosphates through the analysis of kerogen and hydrocarbons (Barbat, 1967; Stone, 1967; Powell *et al.*, 1975; Beyalouni and Trichet, 1980b), of lipids and carbohydrates (Romankevich and Baturin, 1972) and amino compounds (Belayouni, 1978; Belayouni and Trichet, 1980a). This organic matter appears to be essentially of microplanktonic origin and the intensity of its evolution seems to be positively correlated with phosphatogenesis during diagenesis.

These studies, and others, also showed that the sedimentary environments favourable to phosphatogenesis were complex.

Baturin *et al.* (1970), working on recent sediments, stated an inverse correlation between organic carbon and total phosphorus content in sediment, suggesting that the latter resulted from the decomposition of organic matter.

Powell *et al.* (1975) showed that phosphatized sediments contained larger amounts of organic compounds soluble in organic solvents than did shales. The *n*-alkanes of the former confirmed a planktonic origin for the organic matter.

These authors also showed that the phosphatized sediments were rich in nitrogen, sulphur and oxygen, relating to a diagenetic evolution in an anoxic environment.

Burnett (1977) showed that the oxidation of organic matter, coupled with sulphate reduction, was the main mechanism of phosphate liberation in the sediment leading to precipitation of the calcium phosphate.

The same author also suggested that phosphate deposits occurred mainly on the borders of the oxygen minimum zone in areas of intense biological activity (upwelling areas) (Burnett and Veeh, 1977; Burnett, 1978).

Maughan (1980) suggests that if the deposition of abundant organic matter is actually due to an intense biological activity, its evolution towards phosphate deposits or towards oil generation is a function of chemical (oxido-reduction) and hydrodynamic factors within the deposit.

All these results are in agreement with the

observations that can be made in the present marine basins where phosphatized sediments are recorded. The basins are situated at low latitudes, on the western flanks of the continents (where upwelling currents are active) and lie under plankton-rich waters (McKelvey *et al.*, 1953; Emery, 1963; Sheldon, 1964; Baturin *et al.*, 1972; Veeh *et al.*, 1973; Burnett, 1977). The development of this biomass plays a prominent role in phosphorus concentration (Baturin, 1970; Nissenbaum *et al.*, 1972; Brown *et al.*, 1972; Nissenbaum, 1979; Suess, 1981; Val Klump and Martens, 1981). The concentration of phosphate ions (especially at the water–sediment interface) leads to calcium phosphate precipitation by chemical precipitation of apatite either from sea water (Kazakov, 1937; McKelvey *et al.*, 1953; Sheldon, 1964; Nathan and Lucas, 1976), or from phosphate rich interstitial solutions formed in reducing carbon-rich microenvironments (beds of amorphous organic matter, diatom frustules, foraminifer tests, dinoflagellate cysts, radiolaria, faecal pellets, etc.) Baturin *et al.*, 1970; Lamboy, 1975; Fauconnier, 1977; Burnett, 1977; Fauconnier and Slansky, 1980; Slansky, 1980). Apatite growth can cause calcium carbonate substitution (Leckie, 1969; Stumm and Leckie, 1971; Nathan and Lucas, 1972).

This paper is a contribution to the knowledge of the origin, composition and pathways of evolution of the organic matter in Paleocene phosphatized sediments of the Gafsa-Metlaoui Basin (Tunisia).

During the Paleocene, the phosphatized Gafsa-Metlaoui Basin was a marine gulf open to the sea on both sides of an emerging land mass, the island of Kasserine (Cayeux, 1939, 1941, 1950; Visse, 1952; Sassi, 1974; Belayouni and Trichet, 1980b), (Fig. 1).

The phosphatized series, 20 m thick, is made up of nine phosphatized beds (Visse, 1952; Sassi, 1974) interstratified with non-phosphatized or poorly phosphatized sediments of different facies (shales, marls, cherts, or limestones).

The samples studied come from a core (Redeyef S.R. 15) drilled on the western part of the basin, 60 km from the town of Gafsa (Beyalouni and Trichet, 1980b).

The samples were collected from a continuous sequence of phosphate-rich and phosphate-poor beds. The alternation of such phosphate-rich and poor beds provides a model in which the difference in organic matter composition and/or evolution in mineralized and non-mineralized beds *which have been deposited under as nearly identical conditions as possible*, can be studied.

EXPERIMENTAL

Three kinds of studies have been performed:

(1) A thermal characterization of the organic matter (Rock-Eval) (Espitalié *et al.*, 1977a, b) by pyrolysis of the organic matter under a flow of helium in the temperature range 250 °C to 550 °C. The free volatile compounds are then separated into two fractions: in the first one, the quantity of hydrocarbons and tars is measured by a flame ionization detector (S_1 and S_2 peak); in the second one, the oxygen linked to the organic compounds is measured as CO_2 using a catharometer (S_3 peak).

(2) Humic and fulvic acids were obtained by pre-extraction of the sediment ($CHCl_3$), carbonate dissolution (cold HCl, 2 N) and then extraction (NaOH, 0.1 N). Humic acids (HA) were separated from the fulvic acids (FA) by precipitation (HCl 2 N, pH-2) and centrifugation. The HA were then dissolved (NaOH, 0.1 N), purified by dialysis and percolation through H^+ resin, and finally lyophilized, (Schnitzer and Khan, 1972; Huc, 1973; Schnitzer, 1978). The resulting HA contained 5–20% ash, corresponding to alumino-silicates.

(3) Total organic carbon content was obtained by combustion in a Leco furnace. The carbon content of FA and Ha was determined on a Carmograph Wosthoff 8. Elemental analysis (C, H, N) was performed in an autoanalyser Carlo Erba 114 B. Oxygen was measured by pyrolysis of the organic matter incorporating the oxygen atoms into CO molecules. The amount of CO was measured by catharometry after separation of CO from other gases (CH_4, H_2, ...) by chromatography. Sulphur was oxidized and measured as SO_2 by coulometry after oxidation of SO_2 to H_2SO_4. Phosphorus contents were measured colorimetrically from the

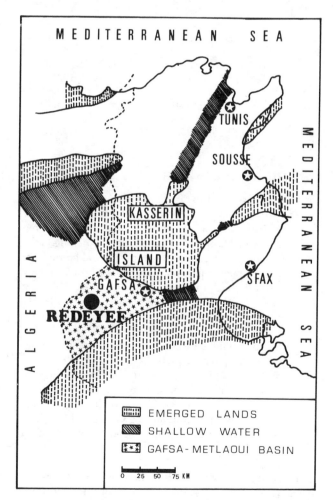

Fig. 1. Paleogeography of the Gafsa Basin during the Paleocene (From Sassi, 1974).

Table 1

Analytical data for sediments from the Gafsa basin (Redeyef core S.R. 15)

Depth of samples (m)	Lithology	Org. C%	P_2O_5 %	Rock-Eval data		
				S_1 Free (Hydrocarbons + tars) mg/g of rock	S_2 Hydrogen index (HI) mg (HC + tars)/g org. C	S_3 Oxygen index (OI) mg CO_2/ g org. C
234.00	limestone	0.27	4.45	0.71	85.10	177.90
236.00	marl	0.87	5.50	0.16	199.20	77.30
236.80	marl	1.46	6.20	0.04	78.00	38.00
237.20	phosphatized marl	0.90	10.50	0.14	155.70	103.80
238.10	phosphate	0.78	25.50	0.54	227.20	27.380
242.20	limestone	0.32	6.55	0.04	108.60	202.90
243.80	phosphate	1.04	21.90	0.20	284.00	209.60
246.40	phosphate	1.35	27.00	0.00	287.50	195.50
249.00	phosphate	1.79	27.00	0.06	185.00	196.00
249.30	marl	1.84	4.75	0.00	283.00	35.00
249.50	limestone	0.44	1.15	0.00	345.00	104.20
250.00	phosphate	1.36	25.70	0.11	200.00	206.50
251.00	phosphate	1.85	27.35	0.09	197.00	123.00
252.30	marl	3.04	7.95	0.00	277.00	53.00
253.60	phosphatized marl	1.67	13.50	0.30	328.80	103.60
254.20	phosphate	1.27	26.30	1.56	259.10	186.20
254.30	limestone	0.24	0.20	0.25	149.40	150.10
256.10	marl	2.88	2.97	0.00	343.00	25.00
256.50	phosphate	1.57	24.40	0.03	206.00	121.00
258.30	marl	1.65	7.60	0.01	374.00	51.00
259.40	phosphate	1.62	25.35	0.06	184.00	114.00
260.90	chert	1.82	0.75	0.00	670.50	42.00
261.30	chert	2.98	0.90	0.00	553.00	34.30
261.60	phosphate	1.20	27.85	0.00	277.60	192.40
262.00	limestone	0.50	0.70	0.00	399.40	88.80
262.90	phosphatized marl	4.30	11.80	0.00	350.00	35.00
263.60	marl	7.80	1.74	0.01	393.00	13.00

vanade–phosphomolybdate complex (Peachey *et al.*, 1973).

RESULTS

A. Rock pyrolysis (Rock-Eval)

This method leads to the calculation or measurement of two kinds of parameters:

(1) hydrogen and oxygen indices (HI and OI) (Espitalié *et al.*, 1977a and b), which can be related to the origin and evolution of the organic matter.

(2) the temperature at the maximum of the pyrolysis peak (S_2 peak) (Table 1). This temperature is related to the thermal maturity of the organic matter (Herbin and Deroo, 1978).

The results concerning the HI and OI values are plotted in Table 1 and in a HI/OI diagram (Fig. 2); the results dealing with the S_2 peak temperature (T°) are plotted in a T°/HI diagram (Fig. 3).

In the Gafsa basin, the points fall in three distinct groups in both diagrams:

1. HI and OI values (Fig. 2).

(a) The first group is characterized by a high hydrogen index ($200 < HI < 700$ mg (HC + tars)/g of TOC) and a low oxygen index ($OI < 150$ mg CO_2/g of TOC). The related samples belong to the marine planktonic series (type II) and come from non- or poorly-phosphatized beds whose lithology is shale, marl, or chert.

(b) The second group is characterized by a $150 < HI < 350$ mg (HC + tars)/g of TOC and a high oxygen index ($100 < OI < 300$ mg CO_2/g of TOC). The points fall between type II and type III curves and correspond to phosphate-rich samples.

(c) In the third group, the points are close to the type III curve. Their hydrogen index is low ($HI < 200$ mg (HC + tars)/g of TOC) and their oxygen index varies between 30 and 300 mg CO_2/g of TOC. The samples come from non- or poorly-phosphatized beds of limestone lithology.

2. Temperature of the maximum of the S_2 pyrolysis peak (Fig. 3). Values of the hydrogen index (HI) are plotted against T_{max} in Fig. 3. Included in this diagram are the evolution pathways for the three

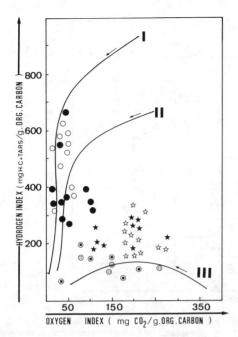

Fig. 2. Types of organic matter in phosphatized and non-phosphatized sediments from the Gafsa-Metlaoui Basin. ●, Non-phosphatized sediments (shales, cherts ...) (Redeyef); ○, Non-phosphatized sediments (shales, cherts ...) (other sites in the Gafsa Basin); ◉ Non-phosphatized sediments (limestones) (Redeyef); ◎ Non-phosphatized sediments (limestones) (other sites in the Gafsa Basin); ★ Phosphatized beds (Redeyef); ☆ Phosphatized beds (other sites in the Gafsa Basin).

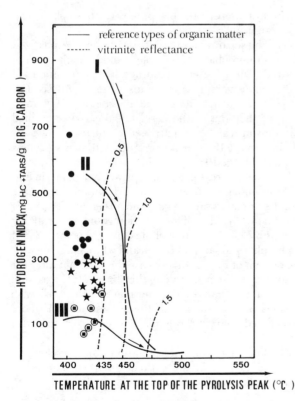

Fig. 3. Thermal maturity of the organic matter in phosphatized and non-phosphatized sediments from the Gafsa-Metlaoui Basin. ● Non-phosphatized sediments (shales, cherts) (Redeyef); ◉ Non-phosphatized sediments (limestones) (Redeyef); ★ Phosphatized beds (Redeyef).

reference types of organic matter (I = algal, II = marine planktonic, III = higher plants or residual organic matter). Along each path, increasing maturity corresponds to lowering HI and increasing T_{max}.

Also included in the diagram are three curves of isoreflectance of vitrinite particles (0.5–1–1.5%). Reflectance values <0.5% are indicative of immature organic matter and correspond to the diagenesis stage. The curve of reflectance values equal to 0.5% is at the boundary between mature and immature organic matter and corresponds to a T_{max} of 435 °C.

Two conclusions can be drawn from the localization of the points relative to the Redeyef sediments in Fig. 3: (a) all the points representative of phosphatized or non-phosphatized samples fall in the diagenesis zone, i.e. the organic matter is thermally immature. This result has been confirmed by the analysis of samples from other cores in the same basin (Belayouni and Trichet, 1980b), and (b) the majority of the points are also localized in the area between the curves of organic matter of types II and III, thus confirming the conclusions deduced from Fig. 2.

B. Study of humic compounds

The amounts of organic carbon in humic acid fractions are reported in Fig. 4.

Three results are evident:

(1) The phosphatized samples generally display a high content of humic compounds. Carbon content in humic acids (HA) varies between 40 and 80% of TOC. Conversely, the non- or poorly-phosphatized beds (shales, marls, cherts, or limestones) generally have a lower humic content (humic carbon <30% of TOC).

(2) In the same strata, the values of HA content, P_2O_5 content, and the oxygen index (OI) show a general positive correlation (Fig. 4). Most of the humic compounds are in the form of humic acids; the amount of carbon in fulvic acids is less than 0.5% of TOC.

(3) The results of the elemental analysis (C, H, O, N, S) of humic acids are reported in Fig. 5. They show that the humic acids in all the samples, phosphatized or poorly phosphatized, have high H/C and S/C ratios. These results are in agreement with those of Brown *et al.* (1972), Huc (1973), Debyser and Gadel (1975), Huc and Durand (1977), who note that a high content of hydrogen and sulphur is characteristic of marine humic acids (versus terrestrial humic acids).

DISCUSSION

1. Origin and evolution of organic matter in the sedimentary sequence as deduced from pyrolysis results

The localization of the points representing samples in a HI/OI diagram is known to be related to the origin and

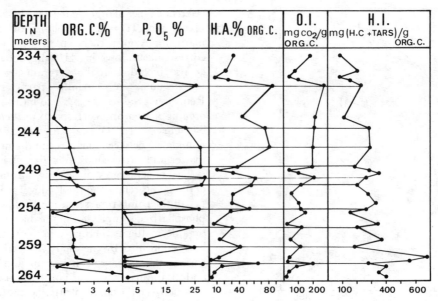

Fig. 4. Variation of total organic carbon content (org. C%), total phosphate content (P$_2$O$_5$%), amount of humic acids (H.A.% org. C), oxygen index (O.I.) and hydrogen index (H.I.), in phosphatized and non-phosphatized sediments from the Gafsa-Metlaoui Basin (core Redeyef S.R. 15).

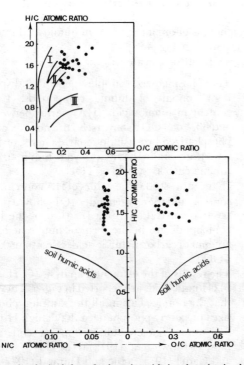

Fig. 5. Analytical data for humic acids in phosphatized and non-phosphatized sediments from the Gafsa-Metlaoui Basin (core Redeyef S.R. 15). 'Soil humic acids' after Debyser and Gadel, 1975.

the evolutionary stage of the organic matter of the sample (Espitalié *et al.*, 1977a, b). Figure 2 includes the reference curves for three fundamental types of organic matter in sediments, differing in origin and in their evolution paths.

The distribution of the points related to the Gafsa Basin samples into three groups would suggest that the organic matter encountered in the different strata could be somewhat different in nature and origin. But optical studies performed on palynological residues (Fauconnier

and Slansky, 1980) from these phosphatized and non-phosphatized samples show that the organic matter in all the samples is essentially the same, i.e. planktonic, rich in Dinoflagellate cysts (up to 40 000 cysts per g of rock). Only very small terrestrial inputs (spores and pollens) can be detected in phosphatized and non-phosphatized strata.

Three reasons can be proposed to explain this localization:

(1) The separation of points related to phosphatized and non-phosphatized samples could result from a 'matrix' effect, itself resulting in a retention of hydrogenous volatile compounds during pyrolysis (low HI, Fig. 2) in limestones and phosphates. It is most unlikely that this is the case in those coarse-grained materials in which the matrix effect during pyrolysis is less important than in fine-grained sediments (shales) (Espitalié *et al.*, 1980).

(2) A second reason for the separation of points in Fig. 2 is the underestimation of the HI values due to the samples' richness in oxygen and other atoms (N, S) (Fourmont, 1981). This phenomenon is probably responsible for the shifting of the cluster of points related to phosphatized samples (black and white stars) towards the bottom of Fig. 2. In any case this does not alter the separation of the points along the abscissa (OI axis) and it is assumed that the organic matter associated with phosphatized samples (and limestones facies) is more oxygenated than the organic matter associated with shales.

(3) The following interpretation can therefore be proposed to explain the existence of three clusters of points in the HI/OI thermal diagram of Fig. 2:

(a)   the non-phosphatized shale, marl, or chert facies sediments have been deposited in an anoxic environment. They are still rich in organic matter ($2 < C_{org} < 8\%$) displaying a high hydrogen index (200–700 mg (HC + tars)/g org. C, Table 1).

(b) The calcareous non-phosphatized sediments are poor in organic carbon ($C_{org} < 0.5\%$, Table 1) and have a low HI (HI < 200 mg (HC + tars)/g of TOC, Table 1). They were deposited in an environment which was either more oxygenated than the previous one or more bioturbated or mechanically reworked, leading to a loss of fine-grained organic matter. This is suggested by the fabric of these limestones which shows evidence of sedimentary reworking.

(c) The phosphatized beds which contain 0.8 to 2% of TOC and display a hydrogen index varying between 150 and 350 mg (HC + tars)/g of TOC (Table 1), suggest a sedimentary environment whose characteristics were intermediate between the two previous ones. In these conditions, the oxidation was mild, leading to a loss of hydrogen compounds and to an oxidation of kerogen intermediate between that in shales and in limestone sediments.

Such a property is confirmed by the positive correlation existing between P_2O_5 contents and the oxygen index (OI) of the rock (Fig. 3). This correlation stresses the role, maybe the control, of oxidation in phosphatogenesis.

2. Maturation of organic matter in phosphatized and non-phosphatized beds

As already stated, all the points representative of samples from the Gafsa Basin fall in the zone characteristic of thermally immature organic matter (diagenesis zone) in Fig. 3. In any case it is interesting to see again how the points, related respectively to the shales, the phosphates, and the limestones are grouped into three clusters. Following the previous interpretation, it is assumed that the different pathways of evolution which occurred under reducing, intermediate and oxidizing conditions (shales, phosphates and limestones respectively), resulted in the dispersion of the points into three clusters. Otherwise, these points would have been grouped along the Type II curve (Fig. 2).

3. Study of humic compounds

Two conclusions can be drawn from the results contained in Fig. 5.

The first one deals with the origin of the organic matter. The similarity of the H/C, O/C and N/C ratios for the humic acids (Fig. 5) confirms their homogeneity and the marine origin of the organic matter. Plots of H/C against O/C for the humic acids show that the samples align along the type II curve (Fig. 5). The O/C and N/C ratios are consistent with a marine origin (cf. Debyser and Gadel, 1975).

The second conclusion is the most important. It concerns the enrichment of humic compounds in the organic matter associated with the phosphatized beds (Fig. 4). Such a richness suggests that the oxidation of the organic matter did not go over the humic stage, i.e. an early stage in diagenesis.

CONCLUSIONS

(1) The bulk of organic matter in the sediments of the Gafsa-Metlaoui Basin is of marine planktonic origin, whatever the lithologic facies of the sediment (shale, marl, chert, phosphate, limestone).

(2) These different strata (shales, marls, cherts, phosphates, limestones) differ by the nature of the diagenetic evolution they have undergone. This nature can be concluded from the thermal analysis of the organic matter and through the relative amounts of humic acids:

(a) The non- or poorly-phosphatized materials such as shales, marls or cherts have an abundant organic content similar to that encountered in anoxic environments. Such an environment does not appear to be suitable for phosphatogenesis. This agrees with the results of recent work showing that the main part of the phosphorus liberated during organic matter decomposition remains soluble as long as the environment remains reductive (Hartmann *et al.*, 1973; val Klump and Martens, 1981). In these conditions, calcium phosphate does not precipitate.

The evolution of organic matter in such an environment will lead to a highly petroligenous kerogen, poor in functional oxygenated groups (humic compounds) (Tissot and Welte, 1978; Demaison and Moore, 1980).

(b) The non- or poorly-phosphatized calcareous sediments have a poor organic content which is a consequence of oxidation or reworking by bioturbation or winnowing by currents. These conditions are not favourable for phosphate precipitation.

(c) The phosphatized series are characterized by a mild oxidation of their organic matter. This oxidation was intermediate between the oxidation undergone in the two previous types. This results first in the existence of a fairly large amount of organic matter in the sediment ($0.8 < C_{org} < 2.5\%$ of TOC), secondly, in an amount of oxygen (incorporated in kerogen) intermediate between the amounts encountered in the former types of organic matter, and thirdly, in an exceptional richness of humic compounds.

(3) The evolution of organic matter up to, and not beyond, the stage of humic compounds appears to be the main feature of organic diagenesis in phosphatized beds.

Two explanations can be given for the fact that the evolution did not go beyond the stage of humic compounds: either humic compounds were the equilibrium forms of organics in the physicochemical conditions prevailing in the phosphatizing sediments, or the humic compounds were unstable but have been sequestred under this form in the sediment, thus inhibiting their further oxidation or evolution.

Several observations support this latter mechanism. Among them, optical examination of phosphatized rocks, performed in collaboration with Mr Slansky and Mrs Fauconnier of BRGM (Bureau de Recherches Géologiques et Minières), reveals that humic compounds are closely associated with phosphate grains (pellets, granules, ooids, ...).

The remaining problem is that of the simultaneous production (followed by an association) of humic compounds and phosphate ions in the sediments. Work by Nissenbaum (1979) first brought to light this humic acid–phosphate association. During the transformation sequence from plankton→dissolved organic matter →fulvic acids→humic acids→kerogen, the main part of the organic phosphorus is liberated during the step fulvic acids→humic acids. The time of genesis of humic acids then appears to be the moment of simultaneous production of large amounts of phosphate ions and humic acids. Observation of the phosphatized sediments still shows the association between the phosphate and humic acids arising from the organic matter's decomposition. It is still not understood how their close association protects the humic acids against further evolution.

REFERENCES

Barbat, W. N. (1967) Crude oil correlation and their role in exploration. *Am. Assoc.Per. Geol.* **51**, pp. 1255–1292.

Baturin, G. N. (1970) Recent authigenic phosphorite formation on the South West African shelf. The geology of the East Atlantic Continental margin. ICSU/SCOR Working Party 31, Symposium Cambridge, Report no. 70/31, pp. 88–97.

Baturin, G. N., Kochenov, A. V. and Petelin, V. P. (1970) Phosphorite formation on the shelf of South Western Africa. *Litol. Polezn. Iskop.* **3**, 15–26.

Baturin, G. N., Merkulova, K. I. and Chalov, P. I. (1972) Radiometric evidence of recent formation of phosphatic nodules in marine shelf sediments. *Mar. Geol.* **10**, 37–41.

Belayouni, H. (1978) Etude des composés aminés contenus dans quelques séries phosphatées. Thèse doctorat de spécialité, Université d'Orléans.

Belayouni, H. and Trichet, J. (1980a) Glucosamine as a biochemical marker for Dinoflagellates in phosphatized sediments. *Phys. Chem. Earth*, **12**, 205–210.

Belayouni, H. and Trichet, J. (1980b) Contribution à la connaissance de la matière organique du bassin phosphaté de Gafsa: informations fournies par l'analyse du potentiel pétrolier. Dans 'Géologie comparée des gisements de phosphates et de pétrole'. Documents B.R.G.M. no. 24, 37–59.

Blackwelder, E. (1916) The geologic role of phosphorus. *Amer. J. Sci.*, 4th series, pp. 285–298.

Brongersma-Sanders, M. (1957) Mass mortality in the sea. *Geol. Soc. Amer. Mem.* **67**, 1, 941–1010.

Brown, F. S., Baedecker, M. J., Nissenbaum, A. and Kaplan, I. R. (1972) Early diagenesis in a reducing fjord, Saanich Inlet, B.C., III. Changes in organic constituents of sediments. *Geochim. Cosmochim. Acta* **36**, 1185–1204.

Burnett, W. C. (1977) Geochemistry and origin phosphorite deposits from off Peru and Chile. *Geol. Soc. Am. Bull.* **88**, 813–823.

Burnett, W. C. and Veeh, H. H. (1977) Uranium series disequilibrium studies in phosphorite nodules from the West coast of South America. *Geochim. Cosmochim. Acta* **41**, 755–764.

Burnett, W. C. (1978) Oceanic phosphate deposits. Proceedings of the Fertilizer Raw Material Resources Workshop, August 20–24, 1979. East West Center, Honolulu, Hawaii.

Cayeux, L. (1939, 1941, 1950) Les phosphates de chaux sédimentaires de France (France métropolitaine et d'Outre-Mer), T. I, II et III, Etude des gites minéraux de la France. Serv. Carte Geol. France.

Debyser, Y. and Gadel, F. (1975) Etude des composés humiques, des kérogènes et de la fraction hydrolysable dans les sédiments. *ORGON II, Atlantique N.E., Brésil*, ed. by Combaz, A. and Pelet, R., pp. 339–356.

Demaison, G. J. and Moore, G. T. (1980) Anoxic environments and oil source bed genesis. *Am. Assoc. Pet. Geol. Bull.* **64**, 8, 1179–1209.

Emery, K. O. (1963) Oceanographic factors in accumulation of petroleum. Contribution no. 1312, of Woods Hole Ocean. Inst., Section I, paper 42, PO 2, USA, pp. 483–491.

Espitalié, J., Madec, M., Tissot, B., Mennig, J. J. and Leplat, P. (1977) Source rock characterization method for petroleum exploration. Off shore technology Conference, Houston, paper O.T.C. 2935.

Espitalié, J., Laporte, J. L., Madec, M., Marquis, F., Leplat, P., Paulet, J. and Boutefeu, A. (1977) Methode rapide de caractérisation des roches mères, de leur potentiel pétrolier et de leur degré d'évolution. *Rev. Inst. Fr. Pet.* **32**, 23–42.

Fauconnier, D. (1977) Les Dinoflagellés de l'Albien et du Cénomanien inférieur du Bassin de Paris. Répartition stratigraphique et relation avec la nature du dépôt. Thèse doctorat d'Université, Orléans.

Fauconnier, D. and Slansky, M. (1980) Relation entre le développement des Dinoflagellés et la sédimentation phosphatée du bassin de Gafsa (Tunisie). Dans 'Géologie comparée des gisements de phosphates et de pétrole'. Documents B.R.G.M. 24, pp. 185–204.

Hartmann, M., Muller, P., Suess, E. and van der Weijden, C. H. (1973) Oxidation of organic matter in recent marine sediments. *Meteor Forsch. Ergebnisse*, Reihe C, 12, pp. 74–86.

Herbin, J. P. and Deroo, G. (1978) Tentative paleogeography of the South Atlantic Ocean during the Cretaceous as deduced from a sedimentological study of organic matter. *Rev. Inst. Fr. Pét., Géol.* 22652, ref. 26248, pp. 1–26.

Huc, A. Y. (1973) Contribution à l'étude de l'humus marin et de ses relations avec le kérogène. Thèse Doctorat ingénieur, Université de Nancy.

Huc, A. Y. and Durand, B. M. (1977) Occurrence and Significance of Humic Acids in Ancient Sediments. *Fuel* **56**, 73–80.

Kazakov, A. V. (1937) The phosphorite facies and the genesis of phosphorites. Geol. Invest. of Agricul. Ores. U.S.S.R., *Proc. Sci. Inst. Fertilizers and Insectofungicides*, 142, 95–113.

Lamboy, M. (1975) Géologie marine et sous-marine du plateau continental au Nord-Ouest de l'Espagne. Genèse des glauconites et des phosphorites. Thèse doctorat es-Sciences, Université de Rouen.

Leckie, Y. O. (1979) Phosphate exchange with sediments. Ph.D. Thesis, Harvard University, Cambridge.

Maughan, E. K. (1980) Relation of phosphorite, organic carbon and hydrocarbons in the Permian Phosphoria Formation, Western United States of America. In *Géologie comparée des gisements de phosphates et de pétrole*. Documents B.R.G.M., 24, pp. 63–91.

McKelvey, V. E., Cathcart, J. B., Altchuler, Z. S., Swanson, R. W. and Ruck, K. L. (1953) Domestic phosphate deposits. In *Soil and Fertilizer Phosphorus*, Vol. 1, Chapter 1, Academic Press, New York, 492 pp.

McKelvey, V. E. (1967) Phosphate deposits, *U.S. Geol. Surv. Bull.* 1252-D, pp. D1–D2.

Murray, J. and Renard, A. F. (1891) *Deep Sea Deposits, Scientific Results of the Exploration Voyage of H.M.S. Challenger, 1872–1876*. Longmans, London, 525 pp.

Nathan, I. and Lucas, J. (1972) Synthèse de l'apatite à partir du gypse; application au problème de la formation des apatites carbonatées par précipitation directe. *Chem. Geol.* **9**, 99–106.

Nathan, I. and Lucas, J. (1976) Expériences sur la précipitation directe de l'apatite dans l'eau de mer: implication dans la genèse des phosphorites. *Chem. Geol.* **18**, 181–186.

Nissenbaum, A., Baedecker, J. J. and Kaplan, I. R. (1972) Studies on dissolved organic matter from interstitial water of reducing marine sediment. In *Advances in Organic Geochemistry*, ed. by Von Gaertner, H. R. and Wehner, H. Pergamon Press, Oxford, pp. 427–440.

Nissenbaum, A. (1979) Phosphorus in marine and non-marine humic substances. *Geochim. Cosmochim. Acta* **43**, 1973–1978.

Peachey, D., Roberts, J. L. and Jane Scot-Baker (1973) Rapid colorimetric determination of phosphorus in geochemical survey samples. *J. Geochem. Explor.* **2**, 115–120.

Powell, T. G., Cook, P. J. and McKirdy, D. M. (1975) Organic geochemistry of phosphorites: relevance to petroleum genesis. *Am. Assoc. Petrol. Geol. Bull.* **59**, 4, 618–632.

Romankevich, Y. A. and Baturin, G. N. (1972) Composition of the organic matter in phosphorites from the continental shelf of South West Africa. *Geochim. Internat. U.S.A.* **3**, 464–469.

Sassi, S. (1974) La sédimentation phosphatée au Paléocène dans le Sud et le Centre-Ouest de la Tunisie. Thèse Doctorat ès-Sciences, Université de Paris-Orsay.

Schnitzer, M. and Khan, S. U. (1972) *Humic Substances in the Environment.* M. Dekker, Inc., New York.

Schnitzer, M. (1978) Humic substances: chemistry and reaction. In *Soil Organic Matter*, Developments in Soil Science 8, ed. by Schnitzer, M. and Khan, S. U. Elsevier, New York, pp. 1–58.

Sheldon, R. P. (1964) Exploration for phosphorite in Turkey. A case history. *Econ. Geol.* **59**, 1159–1175.

Slansky, M. and Fauconnier, D. (1973) Influence possible de certains facteurs biologiques sur la géochimie des sédiments. *Bull. B.R.G.M.,* 4, section 4, 209–228.

Slansky, M. (1980) Géologie des phosphates sédimentaires. *Mémoire B.R.G.M.*, 114, 92 pp.

Stone, D. S. (1967) Theory of Paleozoic oil and gaz accumulation in Big Horn Basin, Wyoming. *Am. Assoc. Pet. Geol. Bull.* **58**, 499–506.

Strakhov, N. M. (1937) Geochemistry of P, V and Cu in marine bituminous rocks. Transactions of the All-Union Scientific Research, Inst. of Mineral Raw Material, Moscow, VII.

Stumm, W. and Leckie, Y. O. (1971) Phosphate exchange with sediments. Its role in the productivity of surface waters. *Advances in Water Pollution Research*, Vol. 2. Pergamon Press, New York, pp. 1–16.

Suess, E. (1981) Phosphate regeneration from sediments of the Peru Continental margin by dissolution of fish debris. *Geochim. Cosmochim. Acta* **45**, 577–588.

Tissot, B. P. and Welte, D. H. (1978) *Petroleum Formation and Occurrence.* Springer Verlag, Berlin, Heidelberg, New York.

Val Klump, J. and Martens, C. S. (1981) Biogeochemical cycling in an organic rich coastal marine basin, II — Nutrient sediment water exchange processes. *Geochim. Cosmochim. Acta* **45**, 101–121.

Veeh, H. H., Burnett, W. C. and Soutar, A. (1973) Contemporary phosphorite on the continental margin of Peru. *Science* **181**, 845–847.

Visse, L. (1952) Genèse des gites phosphatés du Sud-Est algéro-tunisien. XIXe Congrès géologique international, Monographies régionales, série 1, Algérie, 27, 1–58.

Advances in Organic Geochemistry 1981, pp. 336–349
© *John Wiley & Sons Limited, 1983*

Size Fractionation and Analytical Pyrolysis of Suspended Particles from the River Rhine Delta

D. van de Meent[†], A. Los, J. W. Leeuw and P. A. Schenck

Delft University of Technology, Department of Chemistry and Chemical Engineering, Organic Geochemistry Unit, de Vries van Heystplantsoen 2, 2628 RZ Delft, The Netherlands

J. Haverkamp

F.O.M. Institute for Atomic and Molecular Physics, Kruislaan 407, 1098 SJ Amsterdam, The Netherlands

The qualitative and quantitative changes in chemical composition of suspended matter in the IJsselmeer, a major sedimentation basin of the river Rhine, have been studied in order to better understand the organic characteristics of the underlying sediments. Suspended matter was sampled by sequentially passing water through filters of decreasing pore width. Particle size distributions were determined and the fractionated material was studied by means of microscopy, elemental (Al, Si, CO_3, C_{org}, H, N) analysis and analytical pyrolysis. Carbohydrates and peptides make up a substantial fraction of the particulate organic matter, indicating a largely autochthonous origin of this material. The chemical composition of suspended matter in this basin appears to be controlled by sedimentation processes and autochthonous production of suspended matter. At short distances from the river mouth, preferential sedimentation of mineral-rich allochthonous particles predominates, leaving the remaining suspended matter enriched in organics. Sediments from this part of the basin exhibit allochthonous characteristics. At longer distances from the river mouth, extensive autochthonous production of suspended matter (algal bloom) occurs. As a consequence, suspended matter from this part of the basin consist almost exclusively of phytoplankton. Sediments in this area receive a highly autochthonous input.

INTRODUCTION

The river Rhine carries large amounts of suspended matter to the Dutch deltaic area. Most of these solids and their associated pollutants (heavy metals, organic micropollutants) settle in enclosed sea arms and in the large and deep harbours at Rotterdam. The disposal of 20 million tons of polluted Rhine sediments, annually dredged out of the Rotterdam harbours, is a major environmental problem for the Dutch authorities. Suspended matter consists of heterogeneous agglomerates of various types of mineral and organic particles. The mineralogy of suspended matter from the river Rhine delta has been studied extensively (Van Eck, 1982). Clay minerals (mainly illite), quartz, carbonates (mainly dolomite) and hydrous iron oxides are the major mineral constituents. Although it is generally recognized that organic matter can play an important role in the uptake and release of pollutants by suspended matter and sediments (Balistrieri *et al.*, 1981; Förstner and Salomons, 1982) little research has been carried out to chemically characterize the particulate organics present in suspended matter in the river Rhine delta.

† Present address: National Institute for Water Supply, P.O. Box 150, 2260 AD Leidschendam, The Netherlands.

Various investigators have observed a certain resemblance between aquatic organic matter and fulvic acids isolated from soils (Christman and Minear, 1971; Beck *et al.*, 1974; Reuter and Perdue, 1977). This resemblance has been mentioned so often that 'aquatic organic matter' and 'humic substances' have become nearly equivalent in the geochemical literature. Due to this widespread misconception, the present knowledge of the chemical nature of particulate organic matter is often greatly overestimated. Our earlier investigations indicate that the bulk of the organic matter present as suspended solids in the river Rhine delta consists of carbohydrates, peptides, lipids and lignin, originating mainly from autochthonously produced biomass (Van de Meent *et al.*, 1980b). Sigleo *et al.* (1980) and Etcheber *et al.* (1981) arrived at similar conclusions with respect to Chesapeake Bay and the Gironde estuary respectively. Microbiological studies (Uiterwijk Winkel, unpublished data) indicate that particular organic matter in the river Rhine consists mainly of bacterial flocs, similar to those found in the activated sludge of wastewater treatment plants. It should be pointed out here that these findings do not necessarily contradict the observed similarity between soil fulvic acids and aquatic organic matter. Saiz-Jimenez *et al.* (1979) have shown that soil organic matter contains substantial amounts of polysaccharides, presumably of microbial origin. We do want to stress, however, that these studies indicate that, although particulate organic matter may have some humic character, the bulk of this material does not necessarily consist of phenolic polymers.

The aim of the present study was to chemically characterize suspended matter from the downstream course of the river Rhine in order to understand better the chemical characteristics of the underlying sediments and to provide a basis for the study of interaction processes between pollutants and suspended matter. In this study we have used size fractionation in an attempt to reduce the earlier observed chemical complexity of suspended matter (Van de Meent *et al.*, 1980b). Methods based on sedimentation velocity, after destruction of carbonates and organic matter (Hooghoudt, 1945) and density separation (Pilkington and Warren, 1979) have frequently been used to fractionate sediments. As a result of the severe physical and chemical treatment, these methods alter the original particle size distribution of the sample which makes them unsuitable for the fractionation of suspended particles. Thompson and Eglinton (1978) have successfully used a simple sieving technique to fractionate a recent sediment for geochemical analysis. Applied to untreated water samples, sieving is a suitable method to fractionate suspended matter. We have used sequential filtration as a wet sieving technique. Provided that the necessary precautions (thorough stirring and low filter loads) are observed, this fractionation method should yield particle size distributions of suspended matter as originally present in the water column. Data obtained from geochemical analyses of size fractionated suspended matter may therefore be interpreted in relation to the chemical characteristics of the surface sediments.

For this study a simple but comprehensive analytical approach was adopted. Only methods that yield information on the bulk composition of the samples were used. After visual examination (both macroscopically and microscopically) suspended matter was chemically characterized by ashing, elemental analysis and analytical pyrolysis. Pyrolysis–gas chromatography–mass spectrometry (Py–GCMS) was used as a qualitative analysis technique for particulate organic matter. A recently developed semi-quantitative pyrolysis–mass spectrometry (Py–MS) method (Van de Meent *et al.*, 1982) served to estimate the amounts of carbohydrate, peptide and lignin present in suspended matter.

EXPERIMENTAL

Sampling

Shortly after entering the Netherlands, the river Rhine splits into several branches, one of which is the river IJssel. Approximately 10 percent of the Rhine water flows through the river IJssel into the Ketelmeer. This sedimentation basin is part of a larger water body, the IJsselmeer. This artificial freshwater basin was created in 1932 when the former Zuiderzee was shut off from the North Sea by the construction of a dam. Suspended matter and sediments were sampled in the period of July 24 to August 1, 1980, at eight locations in this area (Fig. 1). Site 1 was located at Lobith, near the German–Dutch border. Site 2 was located at Kampen, 10 km upstream the mouth of the IJssel into the Ketelmeer. Sites 3–5 and sites 6–8 were located in the Ketelmeer and IJsselmeer respectively.

Suspended matter was collected simultaneously by two different procedures: centrifugation to collect bulk samples and sequential filtration to obtain fractionated material.

Two continuous flow centrifuges were fed through PTFE tubing by a pump submerged at a depth of 1–2 m. The residence time of water in the centrifuges was ~5 sec at 8000 g. At each location several grams of suspended matter were isolated from 200–500 l water.

Water samples for sequential filtration were taken from the same depth with a 5 l-Friedinger sampler. Filtration was carried out in the field, using home-made, magnetically stirred filtration cells ($\phi = 15$ cm),

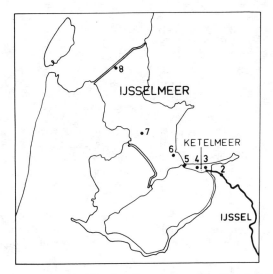

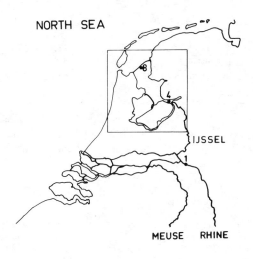

Fig. 1. Geography of the Dutch deltaic area, indicating sampling locations.

pressurized with nitrogen. Filtration speed and particle loads of the filters were kept low and maximum stirring speed was maintained to prevent clogging of the filters. For the first filtration step (60 μm) nylon filtering fabric was used. The next three steps (12 μm, 3 μm and 0.4 μm) were carried out with polycarbonate membrane filters (Nuclepore Co., Pleasanton, CA, USA). Finally, ultrafiltration of the 0.4 μm filtrates was performed using an Amicon model CH4 hollow fibre concentrator, equipped with H1P100 (nominal pore width 5 nm) and H1P2 (nominal pore width 1 nm) cartridges (Amicon B.V., Oosterhout, The Netherlands). The filtration procedure was carried out with four filtration lines simultaneously, processing 5 l of water each. The retentates were quantitatively recovered from the filters and resuspended in a known volume of distilled water. Retentates from two filtration units were combined to finally yield two complete duplicate sets of suspended matter fractions, each sample being the composite of two separate filtration procedures. Of each retentate suspension, a known aliquot was set aside for determination of particle size distributions.

Sediment samples were taken with a small box corer. Only the top few millimeters of the sediment were sampled.

Samples were frozen immediately after collection, transported to the laboratory in dry ice and stored at -35 °C until needed.

Analytical methods

Titration alkalinity and pH of the waters were measured in the field, immediately after sampling. All other analyses were carried out in the laboratory.

Water samples. Hardness, alkalinity, chloride and sulphate were determined according to standard procedures (American Public Health Association, 1976). Ionic strengths were calculated from the above mentioned measurements and published values (Anon., 1981) for sodium.

Suspended matter and sediments. Dry weights of suspended matter for particle size analysis were determined gravimetrically (105 °C) after filtration through pre-weighed polycarbonate membrane filters. Carbonate contents were measured according to Pieters (1948). Total organic matter was determined, after removal of carbonates, as loss of weight on ashing (1 h, 1000 °C). Silicon was measured as loss upon HF treatment of the ash residues. Organic carbon, hydrogen and nitrogen were measured in carbonate-free suspended matter with a Perkin Elmer model 240 CHN analyser.

Pyrolysis–gas chromatography–mass spectrometry (Py–GCMS) was carried out with a Curie-point pyrolysis system as described by Meuzelaar *et al.* (1975), modified for use at high temperatures (Van de Meent *et al.*, 1980a). Small amounts of sample (100–200 μg) in PBS-buffer (0.05 Mol phosphate + 0.15 Mol (NaCl) were applied on ferromagnetic wires (Ni/Fe, Curie temperature 610 °C) and the water was evaporated. Samples were heated for 10 sec. The volatile pyrolysis products were separated on a glass WCOT column (60 m × 0.5 mm) coated with CP-sil 5 (film thickness 1.2 μm). The oven temperature was programmed, after an initial isothermal period of 5 min at -25 °C, at 3 °C/min to 275 °C. Subambient oven temperatures were maintained by means of a cryogenic unit, using liquid nitrogen as a coolant. The gas chromatograph was coupled with a Varian–MAT 44 mass spectrometer, operated at an electron energy of 70 eV and a cycle time of 2 sec. Pyrolysis–mass spectrometry (Py–MS) was carried out with a fully automated instrument, described

Table 1
Some geochemical characteristics of the environment studied

	Sampling Location							
	1	2	3	4	5	6	7	8
Water:								
pH	7.6	7.7	8.01	8.15	8.17	8.14	9.1	9.3
Alkalinity (mMol)	2.0	2.4	2.3	2.2	2.3	2.1	2.1	2.1
O$_2$-saturation (%)	75	72	75	98	82	85	105	140
Ionic strength (mMol)	7.4	8.4	8.1	7.8	7.8	7.4	10.5	11.4
Paticulate matter (mg/l)	35	13	7	16	15	8	9	14
Suspended matter:								
Organic matter (%)	17.6	24	29	25	26	26	60	62
Microscopic observation	diatoms cyano bacteria	diatoms	green algae diatoms	green algae diatoms	green algae diatoms	green algae diatoms cyano bacteria	green algae diatoms	green algae
Sediment:								
Field observation	—	—	pale brown mud	pale brown mud	sandy mud	sand	pale brown mud	green top layer on sand
Organic matter (%)	—	18	18	17	9	—	12	3
Carbonates (% CaCO$_3$)	—	13	12	13	4	—	32	2

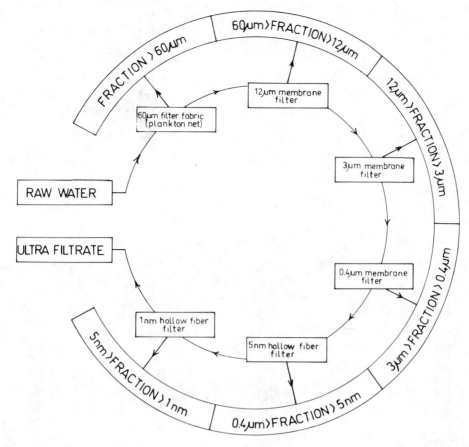

Fig. 2. Size fractionation of suspended particles by sequential filtration.

by Meuzelaar *et al.* (1977). Samples of 25–50 μg were pyrolysed for 1 sec at 510 °C in vacuum. Py–MS data were processed using a discriminant analysis procedure as described by Windig *et al.* (1982).

RESULTS AND DISCUSSION

Chemical characteristics of the water samples

Some of the major characteristics of the waters studied are listed in Table 1. There was a considerable increase in pH, going from the river Rhine (pH = 7.6) to the northern part of the IJsselmeer (pH = 9.3). The titration alkalinity, however, was fairly constant. It can be calculated from known equilibrium data of carbon dioxide–water systems (Stumm and Morgan, 1970) that this means that Rhine water is oversaturated with respect to CO_2, whereas the IJsselmeer water is CO_2^--depleted. Together with the observed O_2^--saturation gradient, this indicates that the pH gradient in these waters is the result of an increase in photosynthetic activity in a downstream direction. As a consequence of the high pH values in the IJsselmeer, $CaCO_3$ precipitates in this area (Salomons and Mook, 1980). This leads to rather high concentrations of calcite in the IJsselmeer sediments (e.g. location 7; Table 1).

The concentrations of most major ions were much lower at the river locations than in the IJsselmeer.

However, quarterly reports on the quality of Dutch waters (Anon., 1980; 1981) show that normally the concentrations of major ions decrease in a downstream direction. The observed low concentrations at the river Rhine can be explained by the exceptionally high river discharge at the time of sampling. As a result of the relatively long residence time of water in the IJsselmeer (~6 months), normal concentrations were measured here.

Extreme hydrodynamic conditions are generally expected to influence the suspended matter load of the river both qualitatively and quantitatively (Jansen *et al.*, 1979; Salomons and Eysink, 1982). However, at the time of sampling (several days after the discharge peak) the total particulate matter concentration at the river Rhine had a rather normal value, which may be taken as an indication that the system had restablized already. Influences of the high discharge on the chemical composition of suspended matter may therefore be limited.

Fractionation of suspended matter

Sampling by sequential filtration resulted in six size fractions of suspended matter (Fig. 2): Fr. > 60 μm, 60 μm > Fr. > 12 μm, 12 μm > Fr. > 3 μm, 3 μm > Fr. > 0.4 μm, 0.4 μm > Fr. > 5 nm and 5 nm > Fr. > 1 nm. The quantitative reproducibility of the fractionation procedure, as characterized by the relative standard deviation in the duplicate analyses on eight sampling

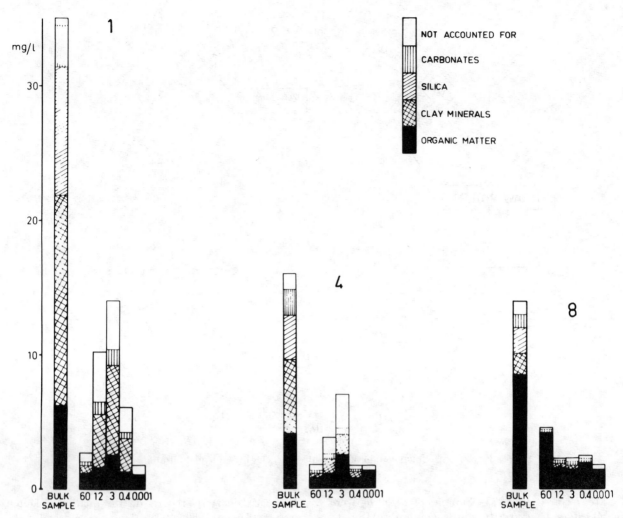

Fig. 3. Particle size distributions and chemical composition of suspended matter from the river Rhine (1), the Ketelmeer (4) and the IJsselmeer (8).

locations, was ~20%. This implies an uncertainty in the mean of two observations (on which the calculation of particle size distributions is based) of 25% at the 90% confidence level. A further source of inaccuracy may be the filtration procedure itself. The actual particle size distribution may have been altered by the various manipulations (exposure to high shear stresses during stirring and passage through narrow holes; temporary high concentrations of particles; temperature changes). Uncertainty remains as to the extent of the alterations.

Particle size distributions of suspended matter from the river Rhine, the Ketelmeer and the IJsselmeer are given in Fig. 3. In these diagrams the fractions obtained by the 5 nm and 1 nm filters are combined in the bars designated '0.001'. It appears that substantial amounts of material that are usually defined as 'dissolved' on the bases of the ability to pass a 0.4 μm filter, are actually ultrafiltrable. It would therefore be better to call this fraction 'colloidal' or preferably 'smaller than 0.4 μm' rather than 'dissolved'. The highest total amounts of particulate matter were observed at the river Rhine. The size distributions of suspended matter from the river Rhine and the Ketelmeer are rather similar. Selective sedimentation of particles with a relatively high density, but with a wide range of grain sizes, would thus be the

most likely way to explain the differences between the sites 1 and 4. Suspended matter from the IJsselmeer had a significantly different particle size distribution. This may be explained by the high productivity in the IJsselmeer water, which causes a high contribution of autochthonously produced biomass to the suspended matter.

Chemical characterization of suspended matter

Suspended matter was characterized in terms of carbonate, silica, clay mineral and organic matter contents. The amounts of these components were estimated from elemental analyses. According to Van Eck (1982) the clay minerals present in suspended matter from the river Rhine (mainly illite with minor amounts of kaolinite) contain approximately 25% aluminium and 14% silicon. In our calculations we assumed that aluminium was present mainly in clay minerals. Silicon in excess of the amount calculated to be present in the clay minerals was assumed to occur as silica (quartz and/or diatom skeletons). Carbonates, expressed as %$CaCO_3$, were either measured directly

Table 2
Chemical composition of suspended matter

Sample		% of total suspended matter	Measured (% dry weight)						Calculated (% dry weight)			
			C_{org}	H	N	Al	Si	Ca	Organic matter	Carbonates	Clay minerals	Silica
no. 1	bulk sample	100	6.0	1.4	1.1	6.35	23.7	3.58	17.6	9	45	27
no. 1	60 μm retentate	8	21	2.2	0.6	3.1	—	2.7	45	7	22	—
no. 1	12 μm retentate	30	7	1	1	5.5	—	3.4	16	9	39	—
no. 1	3 μm retentate	41	8	1	1	6.7	—	3.1	18	8	48	—
no. 1	0.4 μm retentate	18	10	1.6	0.7	5.8	—	2.4	22	6	41	—
no. 1	5 nm retentate	2	21	3.0	4.0	—	—	—	49	—	—	—
no. 1	1 nm retentate	3	37	4.5	—	—	—	—	84	—	—	—
no. 4	bulk sample	100	9.7	1.9	2.6	4.80	18.4	4.98	25.8	12	34	21
no. 4	60 μm retentate	11	20	2.6	2.5	2.9	—	1.9	45	5	21	—
no. 4	12 μm retentate	24	12	2	2	3.4	—	3.7	28	9	31	—
no. 4	3 μm retentate	44	16	2	2	3.8	—	2.7	36	7	36	—
no. 4	0.4 μm retentate	11	20	2.8	3.0	3.5	—	1.7	46	4	30	—
no. 4	5 nm retentate	4	29	3.8	4.1	—	—	—	66	—	—	—
no. 4	1 nm retentate	7	38	4.8	6.4	—	—	—	87	—	—	—
no. 8	bulk sample	100	27.0	4.3	4.4	1.60	9.4	4.30	61.0	7	11	14
no. 8	60 μm retentate	34	41	5.6	5.2	—	—	1.4	93	4	—	—
no. 8	12 μm retentate	17	32	4	5	1.8	—	4.1	73	10	13	—
no. 8	3 μm retentate	18	28	4	4	1.7	—	3.5	64	9	12	—
no. 8	0.4 μm retentate	18	36	5	5	—	—	—	82	7	—	—
no. 8	5 nm retentate	6	37	5.1	5.0	—	—	—	84	—	—	—
no. 8	1 nm retentate	7	37	4.6	3.8	—	—	—	82	—	—	—

(bulk samples) or calculated from the measured calcium contents (suspended matter fractions). Organic matter contents were derived from ashing, or, in those cases where no reliable ash content measurements were available, estimated on the basis of the empirical relationship:

$$\text{organic matter} = 2 \times \%C_{org} + \%H + \%N.$$

Carbonates, silica, clay minerals and organic matter accounted for over 90% of the total dry weight of the bulk samples (Table 2). At all the sampling locations the organic matter content of the fractionated material was significantly higher than that of the bulk samples. Apparently, a considerable fraction of the particulate organic matter of relatively low density (e.g. micro-organisms) was not recovered by the centrifugation procedure. As a consequence of the relatively low amounts of suspended matter sampled by filtration, no silicon determinations could be done on the fractionated material and hence no silica contents were calculated. It may be expected, however, that a large part of the material 'not accounted for' (Fig. 3) is actually silica.

Absolute amounts (per litre water) of clay minerals, silica and carbonates decreased downstream. Organic matter exhibited an opposite trend: the highest abundances of particulate organics were observed in the IJsselmeer. The increase in abundance of organic matter is paralleled by an increase in abundance of phytoplankton, as observed by microscopy. At the river locations, diatoms (*Melosira, Stephanodiscus, Asterionella*) were the most frequently observed organisms, whereas at the IJsselmeer green algae (*Scenedesmus, Coelastrum, Ulothrix*) dominated. Cyanobacteria (mainly *Oscillatoria*)

were only observed in major quantities at site 6, in the southern part of the IJsselmeer (Table 1).

With exception of the fractions retained by the ultrafilters (5 nm and 1 nm) which were very rich in organic matter in all cases, the differences in mineralogical composition between the various size fractions from one location were less pronounced (Table 2). Mineral contents were highest in the fractions retained by the 12 μm and 3 μm filters, whereas organic matter concentrations were relatively high in the 60 μm and 0.4 μm retentates. These results seem to reflect the heterogeneous nature of the suspended matter particles (flocs), differing only slightly in overall chemical composition.

The variations in the chemical composition of suspended matter from various locations in this area are thought to be the result of two simultaneously operating processes. At relatively short distances from the river mouth (Ketelmeer), preferential sedimentation of mineral-rich particles with a relatively high density causes an enrichment of organic matter in the remaining suspended particles. At longer distances from the river mouth (IJsselmeer), further sedimentation of allochthonous (fluvial) suspended matter and extensive production of autochthonous material (algal bloom) results in the occurrence of highly organic lacustrine suspended matter.

Analysis of organic matter

Qualitative analysis by Py–GCMS. Prior to analysis by Py–GCMS all samples were analysed by Py–GC. On the basis of the gas chromatographic

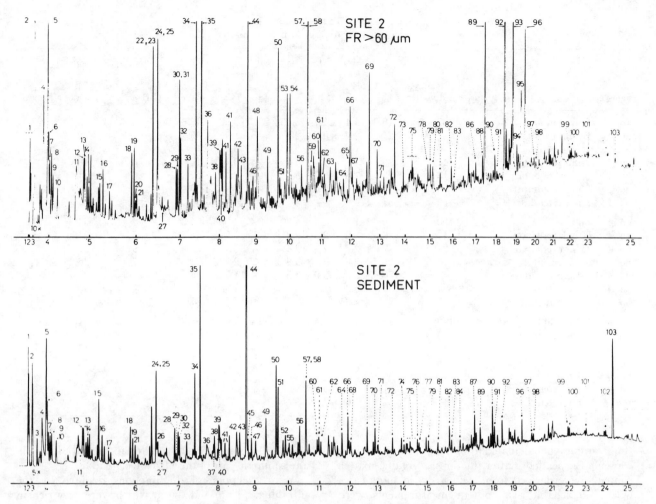

Fig. 4. Py–GCMS of suspended particles > 60 μm and surface sediment from location 2 (Kampen). Peak identifications are given in Table 3. For experimental conditions: see text.

pyrogrammes, samples were selected for analysis by Py–GCMS. Pyrolysis products were identified by comparison of their gas chromatographic retention indices and their mass spectra with literature data (Zweig and Sherma, 1972; Lee *et al.*, 1979; Grzybowski *et al.*, 1980; Ramsey *et al.*, 1980; Schröder, 1980; Stenhagen *et al.*, 1969; Urbach and Stark, 1975). The results of the Py–GCMS analyses of suspended matter, retained by a 60 μm filter (Fr. > 60 μm) and surface sediment, both sampled at location no. 2, are shown in Fig. 4 and Table 3. Most of the major compounds are well-known pyrolysis products of biologically produced substances (carbohydrates, peptides, lipids, chlorophyll), although a number of compounds, especially in the case of the sediment sample, clearly indicate the presence of pollutants: oil, coal, PCBs, synthetic polymers (polystyrene, polymethametacrylate, silicones). A number of peaks can be attributed to the presence of lignin. The origin of this material is uncertain. It may arise from natural sources (terrestrial higher plants) as well as from industrial activity. Wood pulp manufacture has been named as a source of both organic solids and lingosulphonic acids in the river Rhine (IAWR, 1974).

The differences between the various samples were quantitative rather than qualitative: the same products were found in all pyrolysates, albeit in different concentrations. These results agree well with our earlier investigations of particulate organic matter from this area (Van de Meent *et al.*, 1980b, 1980c) and with similar reports of others (Sigleo *et al.*, 1980; Etcheber *et al.*, 1981). We therefore conclude that a substantial part of the organic matter in suspended particles and surface sediments from this area consists of freshly produced biologic material.

Fingerprinting Py–MS. Pyrolysis–MS analyses were carried out in triplicate in order to evaluate the significance of the differences between the mass spectrometric pyrograms of different samples. Py–MS data were processed using a combined factor analysis/discriminant analysis procedure, recently developed by Windig *et al.* (1982). For our data, this procedure resulted in two discriminant functions describing 70% of the significant variance between the spectra of different samples on the basis of 44% of the variance in the original dataset. A plot of these two new variables (Fig. 5) serves to quantitatively evaluate the differences and similarities between the samples. The scores of the various spectra on these discriminant functions indicate to what extent the individual spectra deviate from their mean spectrum.

Table 3

Pyrolysis products of suspended matter and sediment from location 2 (Kampen) as identified by Py–CGMS

Peak no.[a]	Retention index[b]	Compound	Molecular weight	Possible origin[c]	Peak no.[a]	Retention index[b]	Compound	Molecular weight	Possible origin[c]
1	1.00	carbon monoxide	28			6.32	C_6H_8	80	
1		carbon dioxide	44		22	6.36	3-methylbutanal	86	Ps
1		ethylene oxide	42		23	6.36	C_6H_8	80	
1		hydrogen cyanide	27	Pr	24	6.46	2-methylbutanal	86	Ps
					25	6.46	benzene	78	
1		ethene	28		26	6.50	thiophene	84	
1	2.00	ethane	30			6.54	cyclohexane	84	
1	2.30	hydrogen sulphide	34	Pr	27	6.6	acetic acid	60	Ps
1	2.65	ketene	42			6.70	cyclohexene	82	
2	2.85	carbonylsulphide	60	Pr	28	6.88	n-hept-1-ene	98	Lp
2	2.90	propene	42		29	6.91	1-cyano-2-methylpropane	82	Pr
2	3.00	propane	44						
3	3.30	chloromethane	50		30	6.96	2,5-dimethylfuran	96	Ps
	3.50	2-methylpropane	58		31	6.96	methylmetacrylate	100	Pol
4	3.60	acetaldehyde	44	Ps	32	7.00	n-heptane	100	Lp
5	3.85	2-methylpropene	56			7.05	dimethylfuran	96	Ps
6	3.92	n-but-1-ene + buta-1,5-diene	56,54		33	7.18	N-methylpyrrole	81	Pr
						7.28	C_7H_8	92	
7	4.00	n-butane	58		34	7.39	pyrrole	67	Pr
8	4.05	methanethiol	48	Pr	35	7.52	toluene	92	Pr, Lg
9	4.09	trans but-2-ene	56			7.61	methylthiophene	98	
10	4.20	cis but-2-ene	56			7.67	2-methylheptane	114	
	4.51	3-methylpent-1-ene	70		36	7.72	pivalolactam??	99	Pr?
	4.69	2-methylbutane	72		37	7.8	furan derivative	96	Ps
11	4.80	acetone	58	Ps	38	7.89	n-oct-1-ene	112	Lp
12	4.88	n-pent-1-ene	70			7.97	oct-2-ene	112	Lp
13	4.90	furan	68	Ps	39	8.00	n-octane	114	Lp
	4.96	2-methylpent-1-ene	70		40	8.04	2-furaldehyde?	96	Ps
14	5.00	n-pentane	72		41	8.18	methylpyrrole	81	Pr
	5.04	2-methylbuta-1,3-diene (isoprene)	68		41	8.29	methylpyrrole	81	Pr
					42	8.48	ethylbenzene	106	Pr, Lg
	5.09	trans pent-2-ene	70		43	8.57	m- and/or p-xylene	106	Pr, Lg
	5.14	Carbon disulphide	76	Pr	44	8.74	styrene	104	Pol
	5.16	cis pent-2-ene	70		45	8.78	o-xylene	106	Lg
	5.20	2-methylbut-2-ene	70			8.85	furan derivative	110	Ps
15	5.23	dichloromethane + penta-2,3-diene	64,68		46	8.89	n-non-1-ene	126	Lp
16	5.30	cyclopentadiene	66			8.98	C_2-pyrrole	95	Pr
	5.35	penta-2,3-diene	68		47	9.00	n-nonane	128	Lp
17	5.43	2-methylpropanal	72	Pa	48	9.05	unknown		
	5.48	cyclopentene	68		49	9.31	benzaldehyde + $C_{3:1}$-benzene	106, 118	Lg
	5.55	3-methylpent-1-ene	84			9.36	C_3-benzene	120	
	5.69	2-methylpentane	86			9.37	furan derivative	110	Ps
18	5.89	n-hex-1-ene	84	Lp		9.49	cyanobenzene	103	Pr
19	5.95	2-methylfuran	82	Ps		9.51	C_3-benzene	120	
20	5.98	2-cyanopropane	69	Pr		9.57	C_3-benzene	120	
21	6.00	n-hexane	86	PLp	50	9.62	phenol	94	Lg, Pr
	6.04	3-methylfuran	82	Ps	51	9.67	alpha-methyl styrene	118	Pol
	6.06	hexene + hexadiene	84,82			9.77	$C_{3:1}$-benzene	118	
	6.27	C_6H_6	78						

The mean spectrum and the 'factor spectra', corresponding to the first two discriminant functions are given in Fig. 6. Considering the Py–MS data as fingerprints (Fig. 5), it can be seen that the quantitative differences between the spectra reflect both the physical origin and the geographic origin of the samples. Suspended matter fractions, retained by the smallest filters (1 nm, 5 nm, 0.4 μm), from all locations, and sediments from the Ketelmeer area appear to be different from other samples. Disregarding the physical origin, samples from the IJsselmeer (locations 7 and 8)

are different from those taken at the river Rhine (location 1).

The spectral characteristics on which the observed differences are based indicate that the colloidal suspended matter fractions, retained by the 5 nm ultrafilter (0.4 μm > Fr. > 5 nm) contain relatively high amounts of a specific type of carbohydrates, presumably algal exopolymers. This is tentatively concluded from the presence of a characteristic suite of peaks in the negative part of the first discriminant function (m/z = 59, 73, 85, 99, 114, 128), indicative for deoxyhexoses,

Table 3 (continued)

Peak no.[a]	Retention index[b]	Compound	Molecular weight	Possible origin[c]	Peak no.[a]	Retention index[b]	Compound	Molecular weight	Possible origin[c]
	9.81	C$_3$-benzene	120		77	14.53	2,5,9-trimethyltridecane	226	Lp, Pol?
	9.86	dichlorobenzene	146	Pol		14.74	2-methoxy-4-acetylphenol	166	Lg
52	9.89	n-dec-1-ene	140	Lp					
	9.92	dichlorobenzene	146	Pol	78	14.89	n-pentadec-1-ene	210	Lp
53	9.96	unknown	112		79	15.00	n-pentadecane	212	Lp
54	9.98	unknown	112		80	15.06	unknown		
55	10.00	n-decane	142	Lp		15.2	C$_3$-naphthalenes	170	
	10.08	C$_3$-benzene	120		81	15.25	dodecanoic acid	200	Lp
	10.10	C$_{3:1}$-benzene	118		82	15.89	n-hexadec-1-ene	224	Lp
	10.14	dichlorobenzene	146	Pol	83	16.00	n-hexadecane	226	Lp
	10.20	C$_{3:1}$-benzene	118		84	16.33	4-hydroxy-3,5-dimethoxybenzaldehyde	182	Lg
	10.27	indene	116						
56	10.33	o-cresol	108	Lg	85	16.90	n-heptadec-1-ene	238	Lp
	10.37	acetophenone	120	Lg	86	17.00	n-heptadecane	240	Lp
	10.45	C$_4$-benzene	134		87	17.10	pristane	268	Pol
57	10.49	p-cresol	108	Lg, Pr	88	17.36	prist-1-ene	266	Lp
58	10.54	m-cresol	108	Lg	89	17.43	tetradecanoic acid	228	Lp
59	10.62	2-methyoxyphenol (guaiacol)	124	Lg		17.68	phenanthrene	178	Pol
	10.83	dimethylphenol	122	Lg		17.79	anthracene	178	Pol
60	10.89	n-undec-1-ene	154	Lp	90	17.91	n-octadec-1-ene	252	Lp
61	10.93	phenyl cyanomethane	117	Pr	91	18.00	n-octadecane	254	Lp
62	11.00	n-undecane	156	Lp		18.14	phytane	282	Pol
63	11.26	C$_2$-phenol	122	Lg	92	18.36	phytadiene	278	Chl
	11.35	methylindene	130			18.44	phytene	280	Chl
	11.44	C$_2$-phenol	122	Lg		18.56	phytadiene	278	Chl
	11.47	C$_2$-phenol	122	Lg	93	18.73	phytadiene	278	Chl
	11.60	trichlorobenzene	180	Pol	94	18.90	n-nonadec-1-ene	266	Lp
64	11.67	naphthalene	128			19.00	n-nonadecane	268	Lp
65	11.89	n-dodec-1-ene	168	Lp	95	19.20	dibutylphtalate	278	Pol
66	11.92	p-vinylphenol	120	Lg	96	19.40	hexadecanoic acid	256	Lp
67	11.98	unknown			97	19.92	n-eicos-1-ene	280	Lp
68	12.00	n-dodecane	170	Lp	98	20.00	n-eicosane	282	Lp
	12.51	isoquinoline	129	Lg, Pr		20.53	pyrene	202	Pol
69	12.60	indole	117	Pr		20.91	n-heneicos-1-ene	294	Lp
	12.79	2-methylnaphthalene	142			21.00	n-heneicosane	296	Lp
70	12.88	methoxyacetophenone?	150	Lg	99	21.91	n-docos-1-ene	308	Lp
	12.95	1-methylnaphthalene	142		100	22.00	n-docosane	310	Lp
71	13.00	n-tridecane	184	Lp		22.91	n-tricos-1-ene	322	Lp
72	13.68	methylindole	131	Pr	101	23.00	n-tricosane	324	Lp
73	13.89	n-tetradec-1-ene	196	Lp		23.91	n-tetracos-1-ene	336	Lp
74	14.00	1-tetradecane	198	Lp	102	24.00	n-tetracosane	338	Lp
75		C$_2$-naphthalenes	156		103	24.28	1,3-diphenylpropene	194	Pol
76	14.48	2-methoxy-4-propenylphenol (isoeugenol)	164	Lg					

[a] Peak number as shown in Fig. 4.

[b] Measured by linear interpolation from temperature-programmed chromatograms.

[c] Pr-protein; Ps = polysaccharide; Lp = lipid; Chl = chlorophyll; Pol = pollutant.

pentoses and possibly NAc-containing carbohydrates (Meuzelaar et al., 1982). Similar reasoning suggests that the fractions, retained by the 1 nm ultrafilter (5 nm > Fr. > 1 nm) are rich in lignosulphonic acid-type material and that sedimentary organic matter from the Ketelmeer area (locations 2–5) exhibits definite lignin characteristics (negative part of the second discriminant function). Bulk samples of suspended matter, the larger size fractions of suspended matter and surface sediments from the IJsselmeer (locations 7 and 8) appear to be relatively rich in peptides and less specific (storage?)

polysaccharides (positive parts of first and second discriminant functions).

Quantitative analysis of biopolymers. It follows from the above paragraph that pyrolysis mass spectra contain quantitative indications about the chemical composition of particulate organic matter. We have recently shown that Py–MS can be used as a semi-quantitative analysis technique for samples of which the qualitative composition is known (Van de Meent et al., 1982). Basically, this method calibrates the pyrolysis

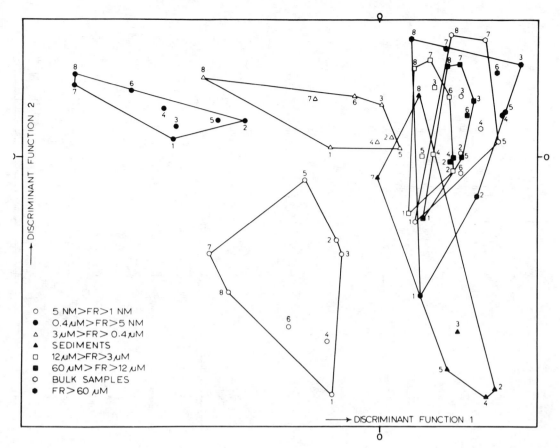

Fig. 5. DF1/DF2-plot for Py–MS data of fractionated suspended matter from the downstream course of the river Rhine. Numbers refer to sampling locations given in Fig. 1.

mass spectra of unknowns against spectra of pure components and mixtures of these components. To do so, plots of discriminant functions as shown in Fig. 5 are used. Sample compositions are then deduced from the orientation of the sample points, relative to the calibration points. As this method of calculation assumes that the pyrolysis mass spectrum of a sample can, in first approximation, be described as a linear combination of spectra of pure components, the method is extremely sensitive to the choice of the calibration components. Based upon the qualitative information obtained by Py–GCMS and fingerprinting Py–MS, we have selected the natural polysaccharide dextran, the protein bovine serum albumin and the higher plant derived lignosulphonic acid as calibration compounds.

Table 4 lists the results of this semi-quantitative analysis of particulate organic matter by Py–MS. For comparison, the results of polysaccharide and protein analyses, obtained after hydrolysis and monomer analysis of the bulk samples, are also given in this table. It is evident that the pyrolysis method results in estimates for the polysaccharide and protein contents much higher than those obtained by classical methods. Two reasons can be proposed to explain this discrepancy. First, the results from Py–MS must be regarded as high estimates since this method assumes that the pyrolysate as analysed by Py–MS represents the total organic matter in the sample. This is not necessarily correct: the sample may contain organic substances, the pyrolysis products of which are not amenable to the mass spectrometric

analysis technique. An example of such substances are lipids, yielding products of low volatility that, under the experimental conditions employed, do not enter the ion source of the mass spectrometer. Secondly, monomer analysis after hydrolysis of the sample always yields conservative estimates, due to incomplete hydrolysis and destruction or repolymerization of the monomeric products. As a result, the true polysaccharide and protein contents are expected to lie somewhere in between these two extremes. In spite of these difficulties, the polysaccharide-to-protein ratios obtained by the two methods agree rather well, taking into account the experimental errors. The semi-quantitative estimates from Py–MS may therefore serve to indicate trends in the biopolymer contents of the various samples. Being aware of the limitations of the analytical method, we observe that the data in Table 4 do indeed contain such trends:

1. The lignin content of suspended matter decreases in downstream direction. Since lignin-rich particulate matter (e.g. higher plant debris) originates from terrestrial or industrial sources, this indicates that there is a downstream decrease in allochthonous contribution to the suspended matter. Combining this observation with the measurements of total suspended matter and the organic matter contents (Fig. 3), we conclude that between site 1 (Rhine) and site 4 (Ketelmeer) a net loss of lignin from the water phase occurs. As a result, surface sediments in

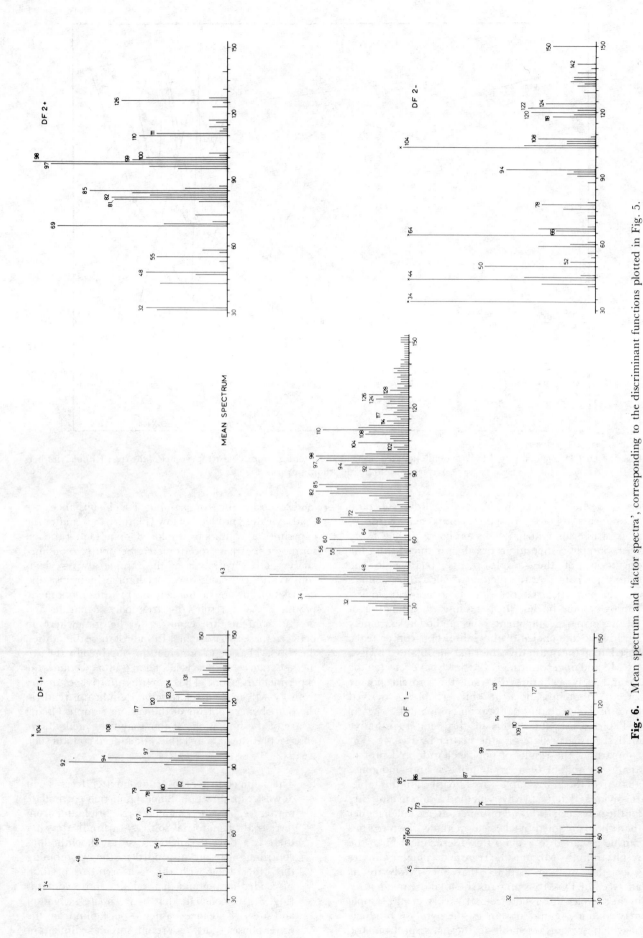

Fig. 6. Mean spectrum and 'factor spectra', corresponding to the discriminant functions plotted in Fig. 5.

Table 4

Semi-quantitative analysis of biopolymers in particulate organic matter based on Py–MS analyses

Sample	Measured by pyrolysis–MS[a]				Measured by hydrolysis[b]		
	Polysaccharide	Protein	Lignin	PS/PR[c]	Polysaccharide	Protein	PS/PR[c]
1 bulk sample	25	60	15	0.4	6	13	0.5
2 bulk sample	30	60	10	0.5	11	17	0.6
3 bulk sample	40	50	10	0.8	20	17	1.2
4 bulk sample	30	60	10	0.5	7	17	0.4
5 bulk sample	30	60	10	0.5	7	20	0.4
6 bulk sample	25	65	10	0.4	7	20	0.4
7 bulk sample	45	55	5	0.8	14	27	0.5
8 bulk sample	50	50	5	1.0	21	25	0.8
1 Fr. >60 μm	30	50	20	0.6	—	—	—
4 Fr. >60 μm	30	65	10	0.5	—	—	—
8 Fr. >60 μm	60	35	5	1.7	—	—	—
1–60 μm > Fr. >12 μm	25	60	15	0.4	—	—	—
4–60 μm > Fr. >12 μm	30	60	15	0.5	—	—	—
8–60 μm > Fr. >12 μm	45	50	10	0.9	—	—	—
1–12 μm > Fr. >3 μm	30	55	20	0.5	—	—	—
4–12 μm > Fr. >3 μm	25	65	10	0.4	—	—	—
8–12 μm > Fr. >3 μm	40	55	10	0.7	—	—	—
1–3 μm > Fr. >0.4 μm	20	60	15	0.3	—	—	—
4–3 μm > Fr. >0.4 μm	20	65	15	0.3	—	—	—
8–3 μm > Fr. >0.4 μm	35	50	15	0.7	—	—	—

[a] Percentage of the pyrolysate.
[b] Percentage ash-free dry weight.
[c] Polysaccharide-to-protein ratio.

the Ketelmeer must be relatively rich in allochthonous organic matter. As stated earlier, Py–MS fingerprints of these samples indicate that this is indeed the case. Beyond the Ketelmeer the absolute amounts of particulate lignin in the water remains constant. The further decrease in lignin content of suspended matter can be attributed to a net autochthonous production of particulate matter. As a consequence, surface sediments from the IJsselmeer are expected to receive a highly autochthonous input. Again, this is supported by the Py–MS analyses which show that these sediments, particularly that from the northerly IJsselmeer (site 8), are relatively rich in polysaccharides.

2. Suspended matter from the IJsselmeer (sites 7 and 8) is relatively rich in polysaccharides. In view of the high amounts of particulate organic matter in these waters and the abundance of green algae observed by microscopy, this must be the result of a high polysaccharide content of the autochthonously produced biomass. Literature data (Huc, 1980; Yen, 1975) suggest that green algae are generally rich in polysaccharides.

3. The variations in polymer contents of the larger size fractions of particulate (>0.4 μm) matter from one location are small in comparison with the differences observed among the samples from different locations.

Similar observations were made with respect to the overall chemical composition of these suspended matter fractions (Table 2). These findings are consistent with the idea that the larger size fractions of suspended matter consist of heterogeneous agglomerates of various types of mineral and organic particles, biologically active material and organic and inorganic colloids. Such flocs were microscopically observed by Uiterwijk Winkel (unpublished data) in various samples of Rhine water.

CONCLUSIONS

1. A substantial part of the particulate organic matter, especially in the IJsselmeer, consists of carbohydrates and peptides, originating from autochthonously produced biomass.

2. Particle size distributions and chemical compositions of suspended matter appear to be controlled by two major processes. At short distances from the river mouth (Ketelmeer), sedimentation of mineral-rich allochthonous material dominates. By this process, suspended matter is enriched in organics. Sediments in this area receive a predominantly allochthonous input, relatively rich in lignin. At longer distances from the river mouth (IJsselmeer), autochthonous production of suspended matter (algal bloom) causes a further increase of the organic matter content of the suspended particles. Chemical compositions of surface sediments in this area reflect the productivity in the overlying water column.

3. At each location size fractions of suspended matter retained by 60 μm, 12 μm and 3 μm filters are chemically rather similar. This indicates that particles of this size consist of heterogeneous aggregates

of various types of mineral and (bio)ortanic matter. Unfiltrable (5 nm) material has a markedly different chemical composition. This highly organic material is rich in carbohydrates. It is suggested that this colloidal matter originates from microbial exopolymers.

4. Carbohydrates, peptides and lignin, major constituents of particulate organic matter, have been semi-quantitatively determined by means of pyrolysis mass spectrometry.

Acknowledgements

This research was sponsored by the Dutch Ministry of Public Health and Environmental Hygiene. We are greatly indebted to the Public Works Department, the crew of the m.v. *Dr. Ir. de Bloc van Kuffeler* and to Irene Rijpstra, Marianne Baas and Hans van der Knaap for technical assistance during the sampling. Microscopic examinations were done by Drs Jaap Olie of the Limnologic Institute (Nieuwersluis, The Netherlands). Elly Bakker of the Chemical Engineering Laboratory (Delft University of Technology) carried out the CHN analyses and the silicon determinations. We thank Mr A. van Estrik and Dr P. J. W. Schuyl of the Organic Chemistry Laboratory (Delft University of Technology) for their contributions to the amino acid determinations and Py–GCMS analyses respectively. Anneke Tom and Bea Brandt of the F.O.M. Institute for Atomic and Molecular Physics (Amsterdam, The Netherlands) are kindly acknowledged for assistance with the Py–MS analyses.

REFERENCES

American Public Health Association (1976) *Standard Methods for the Examination of Water and Wastewater*, 14th edition, ed. by Rand, M. C., Greenberg, A. E. and Taris, M. J. APHA, Washington, D.C.

Anonymous (1980) *Kwaliteitsonderzoek in de Rijkswateren. Verslag over de resultaten van het derde kwartaal.*

Anonymous (1981) *Kwaliteitsonderzoek in de Rijkswateren. Verslag over de resultaten van het derde kwartaal.*

Balistrieri, L., Brewer, P. G. and Murray, J. W. (1981) Scavenging residence times of trace metals and surface chemistry in sinking particles in the deep ocean. *Deep Sea Res.* **28A**, 101–121.

Beck, K. C., Reuter, J. H. and Perdue, E. M. (1974) Organic and inorganic geochemistry of some coastal plain rivers of the Southeastern United States. *Geochim. Cosmochim. Acta* **38**, 341–364.

Christman, R. F. and Minear, R. A. (1971) Organics in lakes. In *Organic compounds in aquatic environments*, ed. by Faust, S. J. and Hunter, J. V. Marcel Dekker, New York, pp. 119–143.

Etcheber, H., Jouanneau, J. M. and Relaxans, J. C. (1981) Seasonal Zn cycles of suspended material in the upper part of the Gironde estuary (France). The role of organic matter. In *Heavy Metals in the Environment, Proceedings of the 5th International Conference, Amsterdam, September 1981*, ed. by Ernst, W. H. O., pp. 363–366.

Förstner, U. and Salomons, W. (1982) Trace element speciation in surface waters: interactions with particulate matter. In *Trace Element Speciation in Superficial Waters and its Ecological Implications, Proceedings NATO Workshop, Genova, Italy, November 1981*, ed. by Leppard. Plenum Press, New York.

Grzybowski, J., Lamparczyk, H., Nasal, A. and Radecki, A. (1980) Relationship between the retention indices of phenols on polar and non-polar stationary phases. *J. Chromatogr.* **196**, 217–223.

Hooghoudt, S. B. (1945) Een gecombineerde zeef- en pipetmethode voor de bepaling van de granulaire samenstelling van gronden. *Versl. Landbouwkd. Onderz.* **50**, 671–693.

Huc, A. Y. (1980) Origin and formation of organic matter in recent sediments and its relation to kerogen. In *Kerogen*, ed. by Durand, B. Editions Technip, Paris, pp. 445–474.

IAWR (1974) *Jahresbericht '74*. Internationale Arbeitsgemeinschaft der Wasserwerke im Rheineinzugsgebiet, Amsterdam.

Jansen, P. Ph., Van Bendegon, L., Van den Berg, J., De Vries, M. and Zanen, A. (1979) *Principles of River Engineering. The Alluvial River*. Pitman Press, London.

Lee, M. L., Vassilaros, D. L., White, C. M. and Novotny, M. (1979) Retention indices for programmed-temperature capillary-column gas chromatography of polycyclic aromatic hydrocarbons. *Anal. Chem.* **51**, 768–773.

Meuzelaar, H. L. C., Ficke, H. G. and Den Harinck, H. C. (1975) Fully automated Curie-point pyrolysis gas–liquid chromatography. *J. Chromatogr. Sci.* **13**, 12–17.

Meuzelaar, H. L. C., Kistemaker, P. G., Eshuis, W. and Engel, H. W. B. (1977) Progress in automated and computerized characterization of microorganisms by pyrolysis mass-spectrometry. In *Rapid Methods and Automation in Microbiology*, ed. by Johnston, H. H. and Newson, S. W. B. Learned Information, Oxford, pp. 225–230.

Meuzelaar, H. L. C., Haverkamp, J. and Hileman, F. D. (1982) *Curie-point Pyrolysis Mass-spectrometry of Biomaterials*. Elsevier, Amsterdam.

Pieters, H. A. J. (1948) Notes on analytical procedures I. Determination of carbon dioxide. *Anal. Chim. Acta* **2**, 263–266.

Pilkington, E. S. and Warren, L. J. (1979) Determination of heavy-metal distribution in marine sediments. *Environ. Sci. Technol.* **13**, 295–299.

Ramsey, J. D., Lee, T. D., Osselton, M. C. and Moffat, A. C. (1980) Gas–liquid chromatographic retention indices of 296 non-drug substances on SE-30 or OV-1 likely to be encountered in toxicological analyses. *J. Chromatogr.* **184**, 206.

Reuter, J. H. and Perdue, E. M. (1977) Importance of heavy metal–organic matter interactions in natural waters. *Geochim. Cosmochim. Acta* **41**, 325–334.

Saiz-Jimenez, C., Haider, K. and Meuzelaar, H. L. C. (1979) Comparison of soil organic matter and its fractions by pyrolysis mass-spectrometry. *Geoderma* **22**, 25–37.

Salomons, W. and Mook, W. G. (1980) Biogeochemical processes affecting metal concentrations in lake sediments (IJsselmeer, The Netherlands). *Sci. Total Environ.* **16**, 217–239.

Salomons, W. and Eysink, W. D. (1982) Pathways of mud and particulate metals to the Southern North Sea. In *Holocene Sedimentation in the North Sea Basin*, ed. by Nio, S. D., Schüttenhelm, R. T. E. and van Weering, T. C. E. Blackwell Scientific Publishers (in Press).

Schröder, H. (1980) Retention indices of hydrocarbons up to C_{14} for the stationary phase squalane. *J. High Resolution Chromatogr. C.C.* **3**, 38–44, 96–100, 200–204, 363–370.

Sigleo, A. C., Hoering, T. C. and Hare, P. E. (1980) The colloidal organic matter in waters of the Chesapeake Bay and the Patuxent River. *Carnegie Institution of Washington Yearbook 79*, pp. 394–399.

Stenhagen, E., Abrahamson, S. and McLafferty, F. W. (1969) *Atlas of Mass-spectral Data.* Interscience, New York.

Stumm, W. and Morgan, J. J. (1970) *Aquatic Chemistry, an Introduction Emphasising Chemical Equilibria in Natural Waters.* Wiley-Interscience, New York.

Thompson, S. and Eglinton, G. (1978) The fractionation of a recent sediment for organic geochemical analysis. *Geochim. Cosmochim. Acta* **42**, 199–207.

Urbach, G. and Stark, S. (1975) The C_{20}-hydrocarbons of butter fat. *J. Agr. Food Chem.* **23**, 20–24.

Van de Meent, D., Brown, S. C., Philp, R. P. and Simoneit, B. R. T. (1980a) Pyrolysis-high resolution gas chromatography and pyrolysis gas chromatography–mass-spectrometry of kerogens and kerogen precursors. *Geochim. Cosmochim. Acta* **44**, 999–1013.

Van de Meent, D., De Leeuw, J. W. and Schenck, P. A. (1980b) Chemical characterization of non-volatile organics in suspended matter and sediments from the river Rhine delta. *J. Anal. Appl. Pyrol.* **2**, 249–263.

Van de Meent, D., De Leeuw, J. W. and Schenck, P. A. (1980c) Origin of unsaturated isoprenoid hydrocarbons in pyrolysates of suspended matter and surface sediments. In *Advances in Organic Geochemistry 1979*, ed. by Maxwell, J. R. and Douglas, A. G. Pergamon Press, Oxford, pp. 469–474.

Van de Meent, D., De Leeuw, J. W., Schenck, P. A., Haverkamp, J. and Windig, W. (1982) Quantitative analysis of biopolymers by pyrolysis–mass-spectrometry. *J. Anal. Appl. Pyrol.* (submitted).

Van Eck, G. T. M. (1982) *Hydrogeochemistry of the Hollands Diep–Haringvliet basin. The Netherlands*, Thesis. Utrecht.

Windig, W., Kistemaker, P. G. and Haverkamp, J. (1982) Chemical interpretation of pyrolysis–mass-spectra by discriminant analysis and graphical rotation *Anal. Chem.* (submitted).

Yen, T. F. (1975) Genesis and degradation of petroleum hydrocarbons in marine environments. In *Marine Chemistry in the Coastel Environment*, ed. by Church, T. M. ACS, Washington, D.C., pp. 231–266.

Zweig, G. and Sherma, J. (editors) (1972) *Handbook of Chromatography, Vol. I.* CRC Press, Cleveland.

Advances in Organic Geochemistry 1981, pp. 350–354
© *John Wiley & Sons Limited, 1983*

Rates of Organic Matter Oxidation and Carbon Transport in Early Diagenesis of Marine Sediments

B. Sundby, G. Bouchard, J. Lebel and N. Silverberg

Département d'Océanographie, Université du Québec à Rimouski, Québec G5L 3A1, Canada

The vertical distributions of organic and inorganic carbon, reactive (hydroxylamine-extractable) manganese and iron, and porewater alkalinity, sulfate and nitrate were measured in a box core from the Laurentian Trough, Gulf of St. Lawrence. The organic carbon content decreased from 1.9% at the top of the core to 1.3% at 45 cm. The amount of carbon mineralized at depth is nearly four times greater than what can be accounted for by the oxidants (O_2, nitrate sulfate and manganese and iron oxides) present at the time of deposition. The sediment is therefore an open system with respect to oxidants. Accumulation of inorganic carbon is insignificant in these sediments and 98% of the mineralized carbon escapes into the overlying water. Escape by molecular diffusion of bicarbonate (the predominant form of dissolved inorganic carbon at the pH of these sediments) can account for only one tenth of the production rate of mineralized carbon. Bioturbation and bioirrigation appear to be the dominant transport mechanisms during early diagenesis. The results imply that mineralization of sedimentary organic matter is more efficient and more complete than would be predicted from closed system considerations.

INTRODUCTION

Sediments accumulating in oxic basins are a mixture of reducing and oxidizing compounds heavily diluted with stable, unreactive mineral components. At the moment of deposition, the reducing part of the mixture consists principally of organic matter. The oxidizing part consists mainly of the oxides of manganese and iron plus the oxygen, nitrate and sulfate which are dissolved in the sediment porewater. Upon burial, microbially mediated reactions lead to the oxidation and mineralization of labile organic compounds and the reduction of the oxidized forms of Mn, Fe, O, N and S. Thus the disappearance of organic carbon and oxidants with depth and the appearance of mineralized carbon and reduced forms of the oxidants can be used as indicators of the evolution of a sediment (Froelich *et al.*, 1979).

In this paper, we use the stoichiometry of organic matter oxidation and mass-balance calculations to examine the early diagenesis of a fine-grained sediment from the Laurentian Trough, Gulf of St. Lawrence. The approach is as follows. Adopting Redfield's formula for the composition of marine plankton in the metabolizable fraction of sedimentary organic matter, we can compare the degree of mineralization of the organic carbon with the oxidizing capacity of the sediment at the moment of burial. The question is whether this oxidizing capacity is sufficient to account for the amount of organic carbon which has been mineralized in the sediment. Then, after establishing that the mineralized carbon has not

accumulated within the sediment, we investigate the escape mechanism by comparing the flux of inorganic carbon out of the sediment, calculated by assuming molecular diffusion, with the rate of mineralization of organic carbon within the sediment.

The results will emphasize the fact that a sediment system is open to exchange of both oxidants and metabolites with the overlying water during the early part of diagenesis. They will also demonstrate the overwhelming importance of transport mechanisms other than molecular diffusion, such as particle and fluid transport due to the burrowing, feeding and irrigation activities of benthic organisms.

METHODS

A sediment core was raised from 350 m depth at a station in the Laurentian Trough, Gulf of St. Lawrence, using a 0.1 m² Hessler-type box corer. The core was subsampled immediately upon recovery after setting aside a 2-cm thick slice for X-radiography. Five subsamples were taken in the top 1 cm of the core by scraping off successive 2-mm thick layers with a teflon-coated spatula. One-cm thick subsamples were then taken at every cm down to 5 cm and then at every 5 cm in the rest of the core. Porewater samples were extracted using a Reeburgh-type squeezer (Reeburgh, 1967).

In the laboratory, the sediment samples were freeze-dried and homogenized. Total and organic carbon were determined by combustion at 950 °C and 475 °C,

Table 1.

Major element composition of box core from the Laurentian Trough, Gulf of St. Lawrence.

Depth (mm)	Al (%)	Si/Al	Ca/Al	Mg/Al
0–2	7.0	3.9	0.06	0.32
2–4	7.0	3.8	0.07	0.31
4–6	6.8	3.8	0.08	0.33
6–8	7.0	3.7	0.06	0.32
8–10	6.6	3.9	0.06	0.34
10–20	6.9	3.7	0.09	0.35
20–30	7.0	3.9	0.06	0.32
30–40	7.1	3.8	0.05	0.31
40–50	7.2	3.7	0.03	0.31
90–100	7.0	3.8	0.03	0.31
140–150	7.1	3.7	0.03	0.30
190–200	7.0	3.7	0.05	0.30
240–250	7.3	3.5	0.04	0.29
290–300	7.3	3.7	0.07	0.29

respectively (Byers *et al.*, 1978). The major elements (Al, Si, Ca and Mg) of the solid phase were determined by atomic absorption spectroscopy after digesting a sample with a mixture of hydrofluoric acid and aqua regia (Rantala and Loring, 1975). The easily reducible (reactive) fractions of Mn and Fe were also determined by atomic absorption after leaching with 1 M hydroxylamine in 30% acetic acid (Chester and Hughes, 1967).

On the porewater samples, nitrate was measured using an automatic analyzer and standard methods (Strickland and Parsons, 1968); total alkalinity was determined by potentiometric titration (Gieskes and Rogers, 1973); and sulfate was measured by barium chloride precipitation and complexometric titration of excess barium (Lebel and Belzile, 1980). pH was measured directly on the sediment by punching an electrode into the core.

RESULTS

Lithology of the core

The sediment consisted of a silty clay. The surface layer was brown-coloured due to the presence of manganese and iron oxides (Sundby *et al.*, 1981). The colour of the subsurface sediment was olive–gray. A radiograph of the core indicated a generally homogenous structure. The presence of worm tubes and mottles indicated some degree of bioturbation. The major element composition (Table 1) did not vary significantly with depth, nor could significant grain-size variations be detected. Below the surface layer the water content was nearly constant around 55%.

Distribution of chemical parameters

The distribution of the chemical parameters which will be used in the stoichiometric calculations are shown in Figs 1 and 2. All values have been recalculated on a common basis (mmol cm^{-3} wet sediment) by adopting a water content of 55% and a wet sediment density of 1.3. This ignores the effect of compaction in the top few cm of the sediment. However, ignoring compaction is justified since the net effect of compaction is to expulse a fraction of the porewater, thus making the oxidants dissolved in this fraction unavailable for oxidizing organic carbon deeper in the sediment.

The following features of the data will be used in the calculations: *Organic carbon* at this station decreased exponentially from 0.92 mmol cm^{-3} at the top of the core to 0.62 mmol cm^{-3} at 45 cm depth. Total *inorganic carbon* was a very small fraction of the total carbon, being less than 0.02 mmol cm^{-3}. *Total alkalinity* increased linearly with depth from 1.7×10^{-3} to 7.2×10^{-3} mmol cm^{-3}. *Nitrate* decreased irregularly from 1.7×10^{-5} to 1.2×10^{-5} mmol cm^{-3}. The concentration of hydroxy-

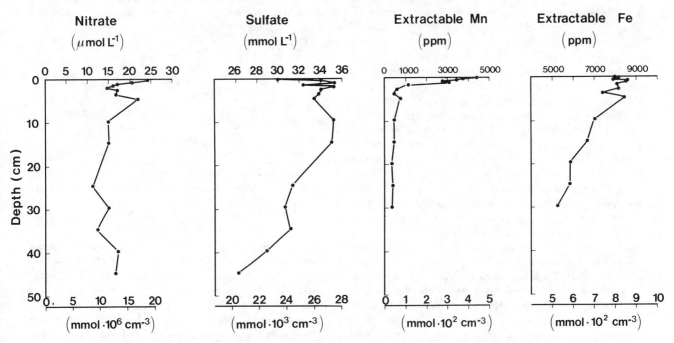

Fig. 1. Distribution of nitrate, sulfate, manganese and iron in a core from the Laurentian Trough, Gulf of St. Lawrence.

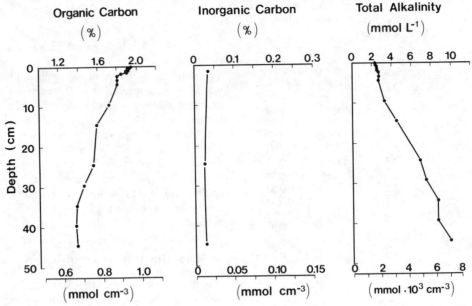

Fig. 2. Distribution of organic and inorganic carbon and total alkalinity in a core from the Laurentian Trough, Gulf of St. Lawrence.

lamine-extractable *iron and manganese* was 0.086 and 0.044 mmol cm^{-3}, respectively, in the top 2 mm of the sediment column. We also noted that the pH decreased from about 7.8 in the top of the core to slightly below 7.0 at depth. *Sulfate* first increased sharply from an initial value of 22×10^{-3} mmol cm^{-3} to 27×10^{-3} mmol cm^{-3} at about 1 cm depth and then decreased slowly to reach 20×10^{-3} mmol cm^{-3} at 45 cm. While this distribution is quite unusual, a discussion of it is beyond the scope of this paper.

DISCUSSION

The decreasing concentration of organic carbon with depth in the core could reflect either a variable rate of organic matter sedimentation or a microbially mediated oxidation of organic carbon. We prefer the second possibility for two reasons. First, the core is lithologically uniform with depth, suggesting a relatively stable sedimentation regime. Second, in view of recent estimates of sedimentation rates in this region (Silverberg, N., unpublished results), the core represents a period of accumulation of about 200 years. No major changes in the productivity of the region are known to have taken place during this period. In Long Island Sound, decreasing concentrations of organic carbon have been attributed to microbial sulfate reduction (Goldhaber *et al.*, 1977). We will assume, therefore, that the decrease of organic carbon with depth is due to the mineralization of organic matter, and also that the condition of steady state applies.

Since mineralization of organic matter cannot occur without the simultaneous consumption of oxidants, it is relevant to ask whether the oxidizing capacity of the sediment at the moment of burial, i.e. that of the surface sediment, is sufficient to account for the amount of organic carbon which has been mineralized in the subsurface sediment. The oxidizing capacity of the sediment is based on the stoichiometry of oxidation (Table 2) and is calculated for the top 2 mm of the sediment according to: oxidizing capacity (mmol cm.^{3}) $= 0.8\,O_2 + 1.1\,NO_3^- + 2.0\,SO_4^{2-} + 0.5\,Mn^{4+} + 0.25\,Fe^{3+}$. All concentrations are expressed on the basis of volume wet sediment. We will assume that the dissolved oxygen concentration of the porewater equals that of the bottom water (6×10^{-5} mmol cm^{-3}) (D'Anglejan and Dunbar, 1968) and that the hydroxylamine-extractable iron and manganese consists of Fe^{3+} and Mn^{4+}. The latter is not strictly correct since the extraction can also solubilize labile compounds of lower-valent iron and manganese. This would lead to an overestimate of the oxidizing capacity of the sediment. However, an overestimate will only reinforce our conclusions.

Using the data in Figs 1 and 2, we obtain for the oxidizing capacity of the sediment:

$$0.8 \times 4.5 \times 10^{-5} + 1.1 \times 1.7 \times 10^{-5} +$$

$$2.0 \times 22 \times 10^{-3} + 0.5 \times 0.044 + 0.25 \times 0.086$$

$$= 0.088 \text{ mmol cm}^{-3}.$$

The fraction of the organic carbon originally deposited which has been mineralized at 45 cm depth is:

$$(0.92 - 0.62) \text{ mmol cm}^{-3} = 0.30 \text{ mmol cm}^{-3}.$$

Thus we conclude that the oxidants initially buried with the organic matter can only account for about 30% of the organic carbon actually mineralized. This means that 70% of the organic carbon must have been mineralized by means of oxidants added to the sediment after the initial burial. It is thus clear that during early diagenesis the sediment constitutes *an open system* with respect to oxidants. It should also be noted that, even at

Table 2.
Stoichiometry of the oxidation of organic carbon (after Froelich *et al.*, 1979).

O_2 Reduction:

$$C_{106}H_{263}O_{110}N_{16}P + 138\ O_2 \rightarrow 106\ CO_2 + 16\ HNO_3 + H_3PO_4 + 122\ H_2O$$

$$\frac{\Delta C_{org}}{\Delta O_2} = \frac{106}{138} = 0.8.$$

MnO_2 Reduction:

$$C_{106}H_{263}O_{110}N_{16}P + 236\ MnO_2 + 472\ H^+ \rightarrow 236\ Mn^{2+} + 106\ CO_2 + 8\ N_2 + H_3PO_4 + 366\ H_2O$$

$$\frac{\Delta C_{org}}{\Delta Mn^{4+}} = \frac{106}{236} = 0.5.$$

Fe_2O_3 Reduction:

$$C_{106}H_{263}O_{110}N_{16}P + 212\ Fe_2O_3 + 848\ H^+ \rightarrow 424\ Fe^{2+} + 106\ CO_2 + 16\ NH_3 + H_3PO_4 + 530\ H_2O$$

$$\frac{\Delta C_{org}}{\Delta Fe^{3+}} = \frac{106}{424} = 0.25.$$

NO_3^- Reduction:

$$C_{106}H_{263}O_{110}N_{16}P + 94\ HNO_3 \rightarrow 106\ CO_2 + 55\ N_2 + H_3PO_4 + 177\ H_2O$$

$$\frac{\Delta C_{org}}{\Delta NO_3^-} = \frac{106}{94} = 1.1.$$

SO_4^{2-} Reduction:

$$C_{106}H_{263}O_{110}N_{16}P + 53\ SO_4^{2-} \rightarrow 106\ CO_2 + 16\ NH_3 + 53\ S^{2-} + H_3PO_4 + 106\ H_2O$$

$$\frac{\Delta C_{org}}{\Delta SO_4^{2-}} = \frac{106}{53} = 2.0.$$

---

45 cm depth, there is still an abundance of oxidants in the form of sulfate and nitrate (Fig. 1).

It is clear from the very low concentrations of inorganic carbon in this core (Fig. 2) that the mineralized organic carbon does not accumulate in the sediment. It is proper to ask, therefore, by which mechanism the mineralized carbon escapes from the sediment. We will test the hypothesis that the escape occurs via molecular diffusion in the sediment porewater.

Mineralized carbon in the form of CO_2 equilibrates with the porewater to form carbonic acid. In carbonate-rich sediments this leads to dissolution of carbonate minerals, increasing the HCO_3^- concentration while maintaining a stable pH. In the absence of carbonate minerals, CO_2 production should increase the HCO_3^-. concentration but also decrease the pH. This was actually observed, supporting the independent observation of very low concentrations of carbonate carbon. Within the pH-range of these sediments, the HCO_3^- ion is by far the predominant species of dissolved inorganic carbon (Gieskes and Rogers, 1973). Furthermore, at the high alkalinity levels observed, it can be assumed that the alkalinity is entirely due to the HCO_3^- ion. Therefore, the vertical gradient of HCO_3^-. equals the alkalinity gradient, 0.13×10^{-3} mmol cm^{-4}. We can then calculate the upward flux of bicarbonate by molecular diffusion from Fick's first law, a whole sediment diffusion coefficient $D_s = 5 \times 10^{-6}$ cm^2 s^{-1}, and a porosity $\Phi = 0.76$:

$$\text{Diffusive flux} = -D_s\Phi\frac{d(HCO_3^-)}{dx}$$

$$= -4.3 \times 10^{-5}\ \text{mmol cm}^{-2}\ d^{-1}.$$

Molecular diffusion can thus remove mineralized carbon at a rate of 4.3×10^{-5} mmol cm^{-2} d^{-1}.

The actual rate of mineralization can be estimated from the sedimentation rate and the difference (0.6%) between the organic carbon content of the surface sediment and that at 45 cm depth. A sedimentation rate of 1.23 mg cm^{-2} d^{-1} was obtained using a sediment trap on a near-by station (Silverberg, N., unpublished data). Thus the rate of mineralization of organic carbon becomes:

$$\frac{1.23\ \text{mg cm}^{-2}\ d^{-1} \times 0.6\%}{100\% \times 12}$$

$$= 6.2 \times 10^{-4}\ \text{mmol cm}^{-2}\ d^{-1}$$

This is over an order of magnitude higher than the rate of removal by molecular diffusion of bicarbonate. Other mechanisms must therefore dominate the transport of mineralized carbon in this sediment.

Our conclusion that the sediment, during the early stage of diagenesis, is a completely open system with efficient exchange of both oxidants and oxidation endproducts, is consistent with recent work which has demonstrated that benthic organisms play an important role in promoting exchange between sediments and the overlying water (Aller, 1977, 1980a, 1980b; Aller and Yingst, 1978; Grundmanis and Murray, 1977; Hammond *et al.*, 1977; Smethie *et al.*, 1981). The implication is that microbial degradation of sedimentary organic matter is more efficient and more complete than would be predicted from closed system considerations.

Acknowledgement

This research was supported by grants from the Natural Sciences and Engineering Research Council of Canada and by the Quebec Ministry of Education. Shiptime was generously provided by the Bedford Institute of Oceanography. Technical assistance was provided by N. Belzile, A. Gendron, C. Gobeil and G. Marquis.

REFERENCES

Aller, R. C. (1977) The influence of macrobenthos on chemical diagenesis of marine sediments. PhD Thesis. Yale University.

Aller, R. C. (1980a) Quantifying solute distributions in the bioturbated zone of marine sediments by defining an average microenvironment. *Geochim. Cosmochim. Acta* **44**, 1955–1965.

Aller, R. C. (1980b) Diagenesis near the sediment–water interface of Long Island Sound. I. Decomposition and nutrient element geochemistry. *Adv. Geophys.* **22**, 235–348.

Aller, R. C. and Yingst, J. Y. (1978) Biogeochemistry of tube-dwellings: A study of the sedentary polychaete *Amphitrityornata* (Leidy). *J. Mar. Res.* **36**, 201–254.

Byers, S., Mills, E. L. and Stewart, P. L. (1978) A comparison of methods of determining organic carbon in marine sediments, with suggestions for a standard method. *Hydrobiologia* **58**, 43–47.

Chester, R. and Hughes, M. J. (1967) A chemical technique for the separation of ferromanganese minerals, carbonate minerals and adsorbed trace elements from pelagic sediments. *Chem. Geol.* **2**, 249–262.

D'Anglejan, B. F. and Dunbar, M. J. (1968) Some observations on oxygen, pH and total alkalinity in the Gulf of St. Lawrence 1966, 1967, 1968. *McGill University Mar. Sci. Centre, Manuscript Rep.* No. 7, 50 pp.

Froelich, P. N., Klinkhammer, G. P., Bender, M. L., Luedtke, N. A., Heath, G. R., Cullen, D., Dauphin, P., Hammond, D., Hartman, B. and Maynard, V. (1979) Early oxidation of organic matter in pelagic sediments of the eastern equatorial Atlantic. Suboxic diagenesis. *Geochim. Cosmochim. Acta* **43**, 1075–1090.

Gieskes, J. M. and Rogers, W. C. (1973) Alkalinity determination in interstitial waters of marine sediments. *J. Sedim. Petrol.* **43**, 272–277.

Goldhaber, M. B., Aller, R. C., Cochran, J. K., Rosenfeld, J. K., Martens, C. S. and Berner, R. A. (1977) Sulfate reduction, diffusion, and bioturbation in Long Island Sound sediments: Report of the FOAM group. *Am. J. Sci.* **277**, 193–237.

Grundmanis, V. and Murray, J. W. (1977) Nitrification and dentrification in marine sediments from Puget Sound. *Limnol. Oceanogr.* **22**, 804–814.

Hammond, D. E., Simpson, H. J. and Mathieu, G. (1977) Rador-222 distribution and transport across the sediment–water interface in the Hudson River estuary. *J. Geophys. Res.* **82**, 3912–3920.

Lebel, J. and Belzile, N. (1980) A simplified automated chelometric method for the determination of sulfate in interstitial water and seawater. *Marine Chem.* **9**, 237–241.

Rantala, R. R. and Loring, D. H. (1975) Multi-element analysis of silicate rocks and marine sediments by atomic absorption spectrophotometry. *At. Absorption Newslet.* **14**, 117–120.

Reeburgh, W. S. (1967) An improved interstitial water sampler. *Limnol. Oceanogr.* **12**, 163–170.

Smethie, Jr. W. M., Nittrouer, C. A. and Self, R. F. L. (1981) The use of radon-222 as a tracer of sediment irrigation and mixing on the Washington continental shelf. *Mar. Geol.* **42**, 173–200.

Strickland, J. D. H. and Parsons, T. R. (1968) A practical handbook of seawater analysis. *Bull. Fish. Res. Bd. Canada* **167**, 311.

Sundby, B., Silverberg, N. and Chesselet, R. (1981) Pathways of manganese in an open estuarine system. *Geochim. Cosmochim. Acta* **45**, 293–307.

Advances in Organic Geochemistry 1981, pp. 355–361
© *John Wiley & Sons Limited, 1983*

Characterization of Organic Matter in Aerosols Over Rural Sites: Phytosterols

B.   R.   T.   Simoneit

School of Oceanography, Oregon State University, Corvallis, Oregon 97331, USA

M. A. Mazurek and W. E. Reed

Department of Earth and Space Sciences, University of California, Los Angeles, California 90024, USA

The fatty alcohol fractions from aerosol samples over various rural and urban areas have been analysed in terms of their molecular marker contents. Phytosterols (C_{27}–C_{29}) and triterpenols ($C_{30} > C_{29}$) were characterized and these compounds could be correlated with dominant geographic sources from floral waxes.

INTRODUCTION

Ambient aerosols sampled from the rural western United States (Simoneit *et al.*, 1980; Simoneit, 1979, 1980), central Africa (Cox *et al.*, 1982) and southeastern Australia (Crisp *et al.*, 1982) have been analysed and compared with urban samples from Los Angeles (Simoneit, 1979). Hydrocarbon, fatty acid, ketone and fatty alcohol fractions of extractable lipids ($\sim C_{15} - C_{36}$) were quantified and also characterized in terms of their contents of homologous compound series and specific molecular markers.

The samples from rural sites contained predominantly vascular plant wax and lesser amounts of higher plant resin residues. Urban samples and, to varying degrees, some rural samples contained primarily higher molecular weight residues of petroleum products (e.g. Simoneit *et al.*, 1980).

Here we describe the molecular markers (phytosterols and triterpenols) of the fatty alcohol fractions from these aerosols. Source correlations are also drawn between these molecular markers present in the aerosol samples with those found in samples of composited vegetation from the respective experimental sites.

EXPERIMENTAL

The descriptions of the sampling procedures of aerosols (high volume filtration) and vegetation have been detailed elsewhere (e.g. Simoneit *et al.*, 1980; Simoneit and Mazurek, 1982a, b). The samples were extracted and then separated into various fractions by thin layer chromatography (Simoneit and Mazurek, 1982a, b). The fatty alcohol fraction was derivatized to the trimethylsilyl ethers and analysed by capillary gas chromatography (GC) and gas chromatography–mass spectrometry (GC–MS) (Simoneit and Mazurek, 1982a, b). Molecular markers were identified by capillary GC and GC–MS comparison with authentic standards and known natural biogenic mixtures.

RESULTS AND DISCUSSION

Common phytosterols that have been encountered in the epicuticular waxes of vascular plants are illustrated in Fig. 1 (Scheuer, 1973; Goad, 1977). These compounds, as well as most plant triterpenols, originate from the same biosynthetic pathway via the cyclization of squalene to form the common intermediate, cycloartenol (Goad, 1977; Goodwin, 1980). Chemical plant taxonomy data have demonstrated that photosynthetic plants and especially higher plants, contain a predominance of the C-24(α)-isomers of the phytosterol structures shown in Fig. 1 (Goad, 1977). Consequently, phytosterols and triterpenols, as single molecular entities, maintain a high degree of structural specificity which is indicative of (1) a recent biogenic origin and of (2) their floral chemotaxonomy. Accordingly, these compounds have been utilized here as molecular markers for the purpose of the characterization of vascular plant constituents that may be present in the lipid fraction of organic aerosols.

The relative amounts of the total C_{27}, C_{28}, and C_{29}-phytosterols, plus that of the C_{29} and C_{30}-triterpenols have been measured for the lipid extracts corresponding to each of the sampling locations (Figs 2, 3, and 4). Representative extracts from composited vegetation epicuticular wax have been similarly assessed and these distributions are compared to the respective aerosol distributions (Figs 5–8). The relative distributions of

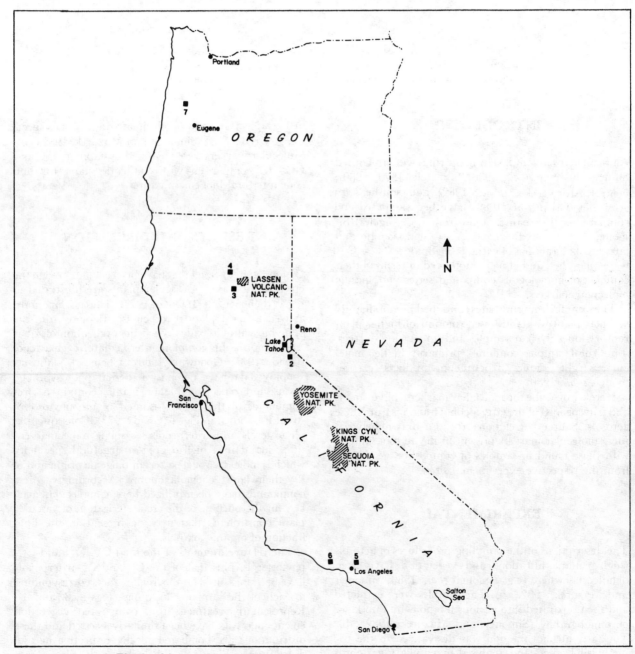

Fig. 1. Phytosterol structures.

Fig. 2. Map of the western United States showing the major aerosol sampling sites.

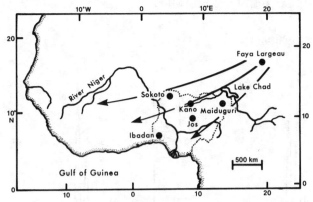

Fig. 3. Map of central Africa depicting Nigerian sampling sites, along with a superimposed Harmattan wind trajectory.

same alcohol signature from higher plant wax input, although the absolute concentrations of the compounds may vary between rural and urban locations.

Aerosol samples from Nigeria (Figs 3 and 7) exhibit a dissimilar phytosterol distribution than those observed from the western United States. Most frequently encountered is an inverted ordering, where the trend of $C_{29} > C_{27} > C_{28}$ is evident. This distribution, with the exception of the Jos 3, Kano and Maiduguri samples, correlates directly with the predominance of the phytosterols found in the wax from both the composited grass and composited desert vegetation. Triterpenols are also present in variable amounts in these plant wax extracts. However, triterpenols are either absent or are present in substantial quantities relative to the

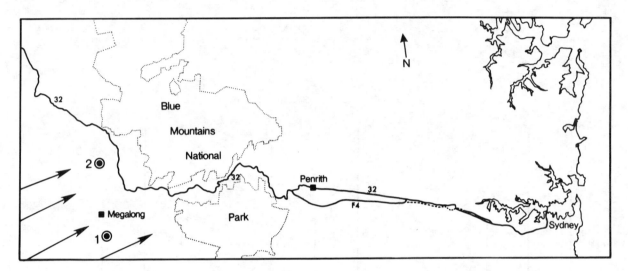

Fig. 4. Location map of southeastern Australia showing Blue Mountain sampling locations.

some examples of *n*-fatty alcohols (Simoneit and Mazurek, 1982a, b) are given for comparison purposes in Fig. 5.

Consistent trends are evident within each geographic subgroup from the comparison of the phytosterol carbon number maximum found in the aerosol to that of the vegetation sample. All urban Los Angeles samples (Figs 2 and 5) show maxima at C_{27} (cholesterol) with lesser amounts of C_{29} (β-sitosterol and some stigmasterol), which in turn is of higher concentration than C_{28}. Similarly, all rural western United States sites (Figs 2 and 6) show the same relationship of $C_{27} > C_{29} > C_{28}$. Varying amounts of C_{29} and mainly C_{30}-triterpenols are also found in each of the samples. The carbon number distribution characteristic of both rural and urban western United States compares directly with the $C_{27} > C_{29} > C_{28}$ distribution of the wax from composited Sierra vegetation (coniferous). This sample of surface wax also contains C_{30}-triterpenols (amyrins). Therefore, in terms of phytosterol and triterpenol molecular marker occurrences, both polluted and non-polluted atmospheres in the western United States contain the

phytosterols found in the wax from both the composited observation may be related to the dissimilar wind trajectories which would result in different input of source material for the various Nigerian Harmattan aerosols. We believe that the samples of Harmattan aerosols collected upwind of Jos, Kano, Sokoto and, to a lesser extent, Maiduguri, contain largely natural organic matter carried with the dusts or adsorbed on the particulates (Cox *et al.*, 1982). The lipid material is composed of primarily plant waxes and secondarily, of compounds derived from degraded microbial detritus, probably mainly of algae; Maiduguri, however, has a large portion of anthropogenic contaminants in addition to these recent biogenic materials. Algal detritus usually contains a different phytosterol distribution from that of vascular plant waxes since the C_{27} analogues generally predominate (Goad, 1977). This bias could explain the noted exception of $C_{27} > C_{29}$ phytosterols in the Jos 3, Kano and Maiduguri samples.

It appears and is further supported here, that the lipids originate predominantly in more fertile areas of Chad and Nigeria, downwind of the source (Cox *et al.*,

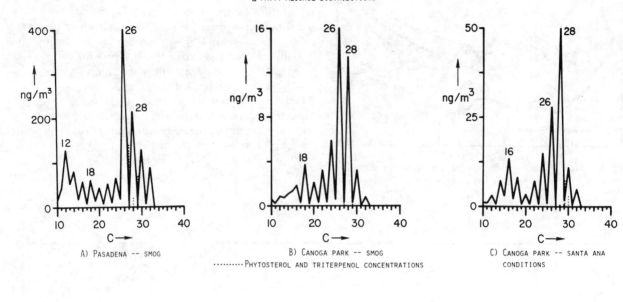

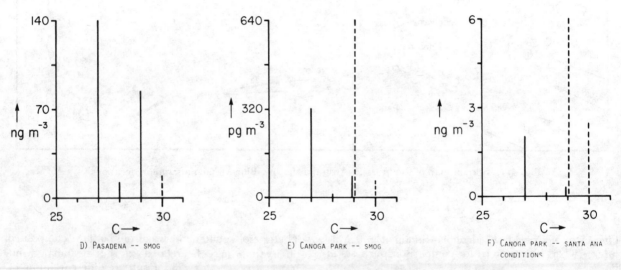

Fig. 5. Relative concentration distributions of some examples of *n*-fatty alcohols from urban Los Angeles aerosols (a–c), presented with the respective phytosterol and triterpenol components (d–f).

1982). Plant wax lipids could be released by a sand blasting effect of the dust on plant surfaces, while the minor microbiological detritus could arise by the remobilization of dust from dried-up wadis, ponds and lakes.

Finally, aerosol samples from the Blue Mountain region (west of Sydney) in southeastern Australia (Figs 4 and 8), show a phytosterol predominance of $C_{29} > C_{27} > C_{28}$, with varying amounts of C_{29} and C_{30}-triterpenols. This distribution coincides with that of wax extracts from Australian gum trees and native grasses at the site of aerosol acquisition.

By comparison of the phytosterol distributions of the temperate sites (western US) to those of the semiarid sites (Nigeria and southeastern Australia), a geographical distinction emerges. The higher molecular weight phytosterol (C_{29}) components predominate in the warmer climatic regions. This may be the result of climatological adaptations by specific plant communities whereby the higher molecular weight epicuticular wax components (i.e. less volatile compounds) are preferentially synthesized in response to the combination of higher ambient temperatures and lower levels of humidity.

CONCLUSIONS

Fatty alcohol fractions have similar ambient concentrations as the natural wax hydrocarbons of aerosols.

The phytosterols are major components of the alcohol fractions of aerosols and are comprised primarily of

RURAL WESTERN UNITED STATES & COMPOSITED SIERRA VEGETATION

PHYTOSTEROL AND TRITERPENOL DISTRIBUTIONS

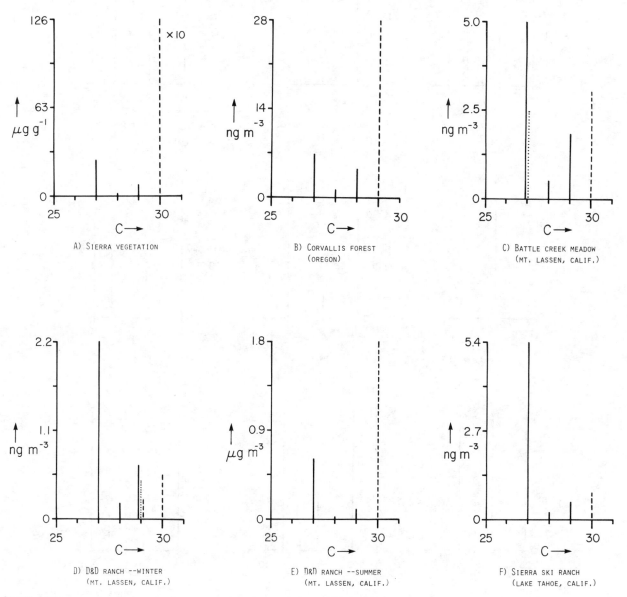

Fig. 6. Phytosterol and triterpenol concentrations for rural western United States aerosols and for composited Sierra vegetation.

cholesterol and β-sitosterol, with lesser amounts of campesterol, stigmasterol and other analogues. Distributions of these compounds are, in general, typical for an origin from higher plants. Geographical distinctions are also present with respect to the phytosterol homologue distribution. The warm, arid regions (Nigeria and southeastern Australia) showed the predominance of β-sitosterol, and the temperate western United States showed the predominance of cholesterol.

Triterpenols and some derivatives are found in aerosols from areas in the proximity of conifer and gum vegetation and also in some grassland environments.

These data confirm that primary biogenic residues (i.e., plant wax) are significant components of ambient aerosols over continental locations in both the northern and southern hemispheres. The molecular detail of the comprehensive analyses of all aerosol fractions permits the definition of major source areas of aerosol parcels, and possibly, also their approximate residence time in the troposphere.

Acknowledgements

We thank Mr Ed Ruth for GC/MS data acquisition and the National Science Foundation, Division of Atmospheric Sciences (Grants ATM79–08645 and ATM81–18101) for financial assistance.

REFERENCES

Cox, R. E., Mazurek, M. A. and Simoneit, B. R. T. (1982) Lipids in Harmattan aerosols of Nigeria. *Nature*, **296**, 848–849.

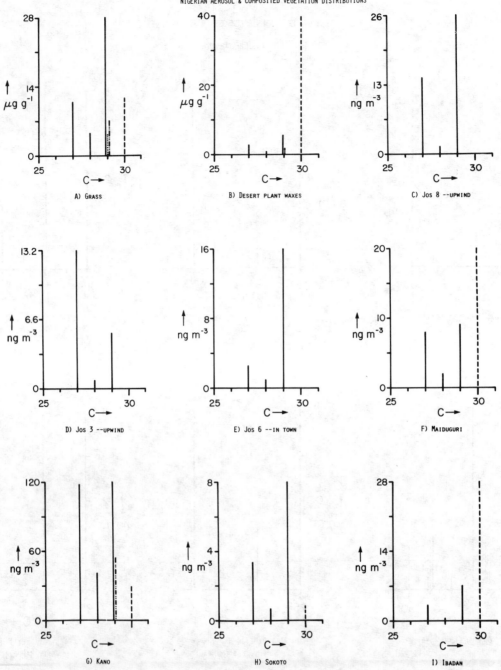

Fig. 7. Concentrations of phytosterol and triterpenol components observed in Nigerian aerosols and in wax extracts from composited grass and desert vegetation.

SOUTHEASTERN AUSTRALIA AEROSOL & COMPOSITED VEGETATION

PHYTOSTEROL AND TRITERPENOL DISTRIBUTIONS

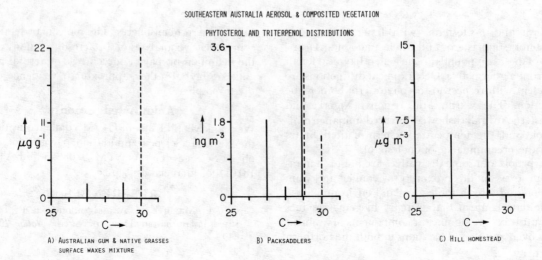

Fig. 8. Distribution of phytosterol and triterpenol components from the aerosols and sample vegetation of the Blue Mountain region of southeastern Australia.

Crisp, P. T., Mazurek, M. A. and Simoneit, B. R. T. (1982) Characterization of extractable organic matter of aerosols from the Blue Mountains of Australia, *Atmos. Environ.* in preparation.

Goad, L. J. (1977) The biosynthesis of plant sterols. In *Lipids and Lipid Polymers in Higher Plants*, ed. by Tevini, M. and Lichtenthaler, H. K. Springer-Verlag, New York, pp. 146–168.

Goodwin, T. W. (1980) The Biosynthesis of Plant Steroids. In *The Biochemistry of Plants*, Vol. 4, ed. by Stumpf, P. W. Academic Press, New York, pp. 485–507.

Scheuer, P. J. (1973) *Chemistry of Marine Natural Products.* Academic Press, New York, pp. 61–82.

Simoneit, B. R. T. (1980) Eolian Particulates from Oceanic and Rural Areas — Their Lipids, Fulvic and Humic Acids and Residual Carbon. In *Advances in Organic Geochemistry 1979*, ed. by Douglas, A. G. and Maxwell, J. R. Pergamon Press, Oxford, pp. 343–352.

Simoneit, B. R. T. (1979) Biogenic Lipids in Eolian Particulates Collected Over the Ocean. In *Proceedings Carbonaceous Particles in the Atmosphere*, ed. by Novakov, T. NSF and Lawrence Berkeley Laboratory, LBL–9037, pp. 233–244.

Simoneit, B. R. T. and Mazurek, M. A. (1982a) Natural Background of Biogenic Organic Matter in Aerosols Over Rural Areas. In *Proceedings Fifth International Clean Air Congress*, Buenos Aires, in press.

Simoneit, B. R. T. and Mazurek, M. A. (1982b) Organic matter of the troposphere: II — Natural background of biogenic lipid matter in aerosols over the rural western United States, *Atmos. Environ.*, **16**, 2139–2159.

Simoneit, B. R. T., Mazurek, M. A. and Cahill, T. A. (1980) Contamination of the Lake Tahoe air basin by high molecular weight petroleum residues, *J. Air Pollut. Control. Assoc.* **30**, 387–390.

Advances in Organic Geochemistry 1981, pp. 362–368
© *John Wiley & Sons Limited, 1983*

Spatial and Temporal Variation of Pelagic Tar in the Eastern Gulf of Mexico

E. S. Van Vleet, W. M. Sackett, F. F. Weber Jr.* and S. B. Reinhardt

Department of Marine Science, University of South Florida, 830 First Street South, St. Petersburg, Florida 33701 USA

Pelagic tar concentrations have been measured for samples collected monthly in the eastern Gulf of Mexico over a one year period. Each month, seven stations were occupied and duplicate neuston tows (to 0.5 m depth) and oblique tows (to 100 m depth) were collected at each station. Gravimetric analysis was carried out on the total extract, as well as on the aliphatic and aromatic fractions. The concentrations of pelagic tar ranged from 0 to 26.5 mg m^{-2} (expressed as the toluene extractable lipid) with an average of 1.60 mg m^{-2} in the neuston tows collected off the west florida shelf and 0.05 mg m^{-2} in neuston tows collected on the west Florida shelf. The concentrations of pelagic tar closely correlated with proximity to the Gulf Loop Current. The occurrence of tar was often associated with floating *Sargassum*. Essentially all of the tar was found in the top 50 cm of the water column with very little occurring in the subsurface waters. The highest pelagic tar concentrations were observed during the spring and summer of 1980. Both the absolute concentrations and spatial distributions of tar decreased during the following fall and winter.

INTRODUCTION

During the past ten to fifteen years, the presence of heavy oil in the open oceans, henceforth referred to as pelagic tar, has been commonly observed. Its source is generally believed to be petroleum production and transportation operations (Butler *et al.*, 1973; McGowan *et al.*, 1974a; NAS, 1975) although some pelagic tar has been attributed to natural seeps (Koons and Monaghan, 1973; Geyer and Giammona, 1980). The concentration of floating tar varies widely in different parts of the world (Wong *et al.*, 1976; Levy, 1977; Jeffrey, 1980). An increased global demand for oil in recent years has led to a concurrent increase in exploration, drilling, and shipping activities. The oil fields offshore Mexico are thought to approach those of the Middle East in size, and will probably be producing 2.5 million barrels per day by the end of the 1980s. Offshore leasing, exploration, and oil well drilling have also recently begun off the west Florida coast and will continue over the next several years. Drilling, production, and marine transportation activities throughout the Gulf of Mexico are expected to increase many fold compared to today's activities. The frequency and magnitude of oil spillage will also probably increase proportionally. For example, two disastrous oil spills occurred in the Gulf of Mexico in 1979 and contributed to the already high background levels of pelagic tar found in the Gulf. The IXTOC-I

drilling blowout and the collision of the oil tanker, *Burmah Agate*, offshore Galveston, Texas, released more than 3 000 000 and 390 000 barrels of petroleum, respectively. It was in the climate of these recorded and likely new disasters that the State of Florida undertook a programme aimed at protecting Florida's coastal ecosystems by maintaining an attentive surveillance of the offshore waters of the west Florida continental shelf. This surveillance was to be carried out by conducting a routine sampling and analysis programme for pelagic crude oil residues in west Florida's coastal waters. The programme was designed not only to give an advance warning of impending danger, but also to recognize and identify any polluting oil.

SAMPLING AND ANALYSIS

To provide regular and comprehensive monitoring, offshore water samples were collected along two standard transects of seven stations each. The two transects, of approximately 300 miles each, were designed to intercept the Gulf Loop Current and detect entrained oil residues along the entire west Florida coastline (FIO/USF, 1981). One transect ran from Tampa Bay southwest toward the Yucatan Peninsula; the other transect ran from Tampa Bay northwest toward the Mississippi Delta region (Fig. 1). The seven stations along each transect were located at standard intervals and were selected so that the outer four stations in each case were in the Loop Current while the inner

* Present address: EXXON Production Research Co., P.O. Box 2189, Houston, Texas 77001 USA.

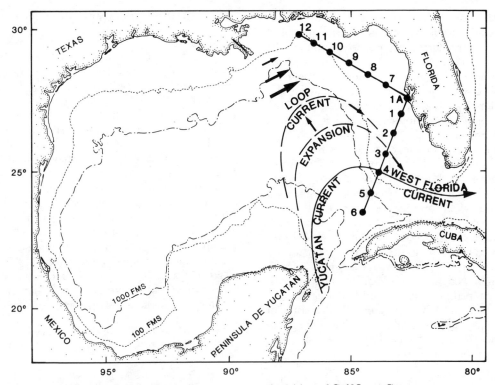

Fig. 1. Standard sampling transects and position of Gulf Loop Current.

three stations were in coastal or marginal shelf waters. The two tracks were originally designed to be occupied alternately, each on a bimonthly basis to ensure that the sampling would reflect the influx of current-borne oil residues in the loop current, regardless of the time of year. As variability in pelagic tar concentrations, loop current intrusions, and temporal tar variations became apparent throughout the year, this sampling pattern was adjusted to ensure intersection with the prevailing loop current and to maximize detection. The position of the Gulf Loop Current was routinely monitored from the NOAA GOES satellite as well as from temperature and salinity data taken aboard ship using STD and XBT profiles.

Pelagic tar was collected using a 1.5 m × 0.5 m neuston net designed after Morris (1971) and equipped with a TSK (Tsurumi–Seiki–Kosakusho, Co., Ltd., Yokohama, Japan) flow metre to monitor the water volume passing through the net. The nylon neuston net had a mesh size of 165 μm, a scope of 5:1, and was towed approximately 50 m off the starboard side of the R/V *Bellows* at 1–2 kt for 10 to 30 min. In this manner, 500–1000 m² of seawater were filtered through the nets during each tow. At each station, two surface neuston tows (to a depth of 0.5 m) and two oblique tows (0 to 100 m) were taken for analysis of floating and suspended tar residues. Duplicate tows were taken at each station to provide information on sampling variability. Pelagic tar passing into the net was collected in a 0.95 l glass jar. After collection, the jar was capped with a Teflon-lined screw cap and refrigerated at 5 °C or kept on ice until returned to the laboratory for analysis.

Table 1

Chemical parameters observed in pelagic tar (from Van Vleet *et al.*, 1982)

Parameter measured	Range	Average
δ^{13}C (total)	−26.5–−28.0‰	−27.2±0.8‰
δ^{13}C (F1)	−26.3–−29.9‰	−27.5±1.4‰
δ^{13}C (F2)	−25.4–−29.6‰	−27.0±1.1‰
aliphatics/aromatics	0.68–7.33	2.69±1.63
nC$_{17}$/pristane	0.14–4.60	1.54±0.79
nC$_{18}$/phytane	0.31–5.21	1.92±0.99
pristane/phytane	0.41–2.79	1.00±0.38
n-alkane range	C$_{12}$–C$_{38}$	C$_{14}$–C$_{38}$
n-alkane maximum	C$_{18}$–C$_{38}$	C$_{19}$–C$_{20}$; C$_{29}$–C$_{35}$
% resolved F1	33.4–94.7	40.2±15.4
% unresolved F1	5.3–71.4	59.8±15.4
% resolved F2	7.9–45.6	25.4±13.8
% unresolved F2	55.4–92.1	74.6±13.8

Tar particles from each tow were then removed from the jars, weighed (to determine the wet weight), and dissolved in toluene to form a homogeneous sample from each tow. In selected instances the wet tar was dried overnight to determine moisture content. All solvents were redistilled prior to use and controls were run periodically for all analyses. The toluene was evaporated from a 1 ml aliquot of the toluene/tar solution under a stream of nitrogen and the sample was weighed to determine the weight of toluene extractable material in the tar. An additional 1 ml aliquot was saponified, extracted, evaporated to near dryness, and passed through a 10 cm × 1 cm diameter activated silica gel column. The F1 (aliphatic hydrocarbon) fraction was eluted with two column volumes of hexane; after which the F2 (aromatic hydrocarbon) fraction was eluted with two column volumes of toluene. Each hydrocarbon fraction was evaporated to dryness in a preweighed Teflon weighing boat and the F1 and F2 hydrocarbon weights determined on a microgram balance. The gas chromatographic and $\delta^{13}C_{PDB}$ isotopic characteristics of the tar were also measured and are being reported in detail elsewhere (Van Vleet et al., 1982). These chemical data are summarized in Table 1.

RESULTS AND DISCUSSION

The concentrations of pelagic tar observed in Florida's coastal waters ranged from 0 to 26.5 mg m^{-2} toluene extractable lipid material (0 to 45.3 mg m^{-2} wet weight) with an overall average surface concentration of 1.01 mg m^{-2}. Beginning with the S1080* cruise, the wet tar was picked from the sample and dried overnight at 45 °C. Based upon these analyses, the floating tar had a moisture content of approximately $59 \pm 21\%$ (observed range = 19–97%). McGowan et al. (1974b) reported moisture contents of tar balls ranging from 0–51% with an average of 21%. In addition to the water associated with the tar particles, the remainder consisted of toluene extractable organic matter (average $\simeq 38\%$ of the wet weight; range = 0 to 86%) plus inorganic and other organic detrital material (generally 1–3% of the wet weight). Thus, about 95% of the dry tar particles was extractable with toluene. A large portion of the toluene extractable material, however, consisted of polar

* Cruises are designated by direction of transect (S = Southern, N = Northern) plus month and year (e.g. S1080 = Southern transect, October, 1980).

Table 2
Average pelagic tar concentrations (expressed in mg m^{-2} of toluene extractable lipid) observed in neustron and oblique tows from each sampling cruise

Transect	Cruise	(I) Concentration (mg m^{-2}) in neuston tows (all stations)	(II) Concentration (mg m^{-2}) in oblique tows (all stations)
Southern	S 480	2.03 ± 4.68	0.00 ± 0.01
	S 580	4.60 ± 7.34	0.04 ± 0.06
	S 680	1.51 ± 3.40	0.00 ± 0.00
	S 780	2.47 ± 4.85	0.00 ± 0.00
	S1080	0.01 ± 0.02	0.00 ± 0.00
	S1180	0.49 ± 1.24	0.01 ± 0.02
	S 181	0.02 ± 0.05	0.12 ± 0.00
	S 281	0.05 ± 0.05	0.00 ± 0.01
	S 381	0.14 ± 0.39	0.00 ± 0.00
Northern	N 880	0.20 ± 0.30	0.00 ± 0.00
	N 980	0.20 ± 0.53	0.00 ± 0.00
	N1280	0.00 ± 0.00	0.00 ± 0.00

Transect	Cruise	(III) Concentration (mg m^{-2}) in neuston tows on west Florida shelf	(IV) Concentration (mg m^{-2}) in neuston tows off west Florida shelf
Southern	S 480	0.00 ± 0.00	3.77 ± 6.03
	S 580	0.00 ± 0.00	6.45 ± 8.04
	S 680	0.57 ± 0.74	2.64 ± 5.03
	S 780	0.00 ± 0.00	3.47 ± 5.48
	S1080	0.00 ± 0.00	0.02 ± 0.00
	S1180	0.00 ± 0.00	1.83 ± 3.24
	S 181	0.00 ± 0.00	0.03 ± 0.05
	S 281	0.00 ± 0.00	0.06 ± 0.04
	S 381	0.00 ± 0.00	0.33 ± 0.56
Northern	N 880	0.07 ± 0.17	0.29 ± 0.34
	N 980	0.00 ± 0.00	0.28 ± 0.61
	N1280	0.00 ± 0.00	0.00 ± 0.00

compounds that were retained by the silica-gel column during chromatographic isolation of the hydrocarbons.

Average pelagic tar concentrations in the neuston and oblique tows observed for each cruise are shown in Table 2. Average concentrations for the neuston tows are also shown for stations taken approximately on the west Florida continental shelf and for stations taken off the west Florida shelf. The stations taken off the shelf are roughly equivalent to those which are associated with the Gulf Loop Current. Concentations of pelagic tar observed in the oblique (0–100 m) tows (Table 2, II) are negligible compared to the concentrations observed in the neuston tows (Table 2, I). Stations that showed significant tar in the oblique tows invariably showed high surface concentrations as well. The nets used for obtaining the neuston samples collected tar to a depth of 50 cm; hence, tar that was floating directly on the surface could not be distinguished from tar at about 50 cm depth. It is likely that most of the tar was floating directly on the surface.

Pelagic tar found in the eastern Gulf of Mexico is primarily associated with the loop current (Table 2, IV). Very little of the total pelagic tar is found on the west Florida continental shelf (Table 2, III). Tar collected from stations along the northern transects (which are also primarily on the Florida continental shelf and outside the loop current) showed concentrations similar to the southern transect stations on the continental shelf. These concentrations are much lower (by about a factor of ten) than the tar associated with the loop current. The entire west Florida continental shelf sampled during this study is apparently quite pristine with respect to floating tar

concentrations. This generalization may not apply to local bays and estuaries where urban run-off and frequent shipping and boating activities can dramatically increase the burden of pelagic tar in these waters.

Pelagic tar concentrations found in the eastern Gulf of Mexico generally comparable to those reported in the western Gulf of Mexico (Jeffrey et al., 1974; Pequegnat, 1979), the Sargasso Sea (Butler and Morris, 1974; McGowan et al., 1974), and the Mediterranean Sea (Zsolany et al., 1978). The concentrations found in the eastern Gulf of Mexico are generally higher than the concentrations reported for most other areas (~2 times higher than the Caribbean Sea to over 46 times higher than in the North Pacific). A method for classifying pelagic tar concentrations has been proposed by Wong et al. (1976) based on samples collected in the Pacific Ocean. These authors arbitrarily assigned the following designations to the floating tar concentrations (wet weights):

$$
\begin{aligned}
\text{No visible tar} &= \text{Zero (0)} \\
<0.1 \text{ mg m}^{-2} &= \text{Trace (T)} \\
0.1\text{–}1 \text{ mg m}^{-2} &= \text{Medium (M)} \\
1\text{–}5 \text{ mg m}^{-2} &= \text{Heavy (H)} \\
>5 \text{ mg m}^{-2} &= \text{Extra Heavy (X)}
\end{aligned}
$$

This classification procedure has subsequently been used by other authors (Shaw and Mapes, 1979; Eagle et al., 1979) and provides a convenient means of comparing pelagic tar data from different areas. Based upon this classification procedure, the pelagic tar concentrations observed in the neuston tows during Year 1 of the present

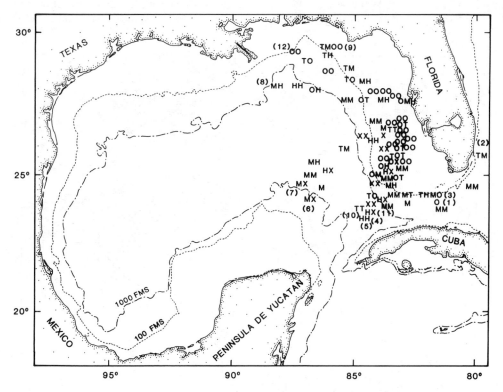

Fig. 2. Distribution of pelagic tar collected in neuston tows (classification of pelagic tar is based upon the procedure of Wong et al., 1976; double letter symbols represent the tar concentrations in duplicate tows at one station, e.g. MX indicates that one of the duplicate tows contained medium tar concentrations, while the other duplicate tow contained extra heavy tar concentration). Numbers in parentheses indicate month of cruise (as in Table 2).

Table 3

Distribution of pelagic tar in individual tows (using the classification procedure of Wong *et al.*, 1976)

	Neuston tows Number of stations with following classification				
	O	T	M	H	X
Northern transects	19	6	10	7	0
Southern transects	44	13	29	14	16
All stations	63	19	39	21	16
	Oblique tows Number of stations with following classification				
	O	T	M	H	X
Northern transects	20	6	1	0	0
Southern transects	49	22	5	0	1
All stations	69	28	6	0	1

Table 4

Average pelagic tar concentrations, in mg m^{-2} wet weight, in neuston tows for each cruise. The classification of the tar (according to the procedure of Wong *et al.*, 1976) is also shown in parentheses

Transect	Cruise	(III') Concentration (mg m^{-2}) in neuston tows on west Florida shelf		(IV') Concentration (mg m^{-2}) in neuston tows off west Florida shelf	
Southern	S 480	0.00	(O)	9.82	(X)
	S 580	0.00	(O)	16.80	(X)
	S 680	1.48	(H)	6.88	(X)
	S 780	0.00	(O)	9.01	(X)
	S1080	0.00	(O)	0.05	(T)
	S1180	0.00	(O)	4.77	(H)
	S 181	0.00	(O)	0.08	(T)
	S 281	0.00	(O)	0.16	(M)
	S 381	0.00	(O)	0.86	(M)
Northern	N 880	0.18	(M)	0.76	(M)
	N 980	0.00	(O)	0.73	(M)
	N1280	0.00	(O)	0.00	(O)

study are shown in Fig. 2. The distribution of the pelagic tar among the various classifications is reported in Table 3. Fig. 2 and Table 3 show that most of the tar is found in the neuston tows of the southern transects. Very little tar is found in the northern transects or in the oblique tows. The oblique tows are heavily skewed toward zero or trace tar concentrations, while the neuston tows show many more stations containing medium, heavy, and extra heavy tar concentrations (Table 3).

The average wet weight concentrations of pelagic tar in the neuston tows, collected both on and off the west Florida shelf, are reported in Table 4 along with the corresponding classification from Wong *et al.* (1976). These classifications were plotted as an average on-shelf

concentration and an average off-shelf concentration for each cruise and contoured to show the average distributions in the eastern Gulf of Mexico (Fig. 3). The stations where zero tar was observed were combined with the stations where trace tar concentrations were observed due to the difficulty in distinguishing very small tar particles from certain other organic detritus and also due to the fact that some of the tar ($<165~\mu$m) may have escaped through the net. The distribution of

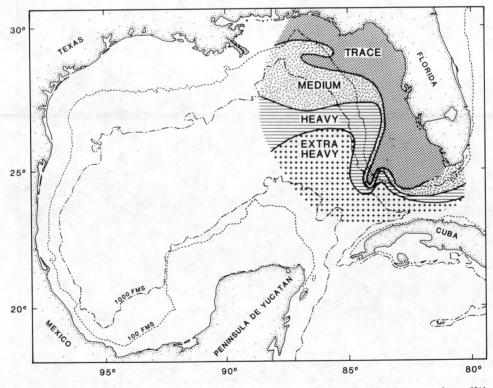

Fig. 3. Average distribution of surface tar in eastern Gulf of Mexico (based upon the classification procedure of Wong *et al.*, 1976).

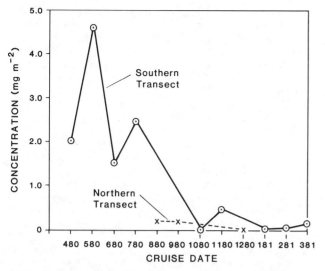

Fig. 4. Average pelagic tar concentrations (expressed in mg m^{-2} of toluene extractable lipid) in neuston tows plotted versus sampling cruise.

pelagic tar is extremely patchy and highly variable. Duplicate neuston tows collected at Station 2 during cruise S580, for example, varied by a factor of 30 (toluene extractable lipid concentrations: tow 1 = 26.4 mg m^{-2}, tow 2 = 0.88 mg m^{-2}. As a result of this patchiness, there is certainly some overlap in the contours shown in Fig. 3. The contours more accurately represent the probability of finding trace, medium, heavy, or extra heavy pelagic tar concentrations in various sectors of the eastern Gulf of Mexico. Comparison of the contour curves to the expected axis of the loop current (Fig. 1) shows that the heaviest tar concentrations again correlate with the loop current while the stations on the west Florida continental shelf (< 100 fathoms) have the lowest tar concentrations. The highest concentrations of pelagic tar were observed in the presence of large amounts of *Sargassum*. Since no quantitative measurements of the *Sargassum* were made, this observation is qualitative only. Butler and Morris (1974) have reported a poor correlation of pelagic tar and floating *Sargassum* in the North Atlantic ($r = 0.39$).

Figure 4 shows the average concentrations of pelagic tar at all stations (from Table 2, I) plotted against cruise date. For the southern transects, the average concentration was highest during the May 1980 cruise (4.6 ± 7.3 mg m^{-2}) and decreased throughout the summer, fall, and winter months. The higher concentrations observed during the spring and summer months were probably due to both calmer sea conditions and higher shipping activities. The rougher sea conditions during the fall and winter months were responsible for the downward mixing of tar in the surface waters which partially led to the lower observed tar concentrations. The variability in these concentrations (from the standard deviations shown in Table 2) indicates that there is not a statistically significant difference between the tar concentrations for any cruise. The overall averages, however, show an apparent seasonal trend in the data. Although the average tar concentrations for the last two cruises (281 and 381) show a very slight increase, they do not approach the tar

levels observed at the beginning of the project (cruise 480). Despite the overall low average concentrations in the latter two cruises, a significantly greater lateral distribution of tar was observed during cruise 281 (measurable tar was observed in 71% of the February neuston tows compared to 27% of the January neuston tows). In addition, higher concentrations of tar were observed at individual stations during the 381 cruise (maximum concentration was 1.40 mg m^{-2} during the March cruise, while the maximum observed concentrations during the January and February cruises were 0.16 and 0.15 mg m^{-2}, respectively). These observations suggest that pelagic tar concentrations were 0.16 and 0.15 mg m^{-2}, respectively). These early spring months of the project.

CONCLUSIONS

Crude oil residues have been monitored by collecting both surface and subsurface samples during monthly cruises in west Florida's coastal waters. Based upon gravimetric analyses of the floating tar, the following conclusions have been reached from this study: (1) the quantities of pelagic tar found in the eastern Gulf of Mexico are about two to forty times higher than concentrations reported in several other coastal areas around the world, but are comparable to levels found in the western Gulf of Mexico, the Sargasso Sea, and the Mediterranean Sea. (2) Pelagic tar found in the eastern Gulf of Mexico is primarily associated with the loop current, with minor amounts found outside the loop current. (3) The distribution of pelagic tar in west Florida coastal waters is extremely patchy. The tar shows a tendency to become associated with floating *Sargassum*. (4) Essentially all of the pelagic tar is found in the upper 0.5 m of the water column. Very little tar was observed in the oblique tows from 0–100 m. (5) The quantitative and spatial distribution of tar showed an apparent seasonal trend with the highest concentrations being found during the summer months.

Acknowledgements

We are especially grateful to Vice-Admiral W. W. Behrens, Jr. and Mr D. M. Milliken of the Florida Institute of Oceanography for logistical and sampling support. We are also grateful to the captain and crew of the R/V *Bellows* for their help during the sampling cruises. We sincerely appreciate the efforts of Dr Karen Steidinger, Director of the Florida Department of Natural Resources, Bureau of Marine Science and Technology. Financial support was provided by The Florida Coastal Protection Trust Fund and the Florida Department of Natural Resources.

REFERENCES

Butler, J. N. and Morris, B. F. (1974) Quantitative monitoring and variability of pelagic tar in the North Atlantic. In *NBS*

Spec. Publ. 409, Marine Pollution Monitoring (Petroleum), pp. 75–78.

Butler, N. J., Morris, B. F. and Sass, J. (1973) Pelagic tar from Bermuda and the Sargasso sea. Bermuda Biological Station Spec. Publ. No. 10. 346 pp.

Eagle, G. A., Green, A. and Williams, J. (1979) Tar ball concentrations in the ocean around the Cape of Good Hope before and after a major oil spill. Mar. Pollut. Bull. 10, 321–325.

FIO/USF (1981) Spatial and Temporal Variation of Crude Oil Residues in Continental Shelf Waters Offshore Western Florida. Final Report submitted to the Florida Department of Natural Resources by the Florida Institute for Oceanography and the University of South Florida, August 1981, 87 pp.

Geyer, R. A. and Giammona, C. P. (1980) Naturally occurring hydrocarbons in the Gulf of Mexico and Caribbean Sea. In Marine Environmental Pollution. I. Hydrocarbons, ed. by Geyer, R. A. Elsevier, New York, pp. 37–106.

Iliffe, T. M. and Calder, J. A. (1974) Dissolved hydrocarbons in the eastern Gulf of Mexico Loop Current and the Caribbean Sea. Deep-Sea Res. 21, 481–488.

Jeffrey, L. M. (1980) Petroleum residues in the marine environment. In Marine Environmental Pollution. I. Hydrocarbons, ed. by Geyer, R. A. Elsevier, New York, pp. 163–179.

Jeffrey, L. M., Pequegnat, W. E., Kennedy, E. A., Vos, A. and Jarnes, B. M. (1974) Pelagic tar in the Gulf of Mexico and Caribbean Sea. In NBS Spec. Publ. 409. Marine Pollution Monitoring (Petroleum), pp. 233–235.

Koons, C. B. and Monaghan, P. H. (1973) Petroleum hydrocarbons in Gulf of Mexico waters. Trans. Gulf Coast Assoc. Geol. Soc. 23, 170–181.

Levy, E. M. (1977) The geographical distribution of tar in the North Atlantic. Rapp. P.V. Reun. Cons. Int. Explor. Mer 171, 55–60.

McGowan, W. E., Saner, W. A. and Hufford, G. L. (1974a) Tar ball distribution in the western North Atlantic. U.S. Coast Guard Rept. CGR&D 24/74. Washington, D.C. 30 pp.

McGowan, W. E., Saner, W. E. and Hufford, G. L. (1974b) Tar ball sampling in the western North Atlantic. In NBS Spec. Publ. 409. Marine Pollution Monitoring (Petroleum), pp. 83–84.

Morris, B. F. (1971) Petroleum: tar quantities floating in the northwestern Atlantic taken with a new quantitative neuston net. Science 173, 430–432.

NAS (1975) Petroleum in the Marine Environment. National Academy of Sciences, Washington, D.C., 107 pp.

Pequegnat, L. H. (1979) Pelagic tar concentrations in the Gulf of Mexico over the South Texas Continental Shelf. Contrib. Mar. Sci. 22, 31–39.

Shaw, D. G. and Mapes, G. A. (1979) Surface circulation and distribution of pelagic tar and plastic. Mar. Pollut. Bull. 10, 160–162.

Van Vleet, E. S., Sackett, W. M., Weber, F. F. Jr. and Reinhardt, S. B. (1982) Input of pelagic tar to the Northwest Atlantic from the Gulf Loop Current: Chemical characterization and its relationship to weathered IXTOC-I oil. Can. J. Fish. Aquat. Sci. In Press.

Wong, C. S., Green, D. R. and Cretney, W. J. (1976) Distribution and source of tar on the Pacific Ocean. Mar. Pollut. Bull. 7, 102–106.

Zsolnay, A., Morris, B. F. and Butler, J. N. (1978) Relationship between aromatic hydrocarbons and pelagic tar in the Mediterranean Sea, 1974–75. Environ. Conserv. 5, 295–297.

Advances in Organic Geochemistry 1981, pp. 369–379
© John Wiley & Sons Limited, 1983

The Use of Sediment Traps to Determine Sterol Sources in Coastal Sediments Off Peru

R. B. Gagosian, J. K. Volkman and G. E. Nigrelli

Department of Chemistry, Woods Hole Oceanographic Institution, Woods Hole, Massachusetts 02543, USA

Sterol distributions of particulate material, organisms and organism egestion products were compared to those of surface sediments to ascertain the sources of sterols in coastal Peruvian sediments. Free drifting sediment trap and seawater particulate matter analyses were undertaken to determine the distribution of sterols on large and small particles in seawater and their vertical flux to the sediments. Zooplankton fecal pellets, molts and carcasses and fecal pellets of anchoveta were analysed for their potential contribution to the sedimentary sterols. Zooplankton (copepods and euphausiids) molts and fecal pellets make significant contributions to some sedimentary sterols (cholest-5-en-3β-ol and cholesta-5, 22E-dien-3β-ol). These sterols are also dominant in the sediment trap material. Sedimentary sterols contain a strong phytoplankton source signal (24-methylcholesta-5, 22E-dien-3β-ol and 24-methylcholesta-5, 24(28)-dien-3β-ol). These diatom derived sterols appear to be delivered to the sediment quickly via sinking anchovy fecal pellets.

INTRODUCTION

Sterols have been used by several investigators as biological markers for the sources and transformations of labile organic matter in Recent sediments (see Gagosian *et al.*, 1980a and Volkman *et al.*, 1981a for recent references). Comparisons of sterol distributions in sediments with those of various organisms have been used to determine the sediment sterol sources. However, rarely have sterol analyses of phytoplankton and zooplankton which inhabit the water column above the sediments been combined with species and biomass determinations. In addition, different sterol distributions in various parts of the organism and their excretion and egestion products (i.e., cytoplasmic fluid, cellular structural framework, and fecal pellets and molts of zooplankton) further complicate sediment sterol source determinations.

We thus decided to study the sterol distributions of the organisms inhabiting the water column above the sediments as well as their egestion products and to compare these distributions to those of surface sediments, Our approach is to compare the sterol distributions of (1) particulate material collected in sediment traps (large particles usually > 20 μm), (2) particulate material from bulk seawater samples (< 20 μm particles), (3) phytoplankton and zooplankton, (4) fecal pellets and molts of zooplankton, (5) fecal pellets of fish, and (6) biota living in the sediments with those sterols found in the sediments to ascertain sediment sterol sources.

In this manuscript, we report initial results from studies conducted in the Peru coastal upwelling region. The intensity of organic matter biosynthesis in this area makes it ideal for such studies. Source organisms are comparatively easy to collect from this region since phytoplankton blooms often contain single species which rise and fall over 3–5 day time scales. This allows several collections of specific species to be made over the duration of one cruise. Vertical migration of zooplankton, principally copepods and euphausiids, to surface waters at night for feeding facilitates collection of these organisms. The transport of organic material from other sources is relatively minor compared with the high concentrations of organic matter produced in the upwelling zone thus simplifying sediment organic matter source determinations.

EXPERIMENTAL

Sampling and extraction

Seawater, free drifting sediment trap (FST) and sediment samples were collected during February–March, 1978 on R/V *Knorr*, cruise 73, leg 2. Detailed hydrographic data for this cruise can be found in Gagosian *et al.* (1980b). Sediment trap samples containing anchoveta fecal pellets were collected in March, 1981 on R/V *Atlantis II* cruise 108, leg 3. Locations of the sediment traps and sediments collected on the 1978 cruise are shown in Fig. 1. A description of the FSTs (a pair of 41 cm diameter cylinders, 0.26 m² total collecting area) as well as bulk parameters of the particulate matter flux is given in Staresinic (1982). Day and night trap deployments were set at 14 m (the base of the euphotic zone) and 52 m (below the seasonal thermocline). Details of the sediment samples (SC5 collected with a Soutar core (0–1 cm) from 15°07.1′ S,

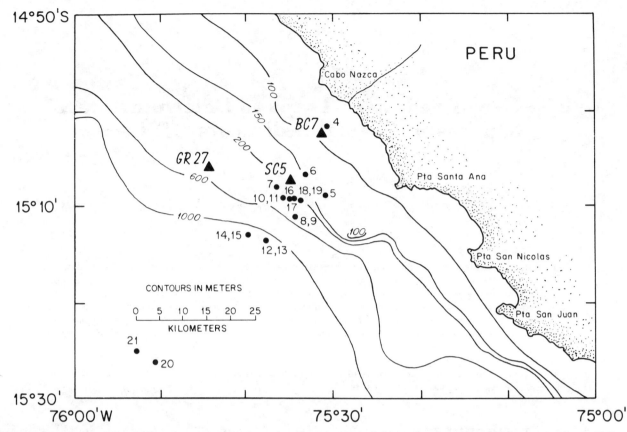

Fig. 1. Locations of sediment samples and sediment trap deployments during R/V *Knorr* cruise 73, leg 2, February to March, 1978 off the Peruvian coast.

75°35.1′ W and GR27 collected with a grab sampler (0–2 cm) from 15°05′ S, 75°43.9′ W) can be found in Volkman *et al.* (1982) and Henrichs (1980). The sediments were diatomaceous oozes located in an oxygen minimum zone (<0.1 ml/l seawater) which either eliminates benthic fauna or restricts it to a few benthic metazoans such as polychaete worms of the family *Ciratulidae*. Filaments of *Thioploca* bacteria (Gallardo, 1977) were conspicuous in each of the surface sediments. A description of the extraction of the sediments and sediment trap material can be found in Volkman *et al.* (1982) and Wakeham *et al.* (1982), respectively. Anchoveta fecal pellets were sonic extracted twice with toluene/methanol. Water samples were collected using glass Bodman bottles (Gagosian *et al.*, 1979), transferred to stainless steel and aluminium containers with polypropylene tubing, and extracted with hexane as previously reported (Gagosian and Nigrelli, 1979).

Analysis

The lipid extract was fractionated into constituent lipid classes by silica gel chromatography (70–230 mesh, deactivated with 5% distilled water). Fourteen fractions were collected by elution with mixtures of hexane, toluene, and ethyl acetate. Fraction VII (15% ethyl acetate in hexane) contained the 4-methylsterols and Δ4-3-ketosteroids; fraction VIII (20% ethyl acetate in hexane) contained the 4-desmethylsterols. These fractions were combined for the seawater and sediment

trap analyses but kept separate for the sediment analyses.

Sterols were acetylated with acetic anhydride in pyridine and analysed by high resolution glass capillary gas chromatography on a Carlo Erba Fractovap 2150 gas chromatograph using a deactivated (by persilyation) SE–52 coated (15 m and 20 m × 0.32 mm i.d.) column (Grob and Grob, 1980). The helium gas flow was 1.5–2 ml per min. The injector and detector were operated at 300 °C. The sediment trap and seawater sterol acetates (1–2 μl) were injected splitless at 80 °C and heated to 265 °C at 3.5 °C/min. The sediment and anchovy fecal pellet sterol acetates were injected at 25 °C, rapidly programmed to 180 °C and then to 300 °C at 2 °C/min.

Structural identification of the free sterols (as acetates) was based on relative retention times obtained by high resolution glass capillary gas chromatography and comparison of mass spectra obtained by gas chromatography/mass spectrometry (GC/MS) with published mass spectra and mass spectra obtained from authentic standards. Electron impact mass spectra were obtained using a Varian Aerograph 1400 gas chromatograph equipped with an SE–52 glass capillary column (25 m × 0.30 mm i.d.) interfaced with a Finnigan 1015C quadrupole mass spectrometer. The carrier gas (He) flow rate was 2–3 ml/min. The mass spectrometer was scanned linearly from 40–550 or 600 amu at 1 sec intervals. Data acquisition used a Finnigan INCOS 2300 data system. Further analytical details can be found in Gagosian *et al.* (1982a).

FREE 4-DESMETHYLSTEROLS

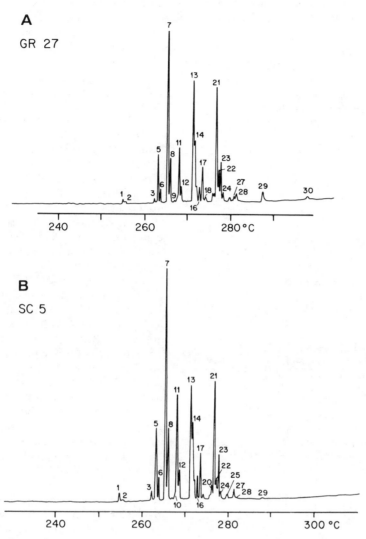

Fig. 2. Glass capillary gas chromatograms of free 4-desmethylsterols (acetates) from surface sediments (a) GR27 and (b) SC5. Peak numbers refer to the structures in Table 1.

RESULTS AND DISCUSSION

Gas chromatograms of the 4-desmethylsterol distributions of two surface sediments collected from the Peruvian shelf are shown in Fig. 2. Hydrocarbon and long chain ketone distributions are reported in Volkman *et al.* (1982). The relative sterol distributions of these two samples are approximately the same and are very similar to another surface sediment sample from 15°02′ S, 75°31′ W, further inshore (BC7). The structural assignments of the compounds can be found in Table 1. Details of these assignments will be presented elsewhere along with the quantitative aspects of the surface sediments and deeper core sections. We will confine our discussion here to the potential sources of this sedimentary material.

There are several important features to note in the sterol distribution. Cholest-5-en-3β-ol (*7*) is the major sterol while cholesta-5,22E-dien-3β-ol (*5*), 24-methylcholesta-5,22E-dien-3β-ol (*11a*), 24-methyl-cholesta-5,24(28)-dien-3β-ol (*13*), and 24-ethyl-cholest-5-en-3β-ol (*21a*) are major components.

The concentration of 4-methylsterols is <10% of the 4-desmethylsterols and of these dinosterol, 4α,23,24-trimethyl-5α-cholest-22E-en-3β-ol is the major component. The stanol/stenol ratio for various sterol pairs (i.e., 5α-cholestan-3β-ol/cholest-5-en-3β-ol) is relatively low compared with other Recent surface sediment studies (Wardroper *et al.*, 1978; Gagosian *et al.*, 1980a). Since bacteria are known to transform stenols into stanols, this low stanol/stenol ratio suggests that the organic matter in the sediments is relatively unreworked by bacteria (Edmunds *et al.*, 1980; Taylor *et al.*, 1981). Indeed, the sedimentation in this area is very high, 1–2 cm/yr (Henrichs, 1980), so that the surface sediments analysed in this study represent less than two years of sediment accumulation.

There are four major sources of marine organic material for the surface sediments of the Peruvian shelf: (1) advection of material produced in other locations, (2) production by meio- and macrofauna living in the sediments, (3) large, fast-sinking particles (e.g. fecal pellets) formed in the upper water column, and (4) small

Table 1

4-Desmethylsterols isolated from sediment trap and sediments
off Peruvian coast at 15° S

GC Peak No.	Identification
1	24-norcholesta-5,22E-dien-3β-ol
2	24-nor-5α-cholest-22E-en-3β-ol
3	27-nor-24-methylcholesta-5,22E-dien-3β-ol
4	27-nor-24-methyl-5α-cholest-24(28)-en-3β-ol
5	cholesta-5,22E-dien-3β-ol
6	5α-cholest-22E-en-3β-ol
7	cholest-5-en-3β-ol
8	5α-cholestan-3β-ol
9	Not identified
10	cholesta-5,24-dien-3β-ol
11	a. 24-methylcholesta-5,22E-dien-3β-ol b. 5α-cholest-7-en-3β-ol
12	24-methyl-5α-cholest-22E-en-3β-ol
13	24-methylcholesta-5,24(28)-dien-3β-ol
14	a. 24-methylcholest-5-en-3β-ol b. 24-methyl-5α-cholest-24(28)-en-3β-ol
15	24-methyl-5α-cholestan-3β-ol
16	23,24-dimethylcholesta-5,22E-dien-3β-ol
17	a. 24-ethylcholesta-5,22E-dien-3β-ol b. 23,24-dimethyl-5α-cholest-22E-en-3β-ol
18	24-ethyl-5α-cholest-22E-en-3β-ol
20	23,24-dimethylcholest-5-en-3β-ol (4,24-dimethyl-5α-cholestan-3β-ol) in sediment traps and seawater
21	a. 24-ethylcholest-5-en-3β-ol b. 23,24-dimethyl-5α-cholestan-3β-ol c. 24-ethylcholesta-5,24(28)E-dien-3β-ol
22	a. 24-ethyl-5α-cholestan-3β-ol b. 24-ethyl-5α-cholest-24(28)E-en-3β-ol
23	24-ethylcholesta-5,24(28)Z-dien-3β-ol
24	24-ethyl-5α-cholest-24(28)Z-en-3β-ol
25	Not identified
26[a]	24-isopropylcholest-5-en-3β-ol
27[a]	24-isopropylcholesta-5,24(28)-dien-3β-ol
28[a]	24-isopropyl-5α-cholest-24(28)-en-3β-ol

[a] Structural identification is tentative. The C–24 alkyl group may be n-propyl.

particles slowly settling through the water column to the sediment (e.g., diatom or coccolithophore fragments or dinoflagellate cysts). Land-derived organic material may be delivered to the Peruvian shelf sediments by either atmospheric of riverine input.

Since the production of organic material in the upwelling zone is 10–100 times greater than in surrounding areas, advection of material from other locations would make a minor contribution to the total quantity of sedimentary sterols. As mentioned earlier, the sediments are anoxic. Meio- and macro-faunal sterol sources can therefore be eliminated. Large quantities of *Thioploca* species bacteria were found in these sediments (Gallardo, 1977; Henrichs, 1980). Although it is still a matter of controversy, it is generally assumed that bacteria do not biosynthesize 4-desmethylsterols from acetate via the squalene cyclization route (Nes and McKean, 1977; Nes *et al.*, 1980). In the cases where they were thought to biosynthesize them, bacteria produced extremely low levels of sterols. Based on this information, we feel that bacteria would be negligible contributors to the overall sterol pool in these sediments. Consequently, this leaves the input of sterols produced in the upper water column and transported by large and small particles as the main source of the marine-derived sedimentary sterols.

Water column particle transport

Recent studies have shown that a large portion of labile, unreworked organic material may be transported to the sea floor in large particles (> 20 μm) (Crisp *et al.*, 1979; Prahl *et al.*, 1980; Wakeham *et al.*, 1980; de Baar *et al.*, 1982; Gagosian *et al.*, 1982a, b; Lee and Cronin, 1982; Repeta and Gagosian, 1982a, b; Wakeham, 1982). This material may be responsible for the major sedimentary input of organic matter produced in the euphotic zone. The importance of large particle transport for sedimentary sterols can be determined by sediment trap experiments. Such an experiment was undertaken in February–March, 1978 on R/V *Knorr* cruise 73, leg 2 during which twenty-one FSTs were deployed (Fig. 1). The sterol distributions of four of these FST samples (FST 8, 9, 10, 11) are shown in Fig. 3. These deployments were made close to sediment samples SC5 and GR27. Although the sterol flux in night samples (FST 10, 11) was approximately ten times that of the day samples (Gagosian *et al.*, 1982b), the sterol distributions were basically the same in all four trap samples. The major source of sterols in the trap material (FSTs 8–11) was determined to be copepod fecal pellets, molts, and carcasses. Visual inspection of a sediment trap sample (FST 3) showed that the sample was almost exclusively made up of these copepod components. The sterol distribution of FST 3 (Fig. 4) was virtually identical to FSTs 8–11. It should be pointed out that euphausiid fecal pellets and molts would probably have a similar sterol distribution to copepod fecal pellets and molts. An important feature of the sterol distribution is the predominance of cholest-5-en-3β-ol (*7*) and cholesta-5,22E-dien-3β-ol (*5*), both of which are well known copepod sterols (Volkman *et al.*, 1980a).

In addition to copepod and euphausiid molts and fecal pellets, sediment traps also contained a number of large (~ 2 mm length and 1 mm diam.) anchoveta (*Engraulis ringens*) fecal pellets. We were able to analyse intact anchoveta fecal pellets collected on R/V *Atlantis II* cruise 108, leg 3, in March, 1981. On this cruise, sediment traps were deployed in the same area as the 1978 cruise. However, almost all of the trap material from 13 deployments contained anchoveta fecal pellets, whereas no more than 17% of the particulate organic carbon found in the 1978 sediment trap samples could be accounted for by anchoveta fecal pellets (Staresinic *et al.*, 1982). The main feature of the sterol distribution of the anchoveta fecal pellets (Fig. 5) is the large amount of 24-methylcholesta-5,24(28)-dien-3β-ol (*13*). This compound has been found in several diatoms, i.e. *Nitzschia alba* (Kates *et al.*, 1978), *Skeletonema costatum* (Ballantine *et al.*, 1979), and *Chaetoceros simplex calcitrans* (Boutry *et al.*, 1979). A culture of cloned *Thalassiosira pseudonana* contained (*13*) as its major sterol (81%) (J. Volkman, L. Brand, unpublished results). Indeed, microscopic analysis of the anchoveta fecal pellets

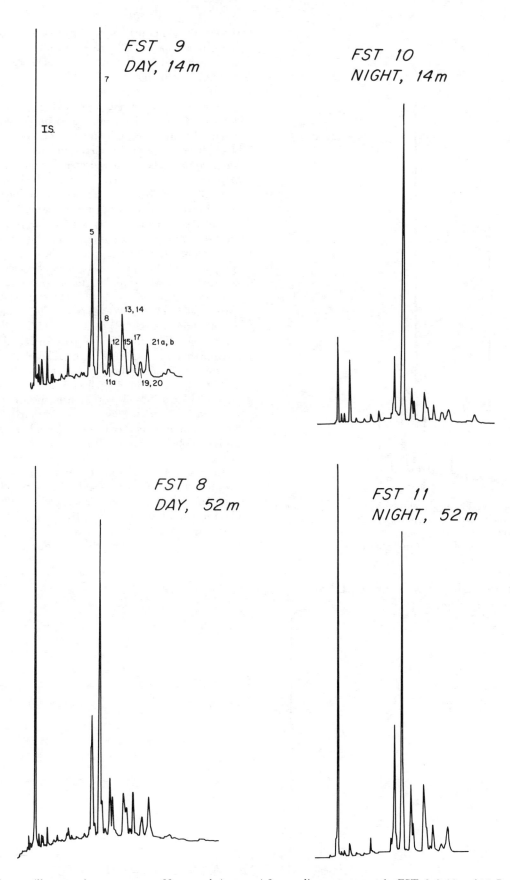

Fig. 3. Glass capillary gas chromatograms of free sterols (acetates) from sediment trap samples FSTs 9, 8, 10 and 11. Peak numbers refer to structures in Table 1.

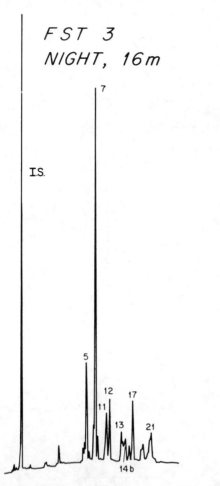

FST 3
NIGHT, 16m

I.S.

Fig. 4. Glass capillary gas chromatograms of free sterols (acetates) from floating sediment trap FST 3 which contained copepod molts, carcasses and fecal pellets. Peak numbers refer to structures in Table 1.

showed the pennate diatom *Thalassionema nitzchoides* and the centric diatom *Thalassiosira eccentrica* to be major components. Intact diatoms in the pellets accounted for >50% of the anchoveta pellet POC in 1978 (Staresinic *et al.*, 1982).

In addition to large, fast-sinking particles, small slowly-sinking particles must also be considered as a potential source of sedimentary sterols. The importance of small particles can be determined by sampling the water column above the sediment under investigation. Selected water samples collected in a depth profile from 15°09.0′ S, 75°31.5′ W are shown in Fig. 6. These samples were collected during the same day as FST 8 and 9 deployments. Water samples were not filtered since 0.45 μm glass fibre filters would not retain all the nannoplankton which could be an important component of the plankton biomass. Surface and 10 m samples showed similar sterol distributions with cholesta-5,22E-dien-3β-ol (*5*), cholest-5-en-3β-ol (*7*), 24-methyl-5α-cholest-22E-en-3β-ol (*12*) and 23,24-dimethyl-5α-cholest-22E-en-3β-ol (*17b*) the major constituents. This distribution pattern is indicative of a phytoplankton, mostly dinoflagellate, input. Microscopic examination of water samples from this profile showed dinoflagellates to be the major phytoplankters. Sterols common in most diatoms (e.g. *11a* and *13*) are in low concentrations. The sterol distribution for seawater below the euphotic zone (~15 m) is completely different from the euphotic zone sterol distributions (Fig. 6): cholest-5-en-3β-ol (*7*) is the dominant sterol in samples from 25 to 50 m. As mentioned earlier, euphausiids and copepods produce compound (*7*) as their major sterol (80%). The observation that predominantly zooplankton derived sterols are associated with small particles (<20 μm) in the water column below the euphotic zone has been

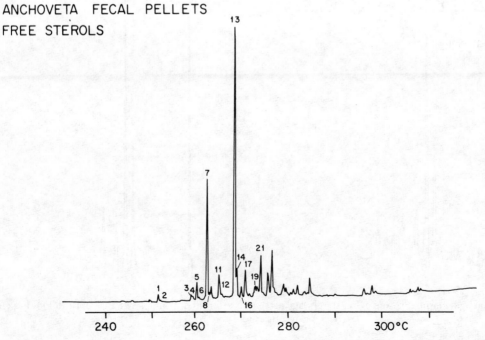

ANCHOVETA FECAL PELLETS
FREE STEROLS

Fig. 5. Glass capillary gas chromatogram of free sterols (trimethylsilylethers of anchoveta fecal pellets. Peak numbers refer to structures in Table 1.

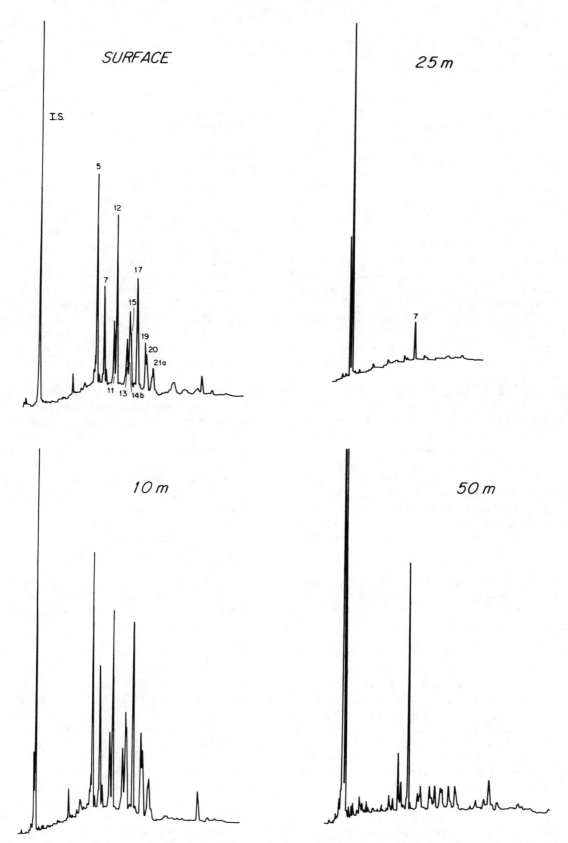

Fig. 6. Glass capillary gas chromatograms of free sterols (acetates) of water samples collected from the surface, 10 m, 25 m, and 50 m (15°09.0′ S, 75°31.5′ W). Peak numbers refer to structures in Table 1.

reported for other oceanic areas such as the oligotrophic Sargasso Sea (Gagosian, 1976; Gagosian and Nigrelli, 1979) and upwelled waters of southwest Africa (Gagosian *et al.*, 1980a).

Sedimentary sterol sources

By comparing the sterol distributions of the large particles (FSTs 8–11), copepod carcasses, molts, and fecal pellets (FST 3), anchoveta fecal pellets and small particles (water samples) with the sterol distribution in the sediments, a preliminary determination of the sources of the sedimentary sterols can be made.

In the sediments, cholest-5-en-3β-ol (7) undoubtedly comes from zooplankton carcasses, molts and fecal pellets with some contribution (perhaps 20%) from anchoveta fecal pellets and a smaller contribution from phytoplankton (<10%). The sediment trap material (FST 8–11) as well as the copepod molts and fecal pellets (FST 3) were rich in cholest-5-en-3β-ol. Sterol (7) was also present in the small particle sterol distribution in surface waters suggesting that this sterol may also have a small phytoplankton source. The source of cholesta-5,22E-dien-3β-ol (5) appears to be from both zooplankton and phytoplankton. This compound was found in high concentrations in water samples taken in the euphotic zone which contained mainly dinoflagellates (Fig. 6). Diatoms have also been found to contain this sterol (Volkman et al., 1980b). FST 3, which contained mainly copepod molts and fecal pellets, also had high concentrations of sterol (5) (Fig. 4).

Anchoveta fecal pellets appear to be a major source for 24-methylcholesta-5,24(28)-dien-3β-ol (13) found in the sediments since this sterol was the major component in the fecal pellets (Fig. 5). These fecal pellets settle at the rate of ~1000 m/day as compared with 10–100 m/day for zooplankton fecal pellets and 1–5 m/day for phytoplankton (Staresinic et al., 1982). Hence, they can deliver fresh, relatively undegraded material to shelf sediments in a matter of hours. Anchoveta fecal pellets may also be the main transport mechanism for 24-methylcholesta-5,22E-dien-3β-ol (11a) into the sediments. Like sterol (13), the source of compound (11a) is most likely diatoms since many species have been found to contain this compound (Rubinstein and Goad, 1974; Orcutt and Patterson, 1975; Ballantine et al., 1979; Volkman et al., 1980b). Some of sterol (11a) may also be derived from coccolithophores such as Emiliania huxleyi (Volkman et al., 1981b), a major phytoplankter in coastal Peruvian waters (Ryther et al., 1971). We observed only a minor amount of sterol (11a) in the anchoveta fecal pellets analysed, however it should be emphasized that these fecal pellets were collected in 1981 and only over a three-week period. It is certainly reasonable to assume that anchoveta fecal pellets analysed from other collections will contain sterols from the major diatoms in the water column at that time. Indeed although sterol (11a) was not found in very significant concentrations in the water column (Fig. 6) or sediment trap samples (Fig. 3) reported in this manuscript, much higher concentrations were observed in other water samples and sediment trap samples collected during diatom blooms on R/V Knorr cruise 73 (Gagosian and Nigrelli, unpublished results).

Since the source for sterols (11a) and (13) in the fecal pellets is undoubtedly diatoms, direct transport of these sterols into the sediments via planktonic settling, rather than incorporation into anchoveta fecal pellets must also be considered. However, water samples collected below the euphotic zone exhibit very low concentrations of sterols (11a) and (13) (Fig. 6). This suggests that this was a minor transport mechanism

during the time of our expedition as compared to anchoveta fecal pellet transport. On the other hand, other investigators (Davies, 1975; R. J. Morris, personal communication) have observed large diatom mats on the sediment surface of coastal sediments. Evidently, these mats occur when a bloom ends and subsequently sinks to the sediment surface before zooplankton grazing becomes effective. Several of these same type of events could occur in Peru upwelling coastal waters as well (Packard, 1977).

These results suggest several fates for phytoplankton sterols. As seen in other oceanic water columns, it appears that sterols in slowly sinking phytoplankton are transformed by zooplankton into cholest-5-en-3β-ol (7) (Gagosian and Nigrelli, 1979) as the particles sink below the euphotic zone. Hence, in deep water, sterol (7) is by far the major compound of the seawater 'standing stock' of sterols associated with small particles. A second fate of phytoplankton sterols in the euphotic zone is consumption by anchoveta, copepods and euphausiids, incorporation into fecal pellets, and release into deep water. A third fate of phytoplankton is offshore transport, away from the sediments directly below the bloom. Offshore flow on the Peru shelf extends to ~20 m depth; below this depth mean flow is onshore (Brink et al., 1980). Dinoflagellates are usually present in low mixing, low-nutrient regimes and tend to be found farther offshore than diatom blooms. This may explain why dinosterol, 4α,22,23-trimethyl-5α-cholest-22E-en-3β-ol, a major dinoflagellate sterol, was observed in such low concentrations in sediment samples SC5 and GC27. Analysis of sediments farther offshore are underway to further test this hypothesis.

Sterols thus far discussed have a clear marine origin. The 24(R) isomer of 24-ethylcholest-5-en-3β-ol (21a) is generally assigned a terrestrial origin. Phytoplankton have also been found to contain a small amount of sterol (21a) but its C-24 stereochemistry is unknown. Our gas chromatographic conditions do not allow us to separate these C–24 epimers. The 24(S) epimer of sterol (21a) has been found in sponges but sponges are not present in the sediment samples from Peru. As the amount of sterol (21a) found in the sediments is much greater than has been found in phytoplankton, the most likely source of sterol (21a) is terrestrial with some phytoplankton contribution. It should be pointed out that gas chromatographic peak 21 contains two other compounds as noted in Table 1. Together these compounds make up <25% of peak 21 in the sediment samples and <5% of the peak 21 components in the seawater and sediment trap samples.

Terrestrial sources may be transported either by atmospheric aerosols or with river run-off. There are few active rivers near 15° S (Zuta and Guillen, 1970) but during El Nino events (recent examples being 1972, 1976) when warm water incursions move south along the Peru shelf, high rainfall occurs. Rivers could then bring large amounts of terrestrial debris down the high (300 m) steep continental land slopes into coastal waters where surface currents could eventually move the material farther offshore. It is difficult to assess the input of atmospheric transport since no studies have been conducted off this coastline. Simoneit (1977) has analysed Saharan dust close to shore off the northwest African shelf but no sterols were detected. The Peru coastline is marked by steep sand cliffs. The strong northwesterly winds cause a constant haze condition for much of the year. A large amount of this dust is undoubtedly transported over the sea but we cannot assess the importance of this atmospheric transport of terrestrially-derived sterols to the sea until aerosol samples collected off the Peruvian coast in 1981 are analysed.

In these two sediment samples other organic markers in the *n*-alkane, fatty acid and wax ester classes show very little terrestrial input as compared to marine sources. They show very little higher land plant contribution unlike a sediment sample closer to the coast which shows a major input (Volkman *et al.*, 1982). Since 24-ethylcholest-5-en-3β-ol is a major sterol in the sediments ($\sim 10\%$), it appears that some portion of it must be produced from a marine source (Lee *et al.*, 1980). The most likely candidate are diatoms, though few analyses have shown this sterol to be biosynthesized by unicellular algae.

A major difficulty in determining the sources of particulate material to the sediments is the different time scales which the various types of samples represent. For example, whereas a water sample represents the standing stock of particles at a single point in time (and not the large infrequent, fast moving particles), sediment traps sample the downward flux of particles through the water column on time scales of hours (this study) to months (Honjo, 1980). On the other hand, surface sediments (1–2 cm depth) represent 1–2 years accumulation in this area (Henrichs, 1980) and up to several hundred to thousands in open ocean areas. The sediments thus integrate hundreds of trap experiments and thousands of water samples. This short time scale variation can clearly be seen in the ten-fold difference in sterol flux at night compared with during the day (Fig. 3) (Gagosian *et al.*, 1982b). We believe this time scale difference is one reason why the strong anchoveta fecal pellet signal (sterol *13*) found in the sediment was not observed in the sediment traps 8–11 (Fig. 3). Sediment traps 8–11 only represent 24 h in a two-year time integration of the particulate matter flux collected at the sediment surface. Typically, plankton blooms and their associated zooplankton grazing events rise and fall in periods of less than one week. Many of these signatures will be left in the surface sediment sampled. The change in anchoveta stocks is expected to track several of these events. In 1978, the maximum amount of POC flux that could be accounted for by anchoveta fecal pellets was 17%; in most of the samples, it was below 5% (Staresinic *et al.*, 1982). However, in 1981, >90% of the POC could be accounted for by anchoveta fecal pellets. Therefore, it is not surprising that high concentrations of sterols associated with anchoveta fecal pellets (*13*) found in the sediment were not found in four 12-hour sediment trap experiments.

CONCLUSIONS

1. The sterol composition of suspended particulate material in seawater ($< 20 \ \mu$m) is very different from

that of large particles ($> 20 \ \mu$m) collected in sediment traps. Zooplankton and anchoveta play an important role in determining this difference.

2. Sedimentary sterols contain a strong phytoplankton source signal (24-methylcholesta-5,22E-dien-3β-ol and 24-methylcholesta-5,24(28)-dien-3β-ol). These phytoplankton derived sterols appear to be delivered to the sediment quickly via sinking anchovy fecal pellets.

3. Zooplankton (copepods and euphausiids) molts and fecal pellets make significant contributions to some sedimentary sterols (cholest-5-en-3β-ol and cholesta-5,22E-dien-3β-ol). These sterols are dominant in sediment trap particulate material.

To understand more fully the relationships between the various sediment sources discussed in this manuscript and the sediments, it is clearly necessary to expand sample coverage both in time and space to approach more fully the accumulation time of the sediments under investigation. Better coverage in the water column, both horizontally and vertically, are needed for both water sampling and sediment trap experiments as well as for the organisms inhabiting the water column at the time these experiments are undertaken. The results reported here are for only one season of the year, austral fall when upwelling off the Peruvian coast is well developed. Seasonal changes in particle fluxes have been observed in oligotrophic waters (Deuser and Ross, 1980) and need to be examined in upwelling zones as well.

Acknowledgements

We thank Drs Nick Staresinic, John Farrington, Cindy Lee and Stuart Wakeham for useful discussions and Dr Nelson Frew for obtaining mass spectra. This work was funded by Grants OCE 77–26084, OCE 79–25352 and OCE 80–18436 from the National Science Foundation, Grant N00014–79–C–0071 from the office of Naval Research and a WHOI Postdoctoral Scholar award to J.K.V.

REFERENCES

Ballantine, J. A., Lavis, A. and Morris, R. J. (1979) Sterols of the phytoplankton-effects of illumination and growth stage. *Phytochem.* **18**, 1459–1466.

Boutry, J. L., Saliot, A. and Barbier, M. (1979) The diversity of marine sterols and the role of algal bio-masses; from facts to hypothesis. *Experientia* **35**, 1541–1684.

Brink, K. H., Halpern, D. and Smith, R. L. (1980) Circulation in the Peruvian upwelling system near 15° S. *J. Geophys. Res.* **85**, 4036–4048.

Crisp, T. P., Brenner, S. M. I., Venkatesan, E., Ruth, E. and Kaplan, I. R. (1979) Organic chemical characterization of sediment trap particulates from San Nicholas, Santa Barbara, Santa Monica, and San Pedro Basins, California. *Geochim. Cosmochim. Acta* **43**, 1791–1801.

Davies, J. M. (1975) Energy flow through the benthos in a Scottish sea loch. *Mar. Biol.* **31**, 353–362.

De Baar, H. J. W., Farrington, J. W. and Wakeham, S. G. (1983) Sediment trap experiment in the equatorial Atlantic Ocean: Vertical flux of fatty acids, regeneration and oxygen consumption. *J. Mar. Res.* In press.

Deuser, W. G. and Ross, E. H. (1980) Seasonal change in the flux of organic carbon to the deep Sargasso Sea. *Nature (London)* **283**, 364–365.

Edmunds, K. L. H., Brassell, S. C. and Eglinton, G. (1980) The short term diagenetic fate of 5α-cholestan-3β-ol: *In situ* radiolabelled incubations in algal mats. In *Advances in Organic Geochemistry, 1979*, ed. by Douglas, A. G. and Maxwell, J. R. Pergamon Press, Oxford, pp. 427–434.

Gagosian, R. B. (1976) A detailed vertical profile of sterols in the Sargasso Sea. *Limnol. Oceanogr.* **21**, 702–710.

Gagosian, R. B., Dean, Jr. J. P., Hamblin, R. and Zafiriou, O. C. (1979) A versatile, interchangeable chamber seawater sampler. *Limnol. Oceanogr.* **24**, 583–588.

Gagosian, R. B. and Nigrelli, G. (1979) The transport and budget of sterols in the western North Atlantic Ocean. *Limnol. Oceanogr.* **24**, 838–849.

Gagosian, R. B., Smith, S. O., Lee, C. L., Farrington, J. W. and Frew, N. M. (1980a) Steroid transformations in Recent marine sediments. In *Advances in Organic Geochemistry, 1979*, ed. by Douglas, A. G. and Maxwell, J. M. Pergamon Press, Oxford, pp. 407–419.

Gagosian, R. B., Loder, T., Nigrelli, G., Mlodzinska, Z., Love, J. and Kogelschatz, J. (1980b) Hydrographic and nutrient data from R/V *Knorr* Cruise 73, Leg 2 — Feb.–March, 1978 — off the coast of Peru. *Woods Hole Oceanographic Institution Technical Report, WHOI–80–1*, 77 pp.

Gagosian, R. B., Smith, S. O. and Nigrelli, G. E. (1982a) Vertical transport of steroid alcohols and ketones measured in a sediment trap experiment in the equatorial Atlantic Ocean. *Geochim. Cosmochim. Acta* **46**, 1163–1172.

Gagosian, R. B., Nigrelli, G. E. and Volkman, J. K. (1982b) Vertical transport and transformation of biogenic organic compounds from a sediment trap experiment off the coast of Peru. *NATO Advanced Research Institute on Coastal Upwelling and its Sediment Record*, ed. by Suess, E. and Thiede, J. Pergamon Press, Oxford (in press).

Gallardo, V. (1977) Large benthic microbial communities in sulphide biota under Peru–Chile subsurface countercurrent. *Nature (London)* **288**, 331–332.

Grob, K. and Grob, G. (1980) Deactivation of glass capillary columns by persilylation, Part 3. Extending the wetability by bonding phenyl groups to the glass surface. *J. High Resolution Chromatogr. and Chromatogr. Commun.* **3**, 197–198.

Henrichs, S. M. (1980) Biogeochemistry of dissolved free amino acids in marine sediments. Ph.D. Thesis, Mass. Inst. Technol./Woods Hole Ocean. Inst. Joint Program, *WHOI Technical Report 80–89*, 253 pp.

Honjo, S. (1980) Material fluxes and modes of sedimentation in the mesopelagic and bathypelagic zones. *J. Mar. Res.* **38**, 53–97.

Kates, M., Tremblay, P., Anderson, R. and Volcani, B. E. (1978) Identification of the free and conjugated sterol in a non-photosynthetic diatom, *Nitzschia alba*, as 24-methylenecholesterol. *Lipids* **13**, 34–41.

Lee, C. L., Gagosian, R. B. and Farrington, J. W. (1980) Geochemistry of sterols in sediments from the Black Sea and the southwest African shelf and slope. *Org. Geochem.* **2**, 103–113.

Lee, C. and Cronin, C. (1982) The vertical flux of particulate organic nitrogen in the sea: decomposition of amino acids in the Peru upwelling area and the equatorial Atlantic. *J. Mar. Res.* **40**, 227–251.

Nes, W. R. and McKean, M. L. (1977) *Biochemistry of steroids and other isopentenoids*. University Press, Baltimore, pp. 412–418.

Nes, W. R., Adler, J. H., Frasinel, C., Nes, W. D., Young, M. and Joseph, J. M. (1980) The independence of photosynthesis and aerobiosis from sterol biosynthesis in bacteria. *Phytochemistry* **19**, 1439–1443.

Orcutt, D. M. and Patterson, G. W. (1975) Sterol, fatty acid and elemental composition of diatoms grown in chemically defined media. *Comp. Biochem. Physiol.* **50B**, 579–583.

Packard, T. T. (1977) The injection of particulate organic matter into the deep sea by a relaxation of oceanic upwelling. *CUEA Newsletter* **6(4)**, 46–47.

Prahl, F. G., Bennett, J. T. and Carpenter, R. (1980) The early diagenesis of aliphatic hydrocarbons and organic matter in sedimentary particulates from Dabob Bag, Washington. *Geochim. Cosmochim. Acta* **44**, 1967–1976.

Repeta, D. J. and Gagosian, R. B. (1982a) Carotenoid transformation products in the upwelled waters off the Peruvian coast: sediment trap, seawater particulate matter, and zooplankton fecal pellet analysis. In *Advances in Organic Geochemistry, 1981*, ed. by Bjorøy, M. Wiley, Sussex. (In press).

Repeta, D. J. and Gagosian, R. B. (1982b) Carotenoid transformations in coastal marine waters. *Nature* **295**, 51–54.

Rubinstein, I. and Goad, L. J. (1974) Occurrence of (24S) 24-methylcholesta-5,22E-dien-3β-ol in the diatom *Phaeodactylum tricornutum*. *Phytochem.* **13**, 485–487.

Ryther, J. H., Menzel, D. W., Hulburt, E. M., Lorenzen, C. J. and Corwin, N. (1971) The production and utilization of organic matter in the Peru coastal current. *Investigacion Pesquera* **35**, 43–59.

Simoneit, B. R. T. (1977) Organic matter in aeolian dust over the Atlantic Ocean. *Mar. Chem.* **5**, 443–464.

Staresinic, N. (1982) Downward flux of bulk particulate organic matter in the Peru coastal upwelling. *J. Mar. Res.* (in press).

Staresinic, N., Farrington, J. W., Gagosian, R. B. Clifford, C. H. and Hulburt, E. M. (1982) Downward transport of particulate matter in the Peru coastal upwelling: Role of the anchoveta, *Engraulis ringens*. *NATO Advanced Research Institute on Coastal Upwelling and its sediment record*, ed. by Suess, E. and Thiede, J. Pergamon Press, Oxford. (In press).

Taylor, C. D., Smith, S. O. and Gagosian, R. B. (1981) Use of microbial enrichments for the study of the anaerobic degradation of cholesterol. *Geochim. Cosmochim. Acta* **45**, 2161–2168.

Volkman, J. K., Corner, E. D. S. and Eglinton, G. (1980a) Transformations of biolipids in the marine food web and in underlying bottom sediments. In *Colloques Internationaux du C.N.R.S. No. 293. Biogeochemie de la matiere organique a l'interface eau sediment marin*, pp. 185–197.

Volkman, J. K., Eglinton, G. and Corner, E. D. S. (1980b) Sterols and fatty acids of the marine diatom *Biddulphia sinensis*. *Phytochem.* **19**, 1809–1813.

Volkman, J. K., Gillan, F. T., Johns, R. B. and Eglinton, G. (1981a) Sources of neutral lipids in a temperate intertidal sediment. *Geochim. Cosmochim. Acta* **45**, 1817–1828.

Volkman, J. K., Smith, D. J., Eglinton, G., Forsberg, T. E. V. and Corner, E. D. S. (1981b) Sterol and fatty acid composition of four marine haptophycean algae. *J. Mar. Biol. Assoc. U.K.* **61**, 509–527.

Volkman, J. K., Farrington, J. W., Gagosian, R. B. and Wakeham, S. G. (1982) Lipid composition of coastal marine sediments from the Peru upwelling region. In *Advances in Organic Geochemistry, 1981*, ed. by Bjorøy, M., Wiley, Sussex (in press).

Wakeham, S. G., Farrington, J. W., Gagosian, R. B., Lee, C., De Baar, H., Nigrelli, G. E., Tripp, B. W., Smith, S. O. and Frew, N. M. (1980) Fluxes of organic matter from a sediment trap experiment in the equatorial Atlantic Ocean. *Nature (London)* **286**, 798–800.

Wakeham, S. G. (1982) Sources and fates of organic matter from a sediment trap experiment in the equatorial north Atlantic: wax esters, steryl esters, triglycerides and glyceryl ethers. *Geochim. Cosmochim. Acta* (in press).

Wakeham, S. G., Farrington, J. W. and Volkman, J. K. (1982) Fatty acids, wax esters, triglycerides and glyceryl ethers associated with particles collected in sediment traps in the Peru upwelling. In *Advances in Organic Geochemistry, 1981*, ed. by Bjorøy, M. Wiley, Sussex (in press).

Wardroper, A. M. K., Maxwell, J. R. and Morris, R. J. (1978) Sterols of a diatomaceous ooze from Walvis Bay. *Steroids* **32**, 203–221.

Zuta, S. and Guillen, O. (1970) Oceanografia de las aguas costeras del Peru. *Boletin, Instituto del Mar del Peru* **2** (5), 157–324.

Advances in Organic Geochemistry 1981, pp. 380–388
© *John Wiley & Sons Limited, 1983*

Carotenoid Transformation Products in the Upwelled Waters Off the Peruvian Coast: Suspended Particulate Matter, Sediment Trap Material, and Zooplankton Fecal Pellet Analyses

D. J. Repeta and R. B. Gagosian

Department of Chemistry, Woods Hole Oceanographic Institution, Woods Hole, Massachusetts 02543, USA

Carotenoids and their transformation products were measured in suspended particulate, sediment trap, and zooplankton fecal pellet samples collected in the Peruvian upwelling system. The carotenoid distribution of suspended particulate matter largely reflects the phytoplanktonic source of the material. However, both sediment trap and zooplankton fecal pellet samples contain significant amounts of carotenoid transformation products. These results are compared to an earlier experiment conducted in Buzzards Bay, Massachusetts (USA) to determine the time scales and mechanisms of the observed transformation reactions.

INTRODUCTION

It has been over half a century since the first report of carotenoids in marine sediments appeared in the geochemical literature (Trask and Wu, 1930). Early studies (Fox *et al.*, 1944, 1954; Vallentyne, 1957; Schwendinger and Erdman, 1963) focused on changes with sample age of the biphasic (ether, aqueous methanol) partition coefficient of pigment extracts as a measure of carotene (epiphasic):xanthophyll (hydrophasic) relative degradation. With the development of increasingly sophisticated analytical techniques for carotenoid isolation and structural identification, the use of partition coefficients (h/e ratios) was largely abandoned in favour of studies focusing on the identification of specific carotenoids as markers of organic matter inputs to Recent and ancient sediments (Peake *et al.*, 1974; Watts and Maxwell, 1977; Watts *et al.*, 1977; Griffiths, 1978). As yet, modern analytical techniques have not been used to readdress the question first raised by the h/e ratio studies: What processes transform and degrade carotenoid pigments once they enter the geochemical cycle? The lability of carotenoids suggests they may be significantly altered by recycling processes that occur in the oceanic water column, in which case, these compounds may serve as useful tracers of biogeochemical cycles that operate over short time scales (<0.1 year).

Our approach to this problem has been to construct a model for organic matter cycling in the water column. This model consists of three parts: (1) the synthesis of carotenoid pigments by phytoplankton in the euphotic zone, (2) consumption and metabolism of some fraction of these pigments by heterotrophic organisms, and (3) removal of metabolic by-products to the sediments by large particle (e.g. fecal pellet) transport. The model separates particulate matter into reservoirs according to the degradation processes that have occurred since synthesis. Our goal is to sample these particulate reservoirs, determine the compositional differences between them, and construct a mechanistic pathway for the transformations that occur as material is transferred between reservoirs.

In practice we separate these reservoirs by particle size. Marine phytoplankton that synthesize carotenoids are typically 5–100 μm. In our model these organisms are consumed by heterotrophs and the solid waste products egested, in part, as rapidly sinking fecal pellets (>100 μm). These large particles, which can be sampled with sediment traps, should reflect both the source (phytoplankton) and the process (heterotrophic metabolism) responsible for their formation.

In an earlier study (Repeta and Gagosian, 1982a), we reported significant concentrations of fucoxanthin (I) transformation products in sediment trap samples collected in the coastal marine waters of Buzzards Bay, Massachusetts. Our analysis led us to propose a degradation pathway for fucoxanthin similar to that illustrated in Fig. 1. Three processes were suggested as responsible for the observed transformations: (1) ester hydrolysis via zooplankton metabolism, (2) dehydration via bacterial metabolism, and (3) epoxide-opening via slow chemical degradation. In order to collect a sufficient amount of material for analysis, traps had to be deployed for a period of one month. As a result, we could not distinguish between short term (hours to days) and long term (weeks to a month) transformation processes.

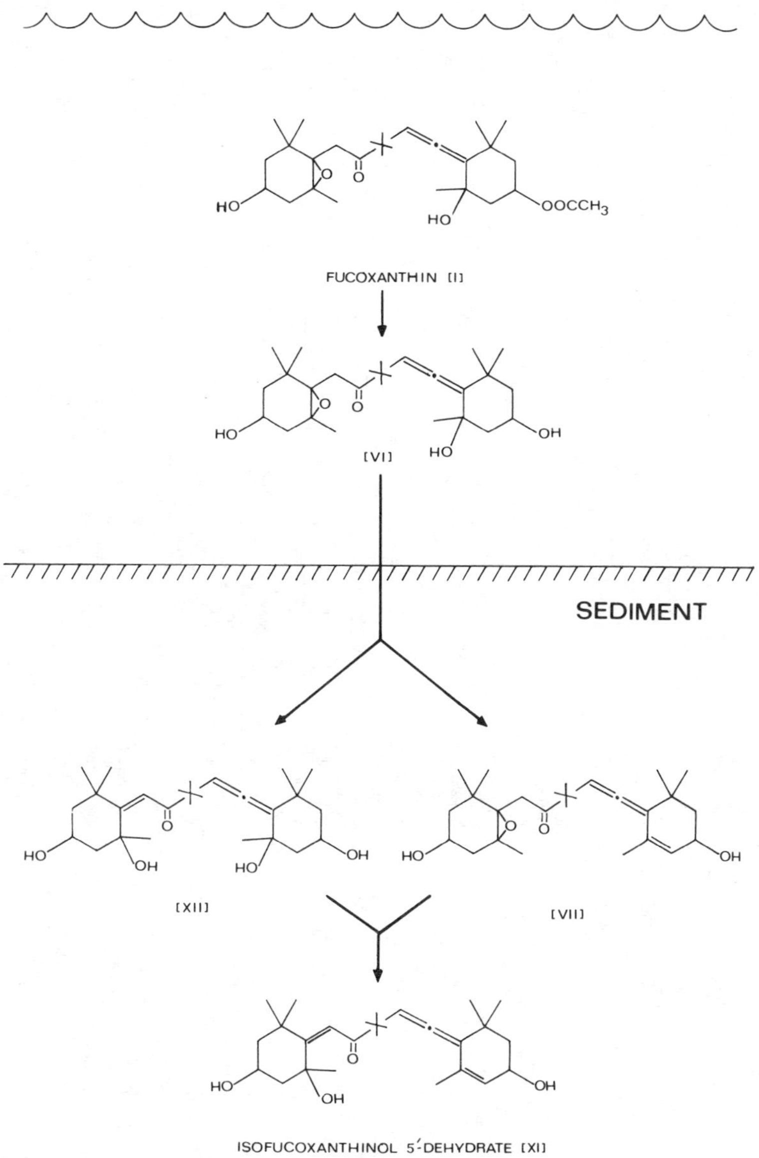

Fig. 1. Proposed transformation pathway showing ester hydrolysis, dehydration, and epoxide opening for fucoxanthin (I).

In addition, there is significant tidal resuspension of bottom sediments throughout the bay (Roman and Tenore, 1978). Input from this source could not be distinguished from the primary vertical flux of material from above the trap.

We report here the preliminary results of a second series of sediment trap experiments conducted in the upwelling waters off the Peruvian coast (15° S, 75° W). We chose this site for the high productivity and low resuspension of bottom sediments that characterize the area. Sediment trap experiments conducted in 1978 at the same location and same time of year demonstrated that the particulate carbon flux at 50 m reached as much as 350 mg C/m²/day (Staresinic, 1982); hence trap deployments of a day or less are sufficient to collect enough material for analysis. Further, values of particulate organic carbon, chlorophyll pigments, and selected classes of organic compounds showed no increase near the bottom of the water column due to sediment resuspension (Gagosian *et al.*, 1980, 1982). Therefore, resuspended material should not contribute

significantly to the material collected in our traps. A comparison of these results with the results from Buzzards Bay will permit us to establish the time scale of observed transformations (days versus months), to distinguish those transformations that occur in the water column from those that occur in the sediment–water interface, and to define more clearly the specific mechanisms for the observed transformations.

EXPERIMENTAL

Sample collection

Suspended particulate matter. All samples were collected on the R/V *Atlantis II* cruise 108, leg 3 in March–April, 1981, off the Peruvian coast at 15° S, 75° W. Vertical profiles of suspended particulate matter were collected with either a 20 l glass Bodman (Gagosian *et al.*, 1979) or a 10 l Nisken water sampler. Sampling

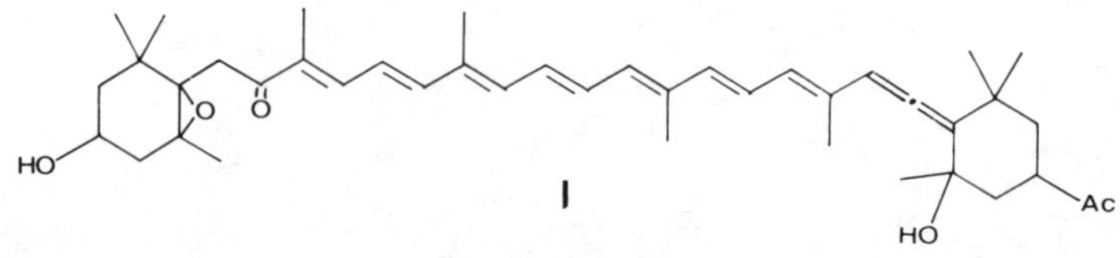

I

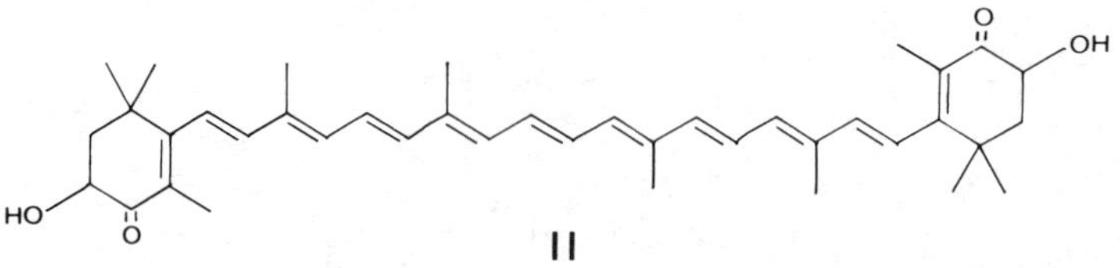

II

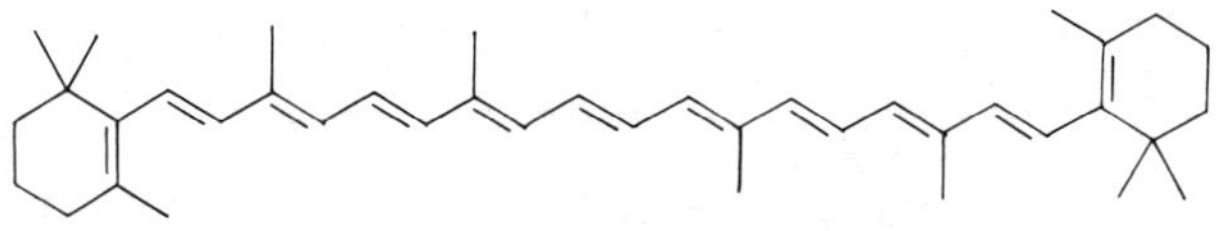

III

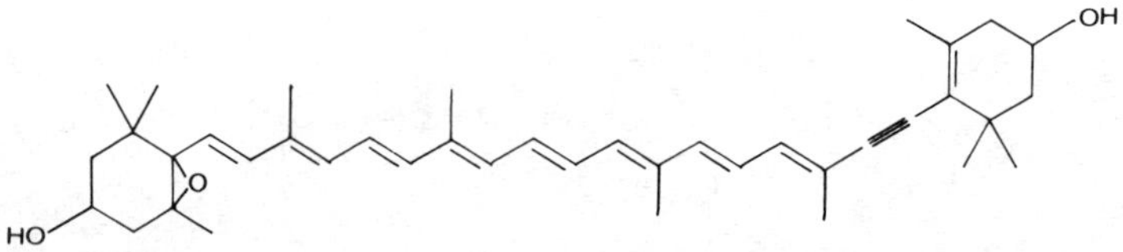

IV

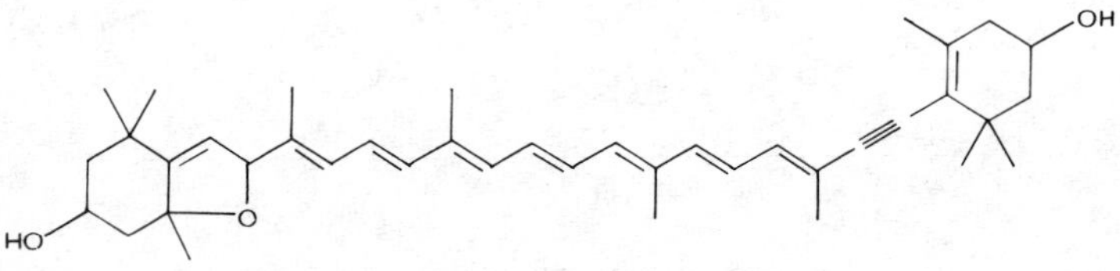

V

locations are given in Table 1. Seawater was immediately filtered through a pre-extracted (dichloromethane, 24 h), precombusted (450 °C, 24 h) Gelman type AE glass fibre filter. Filters were stored at −50 °C in foil wrapped glass vials filled with methanol and capped under ultra-high purity nitrogen. Water samples were collected immediately after the deployment and recovery of the sediment traps. Water profile series no. 36 was collected immediately after the deployment of traps 3 and 4, profile no. 44 after the recovery of traps 3 and 4 and the deployment of traps 6 and 7, profile no. 105 at the deployment of trap 14. In this way the suspended particulates, which serve as the ultimate source for material collected in our sediment traps, could be monitored for their carotenoid composition throughout the course of the trap experiments.

Sediment traps. Moored sediment traps were constructed after the design of Staresinic (1978). Briefly, traps consisted of a 41 cm diameter PVC cylinder with a 3:1 aspect ratio atop a 45° cone with a 3/4 in ball valve

terminus. The traps were deployed empty, allowed to fill with surface water and sink to preset depths. On recovery, traps were drained to the top of the cone, the ball valve opened, and the sample and remaining water collected for filtration. Samples (1–10 g wet weight) were immediately filtered and stored as described above. Altogether thirteen traps were deployed and recovered in this fashion. Deployment times and sampling locations of five representative traps are given in Table 2.

Zooplankton fecal pellets. Studies of material collected in other trap experiments (Honjo., 1978; Knauer *et al.*, 1979; Staresinic, 1982) have shown that fecal pellets from heterotrophic organisms contribute a significant fraction of the particles collected in traps. In order to obtain a fresh sample of this material, fecal pellets were collected from field cultures of zooplanktonic heterotrophs. Zooplankton were collected in a 234 μm mesh net towed 25 m below the surface at 1–2 kt (Table 1). All collections were made between 2000 and 0400 h local time. Immediately after the nets were brought on board, the zooplankton were

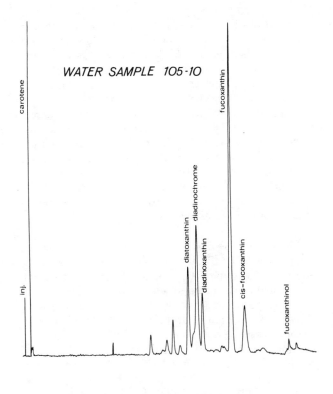

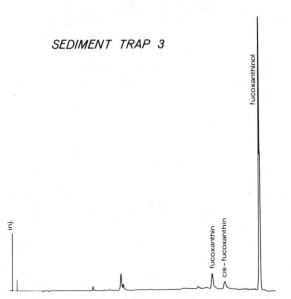

Fig. 2. H.p.l.c. chromatograms of standing crop particulate matter from water sample 105–10 and sediment trap 3. Conditions are given in text.

poured through a 2 mm sieve to remove small particles, and transferred to holding chambers built after the design of La Rosa (1976). Pellets were collected after 8–10 h, filtered, and stored as described above.

Analysis

Extraction. Samples were sonic extracted at ambient temperature with methanol (2×, 20 min each) and dichloromethane (1×, 20 min). Extracts were combined, rotary evaporated under reduced pressure to a small volume, then taken to dryness under ultra-high purity nitrogen. The residue was redissolved in dichloromethane and dried over anhydrous sodium sulphate. Davies (1976) has summarized the difficulties *vis-à-vis* degradation in carotenoid analysis. These pigments are characteristically unstable under relatively mild acid/base, thermal, and photochemical conditions. Therefore, in studies such as ours it is imperative to distinguish degradation products that are initially present in the sample from those that may be produced as artifacts of the analytical method.

Blank filters spiked with fucoxanthin (I), astaxanthin (II), β-carotene (III), and diadinoxanthin (IV), showed that only *cis*⇄*trans* double bond isomerization occurs during our analytical work-up. No transformation products discussed in this report (opened epoxides, hydrolysed esters, and dehydrates) were detected. Recoveries of spikes were > 92%. We have noted the rearrangement of the 5,6-epoxide diadinoxanthin (III) to the corresponding 5,8-furanoxide diadinochrome (V) during storage of sample extracts. Consequently, we do not include diadinochrome as a naturally occurring transformation product at this time. Further studies using a 5,6-epoxide internal standard are in progress to clarify this point. In order to minimize pigment decomposition, analysis were completed within 1 or 2 months after sample collection. All operations were carried out at or below 20 °C and under low light conditions. A more detailed description of the analytical method will appear elsewhere (Repeta and Gagosian, 1982b).

High pressure liquid chromatography (h.p.l.c.). A Waters Associates instrument (model 6000 A pumps, model 660 solvent programmer, U6K injector, and model 440 detector) was used for all h.p.l.c. analyses. Carotenoids were separated from chlorophyll pigments and low molecular weights lipids by gel

VI

VII

Table 1

Depth, time, date, and location of standing crop particulate and zooplankton tow samples.

Sample no.	Depth (m)	Time (local)	Date	Latitude	Longitude
Suspended particulates				(S)	(W)
36–5	5	1130	21/3	15°07′	75°36′
36–10	10	1450	21/3	15°07′	75°36′
36–25	25	1315	21/3	15°06′	75°36′
36–50	50	1735	21/3	15°06′	75°36′
44–3	3	1320	24/3	15°07′	75°35′
44–10	10	1320	24/3	15°07′	75°35′
44–25	25	1320	24/3	15°07′	75°35′
44–45	45	1320	24/3	15°07′	75°35′
105–10	10	1453	3/4	15°00′	75°31′
105–20	20	1453	3/4	15°00′	75°31′
105–30	30	1453	3/4	15°00′	75°31′
Zooplankton tows					
57	25	2240–0310			
			25/3	15°14′	75°30′
67	25	2130–2234			
			26/3	15°13′	75°31′
107	25	2327–0055			
			5/4	15°11′	75°37′

permeation chromatography on three, 100 Å μ-Styragel (Waters Assoc., 300 × 7.9 mm) columns connected in series and eluted with dichloromethane at 1.5 ml/min. The carotenoid fraction was collected, reconcentrated under nitrogen, and separated into its components using a 5 μm Spherisorb amino column (slurry-packed in house, 30 × 3.9 mm) eluted with a linear gradient of hexane and 0–13% THF/methanol (80/20, v/v) at 2 ml/min for 45 min. After 55 min, the mobile phase composition was stepped to 30% THF/methanol for an additional 20 min to elute the more polar carotenoids remaining on the column. The eluate was monitored spectroscopically at 436 nm. Sample chromatograms are given in Fig. 2. Components were collected as they eluted, taken to dryness under nitrogen, then redissolved in hexane for visible spectroscopic analysis. Visible spectra were recorded on a Cary model 118 spectrophotometer. Identification was made on the basis of coinjection with authentic standards (for fucoxanthin (I), astaxanthin (II), β-carotene (III), diadinoxanthin (IV), and diadinochrome (V)), visible spectroscopy, mass spectrometry, and in some instances derivatization (fucoxanthinol (VI) and fucoxanthinol dehydrate (VII)). Since our ability to collect visible and mass spectra is limited by sample size, we could identify only the major carotenoid components in our samples.

Quantification was made by integrating the peak area from h.p.l.c. chromatograms. $E_{1\,cm}^{1\%}$ values from the literature (Bonnett *et al.*, 1969 for fucoxanthin and fucoxanthinol) were used to prepare standard solutions for area/mole determinations. For transformation products where no literature values for $E_{1\,cm}^{1\%}$ have been reported (e.g. dehydrates), the coefficient of the parent compound was used. For example, the extinction coefficient for fucoxanthin was used to quantify fucoxanthin dehydrate. In all instances where extinction coefficients were substituted, the visible spectra of the transformation product were nearly identical to that of the parent compound. Consequently, this substitution should lead to negligible errors.

Mass spectrometry. Mass spectra of selected fractions were collected on a Finnigan 3200 mass spectrometer coupled with an INCOS 2300 data system. The instrument was fitted with a copper-tipped direct insertion probe that allowed the sample to be placed directly into the ion beam (as monitored by changes in the ion plasma). Solutions of the collected fractions in dichloromethane were applied to the probe tip and the solvent allowed to evaporate. The probe was then placed into the instrument and rapidly heated from ambient to 350 °C at approximately 100 °C/min. In this manner, reproducible spectra could be collected on sample sizes of 10 ng (β-carotene) to 50 ng (fucoxanthin). The spectrometer was run in the chemical ionization mode using methane as the reagent gas with an ion source pressure of 0.5 torr, an ionization voltage of 130 eV, and an ionization current of 500 μA.

RESULTS AND DISCUSSION

Suspended particulate matter. Major differences were observed in the carotenoid composition of suspended particulate matter, sediment trap, and zooplankton fecal pellet samples (Fig. 2). Fucoxanthin (I), carotene (III), diatoxanthin (VIII), diadinoxanthin (IV), diadinochrome (V), peridinin (IX), and fucoxanthinol (VI) were the principal carotenoids in suspended particulate matter samples. These pigments, with the exception of diadinochrome and fucoxanthinol, represent the major carotenoids of marine diatoms (Goodwin, 1971; Liaaen-Jensen, 1978) and dinoflagellates (Johansen *et al.*, 1975), the dominant photosynthetic organisms in our sampling area (Blasco, 1971). Additionally, we observed minor amounts of

Table 2

Depth, sampling time, and location of sediment trap samples.

Sample no.	Depth (m) Trap	Depth (m) Station	Deployment Time	Deployment Date	Recovery Time	Recovery Date	Latitude (S)	Longitude (W)
3	30	200	0800	23/3	0820	24/3	15°07′	75°35′
4	50	200	1558	21/3	0820	24/3	15°07′	75°35′
6	40	140	1822	24/3	0920	27/3	15°04′	75°36′
7	90	140	1822	24/3	0920	27/3	15°04′	75°36′
14	40	80	1438	3/4	0908	5/4	15°02′	75°32′

Table 3
Distribution of fuco-pigments in suspended particulate, zooplankton fecal pellet, and sediment trap samples

		% Total fuco-pigments			
				Dehydrates	
Sample no.	Depth (m)	Fucoxanthin	Fucoxanthinol	Fucoxanthin	Fucoxanthinol
Suspended particulates					
36–5	5	94	6	ND[a]	ND
36–10	10	93	7		
36–25	25	87	13		
36–50	50	89	11		
44–3	3	99	1		
44–10	10	98	2		
4–25	25	99	1		
44–45	45	92	8		
105–10	10	99	1		
105–20	20	97	3		
105–30	30	96	4		
Zooplankton fecal pellet collections					
57	25	86	7	7	ND
67	25	70	10	19	tr[b]
107	25	18	19	63	tr
Sediment traps					
3	30	6	94	ND	ND
4	50	85	15	ND	ND
6	40	12	88	tr	tr
7	90	45	55	tr	tr
14	40	26	74	tr	tr
BBST–3	3	5	69(12)[c]	1	6(7)

[a] Not detected.
[b] Trace (1%).
[c] Numbers in parentheses indicate the % of total fuco-pigments in the open epoxide (iso) form.

astaxanthin (II), the principal carotenoid of marine crustacea. The only carotenoid found in our samples that is not considered to be naturally occurring is the 5,8-furanoxide, diadinochrome (V). This pigment arises from an acid catalysed rearrangement of diadinoxanthin (IV) during storage. Fucoxanthinol (VI), which we have hypothesized to be a by-product of heterotrophic metabolism of fucoxanthin (Repeta and Gagosian, 1982a), constituted an average 5% of the total fuco-pigments in suspended particulate matter collected off Peru (Table 3). We know of no reports of naturally

occurring fucoxanthinol in either diatoms (*Bactillariophyceae*) or dinoflagellates (*Dinophyceae*). Berger *et al.* (1977) and Nitsche (1974) have reported finding minor amounts (~4%) of fucoxanthinol in fucoxanthin-synthesizing members of the algal classes *Haptophyceae* and *Phaeophyceae*, respectively. Algal species from these two classes are not typically found in the upwelling area (Blasco, 1971), and we do not consider them a likely source for the fucoxanthinol found in our samples. Liaaen-Jensen (1978) has proposed that fucoxanthinol represents a general metabolic intermediate of fucoxanthin biosynthesis. The presence of metabolite quantities of fucoxanthinol in diatoms and dinoflagellates may account for the trace levels of this pigment in shallower (<20 m, 1–3%) water samples. Alternatively, the presence of fucoxanthinol may be attributed to the detrital background of senescent and partially metabolized phytoplankton cells. Vertical profiles taken through the euphotic zone showed an increase in the relative concentratuon of fucoxanthinol, when expressed as percent total fuco-pigments, with depth (>20 m, 4–13%). This distribution is similar to that observed for chlorophyll and its degradation products (phaeopigments). Typically, chlorophyll displays a shallow concentration maximum near the surface, then a sharp decrease in concentration below the euphotic zone (~ 20 m in our sampling area). The absolute concentration of phaeopigments remains relatively constant with depth. Consequently there is an increase in the phaeopigment/chlorophyll-a ratio due to the decrease in actively photosynthesizing cells with depth. Likewise, the increase in the fucoxanthinol/fucoxanthin ratio below 20 m may be attributable to the decrease in actively photosynthesizing cells below the euphotic zone.

Sediment trap particulate material. Sediment traps are designed to collect rapidly sinking large particles not typically collected by conventional water samplers, such as the Bodman and Niskin water samplers used in this study (McCave, 1975). Microscopic examination of material collected in other sediment traps (Honjo *et al.*, 1978; Staresinic, 1982) has demonstrated that a large fraction of the particles collected represents reworked material in the form of fecal pellets and other debris produced by heterotrophic organisms. Therefore, differences observed in the carotenoid distributions of suspended particulate matter (source term) and material collected in the traps, should arise as a result of heterotrophic recycling. The qualitative distribution of carotene (III), diatoxanthin (VIII), diadinochrome (V), and diadinoxanthin (IV) in our sediment trap samples is strikingly similar to that of suspended particulate matter, suggesting little transformation of these pigments. However, fucoxanthinol, which was present in amounts of only 1–13% in suspended particulate matter, contributed a much larger percentage (15–94%) of the total fuco-pigments (Table 3). Additionally, trace amounts of fucoxanthin dehydrate (X) and fucoxanthinol dehydrate (VII) were present in some samples. This is in contrast to samples analysed from Buzzards Bay, Massachusetts, which contained fucoxanthin dehydrate and fucoxanthinol dehydrate as 1% and 6% of the total fuco-pigments respectively (with isofucoxanthinol dehydrate (XI) contributing another 7%) (Repeta and Gagosian, 1982a). Hence, it appears that the dehydrates observed in our samples from Buzzards Bay come from a resuspended sediment input, or as a result of transformations occurring in the trap during deployment.

We observed no correlation between length of trap deployment or collection depth and the relative per cent transformation of fucoxanthin to fucoxanthinol, or the appearance of the dehydrates (VII) or (X). Therefore, it appears that the degradation of organic matter associated with large particles in the surface waters is not a simple function of depth or time, but is probably more strongly influenced by such factors as the specific heterotroph assemblage and productivity. It is of interest to note that no astaxanthin, the principal pigment of crustacea, was found in the traps.

Zooplankton fecal pellets. The distribution of fuco-pigments from three zooplankton fecal pellet collections is given in Table 2. Previously (Repeta and Gagosian, 1982a) we suggested that zooplankton and other higher heterotrophs metabolize fucoxanthin to fucoxanthinol. The significantly higher fucoxanthinol concentration in the pellet samples (av. 12%) compared to suspended particulate matter (av. 5%) supports this hypothesis. The relative concentration of fucoxanthinol in sediment traps, however, was a factor of five greater than in the pellet samples. In contrast to sediment trap samples collected at the same site in 1978 (Staresinic, 1982. Gagosian *et al.*, 1982), fecal matter from anchoveta rather than zooplankton was the principal source of material collected in the traps. This difference in source term most likely accounts for the disparity in per cent fucoxanthinol between pellet and trap samples.

Summary. The results of these experiments, when compared to those from earlier experiments in Buzzards Bay, Massachusetts (Table 3, BBST–3) permit us to separate transformations that occur in the water column from those that occur in the sediments, and to assign relative time scales to the specific reactions. Our proposed degradation pathway for fucoxanthin is outlined in Fig. 1. Fucoxanthin (I) is synthesized in the euphotic zone by primary producers. These organisms are consumed by heterotrophs that metabolize fucoxanthin to fucoxanthinol (VI). Simultaneously, the phytoplankton are repackaged into larger, more rapidly sinking fecal pellets and transported to the sediment. Sediment trap samples from Buzzards Bay and Peru both contain fucoxanthinol as the major carotenoid pigment. Once incorporated into the surface sediments, fucoxanthinol is slowly dehydrated and isomerized via fucoxanthinol dehydrate (VII) and isofucoxanthinol (XII) to isofucoxanthinol 5′-dehydrate (XI). We do not observe any significant dehydration or epoxide opening of fuco-pigments collected in the Peru traps. Therefore, these transformations occur over time scales greater than the three-day deployment of the traps. We do observe these transformations in the trap samples from Buzzards

X

XI

XII

Bay. As stated previously, these traps collect predominantly resuspended sediments. This suggests that the dehydration and epoxide opening of fuco-pigments occurs at the sediment–water interface, and has a time scale of 0.1–10 years.

CONCLUSIONS

These preliminary results suggest that carotenoid esters synthesized by phytoplankton are hydrolysed to free alcohols in the oceanic water column at a rate determined by the turnover of primary productivity. Dehydration and epoxide opening are not significant water column transformations, but are important in surface sediments. The dehydrated and epoxide-opened intermediates of fucoxanthin degradation that we observed in Buzzards Bay sediment trap samples are associated with resuspended sediments collected in the traps and represent the products of transformations with much longer time scales (0.1–10 yr). A transformation pathway of ester hydrolysis→dehydration→epoxide-opening→further dehydration is proposed for fucoxanthin, and may be applicable to other, structurally similar compounds as well. Further experiments are underway to confirm this sequence and to determine the specific mechanisms involved.

Acknowledgements

This research was supported by the Ocean Sciences Section, National Science Foundation Grants OCE 79–25352 and OCE 81–18436, the Office of Naval Research Contract N00014–74–CO–262 NR 083–004, and the Woods Hole Coastal Research Center Project 25 000067 04. We wish to thank Ms Debbie Maloof for assistance in sample collection, Dr Nelson Frew for assistance in MS analysis, Drs Cindy Lee, Stuart Wakeham, and Nick Staresinic for valuable discussions on the manuscript, and Barbara (Slim) Haskell for editorial comments. We also thank Hoffman–LaRoche, Basel for the generous gift of the astaxanthin standard.

REFERENCES

Berger, R., Liaaen-Jensen, S., McAllister, V. and Guillard, R. R. L. (1977) Carotenoids of Prymnesiophyceae (Haptophyceae). *Biochem. Syst. Ecol.* **5**, 71–75.

Blasco, D. (1971) Composition and distribution of phytoplankton in the region of upwelling off the coast of Peru. *Investigacion Pesquera* **35**, 61–112.

Bonnett, R., Mallams, A. K., Spork, A. A., Tee, J. L., Weedon, B. C. L. and McCormick, A. (1969) Carotenoids and related compounds. Part XX. Structure and reactions of fucoxanthin. *J. Chem. Soc. (C)*, 429–454.

Davies, B. H. (1976) Carotenoids. In *Chemistry and Biochemistry of Plant Pigments*, vol. 2, ed. by Goodwin, T. W. Academic Press, London, pp. 38–165.

Fox, D. L. and Oppenheimer, C. H. (1954) The riddle of sterol and carotenoid metabolism in muds of the ocean floor. *Arch. Biochem. Biophys.* **51**, 323–328.

Fox, D. L., Updegraff, D. M. and Novelli, D. G. (1944) Carotenoid pigments in the ocean floor. *Arch. Biochem. Biophys.* **5**, 1–23.

Gagosian, R. B., Volkman, J. K. and Nigrelli, G. E. (1982) The use of sediment traps to determine sterol sources in coastal sediments off Peru. In *Advances in Organic Geochemistry 1981*, ed. by Bjorøy, J. Wiley, London (in press).

Gagosian, R. B., Dean, J. P., Hamblin, R. and Zafiriou, O. C. (1979) A versatile, interchangeable chamber seawater sampler. *Limnol. and Oceanogr.* **24**, 583–588.

Gagosian, R. B., Loder, T., Nigrelli, G., Mlodzinska, Z., Love, J. and Kogelschultz, J. (1980) Hydrographic and Nutrient Data from R/V Knorr Cruise 73, Leg 2. *Woods Hole Oceanographic Institution Technical Report 80–1*.

Goodwin, T. W. (1971) Algal carotenoids. In *Aspects of Terpenoid Chemistry and Biochemistry*, ed. by Goodwin, T. W. Academic Press, London, pp. 315–356.

Griffiths, M. (1978) Specific blue–green algal carotenoids in sediments of esthwaite water. *Limnol. and Oceanogr.* **23**, 777–784.

Honjo, S. (1978) Sedimentation of Materials in the Sargasso Sea at a 5367 m Deep Station. *J. Mar. Res.* **36**, 469–472.

Johansen, J. E., Svec, W. A. and Liaaen-Jensen, S. (1974) Carotenoids of the Dinophyceae. *Phytochemistry* **13**, 2261–2271.

Knauer, G. A., Martin, J. H. and Bruland, K. W. (1979) Fluxes of particulate carbon, nitrogen, and phosphorus in the upper water column of the northeast Pacific. *Deep Sea Res.* **26A**, 97–108.

La Rosa, J. (1976) A simple system for recovering zooplanktonic faecal pellets in quantity. *Deep Sea Res.* **23**, 995–997.

Liaaen-Jensen, S. (1978) Marine carotenoids. In *Marine Natural Products*, (ed. by Scheuer, P., pp. 1–75.

McCave, I. N. (1975) Vertical flux of particles in the ocean. *Deep Sea Res.* **22**, 491–502.

Nitsche, H. (1974) Neoxanthin and fucoxanthinol in fucus vesiculosus. *Biochim. Biophys. Acta.* **338**, 572–576.

Peake, E., Casagrande, D. J. and Hodgeson, G. W. (1974) Fatty acids, chlorins, hydrocarbons, sterols, and carotenoids from a Black Sea core. In *The Black Sea —*

Geology, Chemistry, and Biology, ed. by Degens, E. T. and Ross, D. A. Am. Assoc. Pet. Geol. Mem. 20, pp. 505–523.

Staresinic, N. (1982) Downward flux of bulk particulate organic matter in the Peru coastal upwelling. *J. Mar. Res.*, in press.

Repeta, D. J. and Gagosian, R. B. (1982a) Carotenoid transformations in coastal marine waters. Submitted to *Nature (London)* **295**, 51–54.

Repeta, D. J. and Gagosian, R. B. (1982b) High pressure liquid chromatography–mass spectrometry of carotenoid pigments of geochemical interest (in preparation).

Roman, M. R. and Tenore, K. R. (1978) Tidal resuspension in Buzzards Bay, Massachusetts. *Estuarine Coastal Mar. Sci.* **6**, 37–46.

Schwendinger, R. B. and Erdman, J. G. (1963) Carotenoids in sediments as a function of environment. *Science* **141**, 808–810.

Staresinic, N. (1978) The vertical flux of particulate organic matter in the Peru coastal upwelling as measured with a free-drifting sediment trap. Ph.D. Thesis, W.H.O.I./M.I.T. Joint Program in Biological Oceanography.

Trask, P. D. and Wu, C. C. (1930) Does petroleum form at the time of deposition? *Bull. Am. Assoc. Pet. Geol.* **14**, 1451–1463.

Vallentyne, J. R. (1957) The molecular nature of organic matter in lakes and oceans, with lesser reference to sewage and terrestrial soils. *J. Fish. Res. Board Can.* **14**, 33–82.

Watts, C. D. and Maxwell, J. R. (1977) Carotenoid diagenesis in a marine sediment. *Geochim. Cosmochim. Acta* **41**, 493–497.

Watts, C. D., Maxwell, J. R. and Kjosen, H. (1977) The potential of carotenoids as environmental indicators. In *Advances in Organic Geochemistry 1975*, ed. by Compos, R. and Goni, J. Enadimsa, Madrid, pp. 391–414.

DSDP/IPOD
ORGANIC GEOCHEMISTRY

Advances in Organic Geochemistry 1981, pp. 391–400
© John Wiley & Sons Limited, 1983

The Role of Organic Geochemistry in the Deep Sea Drilling Project (DSDP/IPOD)

G. Eglinton*, S. C. Brassell, V. Howell and J. R. Maxwell

Organic Geochemistry Unit, University of Bristol, School of Chemistry, Cantock's Close, Bristol BS8 1TS, England

The international community of organic geochemists has already derived much from participation in DSDP/IPOD. The 1981–1983 programme and future possibly extensions offer sediment sampling of improved integrity, geographical extent and depth of penetration. The complexity and specificity of lipid data offers considerable scope for the assessment of aspects of depositional palaeoenvironments. In particular, sediment sequences that show climatic cycles in their $\delta^{18}O$ data should also be evaluated at similar sampling intervals for organic geochemical, notably molecular, evidence of such fluctuations. The major objectives of DSDP/IPOD organic geochemistry are studies of areas of upwelling and of black shale phenomena, which both show fluctuations and depth trends in their organic carbon contents. There is a need for a concerted drilling programme in an area of upwelling to investigate the history of such systems and better documentation of the small scale variability and lateral extent of black shales also warrants further drilling of Cretaceous and Jurassic sediments. DSDP sediments provide the opportunity of evaluating the nature and rates of early-stage diagenetic changes in areas of low geothermal gradients and contrasting such effects with those more rapid processes seen in areas of higher heat flow.

INTRODUCTION

The previous meeting of the European Association of Organic Geochemists, held at Newcastle in 1979, included a detailed paper by Earl Baker and J. William Louda, which was entitled 'Organic geochemistry: highlights in the Deep Sea Drilling Project'. This paper provided an up-to-date summary of much of the organic geochemical studies of DSDP samples with illustrations from specific sites and problems taken from the DSDP literature. The treatment is both comprehensive and detailed and the reader is referred to this paper for an account of the way in which organic geochemists can interact with the DSDP/IPOD programme.

The DSDP programme itself is largely funded by the National Science Foundation, with additional contributions from the participating IPOD countries. Its central organization is based at the Scripps Institution of Oceanography, La Jolla, California, which also houses one of the two DSDP core repositories, the other being at the Lamont-Doherty Geological Observatory. The Glomar Challenger drilling programme operates on a Leg basis, with each Leg lasting about 50 days and being devoted to specific targets in a particular area of the ocean. Ship staffing also operates on this system. The scientific programme of DSDP is formulated by subjects and advisory panels, supplemented by a number of working groups. The current Chairman of the Organic Chemistry Advisory Panel is Dr B. R. T. Simoneit, School of Oceanography, Oregon State University, Corvallis, Oregon 97331, U.S.A.

Several features of the sediment samples available from DSDP merit mention. The 80 Legs drilled to data hve provided suites of oceanic deposits on a world-wide basis, ranging in age from Recent to Jurassic, and in maturity from extremely immature to the threshold of oil generation. In some cases, long sequences of uniform deposition from areas of differing heat flow, and also horizons affected by localized thermal events have been recovered. In contrast, the drilling programme has also sampled sediments of similar age that correspond to differing palaeoenvironments of deposition. One particularly important point is that the samples are not subject to problems of confidentiality, with the results being published freely by those working in industry, in government institutions and in the academic field. In addition, detailed analyses in different areas of expertise eventually become available in the DSDP Initial Report volumes, often for the same samples, thereby allowing interdisplinary studies to be carried out. The organization of the project results in the sharing of samples and knowledge, on the sole basis of scientific need and involvement.

Recent Legs which have been of especial value to organic geochemists are listed in Table 1, with a brief comment as to their significance. The drilling areas are shown in Fig. 1 and well illustrate the global scope of

---

* Addressee for correspondence.

Table 1
Highlights of recent DSDP legs.

Leg number	Location[a]	Aims/Highlights	Cretaceous black shales?	Other features
40	Cape & Angola Basins	SW African continental margin	Yes	
41	Cape Verde Basin	W. African margin	Yes	
42A	Mediterranean	History of basins, especially Messinian salinity crisis		Sapropels
42B	Black Sea	History of stagnant basin		Anoxic sediments
43	Bermuda Rise	W. Atlantic Cenozoic and Mesozoic history	Yes	
44	Blake Bahama Basin	Oldest Atlantic sediments	Yes	
47A	N.W. African Margin	History of rifting of margin; oldest sediments	Yes	Effects of sills
47B			Yes	
48	Bay of Biscay and Rockall	Passive margins; onset of spreading	Yes	
50	Moroccan Basin	Early history of North Atlantic Ocean	Yes	
56	Japan Trench	Processes of subduction; origin of accretion zone		Slow diagenesis
57				
62	Hess Rise	Pacific palaeoenvironments	Yes	
63	California Borderland	History of Pacific boundary currents and Neogene palaeoceanography		Formation parallel to Monterey
64	Gulf of California	Ocean basin formation		Rapid diagenesis and laminated sediments
66	Middle-America Trench	Subduction processes		Gas hydrates
67				
71	Falkland Plateau	History of Plateau and Cenozoic ocean circulation	Yes	
75	Angola Basin/Walvis Ridge	Black shale events and Benguela upwelling system	Yes	Deep HPC
76	W. North Atlantic	Ancient passive margin	Yes	Gas hydrates
77	Florida Straits	Origin of the Gulf of Mexico	Yes	Oil stained cores

[a] The location of each of the Legs is shown in Fig. 1.

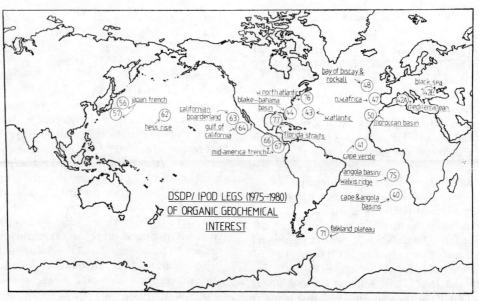

Fig. 1. Locations of recent DSDP/IPOD Legs of organic geochemical interest (*cf* Table 1).

DSDP operations. In this conference volume, there are a number of papers which describe work on samples from several of these DSDP Legs. The present paper is intended as an introduction to the session that highlighted DSDP/IPOD organic geochemistry. The topics represented in this volume include porphyrin diagenesis, gas hydrates and low molecular weight hydrocarbons, biological markers in immature sediments and the changes they show with increasing depth and mild thermal experience, sediments from upwelling regions, anoxic depositional environments, source rock potential of DSDP sediments and palaeoceanography. Much of this research of DSDP sediments bears on marine organic chemistry, especially

Table 2.
Extended scientific schedule (tentative).

Leg number[a]	Scientific objectives
82	N. Atlantic mantle inhomogeneity
83	Costa Rica Rift Deep Hole Layer Two
84	Middle America trench
85	Pacific equatorial paleoenvironments
86	Marine seismometer experiment
87	N.W. Pacific paleoenvironments — Bering Sea
88	Japan trench
89	Old Pacific — mid-plate volcanism
90	S.W. Pacific paleoenvironments — Lord Howe Rise
91	East Pacific Rise submarine hydrogeology
92	U.S. East Coast — passive margin
93	Mid N. Atlantic paleoenvironments
94	N.E. Atlantic paleoenvironments — passive margin
95	U.S. East Coast–New Jersey transect

[a] The location of each of these proposed Legs is shown in Fig. 2.

the study of water column processes by sediment traps and of surficial marine sediments. Indeed, the samples recovered by DSDP provide a link between the shallow sampling of marine sediments by gravity, box and piston coring and the deeper drilling of more mature sediments by the petroleum industry.

In this paper, current plans and future options for drilling at sites of interest to organic geochemists are outlined. The value of sediments recovered by DSDP, in the assessment of depositional palaeoenvironments (notably climatic features) and of diagenesis, are discussed in terms of the insight provided by molecular organic geochemistry.

DSDP/IPOD PROGRAMME 1981–1983

At the time of writing (October 1981) drilling is authorised for a further two years, following a pattern drawn up by the four main panels — ocean palaeoenvironment, passive margin, active margin and ocean crust (Table 2, Fig. 2). Although each Leg is dedicated to the aims of one of these four panels, many of the Holes to be drilled should encounter sediments of interest to organic geochemists, either for the organic geochemistry itself and/or as part of the process of resolving panel problems (Table 3a). Thus, in particular, organic geochemical data should contribute to our understanding of the history of the margins and of oceanic environments overall. Some of the prime sites and areas of interest to organic geochemists are, however, not scheduled at present (Table 3b). Of especial interest during the 1981–1983 drilling will be the large number of hydraulic piston cores (HPC) which should be recovered, in view of the high resolution stratigraphy they afford. This topic will be dealt with later in this article.

DSDP/IPOD POST-1983 DRILLING PROGRAMME

The nature, extent and mode of participation for the ocean drilling programme beyond 1983 have yet to be decided but the main themes have been listed (Table 4). Two ships are under consideration, the Glomar Challenger, after suitable refurbishment, and the Glomar Explorer, after major alteration. Although it is uncertain which ship (or possibly both) is to be used, the post-1983 programme can be considered under two headings: 'Challenger-type' drilling, i.e. a combination of hydraulic piston coring (HPC) and of conventional rotary drilling without riser (blow-out prevention) to sub-bottom depths approaching two kilometres; and 'Explorer-type' rotary drilling with riser, concentrating on very deep penetration. Both offer significant new opportunities to organic geochemists. Thus, 'Challenger-type' drilling could be used to study key

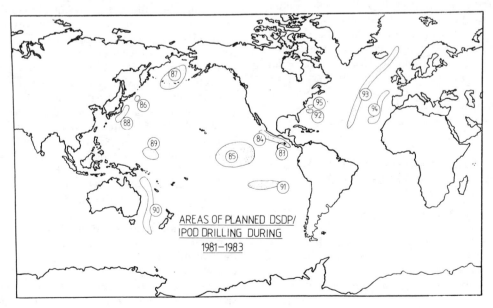

Fig. 2. Locations of drilling planned for Legs 83 through 95 (*cf* Tables 2 and 3A).

Table 3a
Planned palaeoceanographic Legs of organic geochemical interest (1981 onwards).

Leg	Location (Interest)		Aims/Highlights
85	E. Equatorial Pacific	(*)	Equatorial upwelling, Eocene HPC cores and record of productivity and currents
87	N. Pacific	(***)	Miocene varied sediments from the Bering Sea
89	W. Pacific	(*)	Open Pacific sediments of Jurassic age
93	N.E. Atlantic	(**)	Late Cenozoic glacial climatic oscillations

Table 3b
Palaeooceanographic Legs of organic geochemical interest unscheduled at present.

Location (Interest)		Aims/Highlights
N. AFRICA, circum Sahara	(**)	Palaeoclimate and palaeoceanography (aeolian inputs, Niger output and upwelling)
E. CARIBBEAN	(*)	Late Neogene sediments deposited during separation of Atlantic and Pacific. History of Gulf Stream
GULF OF MEXICO (Orca Basic and Cariaco Trough)	(***)	Quaternary climatic oscillations, varved sediments and anoxic and euxinic basins
PERUVIAN MARGIN TRANSECT	(***)	History of upwelling region and O_2 minimum zone

Table 4.
Topics for future scientific ocean drilling programmes.[a]

1. Origin and evolution of oceanic crust.
2. Origin and evolution of marine sedimentary sequences.
3. Tectonic evolution of continental margins and oceanic crust.
4. Causes of long term changes in the atmosphere, oceans, cryosphere, biosphere and magnetic field.
5. Tools, techniques and associated studies.

[a] Steering Committee, Conference on Scientific Ocean Drilling, Austin, Texas, November 16–18, 1981.

geographical areas, through transects involving several holes made with the HPC. The 'Explorer-type' deep drilling on the mature margins would permit the study of diagenesis and catagenesis in thick sedimentary sequences: thus the organic geochemistry of deep sea fans is of major interest for oil production. More detailed discussions must await decisions concerning the drilling ships and shore-based facilities. However, it seems inevitable that organic geochemical parameters will be of considerable use in the post-1983 study of palaeoenvironments, oceanic sedimentation, passive margins and hydrothermal history.

ORGANIC GEOCHEMISTRY STUDIES IN DSDP/IPOD 1983 ONWARDS

The JOIDES Advisory Panel on Organic Geochemistry has submitted a White Paper to the DSDP/IPOD management which outlines seven major themes for special study. These are:
1. Palaeoenvironmental assessment.
2. Thermal history of oceanic sediments and underlying crusts.
3. Establishment of geochemical facies.
4. Global carbon budget over geologic time.
5. Geochemical processes.
6. Hydrocarbon potential.
7. Extent and history of the biosphere.

These themes have been considered in relation to major topics of wide interest in oceanography and geology, and incorporated into a list of major topics which can be addressed by drilling appropriate sites (Table 5, reproduced from the White Paper).

PALAEOENVIRONMENTAL ASSESSMENT

Considerable progress has been made in the routine determination of the gross nature of the insoluble organic matter found in deep sea sediments. Such determinations allow estimates of the contributions of terrestrial and marine material to the bottom sediments (e.g. Tissot et al., 1979). However, it is the solvent-soluble organic matter which presently affords considerable scope for detailed assessment. Thus, solvent extracts of immature marine sediments contain a bewildering variety of lipids. The ability to recognize these compounds has increased greatly in recent years as a result of the introduction of fast scanning, computerized gas chromatographic–mass spectrometric systems. Some 10^3 individual compounds have so far been characterized in such sediments and we must now seek to rationalize the relative abundances of these compounds in terms of the input from organisms and of diagenetic change. The sterol composition of some deep sea sediments is discussed in a separate publication (Brassell and Eglinton, this volume), which demonstrates that their distributions are much more complex than had been realized previously. Indeed, it appears that many of the minor sterols derive from specific inputs to the sediments; thus, the biota reflected in such distributions is highly diverse and includes both

Table 5

Major questions of organic geochemistry of DSDP/IPOD and to geographic areas of interest.[a]

Topics and Areas[b]	DSDP/IPOD Leg[c]
1) Oxygen minima on continental margins and associated upwelling:	
(a) Western North America (eg., off California)	—
b) South America (eg., off Peru)	—
2) Black shale events:	
a) Jurassic (possibly older?) — N. Atlantic Ocean	92,94,95
b) Recent to lower Tertiary (couple with HPC where possible) — California Borderland, Mediterranean, Black Sea, Cariaco Trench, Gulf of California Basins	—
c) Creaceous (especially mid-Cretaceous) — Western North and South Atlantic Ocean, Indian Ocean, Pacific Ocean (eg. Shatsky, Hess, Lord Howe Rises, Manihiki Plateau, etc.)	90, 92, 94, 95
3) The terrestrial component — Fans and eolian deposition:	
a) River influx of terrestrial detritus to deltas and fans — Astoria (temperate conifer vegetation), Amazon, Niger and Mahakam (all tropical vegetation)	poss. 87
b) Eolian Fallout — from Africa in NE Atlantic, from SW America in mid–eastern Pacific	85
4) Thermal history of basins and active hydrothermal systems:	
a) Hydrothermal effects on organic matter — East Pacific Rise versus Guaymas Basin, also Costa Rica Rift	83,84,91,87,88
b) Pacific basins — Japan Trench, Nauru Basin, Bering Sea	
5) Production of organic matter in divergent zones:	
a) Pacific — equatorial transect	85
b) Antarctic — circumpolar current, resultant productivity, erosion and redeposition	—
c) Bering Sea — N. latitude basin	87
d) Outer continental margins — gas hydrates	84,87

[a] From Organic Geochemistry Advisory Panel 'White Paper', July 1981.
[b] Listed in order of long-range importance (1 = highest).
[c] DSDP/IPOD 1981–1983 program will provide some preliminary samples on legs indicated.

pelagic and benthic organisms. Turning to another group of compounds, a series of structurally related long-chain unsaturated ketones, hydrocarbons and carboxylic acids have been identified in a variety of marine sediments, ranging in age from Quaternary to Miocene. These compounds appear to be biological markers for coccolithophore inputs and are present in sediments from the Japan Trench that contain no skeletal remains of these organisms, since they were deposited below the carbonate compensation depth (Brassell et al., 1980a, b; Volkman et al., 1980). Hence, in these organic geochemical markers we seem to have a measure of input which cannot be arrived at through standard micropalaeontological techniques. On a wider basis, it is arguable that organic compounds may provide the basis of a uniquely valuable technique in the assessment of microbial inputs to sediments. In this context the recent work on methanogen microbial lipids offers great scope for the detection of the past activity of such organisms in sediments (Holzer et al., 1979; Brassell et al., 1981). Also of some significance is the possibility that the surface water temperature of palaeo-oceans might be assessed through the study of the planktonic biolipids accumulating in the bottom sediments.

Such potential molecular information is related to the fact that the extent of lipid (e.g. carboxylic acid) unsaturation in an organism is dependent on its growth temperature as part of the biochemical control of membrane flexibility, with a greater extent of unsaturated synthesized under colder conditions (Marr and Ingraham, 1962; Holton et al., 1964). Hence, the occurrence of polyunsaturated carboxylic acids in

Japanese Lake sediments has been shown to correlate with colder climatic episodes over the last 2×10^4 years (Kawamura and Ishiwatari, 1981). The possibility that unsaturated ketones derived from coccolithophores may also reflect water column temperatures needs to be tested in view of the markedly higher values of the di- to triunsaturated ratio in sediments beneath the warm waters of the Middle America Trench compared to those underlying the colder waters of the Japan Trench and elsewhere. The scope of potential lipid markers of water column temperatures, such as these ketones and polyunsaturated carboxylic acids, however, will be limited and confused by the effects of diagenesis.

In summary, the investigation of marine sediments from areas of low geothermal gradient has revealed the preservation of a wealth of labile biolipids. Survival of organic geochemical information at the molecular level constitutes a lipid signature of the depositional environment. How to investigate these signatures in detail represents one major challenge for organic geochemistry in the coming DSDP/IPOD programme. Such signatures could be put to good use in the study of past ocean circulation and climates. The first practical sample requirement is good recovery of undisturbed sediment cores.

The top few hundred metres of ocean sediments are, in general, unlithified or only partly lithified. Hence, the best sedimentary record that can be retrieved is obtained by pistor coring. Rotary drilling greatly disturbs sediments, especially in the unconsolidated upper portion of the sedimentary column. Conventional piston cores penetrate the first 10 m or so, but the new hydraulic

Table 6.
Time resolution with piston cores.

Environment	Sedimentation	Resolution[a] (years)
Anoxic basin	Rapid, no bioturbation	1
Oceanic hemipelagic	Moderate, bioturbation	10^3
centre gyre	Very low productivity, very slow sedimentation	10^5

[a] Minimum number of years which can be sampled; within that timespan the sedimentary record is too sparse and/or blurred (homogenized) due to mixing through bioturbation, bottom currents etc.

piston coring facility of the Glomar Challenger can penetrate as far as the oldest unlithified sediments (its penetration being limited by sediment shear strength), which may be several hundred metres. Piston coring usually affords undisturbed sequences of sediments in which the recovery is very good and the stratigraphy fully retained, making possible continuous 'high-resolution' sampling down the core. With the HPC, the enhanced depth of penetration affords improved access to the sedimentary record on two main counts:

1. much older sediments can be retrieved and examined in detail over significant intervals of time, and
2. in areas of high sedimentation rate, the cores will reach back through substantial periods of time, whereas shallow piston cores might retrieve only the past few thousand years' record.

Of course, the time coverage obtained by HPC coring depends on the site but unlithified cores should routinely yield records spanning in the region of a million years, which is certainly enough for major periodicities to be detected in the climatic record at a resolution of 10^3 y or better, as illustrated in Table 6. The core from the Guaymas Basin (Leg 64) provides a good example of the sedimentary record beneath an oxygen minimum zone.

ORGANIC GEOCHEMICAL INFORMATION IN DEEP SEA SEDIMENTS RELATING TO CLIMATIC HISTORY

Analyses of sequential layers in rock cores taken on land have afforded abundant evidence that, in general, the solvent-soluble organic geolipids do not diffuse out of the layer in which the organic material has been laid down, unless, of course, raised temperatures have resulted in appreciable hydrocarbon generation. Hence, in diagenetically immature sediments especially, there is the possibility of determining the palaeoenvironmental imprint upon a given layer of sediment.

One important aspect of palaeoenvironmental studies is the evaluation of climatic history. Climatic changes effected by one of three major forcing factors (Table 7a) leave their imprint in the sedimentary record as

Table 7.
Aspects of climatic records in sediments.

(a) *Forcing factors for climatic change*
  Astronomic
  Telluric
  Biological

(c) *Cyclic signals in sediments*
  Oxygen isotopes
  Oxygenation imprint
  Carbonate dissolution
  Sediment composition
    — wind-blown detritus
    — faunal abundances
    — organic matter

(c) *Stratigraphic bases*
  Seismic
  Bio- (carbonate, siliceous, organic)
  Magnetic
  Stable isotope
  Molecular

(d) *Resultant patterns in climatic records*
  Cyclicity
  Phase shifts
  Sequences
  Transients

fluctuations or cyclicity in the various signals (Table 7b) from the sediment. The profiles that are generated by the mensuration of such signals form, or can be related to, a suitable stratigraaphic framework (Table 7c) from which patterns (Fig. 7d) reflecting climatic changes may emerge, especially through statistical treatment of the data or the use of other tools (such as power spectrum analysis). From recent research, stable isotopic stratigraphy is beginning to be viewed in the same terms as the well established and widely used geological tools of seismic stratigraphy, biostratigraphy and magnetostratigraphy (Table 7c). It may be possible, in the future, from lipid analysis to build up a stratigraphy based on molecular measurements.

High resolution stratigraphy afforded by the HPC could be used to reveal any climatic signals registered in the lipid content of the layers. This approach requires the lipid analysis of layers taken sequentially at short intervals throughout long sequences of HPC cores. Such analyses should be accompanied by parallel studies of $\delta^{18}O$ and $\delta^{13}C$ values, since stable isotope measurements have already revealed information concerning past water temperatures directly related to climatic conditions. This is a potentially major area for organic geochemical research in DSDP/IPOD. The abundances of organic compounds in suitable lithologies are such that sampling at 5 cm or 10 cm intervals is entirely feasible. The main practical problem will lie in the sheer variety and extent of the molecular data, for which computerized treatment will be essential. The way forward is well seen in oxygen isotopic studies (e.g. Kennett, 1977 and references therein). For example, the HPC core for Site 504 was sampled at 10 cm intervals ($\sim 2 \times 10^3$ y) over some 45 m, corresponding to approximately a million years, and the ensuing $\delta^{18}O$

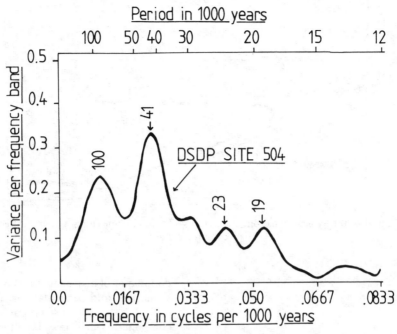

Fig. 3. Variance spectra of Early Pleistocene oxygen isotopic data (Pisias *et al.*).

data then processed so as to display variance per frequency band, as shown in Fig. 3. The results can be interpreted, partially at least, in terms of astronomic forcing: precision of equinoxes, 21×10^3 years; obliquity of ecliptic, 41×10^3 years; and eccentricity of orbit, 105×10^3 years. When undertaken with lipids at individual compound level, molecular stratigraphy may be expected to reveal presently hidden biological responses to astronomic forcing. Key events to be studied could include the pre-Ice Age/Ice Age transition of the order of 10^5 years, in which palaeoceanographers and palaeoclimatologists are seeking to establish whether the onset was smooth or pulsing. Other major questions relate to periods in the Miocene, which exhibit marked variations in the curves for $\delta^{13}C$ and $\delta^{18}O$, indicating rapid changes in the temperature of bottom waters. Another event lies at the Eocene/Oligocene boundary,

where again major changes in the flow of bottom waters may be responsible. In the Cretaceous, black shale events are widely regarded as having their origin in telluric forcing, i.e. as a consequence of palaeogeographic and palaeohydrographic changes. Of especial interest here is Leg 75, Hole 532, discussed elsewhere in this volume (Meyers *et al.*) where the quantities of total organic matter show cycles of around 30–100 thousand years. More detailed work using sequential sampling at narrow intervals together with the results of quantitative molecular analyses is now required.

HISTORY OF COASTAL UPWELLING

Areas of upwelling of cold, nutrient-rich waters in the present oceans are indicated in Fig. 4. The geographic locations of these areas depend mainly on the positions of pressure systems in the atmosphere, the direction and strength of ocean currents and coastal and bottom topography. Hence, the long term geological history of upwelling areas must show a direct relationship with the position of continents, the availability of connecting seaways and similar factors.

Upwelling regimes are of great interest to organic geochemists, as the sediments laid down beneath them are normally rich in organic matter. Such bottom sediments, e.g. those of Walvis Bay, SW Africa, have already been shown to contain a wealth of biological marker compounds, indicative of specific biological inputs (e.g. Boon *et al.*, 1978; Wardroper *et al.*, 1978; Gagosian *et al.*, 1980). What is needed is a major,

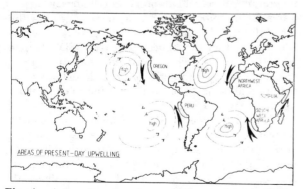

Fig. 4. Areas of present-day upwelling systems and the current systems and schematic positions of isobars of the sea-level atmospheric pressure systems (anticyclones) that influence them (after Barber and Smith 1981).

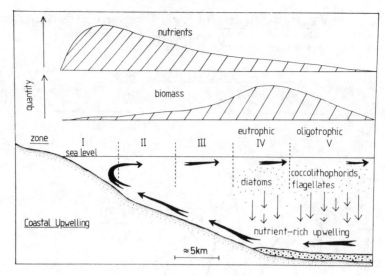

Fig. 5. Scheme illustrating the typical zonation associated with coastal upwelling systems (after R. T. Barber, personal communication).

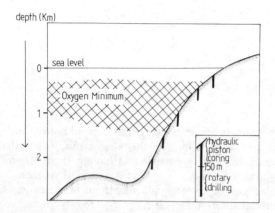

Fig. 6. Proposed drilling on the Peru margin to evaluate impact of upwelling and associated oxygen minimum zone through Neogene.

detailed, interdisciplinary study of a present-day upwelling area as it functions now, in the recent past and back through geological time. The total organic material laid down, including the detailed molecular signatures, should afford a record of input organisms and bottom conditions. Hence, the Organic Geochemistry Advisory Panel is strongly in favour of a programme of drilling transects in an upwelling area, as proposed by the Ocean Palaeoenvironment Panel of DSDP/IPOD for the Peru margin. The features of coastal upwelling are shown schematically in Fig. 5, and an outline proposal for a drilling transect in Fig. 6. Clearly, the history of upwelling in an area is of considerable interest to palaeooceanographers and climatologists, for the nature, size and location of upwelling systems must be affected by and reflect changes in atmospheric and oceanic circulation. The background to the organic geochemical interest in this upwelling problem is summarized as follows.

Organic geochemists can recognise productivity events in the Recent and Neogene — provided geothermal influences have not been major — through quantitation of total organic carbon (TOC), and the dominance of marine marker compounds (i.e. terrestrial v. marine) and particulate organic matter.

Within the 'marine' compounds, there are individual compounds which may be interpreted provisionally as markers for particular organisms. Thus, dinosterol is presently recorded only for dinoflagellates. However, correlations and interpretations should be based on a wide range of compound classes. Thus, while carotenoid pigments are excellent markers for living organisms, communities and Recent bottom sediments (Watts *et al.*, 1977; Tibbetts, 1980; Züllig, 1981; Repeta and Gagosian, this volume), the lability of these compounds restricts their use largely to young sediments. In contrast, the acyclic isoprenoid hydrocarbons offer a long term record as these molecules are rather resistant to biodegradation and physico–chemical diagenesis in sediments.

A vital part of this approach will be the need to improve our understanding of the relationship between conditions throughout the water column and the preservation of organic matter. Sediment trap work, such as that conducted as part of the PARFLUX experiments, and concerted multidisciplinary studies of specific environments, such as those of the ORGON programmes, serve to improve our understanding of water column processes and reactions occurring within the surficial sediments. This oceanographic research, which lies outside the immediate goal of DSDP, helps to address questions such as: just how important is the position of the oxygen minimum zone in relation to the bottom sediments? What is the significance of particle size re survival of organic matter?

If organic chemists and organic geochemists are to contribute to the study of sediments beneath upwelling areas, then the first requirement is that the biology of upwelling regions be defined. For example, the organisms of present-day upwelling areas should be surveyed both in the photic zone and in the rest of the water column in terms of biomass and their position in the food web.

More difficult would be a similar treatment based on

the fossil record. Such studies could then be integrated with lipid analyses for marker compounds and diagenetic products, sea water, plankton tows, sediment traps, bottom sediments and cultures and collections of organisms at different growth stages. Benthic microflora (e.g. *Thioploca* mats) and meiofauna (e.g. foraminifera) require special attention.

Analyses should include not only lipids extracted from the samples but also pyrolysis, microscopy and other techniques applied to the insoluble debris — protokerogen and kerogen. Such studies should result in lists of marker compounds which correlate with appropriate blooms, together with skewing functions for the distributions consequent upon the transformations taking place in the short term in the water column and also over longer time spans (10^6–10^8 y) in the sediments. The remaining and transformed (diagenetic) imprint is seen in the form of the relative and absolute abundances of the marker compounds and diagenetic products. The consequence should be molecular signatures for upwelling events, flexible in regard to time, and semi-quantitative for the intensity of the event and the nature of the water column. Where applied by systematic sampling over an area, these measures should be practicable for the spread of site and depth studies needed to determine the size (geographic distribution) and history of the event.

BLACK SHALE EVENTS

Following on from the theme of coastal upwelling, the second major goal identified in the Organic Geochemistry Advisory Panel 'White Paper' (Table 5) is the evaluation of black shale events. Although such sediments, notably of Cretaceous age, have been recovered from all the major oceans there is much about their formation that requires further investigation. For example, most of the black shale intervals encountered during the first 40 DSDP Legs were not continuously cored, hence the need to return to these sites to further realize the sedimentary setting and extent of such horizons. In addition, the differences between the various time zones (e.g. Apto-Albian v. Cenomanian) of these black shales are in need of investigation, as are the supposed 2–5×10^4 year fluctuations in the organic carbon contents of the Mid-Cretaceous black shales. Indeed, in the southern Angola Basin (Hole 530A) the alkane distribution of a Cenomanian black shale is markedly different from its adjacent green claystone (Brassell *et al.*, this volume) suggesting a discrete change in the inputs of organic matter to these intercalated lithologies. This observation highlights the need to study both the black shales and their adjacent sediment horizons in order to address the question of the nature of their depositional environments. Hence, fine scale sampling is again needed.

Turning to sites of special interest for drilling Cretaceous black shales, a few are mentioned in Table 5, such as rises in the Pacific Ocean. In addition, within the southern part of the North Atlantic Ocean black shales from the Venezuelan margin, from where they have

previously been recovered in small amounts, would present a chance for comparison with the oil-bearing La Luna Formation of the mainland. The Demerara Rise and the south eastern part of the North Atlantic Ocean are also key areas in the understanding of black shale formation in relation to the opening of the Atlantic.

Overall, there is a major need to document the occurrence of Cretaceous black shales in terms of their small scale variability and lateral extension. For example, only two Holes (364 and 530) have been drilled in the entire Angola Basin to date, so that many palaeoceanographic and palaeoenvironmental constructions are based on rather limited sediment data, although geophysical surveys (and hence seismic profiles) are often quite extensive.

DIAGENESIS

Several presentations at this conference deal with the diagenesis of lipids in sediments. In particular, those of Rullkötter and Welte (this volume) and of McEvoy and Maxwell (this volume) are concerned with diagenesis in the sedimentary column in areas of high geothermal gradient. Both of these papers are based on results from DSDP sites. As mentioned above, sedimentary sequences recovered by DSDP provide an important link between shallow piston coring and deeper drilling by the petroleum industry. Hence, in diagenetic terms such sediments provide the only bridge between the largely microbially mediated transformations of early-stage diagenesis and the thermally induced changes of late-stage diagenesis and catagenesis. One of the principal diagenetic processes best seen in DSDP sediment sequences is that of lipid defunctionalization, such as the loss of carbonyl and hydroxyl groups, whereby the biolipids inherited by immature sediments from organisms are converted into the more thermally stable geolipids which are the constituents of mature sediments and petroleums. The latter group are almost exclusively saturated and aromatic hydrocarbons.

McEvoy and Maxwell (this volume) have examined lipid diagenesis in sediments from an area of high heat flow, the California Bight (Leg 63, Site 467), comparing the changes seen in the steroids with those observed in the cold sediment column beneath the Japan Trench (Leg 57, Site 440; Brassell *et al.*, 1980b). In general the two areas show similar diagenetic trends, although lipid defunctionalisation occurs more rapidly in the hotter regime of the California Bight. For example, sterols survive as dominant constituents to the bottom of Site 440 in the Japan Trench (c. 780 m), whereas they are present in only the upper three samples of Site 467 in the California Bight (down to 333 m), where sterenes and steranes are dominant in all but the upper two samples (McEvoy and Maxwell, this volume). These differences illustrate one of the great advantages of the Deep Sea Drilling Project: sediment cores collected from areas of differing heat flow provide vital, direct evidence for the nature and rates of diagenetic changes. Such studies will continue to be a major area for research within DSDP and one which will be aided by future plans to improve downhole temperature measurements.

CONCLUSIONS

Sediments recovered by the Deep Sea Drilling Project (DSDP) present significant opportunities to organic geochemists studying depositional palaeoenvironments and diagenesis. In particular the use of hydraulic piston coring in DSDP offers the unique possibility of fine scale sampling of unconsolidated sediments suitable for the assessment of climatic changes from their imprint on the sedimentary organic matter. In contrast, samples retrieved by deep rotary drilling provide an opportunity to study diagenetic process in the maturity range not normally covered by oceanic piston coring or drilling by the petroleum industry. In these and other respects, future DSDP plans encompass many objectives of organic geochemical interest, notably the drilling of black shale horizons. Indeed it is through the continuation of the drilling programme, and the interaction of organic geochemists with it, that a fuller appreciation of the origin and fate of organic matter in marine sediments will be realized.

Acknowledgements

We thank the Natural Environment Research Council for financial support (GR3/2951 and GR3/3758) and colleagues at Bristol for useful comments. We are grateful to members of the Organic Geochemistry Advisory Panel and fellow delegates to the NATO/ARI Conference on 'Coastal Upwelling; Its sediment record' for helpful discussions.

REFERENCES

Baker, E. W. and Louda, J. W. (1980) Organic geochemistry: Highlights in the Deep Sea Drilling Project. In *Advances in Organic Geochemistry 1979*. Ed. by Douglas, A. G. and Maxwell, J. R. Pergamon, Oxford. pp. 295–319.

Barber, R. T. and Smith, R. L. (1981) Coastal upwelling ecosystems. In *Analysis of Marine Ecosystems*. Ed. by Longhurst, A. R. Academic Press, London. pp. 31–68.

Boon, J. J., de Leeuw, J. W. and Burlingame, A. L. (1978) Organic geochemistry of Walvis Bay diatomaceous ooze III. Structural analysis of the monoenoic and polycyclic fatty acids. *Geochim. Cosmochim. Acta* **42**, 631–639.

Brassell, S. C., Comet, P. A., Eglinton, G., Isaacson, P. J., McEvoy, J., Maxwell, J. R., Thomson, I. D., Tibbetts, P. J. C. and Volkman, J. K. (1980a) Preliminary lipid analyses of sections 440A-7-6, 440B-3-5, 440B-8-4, 440B-68-2 and 536-11-4: Legs 56 and 57, Deep Sea Drilling Project. In *Initial Reports of the Deep Sea Drilling Project Volume 56/57 Part 2*. Ed. by Scientific Parties. U.S. Government Printing Office, Washington. pp. 1367–1390.

Brassell, S. C., Comet, P. A., Eglinton, G., Isaacson, P. J., McEvoy, J., Maxwell, J. R., Thomson, I. D., Tibbetts, P. J. C. and Volkman, J. K. (1980b) The origin and fate of lipids in the Japan Trench. In *Advances in Organic Geochemistry, 1979*. Ed. by Douglas, A. G. and Maxwell, J. R. Pergamon, Oxford. pp. 375–392.

Brassell, S. C., Wardroper, A. M. K., Thomson, I. D., Maxwell, J. R. and Eglinton, G. (1981) Specific acyclic isoprenoids as biological markers of methanogenic bacteria in marine sediments. *Nature (London)* **290**, 693–696.

Gagosian, R. B., Smith, S. O., Lee, C., Farrington, J. W. and Frew, N. M. (1980) Steroid transformations in Recent marine sediments. In *Advances in Organic Geochemistry 1979*. Ed. by Douglas, A. G. and Maxwell, J. R. Pergamon, Oxford. pp. 407–419.

Holton, R. W., Blecker, H. H. and Onore, M. (1964) Effect of growth temperature on the fatty acid composition of a blue–green algae. *Phytochem.* **3**, 595–602.

Holzer, G., Oro, J. and Tornabene, T. G. (1979) Gas chromatographic/mass spectrometric analysis of neutral lipids from methanogenic and thermoacidophilic bacteria. *J. Chromatogr.* **186**, 795–809.

Kawamura, K. and Ishiwatari, R. (1981) Polyunsaturated fatty acids in a lacustrine sediment as a possible indicator of paleoclimate. *Geochim. Cosmochim. Acta.* **45**, 149–155.

Kennett, J. P. (1977) Cenozoic evolution of Antarctic glaciation, the Circum–Antarctic Ocean and their impact on global paleoceanography. *J. Geophys. Res.* **82**, 3843–3860.

Marr, A. G. and Ingraham, J. L. (1962) Effect of temperature on the composition of fatty acids in *Escherichia coli. J. Bacteriol.* **84**, 1260–1267.

Pisias, N. G., Moore, T. G. and Shackleton, N. unpublished results quoted in the DSDP/IPOD program review for 1981.

Tibbetts, P. J. C. (1980) The origin of the Carotenoids of some Quaternary and Pliocene sediments. Phd Thesis, University of Bristol.

Tissot, B. P., Deroo, G. and Herbin, J. P. (1979) Organic matter in Cretaceous sediments of the North Atlantic: contribution to sedimentology and paleogeography. In *Deep Drilling Results in the Atlantic Ocean: Continental Margins and paleoenvironment. Amer Geophys. Union, Maurice Ewing Ser.* **3**, 362–374.

Volkman, J. K., Eglinton, G., Corner, E. D. S. and Sargent, J. R. (1980) Novel unsaturated straight-chain C_{37}–C_{39} methyl and ethyl ketones in marine sediments and a coccolithophore *Emiliania huxleyi*. In *Advances in Organic Geochemistry 1979*. Ed. by Douglas, A. G. and Maxwell, J. R. Pergamon, Oxford. pp. 219–227.

Wardroper, A. M. K., Maxwell, J. R. and Morris, R. J. (1978) Sterols of a diatomaceous ooze from Walvis Bay. *Steroids* **32**, 203–221.

Watts, C. D., Maxwell, J. R. and Kjøsen, H. (1977) The potential of carotenoids as environmental indicators. In *Advances in Organic Geochemistry 1979*. Ed. by Campos, R. and Goni, J. Enadimsa, Madrid. pp. 391–413.

Züllig, H. (1981) On the use of carotenoid stratigraphy in lake sediments for detecting past developments of phytoplankton. *Limnol. Oceanogr.* **26**, 970–976.

Advances in Organic Geochemistry 1981, pp. 401–421
© *John Wiley & Sons Limited, 1983*

Thermal Aspects in Chlorophyll Geochemistry

E. W. Baker and J. W. Louda

Organic Geochemistry Group, College of Science, Florida Atlantic University, Boca Raton, Florida 33431,
USA

Studies on the evolution and maturation of geologic tetrapyrrole pigments within various sedimentary sequences of known thermal profiles recovered by the Deep Sea Drilling Project are presented. The sampling, and possibly the existence, of sedimentary sequences which contain the *entire* geochemical history of chlorophyll derivatives, from deposition to eventual carbonization, is rare at best. The worldwide sampling of marine sediments by DSDP has provided the authors, and past collaborators, the opportunity of piecing together an overview of chlorophyll geochemistry. In keeping with the modern divisions of organic evolution as presented in recent treatises (Hunt, 1979; Tissot and Welte, 1978) we have assigned the following stages to the various reactions and pigment classes within chlorophyll geochemistry: Diagenesis, early — defunctionalization/phorbides, chlorins, purpurins; Middle — aromatization/free-base porphyrins; late — chelation/immature metalloporphyrins; Catagenesis, thermal (alt. thermocatalytic) alteration of metalloporphyrins; Metagenesis, thermal destruction of the tetrapyrrole macrocyclce. Data from past and present studies now enable us to offer description of the thermal regimes in which the various stages of chlorophyll geochemistry have been found. Sedimentary sequences covered include; the Cape Verde Rise (DSDP Leg 41), the Black Sea (DSDP Leg 42B), the Tarfaya Basin (DSDP Leg 47A), the Japan Trench (DSDP Legs 56–57), the San Miguel Gap and Baja California borderlands (DSDP) Leg 63), and the Gulf of California (DSDP Leg 64). Results which are covered include: description of aromatization which yields free-base porphyrins (*ca.* 25–40°C), chelation of nickel (*ca.* 30–60°C), decarboxylation of nickel porphyrins (*ca.* 35–50°C), Ni ETIO generation from Ni DPEP (*ca.* 45°C+), appearance (release, formation) of Ni DPEP homologues above C-32 (<50°C), and the release of vanadyl porphyrins from the overall (asphaltene, kerogen) organic matrix (65°C+). The lower temperature of the ranges given are for geologically older sediments and conversely, the higher temperatures are for younger formations. Variation in geothermal histories show quite clearly that these reactions do indeed follow closely the dictum of time and temperature interdependence. The usefulness of tetrapyrrole pigments as indicators of the geothermal stress applied to sedimentary organic matter is elaborated.

INTRODUCTION

Isolation and identification of desoxophylloerythroetio-porphyrin (DPEP) from a variety of petroleum crudes, shales and sedimentary bitumens, and the suggested linkage to chlorophyll-a (Fig. 1), indicated a biological source for these materials and initiated the field of organic geochemistry (Treibs, 1934a, b; 1935a, b; 1936). The isolation of ETIO-type porphyrins from these

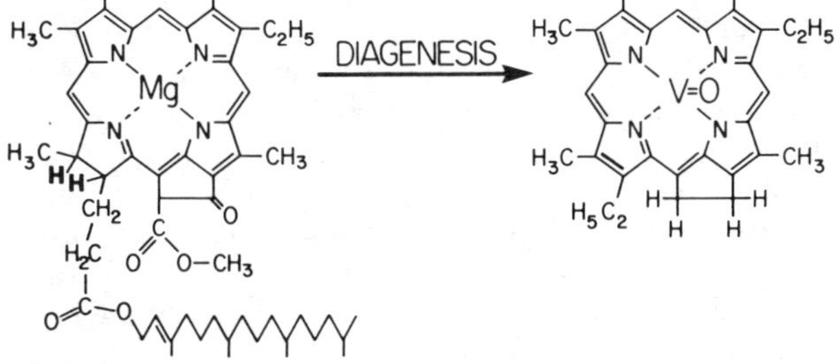

Fig. 1. Structural comparison of chlorophyl-*a* and vanadyl deoxophylloerythroetioporphyrin, a biotic precursor–geologic product pair.

same materials lead to suggestions that their biotic precursors were the heme-based pigments (Treibs, 1934a), even if these were from plant, rather than animal material (Dunning, 1963; Hodgson *et al.*, 1967). The possibility that geologic ETIO-type porphyrins may in fact derive from DPEP, and therefore chlorophyll, rather than from the heme pigments, began to attain notice after the Fifth World Petroleum Congress (Corwin, 1960). Stemming from a comparative study on the metalloporphyrins present in Mahogany Ledge (Green River Formation, Vinta Basin, Colorado, USA) oil-shale and those recovered from the shale-oil, obtained by retort, it was concluded that the ETIO series had increased at the expense of the original DPEP-porphyrins (Morandi and Jensen, 1966). Since that time, the DPEP to ETIO conversion, or crossover, has gained increasing utility as a measure of the thermal history of geologic organic assemblages and their host settings (cf Alturki *et al.*, 1972; Baker, 1969a; Baker and Palmer, 1978; Didyk *et al.*, 1975b).

The unique nature of petroleum porphyrins became apparent only after the application of detailed mass spectrometric analyses to these geologic pigments (Baker, 1966; Baker *et al.*, 1967; Dean and Whitehead,

1963; Morandi and Jensen, 1966; Thomas and Blumer, 1964). The presence of porphyrin homologies extending well above the C–32 compounds directly derived from chlorophyll forced a radical change in thought concerning the original 'Treibs. scheme' for chlorophyll diagenesis (Baker, 1969; Baker *et al.*, 1967; Baker and Palmer, 1978). Thus, alternate biotic sources, such as the *Chlorobium*-chlorophylls, with their unusual alkylation patterns (Holt and Hughes, 1961; Holt *et al.*, 1966; Mathewson *et al.*, 1963; Purdie and Holt, 1965), were suggested as potential biotic sources for the extended alkyl homologies of the petroleum pigments (Baker *et al.*, 1967; Casagrande and Hodgson, 1974; Didyk *et al.*, 1975a; Hodgson *et al.*, 1972). However, the nature and relative abundances of the *Chlorobium*-chlorophylls is such (see Holt, 1966 and references therein) that resultant DPEP-porphyrin homologies would exhibit marked bimodality at C–32 and C–34, assuming simple decarboxylation (viz. $-CO_2$), and extend only to C–37. Even in natural situations where the growth of *Chlorobium* spp. is optimum, the pigment assemblage, as well as the total organic matter, is still attributable to oxic photic zone phytoplankton (Takahashi and Ichimura, 1968). Further, immature porphyrins isolated from the Black Sea sediments, with suggested *Chlorobium* input (Peake *et al.*, 1974), are limited homologies of DPEP extending only from C–27 to C–32 (Baker *et al.*, 1978b). Lastly, analytical oxidation of porphyrins to the resultant maleimides has, to date, failed to show the existence of an iso-butyl substituent (Baker and Palmer, 1978; Barwise and Whitehead, 1980; Didyk *et al.*, 1975a; Hodgson *et al.*, 1972; Mackenzie *et al.*, 1980; Quirke *et al.*, 1980a), an expected product from the *Chlorobium*-chlorophylls (see Holt and Hughes, 1961; Holt, 1966). The possibility of extremely limited *Chlorobium*-chlorophyll input to petroleum pigments should not be dismissed, just as it should not be stressed.

Recently, the bacteriochlorophylls (i.e. tetrahydro-porphyrins) have been suggested as giving rise, in addition to chlorophyll a and b, to the porphyrins of humic coals (Louda and Baker, 1980; Palmer *et al.*, 1982). In this case, the bacteriochlorophylls, as well as with the chlorophylls a, b, c and d (senescence artifact ?), will all blend into the original 'Treibs scheme' (cf. Baker and Palmer, 1978) and yield DPEP with a maximum carbon number of 32, barring subsequent geochemical alkylation.

Thus, in the present treatise we shall treat all geologic porphyrins as being derived essentially from one compound, chlorophyll a. It will be noted that the other chlorophylls, except the *Chlorobium* forms, will blend easily into these scenarios with, usually, only one additional, and often facile, reaction.

Originally, the term 'transalkylation' was invoked as a plausible explanation for the occurrence of extended porphyrin homologies (Baker, 1966, 1969). This was not originally, nor since, meant to infer alkyl transfer *only* between porphyrins, as is the only possible route during *in vitro* experiments with porphyrins as the sole organic (see Bonnett *et al.*, 1972), but rather amongst the entire organic melange. Recently, the possibility that porphyrins form alkyl linkages with, for example, kerogen and are released, as extended homologies, later

via thermal or thermocatalytic cracking has attained growing favour (Baker *et al.*, 1977a; Barwise and Whitehead, 1980; Louda and Baker, 1981; Mackenzie *et al.*, 1980). Thus, we now suggest that the terms alkylation and dealkylation, or the combination alkylation–dealkylation, be utilized to describe what are now known to be two separate processes.

The present paper focuses upon those phases during the geochemical evolution of the tetrapyrrole pigments which are found to be directly attributable to the thermal setting and history of their host environment. Thus, the very early diagenetic reactions during the defunctionalization of phorbides and oxidative destruction of chlorins will, for the most part, be tersely dealt with.

Though each stage or division of tetrapyrrole geochemistry will be primarily discussed as an individual phenomenon it should be noted, and is stressed, that we are dealing with a continuum and that overlap does indeed occur.

EXPERIMENTAL

All samples examined by the authors, except for specific cases mentioned in text, were marine sediments recovered by the Deep Sea Drilling Project vessel D/V *Glomar Challenger*. Detailed sample description, in addition to that given in the text, can be obtained from the appropriate volume (viz.Volume = Leg) of the *Initial Reports of the Deep Sea Drilling Project*, US Government Printing Office, Washington, DC, USA.

Although no tetrapyrrole pigment analysis is truly routine, typical procedures are described.

Sediments were extracted repeatedly with acetone:methanol (9:1, v/v), switching to acetone:benzene (1:1, v/v) afrer 8–10 extractions and continued until no further pigment-like colour or fluorescence was obtained. All extracts were pooled, evaporated *in vacuo*, dissolved with deperoxided distilled ethyl ether and washed several times with ice-cold distilled water. Ethereal extracts were then evaporated in a water bath (T < 40 °C) with a gentle stream of nitrogen. Pigment quality and initial quantitation was performed at this stage via electronic spectroscopy and the subsequent procedures to be utilized were decided upon.

Near-surface, geologically young geochemically immature, sediments usually are dominated by pigments such as pheophytin a, pheophorbide a, phorbides, chlorins and carotenoids. These extracts were initially separated via column chromatography over microcrystalline cellulose (see Baker and Louda, 1982; cf. Holden, 1965; Strain, 1958; Strain and Svec, 1966). The non-polar (viz. phytyl ester and decarboxylated species) mono-carboxylic acid, and di- to poly-carboxylated pigments were then further purified, as *in vitro* methyl esters (via CH_2N_2) where appropriate, by high-performance low-pressure liquid-chromatography using an Ace Glass (Vineland, New Jersey, USA) Michel-Miller System operated at *ca.* 100–250 psig. Typical adsorbants include 13–24 μ silica

(Whatman LPS–1) and 63–200 μ alumina (Merck 1097) and employing acetone, petroleum ether, n-pentane and cyclohexane as typical solvents. Eluates were monitored with a Laboratory Data Control (Riviera Beach, Florida, USA) Spectromonitor-II variable wavelength (160–700 nm) detector fitted with a 10 μl flow cell. The wavelength of maximal tetrapyrrole absorption (viz. Soret or γ band) was usually monitored (e.g. 390–415 nm).

Successively deeper and more thermally mature sediments usually contained a dominance of free-base and/or metalloporphyrins, as well as higher molecular weight products of 'geopolymerization' (see Hunt, 1979). In these cases, as well as petroleum crudes and shale extracts, gel-permeation chromatography (GPC) through/over Sephadex LH–20, with deperoxided tetrahydrofuran as the mobil phase, was utilized to remove large molecular weight (e.g. mw > 2000 daltons) complexes from subsequent interference.

Free-base porphyrins were isolated from extracts or chromatographic fractions via extraction into 2.5–5% aqueous HCl (w/v) and transferred to fresh ether, after neutralization of the acid with sodium carbonate. If required, free-base porphyrins were purified by HPLPLC over silica, as described earlier.

Metalloporphyrin containing extracts, GPC-fractions or petroleum crudes were separated into nickel, or nickel plus copper, and vanadyl porphyrin fractions by chromatography over silica, eluting with toluene and ethyl-acetate/toluene (3:2, v/v), respectively (cf. Barwise and Whitehead, 1980). Nickel, or nickel plus copper, porphyrins were purified by HPLPLC over silica as above. Vanadyl porphyrins were purified by chromatograohy over alumina (Baker et al., 1978a) or recently, 'BP-FUNCTIONALISED-SILICA'[R] after the method of Barwise and Whitehead (1980; cf. Louda and Baker, 1981).

The presence of conjugated carbonyl functions (e.g. 9-keto) was confirmed by treatment of selected isolates with sodium borohydride ($NaBH_4$) in deperoxided ethyl ether containing about 10–20% ethanol (Louda and Baker, 1981; Louda et al., 1980; cf. Holt, 1959).

Electron absorption spectra were recorded with a Perkin-Elmer 575 spectrophotometer coupled to a Perkin-Elmer C570–0729 derivative accessory. Calibration of wavelength and absorbancy was versus holmium oxide and various concentrations of K_2CrO_4 in aqueous 0.05 N KOH (see e.g. Rao, 1967).

Mass spectra were recorded with a DuPont 21–491B instrument at 14 eV (50 μA) and 70 eV (260 μA). Details of mass spectrometric analyses are given elsewhere (see Baker, 1966; Baker and Palmer, 1978; Baker et al., 1967; Louda and Baker, 1981).

All operations were performed either in the dark or under subdued yellow light. Exposure to light, heat and air (viz. O_2), especially in any combination, was strictly avoided. All extracts and isolates were maintained evaporated and stored frozen under nitrogen. Solvents were redistilled prior to usage and ethers (viz. ethyl, tetrahydrofuran) were deperoxided over grade Super-I (viz. 0% H_2O) basic alumina.

Structures of selected tetrapyrrole pigments as well as the carbon and ring position labelling utilized herein are given as an appendix. Systematic and semi-systematic nomenclature of tetrapyrrole pigments may be obtained elsewhere (see e.g. Bonnett, 1978; Seely, 1966; Smith, 1975).

THE GEOCHEMISTRY OF CHLOROPHYLL

In keeping with the modern divisions of organic geochemical evolution as given in recent treatises (see Hung, 1979; Tissot and Welte, 1978), we have assigned the following stages for the reactions and pigment classes involved in chlorophyll geochemistry:

Diagenesis: Early — the *defunctionalization* of phorbides, chlorins and purpurins. Mid — the *aromatization* of phorbides (and chlorins) yielding free-base DPEP (and ETIO) porphyrins. Late — *chelation* of metals (viz. Ni, V = 0) by free-base porphyrins generating metalloporphyrins.

Catagenesis: the thermal and/or thermocatalytic *alteration* of metalloporphyrins including the release of alkylated vanadyl porphyrins, ETIO series generation and dealkylation.

Metagenesis: thermal *destruction* of the tetrapyrrole macrocycle and pigment (viz. chromophore) character.

As we hope to reveal in the subsequent sections, the entire continuum of tetrapyrrole geochemistry closely adheres to the time–temperature interdependence characteristic of organic reactions. That is, geologically younger or older sediments are found to impose stringent requirements for either higher or lower thermal histories, respectively, in order to achieve similar maturational progress and yield somewhat analogous tetrapyrrole pigment assemblages. These patterns, of course, can, and do, fall under certain constrains imposed by the very early stages of sedimentation (viz. paleoenvironment; oxic versus anoxic; etc.).

EARLY DIAGENESIS: DEFUNCTIONALIZATION

Several reactions of the original 'Treibs scheme' diagenesis of chlorophyll (see Baker and Palmer, 1978; Hodgson et al., 1967; Treibs, 1936) are now known to fall more properly into the category of cellular senescence than geochemistry *per se*. That is, the loss of magnesium from chlorophyll, forming pheophytin, is extremely rapid and follows closely the settling out of the photic zone of phytoplankton (see Orr et al., 1958; Yentsch, 1965). Further, much de-esterification of phytol occurs prior to actual sedimentation and is directly attributable to zooplankton predation (Curie, 1962; Lorenzen, 1967; Louda and Baker, unpublished data).

Thus, the initial input of 'chlorophyll' to marine sediments, lying below the photic zone, is as pheophytin a and certain derivatives formed in the water column by biologic activities, most notably pheophorbide a. The geochemistry of 'chlorophyll' then begins with surviving pheophytin and the pheophorbides. Following deposition continued phytyl loss increases the proportion of dihydroporphyrin acids. It has been suggested that reduction of the phytyl double bond, forming dihydrophytyl esters, may lead to longer term retention of the isoprenoid moiety by forcing elimination as phytene rather than as phytadiene (Baker and Smith, 1977).

Aside from the mechanism of post-depositional phytyl or dihydrophytyl loss, the early diagenesis of chlorophyll derivatives has become increasingly clear in recent years. Since these early reactions appear more directly related to biologic factors (viz. sedimentary fauna) and oxygen tension, than strictly to temperature, discussion will be extremely abbreviated. Early tetrapyrrole diagenesis consists of a divergent series of anastomotic pathways initiated and controlled by the relative oxic or anoxic nature of the sedimentary microcosm and, presumably, by the corresponding biota.

Early oxidative conditions are found to lead to extremely rapid removal of tetrapyrrole pigments from the fossil record. This loss of pigments is found to be paralleled, and therefore caused (?), by such reactions as 'allomerization' (see Fischer and Stern, 1940; Seely, 1966 and references in the latter) and the subsequent generation of purpurins and chlorins (viz. e_6 and p_6), isolated recently from various marine sediments (Baker and Louda, 1980a, c, 1982; Louda et al., 1980) and previously from terrestrial grasses (Aronoff, 1953). This we classify as oxidative or oxic diagenesis and only in certain cases where initial chlorophyllous input is high and the bottom waters and surface sediments maintained oxic (e.g. current factors) will minor preservation of chlorins (i.e. lacking the isocyclic ring: Appendix A) lead to survival as immature ETIO porphyrins (see Louda and Baker, 1980; cf. Palmer et al., 1982).

Contrasting early oxidation, and of more interest for longer-term geochemical considerations, is the defunctionalization of phorbides (viz. dihydro-porphyrins retaining the isocyclic ring: Appendix) which occurs in anoxic settings.

Generation of the pyro-pheophorbides, those which have lost the C–10 carbomethoxy (β-keto acid) moiety, removes the ability for these pigments to allomerize (see Hynninen, 1979; Seely, 1966). Thus, we feel that the tentative identification, based upon chromatographic behaviour, of a series of pyro-pheophytins and decarboxylated pyro-pheophorbides from anoxic diatomaceous oozes, deposited within a strong oxygen minimum zone in the Gulf of California, represent major portions of the early diagenetic continuum which leads to eventual tetrapyrrole pigment survival or fossilization (Baker and Louda, 1982).

Retention of 9-keto-phorbide structure has been found to occur within the Pleistocene–Pliocene–Miocene sediment strata of the Japan Trench (Baker and Louda, 1980a; Louda et al., 1980). This setting, the inner trench wall, was found to have an extremely low thermal gradient (viz. ca. 10 °C/km; Shipboard Party — Site 440, 1980) which was taken as the primary factor in the survival of pheophytin-a (pyro-pheophytin-a) to a depth of 456 m sub-bottom and the more highly defunctionalized 9-keto-phorbides to a depth of 722 m

sub-bottom (Baker and Louda, 1980a). This can then be viewed as long-term (viz. Miocene) low-temperature ($< 10 - 15$ °C) early diagenesis.

Contrasting the Japan Trench study is a more recent study on the diagenesis of tetrapyrroles in numerous anoxic diatomaceous oozes from the Gulf of California which were all late Quaternary and exposed to a high thermal gradient (ca. 96°/km; Shipboard Party, in press). In this case, early diagenesis was found to be temporally compressed and free-base porphyrins were generated from defunctionalized phorbides in sediments much less than 1 million years (viz. Pleistocene) old (Baker and Louda, 1982).

Based on the studies mentioned above, as well as previous data (see e.g. Baker and Smith, 1973, 1977; Baker et al., 1978b; Louda and Baker, 1979, 1980), we can now view the early diagenesis of tetrapyrroles as occurring from bottom-water temperatures (e.g. 3–8 °C) to approximately 15–20 °C or 20–30 °C for Miocene or Pleistocene aged lower end-members.

The vast majority of defunctionalized phorbides, free-base and immature metallo-porphyrins isolated from marine sediments are found to be decarboxylated species (Baker and Louda, 1982; Baker and Palmer, 1978; Louda and Baker, 1981). Thus, significant decarboxylation must be functioning in sedimentary environments with maximum in situ temperatures of 25–30 °C, or less. This suggests the possible intervention of microbial action and, due to a lack of direct evidence, requires much additional investigation. Minor amounts of carboxylated porphyrins do survive and the decarboxylation (viz. thermal) of these pigment is covered later in text.

Once the early chlorophyll derivatives (viz. phorbides) have transgressed this period of defunctionalization, and in situ temperatures begin to rise, aromatization ensues and free-base porphyrins are generated.

MID-DIAGENESIS; AROMATIZATION

The aromatization of dihydroporphyrins (viz. defunctionalized phorbides) which yields free-base porphyrins entails the completion of tetrapyrrole aromaticity at the bond between carbons 7 and 8 of ring IV, as shown structurally in Fig. 2. The structures shown

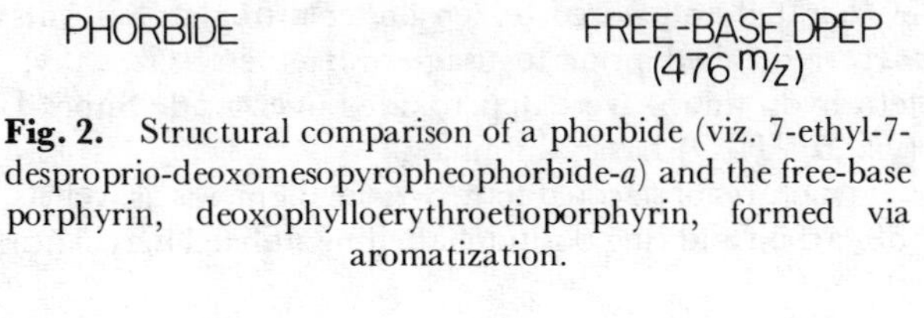

PHORBIDE   FREE-BASE DPEP
                       (476 m/z)

Fig. 2. Structural comparison of a phorbide (viz. 7-ethyl-7-desproprio-deoxomesopyropheophorbide-*a*) and the free-base porphyrin, deoxophylloerythroetioporphyrin, formed via aromatization.

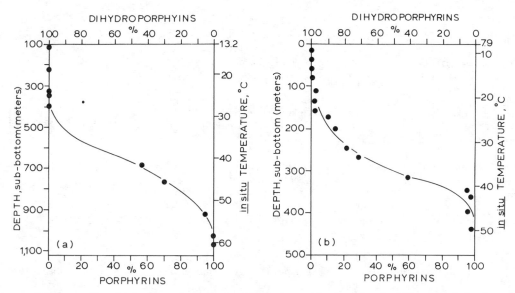

Fig. 3. Aromatization profiles obtained by plotting percent dihydroporphyrins (viz. phorbides, chlorins), alternately percent porphyrins (viz. free-base, metallo-), versus sub-bottom sample depth and *in situ* temperatures. (a) Black Sea, DSDP Leg 42B, Site 380A. Tetrapyrrole data from Baker *et al.*, 178b. Thermal gradient from Erickson and Von Herzen, 1978. (b) Guaymas Basin slope in the Gulf of California, DSDP/IPOD Leg 64, Site 479. Tetrapyrrole data from Baker and Louda, 1982. Thermal gradient from Shipboard Party, 1982.

are the theoretical immediate precursor to DPEP, namely 7-ethyl-7-desproprio-deoxomesopyropheophorbide a, and DPEP itself. Tentative identification has been made for the precursor (i.e. dihydro-DPEP or 7-ethyl-7-desproprio-deoxomesopyropheophorbide a), isolated from diatomaceous oozes recovered from the Gulf of California and also yielding free-base DPEP series porphyrins, but these structural studies, and therefore proof, are still in progress (Baker and Louda, 1982). The mechanism of aromatization is unknown, at present, but the most plausible reactions include didehydrogenation and/or the loss of the angular methyl group (vic. C–8 methyl), the latter finding precedent with the aromatization of steroids (see Streibl and Herout, 1969).

To date, we have been able to observe the entire history of aromatization only within two sample suites, each of which has been characterized as being deposited through anoxic bottom waters. As mentioned earlier, during the latter phases of any one diagenetic stage the initial products of subsequent reactions are often found to co-exist. Thus, to properly investigate down-hole trends in aromatization we must consider only the dihydroporphyrin (viz. phorbides plus chlorins) or porphyrin (viz. free-base plus metallo-species) nature of the macrocycle and *not* exclude the initial metallo-chelates which begin to form towards the completion of mid-diagenesis. Figure 3(a) and (b) are the aromatization trends found when down-hole sequences from the Black Sea (Fig. 3(a): DSDP Site 380A; 42°05.94′ N × 29°36.82′ E, water depth = 2107, see Ross, Neprochnov, *et al.*, 1978) and the Gulf of California (Fig. 3(b): DSDP/IPOD Site 479; 27°50.763′ N × 111°37.492′ W, water depth = 747 m, see Shipboard Party, 1982). Shipboard measurements revealed bottom-water temperatures plus sediment thermal gradients of: 8.4 °C plus ca. 48.8 °C/km (Erickson and Von Herzen, 1978) and 7.9 °C plus *ca.* 95.9 °C/km

(Shipboard Party, 1982), for these Black Sea and Gulf of California sites, respectively. These data were utilized in calculation of the *in situ* sediment temperatures which are co-plotted with sub-bottom depths in Figs 3(a) and (b). In both cases, aromatization was found to begin only when *in situ* temperatures reached approximately 20–25 °C and to be completed by 45–50 °C. The half-life of aromatization (viz. dihydroporphyrins = porphyrins) can be estimated as occurring within these sediments at *ca.* 38–42 °C. The greater depth of burial, within the Black Sea sediments, required for the initiation and completion of aromatization is an overt geochemical manifestation of the lower heat flow at this site, as compared to the Gulf of California sequence. Other salient features of these two studies can be obtained elsewhere (Baker and Louda, 1982; Baker *et al.*, 1978b).

Free-base porphyrins have been isolated from a wide variety of marine sediments and in the main, are only of the DPEP series. Exceptions to this generalization will be pointed out below.

The distribution of free-base porphyrins, both on spatial–temporal and series–homology bases, is extremely important to the understanding of subsequent tetrapyrrole maturation. That is, it is these free-base porphyrin arrays from which the geologic metalloporphyrins (viz. 'petroporphyrins'; see Corwin, 1960) arise. There is, to date, *no* evidence which proves or even strongly implicates, a transmetallation between the magnesium of chlorophyll (or chlorophyllide) and nickel, vanadyl or other metals in the type of sedimentary environment which can be considered as becoming a potential source rock. Therefore, throughout this treatise we shall continue to consider free-base porphyrins as the immediate geochemical precursors to the metalloporphyrins present in sediments, shales, and petroleum crudes.

Table 1 is a compilation of the reports of free-base porphyrin isolates, to date. The 36 isolates listed, with

Table 1

Distribution of geologic free-base porphyrins

Site	Sub-bottom depth, metres[a] (ca. T °C)	Sediment age	Carbon-number distribution and series[b] C range-series [normalized intensities]	DPEP[c] ETIO	=[d] X	References
Serpiano, Switzerland and various in Germany	Unknown (—)	Triassic	Unknown (Various DPEP and ETIO-porphyrins)	—	—	Treibs, 1934 a + b, 1936
Serpiano, Switzerland	Unknown (—)	Triassic	Unknown (DPEP and 'mesoetioporphyrin')	—	—	Blumer and Omenn, 1961
Sea of Japan	175-490 (—)	Pliocene and miocene	Unknown (DPEP dominated)	—	—	Baker and Smith, 1975a
Norwegian-Greenland Sea (Vøring Plateau)	413 (—)	Mid-Miocene	Uknown (DPEP dominated)	—	—	Baker et al., 1976
Cape Basin	1076–1124 (—)	Early Cretaceous	Unknown (DPEP dominated)	—	—	Baker et al., 1978a
Walvis Ridge	140 (—)	Pliocene	C–27 to C–32 DPEP (32/38/51/81/85/100)	—	450.2	Baker et al., 1978a
Angola Basin	1010 (—)	Early Cretaceous	C–29 to C–32 DPEP (8/17/29/100)	—	468.0	Baker et al., 1978a
Cape Verde Basin	650 (—)	Mid-Cretaceous	C–28 to C–32 DPEP (6/18/36/100)	—	466.0	Baker et al., 1978a
Cape Verde Rise	390 (—)	Mid-Eocene	C–28 to C–32 DPEP (10/13/27/51/100)	—	463.2	Baker et al., 1977a
Continental Slope Cape Bojador	340 (—)	Eocene	C–27 to C–32 DPEP (6/34/41/60/63/100)	—	454.3	Baker et al., 1977a
Continental Slope Cape Bojador	450 (—)	Early Cretaceous	C–28 to C–32 DPEP (7/13/27/56/100)	—	463.8	Baker et al., 1977a
Black Sea	500 (33 °C)	Miocene	C–27 to C–32 DPEP (32/49/46/69/72/100)	—	449.2	Baker et al., 1978b
Black Sea	912 (53 °C)	Miocene	C–28 to C–32 DPEP (19/40/34/100/47)	—	454.8	Baker et al., 1978b
Black Sea	1017 (58 °C)	Miocene	C–27 to C–32 DPEP (6/9/26/34/100/46)	—	456.2	Baker et al., 1978b
Black Sea	1062 (60 °C)	Miocene	C–28 to C–32 DPEP (22/37/63/100/94)	—	457.2	Baker et al., 1978b
Bermuda Rise	741 (—)	Late Cretaceous	C–28 to C–32 DPEP (3/7/15/23/100)	—	468.0	Palmer et al., 1979
Blake-Bahama	260–900 (—)	Miocene–Early Cretaceous	5 isolates: DPEP — dominated	—	—	Baker et al., 1978c
Tarfaya Basin	1030 (48°C)	Early Miocene	C–28 to C–32 DPEP (31/44/63/69/100)	—	455.4	Baker and Palmer, 1979

continued on next page

mass spectral data, represent 11 different geographical locations and are Late Quaternary to Early Cretaceous sediments recovered from between 47 and 1115 m, sub-bottom. Except for two cases (viz. San Miguel Gap and the southern rift of the Guaymas), which will be mentioned later, the most apparent fact, stemming from the data given in Table 1, is that *geologic free-base porphyrins are extremely limited homologies of the DPEP series.* Typical distributions include C–28 to C–32 DPEP with maxima at C–32, C–31 or C–30. Further, except in case of high thermal gradients and *in situ* temperatures, greater than 50 °C, there are no free-base porphyrins above C–32 DPEP.

Typical averaged and normalized mass spectral histograms are presented as Figure 4(a) and 4(b), representing free-base porphyrins isolated from Pleistocene greyish–olive diatomaceous mud-oozes recovered from 436 and 394 m sub-bottom respectively,

in the oxygen minimum zone northeast of the Guaymas Basin–Gulf of California (unpublished data; cf. Baker and Louda, 1982). Deposition through anoxic bottom waters coupled with rapid burial, moderate organic carbon content (1.'2–3.5%), and a high thermal gradient (*ca.* 95.9°/km; see Shipboard Party, 1982) afford a distinct possibility for these sediments, upon greater burial, to enter the main zone of oil generation (see Shipboard Party, 1982; cf. Hunt, 1979; Tissot and Welte, 1978). Thus, these examples of sedimentary free-base porphyrins most likely represent the progenitors of petroporphyrins. It should be noted that the examples given (Fig. 4(a) and (b)) contain different carbon-number modes (C–32 versus C–31, respectively), a trait often found when comparing petroleum crudes, source rocks and shales that are known, or suspected to be thermally immature (cf. Baker and Palmer, 1978; Baker et al., 1967; Didyk et al., 1975b;

Table 1 *continued*

Distribution of geologic free-base porphyrins

Site	Sub-bottom depth, metres[a] (ca. 1°C)	Sediment age	Carbon-number distribution and series[b] C range-series [normalized intensities]	DPEP[c]/ETIO	$\overset{=}{\text{X}}$[d]	References
Tarfaya Basin	1068 (50°C)	Early Miocene	C–28 to C–32 DPEP	—	451.1	Baker and Palmer, 1979
			(47/73/100/87/83) (47/73/100/87/83)	—	451.1	Baker and Palmer, 1979
Tarfaya Basin	1115 (52 °C)	Early Miocene	C–28 to C–32 DPEP (57/75/83/97/100)	—	452.5	Baker and Palmer, 1979
Tarfaya Basin	1153 (53 °C)	Early Miocene	C–28 to C–32 DPEP (50/64/79/100/86)	—	452.0	Baker and Palmer, 1979
Japan Trench	47 (<10 °C)	Late Pleistocene (mixed-older)	C–29 to C–32 DPEP (increasing to C–32 Max)	—	—	Baker and Louda, 1980
San Miguel Gap, California borderlands	116–691 (5–47 °C)	Late Pliocene-Late Miocene	11 isolates C–25 to C–32 DPEP with minor amounts ETIO, Maxima at C–30 to C–32 DPEP	4-318	446.4–454.8	Louda and Baker, 1981
Guaymas Basin Slope, Oxygen	343 (41 °C)	Pleistocene	C–27 to C–32 DPEP (2/10/44/68/99/100)	—	458.0	Baker and Louda, 1982
Minimum, Gulf of California	360 (42 °C)	Pleistocene	C–27 to C–32 DPEP (1/13/32/57/100/78)	—	457.9	Baker and Louda, 1982
	394 (46 °C)	Pleistocene	C–27 to C–32 DPEP (4/14/32/55/90/100)	—	458.4	Baker and Louda, 1982
	436 (49 °C)	Pleistocene	C–27 to C–33 DPEP (1/6/22/46/100/91/8) and C–32 to C–33 DiDPEP (4/3)	—	453.1	Baker and Louda, 1982
Guaymas Basin Southern Rift	50 (54 °C)	Late Quaternary	C–27–C–35 DPEP (2/14/33/69/88/100/25/3/1) C–31 to C–35 DiDPEP (3/8/6/1/1) C–27 to C–33 ETIO (6/7/8/9/6/2/1)	8.66 8.66 (9.11)[e]	459.8 459.8	Baker and Louda, 1982

[a] Rounded to nearest metre. Description given is that obtained from the Site Reports published in the appropriate volume (see reference column) of the *initial Reports of the Deep Sea Drilling Project*, US Government Printing Office, Washington, DC.

[b] Determined from 14 eV mass spectra, see text. C–32 DPEP = 476 m/z. C–32 ETIO = 478 m/z. C–32 DiDPEP = 474. m/z. (cf. Baker and Palmer, 1978).

[c] DPEP to ETIO ratio, equal sum of normalized intensities of DPEP divided by the same for the ETIO series. ∞ refers to distributions in which an ETIO component was absent or essentially so (<1%).

[d] $\overset{=}{\text{X}}$, refers to the overall weighted average mass. $\overset{=}{\text{X}} = [\Sigma(IM)_D + \Sigma(IM)_{DiD} + \Sigma(IM)_E / \Sigma ID + \Sigma_{DiD} + \Sigma I_E]$, where I = normalized intensity, M = mass of each series homologic, D = DPEP, DiD = DiDPEP, E = ETIO.

[e] X, Including the DiDPEP component.

Eglinton *et al.*, 1980; Mackenzie *et al.*, 1980).

From the above, it can be surmised that the majority of deviance in the porphyrin distributions found for mature or maturing metalloporphyrins might be due solely to increasing thermal stress and imposed alterations (e.g. ETIO series generation etc., see Catagenesis). While this is primarily true, as will be detailed in a subsequent section, one must contend with the notion of inheritance.

Recently we have characterized a suite of free-base porphyrins which contain both the DPEP and ETIO series and yield DPEP to ETIO ratios between 4.0 and 318.5. These pigments were isolated from Late Pliocene to Late Miocene olive–grey silty to silty-nanno clays and claystones recovered from the San Miguel Gap of the California Borderlands (Louda and Baker, 1981; cf. Shipboard Party, 1981). Representative averaged, normalized and isotopically-corrected mass spectra

histograms for three of these isolates are presented in Fig. 5(a)–(c). The DPEP to ETIO ratios of these free-base porphyrins arrays were found to be 4.0, 20.5 and 237.4, respectively. The mode in all cases, was C–30, C–31 or C–32 DPEP and alkylated members of either series were shown to be absent. When obtaining mass spectra on free-base isolates with DPEP to ETIO ratios over *ca.* 100 to 1, the near trace amounts of the lower carbon-number ETIO-porphyrins (e.g. C–23 to C–25) can only be discerned by extremely carefully controlled volatilization of sample (see Louda and Baker, 1981). The occurrence of free-base ETIO-porphyrins, in any quantity, forces one to consider an inherited DPEP to ETIO ratio. This point will be returned to during consideration of 'immature' geologic nickel porphyrin arrays.

The formation of detectable amounts of ETIO series porphyrins, other than those formed following chelation

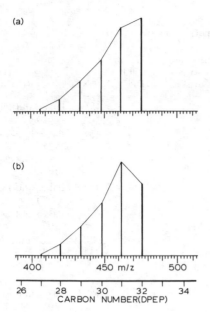

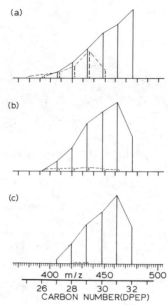

Fig. 4. Averaged, normalized and isotopically corrected low voltage (14 eV) electron impact mass spectra of free-base porphyrins isolated from sediments deposited into the oxygen minimum zone of the Guaymas Basin slope, Gulf of California (cf. Baker and Louda, 1982). (a) C–32 maximized DPEP homology isolated from Pleistocene greyish–olive mud-ooze recovered at 436 m sub-bottom. (b) C–31 maximized DPEP homology isolated from sediments of age and lithology similar to 4a and recovered from 394 m sub-bottom. Geographical setting and lithology is described elsewhere (DSDP/IPOD Leg 64, Silte 479: see Shipboard Party, 1982).

Fig. 5. Averaged, normalized and isotopically corrected mass spectral (14 eV, EIMS) histograms of various free-base porphyrin isolates from the San Miguel Gap, California Borderlands (DSDP/IPOD Leg 63; Site 467: see Louda and Baker, 1981; Shipboard Party, 1981). Solid lines, DPEP series; dashed lines, ETIO series. (a) Isolate from an upper Pliocene olive–grey siliceous silty clay recovered at 165 m sub-bottom. DPEP to ETIO ratio equals 4.0. (b) Isolate from an upper Pliocene olive–grey foraminiferous quartzose-feldspathic sandy silt recovered at 233 m sub-bottom. DPEP to ETIO ratio equals 20.5. (c) Isolate from an upper Miocene olive–grey silty claystone recovered at 446 meters sub-bottom. DPEP to ETIO ratio equals 237.4, essentially infinity (cf. Fig. 4(b)).

and subsequent thermal rupture of the isocyclic-ring, has been alluded to earlier within the section on 'Early-diagenesis'. That is, it is theoretically plausible to evolve small amounts of ETIO-porphyrins from originally large amounts of autochthonous chlorophyll if this material were deposited into oxygenated bottom waters and sediments. The geologic history of the California borderland site, mentioned above, is well outside the scope of this paper. However, it appears that extreme sea-level fluctuations, oceanic transgression and regression, and changes in the oxygen-minimum zone could have yielded just such a setting (see Louda and Baker, 1981 and references therein). Given sufficient input, surviving chlorins, which were originally formed via early oxidative reactions, and intact phorbides might well undergo aromatization and yield the free-base prophyrin arrays described above. The input of autochthonous chlorophyll as chlorins (viz. isocyclic-ring opened) may also occur via resedimentation processes (e.g. turbidites, slumping). Further, the existence of free-base ETIO-porphyrins may, in part, reflect totally allochthonous pigments, such as the coincident highly dealkylated copper and nickel ETIO-porphyrins do. The overall depositional environment and organic matter source at the San Miguel Gap was determined to consist primarily of the anoxic (i.e. sediment–water interface) deposition of autochthonous material to which varying degrees of terrestrial materials were admixed (see Gilbert and Summerhayes, 1981; Rullkotter et al., 1981; Simoneit and Mazurek, 1981; and Whelan and Hunt, 1981). Though the above

hypotheses (cf. Louda and Baker, 1981) require much further testing, the occurrence of geologic free-base ETIO-porphyrins is now a fact.

In the main, metal chelation by geologic free-base porphyrins precedes, temporally and thermally, the appearance of the higher alkyl homologues (i.e. C no. > 32) and the alternate (viz. non-DPEP) series, such as DiDPEP and ETIO. The occurrence of free-base ETIO-porphyrins, presumed to be formed via oxidative reactions during early diagenesis, was detailed above.

To date, we have found only one major exception to the lack of the higher alkyl homologues (> C–32) in free-base porphyrin isolates. The isolate in question was from a late Quaternary olive–grey nanno-daitomaceous ooze recovered from the southern rift of the Guaymas Basin in the Gulf of California (Fig. 6, see Baker and Louda, 1982; Scientific Party, 1982). Though a down-profile is not possible, since an igneous sill *ca.* 91 m below the sample in question has pyrolysed all tetrapyrrole pigments beneath it, aromatization in this sample was found to be only *ca.* 75% completed, even though an *in situ* temperature of approximately 52–54 °C exists. The sill, mentioned above, has not greatly altered tetrapyrrole diagenesis in this sample due to the fact that these sediments were deposited after the igneous event (see Shipboard Party, 1982). However, extremely rapid sedimentation (*ca.* 300–1000 m/my) and a high thermal gradient (14 HFU), due to the proximity of an active margin (Shipboard Party, 1982), yields an

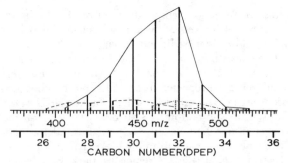

Fig. 6. Averaged, normalized and isotopically corrected low voltage (14 eV) mass spectral histogram of free-base porphyrins isolated from a late Quaternary olive–grey nanno-diatomaceous ooze. Sample recovered from 49.8 m sub-bottom near the southern rift of the Guaymas Basin, Gulf of California, and having an *in situ* temperature of *ca*. 52–54 °C (see Shipboard Party, 1982). Solid lines, DPEP series; dashed lines, ETIO series; dotted plus dashed lines, DiDPEP series.

excellent example of rapid (viz. short term–high temperature) diagenesis. As stated, this sample at 49.8 m sub-bottom yielded 25% defunctionalized phorbides and 75% free-base porphyrins. A less deeply buried sample (viz. 30.7 m sub-bottom, *in situ* T = 24 °C) was found to be dominated by phorbides with only a trace (<1% of total tetrapyrroles) of free-base porphyrins detectable. Review of Fig. 3(a) and (b) will show that aromatization in the present sample is progressing at much higher temperatures (>50° versus <40°) than is required for completion of this reaction within geologically older sediments. This is marked adherence to the time–temperature relationships of organic reaction rates. Further, this compliance of a geochemical reaction with reaction rate laws, worked out *in vitro*, reveals that we are indeed investigating ordered and predictable phenomena.

The most peculiar facet of the free-base porphyrins isolated from the above sample is that detectable amounts of C–33 through C–35 DPEP, C–31 through C–35 DiDPEP, and C–26 through C–33 ETIO-porphyrins are present, in addition to the 'normal' C–27 to C–32 DPEP homology (Fig. 6; cf. Table 1). This array yielded a DPEP (plus DiDPEP) to ETIO ratio of 9:11. That alkylation, or release from an alkyl-linked state (cf. Baker *et al.*, 1977; Louda and Baker, 1981; Mackenzie *et al.*, 1980), has preceded chelation is, at present, an enigma. One may only speculate that local depletion of the metals (esp. Ni) amenable for chelation has occurred (e.g. hydrothermal circulation; see Shipboard Party, 1982), or that the time factor for chelation is such that chelation has not yet begun. These possibilities are presently under further study and, to date, one is not favoured over the other. It must be stressed that the occurrence of this single free-base porphyrin isolate (Fig. 6) is by no means an example of the norm (cf. Figs 4 and 5). That is, this one isolate, out of a total of thirty-six thus far (see Table 1), is truly an exception.

The thermally induced appearance of the higher alkyl homologues of DPEP and DiDPEP and the initiation of ETIO series generation, presumed not to be an inheritance phenomenon, vividly points out the fact that, as mid-diagenesis (aromatization) nears completion and late-diagenesis (chelation)-catagenesis

(alteration) ensues, considerable overlap is possible, and occurs, within the maturational continua of geologic tetrapyrroles.

In general, we now see that the most common sequence of chlorophyll geochemistry leads through a mid-diagenesis stage which evolves a limited homology (r.g. C–27 through C–32) of DPEP-type porphyrins. These reactions are found to transform defunctionalized phorbides into free-base porphyrins through an *in situ* temperature range of *ca*. 20–45 °C, for Pleistocene or older sediments of moderate thermal profiles (e.g. <100 °C/km) and rates of sediment accumulation (e.g. <150 m/my).

LATE-DIAGENESIS; CHELATION

Geologic porphyrins attain longer-term stability, that is, resist total destruction and removal from the fossil record, through the chelation of metals. Metals known to be complexed with geologic porphyrins include nickel [Ni^{+2}], vanadium [V^{+4}, as $V=O$ ...], copper [Cu^{+2}], and gallium [Ga^{+3}, as GaOH ...], (see, e.g.: Baker and Palmer, 1978; Bonnet and Czechowski, 1980; Hodgson *et al.* 1967; Louda and Baker, 1981; Palmer and Baker, 1978; Treibs, 1936). The best known and most widely studied geologic metalloporphyrins are the nickel and vanadyl 'petroporphyrins' (see e.g.: Baker and Palmer, 1978; Dunning, 1963; Glebovskaya and Volkenshtein, 1948; Mackenzie *et al.*, 1980). The present section will be limited to the nickel and vanadyl species as they more directly relate to marine sediments, shales and petroleum crudes.

The formation of the nickel and vanadyl porphyrins now appears to occur via alternate, yet mostly analogous, routes. That is, it is becoming increasingly clear that nickel porphyrins arise and exist with sediments primarily as free, or solvent extractable, species. On the other hand, vanadyl porphyrins appear to form in a bound, or non-extractable, form linked to large geochemical complexes, such as kerogen (?), until the imposed thermal stress is such that alkyl linkages are broken (viz. cracking). Only lately has the nature of immature vanadyl porphyrins come to light (Baker *et al.*, 1977; Louda and Baker, 1981; Mackenzie *et al.*, 1980). Accordingly, the formation of nickel and of vanadyl porphyrins in geologic settings will be covered separately. It should be remembered that both species are usually present in more thermally mature situations.

Nickel porphyrins

The generation of nickel chelates, from free-base porphyrins, within marine sediments was first observed during an investigation on the tetrapyrrole pigments in the Early Cretaceous to Early Miocene calcareous dark grey muds of the Tarfaya Basin, eastern South Atlantic (Baker and Palmer, 1979). Only recently have we re-evaluated these data and coupled the same with the reported thermal profile (viz. bottom water = 4.75 °C plus sub-botton gradient = 42 °C/km; von Rad, Ryan *et al.*, 1979).

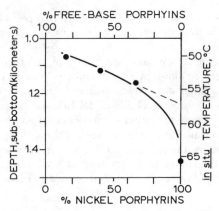

Fig. 7. Tetrapyrrole chelation profile obtained by plotting percent free-base porphyrins, alternately percent metalloporphyrins, versus sub-bottom depth and present *in situ* temperatures for the Tarfaya Basin (cf. Baker and Palmer, 1979; Von Rad, Ryan, *et al.*, 1979). The dotted line indicates chelation probably completed within sediments presently at *ca.* 57 °C. The upper three samples have been reported to contain Type II kerogen, while the lower is predominately Type III (Deroo *et al.*, 1979).

The chelation of nickel is plotted for this sedimentary sequence (Fig. 7) by considering the sum of free-base plus nickel porphyrins to be 100%. That is, the presence of phorbides and chlorins in the less mature samples is ignored. This effectively eliminates the overlap of diagenetic stages stressed earlier, even though the same trend, yet with different numbers, would be observed. From these data, it is found that the realm of most active chelation (viz. Ni) falls into a temperature range of approximately 50–60 °C for this sedimentary profile. Though the initiation of this reactution was not observed, due to simple spacing, one might well expect a gradual beginning, such as observed for aromatization.

Thus, an initiation temperature, of *ca.* 45 °C for the chelation of nickel by free-base porphyrins within Miocene, or older, sediments is suggested.

The coexistence of nickel and free-base porphyrins, suggesting that portions of the chelation process were found, has been reported from studies on the Pliocene–Miocene calcareous dark grey shales of the Black Sea (*ca.* 680–1062 m, sub-bottom; T~40–60 °C, cf. Erickson and Von Hersen, 1978; Baker *et al.*, 1978b) and the mid-Cretaceous black clays from the Blake–Bahama plateau (Baker *et al.*, 1978c). Cretaceous dark gray shales recovered from the continental margin off Morocco yielded only nickel porphyrins (Palmer and Baker, 1980). This latter case appears to be one in which the chelation of nickel is complete and *in situ* thermal stress has not reached the point at which vanadyl porphyrins, if present, are released from a bound state (e.g. kerogen), as will be discussed in the next section.

Recently we have examined 16 samples from the San Miguel Gap of the California borderlands. These samples were of Quaternary to mid-Miocene ages, represent a sediment accumulation of over 1035 m and the thermal gradient was found to be 63 °C/km, plus a bottom-water temperature of 4.5 °C (Shipboard Party, 1981). During initial tetrapyrrole analyses (viz. before mass spectrometry) the quality and quantity of pigment isolates relies solely on electronic spectroscopy and physiochemical behavious patterns (e.g. acid extraction, chromatography). Free-base and metalloporphyrins (viz. nickel or nickel-like) are easily separated quantified by such procedures (see e.g. Baker and Palmer, 1978). Thus, the data from the San Miguel Gap analyses, following quantification, was plotted versus sub-bottom depth and *in situ* temperatures. This preliminary descriptive profile of the chelation process is given here as Fig. 8(a). Immediately obvious from this profile is the marked bimodal, and unexpected, nature of this trend.

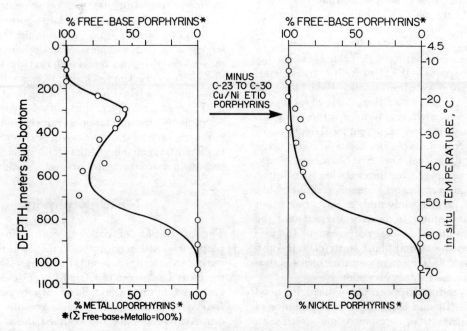

Fig. 8. The uncorrected and corrected profiles of chelation for the San Miguel Gap, California Borderlands (see Louda and Baker, 1981). Left-hand figure includes all metallo-porphyrin species. Right-hand figure is the corrected chelation profile obtained following subtraction of an allochthonous component of highly dealkylated copper and nickel ETIO-porphyrins (cf. Fig. 9 and text).

However, following mass spectrometric analyses, the presence of highly dealkylated copper and nickel ETIO-porphyrins in the sediment samples from 233 to 542 m sub-bottom, inclusive, was found. Since the copper ETIO-porphyrins have been isolated from numerous sites in the Black Sea and the Atlantic and have been linked to inputs of previously oxidized terrestrial organic matter (Palmer and Baker, 1978), we proceeded to totally dissect these metalloporphyrin arrays in an effort to discern autochthonous from allochthonous pigments. Following this process, described below, the chelation reaction was replotted, this time including only the DPEP and traces of the higher alkyl ETIO-members of the nickel species. The resultant plot, Fig. 8(b), reveals the actual *in situ* chelation profile. Thus, chelation for the San Miguel Gap site is found to be occurring within Miocene sediments exposed to *in situ* temperatures between 40 and 60 °C (Louda and Baker, 1981).

Only a short description of the mass spectrometric dissection of mixed assemblages of copper and nickel porphyrins will be presented, as this is given in detail elsewhere (Louda and Baker, 1981). Electronic spectra give the initial clues to the presence of copper porphyrins in a metalloporphyrin isolate (cf. Palmer and Baker, 1978). That is, the copper chelates exhibit the main absorption bands (viz. Soret or γ, β and α) at slightly longer wavelengths than the nickel species.* Once an average-normalized mass spectrum has been obtained, with extreme care to record the *entire* volatility range, isotopic correction for these predominately bi-isotopic metals must be made (see Baker and Palmer, 1978; Louda and Baker, 1981). The resultant corrected mass spectrum of a mixed copper and nickel porphyrin isolate, prior to isotopic correction, is given as Fig. 9(a). Next, the spectrum is corrected for isotopic overlap and each series (viz. CuETIO, NiETIO, NiDPEP) is normalized unto itself (Figs 9(b–c)). Lastly, co-plotting the homologies of Cu and Ni ETIO-porphyrins by carbon-number (Fig. 9(b)) allows one to realize that these highly dealkylated ETIO-porphyrins derive from the same source and that this source is different than from the coincident NiDPEP series (Fig. 9(c)). It should be noted that any overlap between Ni–ETIO porphyrins from the suggested allochthonous grouping and those formed *in situ* from the NiDPEP series (viz. C–28 to C–30) is presently impossible to dissect further. Therefore, only the higher alkyl members of the nickel-ETIO porphyrin homology (e.g. C–30 to C–32), and which do not match the copper ETIO series, are included in the suggested autochthonous assemblage with the nickel DPEP homology (see Louda and Baker, 1981).

The above scenario, reveals that, in addition to the highly dealkylated copper ETIO–porphyrins (cf. Palmer and Baker, 1978), a coincident and

---

* Sample absorption maxima of selected authentic standards recorded in benzene solvent. Maxima in ethyl ether are *ca.* 1–5 nm lower (i.e. hyposochromic).

Copper DPE·ME:402.0, 526.0, 563.5 nm
Copper ETIO-I:399.5, 526.0, 562.5 nm
Nickel DPEP:396.0, 517.0, 554.5 nm
Nickel, OEP:393.5, 517.5, 552.5 nm

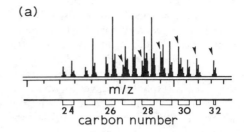

(a)

m/z

24 26 28 30 32
carbon number

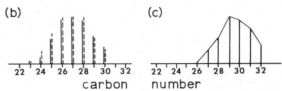

(b) (c)

22 24 26 28 30 32   22 24 26 28 30 32
carbon   number

Fig. 9. Dissection of a copper plus nickel porphyrin assemblage isolated from an upper Miocene olive–grey silty claystone recovered from 446 m sub-bottom at the San Miguel Gap, California Borderlands (see Louda and Baker, 1981; Shipboard Party, 1982). (a) Normalized average mass spectral (14 eV, EIMS) distribution of the total metalloporphyrin isolate. Arrows indicate the position of the Ni[58]–DPEP series, for reference. (b) Copper (dashed lines) and nickel (solid lines) ETIO-porphyrins following isotopic correction,* normalization of each to itself, and co-plotted by carbon-number. (c) Nickel DPEP series normalized to itself, following isotopic correction.*
* Ni–60 = 0.386 × Ni–58; Cu–65 – 0.447 × Cu–63; (M + 2) . .
= 1.10 times the carbon number, divided by 200 (cf. Biemann, 1962).

corresponding array of nickel chelates are most likely also derived from a source which has undergone prior maturation (e.g. terrestrial: Louda and Baker, 1981). However, the recognition of these allochthonous pigments requires the 'handle' provided by the presence of the copper species. Further, the coexistence of copper and nickel porphyrins, without an examination of the mass spectral distributions of each series, does not provide the data required to show possible copper to nickel transmetallation, especially if bitumen is passed over copper to remove sulphur (see Galimov *et al.*, 1980). The large disparities found between the highly dealkylated nickel and copper ETIO–porphyrin homologies and those of the nickel DPEP (including the higher carbon-number nickel ETIO–porphyrins) and free-base porphyrins of a given sediment sample (see Louda and Baker, 1981) strongly reinforces the suggested (cf. Palmer and Baker, 1978) allochthonous and autochthonous sources, respectively, of these pigments.

In general, the investigations described above reveal that the generation of nickel porphyrins (viz. chelation), from free-base porphyrins, is most active, in the Pliocene to Cretaceous sediments studied, when *in situ* temperatures of 45–55 °C are reached. Likewise, the chelation of nickel is found to be essentially completed once temperatures near and exceed 60 °C.

Vanadyl porphyrins

The actual *in situ* chelation of vanadium (viz. vanadyl)

is, at present, rather much of an enigma. That is, a gradual transition of free-base to vanadyl porphyrins has not been observed. To date, only five co-isolations of free-base and vanadyl porphyrins are known, and no trend was revealed, due to sample spacing. In each case these samples were deeply buried, yet thermally immature, Cretaceous shales and were retrieved from the Cape and Angola Basins (Baker et al., 1978a) and the Bermuda Rise (Palmer et al., 1979).

Vanadyl porphyrins, when co-isolated with free-base porphyrins or from known thermally immature sources, more closely resemble what one might expect an immature metalloporphyrin to be, than do the coincident nickel chelates mentioned earlier. That is, immature vanadyl porphyrins consist only of a limited homology of the DPEP series (see Baker et al., 1978a; cf. Didyk et al., 1975b; Palmer et al., 1979), and thus resemble free-base porphyrin distributions more closely. These appear to be examples of vanadyl porphyrins forming in an analogous matter to the chelation of nickel. Specifically, forming as free or solvent-extractable species. The more common isolation of vandyl porphyrins occurs from sediments which have undergone a moderate degree of thermal stress, as detailed below. That is, they appear to be released from a bound state (cf. Baker et al., 1978a; Louda and Baker, 1981; Mackenzie et al., 1980).

The investigation of the San Miguel Gap sediments, described earlier, yielded only one vanadyl porphyrin isolate (Fig. 10). This pigment array was isolated from the most deeply buried sample of the suite studied. This sediment was a mid-Miocene olive-grey calcareous silty claystone recovered from 1035 m sub-bottom and is calculated to have a present in situ temperature of ca. 67 °C (see Louda and Baker, 1981; Shipboard Party, 1981). Less deeply buried strata ($d < 912$ m), with temperatures below 62 °C, were found to be void of detectable vanadyl porphyrins. Since the chelation of nickel had depleted the available free-base supply within the overlying sediments (viz. between 800 and 850 m, the last sample with and the first sample lacking free-base porphyrins), it appears that the vanadyl porphyrins had formed in a

bound non-extractable state. That is, the tetrapyrrole precursors may become bound into a large organic complex (e.g. asphaltene, kerogen) at an earlier stage and then chelate vanadyl, or, the chelation process may be coincident with the complexation into a macromolecular state. In either case, the lock between porphyrin and some unknown portion of a general organic matrix (e.g. kerogen) appears to be via free-radical alkyl linkages. The free-radical nature of this linkage is suggested by the fact that n-alkyl substitution patterns dominate the geologic porphyrins (see Baker and Palmer, 1978; Barwise and Whitehead, 1980; Mackenzie et al., 1980; Quirke et al., 1979). Recently a minor series of porphyrins with a methyl branched-alkyl substitution has been found. However, the methyl branch is at the terminal portion of the substituent (Quirke et al., 1980) and, therefore, the suggested free-radical attachment to porphyrin β-pyrrole positions or substituents still appears valid.

The in vitro rates of formation for various metalloporphyrins (i.e. $Cu > Ni > V = 0$; Corwin, 1964; Erdman et al., 1957) are such that vanadyl porphyrins should form in sediments only after the more rapidly chelated metals become locally limited or an alternate geochemical mechanism enhances reaction between vanadyl and porphyrin. It is known that there is a general, yet hardly direct, correlation between high sulphur–high asphaltene petroleums and source rocks and increased vanadyl, related to nickel, porphyrin content (see e.g. Dunning and Moore, 1957; Eglinton et al., 1980; Hodgson et al., 1963, 1967). Does, then, sulphur act as a geochemical catalyst during the formation of vanadyl porphyrins. Resulting from ESR studies on vanadyl porphyrin rich asphaltenes, it has been suggested that 1S:3 N tetradentate ligands form between sulphur compounds (e.g. thiophenes) and porphyrin nitrogens, about an included vanadyl radical (Yen et al., 1969). Such observations may well explain the chelation of vanadyl but not the vastly extended alkyl homologies of the resultant vanadyl porphyrins. However, it is likewise possible that the chelation of vanadyl occurs with prophyrins that are bound into such macromolecular complexes via alkyl linkages, as mentioned above. The interaction of these two processes, namely sulphur enhanced chelation of vanadyl and alkyl-linked porphyrins, appears, at present, the most plausible interpretation of vanadyl porphyrin generation.

Related studies exist in the literature and lend support to a release mechanism concept for the generation of vanadyl porphyrins. Vanadyl porphyrins, especially those higher in the DPEP series and being of extended alkyl homologies, were found to increase in relative abundance in parallel to an increasing depth of burial (alt. thermal) contuum for the Toarcian shales of the Paris Basin (Mackenzie et al., 1980). Similar results were found for upper Cretaceous black shales from the Cape Verde Rise. In this latter case the gradient of maximum thermal stress was of short duration and reversed, with respect to depth of burial, by the implacement of an igneous sill over the samples studied (Baker et al., 1977, 1978d).

The predominance of n-alkyl substitution within the

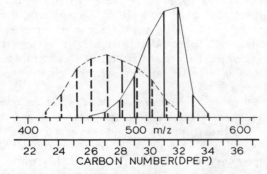

Fig. 10. Normalized, averaged and isotopically corrected mass spectral (14 eV-EIMS) histogram of vanadyl porphyrins isolated from a mid-Miocene olive–grey silty claystone recovered from 1035 m, sub-bottom at the San Miguel Gap, California Borderlands (see Louda and Baker, 1981; Shipboard Party, 1981). Solid lines, DPEP series; dashed lines, ETIO series. DPEP to ETIO ratio equals 1.04.

vanadyl porphyrins, discussed earlier, has led to the suggestion that these alkyl linkages may form via anti-Markovnikov addition at the vinyl moiety inherited from chlorophyll (Mackenzie *et al.*, 1980; Quirke *et al.*, 1979). An early incorporation of tetrapyrrole into a non-extractable organic melange is not at all unlikely. Supporting these concepts are the repeated isolations of a tetrapyrrole pigment or complex which we have labelled 'chlorin-660' (see e.g. Baker and Louda, 1980a, 1982; Louda and Baker, 1981; Louda *et al.*, 1980). This pigment, 'chlorin-660', has proven impossible, to date, to purify, as judged by the presence of a high mixed hydrocarbon-aromatic like background (i.e. generally decreasing absorption from 350 to 800 nm). Further, 'chlorin-660' is always isolated from the fastest migrating (viz. solvent front) fraction during GPC over Sephadex LH-20$^{(R)}$, thus suggesting a molecular weight over 4000 daltons. Electronic spectra of 'chlorin-660' (i.e. band-I = 660 nm $\pm$ 1) is not at all unlike those of various immature humic acid fractions (see e.g. Brassell *et al.*, 1980) and such a complexation would also explain reports that chlorophyll derivatives '... move from the humic to solvent-soluble fractions during diagenesis' (Sato, 1980).

The possibility that such tetrapyrrole containing complexes or geopolymers may form from residues of, or non-degraded, thylalkoids and other chloroplast remnants might well deserve investigation. That is, enhanced preservation of chlorophyll derivatives contained within blue–green algal cells, when compared to free ('neat') chlorophyll, has been observed (Oehler *et al.*, 1974). Fossil tetrapyrrole pigments have also been reported to extent to very high molecular weights (e.g. >1100 daltons) and as dimers and 'complexes' in various shales (Blumer and Rudrum, 1970; Blumer and Snyder, 1967).

The release or appearance of vanadyl porphyrins, as monomeric entities amenable to analysis, is found to occur only after their host environment (e.g. sediment) has been exposed to thermal stress sufficient enough to initiate the breakage (viz. cracking) of the suggested porphyrin-to-organic (asphaltene, kerogen) alkyl linkages. For the mid-Miocene sediments of the San Miguel Gap, discussed above, the requisite *in situ* temperature was found to be 65 °C.

The transition from late diagenesis (chelation) to the initial phases of catagenesis (alteration) is the most vague, due to overlapping reactions, and therefore hardest to delineate. Even though we are dealing with a continuum, we have arbitrarily placed the dividing line between late-diagenesis and catagenesis as follows: The end of tetrapyrrole late-diagenesis is now taken as that point in the time–temperature profile of geologic metalloporphyrin evolution at which all available free-base porphyrins have been chelated, nickel porphyrins are beginning maturation (viz. DPEP to ETIO conversion) and the initial release of vanadyl porphyrins has occurred. In reference to the initial vanadyl porphyrins, these are usually found to be limited homologies (e.g. C–27 to *ca.* C–34) of both series (cf. Louda and Baker, 1981) with increasing amounts of the DPEP series being added as release of the vanadyl chelates continues (see Mackenzie *et al.*, 1980).

CATAGENESIS: THERMAL ALTERATION

Maturing metalloporphyrins which have entered the stage of catagenesis are undergoing alkylation (viz. continued release of the higher alkyl homologues), dealkylation, ETIO series generation and the appearance of the alternate series (i.e. DiDPEP and Benz-porphyrins) occurs.

Increasing thermal stress leads to the appearance of the higher alkyl homologues of both nickel and vanadyl porphyrins. The extent of nickel porphyrin alkylation above C–32 is extremely limited and usually only homologues up to C–34, and rarely C–36, species are found (cf. Baker and Palmer, 1978; Louda and Baker, 1981; Mackenzie *et al.*, 1980). Vanadyl porphyrins, on the other hand, exhibit alkylation patterns up to C–50 and higher (see Baker and Palmer, 1978; Baker *et al.*, 1967; Barwise and Whitehead, 1980; Mackenzie *et al.*, 1980), though the relative abundance of members above C–38 to C–42 is often quite low.

During the initial characterization of petroporphyrins the term 'transalkylation' was invoked in order partially to explain the alkyl extension of porphyrin homologies (Baker *et al.*, 1967). This was not then, nor since, meant to infer alkyl transfer from porphyrin to porphyrin, though this is the only explanation for alkyl extension during *in vitro* experiments with porphyrins as the sole organic (see Bonnett *et al.*, 197s). Thus, we now suggest that the argumentative word 'transalkylation' be dropped from usage and the term alkylation–dealkylation be invoked to describe these separate processes.

Release of the higher alkyl homologues of vanadyl porphyrins apparently continues until all are present as monomeric forms and the alkylation pattern has maximixed. Following this phase of maximal alkylation, dealkylation then becomes the dominate force and these vanadyl homologies shorten with the ETIO series becoming dominant (see Baker *et al.*, 1977; Mackenzie *et al.*, 1980).

Concurrent with patterns of alkylation and dealkylation the appearance of the alternate series (viz. DiDPEP and Benz-porphyrins) usually have appeared and have presumably been generated while porphyrins resided in the bound non-extractable state. The generation of Benz-porphyrins (see Appendix) has been suggested as being by Diels-Alder additions with compounds such as quinones (Baker and Palmer, 1978) or by condensation of side chains during diagenesis (Barwise and Whitehead, 1980). It should be noted that only recently has the proposed benz-porphyrin structure of the 'petro-rhodoporphyrins' (Baker *et al.*, 1967) been proven by the identification of phthalamides after analytical oxidation of Boscan rhodoporphyrins (Barwise and Whitehead, 1980).

The proposed di-DPEP or di-cycloethano-porphyrins (cf. Baker *et al.*, 1967; Barwise and Whitehead, 1980; Yen *et al.*, 1969: see Appendix) awaits verification. Presently, the DiDPEP series is viewed as that series of porphyrin ions in low voltage (12–14 eV) mass spectra which is two mass units lower than the corresponding DPEP compound. The possibility of forming tetrapyrroles containing two isocyclic-rings is not without precedent. During a structural study on the *Chlorobium*-chlorophylls-660 it was reported that reflux in benzene and toluene-*p*-sulphonic acid led to an α-ethylenepheophorbide. Further, this compound, cyclized between the 2-α-hydroxy-ethyl substituent and the α-methine bridge, formed only with the 660 (viz. δ-meso-alkylated) series of *Chlorobium* chlorophylls (Kenner *et al.*, 1978). Thus, meso-alkylation at the δ-bridge, the most available for electrophilic substitution (esp. chlorins: see Furhop, 1975; Zernes and Gouterman, 1966) may aid in the geologic generation of the DiDPEP series. Meso-alkyl substituents have been found not to occur in certain geologic porphyrins viz. the lacustrine Gilsonite (Quirke *et al.*, 1979, 1980a, c), but the DiDPEP series has not yet received such comprehensive examination.

While the DiDPEP and Benz-porphyrin analogues of DPEP and ETIO occur in both vanadyl and nickel porphyrin arrays the generation of considerable amounts of these alternate series appears to be primarily a phenomenon of vanadyl porphyrin geochemistry. Generally nickel porphyrins contain more DiDPEP than benz-porphyrins (see Louda and Baker, 1981; cf. Barwise and Whitehead, 1980).

Concurrent with end of late diagenesis and the alkylation of early catagenesis ETIO series porphyrins are formed from the DPEP series. Emerging from the earliest studies on geologic porphyrins, the ETIO series was considered to be derived from heme-based pigments (see e.g. Dunning and Moore, 1957; Treibs, 1936). Following the suggestion that a geochemical DPEP to ETIO crossover could occur (Corwin, 1960), and the finding that the retort of oil-shale led to increased ETIO–porphyrin content, at the expense of the DPEP series, in the resultant shale-oil (Morandi and Jensen, 1966), the DPEP to ETIO ratio grained favour an indicator of thermal history (Alturki *et al.*, 1972; Baker, 1969; Baker and Palmer, 1978; Didyk *et al.*, 1975b). While we have recently shown that free-base ETIO–porphyrins are present in certain sedimentary environments (Louda and Baker, 1981), presumably derived from early oxidative reactions (cf. Baker and Louda, 1980a, b and in press), the vast majority of ETIO series generation is thermal and occurs during the maturation of metalloporphrins. This is substantiated by the fact that anoxic deposition, presumably favouring petroleum generation in marine sedimentary environments, leads to only free-base porphyrins of the DPEP series (Baker and Louda, 1982; Baker *et al.*, 1980b) and therefore DPEP dominated metalloporphyrins. That increasing thermal stress leads to the continued generation of ETIO series porphyrins, at the expense of the DPEP analogues, is confirmed by *in vitro* heating experiments (Didyk *et al.*, 1975) and porphyrin analyses of samples and sample suites with known thermal histories and depth of burial continua (see Baker and Louda, 1982; Baker *et al.*, 1977, 1978a, c; Didyk *et al.*, 1975a, b; Louda and Baker, 1981; Mackenzie *et al.*, 1980).

The DPEP to ETIO ratio of nickel porphyrins isolated from several suites of marine sediment samples plotted versus sub-bottom depth, is presented here as Fig. 11. The dotted line denoting a DPEP to ETIO ratio

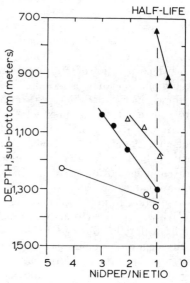

Fig. 11. ETIO series generation. Plot of the DPEP to ETIO ratios of various nickel porphyrin isolates from several Atlantic dark green and black shales versus sub-bottom depth. *Solid triangles*, late Cretaceous samples from the Bermuda Rise (Palmer *et al.*, 1979); *Open triangles*, early Cretaceous samples from the Cape Basin (Baker *et al.*, 1977); *Solid circles*, early Miocene samples from the Tarfaya Basin (Baker and Palmer, 1979; *Open circles*, early Cretaceous samples from the continental margin South of Morocco (Palmer and Baker, 1980). Temperature range for the Tarfara Basin samples (solid circles) is calculated at *ca.* 45–60 °C (cf. Von Rad, Ryan *et al.*, 1979). Half-life (dashed line) is that point when the amount of DPEP is equal to the amount of ETIO series porphyrins (viz. 50% conversion, DPEP to ETIO ratio equal to unity).

(i.e. D/E) equal to unity is given as the half-life, that is 50% conversion to DPEP to ETIO. The overall conversion of the metallo-DPEP series to metallo-ETIO porphyrins, in response to increasing depth of burial (alt. temperature) within marine sedimentary environments, is easily recognized from these data. It should be noted that these profiles are for the nickel chelates which, as pointed out above and previously (Baker *et al.*, 1977; Mackenzie *et al.*, 1980), mature more rapidly than the vanadyl species. The intercept of the DPEP to ETIO ratio at its half-life, as well as the slope (viz. rate) of this change, is taken as reflecting the thermal gradient of the host environment. At the present further study and back-up data (e.g. *in situ* temperatures) are required to characterize adequately these time–temperature relationships and to ascertain the possible catalytic effects of sediment lithology, kerogen types, water contents or combinations of these. From the temperature profile of the Tarfaya Basin samples (Early Miocene, calcareous dark shales) it is found that these sediments had an *in situ* temperature range of *va.* 45–60 °C (cf. Baker and Palmer, 1979; von Rad, Ryan, *et al.*, 1979). Thus, the half-life of the NiDPEP to NiETIO conversion might be expected to occur in Miocene sediments at approximately 60–65 °C. Indeed, nickel porphyrins from the Miocene strata of the San Miguel Gap presently at *ca.* 67 °C revealed a DPEP–ETIO ratio of 0.92 (Louda and Baker, 1981).

Dealkylation becomes a dominant process during the

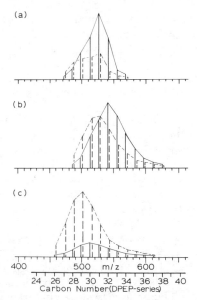

Fig. 12. Maturational changes in the vanadyl porphyrins isolated from selected petroleum crudes (compiled from the data given by Baker *et al.*, 1967). Mass spectral histograms of the two main series: solid lines, DPEP; dashed lines, ETIO. Top: Beldridge petroleum, a Pliocene formation in California (USA), C–31 DPEP maximum, DPEP to ETIO ratio (D/E) equals 1.9 (early Catagenesis). Middle: Boscan petroleum from the Maraciabo Basin of Venezuela, Cretaceous, C–32 DPEP maximum, D/E = 1.2 (Mid-Catagenesis). Bottom: Baxterville petroleum, a Cretaceous formation from Mississippi (USA), C–29 ETIO maximum, D/E = 0.27 (Late Catagenesis to very early Metagenesis).

later phases of catagenesis with the result of lowering the weighted average mass of porphyrin homologies and shifting the mode to lower carbon-numbers. *In vitro* heating experiments with petroporphyrin assemblages have shown the overlap of the DPEP to ETIO conversion and dealkylation (Didyk *et al.*, 1975b) and the random dealkylation of synthetic vanadyl etioporphyrin-I (Yen *et al.*, 1969). Comparisons of maturational profiles of metalloporphyrins in proximity to an igneous sill (Baker *et al.*, 1977) and throughout increasing depth of burial continua (Mackenzie *et al.*, 1980) have confirmed the continued ETIO series generation and dealkylation of these pigments in more thermally stressed geologic settings.

Marine sediment sample suites entering, or in, the stage of organic catagenesis are often difficult to obtain. That is, within such sediments the potential for hydrocarbon generation–accumulation is greatest (cf. Hunt, 1979; Tissot and Welte, 1978) and the sampling programme of DSDP and IPOD, without riser capability, must avoid such situations (Baker and Louda, 1980b). However, a comparison of vanadyl porphyrin distributions from selected petroleum crudes will serve well to illustrate the progress of tetrapyrrole catagenesis. Figure 12 is a comparison of the vanadyl porphyrins reported from three petroleum crudes (after Baker *et al.*, 1967), the minor DiDPEP and Benz-porphyrin series are omitted for clarity. The Pliocene Belridge crude of California (Fig. 12(a)) yielded only a limited (viz. C–26 to C–34) distribution of each

porphyrin series and represents thermally immature tetrapyrroles which are most likely just beginning the release of the higher alkyl homologues. This is also suggested as being an expression of the time factor (viz. lack of) required for the completion of alkylation (viz. release of vanadyl prophyrins). The Cretaceous Boscan (Venezuela) sample, on the other hand, yields homologies of each series extending to C–38 (Fig. 12(b)). Recently, similar Boscan samples were shown to yield vanadyl porphyrins with extended alkylation up to C–40 (Quirke *et al.*, 1980a), and even C–50 (Barwise and Whitehead, 1980). In each of these first examples it is found (cf. Fig. 12(a)–(b)) that the mode of the porphyrin distribution is at C–31 or C–32 DPEP. As pointed out during the discussion of free-base porphyrins, initial free-base and metalloporphyrin assemblages do not always exhibit a maximum at C–32 DPEP but are often at C–31, or rarely C–30, DPEP. Additional maturation of the Boscan (Fig. 12(b)) porphyrins, when compared to the pigments from the Belridge sample (Fig. 12(a)), is seen from the lowering of the DPEP to ETIO ratio, 1.2 versus 1.9 respectively, and the extension of alkylation to higher carbon numbers. The last example is the vanadyl porphyrin isolate from the upper Cretaceous Baxterville (Mississippi, USA) petroleum (Fig. 12(c)). In this case, the dominance of the ETIO series (DPEP/ETIO = 0.27), the lowering of the series maxima (C–29 ETIO, C–30 DPEP), and the presence of the more highly dealkylated homologues (viz. C–26 to C–28), in significant amounts, signals a tetrapyrrole array which is well advanced in catagenetic alteration and, with increased time and temperature, is close to entering metagenesis (viz. destruction).

The complete temperature range for the catagenetic alteration of geologic metalloporphyrins can, at present, only be guessed at. To date, adequate *in situ* time–temperature data is on hand for only one sample suite of marine sediments which reveal the latest portion of late diagenesis and the initiation of early catagenesis. This was the observation of the beginning of vanadyl porphyrin release within Miocene sediments presently at 65–67 °C (Louda and Baker, 1981). Thus, a catagenesis thermal profile for the metalloporphyrins may be tentatively set from *ca.* 70 °C to *ca.* 150–200 °C. The upper temperatures for tetrapyrrole catagenesis are surmised from oil-generation to depth temperature relationships in a recent review of petroleum geochemistry (see Hunt, 1979, pp. 131–143).

METAGENESIS: THERMAL DESTRUCTION

The onset of tetrapyrrole metagenesis has been eluded to in the previous section. That is, completion of the DPEP to ETIO conversion, continued dealkylation and the eventual pyrolysis of the tetrapyrrole macrocycle. Exacting data on the *in situ* metagenesis of metalloporphyrins is very scarce indeed. That extreme thermal stress does destroy these geologic pigments is not only intuitive but has been observed in a few instances.

The implacement of an igneous sill into the Cretaceous black shales of the Cape Verde Rise led to the total destruction of metalloporphyrins in samples close to that body (Baker *et al.*, 1977). Subsequent analyses and data reduction revealed that a theoretical momentary maxima of *ca.* 350 °C had been reacted in samples which were still far enough from the sill to yield detectable pigment (Baker *et al.*, 1978d). Thus, exposure, even for days, to temperatures of 350–400 °C would have led to total destruction. Depending upon reaction conditions, *in vitro* heating experiments have shown limited survival of metalloporphyrins for various time periods (viz. hours, days) at 210 °C (Didyk *et al.*, 1975b), 300 °C (Bonnett *et al.*, 1972) and even 410 °C (Yen *et al.*, 1969). The latter case was of very short duration and the porphyrin distribution reported (cf. Yen *et al.*, 1969), did reveal extreme dealkylation and the probable initiation of destruction.

The relative survival of the nickel and vanadyl chelates in geological settings is actually better understood than is the mechanism of pigment destruction. It is known, from *in vitro* studies, that nickel porphyrins resist thermal destruction better than the vanadyl chelates (Rosscup and Bowman, 1967) and that the stability to catalysed demetallation for the vanadyl species is greater than for nickel porphyrins (Caughey and Corwin, 1955; Erdman *et al.*, 1957; Fleisher *et al.*, 1964). Each of these *in vitro* studies have geologic counterparts. In the first case, thermal destruction, nickel porphyrins were found to be present in samples closer to the previously mentioned sill, whereas the vanadyl chelates had disappeared (Baker *et al.*, 1977; 1978d). Examination of a depth of burial continuum for the Paris Basin Toarcian shales revealed that, with more gradual time–temperature increases (viz. a 'normal' situation), the vanadyl porphyrins survive longer (Mackenzie *et al.*, 1980).

Thus, the relative *in situ* destruction of the nickel and vanadyl porphyrins appears to rest within an interplay of thermal and catalytic (e.g. host environment, lithology) stabilities. It should be noted that actual catalytic effects are unknown and should be the focus of future research. The temperature and age relationships for the later catagenesis and metagenesis are presently unknown, due to a lack of open literature data on such samples.

DECARBOXYLATION OF GEOLOGIC TETRAPYRROLES AND SPECULATIONS ON THE GENERATION OF PETROLEUM

We have delayed discussion of decarboxylation until the end of this treatise since this process has been found to occur within two separate time–temperature settings. That is, there are active low-temperature (microbial?) as well as strictly higher-temperature decarboxylation processes which act upon these geopigments.

As we detailed during the discussion of early and mid-diagenesis, phorbides undergoing defunctionalization and the free-base porphyrins generated from these via aromatization are usually dominated by decarboxylated species (see Baker and Louda, 1982; Louda and

Baker, 1981). Since the majority of these earlier reactions have been found to occur in sediments exposed to temperatures usually between 8 and 20 °C, thermal decarboxylation seems unlikely. Thus, a microbial or purely chemical reduction, or both, must be active. Supportive data for such assumptions is, however, lacking.

To date, we have had the fortune to observe the decarboxylation of nickel porphyrins (viz. nickel deoxophylloerythrins) within only one sample suite. These sediments were middle Miocene olive–grey silty claystones recovered from between 316 and 650 m sub-buttom in the Baja California Borderlands (DSDP/IPOD Leg 63, Site 471 : 23°28.93′ N × 112°29.78′ W; cf. Shipboard Party, 1981). In this case the percentage of carboxylated nickel porphyrins was found to decrease from 74% at 326 m (*ca.* 28 °C) to 8% 468 m (*ca.* 38 °3) and finally all nickel porphyrins were isolated as decarbodylated species at 650 m, sub-bottom (*ca.* 53 °C). Thus, the most active decarboxylation of nickel porphyrin acids appears to be occurring between 30–35 °C and 45–50 °C, at least within these Miocene claystones (Louda and Baker, 1981).

An example of the partial mass spectrum of a nickel deoxophylloerythrin series, from the samples described here, is given as Fig. 13. Due to lack of sample and the thermal instability of geologic porphyrin acid methyl esters in the mass spectrometer, clearly recognizable ions were only attainable at 70 eV and represent the overlapping losses of $-COOCH_3$ (M–59), $-CH_2COOCH_3$ (M–73) and $-CH_2CH_2COOCH_3$ (M–87). The β-cleavage loss (M–73).., is vastly dominant (5–10 ×) over the others (Louda and Baker, unpublished data; NiDPE·ME, authentic; cf. Budzikiewicz, 1978 and references therein). Thus, the ion cluster shown in Fig. 13 represents a C–29 to C–32 (including possible trace C–33) homology of nickel deoxophylloerythrin maximizing at C–31.* This matches closely the mass spectral distribution of decarboxylated nickel DPEP series isolated from the same sample (Fig. 13(b); cf. Louda and Baker, 1981). Both spectra are shown as isotopically corrected, normalized and averaged histograms for clarity. Minor amounts of nickel ETIO-porphyrins in the decarboxylated array were likewise omitted for comprative purposes (cf. Louda and Baker, 1981).

Nickel deoxophylloerythrin (viz. free acid) has been reported from various black water (i.e. trona brines) of the Green River Formation (Uinta Basin, USA). These nickel porphyrin acids were found to be dominated by Ni desmethyl DPE (Smith *et al.*, 1979), a compound which, upon decarboxylation (viz. $-CO_2$), could theoretically give rise to the Ni desmethyl-DPEP 'mineral' (C–31), Abelsonite (cf. Milton *et al.*, 1978).

The decarboxylation of metalloporphyrin-acids appears completed after exposure to *in situ* temperatures of 50–60 °C, when extended over geologic time. This conclusion arises from the above study and the lack of metalloporphyrin acids in sediments with known *in situ*

---

* Carbon number range given does not include the proprionic acid carboxy carbon, but rather infers the expected DPEP series to be generated via 'simple' ($-CO_2$) decarboxylation.

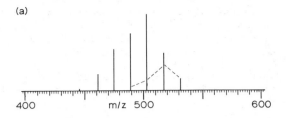

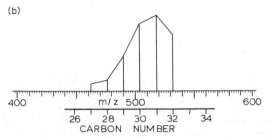

Fig. 13. Nickel porphyrin acids and decarboxylated nickel porphyrins isolated from a mid-Miocene silty-claystone recovered at 316 m sub-bottom (*in situ* T = 28 °C) in the Baja California borderlands (DSDP/IPOD Leg 63, Site 471, see Shipboard Party, 1981; cf. Louda and Baker, 1981). (a) Normalized, averaged and isotopically corrected high-voltage (70 eV-EIMS) mass spectral distribution of the thermal-EI fragment-ion group from an homologous series of nickel deoxophylloerythrin (NiDPE) analysed as *in vitro* methyl esters (viz. NiDPE · ME). Dotted line encompasses the losses of 59, 73, 87 and 102 daltons from NiDPE · ME, *per se*. The β-cleavage decarboxylation (M–73) is vastly dominate and, thus, the mode of the NiDPE series is Ni-desmethyl-DPE (i.e. C–31 NiDPEP plus CO_2). (b) Normalized, averaged and isotopically corrected low voltage mass spectrum (14 eV-EIMS) of the NiDPEP series (ETIO components not shown; cf. Louda and Baker, 1982) co-isolated with the NiDPE series given as above. (Note, C–31 NiDPEP maximum.)

temperatures over *ca.* 50 °C (see, e.g. Baker and Louda, 1982; Baker and Palmer, 1979a; Baker *et al.*, 1978b; Louda and Baker, 1981). These preliminary indications, of total tetrapyrrole decarboxylation within geologic temperature ranges of up to 50 or even 60 °C, cause one to suggest that metalloporphyrin acids in petroleum may not derive directly from that oils' source rock. That is, the presence of metalloporphyrin acids in petroleum crudes has been offered as the proof for the low temperature generation of petroleum (see Dunning, 1963; Dunning and Moore, 1957; Hodgson *et al.*, 1967; Treibs, 1936). However, if the complete decarboxylation of metalloporphyrins we have shown above is verified, with further study, then the implication of the carboxylated pigments in petroleum may be entirely different. As a preliminary suggestion, it seems possible that during migration a petroleum may 'extract' less mature metalloporphyrins from the strata it traverses. Further, if this is the case, one may then well expect a contribution to the overall nickel porphyrin assemblage of a petroleum by a similar process. The overall conclusion from these hypotheses is that the vanadyl porphyrin distribution of a petroleum must be the most conservative indicator of its host's history. This stems from the suggestions that, within immature

sediments, vanadyl porphyrins are bound non-extractable species (cf. Baker *et al.*, 1977; Louda and Baker, 1981; Mackenzie *et al.*, 1980). Thus, a petroleum which is migrating may 'extract' nickel porphyrins and nickel porphyrin acids from transgressed strate but most likely, little if any, of the vanadyl species. Alternatively, in-reservoir oxidation may also contribute to the trace occurrence of metalloporphyrin acids in oil.

The above, long, paragraph is forwarded not only as an example of the authors' propensity for speculation but serves well to illustrate how much more there is to learn of tetrapyrrole geochemistry.

CONCLUDING REMARKS

The geochemistry of chlorophyll derivatives is becoming increasingly well described, yet much in the way of understanding remains ahead. The major phases of tetrapyrrole evolution within geologic setting are now known to parallel the general divisions of geochemical maturation as worked out for overall organic melanges (see Hunt, 1979; Tissot and Welte, 1978).

Aside from the reactions of early diagenesis, which appear more closely related to microbial activities and decreasing Eh than directly to temperature, the later phases of tetrapyrrole maturation have been found to occur in strict parallel to increasing time–temperature regimes. Thus, the reactions of aromatization, chelation of nickel, cracking of vanadyl porphyrins from the general organic matrix, ETIO series generation, dealkylation, thermal decarboxylation and total pigment destruction are found to be sensitive indicators for thermal history of these pigments.

ACKNOWLEDGEMENTS

The authors' studies were funded by grants from the National Science Foundation (OCE-74-12438-AO2 and OCE-77-07273). Samples were obtained from the Deep Sea Drilling Project and are gratefully acknowledged. Past collaborative efforts with Dr. Susan E. Palmer are sincerely appreciated. The following personnel are heartily thanked for assistance in initial sample preparation: Ms. Debra Murphy, Ms. Denise Green, Ms. Inez Suarez, Ms. Cheryl Marshall, Mr. Churchill Barton, Ms. Patricia Ottens-Avery and Mr. Ronald Lane.

REFERENCES

Alturki, Y. I. A., Eglinton, G. and Pillinger, C. T. (1972) The petroporphyrins of Gilsonite. In *Advances in Organic Geochemistry 1971*, ed. by Gaertner H. R. and Wehner, H. Pergamon Press, Oxford, pp. 135–150.

Aronoff, S. (1953) The chemistry of chlorophyll (with special references to foods). *Adv. Food Res.* **4**, 133–184.

Baker, E. W. (1966) Mass spectrometric characterization of petroporphyrins. *J. Am. Chem. Soc.* **88**, 2311–2315.

Baker, E. W. (1969) Porphyrins. In *Organic Geochemistry*, ed. by Eglinton, G. and Murphy, M. T. J. Springer-Verlag, Berlin, pp. 464–497.

Baker, E. W. and Louda, J. W. (1980a) Products of chlorophyll diagenesis in Japan trench sediments. II. DSDP/IPOD sites 438–439 and 440. In *Initial Reports of the Deep Sea Drilling Project — LVII, ed. by E. Honza and the Shipboard Party*, Vols 56–57, part II. U.S. Government Printing Office, Washington, pp. 1397–1408.

Baker, E. W. and Louda, J. W. (1980b) Organic geochemistry: highlights in the deep sea drilling project. In *Advances in Organic Geochemistry 1979*, ed. by Douglas, A. G. and Maxwell, J. R. Pergamon Press, Oxford, 295–319.

Baker, E. W. and Louda, J. W. (1980c) Geochemistry of tetrapyrrole pigments in sediments of the north Philippine sea: DSDP/IPOD Leg 58. In *Initial Reports of the Deep Sea Drilling Project — LVIII, ed. by E. Honza, and the Shipboard Party, Vol. 58. U.S. Government Printing Office, Washington, pp. 737–739.*

Baker, E. W. and Louda, J. W. (1982) Geochemistry of tetrapyrrole, tetraterpenoid, and perylene pigments in sediments from the gulf of California: DSDP–IPOD Leg 64; sites 474–477, 479, and 481 and Guayamas basin survey cruise (S.I.O.) leg 3; sites 10G and 18G. In *Scientific Party, Initial Reports of the Deep Sea Drilling Project — LXIV*, Vol. 64. Pt. II, U.S. Government Printing Office, Washington, pp. 789–817.

Baker, E. W. and Palmer, S. E. (1978) Geochemistry of porphyrins. In *The Porphyrins*, ed. by Dolphin, D. Vol. I. Academic Press, New York, pp. 486–552.

Baker, E. W. and Palmer, S. W. (1979) Chlorophyll diagenesis in IPOD leg 47A, site 397 core samples. In *Initial Reports of the Deep Sea Drilling Project — XLVII, Part I*, ed. by von Rad, V., Ryan, W. B. F. and the Shipboard Party. U.S. Government Printing Office, Washington, v. 47a, 547–551.

Baker, E. W. and Smith, G. D. (1973) Chlorophyll derivatives in sediments, site 147. In *Initial Reports of the Deep Sea Drilling Project — XX*, Vol. 20, ed. by Heezen, B. C., MacGregor, I. D. and the Shipboard Party. U.S. Government Printing Office, Washington, pp. 943–946.

Baker, E. W. and Smith, G. D. (1977) Fossil porphyrins and chlorins in deep ocean sediments. In *Chemistry of Marine Sediments*, ed. by Yen, T. F. Ann Arbor Science Publishers, Ann Arbor, Michigan, pp. 73–100.

Baker, E. W., Palmer, S. E. and Huang, W. Y. (1977) Intermediate and late diagenetic tetrapyrrole pigments, leg 41: Cape Verde Rise and basin. In *Initial Reports of the Deep Sea Drilling Project – XLI*, Vol. 41, ed. by Lancelot, Y., Seibold, W. and the Shipboard Party. U.S. Government Printing Office, Washington, pp. 825–837.

Baker, E. W., Palmer, S. E. and Huang, W. Y. (1978a) Chlorin and porphyrin geochemistry of DSDP leg 40 sediments. In *Initial Reports of the Deep Sea Drilling Project — XL*, Vol. 40, ed. by Bolli, H. M., Ryan, W. B. F. and the Shipboard Party. U.S. Government Printing Office, Washington, pp. 639–647.

Baker, E. W., Palmer, S. E. and Huang, W. Y. (1978b) Early and intermediate chlorophyll diagenesis of Black Sea sediments: Sites 379, 380, and 381. In *Initial Reports of the Deep Sea Drilling Project — XLII*, Vol. 42B, Part 2, ed. by Ross, D. A., Neprochnov, Y. P. and the Shipboard Party. U.S. Government Printing Office. Washington, pp. 707–715.

Baker, E. W., Palmer, S. E. and Huang, W. Y. (1978c) Miocene and cretaceous tetrapyrrole pigments from leg 44, site 391. In *Initial Reports of the Deep Sea Drilling Project — XLVI*, Vol. 44, ed. by Benson, W. E., Sheridan, R. E. and the Shipboard Party. U.S. Government Printing Office, Washington, pp. 639–643.

Baker, E. W., Palmer, S. E., Huang, W. Y. and Rankin, J. G. (1978d) Mass and electronic paramagnetic resonance spectrometric analyses of selected organic components of cretaceous shales of marine origin. In *Analytical Chemistry of Liquid Fuel Sources: Tar Sands, Oil Shale, Coal, and Petroleum*, ed. by Uden, P. C., Siggia, S. and Jensen, H. B. Advances in Chemistry Series Δ170. American Chemical Society, Washington, pp. 159–180.

Baker, E. W., Yen, T. F., Dickie, J. P., Rhodes, R. E. and Clark, L. F. (1967) Mass spectrometry of porphyrins. II. Characterization of petroporphyrins. *J. Am. Chem. Soc.* **89**, 3631–3639.

Barwise, A. J. G. and Whitehead, E. V. (1980) Separation and structure of petroporphyrins. In *Advances in Organic Geochemistry 1979*, ed. by Maxwell, J. R. and Douglas, A. G. Pergamon Press, Oxford, pp. 181–192.

Blumer, M. and Rudrum, M. (1970) High molecular weight fossil porphyrins: evidence for monomeric and dimeric tetrapyrroles of about 1100 molecular weight. *J. Inst. Petr.* **56**, 548, 99–106.

Blumer, M. and Snyder, W. D. (1967) Porphyrins of high molecular weight in a triassic oil shale: evidence by gel permeation chromatography. *Chem. Geol.* **2**, 35–45.

Bonnett, R. (1978) Nomenclature. In *The Porphyrins*, Vol. I, ed. by Dolphin, D. Academic Press, New York, pp. 2–30.

Bonnett, R. and Czechowski, F. (1980) Gallium porphyrins in bituminous coal. *Nature (London)* **283**, 465–467.

Bonnett, R., Brewer, P., Noro, K. and Noro, T. (1972) On the origin of petroporphyrin homologues: the transalkylation of vanadyl octa-alkylporphyrins. *J. Chem. Soc. Chem. Commun.* 1972, 562–563.

Brassel, S. C., Comet, P. A., Eglinton, G., Isaacson, P. J., McEvoy, Maxwell, J. R., Thomson, I. D., Tibbetts, P. J. C. and Volkman, J. K. (1980) Preliminary Lipid Analyses of Sections 440A–7–6, 440B–3–5, 440B—8–4, 440B–68–2, and 436–11–4: Legs 56 and 57, Deep Sea Drilling Project. In *Initial Reports of the Deep Sea Drilling Project*, Volumes LVI, LVII, ed. by Scientific Party. U.S. Government Printing Office, Washington, pp. 1367–1390.

Budzikiewicz, H. (1978) Mass Spectra of Porphyrins and Related Compounds. In *The Porphyrins*, Vol. III, ed. by Dolphin, D. Academic Press, New York, pp. 395–461.

Casagrande, D. J. and Hodgson, G. W. (1974) Generation of homologous porphyrins under simulated geochemical conditions. *Geochim. Cosmochim. Acta* **38**, 1745–1758.

Caughey, W. S. and Corwin, A. H. (1955) The stability of metalloetioporphyrins towards acids. *J. Am. Chem. Soc.* **77**, 1509–1513.

Corwin, A. H. (1960) Petroporphyrins. *Paper V–10*, 5th World Petrol. Congress, New York, 119–129.

Corwin, A. H. and Wei, P. E. (1962) Stabilities of magnesium chelates of porphyrins and chlorins. *J. Org. Chem.* **27**, 4285–4290.

Currie, R. I. (1962) Pigments in zooplankton feces. *Nature (London)* **193**, 956–957.

Dean, R. A. and Whitehead, E. V. (1963) The Composition of High Boiling Petroleum Distillates and Residues. Paper from the Sixth WPC, Frankfurt, June, 1963.

Deroo, G., Herbin, J. P., Roucache, J. and Tissot, B. (1979) Organic geochemistry of some organic-rich shales from DSDP site 397, leg 47A, eastern North Atlantic. In *Initial Reports of the Deep Drilling Project — XLVIIA, ed. by von Rad, V., Ryan, W. B. F., et al.* U.S. Government Printing Office, v. 47A, pp. 523–529.

Didyk, B., Alturki, Y. I. A., Pillinger, C. T. and Eglinton, G. (1975a) The petroporphyrins of cretaceous oil. *Chem. Geol.* **15**, 1192–208.

Didyk, B. M., Alturki, Yl I. A., Pillinger, C. T. and Eglinton, G. (1975b) Petroporphyrins as indicators of geothermal maturation. *Nature* **256**, 563–565.

Dunning, H. N. and Moore, J. W. (1957) Porphyrin research

and origin of petroleum. *Bull. Am. Assoc. Pet. Geol.* **41** (11), 2403–2412.

Dunning, H. N. (1963) Geochemistry of organic pigments. In *International Series of Monographs on Earch Sciences*, Vol. 16, ed. by Breger, A. Pergamon Press, New York, pp. 367–430.

Eglinton, G., Hajibrahim, S. K., Maxwell, J. R. and Quirke, J. M. (1980) Petroporphyrins: structural elucidation and the application of HPLC fingerprinting to geochemical problems. In *Advances in Organic Geochemistry, 1979*, ed. by Douglas, A. G. and Maxwell, J. R. Pergamon Press, Oxford, pp. 193–203.

Erdman, J. G., Walter, J. W. and Hanson, W. E. (1957) The stability of the porphyrin metallo complexes. Preprints, Div. of Pet. Chem. *Am. Chem. Soc.* **2**, 259–266.

Erikson, A. J. and von Hersen, R. P. (1978) Downhole temperature measurements and heat flow data in the Black Sea–DSDP Leg 42B. In *Initial Reports of the Deep Sea Drilling Project — XLII-B*, ed. by Ross, D. A., Neprochnov, Y. P. and the Shipboard Party — Leg 42B. U.S. Government Printing Office, Washington, pp. 1085–1104.

Fischer, H. and Stern, A. (1940) *The Chemistry of Pyrroles*, Vol. 2, Akad. Vrlagsgesellschaft M.B.H., Leipzig, 478 pp.

Fleischer, E. G., Choi, E. I., Hambright, P. and Stone, A. (1964) Porphyrin studies: kinetics of metalloporphyrin formation. *Inorg. Chem.* **2**, 1284–1287.

Galimov, E., Kodina, L. A., Shirinsky, V. G., Drozdova, T. V., Generalova, V. N., Bogachova, M. P., Chinyonov, V. A. and Bannikova, L. A. (1980) A study of the organic matter from deep oceanic bore holes, Deep Sea Drilling Project Sites 415 and 416, in the Moroccan Basin. In *Initial Reports of the Deep Sea Drilling Project, Volume L*, ed. by Lancelot, Y., Winterer, E. L. and the Scientific Party. U.S. Government Printing Office, Washington, pp. 575–603.

Gilbert, D. and Summerhayes, C. P. (1981) Distribution of Organic Matter in Sediments Along the California Continental Margin. In *Initial Reports of the Deep Sea Drilling Project, Vol. 63*, ed. by Haq, B., Yeates, R. S. and the Scientific Party. U.S. Government Printing Office, Washington, pp. 757–761.

Glebovskaya, E. A. and Volkenshtein, M. V. (1948) Spectra of porphyrins in petroleums and bitumens. *J. Gen. Chem. (USSR)* **18**, 1440–1451.

Hodgson, G. W., Baker, B. L. and Peake, E. (1967) Geochemistry of Porphyrins. In *Fundamental Aspects of Petroleum Geochemistry*, ed. by Nagy, B. and Colombo, V. Elsevier, Amsterdam, pp. 1977–260.

Hodgson, G. W., Strosher, M. and Casagrande, D. J. (1972) Geochemistry of Porphyrins Analytical Oxidation of Maliemides. In *Advances in Organic Geochemistry, 1971*, ed. by von Gaertner, H. R. and Wehner, H. Pergamon, Oxford, pp. 151–161.

Hodgson, G. W., Ushijima, N., Taguchi, K. and Shimada, I. (1963) The origin of petroleum porphyrins: pigments in some crude oils, marine sediments and plant material of Japan. *The Science Reports of the Tohoku University, Third Series* **8**, 483–513.

Holden, M. (1965) Chlorophylls. In *Chemistry and Biochemistry of Plant Pigments*, ed. by Goodwin, T. W. Academic Press, London, pp. 461–488.

Holt, A. (1959) Reduction of chlorophyllides, chlorophylls and chlorophyll derivatives by sodium borohydride. *Plant Physiol.* **34**, 310–314.

Holt, A. S. (1966) Recently characterized chlorophylls. In *The Chlorophylls*, ed. by Vernon, L. P. and Seely, G. R. Academic Press, New York, pp. 111–118.

Holt, A. S. and Hughes, D. W. (1961) Studies of chlorobium chlorophylls. III. Chlorobium chlorophyll (650). *J. Am. Chem. Soc.* **83**, 499–500.

Holt, A. S., Purdie, J. W. and Wasley, J. W. F. (1966) Structures of chlorbium chlorophylls. *Can. J. Chem.* **44**, 88–93.

Hunt, J. M. (1979) *Petroleum Geochemistry and Geology.* W. H. Freeman, San Francisco, 617 pp.

Hynninen, P. (1979) Application of elution analysis to the study of chlorophyll transformations by column chromatography on sucrose. *J. Chromatogr.* **175**, 75–88.

Kenner, G. W., Rimmer, J., Smith, K. M. and Unsworth, J. F. (1978) Pyrroles and related compounds. Part 39. Structural and biosynthetic studies of the chlorobium-chlorophylls-660 (bacteriochlorophylls-c). Incorporations of methionine and porphobilinogen. *J. Chem. Soc. Perkin Trans.* I-**1978**, 845–852.

Louda, J. W. and Baker, E. W. (1979) Chlorophyll Diagenesis: Tetrapyrrole Pigments from Deep Sea Drilling Project Core Samples. 178th National A.C.S. Meeting, Division of Geochemistry, Washington, D.C., Sept. 9–14, 1979. Abs. Geoc. II.

Louda, J. W. and Baker, E. W. (1980) Incorporation of the Various Chlorophylls into Marine Sediments and Terrestrial Peats. 179th National A.C.S. Meeting, Division of Geochemistry, Houston, Texas, March 23–28, 1980, Abs. Geoc. 14.

Louda, J. W. and Baker, E. W. (1981) Geochemistry of tetrapyrrole, carotenoid and perylene pigments in sediments from the San Miguel Gap (Site 467) and Baja California borderlands (Site 471): DSDP/IPOD leg 63. In *Initial Reports of the Deep Sea Drilling Project*, ed. by Yeats, R. S., Haq, B. U. and the Shipboard Paety. U.S. Government Printing Office, Washington, pp. 785–818.

Louda, J. W., Palmer, S. E. and Baker, E. W. (1980) Products of Chlorophyll Diagenesis in Japan Trench Sediments. I. Deep Sea Drilling Project Sites 434, 435, and 436. In *Initial Reports of the Deep Sea Drilling Project — LVI*, ed. by Honza, E. and the Shipboard Party. U.S. Government Printing Office, Washington, pp. 1391–1396.

Mackenzie, A. S., Quirke, J. M. E. and Maxwell, J. R. (1980) Molecular parameters of maturation in the Toarcian shales, Paris Basin, France — II. Evolution of metalloporphyrins. In *Advances in Organic Geochemistry, 1979*, ed. by Douglas, A. G. and Maxwell, J. R. Pergamon Press, Oxford, pp. 239–248.

Mathewson, J. W., Richards, W. R. and Rapoport, H. (1963) Chlorobium chlorophylls. Nuclear magnetic resonance studies on a chlorobium pheophorbide-660 and 650. *J. Am. Chem. Soc.* **82**, 2601–2605.

Milton, C., Dwornik, E. J., Epsten-Barnes, P. A., Finkelman, R. B., Prabst, A., and Palmer, S. (1978) Abelsonite, nickel porphyrin, a new mineral from the Green River Formation, Utah. *Am. Mineral.* **63**, 930–937.

Morandi, J. R. and Jensen, H. (1966) Comparison of porphyrins from shale oil, oil shale, and petroleum by absorption and mass spectroscopy. *J. Chem. Eng. Data* **11** (1), 81–88.

Oehler, J. H., Aizenshtat, Z. and Schopp, W. J. (1974) Thermal alteration of blue–green algae and blue green algal chlorophyll. *Am. Assoc. Pet. Geol. Bull.* **58** (1), 124–132.

Orr, W. L., Emery, K. O. and Grady, J. R. (1958) Preservation of chlorophyll derivatives in sediments off southern California. *Bull. Am. Assoc. Pet. Geol.* **42** (5), 925–958.

Palmer, S. E. and Baker, E. W. (1978) Copper porphyrins in deep-sea sediments: a possible indicator of oxidized terrestrial organic matter. *Science* **201**, 49–51.

Palmer, S. E. and Baker, E. W. (1980) Nickel Porphyrins from Deep Sea Drilling Project Sites 415 and 416. In *Initial Reports of the Deep Sea Drilling Project — L*, Vol. 50, ed. by Lancelot, Y., Winterer, E. L. and the Shipboard Party.

U.S. Government Printing Office, Washington, pp. 643–645.

Palmer, S. E., Baker, E. W., Charney, L. S. and Louda, J. W. (1982) Tetrapyrrole pigments in United States humic coals. *Geochim. Cosmochim. Acta* **46**, 1233–1241.

Palmer, S. E., Huang, W. Y. and Baker, E. W. (1979) Tetrapyrrole pigments from Bermuda Rise: DSDP Let 43. In *Initial Reports of the Deep Sea Drilling Project — XLIIIL*, vol. 43, ed. by Tucholke, B. E., Vogt, P. R. and the Shipboard Party. U.S. Government Printing Office, Washington, pp. 657–661.

Peake, E., Casagrande, D. J. and Hodgson, G. W. (1974) Fatty Acids, Chlorins, Hydrocarbons, Sterols and Carotenoids from a Black Sea Core. In *The Black Sea Geology, Chemistry and Biology*, ed. by Degens, E. T. and Ross, D. A. *Am. Assoc. Pet. Geol. Memoir* **20**, 505–523.

Purdie, J. W. and Holt, A. S. (1965) Structures of chlorobium chlorophylls (650). *Can. J. Chem.* **43**, 3347–3353.

Quirke, J. M. E., Eglinton, G. and Maxwell, J. R. (1979) Petroporphyrins. I. A preliminary characterization of the porphyrins of gilsonite. *J. Am. Chem. Soc.* **101** (26), 7693–7697.

Quirke, J. M. E., Shaw, G. J., Soper, P. D. and Maxwell, J. R. (1980) Petroporphyrins — II. The presence of porphyrins with extended alkyl substituents. *Tetrahedron* **35**, 3261–3267.

Rao, C. N. R. (1967) *Ultra-Violet and Visible Spectroscopy*, 2nd Ed., Plenum Press, New York, p. 9.

Ross, D. A., Neprochnov, Y. P., *et al.* (1978) Site Reports. In *Initial Reports of the Deep Sea Drilling Project*, Vol. 42, Part 2, U.S. Government Printing Office, Washington, pp. 27–356.

Rosscup, R. J. and Bowman, D. N. (1967) Thermal stabilities of vanadium and nickel porphyrins. Preprints, Div. Pet. Chem., *Am. Chem. Soc.* **12**, 77–81.

Rullkotter, J., von der Dick, H. and Welte, D. H. (1981) Organic petrography and extractable hydrocarbons of sediments from the eastern north Pacific Ocean, deep sea drilling project leg 63. In *Initial Reports of the Deep Sea Drilling Project, Vol. 63*, ed. by Haq, B., Yeats, R. S. and the Scientific Party. U.S. Government Printing Office, Washington, pp. 819–836.

Sato, S. (1980) Diagenetic alteration of organic matter in leg 57 sediments, deep sea drilling project. In *Initial Reports of the Deep Sea Drilling Project, Vol. LVI, LVII*, ed. by the Scientific Party. U.S. Government Printing Office, Washington, 1305–1312.

Seely, G. R. (1966) The structure and chemistry of functional groups. In *The Chlorophylls*, ed. by Vernon, L. P. and Seely, G. R. Academic Press, New York, pp. 67–110.

Shipboard Party (1980) Site reports. In *Initial Reports of the Deep Sea Drilling Project, Vols 56, 57, Pt. 1*, ed. by Vernon, L. P. and Seely, G. R. U.S. Government Printing Office, Washington, pp. 225–446.

Shipboard Party (1981) DSDP/IPOD leg 63, site reports. *Initial Reports of the Deep Sea Drilling Project, LXIII*, Vol. 63. U.S. Government Printing Office, Washington, pp. 3–412.

Shipboard Party (1982) DSDP/IPOD leg 64, site reports. *Initial Reports of the Deep Sea Drilling Project, LXIV*, Vol. 64, Pt. I, U.S. Government Printing Office, Washington.

Simoneit, B. R. T. and Mazurek, M. A. (1981) Organic geochemistry of sediments from the southern California borderland, deep sea drilling project leg 63. In *Initial Reports of the Deep Sea Drilling Project, Vol. 63*, ed. by Haq, B., Yeats,

R. S. and the Scientific Party. U.S. Government Printing Office, Washington, pp. 837–853.

Smith, K. M. (1975) General features on the structure and chemistry of porphyrin compounds. In *Porphyrins and Metalloporphyrins*, ed. by Smith, K. M. Elsevier, Amsterdam, pp. 3–28.

Smith, E. W., Branthaver, J. F. and Robinson, W. E. (1979) Characterization of Organic Substances from Black Water and Green River Oil Shale. 177th National ACS Meeting, Honolulu, Division of Geochemistry, Abstracts: Geoc. 20.

Strain, H. H. and Svec, W. A. (1966) Extraction, separation, estimation, and isolation of the chlorophylls. In *The Chlorophylls*, ed. by Vernon, L. P. and Seely, G. R. Academic Press, New York, pp. 21–66.

Strain, H. H. (1958) Chloroplast Pigments and Chromatographic Analysis, 32nd Ann. Priestly Lectures. Penn. Univ. 180 pp.

Streibl, M. and Herout, V. (1969) Terpenoids — especially oxygenated mono-, sesqui-, di- and triterpenes. In *Organic Geochemistry*, ed. by Eglinton, G. and Murphy, M. T. J. Springer-Verlag, Berlin, pp. 402–424.

Takahashi, M. and Ichimura, S. (1968) Vertical distribution and organic matter, production of photosynthetic sulfur bacteria in Japanese lakes. *Limnol. Oceanogr.* **13**, 644–655.

Thomas, D. W. and Blumer, M. (1964) Porphyrin pigments of a Triassic sediment. *Geochim. Cosmochim. Acta* **28**, 1147–1154.

Tissot, B. P. and Welte, D. H. (1978) *Petroleum Formation and Occurrence: A New Approach to Oil and Gas Exploration*. Springer-Verlag, Berlin, 538 pp.

Treibs, A. (1934a) Organic mineral substances. II. Occurrence of chlorophyll derivatives in an oil shale of the Upper Triassic. *Ann. Chem.* **509**, 103–114.

Triebs, A. (1934b) Chlorophyll- and Haemin derivatives in bituminous rocks, petroleum, mineral waxes and asphalts. *Ann. Chem.* **510**, 42–62.

Treibs, A. (1935a) Organic mineral substances. IV. Chlorophyll and hemin derivatives in bituminous rocks, petroleums, coals and phosphorites. *Ann. Chem.* **517**, 172–196.

Treibs, A. (1935b) Porphyrins in coal. *Ann. Chem.* **520**, 144–151.

Treibs, A. (1936) Chlorophyll and hemin derivatives in organic mineral substances. *Angew. Chem.* **49** (38), 682–686.

von Rad, V., Ryan, W. B. F. and the Shipboard Party (1979) Site Report — 397A — Leg 47A. In *Initial Reports of the Deep Sea Drilling Project XLVII–A*, vol. 47, part 1, ed. by von Rad, V., Ryan, W. B. F. and the Shipboard Party — Leg 47A. U.S. Government Printing Office, Washington, pp. 17–218.

Whelan, J. K. and Hunt, J. M. (1981) C_1–C_8 hydrocarbons in IPOD leg 63. Sediments from outer California and Baja California borderlands. In *Initial Reports of the Deep Sea Drilling Project, vol. 63*, ed. by Haq, B., Yeats, R. S. and the Scientific Party, U.S. Government Printing Office, Washington, pp. 775–784.

Yen, T. F. Boucher, L. J., Dickie, J. P., Tynan, E. C. and Vaughan, G. B. (1969) Vanadium complexes and porphyrins in asphaltenes. *J. Inst. Petrol.* **55** (542), 87–99.

Yentsch, C. S. (1965) Distribution of chlorophyll and pheophytin in the open ocean. *Deep Sea Res.* **12**, 653–666.

Zerner, M. and Gouterman, M. (1966) Porphyrins. V. Extended nickel calculations on vanadyl (VO^{+2}) and vanadium (II) complexes. *Inorg. Chem.* **5**, 1699–1706.

APPENDIX

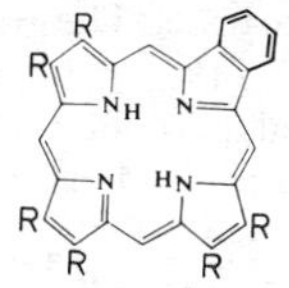

a)- Nomenclature: peripheral carbons = 1 to 10; methine bridges = α to δ; rings = I to IV; isocyclic ring (6,γ-cycloethano) = V.

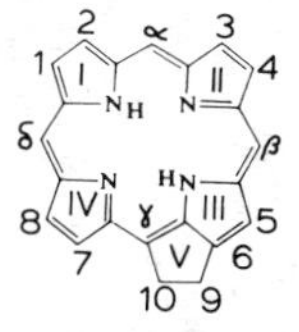

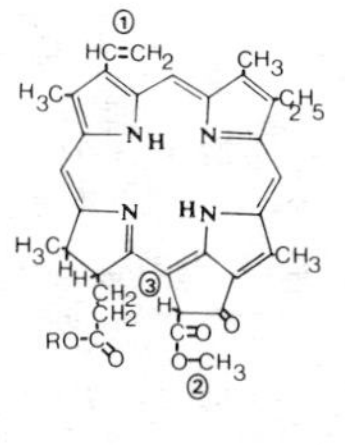

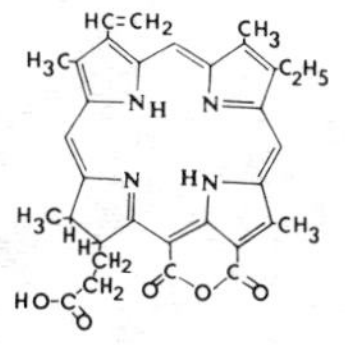

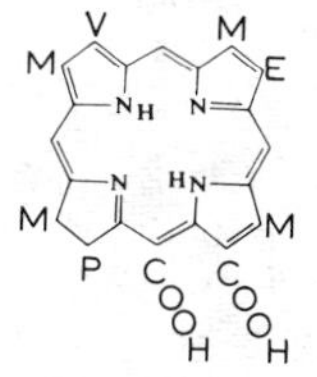

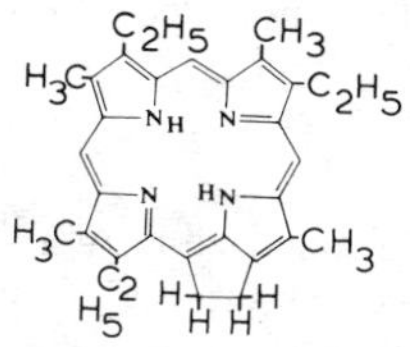

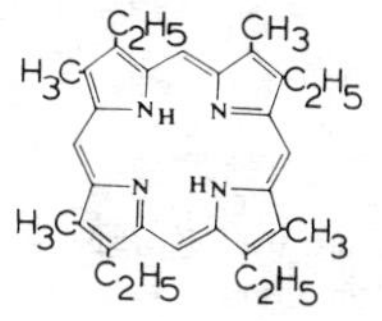

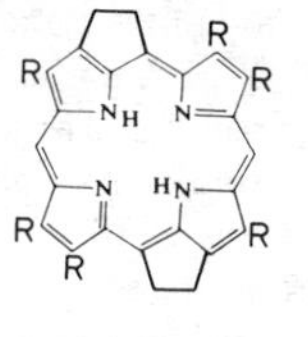

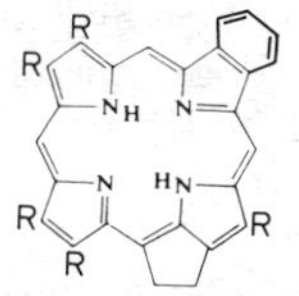

b)- Pheophorbides: Pheophytin-a (R=phytyl), Dihydrophytyl-pheophorbide-a (R =dihydro-phytyl); Pheophorbide-a (R = H), 7-Ethyl-7-desproprio structures (R=H, and -CO$_2$ from 7-proprionic acid moiety; cf."a").
①if ethyl, prefix = meso. ②if carbomethoxy is absent, prefix = pyro. ③if -OH, prefix = 10-hydroxy (i.e."Allomerized").

c)- Purpurin-18.

d)- Chlorin-p_6.

e)- Desoxophylloerythroetioporphyrin (DPEP).

f)- Etioporphyrin-III (an ETIO-type).

g)- Di-DPEP.

h)- Benz-DPEP.

i)- Benz-ETIO

re-d,g,h, and i (V=vinyl, P=proprionic acid; M =methyl; E= ethyl, R =M,E,H, or n-alkyl).

Advances in Organic Geochemistry 1981, pp. 422–430
© John Wiley & Sons Limited, 1983

Geochemistry of Natural-Gas Hydrates in Oceanic Sediment

K. A. Kvenvolden

US Geological Survey, MS-99, Menlo Park, California 94025

L. A. Barnard, J. M. Brooks, and D. A. Wiesenburg

Department of Oceanography, Texas A and M University, College Station, Texas 77841

The occurrence of natural-gas hydrates in oceanic sediment has been indicated by both geophysical and geochemical evidence. The geophysical evidence consists mainly of the appearance of a seismic reflection that mimics the bathymetry of the sea floor, commonly follows a predictable pressure–temperature surface, and lies between 100 and 1100 m below the bottom at water depths that usually exceed 500 m. This bottom-simulating reflector, which may mark the base of the zone of gas hydrates, has been observed in outer continental margins in all of the major oceans. The geochemical evidence for gas hydrates in oceanic sediment comes principally from Deep Sea Drilling Project Legs 66 (Mid-America Trench off southern Mexico), 67 (Mid-America Trench off Guatemala), and, particularly, 76 (Blake Ridge off southeastern United States). Cores recovered at sites on these three legs contained frothing sediment with ice-like properties that released mainly methane and small amounts (less than 1 per cent) of ethane and hydrocarbon gases of higher molecular weight, and carbon dioxide. Large methane to ethane ratios indicate that the methane is dominantly biogenic and not thermogenic. At one site on Leg 76 the carbon-isotopic contents of methane range from −88 to −67 permil relative to the Peedee belemnite standard (PDB); such values support the contention that the methane is biogenic. Experiments conducted on Leg 76 confirmed the presence of marine gas hydrates. The molecular distribution of hydrocarbon gases in the decomposition products of one sediment sample that appeared to contain gas hydrates suggested that gas hydrates of Structure I and some Structure II had been formed. Methane, ethane, propane, and isobutane were present in measurable quantities, but n-butane and higher molecular weight hydrocarbon gases that cannot fit inside either of the gas hydrate structures were present only in trace amounts. The volume of gas released during decomposition of the sample was about twenty times the volume of pore fluid and indicated that gas hydrate was present because more gas was present than could be dissolved in the pore fluid. These observations also suggest the gas–hydrate structures are only partially filled. Finally, experiments on cores obtained with a pressure-core barrel showed that during degassing at constant temperature the pressure release followed a pattern tentatively suggestive of gas hydrates.

INTRODUCTION

Natural gas is composed for the most part of methane, but that methane is often accompanied by hydrocarbons of higher molecular weight as well as inorganic gases such as nitrogen, carbon dioxide, and hydrogen sulfide. When natural gas is in excess of the amount soluble in water at appropriate conditions of pressure and temperature that are found in deep oceanic sediments, it may interact with water to crystallize as a clathrate, i.e. a three-dimensional framework of water molecules that is stabilized by the included molecules of natural gas (Hand et al., 1974; Hitchon, 1974). The water clathrate of natural gas is commonly called a 'natural-gas hydrate'. The approximate pressure–temperature region in which gas hydrates are stable is shown in Fig. 1 (Kvenvolden and McMenamin, 1980). This region was determined for a pure methane and pure water system

(Katz et al., 1959). Because the effects of salt water and of gaseous components in the methane more or less cancel each other, the location of the phase boundary between free natural gas and natural gas hydrate in oceanic sediments is best estimated by using the pure methane/pure water system (Claypool and Kaplan, 1974).

The geothermal gradient limits the depths within sediment at which gas hydrates can occur. That is, the temperature of sediments increases with depth until temperature conditions are reached at which gas hydrates are no longer stable and therefore decompose. The base of the gas hydrate zone coincides with a pressure–temperature surface that represents the maximum depths at which the gas hydrate is stable. Gas hydrates form in oceanic sediments at water depth greater than about 500 m where bottom-water temperatures approach 0 °C. The base of the gas hydrate

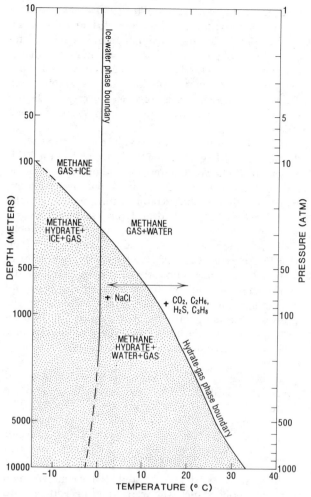

Fig. 1. Diagram showing the phase boundary between free methane gas and methane hydrate (pattern) in a pure water and pure methane system. Addition of NaCl to water shifts the curve to the left. Additions of CO_2, H_2S, C_2, and C_3 to C_1, shift the boundary to the right. Arrows indicate the direction but not the magnitude of the shifts. Depth scale is an approximation based on the assumption that lithostatic and hydrostatic pressure gradients are both 0.1 atmosphere per meter. Redrawn after Katz *et al.* (1959) and taken from Kvenvolden and McMenamin (1980).

lies in sediment between 100 and 1100 m subbottom; the thickness of the zone increases with increasing water depths.

The base of the gas hydrate zone has often been correlated with anomalous acoustic reflectors in marine seismic records obtained from a number of areas on outer continental margins (Shipley *et al.*, 1979). These anomalous reflectors approximately parallel the sea-floor but deepen with increasing water depths. If the geothermal gradient is known, the depth at which such a reflector will appear can be predicted on the basis of the pressure–temperature stability field for gas hydrates (Fig. 1). This bottom-simulating reflector probably results from the velocity contrast between sediment containing gas hydrates and the underlying sediment where lower velocities result from the absence of gas hydrate and the possible presence of free gas. Figure 2 is an example of a seismic profile with a well-developed bottom-simulating reflector. The acoustically transparent region above the reflector may result from the reduction of acoustic impedance differences between strata caused by the presence of gas hydrate. Bottom-simulating reflectors have been noted on marine seismic records of outer continental margins around the world (Kvenvolden and McMenamin, 1980; Kvenvolden and Barnard, 1982). The rather common occurrence of such reflectors implies the widespread occurrence of gas hydrates in oceanic sediments.

Indirect geochemical evidence for gas hydrates in oceanic sediments has been recognized since the early 1970s. Stoll *et al.* (1971), pointed out that 'marine sediments that emit considerable quantities of gas when exposed to surface conditions are found in many parts of the sea'. Coring by the Deep Sea Drilling Project (DSDP) has produced samples which have outgassed methane. For example, gas in quantities sufficient to sample and measure was found at about 33 of the drilled sites on DSDP Legs 10 through 23 (Claypool *et al.*, 1973; McIver, 1974). Most of these sites have pressure–temperature conditions that fall within the zone of gas-hydrate stability (Fig. 1). These observations provided necessary but insufficient evidence for the identification of gas hydrates, however.

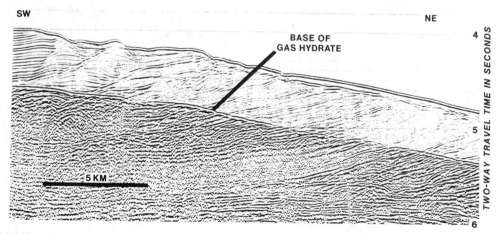

Fig. 2. A 12-fold multichannel seismic reflection profile from the crest and eastern flank of the Blake Outer Ridge. The reflector probably marks the base of the gas hydrate; it follows the bathymetry of the sea floor and transects dipping bedding reflectors (Shipley *et al.* (1979), Fig. 3, p. 2206).

The first direct observation of solid gas hydrates in oceanic sediment was made by Yefremova and Zhizhchenko (1974) in samples from the Black Sea. They reported that methane and carbon dioxide gas bubbled off the surfaces of some cores, leaving numerous cavities because of the gas expansion. Crystal hydrates of gas were observed in a core taken in the Black Sea at a water depth of 2000 m. These hydrates occurred in cavities 6.5 m below the sea floor as microcrystalline aggregates that resembled frost and tended to quickly disappear. Coring during DSDP Leg 42B in the Black Sea failed to recover solid gas hydrates, but most cores taken on that leg contained high concentrations of gas composed mainly of methane together with small amounts of other hydrocarbon gases and of carbon dioxide (Hunt and Whelan, 1978).

The only other direct geochemical evidence, i.e. evidence from direct observation and measurement, of gas hydrates in oceanic sediment comes from coring by DSDP on Legs 66, 67, and 76. Unfortunately, the 'Initial Reports of DSDP', where information on these legs will be fully documented, are not yet available (Moore, Watkins, et al., 1982; von Huene, Aubouin, et al., 1982; Sheridan, Gradstein, et al., 1983). Therefore, this paper can consider only some of the preliminary geochemical results which lead to initial generalizations about gas hydrates in oceanic sediment.

Gas hydrates observed by deep sea drilling

Sediments containing solid gas hydrate have been recovered by DSDP from three areas (Fig. 3): the Pacific continental margin off Mexico (Leg 66), and Guatemala (Leg 67), and the Atlantic continental margin off southeastern United States (Leg 76).

Seismic records from the area of Leg 66 that lies on the landward wall of the Mid-American Trench showed a bottom-simulating reflector that suggested the presence of gas hydrates. Drilling at three sites in water depths ranging from about 1780 to 2870 m confirmed that gas

hydrates are present. At Site 490, gassy ice was recovered at 137 m subbottom, and at Sites 491 and 492 gassy frozen sediment was obtained that produced about 20 ml of gas per ml of pore fluid. The gas was mainly methane, and the volume of methane produced represented about five times the amount of methane that is soluble in sea water at equivalent conditions; such a result indicates the presence of gas hydrates (Moore, Watkins, et al., 1979).

Gas hydrates were unexpectedly encountered while drilling during Leg 67 on the landward wall of the Mid-American Trench off Guatemala. Although the geologic setting is similar to that of Leg 66, no bottom-simulating reflector had been observed on seismic records from the area. Nevertheless, gas hydrates were recovered in vitric sands near the bottom of holes in water depths of about 2350 and 5490 m at Sites 497 and 498, respectively (von Huene, Aubouin, et al., 1980). Evidence for gas hydrates included the observation that decomposition of the suspected gas hydrate produced much greater quantities of methane than are soluble in sea water at in situ pressures and temperatures. Methane was abundant in samples from Site 496 as well. High gas pressures in cores taken at all three sites also indicated the presence of gas hydrates.

To recover samples of gas hydrates was a principal objective at DSDP Site 533 on Leg 76 along the Blake Outer Ridge in the Atlantic Ocean (Fig. 4). The presence of gas hydrates here had been predicted on the basis of a well-developed bottom-simulating reflector (Fig. 2) and previous observations made in the same area at three sites on DSDP Leg 11 (Ewing and Hollister, 1972). At Sites 102, 103, and 104 (Fig. 4), high concentrations of methane were found in sediments. In many cases, gas expansion was sufficient to cause sediment to extrude from core liners. When cores were opened, degassing occurred immediately and many cores continued to produce gas for several hours (Lancelot and Ewing, 1972). No obvious solid gas hydrates were reported, however.

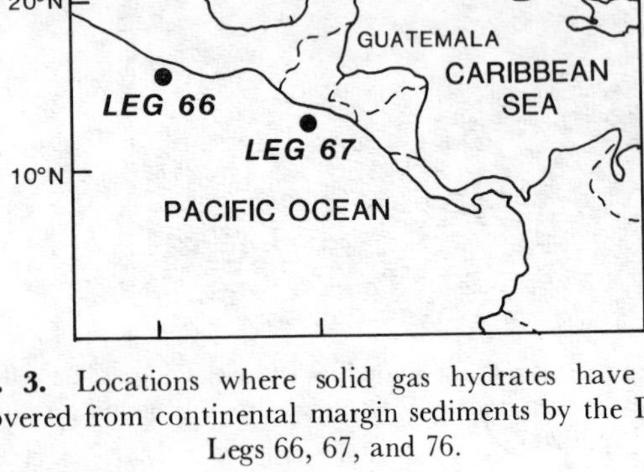

Fig. 3. Locations where solid gas hydrates have been recovered from continental margin sediments by the DSDP Legs 66, 67, and 76.

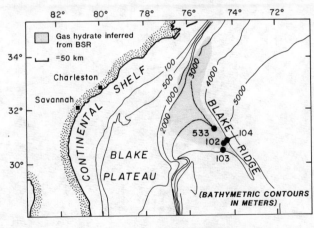

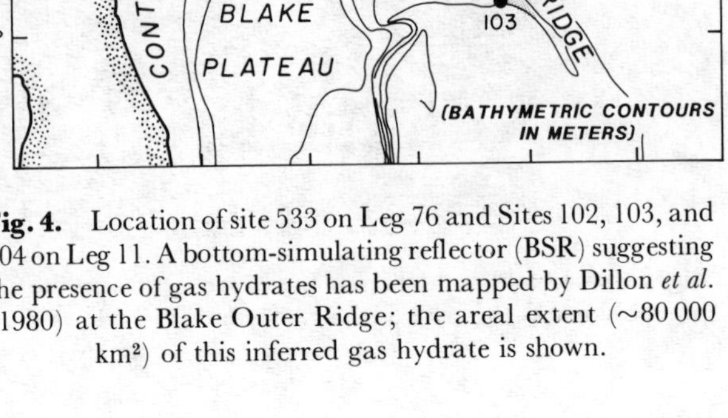

Fig. 4. Location of site 533 on Leg 76 and Sites 102, 103, and 104 on Leg 11. A bottom-simulating reflector (BSR) suggesting the presence of gas hydrates has been mapped by Dillon *et al.* (1980) at the Blake Outer Ridge; the areal extent (~80 000 km²) of this inferred gas hydrate is shown.

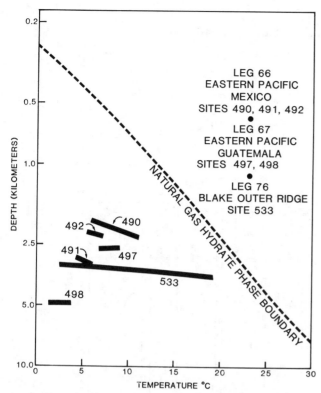

Fig. 5. Preliminary depth and temperature information for DSDP sites at which solid gas hydrates were recovered. Total depth (water plus sediment) is indicated. The phase boundary is the same as in Fig. 1. All sites are within the pressure–temperature field for gas hydrate stability. The temperature gradient of about 36 °C/km for Site 533 was established by three downhole measurements (Sheridan, Gradstein *et al.*, 1982). Depth and temperature information for Sites 490, 491, and 492 are from Shipley and Didyk (1982) and for Sites 497 and 498 from Harrison and Curiale (1982).

Geochemical analyses of sediments from Site 533 of Leg 76, taken in 3184 m of water, showed that below a sediment depth of 50 m the sediment contains high concentrations of methane at pressures sufficient to cause sediment separations in the core liner (Sheridan, Gradstein *et al.*, 1982). At 238 m subbottom, conclusive evidence for gas hydrates was obtained when a frothing sediment sample containing rapidly disappearing, matlike layers of white crystals was recovered. The volume of gas (mainly methane) released upon sample decomposition was about 20 times the volume of pore fluid, a result similar to that obtained from a gas-hydrate-containing sediment from Leg 66.

Preliminary information relating total depths and temperatures at the sites on Legs 66, 67, and 76 where gas hydrates were observed, is summarized in Fig. 5. Pressure–temperature conditions for all of these sites fall within the natural gas–hydrate stability field shown in Fig. 1.

Hydrocarbon gases at Site 533

The hydrocarbon gases methane (C_1), ethane (C_2), propane (C_3), isobutane (i-C_4), normal butane (n-C_4), isopentane (i-C_5), normal pentane (n-C_5), isohexane (i-C_6), and normal hexane (n-C_6) are present in sediments at Site 533. C_1 is the most abundant hydrocarbon gas; it constitutes more than 99 per cent of the hydrocarbon gas mixture. The inorganic gases identified are carbon dioxide and nitrogen.

Two methods were used for gas analyses. In the first procedure, gases were recovered directly from separations in the sediment that developed as the gases expanded during the time the sediment was confined in the core liner. These gas pockets were sampled by means of a hollow punch equipped with a valve designed to prevent immediate release of gas. After the punch penetrated the core liner, gas was vented through the valve into 20 ml evacuated containers (vacutainers). The vacutainers have a residual background of air, which affects volumetric measurements. The collected gases were analyzed by gas chromatography and (except as otherwise indicated) were reported in terms of volume per cent for C_1 and CO_2 and parts per million by volume (ppm) for other hydrocarbons. Concentrations of C_1 through C_5 hydrocarbons and of CO_2 were determined by means of this procedure. Hydrocarbons larger than C_5 could not be measured because contamination in the vacutainers interfered with chromatographic detection. The second procedure was a headspace analysis. By means of this procedure, described by Kvenvolden and Redden (1980), gases were extracted from sediment samples and were equilibrated with a helium-filled headspace; a portion of the headspace was then analyzed by gas chromatography. Concentrations of C_1 through C_6 and of CO_2 were measured.

Gas chromatography was done on shipboard utilizing two instruments.

1. The Carle Model 800* utilizing a thermal conductivity detector and a $1/8'' \times 5'$ stainless steel column packed with 8% Carbowax 1540* on 90–100 mesh Anakrom ABS*. This instrument measured C_1 and CO_2. At Site 533, C_2 never reached concentrations sufficient to be detected by this chromatographic system.

2. The Hewlett-Packard Model 5710A* with dual columns, each of which is made up of two connected stainless steel columns, one of them $1/8'' \times 4'$ packed with Spherosil* and the other $1/8'' \times 12'$ packed with 20% OV 101 on 100–110 mesh Anakrom AS*. This latter instrument has dual-flame ionization detectors; it was used to measure C_2 through C_6. In the injection procedure for this instrument, C_1 was removed because it would interfere with the detection of the other hydrocarbon gases. This chromatographic system was first used on the *Glomar Challenger* on Leg 47A (Whelan, 1979). The isotopic composition of carbon in C_1 from selected samples has been measured at the US Geological Survey in Denver, Colorado (Claypool, written communication), and at Texas A and M University.

Drilling at Site 533 involved two holes. The first was continuously cored from the surface to a subbottom depth of 168 m, using an hydraulic piston core. A second hole at the same site was rotary cored from 57 m, with

---

* Use of trade names is for descriptive purposes only and does not constitute endorsement by the US Geological Survey.

Table 1
Concentrations in Microliters of Gas per Liter of Wet Sediment

Core	Depth (m)	C_1	C_2	C_3	i-C_4	n-C_4	i-C_5	n-C_5	CO_2
1	1.5	30	0.02	0.02	0.03	0.04	—	—	1800
2	3.5	40	0.02	0.02	0.02	—	—	—	—
6	14.3	30	0.05	0.04	0.01	0.01	—	—	300
8	21.6	22 000	0.09	0.2	0.1	0.01	—	—	1400
10	32.3	57 000	1.7	0.5	0.2	0.04	0.01	0.01	3400
12	39.8	82 000	2.1	0.5	0.2	0.02	0.04	0.02	5300
14	48.4	55 000	2.0	0.6	0.2	0.04	0.02	—	3300

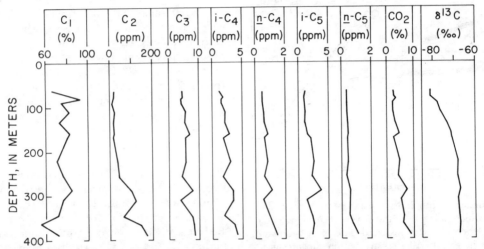

Fig. 6. Concentration profiles with depth (subbotom) for C_1, C_2, C_3, i-C_4, n-C_4, i-C_5, n-C_5, CO_2, and $\delta^{13}C_1$ for Site 533, Leg 76. $\delta^{13}C_1$ values provided by Claypool (written communication).

continuous core recovery from 143 to 399 m. The cores of near-surface sediment samples (0 to 25 m) did not contain gas in sufficient quantities to produce gas pockets in the core liners; therefore, direct recovery of the gas through vacutainers was not possible. Instead, gas was extracted from the sediments by means of the headspace procedure in order to estimate the relative amounts of gases in these sediments. Table 1 lists the concentrations of gases in the first 50 m of sediment. The amounts of all hydrocarbon gases and CO_2 increase with depth in this interval. Particularly striking is the rapid increase in amounts of C_1 and C_2. Below 50 m, C_1 concentrations decrease whereas the concentrations of the other hydrocarbon gases and CO_2 increase slightly.

Gas pockets were observed sporadically in cores taken from 25 to 50 m subbottom. Most cores from depths greater than 50 m contained gas pockets from which samples could be removed for analysis. Figure 6 shows the concentrations of hydrocarbons and CO_2 at various depths for those samples of gas removed from gas pockets in the cores for which carbon isotopic compositions of C_1 are available. Trends of the data show that the concentrations of C_2 through C_5 hydrocarbons all increase with depth, as do the concentrations of CO_2. C_2 shows the greatest rate of increase in concentration with depth. The amount of C_1 in the gas mixture decreases with depth, and the carbon isotopic composition of C_1 follows a systematic but nonlinear change with depth from −81 to −67 permil relative to the Peedee belemnite standard (PDB). The ratio of C_1 to C_2

decreases exponentially with depth from about 35 000 to about 4000. The high values of the C_1/C_2 ratios suggest that the C_1 is of biologic origin (Bernard et al., 1976) and the $\delta^{13}C_1$ values (−81 to −67 permil) support this interpretation (Claypool et al., 1973). Superimposed on the microbial production of C_1 is the probable low-temperature generation of the other hydrocarbon gases exemplified particularly by C_2 (Fig. 6). In general, the isohydrocarbons (i-C_4 and i-C_5) were more abundant than their respective normal isomers (n-C_4 and n-C_5). However, the ratio of iso- to normal hydrocarbons tended to decrease with depth, especially near the bottom of the hole. The ratios (C_1/C_2, i-C_4/n-C_4, i-C_5/n-C_5) decreasing with depth, can all be interpreted to be the result of early diagenesis. None of the information discussed above concerning the concentrations of hydrocarbon gases and CO_2 in these sediments points diagnostically to the presence of gas hydrates.

Gas-hydrate composition

At Site 533 only one sample of sediment containing obvious gas hydrate was recovered for physical and chemical measurements, and that sample came from a subbottom depth of 238 m as has been noted. The volumetric expansion of the gas (20 times the volume of pore water) was determined; in addition, the composition of the gas was measured gas chromatographically. For this analysis a part of the gas

Table 2

Concentrations of gases recovered from decomposed gas hydrate.

C_1 (%)	C_2 (ppm)	C_3 (ppm)	i-C_4 (ppm)	n–C_4 (ppm)	i-C_5 (ppm)	n–C_5 (ppm)	i-C_6 (ppm)	n–C_6 (ppm)	CO_2 (%)
36	123	2	2	0.06	0.15	0.13	0.02	—	0.5

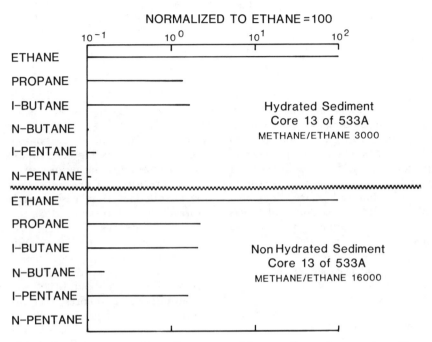

Fig. 7. Comparison of the hydrocarbon compositions of gas recovered from a sediment that contains evident gas hydrates and gas removed from a gas pocket in the same core. The concentrations are normalized to ethane = 100.

that had accumulated in the pressure-measuring device was used. The results are given in Table 2. C_1 constitutes about 36 per cent of the volume of gas in the container; most of the gas remaining is air. An interesting distributional relationship shown in Table 2 is the low concentration of n-C_4, i-C_5, and n-C_5 relative to the much higher concentrations of C_1, C_2, C_3, and i-C_4. This distribution of gases recovered from the decomposed gas hydrate contrasts with the distributions of hydrocarbon gas recovered from all gas pockets in the cores (Fig. 6); that contrast is illustrated in Fig. 7. The hydrocarbon gases from gas pockets do not show the abrupt decrease in concentrations of all molecules larger than i-C_4 (i.e. n-C_4, i-C_5, and n-C_5). The distribution of hydrocarbons released from the decomposing gas hydrate may be explained on the basis of the sizes of cages in the gas hydrate structure.

The framework of water molecules in a gas hydrate is a cubic lattice that contains cages large enough to accommodate molecules of gas. Two structures of such a cubic lattice are possible. In Structure I the cages are arranged in body-centered packing, and they include small hydrocarbon molecules such as C_1 and C_2 as well as nonhydrocarbons such as CO_2, N_2, and H_2S. Structure II has diamond packing, and not only can C_1 and C_2 be included in the cages, but C_3 and i-C_4 are also required to occupy some of the larger cages in order to stabilize the structure. Apparently, gases larger than i-C_4 (for example, n-C_4, i-C_5, n-C_5, etc.) cannot be included in either Structure I or Structure II (Hand *et al.*, 1974;

Hitchon, 1974). The molecular distribution of hydrocarbon gases from the decomposing gas hydrate seems to follow the pattern predictable from gas-hydrate crystallography. Our results suggest that Structure I gas hydrate was present because C_1 was the dominant hydrocarbon; C_2 would also fit in the cages of Structure I. C_3 and i-C_4 were measured in amounts of only a few parts per million. Only traces (less than 1 ppm) of n-C_4 and larger molecules were measured. Thus, a few crystals of Structure II gas hydrate may have been present to account for the observed molecular distribution of hydrocarbon gases.

The results of this experiment imply that much of the gas removed from cores at Site 533 is not in hydrate form because most of the gas samples removed from gas pockets or extracted from sediment contained the higher molecular weight hydrocarbons (n-C_4, i-C_5, n-C_5, etc.). Only when a sediment sample containing a large amount of gas hydrate is analyzed does the influence of the sizes of the gas hydrate cages become apparent in the distribution of the hydrocarbon gases.

How the gas hydrate is distributed in the hemipelagic sediment at Site 533 is not known. From 0 to 152 m depth subbottom the cores show no unusual features except for the gaps (gas pockets) which are common in cores deeper than 50 m. Below 152 m the following intervals contain disrupted sediment or evidence of frothing, suggestive of gas hydrate decomposition: 152–155 m, 171–190 m, 209–218 m, 228–250 m. At the depths between these intervals the sediment was semiconsolidated, with little

Table 3

Results from the pressure-core barrel at DSDP site 533.

PCB No.	Subbottom depth[b] (m)	Core recovered (m)	Pressure (MPa)	C_1/C_2 (average)	$\delta^{13}C_1$‰ (average)
PCB-1	152	6.4	27.5	—	—
PCB-2	247	1.6[a]	0	—	—
PCB-3	333	6.1	32.3	6000	− 66
PCB-4	361	6.1	10.3	5400	− 64
PCB-5	392	6.2	30.2	4100	− 69

[a] Unpressurized core.
[b] Top of cored interval.

evidence for gas except for occasional gaps. Below 250 m the sediment remained semiconsolidated to the bottom of the hole (399 m) with disruption and gaps but no obvious characteristics attributable to the presence of gas hydrates. Apparently the gas hydrates here do not form a massive, solid layer, as had been inferred from seismic records (Fig. 2), but rather are distributed unevenly in the sediment. Alternatively, much of the gas hydrate may be finely dispersed throughout the core, so that upon decomposition there is little evidence of sediment disruption except in the interval between 150 m and 250 m where visual evidence suggests that the gas hydrate is more concentrated.

Pressure core barrel

A pressure-core barrel (PCB), described by Larson *et al.* (1980), was deployed five times at Site 533 (Table 3). Three cores were recovered at *in situ* pressures of approximately 27.5 to 32.3 megaPascals (MPa). PCB-4 had only 10.3 MPa pressure due to a leaking assembly, and PCB-2 had no pressure because of a missing plug; this PCB recovered only a short unpressurized core. Pressurized sediment cores were intermittently degassed; i.e. at varying intervals of time portions of the gas were collected for analysis by drawing the gas through a transfer manifold and high-pressure regulator into steel sampling cylinders. Gas was released intermittently from PCB-1, PCB-3, and PCB-5 at intervals spanning about three hours; PCB-4 was vented immediately. The pressure-release curves from PCB-1, PCB-3, and PCB-5 show some pressure recovery after partial degassing. This behavior suggested that gas hydrates were present; however, inefficient transfer of gases coming out of solution could produce similar results. Figure 8 shows the pressure release diagram for PCB-5, which was degassed at two temperatures by transferring the barrel from an ice bath at 0 °C to a seawater bath at 29 °C (Sheridan, Gradstein, *et al.*, 1982). The pattern of the diagram suggests that if gas hydrates are present at all, they occupy only a small portion of the sediment pore space.

Gas samples were collected during the degassing of PCB-3, PCB-4, and PCB-5; no gas samples could be collected from PCB-1 because its gas came out as a slurry of mud, or from PCB-2 because there was no pressurized core. This lack of gas samples was disappointing because these PCB cores were taken from the sediment interval between 150 and 250 m where rotary cores had provided

the best visible evidence for gas hydrates. Gas samples from PCB-3, PCB-4, and PCB-5 were analyzed by gas chromatography and the carbon-isotopic composition of their C_1 was measured. The ratios of C_1 to C_2 did not vary significantly during degassing. Average values of C_1/C_2 are listed in Table 3; these ratios are similar to the ratios obtained from gases that had been recovered directly from unpressurized cores taken from adjacent sediment intervals. This result contrasts with observations made at Site 380 of DSDP Leg 42B in the Black Sea (Ross *et al.*, 1978). There a pressure core barrel retained formation pressure, and the C_1/C_2 ratio of the released gas was about 18 000 whereas gas recovered from unpressurized cores taken from nearby sediment intervals had C_1/C_2 ratios of about 2000. The difference between the C_1/C_2 ratios observed at Site 380 is probably an artifact of the sampling procedure.

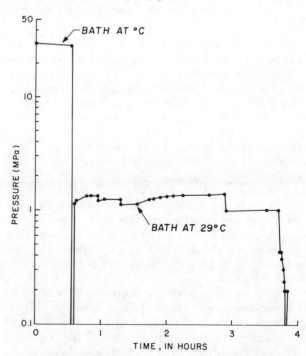

Fig. 8. Pressure release pattern for PCB-5. The PCB was recovered at a pressure of 30.2 MPa and immersed in a bath at 0 °C. The hydrostatic pressure was released at about 0.6 h. After the pressure release valve was closed, pressure recovered to about 1.2 MPa. Dots record times and pressures when samples were collected for analyses. At about 1.5 h the PCB was removed from the ice bath and immersed in a bath of seawater at 29 °C. The degassing curve suggests that gas hydrates, if present, form only a minor part of the sediment in the core.

Besides the nearly constant C_1/C_2 ratios observed at Site 533 during degassing of PCB-3 and PCB-5, the carbon-isotopic composition of C_1 from each core also remained about the same and averaged -66 and -69 permil, respectively (Table 3), values similar to those obtained for C_1 recovered from the unpressurized cores of sediment taken above and below the interval cored by the PCB (Fig. 6). In general, although C_1/C_2 ratios and $\delta^{13}C_1$ values remained about the same during degassing, the relative amounts of C_3, i-C_4, n-C_4, i-C_5, n-C_5, and CO_2 increased.

The results of the pressure core barrel experiments provide tentative evidence for the presence of gas hydrates at Site 533. The amount of gas hydrate indicated is very small, however, and this conclusion agrees with the visual evidence for gas hydrates at this site.

Source and significance of gas hydrates

Marine gas hydrates have been sampled at only four areas thus far, and information from all of these areas is still incomplete. However, sufficient information is available to enable some generalizations. The gases associated with these marine gas hydrates are predominantly C_1; that is, C_1 generally constitutes more than 99.9 per cent of the hydrocarbons present. C_2 and hydrocarbons of higher molecular weight are present in very low concentrations. This molecular composition of the gas occurring in shallow marine sediments suggests that the C_1 has been formed by microbial processes; furthermore, the light carbon isotopic compositions of C_1 support the hypothesis of its biologic origin. The gases involved in the formation of gas hydrates apparently are generated in place by microorganisms that operate on organic matter and reduce CO_2. A model for the origin of gas hydrates from biogenic methane has been outlined by Kvenvolden and Barnard (1982) after ideas put forward by Claypool and Kaplan (1974) and Rice and Claypool (1981). Conditions conducive to the generation of C_1 include high rates of sedimentation, deposition of sufficient organic matter to sustain a microbial population, and establishment of an oxygen-free environment. In the model advocated here, the production of C_1 by microorganisms goes on concurrently with the process of sedimentation. When sufficient C_1 has been generated to saturate the pore water, gas hydrate begins to form, and it will gradually thicken until its base subsides to depths at which the temperatures are sufficiently high to cause the gas hydrate to decompose. This depth is determined by the pressure–temperature stability field of the gas hydrate (Fig. 1) and the geothermal gradient of the sediment column. Below depths at which the gas hydrate is stable, free gas can occur.

An alternate way to explain the formation of marine gas hydrates is to call upon the migration of gas from below into the zone of gas-hydrate stability. Upward migration of C_1 from deeper parts of the sedimentary section for the formation of gas hydrates has been suggested (Lancelot and Ewing, 1972; Hedberg, 1980; Dillon et al., 1980). Upward migration of C_1 would be a

particularly attractive hypothesis if C_1 from the thermal alteration of deeply buried organic matter were available in deep-sea sedimentary sections. However, the molecular composition of the hydrocarbons as well as the isotopic composition of C_1 in sampled marine gas hydrates indicate that the C_1 is biogenic, not thermogenic. Of course, biogenic C_1 might migrate from below the zone of gas hydrate stability, but this source would be limited by the lack of significant biologic activity in deeply buried sediment. The geochemical observations made thus far of gas hydrates in oceanic sediments favor a biologic origin for the C_1 and oppose the hypothesis that gas migration from depth is an important process in gas hydrate formation.

Gas hydrates include large quantities of gas within their crystal-lattice structure. This fact, coupled with the common occurrence of gas hydrates in oceanic sediments inferable from marine seismic records, suggests that marine gas hydrates may provide a source of natural gas in the future. However, current technology probably cannot produce the hydrated gas economically even if production wells were able to reach the appropriate water and sediment depths. Furthermore, marine gas hydrates may act as a barrier or seal to trap C_1 beneath the gas hydrate itself. In such cases, the reservoir characteristics of the sediments beneath the gas hydrate become very important. Therefore, circumstances can be envisioned for the development of continental slope and rise hydrocarbon deposits involving gas hydrates if gas trapped beneath the gas hydrates is in producible reservoir sediments.

REFERENCES

Bernard, B. B., Brooks, J. M. and Sackett, W. M. (1976) Natural gas seepage in the Gulf of Mexico. *Earth and Planet. Sci. Lett.* **31**, 48–54.

Claypool, G. E. and Kaplan, I. R. (1974) The origin and distribution of methane in marine sediments. In *Natural Gases in Marine Sediments*. Ed. by Kaplan, I. R. Plenum, New York. pp. 94–129.

Claypool, G. E., Presley, B. J. and Kaplan, I. R. (1973) Gas analysis of sediment samples from Legs 10, 11, 13, 14, 15, 18 and 19. In *Initial Reports of the Deep Sea Drilling Project*. Ed. by Creager, J. S., Scholl, D. W., et al. **19**, US Govt. Printing Office, pp. 879–884.

Dillon, W. P., Grow, J. A. and Paull, C. K. (1980) Unconventional gas hydrate seals may trap gas off southeast US. *Oil and Gas J.* **78**, No. 1, 124–130.

Ewing, J. I. and Hollister, C. H. (1972) Regional aspects of deep sea drilling in the western North Atlantic. In *Initial Reports of the Deep Sea Drilling Project* **11**. Ed. by Hollister, C. H., Ewing, J. I., et al. US Govt. Printing Office. pp. 951–973.

Hand, J. H., Katz, D. L. and Verma, V. K. (1974) Review of gas hydrates with implications for ocean sediments. In *Natural Gases in Marine Sediments*. Ed. by Kaplan, I. R. Plenum, New York. pp. 179–194.

Harrison, W. E. and Curiale, J. A. (in press) Gas hydrates. In *Initial Reports of the Deep Sea Drilling Project* **67**. Ed. by von Huene, R., Aubonin, J. et al. US Govt. Printing Office.

Hedberg, H. D. (1980) Methane generation and petroleum migration: Problems of Petroleum Migration, SG-10, *Am.*

Ass. Petrol. Geol., Tulsa, Oklahoma. pp. 179–206.

Hitchon, B. (1974) Occurrence of natural gas hydrates in sedimentary basins. In *Natural Gases in Marine Sediments*. Ed. by Kaplan, I. R. Plenum, New York. pp. 195–225.

Hunt, J. M. and Whelan, J. K. (1978) Dissolved gases in Black Sea sediments. In *Initial Reports of the Deep Sea Drilling Project* **42**. Ed. by Ross, D. A., Neprochnov, Y. P. *et al.*, Part 2. US Govt. Printing Office. pp. 661–665.

Katz, D. L., Cornell, D., Kobayashi, R., Poettmann, F. H., Vary, J. A., Elenblass, J. R. and Weinaug, C. F. (1959) Handbook of Natural Gas Engineering, McGraw-Hill, New York, 802 pp.

Kvenvolden, K. A. and Barnard, L. A. (in press) Hydrates of natural gas in continental margins. *Proceedings of Hedberg Conference, Am. Ass. Petrol. Geol.*

Kvenvolden, K. A. and McMenamin, M. A. (1980) Natural gas hydrates: a review of their geologic occurrence. US Geological Survey Circular 825, 11 pp.

Kvenvolden, K. A. and Redden, G. D. (1980) Hydrocarbon gas in sediment from the shelf, slope, and basin of the Bering Sea. *Geochim. Cosmochim. Acta* **44**, 1145–1150.

Lancelot, Y. and Ewing, J. I. (1972) Correlation of natural gas zonation and carbonate diagenesis in Tertiary sediments from the north–west Atlantic. In *Initial Reports of the Deep Sea Drilling Project* **11**. Ed. by Hollister, C. H., Ewing, J. I., *et al.* US Govt. Printing Office. pp. 791–799.

Larson, V. F., Robson, V. B. and Foss, G. N. (1980) Deep Ocean coring — recent operational experience of the Deep Sea Drilling Project, 55th Ann. Fall Tech. Conference and Exhibition, Soc. of Petroleum Engineers of AIME, SPE 9409, pp. 1–9.

McIver, R. D. (1974) Hydrocarbon gas (methane) in canned Deep Sea Drilling Project core samples. In *Natural Gases in Marine Sediments*. Ed. by Kaplan, I. R. Plenum Press, New York. pp. 65–69.

Moore, J. C., Watkins, J. S., *et al.* (1979) Middle American Trench. *Geotimes* **24**, No. 2, 20–22.

Moore, J. C., Watkins, J. S., *et al.* (in press) *Initial Reports of the Deep Sea Drilling Project* **66**. US Govt. Printing Office.

Rice, D. D. and Claypool, G. E. (1981) Generation, accumulation, and resource potential of biogenic gas. *Am. Ass. Petrol. Geol. Bull.* **65**, 5–25.

Ross, D. A., *et al.* (1978) Site 380. In *Initial Reports of the Deep Sea Drilling Project*. Ed. by Ross, D. A., Neprochnov, Y. P., *et al.* Part 2. US Govt. Printing Office. pp. 119–291.

Sheridan, R. E., Gradstein, F., *et al.* (1982) Early history of the Atlantic Ocean and gas hydrates on the Blake Outer Ridge: Results of the Deep Sea Drilling Project Leg 76. *Geol. Soc. Am. Bull.* **93**, 876–885.

Sheridan, R. E., Gradstein, F., *et al.* (in press) *Initial Reports of the Deep Sea Drilling Project* **76**. US Govt. Printing Office.

Shipley, T. H. and Didyk, B. M. (1982) Occurrence of methane hydrates offshore southern Mexico. In *Initial Reports of the Deep Sea Drilling Project* **66**. Ed. by Watkins, J. S., Moore, J. C., *et al.* US Govt. Printing Office.

Shipley, T. H., Houston, M. H., Buffler, R. T., Shaub, F. J., McMillan, K. J., Ladd, J. W. and Worzel, J. L. (1979) Seismic evidence for widespread possible gas hydrate horizons on continental slopes and rises. *Am. Ass. Petrol. Geol. Bull.* **63**, 2204–2213.

Stoll, R. D., Ewing, J. I. and Bryan, G. M. (1971) Anomalous wave velocities in sediments containing gas hydrates. *J. Geophys. Res.* **76**, 2090–2094.

von Huene, R., Aubouin, J., *et al.* (1980) Leg 67. The Deep Sea Drilling Project Mid-American Trench transect off Guatemala. *Geol. Soc. Am. Bull.*, Part 1, **91**, 421–432.

von Huene, R., Aubouin, J., *et al.* (in press) *Initial Reports of the Deep Sea Drilling Project* **67**. US Govt. Printing Office.

Whelan, J. K. (1979) C_1 to C_7 hydrocarbons from IPOD Holes 397 and 397A. In *Initial Reports of the Deep Sea Drilling Project* **47**, Part 1. Ed. by von Rad, V., Ryan, W. B. F., *et al.* US Govt. Printing Office. pp. 531–539.

Yefremova, A. G. and Zhizhchenko, B. P. (1974) Obnaruzheniye kristall-gidradov gazov osadkakh sovremennykh akvatoriy 'Occurrence of crystal-hydrates of gases in the sediments of modern marine basins.' *Dokl. Akad. Nauk. SSSR* **214**, 1179–1181 (in Russian); *Dokl.-Earth Sci. Sect* (1975) **214**, 219–220 (in English).

Advances in Organic Geochemistry 1981, pp. 431–437
© *John Wiley & Sons Limited, 1983*

Organic Matter in Oceanic Sediments of High Thermogradient (DSDP Leg 64, Gulf of California)

E. M. Galimov and L. A. Kodina

V. I. Vernadsky Institute of Geochemistry and Analytical Chemistry of the Academy of Sciences of the USSR, Moscow

Core samples from Holes drilled during DSDP Leg 64 have been studied in order to specify characteristics of the organic matter which depend on thermal effects. Relative hydrocarbon content, composition of the bitumen, *n*-alkane distribution, character and content of tetrapyrrole pigments, carbon isotope distribution between bitumen fractions have all been found to be changed under thermal stress. The observed picture of thermal alteration in organic matter is similar but not absolutely equivalent to the long-term maturation under normal temperature gradient.

INTRODUCTION

The sedimentary sequence of the Gulf of California is characterized by extremely diverse thermal conditions due to recent tectonic activity. Some of the sediments have been subjected to very high thermal stress. But in the same sedimentary basin there are sites where heat flows do not exceed the normal level. Thus the geological environment of the Gulf of California allows a study of the transformation of organic matter under a wide range of thermal conditions with other conditions, including age of the deposits, type and source of organic matter, lithology–facies composition, being more or less uniform.

We studied core samples collected during Deep Sea Drilling Project Leg 64. Locations of Leg 64 drill sites are shown in Fig. 1. Sites 474 to 476 are at the mouth of the Gulf of California and within the boundary of the continental slope. The heat flow in this region is about 3 units (μcal cm^{-2} s^{-1}). Holes 477, 478 and 481A are in the Guaymas Basin, which is an active rift zone and has a typical oceanic crust (Moore *et al.*, 1980). The geological structure of the basin is determined by two short rifting axes separated by a short minor transform fault and confined by two long transform faults. Hole 477 is located in the southern rift zone. Measurements showed extremely high values of heat flow at this site. The sediments were intruded by the thick dolerite sill at the level 58–105.5 m. Below the sill, sediments have undergone extensive hydrothermal alteration. Hydrothermal mineral paragenesis indicate temperatures up to 300 °C (Einsele, *et al.*, 1980). The heat flow at this site exceeds 20 units. Hole 481A is located in the northern rift of the Guaymas Basin. The heat flow is also considerable but much lower than in

Hole 477. The temperature in this Hole is thought to not exceed 150 °C. Hole 478 is located outside the present rifting zone. The heat flow is 3.65 units. Hole 479 is located on the continental slope of the northeastern flank of the Guaymas Basin. The temperature conditions in this Hole are normal. Magmatic intrusions do not occur. The measured value of the heat flow is 2.36 units.

The sedimentary strata recovered by the Holes is commonly represented by hemipelagic diatomaceous ooze with interlayers of turbidites. The basin has a rather high rate of sediment accumulation associated with high biological productivity. The oldest sediments recovered by Hole 474 are early Pliocene, Hole 477 — late Quaternary, Hole 478 — late Pleistocene, Hole 479 — Pleistocene and Hole 481A — late Quaternary.

EXPERIMENTAL

We obtained 26 core samples from the Organic Geochemistry Panel. Details of experimental procedure applied are described elsewhere (Galimov *et al.*, 1980). The general scheme of fractionation of organic matter is shown in Fig. 2. Dry core samples were exhaustively extracted with benzene–methanol mixture (9:1). The extract (bitumen) was fractionated into five fractions. Asphaltenes were precipitated by a 50-fold volume of pentane. Pentane solution was fractionated on a silica-gel column by using for the elution the solvents in the following sequence: hexane, hexane–benzene (1:1), benzene, benzene–methanol (1:1). The hexane fraction contains hydrocarbons. The next three fractions represent resins that differ from each other by their polarity.

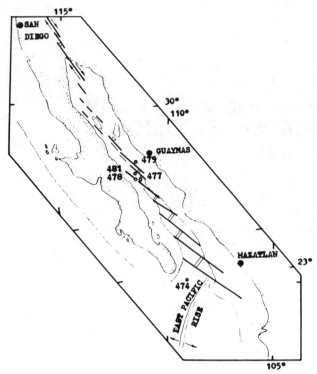

Fig. 1. Location of Leg 64 drill sites.

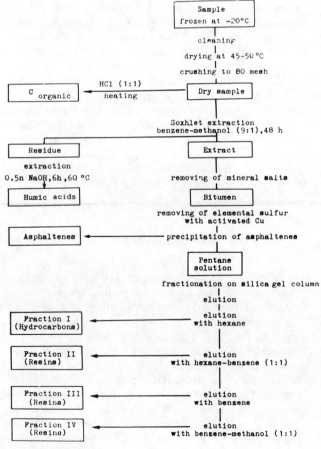

Fig. 2. Flow sheet for separation and fractionation of the organic matter of samples from Holes 474, 477, 478, 479 and 481A.

The hexane fraction was analysed by gas–liquid chromatography (GC). The data on *n*-alkanes and isoprenoid alkanes (pristane and phytane) distribution were obtained. To study tetrapyrrole pigments, absorption spectra in the visible light region from 320 to 700 nm as well as electron spin resonance (ESR) spectra of some bitumen fractions (especially hexane–benzene) were recorded. Carbon isotope composition of all bitumen fractions and the total organic matter in the core samples after removal of carbonate material was measured as described elsewhere (Galimov *et al.*, 1980).

The results obtained are described in detail in the Initial Report of DSDP Leg 64 (Galimov *et al.*, 1981). The purpose of this paper is to specify some of the characteristics of the organic matter which are affected by the temperature factor.

RESULTS AND DISCUSSION

The data on organic carbon and bitumen content are given in Fig. 3. The sediments are characterized by a rather high concentration of organic matter with an average value about 1.5%.

The extractable part of the organic matter varies from about 80–100 ppm to more than 3000 ppm and reveals clear dependence on the thermal factor. The extract content normalized to organic carbon content amounts to 2–10 per cent in unaltered sediments, increases dramatically up to 36% in the thermally altered sample 477-7-1 and gets low again in the sediments which were intensively thermally stressed as core samples 477-16-5, 477-20-1 and 481A-13-6.

Somewhat different dependence on the temperature factor is revealed in the composition of the bitumens. The relative concentration of the bitumen fractions is given in Fig. 4. In the unaltered samples, asphaltenes are the prevalent part of the extract. The hydrocarbon concentration in these samples does not exceed 10 per cent of the whole extract. But the percentage of hydrocarbons reaches 13–20 in the samples thermally affected like cores 477-7-1, 474A-40-3, 479-43-1. Severe thermal stress causes asphaltenes to decrease essentially and fractions of low polarity to be the main ones in the bitumen (hydrocarbon amounts to more than 30% in core 481A-13-6 and up to 50% in core 477-16-5).

In order to find out the regularities in changes of carbon isotope composition of different organic matter fractions depending on the intensity of thermal effect, we attempted to arrange the core samples from different holes according to the component composition of the bitumen and especially the percentage of hydrocarbons in the extract (Fig. 5). The regular increase in percentage of components of low polarity and hydrocarbons in the first place was established for organic matter of different genetic types as the degree of maturity of organic matter grew, the depth of subsidence increased (up to 5 km) and the temperature of rocks rose (Korchagina and Chetverikova, 1979). In the basin under investigation, organic matter and lithological composition of sediments are uniform throughout the thickness recovered. From these considerations we

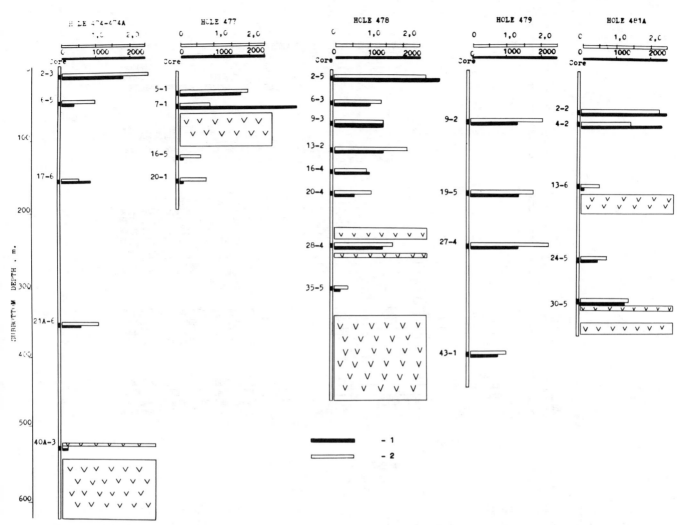

Fig. 3. Organic carbon and bitumen in samples from Holes 474, 477, 478, 479 and 481A. 1. Bitumen, ppm; 2. C_{org}, %.

suggest the component composition of bitumen to be due to the temperature effect rather than other factors. The position of the core samples on a vertical scale in Fig. 5 corresponds to the percentage of hydrocarbon fraction in the extract.

Along with this, the bitumen coefficient, (the yield of extractable organic matter normalized to the organic carbon), increases to a certain limit and drops back after passing through a maximum. The hydrocarbon content normalized to the organic carbon shows the same behaviour. This is just the same pattern which can be observed in the natural process of maturation of organic matter with depth in a sedimentary basin with normal thermal gradient. The maximum presented here by the sample 477-7-1 can be paralleled with the main stage of hydrocarbon generation.

Tetrapyrrole pigment distribution in the sample range also gives evidence of gradual maturation of organic matter when affected by the temperature factor. Tetrapyrrole compounds appear to be the most sensitive indicator of the thermal history of sediments. Organic matter in early diagenesis stages contains chlorins as free bases or Cu–complexes. As sediments subside, chlorines are replaced by porphyrins, mainly as complexes with Cu, Ni and V. The presence of vanadyl porphyrins is characteristic of mature organic matter. Under high

temperatures the porphyrin nucleus is destroyed. Data on the presence of specific tetrapyrrol obtained from ultraviolet, visible and ESR spectra are given in Fig. 6. In this figure, cores are arranged in the same sequence as in Fig. 5 with two exceptions which will be discussed below. Chlorins are present in immature samples 477-5-1, 479-19-5, 481A-2-2, 478-16-4 and 478-9-3. The characteristics of the former two shown in Fig. 6 are typical for this set of the samples. They have visible-light spectra with maxima at 400, 600 and 655 nm, as shown in Fig. 7a. These cores are followed by the set of samples in which porphyrins are present mainly as Ni–complexes along with trace amounts of Cu–complexes. The presence od vanadyl porphyrins distinguishes core 477-7-1 from the rest of the set. Vanadyl complexes were identified in the benzene resin fraction by the specific maxima at 530 and 580 nm (Fig. 7b) in visible-light spectra and by ESR spectra. Ni–complexes are present in the hexane–benzene resin fraction. Visible-light spectra of the fraction has maxima at 522 and 552 nm specified by the Ni–complexes and a shoulder at 562 nm specified by the Cu–porphyrin complexes (Fig. 7b). The core samples which are arranged below core 477-7-1 in Fig. 6 do not contain any porphyrin structures. Core 477-16-5 is an example (Fig. 7c). Visible-light spectra of benzene, and hexane–benzene resin fractions of the sample have

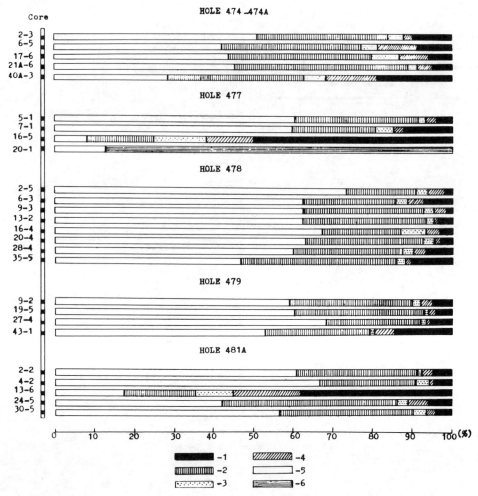

Fig. 4. Relative concentrations (%) of different bitumen fraction. 1. Hydrocarbons, 2. Benzene–methanol (1:1) soluble resins, 3. Benzene soluble resins, 4. Hexane–benzene (1:1) soluble resins, 5. Asphaltenes, 6. Pentane solution (hydrocarbons and resins in the total).

no maxima. In cores 477-16-5, 477-20-1 and 481A-13-6, porphyrins were destroyed as a result of severe thermal stress. Decrease in the values HC/C_{org} and $Extract/C_{org}$ for these cores is due to destructive processes as well. When we compare the core sample succession in Figs 5 and 6 we can see their identity with the exception of cores 479-43-1 and 474A-40-3. In Fig. 5 they proved to be in descending branches of the $Extract/C_{org}$ and $Hydrocarbons/C_{org}$ curves. However other geochemical properties, particularly the presence of Ni–porphyrins only, with absence of VO–porphyrins, indicate that the organic matter in these samples is at a lower stage of geochemical maturation compared with core 477-7-1. Therefore they should be placed on the maturation scale below core sample 477-7-1.

Alkane distribution in the core succession in Fig. 6 has some special features resulting from thermal alteration of the organic matter. All the sediments investigated are composed mainly of diatomaceous muds and contain organic matter of marine genesis. Therefore the CPI-value for n-alkanes $> C_{15}$ is nearly 1 and ranges from 0.89 to 1.41 in the cores under investigation. Against this background even the values of 1.09, 0.99 and 1.11 (samples 481A-13-6, 477-16-5, 477-20-1) cannot be treated as unambiguous evidence for thermal stress.

However the CPI value for high molecular weight alkanes $(> C_{25})$, which is more representative in this respect, is also close to unity for these samples. In addition they are characterized by the lowest values of phytane to n-C_{18} ratio. In chromatograms of hexane fractions of samples 481A-13-6, 477-16-5 and 477-20-1, numerous peaks in the region C_{19}–C_{23} appear which have not been observed in the other samples (Galimov *et al.*, 1981). Taking these pieces of evidence together convince us that the three samples mentioned actually represent the descending branch of the 'maturation curve'.

Thus the samples collected from different Holes and depths when properly arranged makes up a consequential series which simulates progressive maturation of organic matter with depth.

Carbon isotope composition of the organic matter and the bitumen as a whole does not show any dependence on temperature in studied samples, but carbon isotope distribution between the bitumen fractions reveals an interesting temperature effect.

Variations of the carbon isotope composition of the total organic matter and the bitumen throughout the Holes studied are shown in Fig. 8. Relatively high $\delta^{13}C$-values and a narrow range of variations, indicate a

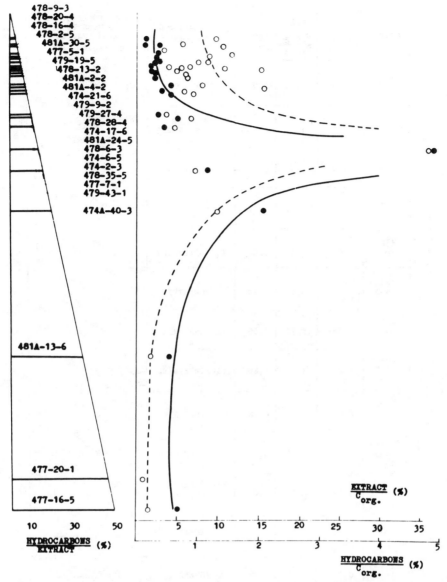

Fig. 5. Trends of change of the extract/C_{org} (black circles) and hydrocarbons/C_{org} (white circles) values in core samples arranged according to the percentages of hydrocarbons in extract (hydrocarbon/extract values).

predominantly marine source of the organic matter with a rather small and constant input of the terrestrial material.

Carbon isotope distribution between the bitumen fractions as we have shown previously (Galimov *et al.*, 1980) is characterized by a certain regularity which consists of depletion of the carbon in the light ^{12}C isotope with an increase of polarity of the bitumen fraction. This is a consequence of thermodynamically ordered carbon isotope distribution in biological systems (Galimov, 1981).

In Fig. 6 one can see that carbon isotope distribution between fractions of the bitumen from slightly and moderately thermally altered samples obey the relationship mentioned above: hydrocarbons are relatively enriched and asphaltenes are depleted in ^{12}C-isotope. But in the samples 477-16-5, 477-20-1 and 481A-13-6 the character of the isotope distribution sharply changes. Carbon isotope composition of the bitumen components flattens or varies irregularly.

It means that in this stage of thermal alteration, fossil organic molecules lose the ordered isotope distribution which was characteristic of their biological precursors. The change in isotope distribution between the bitumen components in the samples belonging to the descending branch of the 'maturation curve' testifies that a decrease in hydrocarbon content in the corresponding stage of maturation of organic matter is due to degradation of hydrocarbons and disproportionation of them into gas and high molecular weight compounds rather than introduction of hydrocarbons from source rocks as is often believed. Indeed, redistribution of isotopes between bitumen fractions cannot be due to input or output of organic compounds. On the contrary, the observed pattern is easily explained by the disproportionation process since it brings about generation of high molecular weight condensation products, from initially ^{12}C-enriched sources, i.e. hydrocarbons, whereas the hydrocarbons themselves are depleted in the ^{12}C isotope because of a kinetic isotope effect which

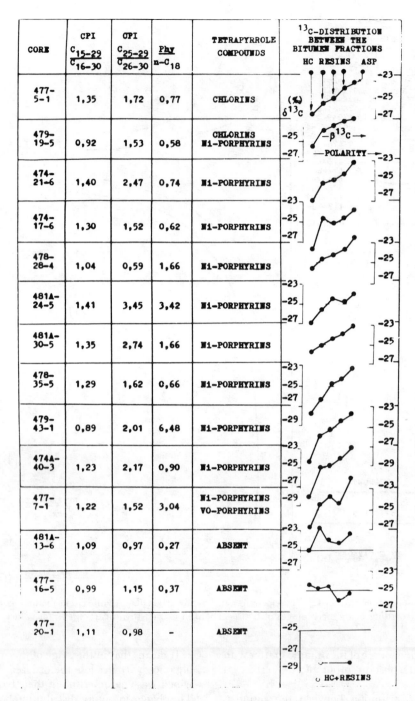

Fig. 6. Change in carbon isotope distribution between the bitumen fractions with increase in thermal effect, as deduced from alkane and tetrapyrrole composition in the core arrangements.

accompanies their cracking.

Thus some features of organic matter clearly change depending on the degree of thermal effect. This change is in agreement with the classical pattern of geochemical evolution of organic matter. At the same time it should be noted that the observed picture of the thermal alteration of organic matter is not completely equivalent to long-term maturation under a normal temperature gradient. Indeed, organic matter from the sample 477-7-1, which corresponds to the main stage of hydrocarbon generation seems to be immature from the standpoint of relatively high CPI, high phytane: $n\text{-}C_{18}$ ratio and the

presence of Cu–porphyrins. On the other hand, strongly thermal degraded samples 477-16-5, 477-20-1 and 481A-13-6 have CPI values close to unity just like oil, but these samples do not contain any tetrapyrrole pigments whereas crude oils do. They lose the regular biomolecular carbon isotope distribution, inheritable from parent which is still preserved to a great extent in crude oils and is revealed in core 477-7-1. These deviations are probably due to a change of chemical reaction mechanism under increased temperature compared with those which occur during long-term maturation of organic matter under conditions of

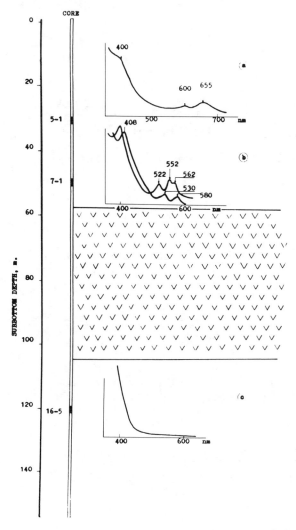

Fig. 7. Visible-light spectra of tetrapyrrole compounds in samples throughout the section, Hole 477.

normal sedimentary sequence where organic matter evolves as part of an energetically conjugated mineral phase–organic matter assemblage (Galimov, 1973).

REFERENCES

Einsele, G., Gieskes, J. M., Curray, G., *et al.* (1980) Intrusion of basaltic sills into highly porous sediments, and resulting hydrothermal activity. *Nature* **283**, N5746, 441–445.

Galimov, E. M. (1975) Carbon isotopes in oil–gas geology. Washington, D.C. *NASA TT F-682* **395**.

Galimov, E. M. (1981) Nature of biological fractionation of isotopes. Nauka, Moscow, **250** (in Russian).

Galimov, E. M., Kodina, L. A., *et al.* (1980) A study of organic matter from deep oceanic bore holes, Deep Sea Drilling Project Sites 415 and 416, in the Moroccan Basin. In *Initial Reports of the Deep Sea Drilling Project* **50**. Ed. by Lancelot, Y., Winterer, E. L., *et al.* US Govt. Printing Office, Washington. pp. 575–600.

Galimov, E. M., Kodina, L. A., Bogacheva, M. P. and Shirinsky, V. G. (1981) Organic geochemical studies of samples from DSDP Leg 64 Sites 474, 477, 478, 479 and 481A in the Gulf of California. In *Initial Reports of the Deep Sea Drilling Project* **64**. Ed. by Curray, J. R., Moore, D. G., *et al.* US Govt. Printing Office, Washington.

Korchagina, J. I. and Chetverikova, O. P. (1980) Methods of interpretation of the analytical data on the composition of organic matter in sedimentary rocks. Nedra, Moscow, **227** (in Russian).

Moore, D. G., Surray, I. R. and Lavfer, L. A. (1978) Tectonic and geological history of the Gulf of California. CIBCASIO Trans. 3rd **3**, 66–75.

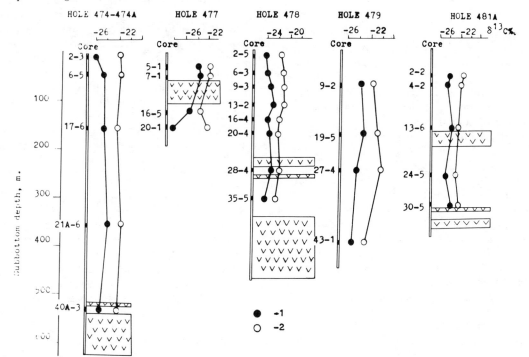

Fig. 8. Carbon isotopic composition of the total organic matter (2) and bitumen (1), Holes 474, 477, 478, 479, 481A.

Advances in Organic Geochemistry 1981, pp. 438–448
© *John Wiley & Sons Limited, 1983*

Maturation of Organic Matter in Areas of High Heat Flow: A Study of Sediments from DSDP Leg 63, Offshore California, and Leg 64, Gulf of California

J. Rullkötter and D. H. Welte

Institute of Petroleum and Organic Geochemistry (ICH-5), Kernforschungsanlage Jülich GmbH, PO Box 1913, D-5170 Jülich 1, F. R. Germany

Sediments from Deep Sea Drilling Project Legs 63 and 64, recovered in areas of high heat flow, were analysed to determine trends of organic matter maturation with increasing depth of burial. Capillary column chromatography and combined gas chromatography–mass spectrometry were employed to study the distribution of extractable hydrocarbons. Distinct maturation effects were observed in the organic matter of the Leg 63 samples (offshore California). As a function of depth, there was an increase in the amount of total extract, normalized to organic carbon, an increasing tendency for the conversion of regular sterenes to steranes, systematic changes in the aromatic hydrocarbon composition, and an increase in vitrinite reflectance. Comparison of these data with those obtained on sediments of similar age, buried more deeply in an area of lower heat flow (off Northwest Africa), indicates an advanced maturity stage of the Leg 63 sediments based on the molecular parameters, e.g. conversion of sterenes to steranes. The Pleistocene sediments of Leg 64 (Gulf of California) did not exhibit the expected pronounced maturation trend. This indicates that, in this case, the higher heat flow did not compensate for the lack of time. Within the investigated range of relatively low maturity, molecular maturation parameters appear to be more sensitive than vitrinite reflectance values.

INTRODUCTION

Several attempts have been made to study the hydrocarbon generation potential of deep sea sediments in terms of total amount and type of organic matter (e.g., Kendrick *et al.*, 1977, 1979; Dow, 1978; Welte *et al.*, 1979; Tissot *et al.*, 1980; Rullkötter *et al.*, 1981, 1982, in press). Investigation of another important prerequisite for hydrocarbon generation in sediments, i.e. maturity of organic matter, is limited by the present deep sea drilling capabilities of the *Glomar Challenger* which are related to safety and pollution prevention aspects. Deep sea drilling in various areas of the world's oceans on the other hand has encountered sediments which, after deposition, were subjected to different degrees of thermal stress due to differences in geothermal heat flow. Because one or several of the above-mentioned important prerequisites for hydrocarbon generation were not fulfilled, the zone of major hydrocarbon generation has never been reached. Furthermore, when approaching this zone, in some cases, drilling had to be terminated because gaseous hydrocarbon concentrations started to increase. However, trends of progressive diagenetic alteration of organic matter with depth could be observed in sediment cores recovered by the Deep Sea Drilling Project (DSDP).

This paper compares the effect of different geothermal gradients on the composition of sedimentary organic matter. Based on several diagenetic maturation parameters the influence of differing heat flow is studied in areas with very high (Gulf of California, DSDP Leg 64), high (eastern North Pacific Ocean off California and Baja California, DSDP Leg 63) and moderate (eastern North Atlantic Ocean off Northwest Africa, DSDP Leg 47a) geothermal gradients. Preliminary results of organic geochemical investigations on these sediments have been published by Cornford *et al.* (1979) and Rullkötter *et al.* (1981, in press).

EXPERIMENTAL

The origin and lithology of the samples investigated during this study as well as the analytical procedures applied for extraction, liquid chromatography, gas chromatography, combined gas chromatography–mass spectrometry (GC–MS) (full mass spectra) and kerogen microscopy have been described in detail by Cornford *et al.* (1979) and Rullkötter *et al.* (1981).

All mass spectra shown in this paper were corrected by background subtraction. Molecular and fragment ion traces of aromatic steroid hydrocarbons were obtained

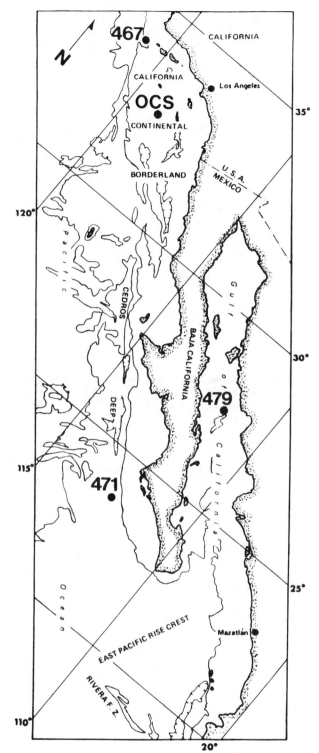

Fig. 1. Map showing the locations of DSDP Sites 467 and 471 (Leg 63, eastern North Pacific), DSDP Site 479 (Leg 64, Gulf of California) and the Southern California Deep Stratigraphic Test OCS-CAL 75–70 No. 1.

by multiple peak monitoring mass spectrometry. Samples were injected splitless onto a 25 m × 0.3 mm i.d. glass capillary column, coated with SE 54. The column was fitted in a Carlo Erba Fractovap model 4160 gas chromatograph and connected via an open-split coupling device to a Kratos MS 3074 mass spectrometer. The oven temperature was programmed from 100 to 270

°C at a rate of 4°C min^{-1}. The mass spectrometer was operated at an ionization energy of 70 eV, the source temperature was 220 °C. Cyclic peak switching to a series of six masses, with a residence time of 200 ms each, resulted in a cycle time of 2.3 s/scan. All data were acquired and processed using an on-line DS-50S data system (Kratos).

4-Methyl-19-norcholesta-1,3,5(10)-triene was prepared by dienol-benzene rearrangement of cholesta-1,4-dien-3-ol under acidic conditions (Gentles *et al.*, 1958; Dannenberg and Doering, 1958). The starting material was synthesized following standard procedures (Fried and Edwards, 1972) from cholest-4-en-3-one (Fluka AG). Dehydrogenation of cholest-4-en-3-one with 2,3-dichloro-5,6-dicyanobenzoquinone (DDQ) gave cholest-1,4-dien-3-one which was reduced to the corresponding alcohol with sodium borohydride. An earlier synthesis under badly controlled conditions afforded a second product which from its mass spectrometric fragmentation pattern was inferred to be a ring B aromatized anthrasteroid (P. Albrecht, private communication). The formation of these compounds in steroid aromatization reactions is known from Ogilvie and Hanson (1972).

SAMPLES

The results presented here were obtained on sediment samples from three different deep sea areas. Sites 467 and 471 (DSDP Leg 63) are located in the eastern North Pacific Ocean offshore California (Patton Escarpment) and Baja California (Fig. 1), and the sediments investigated range from Middle Miocene to Quaternary (Haq *et al.*, 1981a, b). Site 479 (DSDP Leg 64) is on the slope of the Guaymas Basin in the Gulf of California (Fig. 1) within the present oxygen-minimum zone, and the sediments are all of Pleistocene age (Curray *et al.*, in press). The Site 397 (DSDP Leg 47a) samples are from the Early to Middle Miocene slump sequences deposited at the continental rise off Northwest Africa, 120 km south of the Canary Islands (von Rad *et al.*, 1979).

RESULTS

The results obtained for a number of different maturation-relevant parameters are compiled in Figs 2–5 for sediments from all four DSDP sites. The vitrinite reflectance values for the deepest sample at each site are close to 0.4% $\bar{R}_0$.

Organic carbon and total extracts

Total organic carbon values vary between 1 and 5% in the Site 467 samples (Fig. 2), whereas they are fairly constant at about 1% down the hole at Site 471 (Fig. 3). In both cases, however, starting from a constant level around 10 mg/g C_{org} in the shallower sediment sections, the amounts of total extractable organic matter progressively increase up to nearly 40 mg/g C_{org} below 600 m and 300 m (early Late Miocene) at Sites 467 and

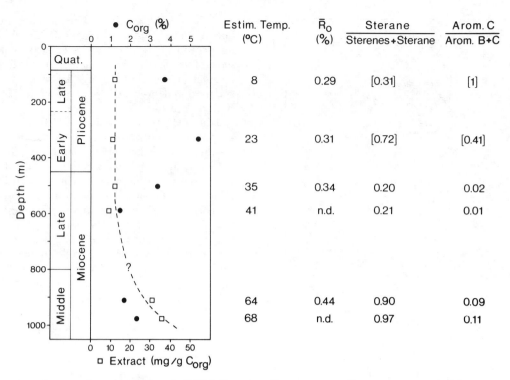

Fig. 2. Summary of maturation relevant data for DSDP Site 467 sediment samples. The estimated temperatures were calculated from the lower limit of the geothermal gradient values measured at DSDP Site 471 (70–154 °C km⁻¹, Haq *et al.*, 1981b). Vitrinite reflectance values were taken from Rullkötter *et al.* (1981). For the definition of the Sterane/(Sterenes + Sterane) and Arom C/(Arom B + C) parameters see text. Values in brackets are influenced by rederived organic matter or large experimental errors due to low concentrations; n.d. = not determined.

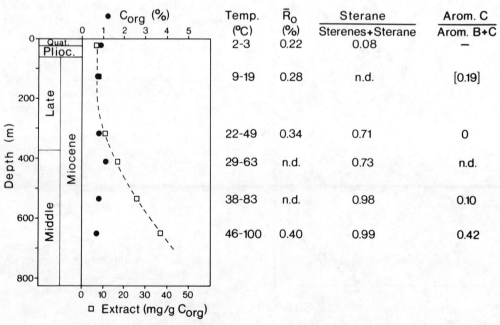

Fig. 3. Summary of maturation relevant data for DSDP Site 471 sediment samples. The temperatures were calculated from the geothermal gradient values measured at this site (70–154 °C km⁻¹; Haq *et al.*, 1981b). Vitrinite reflectance values were taken from Rullkötter *et al.* (1981). Cf. also Fig. 2 legend.

471, respectively. In contrast to this, the extract amounts are constant around 10 mg/g C_{org} in the Gulf of California Site 479 sediments with the organic carbon content varying between 1 and 4% (Fig. 4). The sediments from DSDP Site 397 do not exhibit a similar definite trend (Fig. 5), and these data should not be compared with those reported for the other sites. The absolute values of the total extracts are higher because a more polar solvent has been used (toluene/methanol instead of dichloromethane; Cornford *et al.*, 1979). The scatter in the extract values, normalized to organic carbon, may partly be related to a relatively

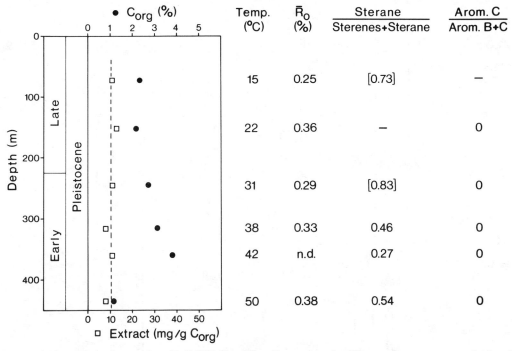

Fig. 4. Summary of maturation relevant data for DSDP Site 479 sediment samples. The temperatures were calculated from the geothermal gradient value measured at this site (95.9 °C, sea bottom temperature 7.9 °C; Curray *et al.*, in press). Vitrinite reflectance values were taken from Rullkötter *et al.* (in press). Cf. also Fig. 2 legend.

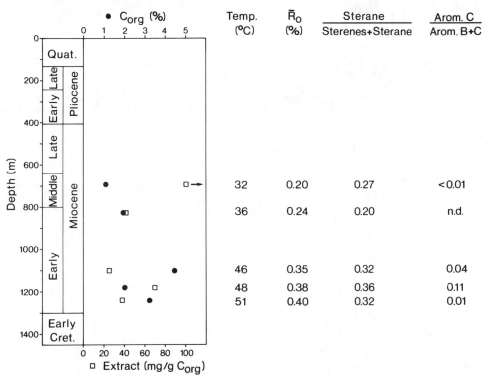

Fig. 5. Summary of maturation relevant data for DSDP Site 397 sediment samples. The temperatures were taken from the values calculated by Yükler *et al.* (1979). Vitrinite reflectance values are from the trend reported for this site by Cornford *et al.* (1979). Cf. also Fig. 2 legend.

inhomogeneous nature of the slumped sediments. In addition, there may be some influence of the experimental procedure, i.e. the lower reproducibility of soxhlet extraction compared with the flow-through extraction method (Radke *et al.*, 1978) which has been used for the Northeastern Pacific and Gulf of California sediments.

Sterane/sterene ratios

The diagenesis of biogenic sterols, in a general sense, is fairly well understood. It involves hydrogenation of sterols to stanols in the uppermost sediment layers, transformation into sterenes and hydrogenation to saturated steranes during later diagenesis (e.g.,

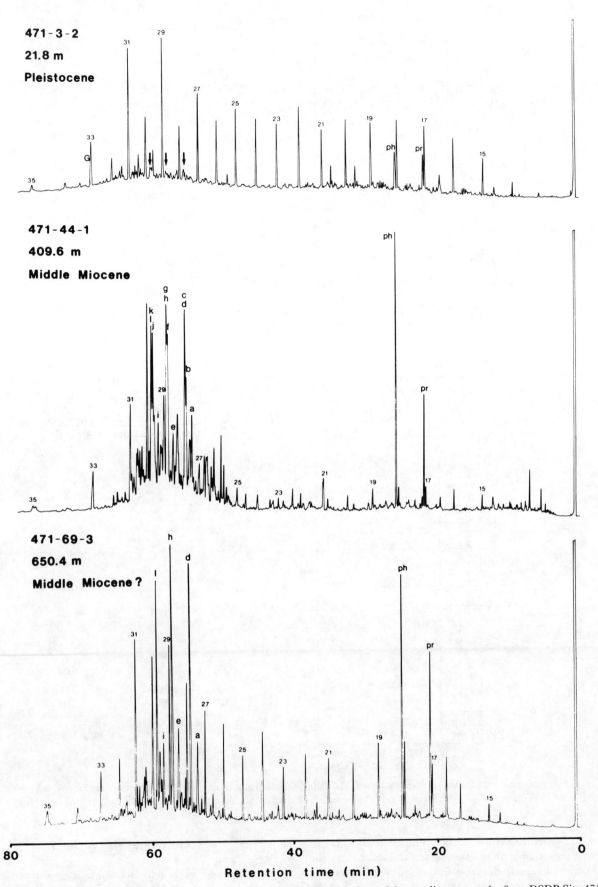

Fig. 6. Capillary column chromatograms of non-aromatic hydrocarbon fractions of three sediment samples from DSDP Site 471 showing increase of steroid hydrocarbon concentrations and conversion to saturated steranes down the hole. Arrows in the upper trace mark positions of C_{27} to C_{29} ster-4-enes/ster-5-enes. Lettered compounds are C_{27}–$C_{29}5\beta(H)$-steranes (a, e, i), ster-4-enes (b, f, j), ster-5-enes (c, g, k) and $5\alpha(H)$-steranes (d, h, l). Pr = pristane, ph = phytane, *n*-alkanes are marked by numbers.

Dastillung and Albrecht, 1977). This is illustrated in Fig. 6 by the capillary column chromatograms of the non-aromatic hydrocarbon fractions extracted from three sediment samples from different depth levels of DSDP Site 471. In the shallowest sample, the absolute concentration of sterenes is very low (position of Δ^4/Δ^5-sterenes marked with arrows in Fig. 6, top). In the Middle Miocene sample from 409.6 m the sterenes are dominant components in the non-aromatic hydrocarbon fraction, but are accompanied by significant amounts of saturated $5\alpha(H)$- and $5\beta(H)$-steranes with the biogenic 2OR-configuration (cf. figure legend for compound identification). In the deepest sample shown in Fig. 6 only the saturated steranes can be identified in the chromatogram.

For the four series of deep sea sediments the conversion of sterenes to steranes has been quantitated by measuring ratios of mass spectrometric key fragment intensities. The sterane/(sterenes + sterane) value in Figs 2–5 is based on the ratio of the absolute abundance (total ion count) represented by the peak in the m/z 217-fragmentogram which corresponds to $5\alpha(H)$-cholestane in the same figure and the abundances represented by the peaks in the m/z 215-fragmentograms which correspond to cholest-4-ene ('b') and cholest-5-ene ('c').

As can be seen in Figs 2 and 3, the hydrogenation of sterenes proceeds rapidly at the Northeastern Pacific DSDP sites in the interval where the increase of organic-carbon-normalized total extracts has been observed. The conversion, measured by the sterane/(sterenes + sterane) ratio, proceeds to 97 and 99% in the deepest samples from Sites 467 and 471, respectively. In the Gulf of California, the relative concentration of steranes has also reached a significant level in the deepest sample (54%, Fig. 4). Some scatter in the values is due to the fact that, in contrast to the other three sites, there is a strong variation in absolute steroid hydrocarbon concentrations in the DSDP Site 479 samples (Rullkötter *et al.*, in press). The Miocene sediments from Site 397 exhibit by far a lower sterene/sterane conversion rate leading to a value of only about 35% at the 1200 m depth level. Values in brackets in Figs 2–5 indicate that the absolute concentrations in the shallow sediments were too low for reliable measurements and the data were sometimes obscured by a contribution of rederived, more mature organic matter.

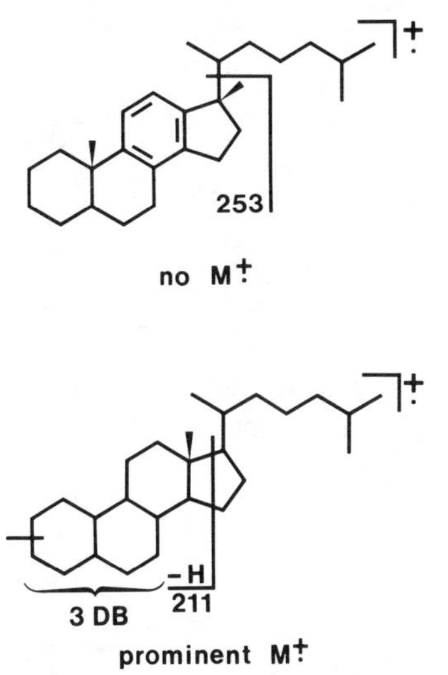

Aromatic steroid hydrocarbons

Diagenetic alteration of biogenic sterols also leads to the formation of aromatic steroid hydrocarbons, probably by dehydrogenation of sterenes. So far, C-ring aromatic steroids (Fig. 7, top) were found to be common in mature sediments and petroleum. They were used for correlation (e.g. Seifert and Moldowan, 1978) and maturation studies (Mackenzie *et al.*, 1981). Some steroid aromatization reactions, however, like triterpenoid aromatization (Spyckerelle *et al.*, 1977; Corbet *et al.*, 1980) seem to be initiated at a very early stage of diagenesis. Ring A monoaromatic steroid hydrocarbons have recently been detected in relatively immature Cretaceous black shales by Hussler *et al.* (1981). Preliminary analysis of deep sea sediments from

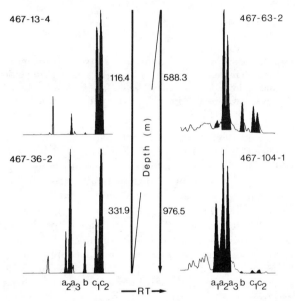

Fig. 7. Scheme of mass spectrometric key fragment formation for ring C aromatic steroid hydrocarbons (top) and ring A/B monoaromatic steroids (bottom).

Fig. 8. Mass fragmentograms of the molecular ions (m/z 366) of C_{27} ring A/B monoaromatic steroids for DSDP Site 467 sediment samples (cf. text for compound identification).

DSDP Legs 63 and 64 have indicated the presence of steroid hydrocarbons most probably aromatized in the A/B-ring part of the molecules (Fig. 7, bottom; Rullkötter *et al.*, 1981, in press). A more systematic investigation of these sediments has now revealed more structural information and indicates compositional changes during diagenesis.

The most important mass spectrometric features of the ring A/B monoaromatic steroid hydrocarbons are a prominent molecular ion and a base peak from ring D fragmentation at m/z 211, whereas the ring C aromatic steroid hydrocarbons show a base peak at m/z 253 from side-chain cleavage and a weak molecular ion usually not detectable under electron impact GC–MS conditions (Fig. 7). Figure 8 shows the molecular ion mass fragmentograms (m/z 366 for C_{27} compounds) for four sediment samples from DSDP Site 467. With

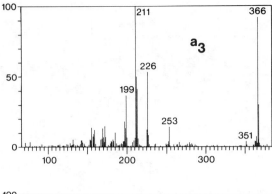

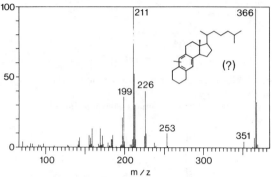

Fig. 9. Mass spectra of compound a₃ (cf. Fig. 8) and a synthetic compound which according to its mass spectrometric fragmentation pattern may be a ring B aromatized anthrasteroid (P. Albrecht, private communication).

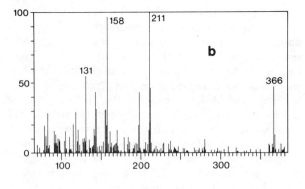

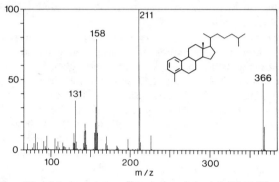

Fig. 10. Mass spectra of compound b (cf. Fig. 8) and synthetic 4-methyl-19-norcholesta-1,3,5(10)-triene.

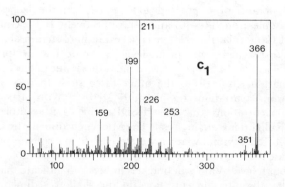

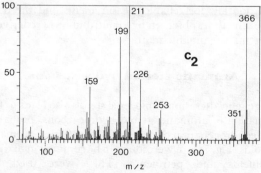

Fig. 11. Mass spectra of compounds c₁ and c₂ (cf. Fig. 8).

increasing depth there is a systematic change in the composition of the ring A/B monoaromatic steroids which may be divided into three different groups.

The group 'a' compounds apparently become more abundant relative to the others with depth. The mass spectrum of compound a₃ is shown in Fig. 9. It is virtually identical with that of a coeluting by-product in the synthesis of 4-methyl-19-norcholesta-1,3,5(10)-triene (cf. Experimental section). The mass spectrum of a₂ is nearly identical with that of a₃, so it may be speculated that a₂ is an isomer of a₃. The mass spectrometric fragmentation patterns of these compounds indicate that they may be anthrasteroids aromatized in Ring B (P. Albrecht, private communication) which under certain conditions are obtained as by-products in the laboratory ring A aromatization of steroids (e.g., Ogilvie and Hanson, 1972). Compound a₁, which has a significant abundance only in the deepest sample from 976.5 m (Fig. 8), according to its mass spectrum has lost the methyl group at C-10 during aromatization. The characteristic ring D fragment and related peaks in the mass spectrum are shifted by 14 mass units to lower masses compared with compound a₃ (Fig. 9).

Compound b, which is a minor component in most of the samples investigated and which seems to be lost during diagenesis (Fig. 8), has a mass spectrum similar to that of 4-methyl-19-nor-1,3,5(10)-cholestatriene, and coinjection on a SE 54 capillary column showed that the synthetic compound coelutes with b (Fig. 10). Compounds c₁ and c₂, which are relatively abundant in the shallower sediments but are progressively reduced with increasing maturation (Fig. 8), could not be

identified. Their mass spectra (Fig. 11) being nearly identical to each other, resemble that of compound a₃ (Fig. 9). Differences are the higher abundance of the $(M - 2)^+$ peaks (m/z 364) and of the m/z 199 and m/z 159 fragments in the mass spectra of compounds c₁ and c₂, whereas the peak at m/z 213 has a higher relative intensity in the mass spectrum of a₃.

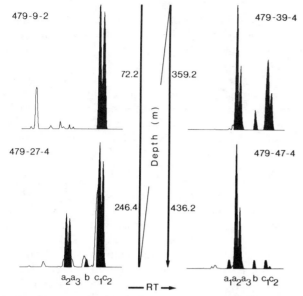

Fig. 12. Mass fragmentograms of the molecular ions (m/z 366) of C_{27} ring A/B monoaromatic steroids for DSDP Site 479 sediment samples (cf. text for compound identification.

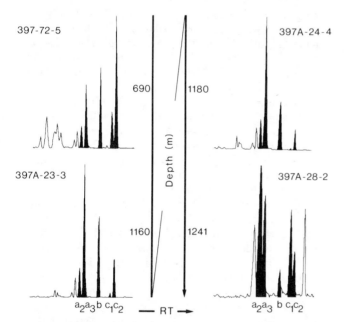

Fig. 13. Mass fragmentograms of the molecular ions (m/z 366) of C_{27} ring A/B monoaromatic steroids for DSDP Site 397 sediment samples (cf. text for compound identification).

The diagenetic development affecting the ring A/B monoaromatic steroid hydrocarbons is obvious from the m/z 366 mass chromatogram of the DSDP Site 467 samples in Fig. 8. Compounds b, c_1 and c_2 are reduced in abundance relative to compounds a_2 and a_3 with increasing depth of burial. Compound a_1 which has lost a methyl group during aromatization starts to gain importance only at a relatively late stage. Very similar results were obtained for the Site 471 sediments where in the deepest sediment sample only the group 'a' compounds were found to be present.

In the Gulf of California sediments (DSDP Site 479) this diagenetic process could only be observed to a level where compounds a_2 and a_3 were greatly enhanced at

the expense of compounds b, c_1 and c_2 (Fig. 12). The formation of the ring A/B desmethyl compound (a_1) has apparently just started in the deepest sediment investigated. An even lower diagenetic stage was observed in the North Atlantic sediments from DSDP Site 397 at 1241 m depth, where compounds c_1 and c_2 are still present in significant amounts (Fig. 13). The compound eluting before a_2 in the Site 397 samples (Fig. 13) is not a_1 as was noticed from the absence of the corresponding fragment in the m/z 197 mass fragmentograms.

A process operating parallel to the changes in the ring A/B monoaromatic steroids is the progressive formation of ring C monoaromatic steroid hydrocarbons. As can be seen from Figs 2–5 the ring C aromatic steroids increase in abundance relative to the ring B aromatic compounds indicating that a higher energy level is required for the formation of the ring C monoaromatic steroid hydrocarbons. Again, different levels of diagenetic development were observed for the different DSDP sites investigated when the abundance of the m/z 253 fragment ('Arom C') of the first-eluting C_{27} ring C monoaromatic steroid hydrocarbon (Mackenzie et al., 1981) was measured relative to the sum of the m/z 211 fragments of the tentatively identified ring B monoaromatic compounds a_2 and a_3 ('Arom B'). The ratio Arom C/(Arom B + C) reaches the highest value in the deepest sample from DSDP Site 471 (0.42; Fig. 3), but an increase was also obvious at Site 467 (Fig. 2). No C-ring aromatic steroid hydrocarbons were detected in the DSDP Site 479 samples (Fig. 4), which may be partly due to the low concentration level of steroid hydrocarbons in most of the sediments from this site. The value of the Arom C/(Arom B + C) ratio in the deepest DSDP Site 397 sediment (1241 m; Fig. 5) is still very low. Higher values in the overlying sediments at this site confirm the scatter in the downhole trends observed for other maturation parameters as well (cf., e.g., Fig. 13).

DISCUSSION

The investigation of the extractable hydrocarbon fractions has revealed that the organic matter in the sediments from the three different deep sea areas has undergone different diagenetic maturation developments, although the vitrinite reflectance values indicated that the deepest sediments analysed in each case should have reached approximately the same maturation levels. According to the parameters used, i.e. the amount of total extracts normalized to organic carbon (disregarding the values for the DSDP Site 397 sediments for experimental reasons), the ratio of sterene to sterane conversion, the changes in the composition of ring A/B monoaromatic steroids and the ratio of ring C aromatic relative to ring B aromatic steroid hydrocarbons, the highest maturity levels are reached in the Middle Miocene sediments from the eastern North Pacific (DSDP Sites 467 and 471). The normalized total extracts and the degree of sterene hydrogenation, which is nearly complete in the deepest samples at both sites (Figs 2 and 3) indicate that sediments of comparable age are slightly more mature at DSDP Site 471 than at Site

467 farther north, although these sediments are less deeply buried at Site 471. The more advanced maturity at Site 471 becomes even more obvious when the ratio of C- and B-ring aromatized steroids are compared (Figs 2 and 3).

The present geothermal gradient at Site 471 has been measured to lie between 70 and 154 °C km^{-1} (Haq *et al.*, 1981b). Unfortunately, this wide span already indicates that the measured data cannot be taken as very reliable, and so they may merely indicate that the geothermal gradient is high offshore Baja California. In Fig. 2 estimated temperatures are given for the Site 467 sediments based on the lower value of the range determined at Site 471 (70 °C km^{-1}), because the chemical data indicate that the heat flow at Site 467 must also be relatively high but slightly lower than at Site 471. In contrast to this estimate are probably more reliable temperature values measured on the Southern Californian outer continental shelf during drilling of a deep stratigraphic test well (OCS-CAL 75–70 No. 1; Fig. 1) which revealed a present geothermal gradient of only 33 °C km^{-1} and an immature/mature transition (from pyrolysis) between 2400 and 2700 m (Paul *et al.*, 1976). Gas chromatograms of non-aromatic hydrocarbon fractions comparable to that in Fig. 6 (bottom) were not obtained above about 1500 m depth in the OCS-CAL well (Paul *et al.*, 1976) indicating a considerably higher geothermal gradient at the continental rise off Southern California than on the shelf.

The sediments from DSDP Site 397 are slightly older (Early to Late Miocene) than those from the eastern North Pacific Sites and buried several hundred metres deeper. Nevertheless, all hydrocarbon maturity parameters used (Figs 5 and 13) exhibit that the organic matter in the Site 397 sediments is still very immature. The geothermal gradient at this site off Northwest Africa has been calculated by Yükler *et al.* (1979) to be 44 °C km^{-1} above and 36 °C km^{-1} below 410 m sediment depth which is consistent with downhole temperature measurements. The temperature data and the analytical results for Site 397 thus indicate that the estimated temperatures for Site 467 most probably are not too high.

Still, there is the discrepancy between the measured vitrinite reflectance values, which are nearly the same in the deepest samples from the North Atlantic and Northeastern Pacific sites, and the hydrocarbon maturity parameters, which differ greatly in these two areas. The mere fact that huminite–vitrinite reflectance values usually show a relatively large standard deviation in the immature range below 0.5% $\bar{R}_0$ due to the presence of vitrinite subtypes (e.g., Dow, 1977) cannot explain the substantial differences observed in the hydrocarbon fractions. More likely, there is an additional effect of the absolute temperature levels reached in the sediments. It has been shown that some chemical processes seem to proceed faster in the bitumen of sedimentary rocks than in the related kerogen (Seifert, 1978). Thus, if the data from DSDP Site 397 are taken as representing the result of 'normal' maturation, then the higher temperatures at the eastern North Pacific sites mainly initiated the release of loosely bound compounds from the kerogen and affected the chemical composition

in the bitumen but had no or only little effect on those processes which are responsible for the changes in vitrinite reflectance.

The Pleistocene sediments from the Gulf of California (DSDP Site 479) according to their hydrocarbon characteristics (Figs 4 and 12) have reached a maximum maturity stage in between that of the North Atlantic and Northeastern Pacific sediments. The geothermal gradient has been determined to be 95.9 °C km^{-1} (Curray *et al.*, in press) which leads to an extrapolated temperature of 50 °C for the deepest sample analysed from DSDP Site 479. With the wide span for the geothermal gradient at DSDP Site 471 in mind, however, comparison of the analytical results with other sites based on the temperature values may be too speculative. The differences in age of the sediments and the uncertainty about the reliability of the temperature values make it difficult to compare the results of DSDP Site 479 with those of the other sites. They also make it difficult to delineate exactly the effects of time and temperature on the organic matter maturation in the different areas. Assuming the highest heat flow in the Gulf of California, however, it is clear that higher temperatures have compensated for many million years compared with the North Atlantic site. On the other hand, it is obvious that the probably higher heat flow in the Gulf of California did not compensate for the lack of time when compared with the deep sea area offshore California and Baja California.

In the relatively young and immature sediments investigated, the chemical maturation parameters in the hydrocarbon fractions seem to be more sensitive than the measurements of huminite–vitrinite reflectance. Nevertheless, more reliable temperature information is needed to relate the observed discrepancies to the kinetics of diagenetic processes.

The maturation parameters for immature organic matter described here add to a number of other hydrocarbon maturation parameters mainly useful in the 'oil window' (e.g. Mackenzie *et al.*, 1980, 1981; Seifert and Moldowan, 1980; Radke and Welte, this volume). The hydrogenation of sterenes to steranes leads over to the isomerization reactions in the sterane skeleton at higher maturity levels, i.e. during catagenesis (Mackenzie *et al.*, 1980). The changes observed in the ring A/B monoaromatic steroid hydrocarbons and the increase of relative abundance of ring-C aromatized steroid hydrocarbons are followed by an increase in triaromatic/monoaromatic steroid ratios and later by an increase in side-chain cleavage in the aromatic steroid hydrocarbons (Mackenzie *et al.*, 1981).

CONCLUSIONS

Chemical maturation parameters have been shown to demonstrate the differences in organic matter maturation between sediments from deep sea areas with different geothermal heat flows. These parameters, i.e. the conversion of sterenes to steranes, changes in the composition of ring A/B monoaromatic steroids and in the ratio of ring C to ring B aromatic steroid hydrocarbons, seem to be more sensitive than huminite–vitrinite reflectance at least in the diagenetic stage investigated here. The most likely reason for this are differences in the kinetics between reactions of isolated molecules in solution and solid state reactions in the vitrinite particles. The chemical maturation parameters described here for the diagenetic level add to known hydrocarbon maturation parameters, e.g. sterane and triterpane isomerization (Mackenzie *et al.*, 1980; Seifert and Moldowan, 1980), steroid aromatization (Mackenzie *et al.*, 1981) and alkylphenanthrene ratios (Radke and Welte, this volume), which are mostly applicable in more mature sediments.

Middle Miocene sediments in the eastern North Pacific, exposed to high heat flow, have reached a higher maturity than slightly older sediments buried more deeply in the eastern North Atlantic. Pleistocene sediments from the very high heat flow area in the Gulf of California based on the hydrocarbon maturation parameters show a higher maturity than the Early Miocene sediments in the North Atlantic but are slightly less mature than the Middle Miocene sediment from offshore California and Baja California.

Acknowledgements

We would like to thank Mr F. J. Keller for his technical assistance. Financial support by the Deutsche Forschungsgemeinschaft (Bonn), grants No. We 346/23 and We 346/25, is gratefully acknowledged.

REFERENCES

Corbet, B., Albrecht, P. and Ourisson, G. (1980) Photochemical or photomimetic fossil triterpenoids in sediments and petroleum. *J. Am. Chem. Soc.* **102**, 1171–1173.

Cornford, C., Rullkötter, J. and Welte, D. H. (1979) Organic geochemistry of DSDP Leg 47a, Site 397, eastern North Atlantic: organic petrography and extractable hydrocarbons. In *Initial Reports of the Deep Sea Drilling Project* (ed. by von Rad, U., Ryan, W. B. F., *et al.*), Vol. 47, part 1, pp. 511–522. U.S. Government Printing Office, Washington.

Curray, J. R., Moore, D. G. and Shipboard Party (in press) Site Chapter DSDP Site 479. In *Initial Reports of the Deep Sea Drilling Project* (ed. by Curray, J. R., Moore, D. G., *et al.*), Vol. 64, U.S. Government Printing Office, Washington.

Dannenberg, H. and Doering, C. (1958) Dehydrierung von Steroiden, II. Ring A-benzoide Steroide. *Hoppe Seyler's Z. Physiol. Chem.* **311**, 84–86.

Dastillung, M. and Albrecht, P. (1977) Δ²-sterenes as diagenetic intermediates in sediments. *Nature (London)* **269**, 678–679.

Dow, W. G. (1977) Kerogen studies and geological interpretations. *J. Geochem. Explor.* **7**, 79–99.

Dow, W. G. (1978) Petroleum source beds on continental slopes and rises. *AAPG Memoir 29*, pp. 423–442.

Fried, J. and Edwards, J. A. (1972) *Organic Reactions in Steroid Chemistry*, Vol. 1, Van Nostrand Reinhold Co., New York.

Gentles, J. M., Moss, J. B., Herzog, H. L. and Hershberg, E. B. (1958) The dienol-benzene rearrangement. Some chemistry of 1,4-androstadiene-3,17-dione. *J. Am. Chem. Soc.* **80**, 3702–3705.

Haq, B., Yeats, R. S. and Shipboard Party (1981a) Site Chapter DSDP Site 467. In *Initial Reports of the Deep Sea Drilling Project*, Vol. 63, ed. by Haq, B., Yeats, R. S., *et al.* U.S. Government Printing Office, Washington, pp. 23–112.

Haq, B., Yeats, R. S. and Shipboard Party (1981b) Site Chapter DSDP Site 471. In *Initial Reports of the Deep Sea Drilling Project* Vol. 63, ed. by Haq, B., Yeats, R. S., *et al.* U.S. Government Printing Office, Washington, pp. 269–349.

Hussler, G., Chappe, B., Wehrung, P. and Albrecht, P. (1981) C_{27}–C_{29} ring A monoaromatic steroids in Cretaceous black shales. *Nature (London)* **294**, 556–558.

Kendrick, J. W., Hood, A. and Castaño, J. R. (1977) Petroleum-generating potential of sediments from Leg 41, Deep Sea Drilling Project. In *Initial Reports of the Deep Sea Drilling Project*, Vol. 41, ed. by Lancelot, Y., Seibold, E., *et al.* U.S. Government Printing Office, Washington, pp. 817–819.

Kendrick, J. W., Hood, A. and Castaño, J. R. (1979) Petroleum-generating potential of sediments from Leg 47, Deep Sea Drilling Project. In *Initial Reports of the Deep Sea Drilling Project*, Vol. 47, part 2, ed. by Sibuet, J.-C., Ryan, W. B. F., *et al.* U.S. Government Printing Office, Washington, pp. 547–551.

Ludwig, B., Hussler, G., Wehrung, P. and Albrecht, P. (1981) C_{26}–C_{29} Triaromatic steroid derivatives. *Tetrahedron Lett.* **22**, 3313–3316.

Mackenzie, A. S., Patience, R. L., Maxwell, J. R., Vandenbroucke, M. and Durand, B. (1980) Molecular parameters of maturation in the Toarcian shales, Paris Basin, France I. Changes in the configuration of acyclic isoprenoid alkanes, steranes and triterpanes. *Geochim. Cosmochim. Acta* **44**, 1709–1721.

Mackenzie, A. S., Hoffmann, C. F. and Maxwell, J. R. (1981) Molecular parameters of maturation in the Toarcian shales, Paris Basin, France III. Changes in aromatic steroid hydrocarbons. *Geochim. Cosmochim. Acta* **45**, 1345–1355.

Ogilvie, A. G. and Hanson, J. R. (1972) The aromatization of some 3-substituted 5α,6α-epoxysteroids. *J. Chem. Soc. Perkin Trans.* **1**, 1981–1983.

Paul, R. G., Arnal, R. E., Baysinger, J. P., Claypool, G. E., Holte, J. L., Lubeck, C. M., Patterson, J. M., Poore, R. Z., Slettene, R. L., Sliter, W. V., Taylor, J. C., Tudor, R. B. and Webster, F. L. (1976) Geological and operational summary, Southern California Deep Stratigraphic Test OCS-CAL 75–70 No. 1, Cortes Bank area offshore Southern California. *U.S. Geological Survey Open File Report* No. 76–223, 65 pp.

von Rad, U., Ryan, W. B. F. and Shipboard Party (1979) *Initial Reports of the Deep Sea Drilling Project*, Vol. 47, part 1. U.S. Government Printing Office, Washington, 835 pp.

Radke, M., Sittardt, H. G. and Welte, D. H. (1978) Removal of soluble organic matter from rock samples with a flow-through extraction cell. *Anal. Chem.* **50**, 663–665.

Rullkötter, J., von der Dick, H. and Welte, D. H. (1981) Organic petrography and extractable hydrocarbons of sediments from the eastern North Pacific Ocean, Deep Sea Drilling Project Leg 63. In *Initial Reports of the Deep Sea Drilling Project*, Vol. 63, ed. by Haq, B., Yeats, R. S., *et al.* U.S. Government Printing Office, Washington, pp. 819–836.

Rullkötter, J., Cornford, C. and Welte, D. H. (1982) Geochemistry and petrography of organic matter in Northwest African continental margin sediments: quantity, provenance, depositional environment, and temperature history. In *Geology of the Northwest African Continental Margin*, ed. by von Rad, U., *et al.* Springer-Verlag, Heidelberg, pp. 686–703.

Rullkötter, J., von der Dick, H. and Welte, D. H. (in press)

Organic petrography and extractable hydrocarbons of sediments from the Gulf of California, Deep Sea Drilling Project Leg 64. In *Initial Reports of the Deep Sea Drilling Project*, Vol. 64, ed. by Curray, J. R., Moore, D. G., *et al.* U.S. Government Printing Office, Washington.

Seifert, W. K. (1978) Steranes and terpanes in kerogen pyrolysis for correlation of oils and source rocks. *Geochim. Cosmochim. Acta* **42**, 473–484.

Seifert, W. K. and Moldowan, J. M. (1978) Application of steranes, terpanes and monoaromatics to the maturation, migration and source of crude oils. *Geochim. Cosmochim. Acta* **43**, 111–126.

Seifert, W. K. and Moldowan, J. M. (1980) The effect of thermal stress on source-rock quality as measured by hopane stereochemistry. In *Advances in Organic Geochemistry — 1979*, ed. by Douglas, A. G. and Maxwell, J. R. Pergamon Press, Oxford, pp. 229–237.

Spyckerelle, C., Greiner, A. Ch., Albrecht, P. and Ourisson, G. (1977) Hydrocarbures aromatiques d'origine géologique. III. Un tetrahydrochrysène, dérivé de triterpènes, dans des sédiments récents et anciens: 3,3,7-triméthyl-1,2,3,4-tetrahydrochrysène. *J. Chem. Res. (M)*, 3746–3777.

Tissot, B., Demaison, G., Masson, P., Delteil, J. R. and Combaz, A. (1980) Palaeoenvironment and petroleum potential of the mid-Cretaceous black shales in the Atlantic Basins. *Bull. Am. Ass. Petrol. Geol.* **64**, 2051–2063.

Welte, D. H., Cornford, C. and Rullkötter, J. (1979) Hydrocarbon source rocks in deep sea sediments. *Proceedings of the 11th Annual Offshore Technology Conference (Houston)*, Vol. 1, pp. 457–464.

Yükler, M. A., Cornford, C. and Welte, D. H. (1979) Simulation of geologic, hydrodynamic, and thermodynamic development of a sediment basin — a quantitative approach. In *Initial Reports of the Deep Sea Drilling Project*, Vol. 47, part 1, ed. by von Rad, U., Ryan, W. B. F., *et al.* U.S. Government Printing Office, Washington, pp. 761–771.

Advances in Organic Geochemistry 1981, pp. 449–464
© *John Wiley & Sons Limited, 1983*

Diagenesis of Steroidal Compounds in Sediments from the Southern California Bight (DSDP Leg 63, Site 467)

J. McEvoy and J. R. Maxwell

Organic Geochemistry Unit, University of Bristol, School of Chemistry, Cantock's Close, Bristol BS8 1TS, England

The distributions of several classes of steroidal compounds (alkanes, alkenes and alcohols) have been examined in sediments (Quaternary to Middle Miocene) collected at Site 467 (Southern California Bight; DSDP Leg 63) using gas chromatography and combined gas chromatography–mass spectrometry. The high relative abundances of steroidal components in their respective fractions reflect a high productivity and good preservation at the time of deposition for the samples which are discussed in detail. Abundant evidence has been obtained for the diagenesis of steroidal compounds occuring at a faster rate in this area of high geothermal gradient that in the Japan Trench (DSDP Legs 56/57), an area of low geothermal gradient; for example, sterols have disappeared by the Late Miocene at Site 467 but are still present in high relative abundance in the Late Miocene samples of the Japan Trench. These differences are not accounted for in terms of differences in burial depth. The results are in keeping with those obtained from a number of other compound classes in the same sediments from Site 467 in that defunctionalization (e.g. disappearance of ketones and chlorins) has occurred to a marked extent by the Early Pliocene/Late Miocene.

INTRODUCTION

A major objective of Leg 63 of the Deep Sea Drilling Project (DSDP) was to investigate palaeoclimatic fluctuations of the southward flowing Southern California Current, seven sites (Sites 467–473) being drilled in a north–south transect (Fig. 1). The sites are situated in areas of high geothermal gradient (e.g. *c.* 80 °C km^{-1} at Site 471; Site Reports, 1981). Since it was expected that Miocene sediments rich in organic matter would be recovered, another major objective was to investigate the diagenesis of organic matter.

In the present study, Site 467 (Fig. 1) was chosen because sediment cores were available from the Quaternary to the Middle Miocene, spanning a depth range of about 1 km (Fig. 2). With the exception of samples 74-1 and 85-4 (Tuff, Fig. 2), the samples are clay-rich and have high concentrations of organic matter (3-3 = 2.4, 36-2 = 5.7, 54-2 = 5.1, 110-3 = 2.9% TOC respectively). The TOC value of a small sample (chips) of 85-4 (74-1 not measured) was also relatively high (1.6%) but the remainder of the sample extracted after crushing had very low concentrations of lipids (as did 74-1), possibly reflecting the inhomogeneity of the tuff core samples which was also apparent from visual inspection. With the exception of samples 74-1 and 85-4, the distributions of a variety of lipid and geolipid classes (see below) have been examined. It was hoped that the biological marker compounds of the sediments from this area of relatively high heat flow would (i) reveal extensive changes in their distributions as a result of diagenesis, (ii) provide a comparison with those examined previously (Brassell *et al.*, 1980b and c) in sediments of comparable ages from the Japan Trench (DSDP Legs 56 and 57) where the geothermal gradient is much lower (*c.* 24 °C km^{-1} at Site 440; Langseth and Burch, 1980). Although several compound types have been examined, only compounds based on the steroidal skeleton are discussed here.

EXPERIMENTAL

Isolation

The extraction and separation procedures are described in detail elsewhere (Barnes *et al.*, 1979). The solvent extract was fractionated by thin layer chromatography into appropriate compound classes (aliphatic hydrocarbons, aromatic hydrocarbons, metallo-porphyrins, ketones, alcohols, carboxylic acids and 'polars'). Fractions, except metalloporphyrins, were analysed (after derivatization where appropriate, i.e. silylation of alcohols and methylation of carboxylic acids) by gas liquid chromatography (GC) and computerised gas chromatography–mass spectrometry (GC–MS).

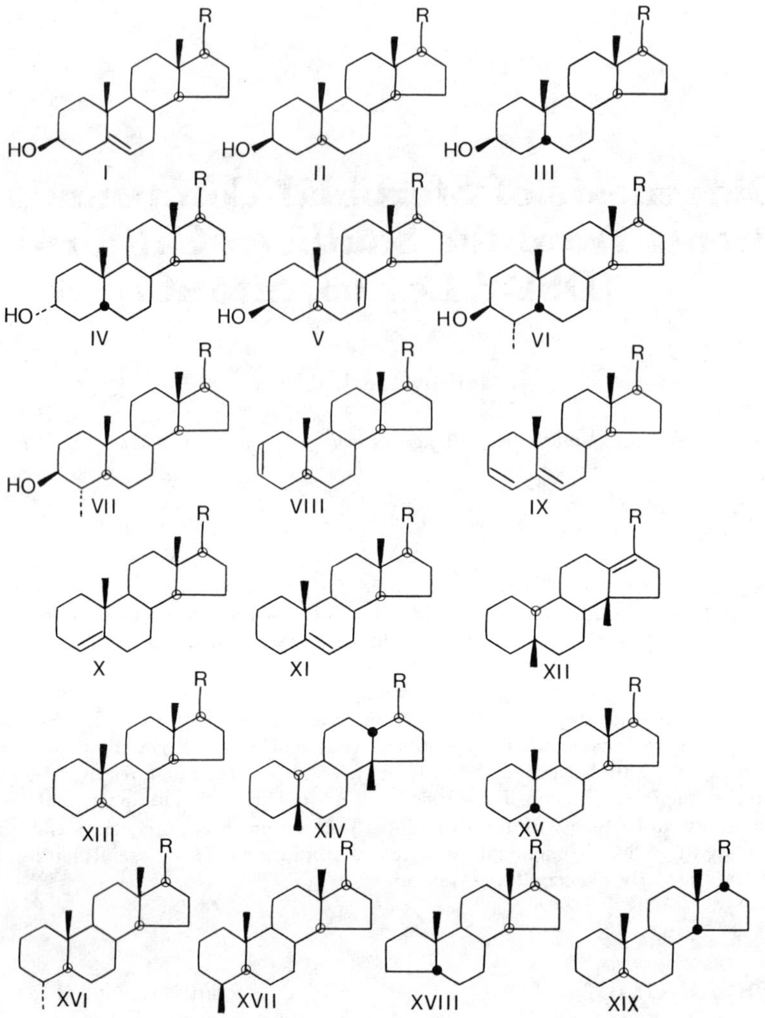
I
II
III
IV
V
VI
VII
VIII
IX
X
XI
XII
XIII
XIV
XV
XVI
XVII
XVIII
XIX

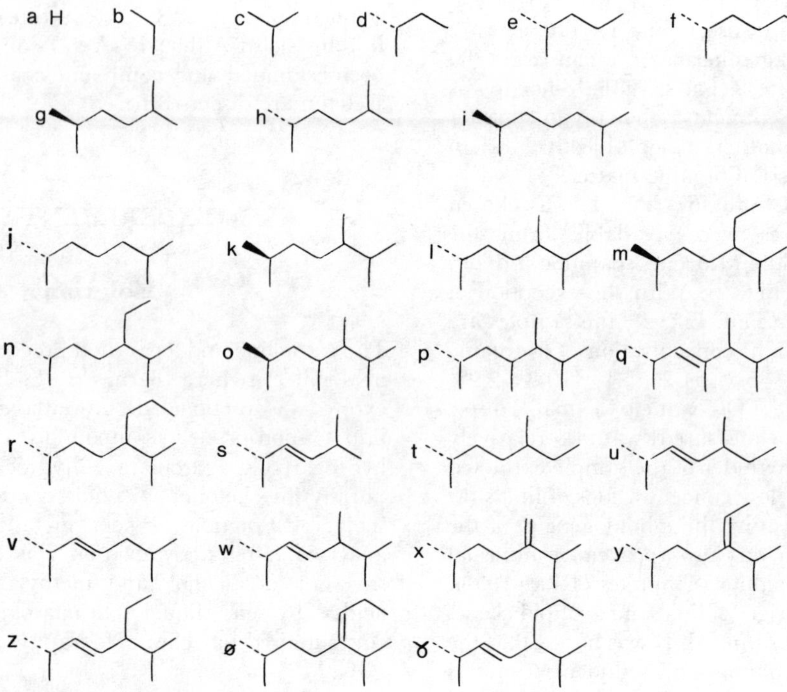
a H
b
c
d
e
f
g
h
i
j
k
l
m
n
o
p
q
r
s
t
u
v
w
x
y
z
ø
ɤ

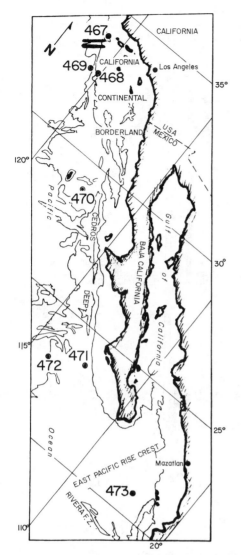

Fig. 1. Locations of drilling sites for Leg 63, including Site 467 studied herein (taken from Site Reports, 1981).

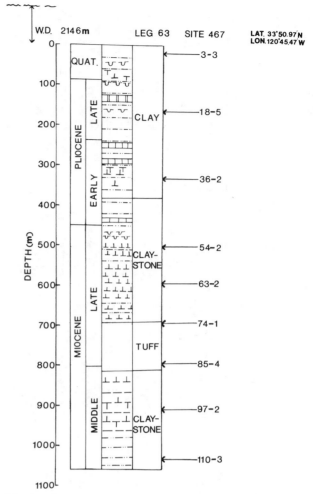

Fig. 2. Stratigraphic summary of Leg 63, Site 467 (adapted from Site Reports, 1981). Arrows indicate the approximate locations of the sediments examined herein.

GC and GC–MS

Typical GC conditions were: Carlo Erba 2151, SL 490 splitless injector, 20 m OV-1 glass capillary, typically programmed from 50–270 °C at 4 °C min^{-1}. The GC/MS system comprised a Finnigan 9610 chromatograph (coupled directly to a Finnigan 4000 mass spectrometer equipped with an INCOS 2300 data system). Typically, splitless injection was used with programming from 50–100 °C at 6 °C min^{-1}, then to 265 °C at 4 °C min^{-1}. Samples were analysed using either a glass capillary column (20 m OV-1, Jaeggi) or a fused silica column (25 m, methyl silicone fluid, Hewlett–Packard).

Individual components were either assigned from mass spectral interpretation, consideration of elution orders, and by comparison with previous assignments, where possible (e.g. Wardroper, 1979; Brassell, 1980; Mackenzie *et al.*, 1980; Brassell and Eglinton, 1981, and references therein), or were identified by comparison of spectra with those of standards. Mass fragmentography was used extensively to aid compound identification, especially when coelution occurred. Quantitation of

individual components was carried out by measurement of GC peak areas. For minor or coeluting components, mass fragmentography was used, approximate quantitation being achieved by comparing the abundance of the chosen ion in the spectrum of the compound with the abundance of the same ion in a homologue (quantitated by GC), then with reference to the peak areas in the appropriate fragmentograms. Such quantitation, although internally consistent, does not allow for differences in GC response factors in the various compound classes (alkanes, alkenes and alcohols).

RESULTS AND DISCUSSION

General

A preliminary discussion of the distributions of the various lipid and geolipid classes in the sediments (samples 3-3 and 97-2 only) has appeared elsewhere (McEvoy *et al.*, 1981). The present discussion is restricted mainly to the changes observed with increasing depth of burial in the distributions of certain classes (alkanes, alkenes and alcohols) of steroidal

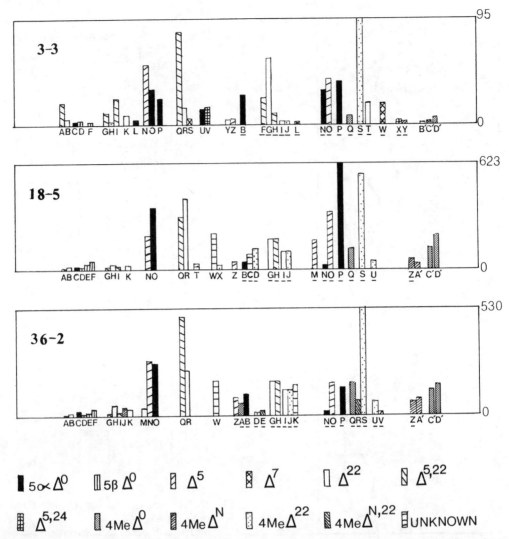

Fig. 3. Histograms showing the distributions of sterols in samples 3-3 (c. 23 m sub-bottom depth), 18-5 (c. 163 m) and 36-2 (c. 334 m). Shading corresponds to the different structural types shown; the letters correspond to assignments in Table 1. Concentrations in ng g^{-1} dry weight of sediment.

compounds, which tended to dominate their respective fractions. For brevity, the overall changes in the distributions of the classes are discussed rather than the significance of the occurrence of individual components.

Sterols

In the three shallowest samples (3-3, 18-5 and 36-2), sterols were observed in high relative abundance down to the Early Pliocene (Fig. 3). The concentrations were much higher in the Pliocene sediments than in the Quaternary sample (3-3; Fig. 3). This difference may reflect higher productivity in the Pliocene as the sedimentation rates of the samples are thought to have been similar (Site 467 Reports, 1981). The distributions are complex and contain both stanols and stenols, including components with a methyl substituent at C-4, with a variety of side chain structures and a carbon number range extending from C_{26} to C_{30}. Such complexity is typical of sediments with inputs from a variety of marine organisms (Wardroper et al., 1978; Lee et al., 1979; Brassell et al., 1980b). Consideration of

reviews of sterols in algae and invertebrates (e.g. Patterson, 1971; Goad, 1978) can provide some insight into the contributions from different types of organisms at the time of deposition. For example, dinosterol (S in Table 1; structure VIIq; Shimizu et al., 1978) is the most abundant sterol in 3-3 and 36-2 and the second most abundant in 18-5. It is thought (Boon et al., 1979) to be a characteristic marker compound for dinoflagellates and the high relative abundance of this stanol in the shallow Site 467 samples indicates a significant contribution of organic matter from such a source, as has been observed for other marine sediments (Boon et al., 1979; Lee et al., 1980; Comet et al., 1981).

The C_{28} sterol, 24-methylcholesta-5,22-dien-3β-ol (Q; Iw) is the second most abundant sterol in 3-3 and 36-2 and one of the most abundant in 18-5. Although it has been found in a variety of marine algae (see Goad, 1978), it is often the dominant sterol in diatoms (e.g. Ballantine et al., 1979; Rubinstein and Goad, 1974) and may reflect an input from this source. However, this sterol is also dominant in some coccolithophorids (Volkman et al., 1981) and is probably contributed to these sediments

Table 1

Sterols assigned in samples 3–3, 18–5 and 36–2 from Site 467.

Peak (Fig. 3)	Assignment	Structure
A	24-Norcholesta-5,22(E)-dien-3β-ol	Is
B	24-Nor-5α(H)-cholest-22(E)-en-3β-ol	IIs
C	24-Nor-5α(H)-cholestan-3β-ol	IIh
D	5β(H)-Cholestan-3β-ol	IIIj
E	27-Nor-24-methyl-5β(H)-cholestan-3β-ol?	IIIt
F	5β(H)-Cholestan-3α-ol	IVj
G	27-Nor-24-methylcholesta-5,22(E)-dien-3β-ol[a]	Iu
H	27-Nor-24-methyl-5α(H)-cholest-22(E)-en-3β-ol[a]	IIu
I	Cholesta-5,22(E)-dien-3β-ol	Iv
J	Unknown C_{28} 4-methylsterol	—
K	5α(H)-Cholest-22(E)-en-3β-ol	IIv
L	Unknown C_{27} stanol	—
M	24-Methyl-5β(H)-cholest-22(E)-en-3β-ol?	IIIw
N	Cholest-5-ene-3β-ol	Ij
O	5α(H)-Cholestan-3β-ol	IIj
P	27-Nor-24-methyl-5α(H)-cholestan-3β-ol	IIt
Q	24-Methylcholesta-5,22-dien-3β-ol	Iw
R	24-Methyl-5α(H)-cholest-22(E)-en-3β-ol	IIw
S	5α(H)-Cholest-7-en-3β-ol?	Vj
T	Unknown C_{28} 4-methylsterol	—
U	Unknown C_{28} stanol	—
V	24-Methylenecholest-5-en-3β-ol	Ix
W	Unknown C_{29} sterol	—
X	4,24-Dimethylcholest-22-en-3β-ol?	—
Y	24-Methylene-5α(H)-cholestan-3β-ol	IIx
Z	24-Methylcholest-5-en-3β-ol	Il
A	4α-Methyl-5α(H)-cholestan-3β-ol?	VIIj
B	24-Methyl-5α(H)-cholestan-3β-ol	III
C	Unknown C_{29} sterol	—
D	4α,24-Dimethyl-5β(H)-cholest-22(E)-en-3β-ol?	VIw
E	4,23,24-Trimethyl-cholesta-N,22-dien-3β-ol[b]?	—
F	23,24-Dimethylcholesta-5,22(E)-dien-3β-ol	Iq
G	23,24-Dimethyl-5α(H)-cholest-22(E)-en-3β-ol	IIq
H	24-Ethylcholesta-5,22(E)-dien-3β-ol	Iz
I	24-Ethyl-5α(H)-cholest-22(E)-en-3β-ol	IIz
J	4α-24-Dimethyl-5α(H)-cholest-22(E)-en-3β-ol?	VIIw
K	Unknown C_{30} sterol	—
L	24-Methyl-5α(H)-cholest-7-en-3β-ol?	Vl
M	23,24-Dimethylcholest-5-en-3β-ol	Ip
N	23,24-Dimethyl-5α(H)-cholestan-3β-ol	IIp
O	24-Ethylcholest-5-en-3β-ol	In
P	24-Ethyl-5α(H)-cholestan-3β-ol	IIn
Q	4α,24-Dimethyl-5α(H)-cholestan-3β-ol?	VIIl
R	4,23,24-Trimethylcholesta-N,22-dien-3β-ol[b]?	—
S	4α,23,24-Trimethyl-5α(H)-cholest-22(E)-en-3β-ol	VIIq
T	24-Propyl-5α(H)-cholest-22(E)-en-3β-ol?	IIγ
U	Unknown C_{30} 4-methyl-Δ^{22}-sterol	—
V	Unknown C_{31} sterol	—
W	24-Ethyl-5α(H)-cholest-7-ene-3β-ol?	Vn
X	24(Z)-Propylidenecholest-5-en-3β-ol?	Iφ
Y	Unknown C_{30} 4-methyl-Δ^N-sterol[b]	—
Z	Unknown C_{30} 4-methyl-Δ^N-sterol[b]	—
A'	Unknown C_{30} 4-methyl-Δ^N-sterol[a]	—
B'	Unknown C_{30} steradienol	—
C'	4α,22,24-Trimethyl-5α(H)-cholestan-3β-ol?	—
D'	4α,23,24-Trimethyl-5α(H)-cholestan-3β-ol	VIIp

[a] G and H could also be the Δ^{22}(Z) isomers of I and K respectively.

[b] N designates nuclear double bound in an uncertain position.

? Tentative assignment only.

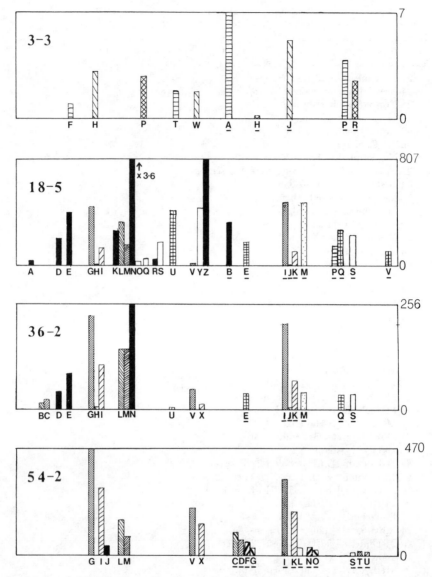

Fig. 4. Histograms showing the distributions of sterenes and steradienes in sediments from Site 467. Shading corresponds to the different structural types shown; the letters correspond to the assignments in Table 2, except for the diasterenes (numbered; Table 3). Concentrations in ng g^{-1} dry weight of sediment.

from this source also. In the Quaternary sample (3-3) a minor series of Δ^7-sterols (S, L and W in Fig. 3 and Table 1) was assigned tentatively on the basis of retention times and mass spectral interpretation (Gupta and Scheuer, 1968; Sheikh *et al.*, 1973; Ballantine *et al.*, 1981). Such components are known to occur in certain sponges where they are sometimes the major sterols (e.g. Voogt, 1976), so their presence in sample 3-3 may reflect a minor contribution of sterols from such a source. Sponge spicules have also been observed in sediment samples from this site (Site 467 Reports, 1981). Δ^7-Sterols also occur widely, however, in echinoderms (e.g. Gupta and Scheuer, 1968; Goad *et al.*, 1972) and cholest-7-en-3β-ol) (S in Fig. 3) has been observed in a diatom (Volkman *et al.*, 1980a). They cannot, therefore, be assigned unambiguously to a particular source.

In the three samples, Δ^5-monoenols and $\Delta^{5,22}$-dienols are abundant, as are their nuclear saturated stanols, the Δ^0-5α(H)-stanols and the Δ^{22}-5α(H)-stanols (e.g. compare in Fig. 3 N and Q with O and R respectively),

with the stanols being particularly abundant in sample 18-5. Both Δ^0- and Δ^{22}-5α(H)-stanols have been reported as being present in a wide variety of marine organisms, for example red algae (Chardon-Loriaux *et al.*, 1976), sponges (Erdman and Thomson, 1972; Edmonds *et al.*, 1977) and benthic fauna (Ballantine *et al.*, 1981). Thus, their presence in sediments may reflect a direct biological contribution, their abundance to unsaturated counterparts being enhanced during deposition (Nishimura and Koyama, 1976, 1977).

The presence of the nuclear saturated compounds may also arise from microbial reduction of their unsaturated analogues (Gaskell and Eglinton, 1975). If this is the major source of the stanols, their higher relative abundance in sample 18-5 may reflect a greater extent of reduction of the Δ^5-double bond than in samples 3-3 and 36-2.

Sterols were present in low abundance in sample 54-2 and were not present in sample 63-2, both samples corresponding to the Late Miocene (505 and 590 m

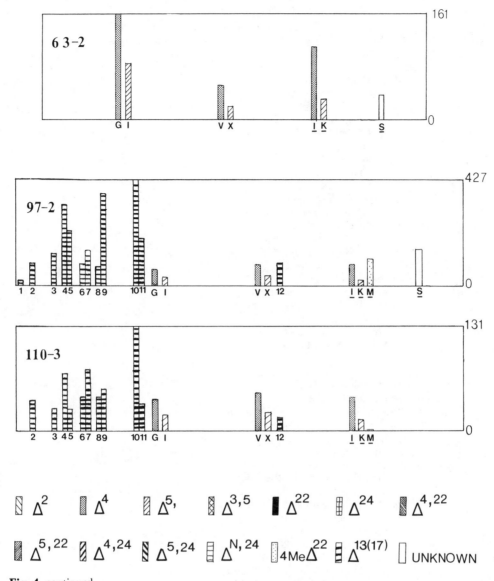

Fig. 4. continued

respectively (Fig. 2)). This is in marked contrast to sediments from the Japan Trench. Here, sterols were still the dominant steroidal components detected in the Late Miocene, corresponding to a greater burial depth of 779 m (Brassell *et al.*, 1980b). The more rapid disappearance of sterols at Site 467 probably reflects, therefore, a greater extent of diagenetic conversion (see below) as a result of the high geothermal gradient compared to the Japan Trench.

Sterenes and steradienes

With one exception (Hamilton *et al.*, 1975) steroidal alkenes have not been observed in living organisms. Their presence in sediments results from dehydration of sterols; the process may be microbially assisted (Dastillung and Albrecht, 1977; Gagosian and Farrington, 1978). Sample 3-3 shows a simple distribution of Δ^2-sterenes and of $\Delta^{N,24}$- (position of nuclear double bond unknown) and $\Delta^{3,5}$-steradienes in

very low concentration relative to the other samples (Fig. 4 and Tables 2 and 3). There is a reasonably good carbon number comparison between the Δ^2-sterenes (components H, W and $\mathcal{J}$ in Fig. 4) and their precursors, the Δ^0-5α(H)-stanols (O, B and P in Fig. 3) and between the $\Delta^{3,5}$-dienes (P, H and R in Fig. 4) and their precursors, the Δ^5-monoenols (N, Z and O) as expected. The low concentration of the hydrocarbons indicates, however, that the dehydration has not progressed to any significant extent within the sediment. Indeed, it may have occurred in the water column prior to deposition (Wakeham *et al.*, 1980). The significant abundance of $\Delta^{N,24}$-steradienes (F, T, A and P in Fig. 4) contrasts with the low relative abundance of sterols with unsaturation at C-24 (e.g. V in Fig. 3) so there must have been selectivity in the dehydration process. The same effect (high relative abundance of sterenes with unsaturation at C-24) has also been observed in Recent sediments from the Middle America Trench (DSDP Leg 66; Brassell *et al.*, 1981).

Table 2
Sterenes and steradienes assigned in samples from Site 467.

Peak (Fig. 4)	Assignment	Structure
A	5β(H)-Cholest-22-ene?	XVj
B	Cholesta-4,22-diene	Xv
C	Cholesta-5,22-diene	XIv
D	27-Nor-24-methyl-5α(H)-cholest-22-ene?	XIIIu
E	5α(H)-Cholest-22-ene	XIIIv
F	Unknown cholesta-N,24-diene[a]	—
G	Cholest-4-ene	Xj
H	5α(H)-Cholest-2-ene	VIIIj
I	Cholest-5-ene	XIj
J	Unknown $C_{27}\Delta^{22}$-sterene	—
K	24-Methyl-5β(H)-cholest-22-ene?	XVw
L	24-Methylcholesta-4,22-diene	Xw
M	24-Methylcholesta-5,22-diene	XIw
N	24-Methyl-5α(H)-cholest-22-ene	XIIIw
O	Unknown C_{29} steradiene	—
P	Cholesta-3,5-diene	IXj
Q	24-Methylcholest-N-ene[a]?	—
R	24-Ethyl-5β(H)-cholest-22-ene?	XVz
S	Unknown 24-methylcholestatriene	—
T	24-Methylcholesta-N,24-diene[a]?	—
U	24-Methylcholest-24(28)-ene?	—
V	24-Methylcholest-4-ene	Xl
W	24-Methyl-5α(H)-cholest-22-ene	VIIIl
X	24-Methylcholest-5-ene	XIl
Y	24-Ethylcholest-N-ene[a]?	—
Z	23,24-Dimethyl-5α(H)-cholest-22-ene?	XIIIp
A	24-Methylcholesta-N,24-diene[a]?	—
B	24-Ethyl-5α(H)-cholest-22-ene	XIIIz
C	24-Ethylcholesta-4,22-diene	Xz
D	24-Ethylcholesta-5,22-diene	XIz
E	24-Methyl-5α(H)-cholest-24(28)-ene?	XIIIx
F	24-Methylcholesta-4,24(28)-diene?	Xx
G	24-Methylcholesta-5,24(28)-diene?	XIx
H	24-Methylcholesta-3,5-diene	IXl
I	24-Ethylcholest-4-ene	Xn
J	24-Ethyl-5α(H)-cholest-2-ene	VIIIn
K	24-Ethylcholest-5-ene	XIn
L	4,23,24-Trimethylcholesta-N,22-diene[a]?	—
M	4α,23,24-Trimethyl-5α(H)-cholest-22-ene?	XVIq
N	24-Ethylcholesta-4,24(28)-diene?	Xy
O	24-Ethylcholesta-5,24 (28)-diene?	XIy
P	24-Ethylcholesta-N,24-diene[a]?	—
Q	24-Ethyl-5α(H)-cholest-24(28)-ene?	XIIIy
R	24-Ethylcholesta-3,5-diene	IXn
S	4,23-24-Trimethylcholest-N-ene?	—
T	24-Propylcholest-4-ene?	Xr
U	24-Propylcholest-5-ene?	XIr
V	24-Propyl-5α(H)-cholest-24(28)-ene?	XIIIϕ

[a] N designates nuclear double bond in an uncertain position.
? Tentative assignment only.

The steroidal alkene distribution of sample 18-5 is much more complex (Fig. 4, and Tables 2 and 3). This, taken with the much higher relative abundance of the components (Fig. 4) in comparison with sample 3-3, indicates that diagenesis has occurred extensively within the sediment between the Quaternary and the Late Pliocene. Of the monoenes, Δ^2-sterenes are present in only trace amounts (see e.g. H in Fig. 4); Δ^4- and Δ^5-sterenes (e.g. G and I in Fig. 4) are now present in significant relative abundance. These components are thought to arise with increasing extent of diagenesis (Wardroper, 1979) as a result of isomerisation of the Δ^2-sterenes commonly found in surface or very young sediments (Dastillung and Albrecht, 1977). If so, the Δ^2-monoenes have presumably been short-lived in intermediates in sample 18-5 between the Δ^0-5α(H)-stanols and the Δ^4- and Δ^5-monoenes. Again, there is a reasonably good comparison of carbon number distributions between the Δ^0-5α(H)-stanols (O, B and P in Fig. 3) and the Δ^4- and Δ^5-monoenes (G, I, V, X, *I* and *K* in Fig. 4). A comparable situation exists for the $\Delta^{4,22}$- and $\Delta^{5,22}$-steradienes (Fig. 4); the presumed

Table 3

Diasterenes assigned in samples 97-2 and 110-3 from Site 467.

Peak (Fig. 4)	Assignment	Structure
1	20*R* 24-Nordiacholest-13(17)-ene?	XIIh
2	20*S* Diacholest-13(17)-ene	XIIi
3	Unknown diacholestene[a]	—
4	20*R* Diacholest-13(17)-ene	XIIj
5	20*S* 24-Methyldiacholest-13(17)-ene	XIIk
6	Unknown methyldiacholestene	—
7	Unknown methyldiacholestene	—
8	20*S* 24-Ethyldiacholest-13(17)-ene	XIIm
9	20*R* 24-Methyldiacholest-13(17)-ene	XIII
10	20*R* 24-Ethyldiacholest-13(17)-ene	XIIn
11	Unknown C_{30} 4-methyldiacholestene	—
12	Unknown C_{30} 4-methyldiacholestene	—

[a] Coelutes with an unknown methyldiacholestene.

? Tentative assignment only.

intermediates ($\Delta^{2,22}$-steradienes) are not observed in 18-5, the major $\Delta^{4,22}$ and $\Delta^{5,22}$ components (L and M in Fig. 4) being C_{28} as is the major $5\alpha(H)$-$\Delta 22$-stanol (R in Fig. 3). No $C_{29}\Delta^{4,22}$- and $\Delta^{5,22}$-steradienes were observed, however, although two $C_{29}5\alpha(H)$-Δ^{22}-stanols (G and I in Fig. 3) were present in measurable abundances. The most abundant sterenes are Δ^{22}-monoenes (n.b. multiplication factor for N in sample 18-5 in Fig. 4). These components (D, E, K, N, Z and B in Fig. 4) presumably arise from $5\alpha(H)$-Δ^{22}-stanols via reduction of $\Delta^{2,22}$-steradienes, the latter again being short-lived intermediates as they were not present (see above). This evidence for reduction having occurred to a marked extent in the Late Pliocene is substantiated by the high relative abundances of steranes (see below).

With the exception of the $C_{28}\Delta^{22}$-sterene (N; XIIIw) sample 36-2 is dominated by Δ^4- and Δ^5-sterenes (G, I, V, X, *I* and *J* in Fig. 4). Again, there is a reasonably good carbon number comparison with the presumed precursors, the Δ^0-$5\alpha(H)$-stanols (O, B and P in Fig. 3). The Δ^4- and Δ^5-monoenes continue to dominate in the Late Miocene (samples 54-2 and 63-2; Figs 2 and 4), no dienes being detected in sample 63-2.

No diasterenes were observed in the Quaternary and Pliocene and were only present in small concentrations in the Late Miocene. They were present in significant concentrations, however, by the Middle Miocene (samples 97-2 and 110-3) where they dominate the steroidal alkenes. These components (1 to 10 in Fig. 4; Table 3) arise (Rubinstein *et al.*, 1975) from acid catalysed rearrangement of sterenes, presumably from the Δ^4- and Δ^5-sterenes in samples 97-2 and 110-3 since no Δ^2-sterenes are present. That these rearranged components appear here only in the Middle Miocene is not thought to be the result of differences in the lithology between samples 97-2 and 110-3 and the younger samples, as all the samples are rich in clay minerals. Rather, it is thought to reflect the fact that diasterenes form at a later stage of diagenesis. A similar situation has been observed in other DSDP samples (Brassell *et al.*, 1980a). In both samples 97-2 and 110-3, minor amounts of 4-methyldiasterenes (11 and 12 in Fig. 4; Table 3) are also present. In several of the samples a C_{30} 4-methylsterene with Δ^{22} unsaturation was observed

(component *M* in Fig. 4) and is tentatively proposed from its mass spectrum as a diagenetic product (XVIq) from dinosterol (*S* in Fig. 3; VIIq) which is observed in abundance in the three samples where sterols were observed. Its presence is explicable in terms of a pathway analogous to that giving rise to the Δ^{22}-monoenes (see above) and it is first observed in sample 18-5 where the Δ^{22}-monoenes are first observed.

Steranes

The Quaternary sample, 3-3 has a complex mixture of steranes present in very low concentration, including rearranged components (1 to 6 in Fig. 5; e.g. XIV), components of the $5\alpha(H)$, $14\alpha(H)$, $17\alpha(H)$ configuration (both 20*S* and 20*R*, e.g. S and Z for C_{29}, XIIIm and n) and of the $5\alpha(H)$, $14\beta(H)$, $17\beta(H)$ configuration (both 20*R* and *S*, e.g. T and V for C_{29}, XIX n and m). The low concentrations and the multiplicity of stereoisomers indicates the presence of a minor component from a non-indigenous source. For example, the relatively high 20*S* to 20*R* ratio for the C_{29} $5\alpha(H)$, $14\alpha(H)$, $17\alpha(H)$ components (S and Z in Fig. 5) and the presence of the stable $5\alpha(H)$, $14\beta(H)$, $17\beta(H)$-steranes would not be expected for such an immature young sample (Seifert and Moldowan, 1978, 1979; Mackenzie *et al.*, 1980). The mixture, therefore, probably contains either a reworked mature component or a component from shipboard contamination (Thomson *et al.*, 1981).

In contrast, the sterane distribution of sample 18-5 is much less complex and is dominated by the $5\alpha(H)$, $14\alpha(H)$, $17\alpha(H)$ 20*R* components (XIII; K, R and Z in Fig. 5). Such a simple distribution shows clearly that these steranes are indigenous and their high concentration (Fig. 5) indicates extensive reduction has occurred in this Late Pliocene sample (cf. Δ^{22}-sterenes above). Again, there is a marked contrast to the sediments from the Japan Trench where steranes were not formed in any significant abundance by the Late Miocene (Brassell *et al.*, 1980b and c). In terms of the other steroidal components, the diagenetic origin of the steranes in this particular sample is not obvious; the major sterane is 20*R* $5\alpha(H)$-cholestane, the $5\beta(H)$

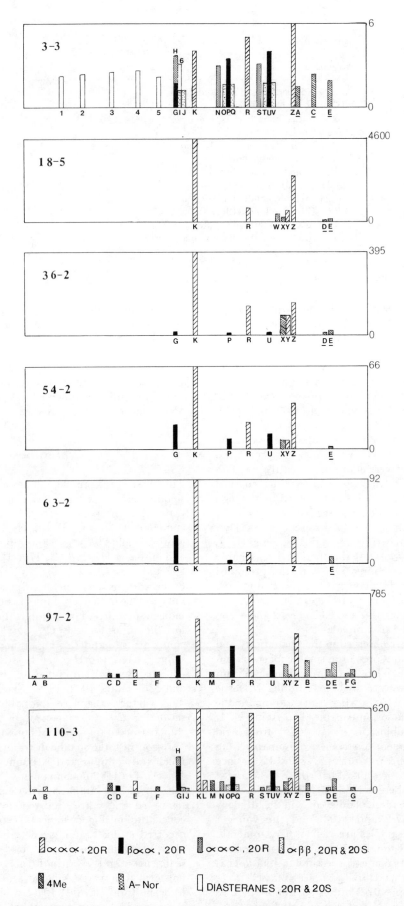

Fig. 5. Histograms showing the distribution of steranes in sediments from Site 467 and of diasteranes in sample 3-3. Shading corresponds to the different structural types shown; the letters correspond to the assignments in Table 4, except for the diasteranes (numbered; Table 5) in sample 3-3. Concentrations in ng g^{-1} dry weight of sediment.

Table 4

Steranes assigned in samples 3–3, 18–5, 36–2, 54–2, 63–2, 97–2 and 110–3 from Site 467.

Peak (Fig. 5)	Assignment	Structure
A	5α(H),14α(H)-Androstane	XIIIa
B	5α(H),14α(H),17α(H)-Pregnane	XIIIb
C	20R A-nor-5β(H),14α(H),17α(H)-cholestane	XVIIIj
D	20R 24-Nor-5β(H),14α(H),17α(H)-cholestane?	XVh
E	20R 24-Nor-5α(H),14α(H),17α(H)-cholestane?	XIIIh
F	20R A-nor-24-methyl-5β(H),14α(H),17α(H)-cholestane	XVIIIl
G	20R 5β(H),14α(H),17α(H)-Cholestane ⎫	XVj
H	20S 5α(H),14α(H),17α(H)-Cholestane ⎭	XIIIi
I	20R 5α(H),14β(H),17β(H)-Cholestane	XIXj
J	20S 5α(H),14β(H),17β(H)-Cholestane	XIXi
K	20R 5α(H),14α(H),17α(H)-Cholestane	XIIIj
L	20R 27-Nor-24-methyl-5α(H),14α(H),17α(H)-cholestane?	XIIIt
M	20R A-nor-24-ethyl-5β(H),14α(H),17α(H)-cholestane	XVIIIn
N	20S 24-Methyl-5α(H),14α(H),17α(H)-cholestane	XIIIk
O	20R 24-Methyl-5α(H),14β(H),17β(H)-cholestane ⎫	XIXl
P	20R 24-Methyl-5β(H),14α(H),17α(H)-cholestane ⎭	XVl
Q	20S 24-Methyl-5α(H),14β(H),17β(H)-cholestane	XIXk
R	20R 24-Methyl-5α(H),14α(H),17α(H)-cholestane	XIIIl
S	20S 24-Ethyl-5α(H),14α(H),17α(H)-cholestane	XIIIm
T	20R 24-Ethyl-5α(H),14β(H),17β(H)-cholestane ⎫	XIXn
U	20R 24-Ethyl-5β(H),14α(H),17α(H)-cholestane ⎬	XVn
V	20S 24-Ethyl-5α(H),14β(H),17β(H)-cholestane ⎭	XIXm
W	4,14-Dimethylcholestane?	—
X	20R 4,24-Dimethyl-5α(H),14α(H),17α(H)-cholestane?	XVIl
Y	Unknown C₂₉ 5α(H),14α(H),17α(H)-sterane	—
Z	20R 24-Ethyl-5α(H),14α(H),17α(H)-cholestane	XIIIn
A	4,23,24-Trimethylcholestane?	—
B	20R,4β,24-Dimethyl-5α(H),14α(H),17α(H)-cholestane?	XVIIl
C	4,23,24-Trimethylcholestane?	—
D	20R 4α,23,24-Trimethyl-5α(H),14α(H),17α(H)-cholestane?	XVIp
E	20R 4α,23,24-Trimethyl-5α(H),14α(H),17α(H)-cholestane?	XVIp
F	20R 4β,23,24-Trimethyl-5α(H),14α(H),17α(H)-cholestane?	XVIIp
G	20R 4β,23,24-Trimethyl-5α(H),14α(H),17α(H)-cholestane?	XVIIp

? Tentative assignment only.
Brackets indicate coeluting components.

isomer not being detected. Such a predominance of the C_{27} skeleton is not observed in the corresponding Δ^0-5α(H)-stanols (O, B and P in Fig. 3), although the C_{28} skeleton (R in Fig. 5 and B in Fig. 3) is by far the least abundant in the 5α(H), 14α(H), 17α(H) 20R steranes and Δ^0-5α(H)-stanols. A similar situation exists for the Δ^4- and Δ^5-sterenes (cf. Figs. 4 and 5). There is also no carbon number relationship with the Δ^{22}-sterenes, the C_{28} 5α(H) compound (N in Fig. 4) in the latter being by far the most abundant sterene. It is perhaps significant that this sample was the only one at Site 467 in which sterol ethers with a long chain (up to C_{10}) ether moiety at C-3, were detected. Such components, which have been observed previously (Brassell et al., 1980b; Boon and De Leeuw, 1979) are present in high relative concentration (up to c. 0.3 μg g⁻¹ individual component) with components having the C_{27} steroidal skeleton predominant. It is unclear, however, what relationship, if any, these components could have with the steranes. Downhole from sample 36-2 to sample 97-2 the distributions of the major steranes are quite similar. In each case 20R 5β(H), 14α(H), 17α(H)-steranes (G, P and U in Fig. 5; Table 4) are present in carbon number distributions which compare well with their 5α(H)

counterparts (N.B. in sample 63-2 the 5β(H) component with the C_{29} skeleton could not be detected because of the presence of a very high concentration of a C_{28} pentacyclic triterpane (9.3 μg g⁻¹) at its retention position). In each case the carbon number distribution of the 5α(H)- and the 5β(H), 14α(H), 17α(H) components shows a reasonably good carbon number comparison with the co-occurring Δ^4- and Δ^5-sterenes, providing circumstantial evidence that the steranes are formed from these sterenes by reduction. In samples 36-2 to 110-3 varying concentrations of other minor steranes were present, which may reflect differences in the source organisms by way of differences in their sterol distributions: (i) 4-methylsteranes (e.g. X, D and E in Fig. 5), (ii) low molecular weight components in 97-2 and 110-3, including 5α(H), 14α(H)-androstane (A in Fig. 5; XIIIa) and 5α(H), 14α(H), 17α(H)-pregnane (B; XIIIb) along with trace concentrations (not shown in Fig. 5) of the C_{22} to C_{25} homologues (XIIIc to XIIIf); the origin of these steranes with short side chains is uncertain but they may have originated from stanols with degraded side chains which have been detected in sponges (Ballantine et al., 1977), (iii) a series of C_{26} to C_{28} steranes (C, F and M in Fig. 5) in samples 97-2 and 110-

Table 5

Diasteranes assigned in sample 3–3 from Site 467.

Peak (Fig. 5)	Assignment	Structure
1	20S 13β(H),17α(H)-Diacholestane	XIVi
2	20R 13β(H),17α(H)-Diacholestane	XIVj
3	20S 24-Methyl-13β(H),17α(H)-diacholestane	XIVk
4	20R 24-Methyl-13β(H),17α(H)-diacholestane	XIVl
5	20S 24-Ethyl-13β(H),17α(H)-diacholestane	XIVm
6	20R 24-Ethyl-13β(H),17α(H)-diacholestane	XIVn

3. Mass spectral interpretation shows that these compounds have the expected side chains for C_{27} to C_{29} steranes, but appear to have either lost a methyl group from the nucleus or ring A has been modified to give A-norsteranes of type XVIII. Interpretation of the mass spectra of C_{26} to C_{28} stanones (not discussed herein) in a number of the samples suggested (Van Horn and Djerassi, 1967) that the steranes are of type XVIII. It has come to our attention (De Leeuw, personal communication) that these components are indeed of type XVIII, the configuration at C-5 being β(H). In addition, the C_{26} component coeluted with a standard. These alkanes have also been found in a Cretaceous Black shale (Van Graas et al., 1982) and could have arisen from sterols of this skeletal type which have been isolated from some sponges in high relative abundance (Minale and Sodano, 1974). Labelling experiments have shown that the sponge *Axinella verrucosa* can transform cholesterol into 3β-hydroxymethyl-5α(H)-cholestane (De Rosa *et al.*, 1975, 1976).

The oldest and deepest sample, 110-3, in the Middle Miocene has a more complex distribution (Fig. 5) of steranes than samples 18-5 (Late Pliocene) to 97-2 (Middle Miocene). The increase in complexity over sample 97-2 arises from the presence of trace components with the 20S 5α(H), 14α(H), 17α(H) configuration (e.g. S for C_{29}; XIIIm) and with the 5α(H), 14β(H), 17β(H) configuration (both 20S and 20R; e.g. for C_{29} T and V; XIXn and m). The overall distribution is reminiscent of those in the less mature Toarcian shales of the Paris Basin (e.g. Semécourt, Mackenzie *et al.*, 1980). Although the major steranes are certainly indigenous (cf. above), it is not clear whether these minor stereoisomers are also indigenous or whether they originate from a mature source (cf. sample 3-3 above). If the latter situation is the case, the source of the minor components must be different from that giving rise to the steranes in sample 3-3 because the Quaternary sample contains diasteranes (XIV), which are not observed in sample 110-3. Also, sample 3-3 was an unconsolidated mud whereas sample 110-3 was a claystone, the exterior surfaces being extracted with solvent prior to crushing. It seems unlikely, therefore, that the minor steranes in 110-3 arise from shipboard contamination. If they originate from a mature reworked component, this component would have to be devoid of diasteranes. If they are indigenous, then it appears that this Middle Miocene sample may have reached a maturity at which the appearance of steranes with the 'non-biological' configuration is just beginning to be observed, such components being present in high relative abundance at maturity levels

greater than 110-3 (e.g. Mackenzie *et al.*, 1980). On the other hand, the major hopanes present in sample 110-3 have the less stable 17β(H), 21β(H)-configuration and there is little evidence of isomerization of the 22R 17α(H), 21β(H)-hopanes to their 22S isomers (see sample 97-2; McEvoy *et al.*, 1981), both of the isomerizations (17β(H) to 17α(H) and 22R to 22S in the 17α(H)-hopanes) being thought to occur at an earlier stage than the isomerizations at C-14, C-17 and C-20 in the steranes (Mackenzie *et al.*, 1980).

It is noteworthy that the diasterenes (XII) present in high abundance relative to the other alkenes in sample 110-3 (Fig. 4) have not been reduced to their corresponding alkanes (XIV). Again, this situation is reminiscent of the immature Toarcian shales of the Paris Basin, which still contain diasterenes (Ensminger, 1977).

SUMMARY AND CONCLUSIONS

The distributions of a number of types of steroidal compounds (alkanes, alkenes and alcohols) in sediments at Site 467 have been examined. The high relative abundance of steroidal components in their respective fractions reflects high productivity and good preservation at the time of deposition of the samples examined. Sterols are present down to the Early Pliocene. Where sterols are present, 4α,23,24-trimethylcholest-22(E)-en-3β-ol (dinosterol; VIIq) and 24-methylcholesta-5,22(E)-dien-3β-ol (Iw) occur in high relative abundance, suggesting significant inputs from dinoflagellates, diatoms and/or coccolithophorids respectively. In certain of the deeper samples, the presence of low molecular weight steranes (XIIIc) and of A-norsteranes (XVIII) suggest inputs of organic matter from sponges at the time of deposition.

Consideration of the distributions of the various components has allowed a number of diagenetic steps relating to the sedimentary fate of sterols to be proposed for the samples. These are summarized in Fig. 6, which also shows the stages at which the proposed transformations are observed. Thus, $\Delta^{3,5}$- and $\Delta^{N,24}$-steradienes are the first diene transformation products to be recognised and rapidly disappear. The same situation is observed for the Δ^2-sterenes in the monoene series; in the latter series, Δ^4- and Δ^5-sterenes are formed after, and apparently from, Δ^2-sterenes which appear to be short-lived intermediates (Fig. 6). In the diene series, $\Delta^{4,22}$- and $\Delta^{5,22}$-dienes are thought to be formed by isomerization of $\Delta^{2,22}$-dienes (cf. Δ^2-sterenes) which are

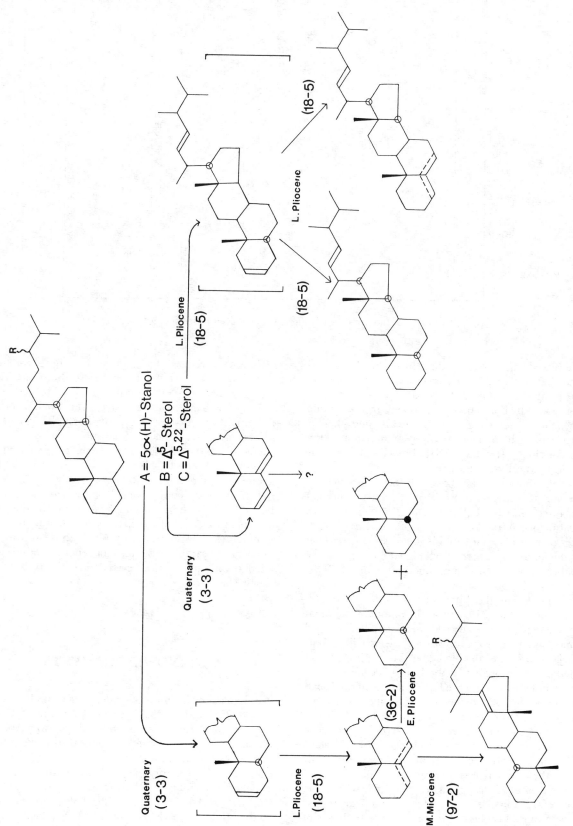

Fig. 6. Proposed transformation pathways of steroidal compounds observed in sediment samples from Site 467, and stages at which they occur.

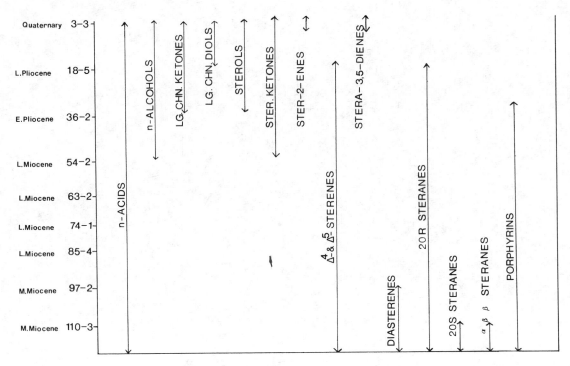

Fig. 7. Summary of the presence of different lipid classes in sediments from Site 467.

not observed, and are also thought to be short-lived intermediates. Rearranged sterenes are formed in the pathway after all other steroidal alkenes. There is no evidence of reduction of these components by the Middle Miocene to the corresponding alkanes although there is evidence of reduction of Δ^4- and Δ^5-sterenes to the corresponding $5\alpha(H)$ and $5\beta(H)$, $14\alpha(H)$, $17\alpha(H)$ $20R$ steranes by the Early Pliocene.

The distributions of the above steroidal compounds in sediments at Site 467, in an area of high geothermal gradient contrast (cf. Eglinton *et al.*, this volume) with those from Site 440 in the Japan Trench, an area of much lower geothermal gradient, as follows: (i) steroidal components are present in much higher concentrations, probably reflecting a higher productivity at Site 467; (ii) sterols have disappeared by the Late Miocene (sample 63-2) whereas in the Japan Trench they were still detected in the Late Miocene as the dominant steroidal components; (iii) Δ^2-sterenes were barely detected beyond the Quaternary, whereas they were still present in the Late Miocene from the Japan Trench; (iv) Δ^4- and Δ^5-sterenes were present in the Late Pliocene whereas they did not appear until the Late Miocene in the Japan Trench; (v) stera-3,5-dienes have disappeared by the Late Pliocene but were still present in the Late Miocene in the Japan Trench. Figure 7 summarizes the presence of the above steroidal compound classes in the sediments of different ages obtained from Site 467. Apart from (i) above, these differences appear to result from an increased rate of diagenesis at Site 467 where the geothermal gradient is much higher. They do not appear to arise from differences in lithology since both sets of sediments are clay-rich with some similarity in the clay minerals present. Furthermore, they do not appear to arise from burial rate differences since the Japan Trench sediments occur at deeper depths for comparable ages.

The occurrences of a number of other compound classes, not reported in detail here, are also summarized in Fig. 7 (McEvoy, unpublished results; McEvoy *et al.*, 1981). It is obvious that extensive defunctionalization of the lipids has occurred by the Early Pliocene/Late Miocene. Apart from the diagenetic changes in the steroidal compounds discussed above, it can be seen, for example, that the C_{37} to C_{39} very long, straight chain ketones (Volkman *et al.*, 1980b; de Leeuw *et al.*, 1980), thought to be coccolithophorid markers, are not present beyond sample 36-2, although *n*-alkanes of the same carbon number are observed in significant abundance in sample 97-2. Also, chlorins were abundant in the Quaternary sample 3-3, their diagenetic products, the alkyl metalloporphyrins, even being observed in the Early Pliocene.

ACKNOWLEDGEMENTS

We thank the Natural Environment Research Council (GR3/2951 and GR3/3758) for providing GC–MS facilities and for a Research Studentship (J.M.). We also thank Mr G. P. Cooles of The British Petroleum Company Limited, and Dr S. P. Lowe of Paleochem Ltd., for providing organic carbon determination and palynological analyses. We are grateful to Mrs A. P. Gowar and Dr G. J. Shaw for help with GC–MS analyses and to Drs S. C. Brassell, A. S. Mackenzie, J. Volkman and J. Rullkötter for useful discussions. We also wish to thank Dr N. A. Lamb and Dr J. W. De Leeuw for making available 24-ethylcholesta-4,22-diene and A-nor-5β(H)-cholestane respectively.

REFERENCES

Ballantine, J. A., Williams, K. and Burke, B. A. (1977) Marine sterols. IV. C_{21} sterols from marine sources. Identification of pregnane derivatives in extracts of the sponge *Haliclona rubens*. *Tetrahedron Lett.* 1547–1550.

Ballantine, J. A., Lavis, A. and Morris, R. J. (1979) Sterols of the phytoplankton — effects of illumination and growth stage. *Phytochem.* **18**, 1459–1466.

Ballantine, J. A., Lavis, A. and Morris, R. J. (1981) Marine sterols — XV. Sterols of some oceanic holothurians. *J. Exp. Mar. Biol. Ecol.* **53**, 89–103.

Barnes, P. J., Brassell, S. C., Comet, P. A., Eglinton, G., McEvoy, J., Maxwell, J. R., Wardroper, A. M. K. and Volkman, J. K. (1979) Preliminary lipid analyses of core sections 18, 24 and 30 from Hole 402A. In *Initial Reports of the Deep Sea Drilling Project*, Vol. 48. Ed. by Montadert, L. and Roberts, D. G. *et al.* US Govt. Printing Office, Washington. pp. 965–976.

Boon, J. J. and De Leeuw, J. W. (1979) The analysis of wax esters, very long mid-chain ketones and sterol ethers isolated from Walvis Bay diatomaceous ooze. *Mar. Chem.* **7**, 117–132.

Boon, J. J., Rijpstra, W. I. C., De Lange, F., De Leeuw, J. W., Yoshioka, M. and Shimizu, Y. (1979) The Black Sea sterol — A molecular fossil for dinoflagellate blooms. *Nature* **277**, 125–127.

Brassell, S. C. (1980) The lipids of deep sea sediments: their origin and fate in the Japan Trench. *Ph.D. Thesis*, University of Bristol.

Brassell, S. C. and Eglinton, G. (1981) Biogeochemical significance of a novel sedimentary C_{27} stanol. *Nature* **290**, 579–582.

Brassell, S. C., Comet, P. A., Eglinton, G., McEvoy, J., Maxwell, J. R., Quirke, J. M. E. and Volkman, J. K. (1980a) Preliminary lipid analyses of core sections 14, 18 and 28 from Hole 416A. In *Initial Reports of the Deep Sea Drilling Project*, Vol. 50. Ed. by Lancelot, Y., Winterer, E. L. *et al.* US Govt Printing Office. pp. 647–663.

Brassell, S. C., Comet, P. A., Eglinton, G., Isaacson, P. J., McEvoy, J., Maxwell, J. R., Thomson, I. D., Tibbetts, P. J. C. and Volkman, J. K. (1980b) Preliminary lipid analyses of Core 7 from 440A, Cores 3, 8 and 68 from 440B and Core 11 from Hole 436. In *Initial Reports of the Deep Sea Drilling Project*, Vol. 56/57. Ed. by von Huene, R., Nasu, N., *et al.* US Govt Printing Office, pp. 1367–1390.

Brassell, S. C., Comet, P. A., Eglinton, G., Isaacson, P. J., McEvoy, J., Maxwell, J. R., Thomson, I. D., Tibbetts, P. J. C. and Volkman, J. K. (1980c) The origin and fate of lipids in the Japan Trench. In *Advances in Organic Geochemistry* 1979. Ed. by Douglas, A. G. and Maxwell, J. R. Pergamon Press. pp. 375–392.

Brassell, S. C., Eglinton, G. and Maxwell, J. R. (1981) Preliminary lipid analyses of two Quaternary sediments from the Middle American Trench, Southern Mexico transect. In *Initial Reports of the Deep Sea Drilling Project*, Vol. 66. Ed. by Moore, J. C., Watkins, J. S., *et al.* US Govt Printing Office, pp. 557–580.

Chardon-Loriaux, I., Morisaki, M. and Ikekawa, N. (1976) Sterol profiles of red algae. *Phytochem.* **15**, 723–725.

Comet, P. A., McEvoy, J., Brassell, S. C., Eglinton, G., Maxwell, J. R. and Thomson, I. D. (1981) Lipids of an Upper Albian limestone, Section 465A-38-3. In *Initial Reports of the Deep Sea Drilling Project*, Vol. 62. Ed. by Thiede, J., Vallier, T., *et al.* US Govt Printing Office, pp. 923–937.

Dastillung, M. and Albrecht, P. (1977) Δ^2-Sterenes as diagenetic intermediates in sediments. *Nature* **269**, 678–679.

De Leeuw, J. W., Van De Meer, F. W. and Rijpstra, W. I. C.

(1980) On the occurrence and structural identification of long chain unsaturated ketones and hydrocarbons in Recent and sub-Recent sediments. In *Advances in Organic Geochemistry* 1979. Ed. by Douglas, A. G. and Maxwell, J. R. Pergamon Press. pp. 211–217.

De Rosa, M., Minale, L. and Sodano, G. (1975) Metabolism in Porifera IV. Biosynthesis of the 3β-hydroxymethyl-A-nor-5α-steranes from cholesterol by *Axinella verrucosa*. *Experientia* **31**, 408–410.

De Rosa, M., Minale, L. and Sodano, G. (1976) Metabolism in Porifera VI. Role of the 5,6 double bond and the fate of the C-4 of cholesterol during the conversion into 3β-hydroxymethyl-A-nor-5α-steranes in the sponge *Axinella verrucosa*. *Experientia* **32**, 1112–1113.

Edmonds, C. G., Smith, A. G. and Brooks, C. J. W. (1977) Analysis of sponge sterols as the trimethylsilyl ethers and as the corresponding 5α- and Δ^4-3-ketosteroids using open-tubular gas chromatography–mass spectrometry. Application of selective enzymic oxidation. *J. Chromatogr.* **133**, 372–377.

Eglinton, G., Brassell, S. C., Howell, V. and Maxwell, J. R. (this volume) The role of organic geochemistry in the Deep Sea Drilling Project (DSDP).

Ensminger, A. (1977) Evolution de composés polycycliques sédimentaires. *Thèse de docteur ès Sciences*, Université Louis Pasteur, Strasbourg.

Erdman, T. R. and Thomson, R. H. (1972) Sterols from the sponges *Cliona celata* Grant and *Hymeniacidon perleve* Montague. *Tetrahedron* **28**, 5163–5173.

Gagosian, R. B. and Farrington, J. W. (1978) Sterenes in surface sediments from the southwest African shelf and slope. *Geochim. Cosmochim. Acta* **42**, 1091–1101.

Gaskell, S. J. and Eglinton, G. (1975) Rapid hydrogenation of sterols in a contemporary lacustrine sediment. *Nature* **254**, 209–211.

Goad, L. J. (1978) The sterols of marine invertebrates: composition, biosynthesis and metabolites. In *Marine Natural Products*, Vol. II. Ed. by Scheuer, P. J. Academic Press. pp. 75–172.

Goad, L. J., Rubinstein, I. and Smith, A. G. (1972) The sterols of echinoderms. *Proc. Royal Soc. London Ser. B.* **180**, 223–246.

Van Graas, G., De Lange, F., De Leeuw, J. W. and Schenck, P. A. (1982) A-norsteranes, a novel class of sedimentary hydrocarbons. *Nature* **296**, 59–61.

Gupta, K. C. and Scheuer, P. J. (1968) Echinoderm sterols. *Tetrahedron* **24**, 5831–5837.

Hamilton, R. J., Raie, M. Y., Weatherston, I., Brooks, C. J. and Borthwick, J. H. (1975) Crustacean surface waxes. Part I. The hydrocarbons from the surface of *Ligia oceanica*. *J. Chem. Soc. Perkin I*, 354–357.

Van Horn, A. R. and Djerassi, C. (1967) Mass spectrometry in structural and stereochemical problems CXXVIII. Further studies on the mass spectrometry of 15-keto steroids. *Steroids* **9**, 163–175.

Langseth, M. and Burch, T. (1980) Geothermal observations of the Japan Trench transect. In *Initial Reports of the Deep Sea Drilling Project*, Vol. 56/57, Part 2. Ed. by Von Huene, R., Nasu, N., *et al.* US Govt. Printing Office. pp. 1207–1210.

Lee, C., Farrington, J. W. and Gagosian, R. B. (1979) Sterol geochemistry of sediments from the western North Atlantic Ocean and adjacent coastal areas. *Geochim. Cosmochim. Acta* **43**, 35–46.

Lee, C., Gagosian, R. B. and Farrington, J. W. (1980) Geochemistry of sterols in sediments from the Black Sea and the southwest African shelf and slope. *Organic Geochem.* **2**, 103–113.

McEvoy, J., Eglinton, G. and Maxwell, J. R. (1981) Preliminary lipid analyses from Sections 467-3-3 and 467-97-2. In *Initial Reports of the Deep Sea Drilling Project*, Vol. 63.

Ed. by Haq, B., Yeats, R., *et al.* US Govt Printing Office. pp. 763–774.

MacKenzie, A. S., Patience, R. L., Maxwell, J. R., Vandenbroucke, M. and Durand, B. (1980) Molecular parameters of maturation in the Toarcian shales, Paris Basin, France I. Changes in the configurations of acyclic isoprenoid alkanes, steranes and triterpanes. *Geochim. Cosmochim. Acta* **44**, 1709–1721.

Minale, L. and Sodano, G. (1974) Marine sterols: unique 3β-hydroxymethyl-A-nor-5α-steranes from the sponge *Axinella verrucosa*. *J. Chem. Soc. Perkin I*, 2380–2384.

Nishimura, M. and Koyama, T. (1976) Stenols and stanols in lake sediments and diatoms. *Chem. Geol.* **17**, 229–239.

Nishimura, M. and Koyama, T. (1977) The occurrence of stanols in various living organisms and the behaviour of sterols in contemporary sediments. *Geochim. Cosmochim. Acta* **41**, 379–385.

Patterson, G. W. (1971) The distribution of sterols in algae. *Lipids* **6**, 120–127.

Rubinstein, I. and Goad, L. J. (1974) Occurrence of (24S)-24-methylcholesta-5,22E-dien-3β-ol in the diatom *Phaeodactylum tricornutum*. *Phytochemistry* **13**, 485–487.

Rubinstein, I., Sieskind, O. and Albrecht, P. (1975) Rearranged sterenes in a shale: occurrence and simulated formation. *J. Chem. Soc. Perkin I*, 1833–1835.

Seifert, W. K. and Moldowan, J. M. (1978) Applications of steranes, terpanes and monoaromatics to the maturation, migration and source of crude oils. *Geochim. Cosmochim. Acta* **42**, 77–92.

Seifert, W. K. and Moldowan, J. M. (1979) The effect of biodegradation on steranes and terpanes in crude oils. *Geochim. Cosmochim. Acta* **43**, 222–236.

Sheikh, Y. M., Kaisin, K. and Djerassi, C. (1973) Steroids from starfish. *Steroids* **22**, 835–850.

Shimizu, Y., Alam, M. and Kobayashi, A. (1976) Dinosterol, the major sterol with a unique side chain in the toxic dinoflagellate, *Gonyaulax tamarensis*. *J. Amer. Chem. Soc.* **98**, 1059–1060.

Site 467 Reports (1981) In *Initial Reports of the Deep Sea Drilling Project*, Vol. 63. Ed. by Haq, B., Yeats, R., *et al.* US Govt Printing Office, pp. 23–112.

Thomson, I. D., Brassell, S. C., Comet, P. A., Eglinton, G., Isaacson, P. J., McEvoy, J. and Maxwell, J. R. (1981) Preliminary lipid analyses of cores 49, 54 and 59 from Hole 462. In *Initial Reports of the Deep Sea Drilling Project*, Vol. 61. Ed. by Schlanger, S. O., Larson, R. L., *et al.* US Govt Printing Office. pp. 613–618.

Volkman, J. K., Eglinton, G. and Corner, E. D. S. (1980a) Sterols and fatty acids of the marine diatom *Biddulphia sinensis*. *Phytochemistry* **19**, 1809–1813.

Volkman, J. K., Eglinton, G., Corner, E. D. S. and Sargent, J. R. (1980b) Novel unsaturated straight chain C_{37}–C_{39} methyl and ethyl ketones in marine sediments and a coccolithophore *Emiliania huxleyi*. In *Advances in Organic Geochemistry 1979*. Ed. by Douglas, A. G. and Maxwell, J. R. Pergamon Press. pp. 219–227.

Volkman, J. K., Smith, D. J., Eglinton, G., Forsberg, T. E. V. and Corner, E. D. S. (1981) Sterol and fatty acid composition of four marine *Haptophycean* algae. *J. Mar. Biol. Assoc. UK* **61**, 509–527.

Voogt, P. A. (1976) Composition and biosynthesis of sterols in some sponges. *Netherlands J. Zool.* **26**, 84–93.

Wakeham, S. G., Farrington, J. W., Gagosian, R. B., Lee, C., DeBarr, H., Nigrelli, G. E., Tripp, B. W., Smith, S. O. and Frew, N. M. (1980) Organic matter fluxes from sediment traps in the equatorial Atlantic Ocean. *Nature* **286**, 798–800.

Wardroper, A. M. K. (1979) Aspects of the geochemistry of polycyclic isoprenoids. *Ph.D. Thesis*, University of Bristol.

Wardroper, A. M. K., Maxwell, J. R. and Morris, R. J. (1978) Sterols of a diatomaceous ooze from Walvis Bay. *Steroids* **32**, 203–221.

Advances in Organic Geochemistry 1981, pp. 465–470
© *John Wiley & Sons Limited, 1983*

Organic Matter Patterns in South Atlantic Sediments Deposited Since the Late Miocene Beneath the Benguela Upwelling System

P. A. Meyers

Oceanography Program, Department of Atmospheric and Oceanic Science, The University of Michigan, Ann Arbor, Michigan 48109, USA

A. Y. Huc*

Laboratoire de Geologie Appliquée, Université d'Orleans, 45046 Orleans, France

S. C. Brassell

Organic Geochemistry Unit, Department of Chemistry, University of Bristol, Bristol BS8 1TS, UK

DSDP Leg 75 Shipboard Party

Hydraulic piston coring done during Deep Sea Drilling Project Leg 75 recovered organic-rich biogenic sediments of Late Miocene through Holocene age from two sites under the Benguela upwelling system in the southeastern Atlantic Ocean. These sediments contain up to 6% organic carbon. Based upon data from Rock-Eval Eval pryolysis and lipid analysis, the organic matter source is predominantly marine. A pattern of increasing organic carbon content from Late Miocene to Late Pliocene sediments and a decrease thereafter indicates a progressive intensification and subsequent weakening of the upwelling system. Carbon content fluctuations occur at 30 to 50 thousand year time intervals throughout this overall pattern and may reflect glacial/interglacial changes. DSDP Site 532 on the Walvis Ridge contains bioturbated pelagic sediments in which organic matter preservation is due to high sedimentation rates. In contrast, DSDP Site 530 at the edge of the Angola Basin contains organic-rich turbidites and debris flows interbedding organic-lean nannoplankton oozes. These cores represent examples of two modes of accumulation under oxic conditions of sediments high in organic matter. In both cases an abundant supply of organic matter is provided by high biological productivity in the upwelling. Preservation occurs by rapid burial, either by a high rate of pelagic sedimentation or by turbidity flows, thus limiting the exposure to biochemical degradation.

INTRODUCTION

Deep-sea sediments typically contain about 0.2% by weight of organic matter (Degens and Mopper, 1976). This material represents the residue of organisms formed by biosynthesis in the photic zone of the overlying waters, augmented by land-derived biological detritus transported to the ocean basins by rivers and winds. The bulk of marine biological organic matter production is rapidly remineralized in the upper waters of the oceans. Analysis of sediment trap contents has shown that only a few per cent of the original mass of organic matter reaches a water depth of 500 m (Knauer and Martin, 1981) and that even less material survives to become incorporated into the bottom (Müller and Suess, 1979). However, factors such as high rates of primary production, enhanced sinking rates of detritus, an

expanded oxygen minimum zone and high sedimentation rates can combine to allow large concentrations of organic matter to accumulate in oceanic sediments. The interaction of the many factors important to organic matter biosynthesis and preservation in sediments has been discussed by Tissot and Welte (1978), Hinga *et al.* (1979), and Demaison and Moore (1980).

Upwellings are good areas in which to study the conditions important to organic matter inputs to sediments. Upwelling patterns are best developed in coastal areas where prevailing wind patterns result in offshore transport of oceanic surface waters. Deeper water rises to replace the surface water, bringing with it dissolved nutrients. Conditions are thus maintained that encourage the sustained growth of high numbers of marine plants and of the animals that graze upon them. When these organisms die, their remains sink, and a portion of their organic matter reaches underlying

---

* *Present address*: Institut Francais du Petrole, 92506 Rueil Malmaison, France.

sediments and becomes incorporated in the bottom. At the same time, the sinking of large masses of biological debris expands the oxygen minimum zone and contributes to an enhanced sediment accumulation rate. Consequently, bottom sediments contain sufficiently high concentrations of organic matter to permit detailed analyses of relatively short-term fluctuations in input rates and character. As an example of this type of study, Summerhayes (1981) discusses the geological history of organic matter accumulation in sediments under the California upwelling system.

The Benguela Current offshore of Namibia (South West Africa) in the South Atlantic Ocean is another example of a major upwelling system, and the ocean bottom sediments beneath this system contain as much as 25% organic carbon. A special feature aiding identification of sources of organic matter input to these sediments is the Namib Desert which forms the African coastline along the Benguela Current. Virtually no land-derived organic matter can be provided by land run-off or river input although air-borne inputs from distant sources remain probable but small.

Several locations under the Benguela Current have been sampled as part of the Deep Sea Drilling Project (DSDP). During DSDP Leg 40 in 1975, sediments were obtained from Site 362, and Sites 530 and 532 yielded more samples during DSDP Leg 75 in 1980. Erdman and Schorno (1978) report organic carbon concentrations as high as 7.2% in upper sections of sediments obtained by rotary drilling at Site 362. Based upon concentration patterns of organic carbon, diatom

abundances, and nutrient incorporation in the Leg 40 sediments, a late Miocene onset of upwelling off South West Africa has been proposed by Siesser (1980).

We report here the results of organic geochemical analyses performed on board D/V *Glomar Challenger* during DSDP Leg 75. More sophisticated procedures employed in land-based laboratories are expected to provide additional information that will allow the conclusions presented in this report to be better refined. Nonetheless, the shipboard data are a useful base for future studies and reveal interesting patterns of organic matter deposition over the history of the Benguela upwelling system.

SAMPLING AND ANALYSIS

D/V *Glomar Challenger* occupied two sites under the oceanic edge of the Benguela upwelling in August 1980. Sediments were sampled by continuous hydraulic-piston coring to a subbottom depth of 180 m at Site 530 and to 291 m at Site 532 (Figure 1). Water depths at these locations are 4639 m and 1341 m, respectively. This newly developed coring procedure gives minimal sediment disturbance, thus allowing observation and study of closely spaced variations in sediment character. Standard rotary drilling procedures were used to obtain samples deeper than 180 m at Site 530. A description of the Pleistocene to Miocene sediments from these two sites is given by Hay *et al.* (1982). Samples of these

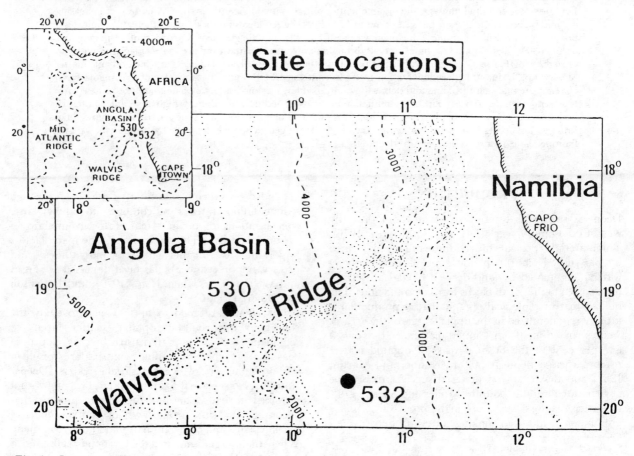

Fig. 1. Locations of Site 530 (4639 m) and Site 532 (1341 m) occupied during Deep Sea Drilling Project Leg 75 in 1980.

sediments were selected from representative sequences and also from sedimentary features believed to be of special interest to organic geochemistry. Other samples were frozen immediately after collection in order to preserve their organic matter constituents for subsequent study. In addition, a separate, 235 m long core was obtained from Site 532 for future organic geochemical study. This site and Site 362 of Leg 40 share nearly the same location.

Shipboard organic carbon analyses were done using a Hewlett-Packard 185-B CHN Analyzer. Portions of samples selected for carbonate measurements were treated with dilute HCl to remove carbonate, washed with deionized water, and dried at 110 °C. A Cahn Electrobalance was used to weigh 20 mg samples of sediment for CHN analysis. Samples were combusted at 1050 °C in the presence of an oxidant, and the volumes of the evolved gases determined as measures of the C, H, and N contents of sediment organic matter. Total organic carbon concentrations and atomic C/N ratios were calculated using response factors determined from standards and were corrected for the small blank of the complete procedure.

Numerous samples were analysed with the Girdel Rock-Eval instrument which used the IFP-Fina Process (Espitalié *et al.*, 1977) to measure both the free hydrocarbons and the hydrocarbon generating potential of rock samples. This instrument was used routinely to monitor the nature and maturity of sediment organic matter. Small samples of sediment (~0.5 g) were allowed to dry at room temperature and then were coarsely ground. One-hundred milligram portions of dry sediment were placed in the instrument and heated at 25 °C min^{-1} in a helium stream from 250 to 500 °C. Free hydrocarbons contained in the sediment are expressed as an S_1 peak; those released by the thermal breakdown of kerogen appear as an S_2 peak. Finally, an S_3 peak representing CO_2 produced from the kerogen appears as a reflection of the oxygen content of the organic matter.

RESULTS AND DISCUSSION

Different types of sedimentary sequences were found at the two sites in Fig. 1. Site 530 in the Angola Basin sediments consists of turbidities and debris flow deposits, presumably originating from biogenic oozes originally laid down on the Walvis Ridge. The sediments at Site 532 on the Walvis Ridge are made up of alternating sequences of light and dark pelagic oozes and are heavily bioturbated. As noted by Hay *et al.* (1982), these light–dark cycles occurred over an estimated average time span of 30 000–50 000 years. The dark layers are richer in organic carbon, clay and pyrite. A possible explanation for this pattern is episodic increases in planktonic productivity, creating relative increases in organic matter and its rapid sedimentation via fecal pellets and biological transport and eventual preservation as the darker sediment layers. The increased non-biogenic component of the dark layers may be, in part, due to an increased eolian input of clay-size material. There is little evidence that the light–dark cycles were caused by carbonate dissolution within the sediment.

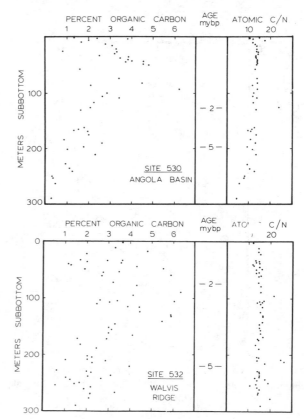

Fig. 2. Organic carbon concentrations and atomic C/N ratios of organic matter in sediment samples from DSDP Sites 530 and 532. Approximate depths of the 2 and 5 million-year-before-present horizons are shown. Concentrations are expressed as percentages of whole sediment dry weight.

There exists evidence for the presence and activity of bacteria in the sediments underlying these highly productive surface waters. Among the manifestations of their existence are high concentrations of biogenic gas, including hydrogen sulphide, detected during Leg 75 at Site 532 and during Leg 40 at Site 362.

Although lithologically different, the sediments at Sites 530 and 532 share similar organic matter patterns and compositions. Figure 2 shows individual values for organic carbon concentrations and for organic matter atomic C/N ratios in samples from these sites. The percentages of organic carbon are relatively high, particularly in view of the amount of bioturbation evident in sediments from both locations (Hay *et al.*, 1982). Maximum values of 5 to 6% TOC are found at subbottom depths of 40 to 110 m at Site 530 and 50 to 150 m at Site 532. Below this, values tend to decrease with depth, but are still *c.* 2% in the upper Miocene layers of these sediments. There is considerable variability in TOC of individual samples, with light-coloured oozes possessing lower organic carbon contents than the darker, olive-coloured samples.

The overall trends of organic carbon contents are clearly shown in Fig. 3, in which averaged values for one-million-year intervals are plotted against sediment age, rather than against depth as in Fig. 2. The increase in organic carbon values from Upper Miocene–Lower Pliocene sediments to maxima in Upper Pliocene to Lower Pleistocene oozes and subsequent decrease to

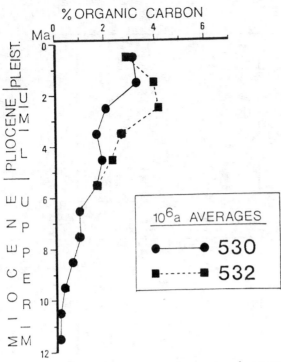

Fig. 3. Organic carbon concentrations averaged over one-million-year intervals and plotted against sediment age in millions of years.

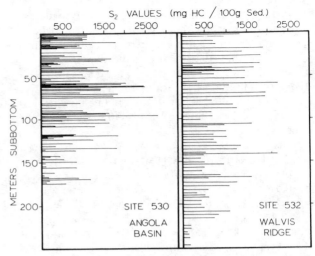

Fig. 4. Rock-Eval S_2 values of sediment samples from DSDP Sites 530 and 532. Data are from samples obtained by hydraulic-piston coring only. S_2 values represent hydrocarbons released from the thermal breakdown of kerogen below 500 °C.

Upper Pleistocene strata parallels the general trend of Site 362 (Erdman and Schorno, 1978; Kendrick *et al.*, 1978). As proposed by Siesser (1980), these patterns in the organic carbon contents appear to reflect:

(1) The advent of the Benguela upwelling system in Late Miocene time with a concomitant increase in the input of organic matter to the underlying sediments.
(2) An intensification of upwelling and productivity continuing to the Upper Pliocene–Lower Pleistocene.
(3) A subsequent decline in productivity levels during the Pleistocene.

In contrast to the variability and depth changes in the organic carbon contents of Site 532 sediments, the atomic C/N ratios change little from a value of 15 throughout the sediment sequence. This monotonous depth trend suggests that the nature of the organic matter preserved in the sediments has not changed significantly since the initiation of the Benguela upwelling system. A C/N ratio of *c.* 15, as found here, suggests a preferential loss of proteinaceous material from phytoplankton organic detritus (C/N = 6, Goodell, 1972; Müller, 1977). Since C/N values of upper water column particulate matter average 7.3 in this area of the Atlantic Ocean (Bishop *et al.*, 1978) a selective loss of nitrogen may occur after particles settle out from the photic zone, but prior to their incorporation into the bottom sediments, as suggested by Suess and Müller (1980).

A downhole log of S_2 (mg of hydrocarbons released by pyrolysis per 100 g of dry sediment) was drawn up as drilling progressed using sediment from the core catcher. The logs of the Rock-Eval S_2 response values in Fig. 4

show a trend generally similar to those of the organic carbon values, although the Upper Pliocene–Lower Pleistocene maximum is not so apparent, probably due to differences in sample selection. Sediments throughout the entire core exhibit a high oil potential.

The organic carbon values and the S_2 response both show considerable variability between closely spaced sediment samples (Figs 2 and 4). In general, the lighter coloured oozes possess lower organic carbon contents and give smaller S_2 responses than the darker, olive-

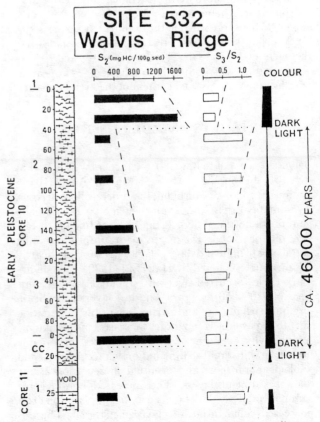

Fig. 5. Changes in Rock-Eval responses over a sediment light–dark cycle in Core 10 from DSDP Site 532.

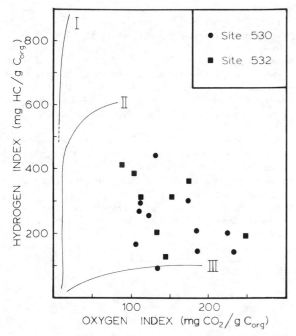

Fig. 6. Van Krevelen-type plot of hydrogen indexes and oxygen indexes of organic matter in sediments from DSDP Sites 530 and 532. Hydrogen indexes are calculated from Rock-Eval S_2 values and TOC; oxygen indexes from S_3 values and TOC.

coloured samples. These variations suggest that there are additional factors superimposed upon the overall trend in upwelling and productivity which are influencing the accumulation of organic matter in the underlying sediments. In many parts of the sedimentary section the colour appears to change from dark to light in rhythmic cycles. One such cycle in Site 532, Core 10, was studied by Rock-Eval pyrolysis to assess the relationship between sediment colour and organic matter content. As Fig. 5 shows, the S_2 response is high (*c.* 1500 mg HC/100 g sediment) for the darker (5Y 4/4) sediment horizons and decreases to low values (*c.* 300) for the lighter (10Y 7/2) sediment intervals. Hence, the colour of the sediments is indeed related to their organic matter content, and its fluctuations may reflect episodes of midwater or bottom anoxia, variations in upwelling strength or in pelagic biological populations, or changes in sediment accumulation rates.

The values of the hydrogen and oxygen indices calculated for these sediments from Rock-Eval pyrolysis data and from their organic carbon contents are shown in Fig. 6. These values are between Type II and Type III kerogen and suggest that the sedimentary organic matter is predominantly of marine origin and was deposited under slightly oxic conditions. Shore-based studies using Rock–Eval pyrolysis and investigations of humic acids support this result (Deroo, personal communication). In addition, the lipid contents in sediments from Site 362 (Boon *et al.*, 1978), as well as carbon isotope data (Erdman and Schorno, 1978), indicate predominantly marine sources. Thus, the organic geochemical studies suggest that local aquatic productivity is the primary origin of most of the organic matter in the sediments of this part of the southeastern Atlantic Ocean.

CONCLUSIONS

At DSDP Sites 530 and 532 the high organic carbon content of the sediments, the marine character of the organic matter, the abundance of pelagic microfossils and the pelagic nature of the sedimentological features uniformly indicate that the sediments are directly related to and reflect the productivity of the Benguela upwelling system. The good preservation of organic matter despite extensive evidence of reworking of sediments by burrowing fauna is surprising and may be at least partially explained by sedimentation rates that are relatively high for pelagic sediments (up to 6 cm/10³ years, Hay *et al.*, 1982). Organic matter is diagenetically immature, and sediment gases generated by active microbial populations are abundant at Site 532. In the monotonous sequences of dark and light pelagic sediments at Site 532, as well as in the turbidite and debris flow deposits from Site 530, the higher concentrations of organic carbon occur in diatomaceous oozes. The geological record at these sites shows that an increase in the organic carbon content of the sediments began during the Late Miocene, apparently reflecting the advent of the Benguela upwelling system as suggested by Siesser (1980), and that upwelling conditions peaked in the Late Pliocene.

Acknowledgements

We thank the Deep Sea Drilling Project (International Program for Ocean Drilling) for the opportunity to participate in Leg 75. The shipboard Scientific Party consisted of W. W. Hay and J.-C. Sibuet, Co-Chief Scientists, E. J. Barron, R. E. Boyce, W. E. Dean, B. H. Keating, C. L. McNulty, M. Nohara, R. E. Schallreuter, J. C. Steinmetz, D. Stow, H. Stradner, and the authors.

REFERENCES

Bishop, J. K. B., Ketten, D. R. and Edmond, J. M. (1978) The chemistry, biology and vertical flux of particulate matter from the upper 400 m of the Cape Basin in the southeast Atlantic Ocean. *Deep Sea Res.* **25**, 1121–1161.

Boon, J. J., *et al.* (1978) Organic geochemical analysis of core samples from Site 362, Walvis Ridge, DSDP, Leg 40. In *Init. Repts. DSDP 40*, ed. by Bolli, H. M., Ryan, W. B. F., *et al.* U.S. Government Printing Office, Washington, pp. 627–637.

Degens, E. T. and Mopper, K. (1976) Factors controlling the distribution and early diagenesis of organic material in marine sediments. In *Chemical Oceanography*, Vol. 6, Chapt. 3, ed. by Riley, J. P. and Chester, R. Academic Press, London, pp. 59–113.

Demaison, G. J. and Moore, G. T. (1980) Anoxic environments and oil source bed genesis *Org. Geochem.* **2**, 9–31.

Erdman, J. G. and Schorno, K. S. (1978) Geochemistry of Carbon: Deep Sea Drilling Project Leg 40. In *Init. Repts. DSDP 40*, ed. by Bolli, H. M., Ryan, W. G. F., *et al.* U.S. Government Printing Office, Washington, pp. 651–658.

Espitalié, J., Madec, M. and Tissot, B. (1977) Source rock characterization method for petroleum exploration. *OTC* 399–404.

Goodell, H. G. (1972) Carbon/nitrogen ratio. In *Encyclopedia of Geochemistry and Environmental Science*, ed. by Fairbridge, R. W. Van Nostrand Reinhold, New York, pp. 136–142.

Hay, W. W., Sibuet, J.-C. and Leg 75 Shipboard Party (1982) Sedimentation and accumulation of organic carbon in the Angola Basin and on Walvis Ridge: Preliminary results of Deep Sea Drilling Project Leg 75. *Geol. Soc. Am. Bull.* in press.

Hinga, K. R., Sieburth, J. McN. and Heath, G. R. (1979) The supply and use of organic material at the deep-sea floor. *J. Mar. Res.* **37**, 557–579.

Kendrick, J. W., *et al.* (1978) Petroleum-generating potential of sediments from Leg 40, Deep Sea Drilling Project. In *Init. Repts. DSDP 40*, ed. by Bolli, H. M., Ryan, W. B. F., *et al.* U.S. Government Printing Office, Washington, pp. 671–676.

Knauer, G. A. and Martin, J. H. (1981) Primary production and carbon–nitrogen fluxes in the upper 1500 m of the northeast Pacific. *Limnol. Oceanogr.* **26**, 181–186.

Müller, P. J. (1977) C/N ratios in Pacific deep-sea sediments: Effect of inorganic ammonium and organic nitrogen compounds sorbed by clays. *Geochim. Cosmochim. Acta* **41**, 765–776.

Müller, P. J. and Suess, E. (1979) Productivity, sedimentation rate and sedimentary organic matter in the oceans: I. Organic carbon preservation. *Deep-Sea Res.* **26**, 1347–1362.

Siesser, W. G. (1980) Late Miocene origin of the Benguela upwelling system off northern Namibia. *Science* **208**, 283–285.

Suess, E. and Müller, P. J. (1980) Productivity, sedimentation rate and sedimentary organic matter in the oceans: II. Elemental fractionation. *Colloq. Int. CNRS* No. 293, 17–26.

Summerhayes, C. P. (1981) Oceanographic controls on organic matter in the Miocene Monterey Formation, offshore California. In *The Monterey Formation and Related Siliceous Rocks of California*, pp. 213–219. Soc. Ec. Paleont. Mineral.

Tissot, B. P. and Welte, D. H. (1978) *Petroleum Formation and Occurrence*. Springer-Verlag, Berlin.

Advances in Organic Geochemistry 1981, pp. 471–476
© *John Wiley & Sons Limited, 1983*

Origin of the Organic Matter in a Cretaceous Black Shale Deposit in the Central Apennines (Italy)

G. van Graas, T. C. Viets, J. W. de Leeuw and P. A. Schenck

Delft University of Technology, Department of Chemistry and Chemical Engineering, Organic Geochemistry Unit, De Vries van Heystplantsoen 2, 2628 RZ Delft, The Netherlands

The organic matter in a Cretaceous sequence of alternating limestones and marls from the central Apennines, Italy, has been investigated microscopically and through detailed analysis of the extracts. Black layers are different from the other layers in that they contain remains of bacteria in the insoluble material; the composition of the extracts points to a bacterial contribution too. A paleoreconstruction based on chemical data shows a low productivity in the water column and an oxic environment of sedimentation for the limestones and an anoxic environment of sedimentation for the black marls. Eolian input probably accounts for the presence of n-alkanes of terrestrial origin in all samples. This reconstruction is in agreement with paleontological and sedimentological data.

INTRODUCTION

During some intervals of the Cretaceous (~140 to 64 My b.p.), dark coloured (black) shales, whether or not interbedded with lighter coloured, carbonate-richer beds, have been deposited more frequently and more abundantly than during any other geological period.

Cretaceous black shales are encountered especially in the North and South Atlantic (e.g. Deep Sea Drilling Project (DSDP) leg 11, Hollister *et al.*, 1972; leg 40, Bolli *et al.*, 1978; leg 44, Benson *et al.*, 1978; leg 48, Montadert *et al.*, 1979) but also in the Pacific at the flanks of seamounts and continents (e.g. leg 32, Larson *et al.*, 1975; leg 33, Schlanger *et al.*, 1976).

Several authors have discussed the origin of the Cretaceous black shales. Schlanger and Jenkyns (1976) and Thiede and Van Andel (1977) suggest that the expansion of the mid-water oxygen minimum layer and its oxygen exhaustion caused the formation of the dark coloured, often organic rich layers, while Ryan and Cita (1977) emphasize the possibility of an ocean-wide stagnation. These theories are not conflicting; a full depletion of oxygen in the oxygen minimum layer will be favoured by a waning of circulation velocity. In case of complete stagnation (if possible), oxygen exhaustion is likely to start in this mid-water oxygen minimum zone.

The frequent depletion of oxygen in deeper parts of the Mid-Cretaceous oceans, which allowed the formation of organic rich sediments, is obviously related to both tectonic and climatic factors.

The Mid-Cretaceous (110–85 My b.p.) is characterized by relatively high temperatures and low temperature differences between high and low latitudes

(Frakes, 1979) as a consequence of a great rise of the sea level (up to 350 m; Pitman, 1978) which in turn was caused by an increase of total volume of mid-oceanic ridges (van Straaten, 1973; Hays and Pitman, 1973). In such a situation a relatively low circulation velocity of oceanic water results and hence a decrease in replenishment of oxygen in deep water is expected. This depletion of oxygen has favoured the deposition of organic rich sediments in the oceans.

Depending on the place of deposition relative to the position of land areas, the organic matter in Mid-Cretaceous pelagic sediments is composed of varying ratios of terrestrial and marine organic matter (Tissot *et al.*, 1980).

In spite of its large size, the rate of sea level rise during the Cretaceous has been relatively slow. Therefore, it is unlikely that the Cretaceous transgression would have caused a catastrophic transfer of terrestrial organic matter into the oceans, as was suggested by Jenkyns (1980).

Our current research is part of a project concerning sedimentological, paleontological and organic geochemical investigations of Mid-Cretaceous black shale deposits from outcrops in northern Italy and southern France. In this paper we report the results obtained on samples from a location in the north central Apennines, Italy, which covers a large part of the Cretaceous in this area. The sampled section forms part of a pelagic sequence. This sequence consists of a more or less regular alternation of carbonate-rich and carbonate-poorer beds, the latter of which are characterized by a grey to black colour and therefore are indicated as black shales.

The carbonate of the samples consists mainly of the remains of coccolithophores and to a smaller extent of planktonic and benthonic foraminifera (Wonders, 1980).

De Boer and Wonders (1981) show the rhythmicity of the carbonate–marl alternations in the Albian–Cenomanian interval to be the result of a rhythmic variation of production of carbonate, which is related to the influence of astronomical parameters upon the Earth's climate.

Analysis of the extractable organic matter from the limestones and marls, in combination with microscopic, sedimentological and paleontological data, made possible the construction of a model for the origin of this sedimentary sequence.

EXPERIMENTAL

The samples have been taken from a location along the Moria-Monte Petrano road near the cemetery of Moria (43°33′ N, 12°41′ E), 6.5 km southwest of Cagli in the north central Apennines, Italy (Wonders, 1980), from the lower part of the Scaglia Bianca Formation which is of Late Albian age (108–100 My b.p.). An interval of 1.30 m with 13 limestone/marl couplets was sampled (Fig. 1). In a number of couplets the marly layer is very thin. Several marly layers are partially or totally dark coloured. In the case of partially dark coloured marls (samples 5, 14, 16 and 24) a subdivision was made as indicated in Fig. 1. In order to obtain fresh material about 30 cm of rock were removed before actual sampling.

In the laboratory six samples have been selected for a detailed analysis of the extracts: two carbonate layers (27 and 29); two integral marly layers, one with a black middle part (24-total) and one without a black middle part (28) and the black parts of two marly layers (24B and 26). The samples were ground in a rotary disc mill and Soxhlet-extracted with toluene/methanol (1/3 v/v) for 20 h. The organic carbon content of the extraction residues was measured after removal of carbonate with 2N HCl. The carbonate content of the samples was calculated from the weight loss upon 2N HCl treatment.

The total extracts were investigated by thin-layer chromatography (TLC) using an Iatron Iatroscan TH-10 instrument equipped with Chromarods S II; hexane/diethylether/formic acid (95/5/1 v/v/v) was used as eluent (Kramer et al., 1980). The hydrocarbons were isolated by preparative TLC on silica gel with petroleum ether 40–60/diethyl ether/acetic acid (89/10/1 v/v/v) as developer. Gas chromatography (GLC) was performed using a Carlo Erba 4160 instrument equipped with a 25 m glass WCOT column (i.d. 0.31 mm) coated with SE-52.

Gas chromatography–mass spectrometry (GCMS) was carried out on a Varian 3700 gas chromatograph equipped with a 25 m glass WCOT column (i.d. 0.25 mm) coated with CP-Sil-5, coupled to a MAT 44 quadrupole mass spectrometer operating at 70 eV with mass range m/z 50–500 and a cycle time of 2 s. In both GC and GCMS helium was used as carrier gas.

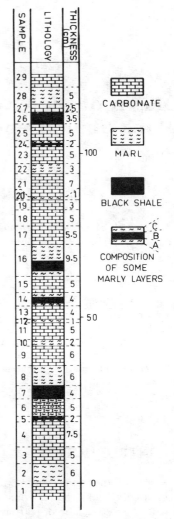

Fig. 1. Stratigraphy of the sampled section.

A blank procedure was carried out using quartz sand which was first heated for 16 h at 900 °C. Samples 26, 27, 28 and 29 have been investigated by incident light (UV, 365 nm) microscopy.

RESULTS

Carbonate and organic carbon content of the samples are listed in Table 1. Extraction yields are in the order of magnitude of 10–100 ppm. Further quantitation was not attempted.

TLC analysis showed that the extracts contain mainly saturated hydrocarbons (Rf 0.95–1.0) and highly polar material (Rf 0.0–0.1). Separate bands of aromatic hydrocarbons were not present.

The saturated hydrocarbon fractions of the extracts were analysed by GLC and GCMS. The chromatograms of the hydrocarbon fraction of samples 26 and 28 are shown in Fig. 2. Identification of the numbered compounds is given in Table 2. Identification of hopanes and hopenes is based on mass spectral and GLC-retention data (Ensminger, 1974; Van Dorsselaer, 1974; Wardroper, 1979).

Table 1

Carbonate and organic carbon content of the samples.

Sample	Carbonate (% wt)	Organic carbon (% wt)
3	73	0.03
4	75	0.02
5A	75	0.03
5B	64	0.08
5C	69	0.05
6	71	0.06
7	71	0.57
8	75	0.03
9	75	0.01
10	74	0.02
11	72	0.03
12	71	0.04
13	70	0.03
14	65	0.08
15	70	0.04
16A	65	0.09
16B	67	0.21
16C	68	0.09
17	78	0.02
18	79	0.01
19	77	0.02
20	75	0.05
21	77	0.02
22	71	0.02
23	75	0.02
24-total	65	0.14
24A	72	0.10
24B	63	0.26
24C	54	0.62
25	73	0.13
26	67	0.66
27	73	0.04
28	70	0.23
29	77	0.02

Table 2

Compounds identified by GCMS in the hydrocarbon fractions of samples 26 and 28 (see Fig. 2).

1. n-hexadecane
2. 2,6,10-trimethyl pentadecane
3. n-heptadecane
4. pristane
5. n-octadecane
6. phytane
7. n-nonadecane
8. n-eicosane
9. n-heneicosane
10. n-docosane
11. n-tricosane
12. n-tetracosane
13. n-pentacosane
14. phthalate ester (contaminant)
15. n-hexacosane
16. n-heptacosane
17. n-octacosane
18. squalene (contaminant)
19. 17α(H)-22, 29, 30-trisnorhopane
20. n-nonacosane
21. 17β(H)-22, 29, 30-trisnorhopane
22. unidentified hopane-like compound
23. n-triacontane
24. 30-norneohop-13(18)-ene
25. 17α(H), 21β(H)-30-norhopane
26. 17β(H), 21α(H)-30-norhopane
27. n-hentriacontane
28. 17α(H), 21β(H)-hopane
29. 17β(H), 21β(H)-30-norhopane
30. n-dotriacontane
31. 17α(H), 21β(H)-homohopane
32. 17β(H), 21β(H)-hopane
33. 17β(H), 21α(H)-homohopane
34. n-tritriacontane
35. 17β(H), 21β(H)-homohopane
36. n-tetratriacontane
37. n-pentatriacontane

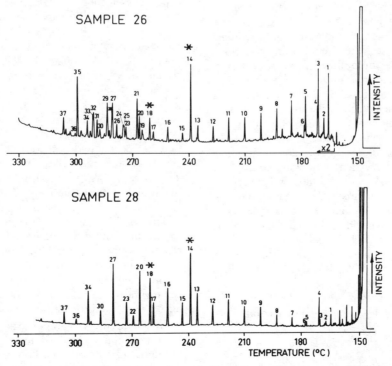

Fig. 2. Chromatograms of the hydrocarbon fractions of sample 26 (dark marl) and sample 28 (light marl). Identifications of numbered compounds are listed in Table 2. The asterisks indicate the presence of a contaminant.

All samples contain *n*-alkanes with a moderate odd/even predominance* (CPI$_{24-34}\approx2$) and squalene. The presence of the latter compound is due to contamination from an unknown source, since it is the major compound showing up in the blank procedure. In the light layers (27, 28, 29) these alkanes were the only compounds that could be identified. The dark layers (24-total, 24B, 26) also contained C$_{27}$ and C$_{29-32}$ hopanes. The major isomers are 17β(H), 21β(H)-hopanes, but 17α(H), 21β(H)- and 17β(H), 21α(H)-hopanes are also present. Other hopanoid compounds are present in some samples: hop-17(21)-ene was identified in sample 24 and 30-norneohop-13(18)-ene was tentatively identified in sample 26. Steroidal hydrocarbons were not detected in any of the samples. The saturated hydrocarbon fractions of samples 24-total and 24B did not differ significantly.

The organic matter of sample 26, showing a brownish fluorescence under incident UV light, is defined as structureless organic matter (SOM). This SOM — especially when it is associated with relatively large amounts of framboidal pyrite, as in this case — is assumed to be the fossil form of bacterial biomass (Lijmbach, 1975). Moreover, this same qualitative analysis showed the presence of pelagic foraminifera and a fairly large amount of pollen and spores. Upon demineralization (HCl/HF treatment) the pollen turned out to be of the bisaccate type (conifers).

The other samples (27, 28, 29) also contained SOM but in significantly smaller amounts.

DISCUSSION

The amounts of organic carbon in the black marly layers investigated (maximum 0.66%) are low as compared with values obtained for some Cretaceous black shales from the Atlantic Ocean (values up to 17%; e.g. Tissot *et al.*, 1980) or from other locations in the Apennines (values up to 14% at the Cenomanian–Turonian boundary; van Graas, unpublished results). However, on a number of other locations (e.g. DSDP leg 43, Tucholke *et al.*, 1979; leg 47B, Sibuet *et al.*, 1979) sediments occur which have been characterized as black shales and have organic carbon contents of less than 1%. Hence one might wonder whether it would be recommendable to reconsider the common definition of black shales being 'organic-rich' dark-coloured marly or clayey sediments (e.g. Wonders, 1980). Microscopical studies indicate that pyrite instead of organic matter is responsible for the dark colour of the samples. The hopanes present exclusively in the black layers probably are diagenetic products of bacteriohopanes (e.g. Van Dorsselaer *et al.*, 1974) which are present in bacteria (e.g. Rohmer and Ourisson, 1976). Two layers contain a hopene in addition to the hopanes.

Hop-17(21)-ene is present in sample 24 and 30-norneohop-13(18)-ene in sample 26. These compounds

$$\text{CPI}_{24-34} = \frac{1}{2}\left(\frac{C_{25}+C_{27}+C_{29}+C_{31}+C_{33}}{C_{24}+C_{26}+C_{28}+C_{30}+C_{32}} + \frac{C_{25}+C_{27}+C_{29}+C_{31}+C_{33}}{C_{26}+C_{28}+C_{30}+C_{32}+C_{34}}\right).$$

were also found in Cretaceous black shales by Barnes *et al.* (1979) but together with their C$_{27}$ and C$_{29}$ or C$_{30}$ homologues. They were thought to have arisen through rearrangement of the original double bond position. Recently Brassell *et al.* (1981) interpreted hop-17(21)-ene and neohop-13(18)-ene in Japan Trench samples as bacterial markers following their identification in a bacterium by Howard (1980). The presence of these bacterial marker molecules in the extracts is in accordance with the microscopic indication of bacterial organic matter in sample 26 (Gutjahr, personal communication).

Three isomeric types of hopanes are present in the samples: 17β(H), 21β(H), 17α(H), 21β(H) and 17β(H), 21α(H). The dominating presence of the 17β(H), 21β(H)-type indicates a relatively low degree of maturation (Van Dorsselaer, 1974; Mackenzie *et al.*, 1980).

The *n*-alkane distribution in the samples (CPI≈2) indicates an origin from higher plant material (e.g. Maxwell *et al.*, 1971). It also confirms the relatively low maturity of the sediments. Apart from the *n*-alkanes no other higher-plant-related compounds such as steroidal or diterpenoid hydrocarbons could be detected in the saturated hydrocarbon fractions. Since the TLC-analysis has shown the absence of aromatic hydrocarbon bands separated from the saturated hydrocarbons, partially or totally aromatized steroidal or diterpenoid hydrocarbons are also not present. The samples did not contain microscopically visible higher plant tissues although a number of spores and pollen grains were present.

An explanation for the exclusive presence of *n*-alkanes as higher plant marker molecules could be the input of eolian dust into the sediments. The organic matter of eolian dust mainly consists of higher-plant waxes (*n*-alkanes, *n*-alcohols, *n*-carboxylic acids) but does not contain diterpenoids or steroids (Simoneit, 1977; Simoneit and Eglinton, 1977). The supposed open marine environment of sedimentation of the samples (de Boer, 1982) does not at all exclude the possibility of eolian input since eolian transport can cover large distances (Simoneit, 1977). The presence of bisaccate pollen (conifers) is also in agreement with eolian input since they can be airborne over large distances. In case of potamic input of terrestrial material one would expect to find diterpenoid hydrocarbons which are present in high concentrations in the resins of conifers (Thomas, 1969). The spores present in the samples are fairly large which makes eolian input unlikely. The way in which they reach the sediment remains uncertain.

The complete absence of steroidal hydrocarbons in the extracts and of visible organic algal remains in the sediments upon microscopical investigation indicate a low productivity in the water column and an aerobic environment of sedimentation. The low mean sedimentation rate (0.7 cm/1000 years; de Boer, 1982) agrees with the proposed low productivity.

In conclusion we can construct the following model for the origin of this sedimentary sequence. The low amounts of organic carbon and the absence of substantial amounts of algal-related compounds, together with the low rate of sedimentation, indicate that the sediments have been deposited in a low productive environment with enough oxygen available in the water column to oxidize the algal products.

Black marly layers were formed when enough organic material could reach the sediment surface to enable growth of bacteria as represented by the hopanes and the presence of structureless bacterial residues in the samples. This relatively high input of organic matter into the sediment probably is the result of a lower availability of oxygen. According to sedimentological evidence, marly layers were deposited during times of low productivity (de Boer, 1982). Hence the origin of black layers is probably due to a lower availability of oxygen caused by a restricted water circulation. During such periods, absence of oxygen in the top of the sediment gave rise to activity of sulphate reducing bacteria which must have lead to the formation of pyrite which causes the dark colour of the samples. Eolian input explains the sole presence of *n*-alkanes as higher plant marker molecules and is in agreement with the paleoreconstruction of the site as being a pelagic environment located at considerable distance from the mainland (de Boer, unpublished).

The relatively low maturity of the samples as indicated by the distribution of the hopanes and the *n*-alkanes is in agreement with the burial history, which shows an overburden of ± 500 m until the Miocene, an increase to 2000–2500 m during the Miocene and upheaval and erosion afterwards (Wonders, 1980).

Acknowledgements

The authors are grateful to Mr P. L. de Boer for valuable discussions and suggestions regarding the geological aspects of this investigation. Dr C. C. M. Gutjahr (Koninklijke/Shell Exploratie and Produktie Laboratorium, Shell Research B.V., Rijswijk, The Netherlands) kindly performed the microscopical analyses. Mr F. de Lange is thanked for technical assistance during the course of this investigation. This research is supported by the Netherlands Foundation for Earth Science Research (AWON) with financial aid from the Netherlands Organization for the Advancement of Pure Research (ZWO).

REFERENCES

Barnes, P. J., Brassell, S. C., Comet, P., Eglinton, G., McEvoy, J., Maxwell, J. R., Wardroper, A. M. K. and Volkman, J. K. (1979) 50. Preliminary lipid analyses of core sections 18, 24 and 30 from hole 402A. In *Initial Reports of the Deep Sea Drilling Project*, Vol. 48, ed. by Montadert, L., Roberts, D. G., *et al*. U.S. Government Printing Office, Washington, pp. 965–975.

Benson, W. E., Sheridan, R. E., *et al*. (Eds), (1978) *Initial Reports of the Deep Sea Drilling Project*, Vol. 44. U.S. Government Printing Office, Washington.

de Boer, P. L. (1982) Cyclicity and storage of organic matter in Middle Cretaceous pelagic sediments (unpublished).

de Boer, P. L. and Wonders, A. A. H. (1981) Milankovitch parameters and bedding rhythms in Umbrian Middle Cretaceous pelagic sediments. *I.A.S. 2nd Eur. Meeting, Bologna Abstr.*, 10–13.

Bolli, H. M., Ryan, W. B. F., *et al*. (Eds) (1978) *Initial Reports of the Deep Sea Drilling Project*, Vol. 40. U.S. Government Printing Office, Washington.

Brassell, S. C., Wardroper, A. M. K., Thompson, I. D., Maxwell, J. R. and Eglinton, G. (1981) Specific acyclic isoprenoids as biological markers of methanogenic bacteria in marine sediments. *Nature (London)* **290**, 693–696.

Ensminger, A. (1974) Triterpénoides du schiste de Messel. Thesis, University of Strasbourg.

Frakes, L. A. (1979) *Climates throughout Geologic Time*, Elsevier, Oxford.

Hays, J. D. and Pitman, W. C. (1973) Lithospheric plate motion, sea level changes and ecological consequence. *Nature (London)* **246**, 18–22.

Hollister, C. D., Ewing, J. I. *et al*. (Eds) (1972) *Initial Reports of the Deep Sea Drilling Project*, Vol. 11. U.S. Government Printing Office, Washington.

Howard, D. L. (1980) Polycyclic triterpenes of the anaerobic photosynthetic bacterium. Rhodomicrobium vaniellii. Thesis, University of California, Los Angeles.

Jenkyns, H. C. (1980) Cretaceous Anoxic Events: From Continents to Oceans. *J. Geol. Soc. London* **137**, 171–188.

Kramer, J. K. G., Fouchard, R. C. and Farnworth, E. R. (1980) Effect of solvents on the resolution of neutral lipids on chromarods. *J. Chromatogr.* **198**, 279–285.

Larson, R. L., Moberly, R. M., *et al*. (Eds) (1975) *Initial Reports of the Deep Sea Drilling Project*, Vol. 32. U.S. Government Printing Office, Washington.

Lijmbach, G. W. M. (1975) SP 1. On the origin of petroleum. In *9th World Petroleum Congress*, Vol. 2. Applied Science Publishers, London, pp. 357–374.

Mackenzie, A. S., Patience, R. L., Maxwell, J. R., Vandenbroucke, M. and Durand, B. (1980) Molecular parameters of maturation in the Toarcian shales, Paris Basin, France. I. Changes in the configurations of acyclic isoprenoid alkanes, steranes and triterpanes. *Geochim. Cosmochim. Acta* **44**, 1709–1721.

Maxwell, J. R., Pillinger, C. T. and Eglinton, G. (1971) Organic geochemistry. *Q. Rev. Chem. Soc.* **25**, 571–628.

Montadert, L., Roberts, D. G., *et al*. (Eds) (1979) *Initial Reports of the Deep Sea Drilling Project*, Vol. 48. U.S. Government Printing Office, Washington.

Pitman, W. C. (1978) Relationship between eustacy and stratigraphic sequences of passive margins. *Geol. Soc. Am. Bull.* **89**, 1389–1403.

Rohmer, M. and Ourisson, G. (1976) Structure des bacteriohopanetetrols d'Acetobacter xylinum. *Tetrahedron Lett.* **40**, 3633–3636.

Ryan, W. B. F. and Cita, M. B. (1977) Ignorance concerning episodes of ocean-wide stagnation. *Mar. Geol.* **23**, 197–215.

Schlanger, S. O. and Jenkyns, H. C. (1976) Cretaceous oceanic anoxic events: causes and consequences. *Geol. Mijnbouw* **55**, 179–184.

Schlanger, S. O., Jackson, E. D., *et al*. (Eds) (1976) *Initial Reports of the Deep Sea Drilling Project*, Vol. 33. U.S. Government Printing Office, Washington.

Sibuet, J. C., Ryan, W. B. F., *et al*. (Eds) (1979) *Initial Reports of the Deep Sea Drilling Project*, Vol. 47, part 2. U.S. Government Printing Office, Washington.

Simoneit, B. R. T. (1977) Organic matter in eolian dusts over the Atlantic Ocean. *Mar. Chem.* **5**, 443–464.

Simoneit, B. R. T. and Eglinton, G. (1977) Organic matter of eolian dust and its input to marine sediments. In *Advances in Organic Geochemistry 1975*, ed. by Campos, R. and Goni, J. Enadimsa, Madrid, pp. 415–430.

van Straaten, L. M. J. U. (1973) Eustatische zeespiegelbewegingen en verschuiving der continenten. *K.*

Ned. Akad. Wet. Versl. Gewone Vergad. Afdl. Natuurkd. **82**, 6–8.

Thiede, J. and Van Andel, T. H. (1977) The paleoenvironment of anaerobic sediments in the Late Mesozoic South
Atlantic Ocean. *Earth Planet. Sci. Lett.* **33**, 301–309.

Thomas, B. R. (1969) Kauri resins — modern and fossil. In
Organic Geochemistry — Methods and Results, ed. by Eglinton,
G. and Murphy, M. T. J. Springer-Verlag, Berlin, pp. 599–
618.

Tissot, B., Demaison, G., Masson, P., Delteil, J. R. and
Combaz, A. (1980) Paleoenvironment and petroleum
potential of Middle Cretaceous black shales in Atlantic
basins. *Am. Assoc. Pet. Geol. Bull.* **64**, 2051–2063.

Tucholke, B. E., Vogt, P. R., *et al.* (Eds) (1979) *Initial Reports of
the Deep Sea Drilling Project*, Vol. 43. U.S. Government

Printing Office, Washington.

Van Dorsselaer, A. (1974) Triterpènes de sediments. Thesis,
University of Strasbourg.

Van Dorsselaer, A., Ensminger, A., Spyckerelle, C., Dastillung,
M., Sieskind, O., Arpino, P., Albrecht, P., Ourisson, G.,
Brooks, P. W., Gaskell, S. J., Kimble, B. J., Philp, R. P.,
Maxwell, J. R. and Eglinton, G. (1974) Degraded and
extended hopane derivatives (C_{27} to C_{35}) as ubiquitous
geochemical markers. *Tetrahedron Lett.* 1349–1352.

Wardroper, A. M. K. (1979) Aspects of the geochemistry of
polycyclic isoprenoids. Thesis, University of Bristol.

Wonders, A. A. H. (1980) Middle and Late Cretaceous
planktonic Foraminifera of the western Mediterranean
area. *Utrecht Micropaleontol. Bull.* 24.

Advances in Organic Geochemistry 1981, pp. 477–484
© *John Wiley & Sons Limited, 1983*

Lipid Geochemistry of Cretaceous Sediments Recovered by the Deep Sea Drilling Project

S. C. Brassell, V. J. Howell, A. P. Gowar and G. Eglinton

Organic Geochemistry Unit, University of Bristol, School of Chemistry, Cantock's Close, Bristol BS8 1TS,
UK

The extractable lipid distributions of Cretaceous deep sea sediments from various locations have been examined using computerized gas chromatography–mass spectrometry. Among the aliphatic hydrocarbons, compounds indicative of inputs from terrigeneous (e.g. long chain *n*-alkanes), marine algal (e.g. steroids), and bacterial (e.g. specific acyclic isoprenoids and hopanoids) sources are recognized. Overall, the aliphatic hydrocarbon compositions reflect the relative proportions of terrigenous and marine (both algal and bacterial) sources for the organic matter and attest the immaturity of these sediments. There are significant differences in the lipid composition of the sediments that reflect their different environments of deposition (e.g. between Leg 50 and Leg 62 samples), whereas the marked similarity in certain distributions, such as hopanoids in Leg 48 and Leg 50 samples, presumably reflects similar sources for that part of the organic matter or similar depositional conditions.

INTRODUCTION

Sediments of Cretaceous age that are rich in organic matter have been recovered from all the major oceans during the Deep Sea Drilling Project (DSDP) and have been conveniently called 'black shales'. Attempts to classify the term 'black shale' (Spears, 1980; Hallam, 1980) have not become generally accepted and it continues to be used in the description of sediments that differ greatly in their lithology and organic carbon content. Indeed, the blackness of the sediments is principally associated with the presence of sulphides and is therefore often only indirectly linked to the quality and quantity of the sedimentary organic matter.

The enigma of oceanic Cretaceous black shales is their widespread occurrence during discrete time intervals, observations that have led to the term oceanic anoxic events (e.g. Schlanger and Jenkyns, 1976). Black shales, however, are often intercallated with other lithologies, which suggests that conditions appropriate for their deposition occurred only intermittently. In some instances, evidence for bioturbation in the sediment sequence argues against deposition under anoxic conditions, although the presence of reduced sulphide species in the sediments confirms subsurface anoxic conditions. In general, however, the tendency to group black shales in a single category belies their different sedimentological settings.

To date, the most comprehensive organic geochemical studies of DSDP black shales have been those of Tissot and co-workers (Tissot *et al.*, 1979, 1980). Their investigations of Atlantic black shales have assessed the origin of the organic matter and its petroleum potential from characterization of the kerogen. The results show that these sediments can be principally composed of marine or terrestrial or residual organic matter in variable proportions. The petroleum potential of the black shales also differs considerably.

No detailed comparison of the lipid constituents of DSDP black shales from various locations has been published, although the composition of examples from specific regions has been evaluated (Cornford *et al.*, 1980; Rullkötter *et al.*, 1982), in conjunction with organic petrographic studies. In this paper selected extractable hydrocarbon distributions of nine Cretaceous DSDP samples (Table 1) are described and used in the evaluation of the source (i.e. whether terrestrial or marine), depositional environment and maturity of the sediments. These lipid distributions are also used to compare and contrast the various samples.

EXPERIMENTAL

The analytical methods used in our investigations of sedimentary lipid distributions have been described in detail elsewhere (Barnes *et al.*, 1979; Brassell *et al.*, 1980a, b, d). In brief, the lipids are solvent-extracted by ultrasonication, separated into fractions composed principally of a specific compound class (hydrocarbons, alcohols, ketones etc.) by thin layer chromatography and each fraction is analysed by gas chromatography (GC) and computerized gas chromatography–mass spectrometry (C-CH-MS). The conditions of such GC and C-GC-MS analyses have differed somewhat from sample to sample and the reader is referred to the individual publications cited above and in Table 1 for full details. Extensive use is made of mass fragmentography (MF) for both the identification and the quantitation of the various compound classes

Table 1

Sample descriptions

| Location | Sample (DSDP Code) | | | Age | Lithology | Reference[a] |
	Leg	Site, Core, Section, interval	Depth (m subbottom)			
Angola Basin	75	530A-96-5 72–77 cm	1024	Cenomanian	Green claystone	—
	75	530A-96-5 77–82 cm	1024	Cenomanian	Black shale	—
Rio Grande Rise	72	516F-122-2 0–13 cm	1224	Coniacian–Santonian	Calcareous black claystone	—
Falkland Plateau	71	511-70-3 140–150 cm	625	Neocomian[b]	Mudstone (laminated)	—
Hess Rise	62	465A-38-3	394	Upper Albian	Light olive to dark olive grey finely laminated limestone	Comet et al., 1981
Moroccan Basin	50	416A-18-3 75–91 cm	1266	Valanginian	Calcareous mudstone/marlstone (laminated)	Brassell et al., 1980a
	50	416A-28-4 124–145 cm	1361	Valanginian	Calcareous claystone/mudstone	Brassell et al., 1980a
Bay of Biscay Abyssal Plain	48	402A-24–1 0–20 cm	356	Lower Albian	Brownish to olive black carbonaceous marly chalk	Barnes et al., 1979
	48	402A-30-4 65–75 cm	418	Upper Aptian	Olive grey to olive black carbonaceous marly chalk	Barnes et al., 1979

[a] References for DSDP papers concerned with these samples.
[b] Possibly Upper Jurassic in age.

discussed herein; the details are given in the appropriate results sections. In general, relative rather than absolute quantitations are given.

RESULTS

From the wide range of compounds identified in the various samples, a few key classes have been selected to illustrate the type of information realized through lipid analysis. All of these are hydrocarbon classes, but functionalized components are also present in several of these samples.

n-Alkanes and acyclic isoprenoids

The distributions of n-alkanes and acyclic isoprenoid alkanes in the samples are shown in Fig. 1. n-Alkanes were recognized, characterized and quantitated from their GC or m/z 85 MF response. Acyclic isoprenoid alkanes were identified on the basis of their individual mass spectra and GC retention times. The samples show considerable variation in their n-alkane distributions with three features or modes evident: (i) low carbon number (C_{13}–C_{22}); (ii) intermediate carbon number (C_{22}–C_{26}), both with little or no odd over even preference (OEP) and (iii) higher carbon number (C_{23}–C_{35}) with a prominent OEP.

The acyclic isoprenoid alkanes recognized include C_{16}, C_{18}–C_{21}, C_{25}, C_{30} and C_{40} components (a–h in Fig. 1, respectively). Of these, pristane (C_{19}) and phytane (C_{20}) tend to be the most abundant, although lycopane (C_{40}, III) dominates the distribution in Section 62-465A-38-3. The occurrence of the other acyclic isoprenoids is somewhat sporadic. In terms of their acyclic alkane distributions, the two Leg 48 samples resemble one another (Fig. 1H and I), as do the Leg 50 sediments (Fig. 1F and G). In contrast, the Leg 75 black shale (Fig. 1B) is markedly different from its adjacent green claystone (Fig. 1A), yet is similar to the Leg 71 black shale (Fig. 1D).

Steroids

Alkanes The sterane distributions, characterized from m/z 217 MF, of five of the samples are shown in Fig. 2. Steranes were only present as minor or trace compounds in the other sections. In all cases only $5\alpha(H)$ and $5\beta(H)$ regular ($14\alpha(H)$, $17\alpha(H)$) steranes (IV and V) were recognized as prominent components; steranes with $14\beta(H)$, and $17\beta(H)$ stereochemistry, or with $20S$ configurations and diasteranes (VI) were not detected

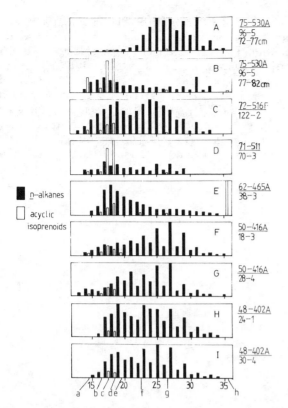

Fig. 1. Distributions of n-alkanes (numbers) and acyclic isoprenoid alkanes (letters; identities given in Table 2).

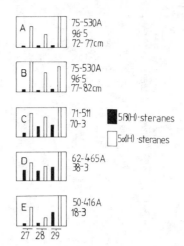

Fig. 2. Distributions of steranes. C_{27}, C_{28} and C_{29} components are cholestanes (a in IV and V) 24-methylcholestanes (b in IV and V) and 24-ethylcholestanes (c in IV and V), respectively.

using MF (e.g. for m/z 218, 259). There are minor differences in the carbon number distributions of the C_{27}–C_{29} components of the various samples, with $5\alpha(H)$-cholestane (IVa) the predominant component in Section 96-5, 77–82 cm (Fig. 2B) whereas 24-ethyl-$5\alpha(H)$-cholestane (IVc) dominates the other samples. One significant difference between the sections is the markedly lower amount of $5\beta(H)$-steranes (V), relative to their $5\alpha(H)$ counterparts (IV), in the Leg 75 samples (Fig. 2A and B).

Alkenes The major steroidal alkenes in most of the samples were series of $20(S)$- and $20(R)$-diasterenes (VII and VIII, respectively). Their distributions, quantitated from MF m/z 257 responses, are shown in Fig. 3. Incomplete GC resolution of $20(R)$-24-methyldiacholest-13(17)-ene (VIIIb) and $20(S)$-24-

ethyldiacholest-13(17)-ene (VIIc) complicated their quantitation, hence they are shown (Fig. 3) to be present in equal amounts, although the former is generally the more abundant based on $20(R)/20(S)$ ratios and MF of their molecular ions (m/z 384 and 398, respectively). The diasterene distributions of the samples are broadly similar, although the relative proportions of C_{27}, C_{28} and C_{29} components vary; for example, $20(R)$-diacholest-13(17)-ene (VIIIa) is predominant in only the Leg 75 samples. The $20(R)$-diasterenes (VIII) are more abundant than their $20(S)$ counterparts in all of the samples, although the $20(S)/20(R)$ ratios vary, as seen, for example, in the diacholest-13(17)-enes (VIIa and VIIIa). 4-Methyldiasterenes (IX) were present in significant amounts in many of the samples, but are not discussed herein. Diasterenes and 4-methyldiasterenes were not detected in two of the samples, those from Legs 72 and 62, although ster-4-enes (X) and ster-5-enes (XI) were prominent components of the latter.

Hopanes and hopenes

The relative distributions of hopanes and hopenes characterized from their individual mass spectra and by MF of key ions (e.g. m/z 177, 149, 205, 218, 189, 231;

Table 2
Acyclic isoprenoid alkanes (Fig. 1)

Peak	Identity	C No.
a	2,6,10-Trimethyltridecane	16
b	2.6.10-Trimethylpentadecane	18
c	2,6,10,14-Tetramethylpentadecane (pristane)	19
d	2,6,10,14-Tetramethylhexadecane (phytane)	20
e	2,6,10,14-Tetramethylheptadecane	21
f	2,6,10,15,19-Pentamethyleicosane (I)[†]	25
g	2,6,10,15,19,23-Hexamethyltetracosane (squalane, II)	30
h	2,6,10,14,19,23,27,31-Octamethyldotriacontane (lycopane, III)	40

[†] Assignment recently confirmed by Rowland *et al.* (1982).

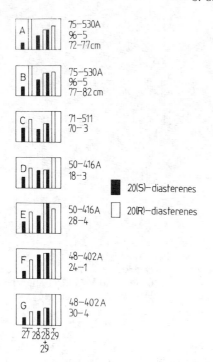

Fig. 3. Distributions of diasterenes. C_{27}, C_{28} and C_{29} components are diacholestenes (a in VII and VIII), 24-methyldiacholestenes (b in VII and VIII) and 24-ethyldiacholestenes (c in VII and VIII), respectively.

Table 3; cf. Barnes *et al.*, 1979; Brassell *et al.*, 1980a) and quantitated according to their m/z 191 response are shown in Fig. 4. The range of hopanoids present in the various samples is generally similar, although certain components, for example the extended (C_{32}, C_{33} and C_{35}) hop-17(21)-enes (XIII), are of more limited occurrence. $17\beta(H)$, $21\beta(H)$-Hopanes (XVI) tend to be prominent components of the samples and are generally greater than their $17\alpha(H)$, $21\beta(H)$ and $17\beta(H)$, $21\alpha(H)$ counterparts (XIV and XV, respectively); they are also

Table 3
Hopanes and hopenes (Fig. 4)

Peak	Identity	Structure
a	22,29,30-Trisnorneohop-13(18)-ene	(XIIa)
b	22,29,30-Trisnorhop-17(21)-ene	(XIIIa)
c	$17\alpha(H)$-22,29,30-Trisnorhopane	(XIVa)
d	$17\beta(H)$-22,29,30-Trisnorhopane	(XVa)
e	30-Norneohop-13(18)-ene	(XIIb)
f	30-Norhop-17(21)-ene	(XIIIb)
g	$17\alpha(H),21\beta(H)$-30-Norhopane	(XIVb)
h	Hop-17(21)-ene	(XIIIc)
i	$17\alpha(H),21\beta(H)$-Hopane	(XIVc)
j	Neohop-13(18)-ene	(XIIc)
k	$17\beta(H),21\alpha(H)$-30-Norhopane	(XVb)
l	$17\beta(H),21\beta(H)$-30-Norhopane	(XVIb)
m	22(S)-Homohop-17(21)-ene	(XIIId)
n	22(R)-Homohop-17(21)-ene	(XIIIe)
o	$17\beta(H),21\alpha(H)$-Hopane	(XVc)
p	22(S)-$17\alpha(H),21\beta(H)$-Homohopane	(XIVd)
q	22(R)-$17\alpha(H),21\beta(H)$-Homohopane	(XIVe)
r	$17\beta(H),21\beta(H)$-Hopane	(XVIc)
s	$17\beta(H),21\alpha(H)$-Homohopane	(XVe)
t	22(S)-Bishomohop-17(21)-ene	(XIIIf)
u	22(R)-Bishomohop-17(21)-ene	(XIIIg)
v	$17\beta(H),21\alpha(H)$-Bishomohopane	(XVg)
w	$17\beta(H),21\beta(H)$-Homohopane	(XVIe)
x	22(S)-Trishomohop-17(21)-ene	(XIIIh)
y	22(R)-Trishomohop-17(21)-ene	(XIIIi)
z	$17\beta(H),21\beta(H)$-Bishomohopane	(XVIg)
aa	$17\beta(H),21\beta(H)$-Trishomohopane	(XVIi)
ab	22(S)-Pentakishomohop-17(21)-ene	(XIIIk)
ac	22(R)-Pentakishomohop-17(21)-ene	(XIIIl)
ad	$17\beta(H),21\beta(H)$-Tetrakishomohopane	(XVIj)
ae	$17\beta(H),21\beta(H)$-Pentakishomohopane	(XVIl)

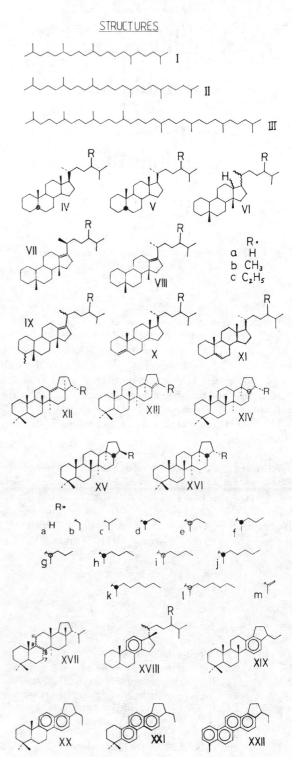

STRUCTURES

N.B. Fernene structure XVII should be $13\alpha,14\beta,17\alpha$-trimethyl not $13\beta,14\alpha,17\beta$-trimethyl as shown.

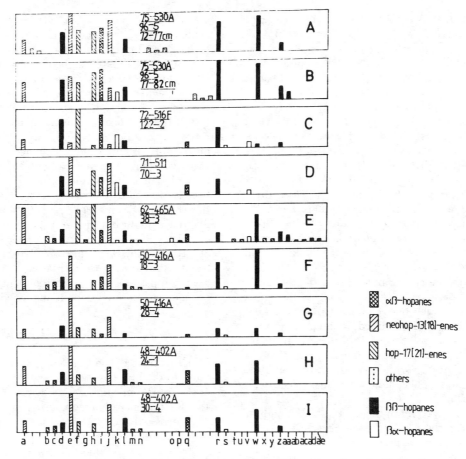

Fig. 4. Distributions of hopanes and hopenes (identities given in Table 3).

present as a fuller range of carbon numbers (e.g. C_{27} and C_{29}–C_{35}). 30-Norneohop-13(18)-ene is the dominant component of several of the distributions; indeed, neohop-13(18)-enes tend to be more prominent than hop-17(21)-enes, with the exception of Leg 72 and 62 samples (Fig. 4C and E, respectively). The histograms of hopanoid distributions shown in Fig. 4 do not represent the full range of hopanes and hopenes in some of the samples, where additional minor or unrecognised components were present (cf. Comet *et al.*, 1981). Fernenes (XVII) were also detected in the Leg 75 and Leg 62 sediments, but are not further reported herein.

Other components

Aromatic hydrocarbons A wide range of aromatic hydrocarbons are present in these samples (e.g. Barnes *et al.*, 1979; Brassell *et al.*, 1980a, b, c; Comet *et al.*, 1981). These include series of C-ring aromatic steroids (XVIII, e.g. Mackenzie *et al.*, this volume) which were recognised by MF of *m/z* 253, and a number of aromatized hopanoids (with from 1–4 aromatic rings; e.g. XIX–XXII) characterized from their individual mass spectra (Greiner *et al.*, 1976, 1977).

Ketones, alcohols and carboxylic acids A variety of functionalized components were recognized in several of the samples (Barnes *et al.*, 1979; Wardroper, 1979; Brassell *et al.*, 1980a; Comet *et al.*, 1981; Brassell and Eglinton, this volume) and the principal results

are given below, although they are not discussed in detail here. Monocarboxylic acids, including hopanoid acids (cf. Barnes *et al.*, 1979), are prominent components of many of the samples. Indeed, in the Leg 62 sample the total concentration of *n*-alkanoic acids is thrice that of the *n*-alkanes (Comet *et al.*, 1981). C_{27}–C_{29} sterols and steroidal ketones occur in several of the samples, with the latter generally the more abundant (e.g. Comet *et al.*, 1981); series of hopanoid ketones are also found (Wardroper, 1979; Brassell and Eglinton, this volume).

DISCUSSION

Input consideration

The prominence of *n*-heptadecane in the Leg 71 and Leg 62 samples and, to a lesser extent, the Leg 75 black shale suggests autochthonous inputs to these sediments, possibly from marine phytoplankton (e.g. Gelpi *et al.*, 1970). The lack of any predominance of the odd numbered *n*-alkanes in the C_{13}–C_{22} range in these sediments is, however, more characteristic of bacterial distributions (Han, 1970), since the immaturity of the samples (see below) precludes the loss of *n*-alkane carbon preference as a thermal effect. The predominance of odd numbered higher *n*-alkanes in several of the samples reflects lipid inputs from terrigenous sources (Simoneit, 1978; Barnes *et al.*, 1979; Brassell *et al.*, 1980a). The preferential biodegradation of lower *n*-alkanes (Johnson and Calder, 1973; Brassell *et al.*, 1978 and references therein) can serve, however, to enhance the apparent size of the terrigenous contributions of *n*-alkanes. The significance of the intermediate carbon numbered *n*-alkanes with little carbon number preference is unclear.

2,6,10,15,19-Pentamethyleicosane, squalane and lycopane reflect lipid contributions from methanogenic bacteria to the sediments (Brassell *et al.*, 1981; Rowland *et al.*, 1982), whereas the biological source of the other acyclic isoprenoid alkanes is less clear. Pristane, phytane and 2,6,10-trimethylpentadecane may represent diagenetic products of phytol (e.g. Didyk *et al.*, 1978), or may be derived from methanogens (Holzer *et al.*, 1979). A mixed source of these compounds seems likely. The C_{16} and C_{21} acyclic isoprenoid alkanes (Table 2) have been recognized as constituents of archaebacteria (Holzer *et al.*, 1979) and may therefore also derive from such sources.

The carbon number distributions of both the steranes (Fig. 2) and diasterenes (Fig. 3) suggest that these components are largely derived from marine sources, in view of the absence of a marked dominance of any of series members (an assessment partly based on Huang and Meinschein, 1979). The greater prominence of C_{29} components in the Leg 48 and Leg 50 samples points to a larger terrigenous input to these sediments, as seen in the *n*-alkane distributions.

The hopanoids present in the samples are thought to principally derive from bacterial sources (Ourisson *et al.*, 1979). In particular, extended hopanoids ($>C_{30}$) have only been recognized as constituents of procaryotes, which strongly suggests bacterial inputs for such components in that blue–green algae are not abundant in the marine system. Neohop-13(18)-ene (XIIc), until recently, was envisaged as either a direct input from ferns or a diagenetic isomerisation product of $17\beta(H)$, $21\beta(H)$-hop-22(29)-ene (XVIm; Ensminger, 1977; Brassell *et al.*, 1980c). It has now been identified as a bacterial constituent (Howard, 1980) and may therefore also represent sediment inputs from these organisms (Brassell *et al.*, 1981). Similarly, fernenes now appear to derive from microbes rather than from terrestrial ferns (Brassell *et al.*, 1980c). Direct sources for several of the hopanes and hopenes reported herein (Fig. 4; Table 3) are unknown, but, in the absence of evidence to the contrary, are assumed to be derived from bacterial sources, either directly or through diagenetic processes.

In summary, the hydrocarbon classes discussed herein provide evidence of marine algal, terrigenous and bacterial inputs to the sediments. Many of the components considered are direct inputs from organisms, whereas others represent diagenetic products which retain structural features, notably their carbon skeletons, that attest their origin. Hence, it remains possible at the maturity state of these samples (see below) to assign the origin of many of their lipid constituents.

Depositional environment considerations

Perhaps the most significant objective of palaeoenvironmental assessment of Cretaceous black shales is the assignment of the oxicity/anoxicity of their depositional conditions. The presence of lipid markers of methanogenic activity in such sediments provides evidence for anoxic conditions, although these may be subsurface. The pristane/phytane (Pr/Ph) ratio may serve as a guide to depositional conditions (Didyk *et al.*, 1978), but may need revision in view of the importance now attached to methanogenic sources for acyclic isoprenoid alkanes (Holzer *et al.*, 1979; Brassell *et al.*, 1981). In the black shales investigated herein the Pr/Ph ratios (typically ≈ 1) do, however, suggest anoxic deposition, although the abundance of hopanoids also suggests extensive aerobic bacterial activity. Clearly the preservation of the organic matter in the black shales has been facilitated by a variety of factors (cf. Eglinton *et al.*, this volume; Tissot *et al.*, 1979, 1980), as shown by the differences in the nature of organic matter itself (Tissot *et al.*, 1979, 1980; see above). No specific lipids are known at present, however, that are definitive markers for oxicity status during sedimentation although the overall lipid composition of a given sediment does provide a general indication of depositional conditions.

Diagenetic considerations

Many features of the lipid composition of the samples attest to the immaturity of these Cretaceous sediments. Such features include:

1. the presence of functionalized components, such as carboxylic acids, sterols, sterones and hopanones;
2. the odd over even preference of many of the *n*-alkane distributions;
3. the presence of diasterenes as significant components of several of the samples;
4. the recognition of only $5\alpha(H)$, $14\alpha(H)$, $17\alpha(H)$- and $5\beta(H)$, $14\alpha(H)$, $17\alpha(H)$-20(*R*) steranes (cf. Mackenzie *et al.*, 1980) and the absence of diasteranes;
5. the abundance of hopenes among the hopanoid distributions; and
6. the dominance of $17\beta(H)$, $21\beta(H)$-hopanes over $17\beta(H)$, $21\alpha(H)$ and $17\alpha(H)$, $21\beta(H)$ isomers (Ensminger, 1977; Mackenzie *et al.*, 1980).

The absence of diasterenes in the Leg 62 sample can perhaps be explained in terms of their calcareous lithology (Table 1) in that the steroidal backbone rearrangement is clay-catalysed (Rubinstein *et al.*, 1975). Overall, the maturity of these Cretaceous sediments is in significant contrast to that of most land-based formations of similar age, illustrating the advantages of such samples in attempts to assess palaeoenvironments (e.g. Brassell and Eglinton, this volume; Comet *et al.*, 1981).

Sample comparisons

The lack of full quantitative data for the abundance of the various lipid distributions presented herein precludes a detailed comparison of samples. Hence, this section serves to provide an impression of their similarities and differences rather than a detailed evaluation in quantitative terms.

The estimated relative size of the inputs of organic matter to the samples, assigned from consideration of the

Table 4.

Estimated relative importance of lipid inputs from terrigenous, bacterial and marine algal sources to each sample.

Sample	Inputs[a]		
	Terrigenous	Bacterial	Marine algal
75-530A-96-5 (72–77 cm)	+ + +	+	+
75-530A-96-5 (77–82 cm)	+	+ +	+ + +
72-516F-122-2	+ +	+ +	+ + +
71-511-70-3	+	+ +	+ + +
62-465A-38-3	+	+ + +	+ + +
50-416A-18-3	+ + +	+ +	+ +
50-416A-28-4	+ + +	+ +	+ +
48-402A-24-1	+ +	+ + +	+
48-402A-30-4	+ +	+ + +	+

[a] The lipid components used as criteria for assessing the relative importance of the different input sources are as follows: Terrigenous: prominence of long chain n-alkanes and relative abundance of C_{29} steroidal components. Bacterial: abundance of 2,6,10,15,19-pentamethyleicosane, squalane and lycopane and predominence of hopanoids. Also presence of fernenes. Marine algal: prominence of n-C_{17} alkane and abundance of steroidal components.

abundance of the various compound classes, is given in Table 4 (derived in part from Comet *et al.*, 1981). For example, the lipids of the Leg 48 samples are dominated by hopanoids that attest bacterial inputs, whereas the prominance of steroids diagenetically derived from algal sterols in the Leg 75 black shale (Section 96-5, 77–82 cm), reflects major marine inputs. The individual lipid distributions of the samples show some major differences (e.g. Fig. 1), but also certain marked similarities (e.g. Fig. 4F–I; Brassell *et al.*, 1980a). The differences can be explained in various terms, such as the relative proportion of organic matter derived from allochthonous and autochthonous sources, or different sedimentary biological populations (e.g. of methanogens contributing different proportions of specific acyclic isoprenoid alkanes, cf. Brassell *et al.*, 1981). In contrast, the similarities suggest common lipid contributions, originating either from similar inputs or from similar depositional conditions.

Certain minor differences in the maturity of the sediments can be recognised from their lipid compositions. For example the abundance of alcohols and acids in the Leg 62 black shale (Comet *et al.*, 1981) suggests that it is marginally less mature than the other sediments, which contain such components in rather smaller amounts. It is not proposed, however, to discuss such differences herein.

A particularly significant result presented here is the difference in the n-alkane and acyclic isoprenoid distributions of the Leg 75 green claystone and its adjacent black shale. It shows that the inputs of organic matter to these lithologies are qualitatively, as well as quantitatively, different suggesting a marked change in depositional environments or sediment inputs.

CONCLUSIONS

This preliminary survey of the lipid constituents of various Cretaceous DSDP sediments shows that they contain a variety of lipid indicators that attest sediment inputs of marine algal, bacterial or terrigenous origin. The sediments differ, however, in the relative sizes of their inputs from such allochthonous and autochthonous sources. All of the samples are immature.

These studies represent a prelude to a more systematic sampling of black shales on a finer time scale to provide a better definition of their lipid characteristics (cf. Eglinton *et al.*, this volume). To this end the differences between the Leg 75 black shale and green claystone considered herein highlight the need to consider black shales with reference to their sedimentological context, if their palaeoenvironmental conditions of deposition are to be properly understood.

Acknowledgements

We thank the NERC for financial support (GR3/2951 and GR3/3758) and colleagues at Bristol for helpful discussions. The samples were supplied with the assistance of the National Science Foundation.

REFERENCES

Barnes, P. J., Brassell, S. C., Comet, P. A., McEvoy, J., Maxwell, J. R., Wardroper, A. M. K. and Volkman, J. K. (1979) Preliminary lipid analyses of core sections 18, 24 and 30 from Hole 402A. In *Initial Reports of the Deep Sea Drilling Project*, Vol. 48. Ed. by Montadert, L., Roberts, D. G. *et al.* U.S. Government Printing Office, Washington. pp. 965–976.

Brassell, S. C., Eglinton, G., Maxwell, J. R. and Philp, R. P. (1978) Natural background of alkanes in the aquatic environment. In *Aquatic Pollutants, Transformation and Biological Effects*. Ed. by Hutzinger, O., van Lelyveld, I. H. and Zoetman, B. C. J. Pergamon, Oxford. pp. 69–86.

Brassell, S. C., Comet, P. A., Eglinton, G., McEvoy, J., Maxwell, J. R., Quirke, J. M. E. and Volkman, J. K. (1980a) Preliminary lipid analyses of cores 14, 18 and 28 from Deep Sea Drilling Project Hole 416A. In *Initial Reports of the Deep Sea Drilling Project*, Vol. 50. Ed. by Lancelot, Y., Winterer, E. L. *et al.* US Government Printing Office, Washington. pp. 647–664.

Brassell, S. C., Comet, P. A., Eglinton, G., Isaacson, P. J., McEvoy, J., Maxwell, J. R., Thomson, I. D., Tibbetts, P. J. C. and Volkman, J. K. (1980b) Preliminary analyses of sections 440A-7-6, 440B-3-5, 440B-8-4, 440B-68-2 and 436-11-4: Legs 56 and 57, Deep Sea Drilling Project. In *Initial Reports of the Deep Sea Drilling Project*, Vol. 56/57, Part 2. Ed. by Scientific Party. US Government Printing Office, Washington. pp. 1367–1390.

Brassell, S. C., Comet, P. A., Eglinton, G., Isaacson, P. J., McEvoy, J., Maxwell, J. R., Thomson, I. D., Tibbetts, P. J. C. and Volkman, J. K. (1980c) The origin and fate of lipids in the Japan Trench. In *Advances in Organic Geochemistry 1979*. Ed. by Douglas, A. G. and Maxwell, J. R. Pergamon, Oxford. pp. 375–391.

Brassell, S. C., Gowar, A. P. and Eglinton, G. (1980d) Computerised gas chromatography–mass spectrometry in analyses of sediments from the Deep Sea Drilling Project. In

Advances in Organic Geochemistry 1979. Ed. by Douglas, A. G. and Maxwell, J. R. Pergamon, Oxford. pp. 421–426.

Brassell, S. C., Wardroper, A. M. K., Thomson, I. D., Maxwell, J. R. and Eglinton, G. (1981) Specific acyclic isoprenoids as biological markers of methanogenic bacteria in marine sediments. *Nature (London)* **290**, 693–696.

Comet, P. A., McEvoy, J., Brassell, S. C., Eglinton, G., Maxwell, J. R. and Thomson, I. D. (1981) Lipids of an Upper Albian limestone, Deep Sea Drilling Project Site 465, Section 465A-38-3. In *Initial Reports of the Deep Sea Drilling Project*, Vol. 62. Ed. by Thiede, J., Vallier, T. L., *et al.* US Government Printing Office, Washington. pp. 923–937.

Cornford, C., Rullkötter, J. and Welte, D. H. (1980) A synthesis of organic petrographic and geochemical results from DSDP sites in the eastern central North Atlantic. In *Advances in Organic Geochemistry 1979.* Ed. by Douglas, A. G. and Maxwell, J. R. Pergamon, Oxford. pp. 445–453.

Didyk, B. M., Simoneit, B. R. T., Brassell, S. C. and Eglinton, G. (1978) Organic geochemical indicators of palaeoenvironmental conditions of sedimentation. *Nature (London)* **272**, 216–222.

Ensminger, A. (1977) Evolution de composés polycycliques sédimentaires. PhD Thesis, Université Louis Pasteur, Strasbourg.

Gelpi, E., Schneider, H., Mann, J. and Oró, J. (1970) Hydrocarbons of geochemical significance in microscopic algae. *Phytochem.* **8**, 603–612.

Greiner, A. Ch., Spyckerelle, C. and Albrecht, P. (1976) Aromatic hydrocarbons from geological sources I: new naturally occurring phenanthrene and chrysene derivatives. *Tetrahedron* **32**, 257–260.

Greiner, A. Ch., Spyckerelle, C., Albrecht, P. and Ourisson, G. (1977) Aromatic hydrocarbons from geological sources V: mono and diaromatic hopane derivatives. *J. Chem. Res.* (S) **334**, (M) 3829–3871.

Hallam, A. (1980) Black shales, *J. Geol. Soc. London* **137**, 123–124.

Han, J. (1970) Chemical studies of terrestrial and extraterrestrial life. PhD Thesis, University of California, Berkeley.

Holzer, G., Oro, J. and Tornabene, T. G. (1979) Gas chromatographic/mass spectrometric analysis of neutral lipids from methanogenic and thermoacidophilic bacteria. *J. Chromatogr.* **186**, 795–809.

Howard, D. L. (1980) Polycyclic triterpenes of the anaerobic photosynthetic bacterium *Rhodomicrobium vanielli*, PhD Thesis, University of California, Los Angeles.

Huang, W.-Y. and Meinschein, W. G. (1979) Sterols as ecological indicators. *Geochim. Cosmochim. Acta* **43**, 739–745.

Johnson, R. W. and Calder, J. A. (1973) Early diagenesis of fatty acids and hydrocarbons in a salt marsh environment. *Geochim. Cosmochim. Acta* **37**, 1943–1955.

Mackenzie, A. S., Patience, R. L., Maxwell, J. R., Vandenbroucke, M. and Durand, B. (1980) Molecular parameters of maturation in the Toarcian shales, Paris Basin, France I. Changes in the configurations of acyclic isoprenoid alkanes, steranes and triterpanes. *Geochim. Cosmochim. Acta* **44**, 1709–1721.

Ourisson, G., Albrecht, P. and Rohmer, M. (1979) The hopanoids. Palaeochemistry and biochemistry of a group of natural products. *Pure Appl. Chem.* **51**, 709–729.

Rowland, S. J., Lamb, N. A., Wilkinson, C. F. and Maxwell, J. R. (1982) Confirmation of 2,6,10,15,19-pentamethyleicosane in methanogenic bacteria and sediments. *Tetr. Lett.* **23**, 101–104.

Rubinstein, I., Sieskind, O. and Albrecht, P. (1975) Rearranged sterenes in a shale: occurrence and simulated formation. *J. Chem. Soc. Perkin* **I**, 1833–1835.

Rullkötter, J., Cornford, C. and Welte, D. H. (1982) Geochemistry and petrography of organic matter in Northwest African continental margin sediments: Quality, provenance, depositional environment and temperature history. In *Geology of the Northwest African Continental Margin.* Ed. by von Rad, U., *et al.* Springer Verlag, Heidelberg. pp. 686–703.

Schlanger, S. O. and Jenkyns, H. C. (1976) Cretaceous oceanic anoxic events: causes and consequences. *Geol. Mijnbouw* **55**, 179–184.

Simoneit, B. R. T. (1978) The organic chemistry of marine sediments. In *Chemical Oceanography* Vol. 7. Ed. by Riley, J. P. and Chester, R. Academic Press, New York. pp. 233–311.

Spears, D. A. (1980) Towards a classification of shales. *J. Geol. Soc. London* **137**, 125–129.

Tissot, B. P., Deroo, G. and Herbin, J. P. (1979) Organic matter in Cretaceous sediments of the North Atlantic: contribution to sedimentology and paleography. In *Deep drilling results in the Atlantic Ocean: continental margins and paleoenvironment. Amer. Geophys. Union Maurice Ewing Ser. 3.* pp. 362–374.

Tissot, B., Demaison, G., Masson, P., Delteil, J. R. and Combaz, A. (1980) Paleoenvironment and petroleum potential of middle Cretaceous black shales in Atlantic basins. *Amer. Ass. Petrol. Geol. Bull.* **64**, 2051–2063.

Wardroper, A. M. K. (1979) Aspects of the geochemistry of polycyclic isoprenoids. PhD Thesis, University of Bristol.

Diagenesis/Catagenesis and Organic Geochemistry of Coal and Kerogens

Advances in Organic Geochemistry 1981, pp. 487–495
© *John Wiley & Sons Limited, 1983*

Qualitative and Quantitative Aspects of Gas Generation during Maturation of Sedimentary Organic Matter. Examples from Canadian Frontier Basins

F. Monnier*, T. G. Powell and L. R. Snowdon

Institute of Sedimentary and Petroleum Geology, Geological Survey of Canada, 3303-33rd Street, NW Calgary, Alberta T21 2A7

The current dispute concerning the generation of gas at low levels of thermal maturation has prompted a study of the quantitative and qualitative aspects of gas generation in several Canadian basins utilizing data from canned cuttings. In order to eliminate the effects of lithology, organic matter type and migration effects, gas generation has been followed in single lithostratigraphic units at varying levels of maturation in Arctic Basins. Qualitative changes in the composition of gases evolved from Type II and Type III kerogen occur at vitrinite reflectance levels as low as $0.4\% R_0$. There is a five-fold or more increase in the gas yield per unit weight of organic carbon from Type III kerogen in the reflectance range 0.55 to $0.65\% R_0$. This immediately precedes the onset of generation of liquid hydrocarbons. In contrast, the initial gas yield per unit weight of organic carbon is higher from Type II kerogen, but no dramatic increase in gas yield occurs during liquid hydrocarbon generation above reflectance levels of $0.5\% R_0$. No dramatic change in gas yield occurs in the transition from the mature to overmature with respect to Type III organic matter but there is an increase in gas yield during this transition with respect to Type II organic matter. This data suggests that significant gas generation can occur from Type III kerogen at reflectance levels as low as $0.6\% R_0$ and has been used to establish threshold values for determining gas source potential.

INTRODUCTION

Many studies have shown that oil and gas are generated from sedimentary organic matter at elevated temperatures encountered during burial. The extent of thermal alteration (maturation or catagenesis) and the nature of the organic matter, determines the composition of the hydrocarbons produced. The atomic hydrogen to carbon ratio of the kerogen can be used to determine the nature of the organic matter (Tissot *et al.*, 1974) and the vitrinite reflectance scale can be used as a universal scale in order to make a comparison of the levels of maturation at which different organic matter types produce hydrocarbons (Powell and Snowdon, 1980).

Hydrogen rich organic matter (atomic H/C 1.0–1.5, Types I and II of Tissot *et al.*, 1974) generates mainly oil between reflectance levels of 0.5% to 1.3% R_0. At higher levels of reflectance thermal cracking becomes dominant and oil gives way to gas. Organic matter with intermediate hydrogen to carbon ratios in the immature stage (atomic H/C 1.0–0.8, Type III of Tissot *et al.*, 1974) generates wet gas and some oil above reflectance

* Present address: Canterra Energy Co. 555-4th Avenue SW, Calgary, Alberta.

levels of 0.7% R_0 and again with extensive maturation the main product is gas. Organic matter with lower hydrogen to carbon ratios (Type IV of Harwood, 1977) may generate dry gas upon extensive maturation. A feature of the hydrocarbon generation model summarized above, is that for all organic matter types the main phase of thermogenic gas generation is a late catagenic event (vitrinite reflectance levels $\geqslant 0.8\% R_0$), although numerous cuttings gas analyses show that methane is ubiquitous in sub-surface sediments at all stages of maturation (e.g. Evans and Staplin, 1970; Snowdon and McCrossan, 1972; Snowdon and Roy, 1975).

The question arises as to the significance of the gas present in sediments at the earlier stages of maturation (vitrinite reflectance $\leqslant 0.7\% R_0$) from the standpoint of gas source potential. This question is particularly relevant for the evaluation of areas of low geothermal gradient where the lower levels of maturation are encountered over many thousands of feet of section and yet sediments in these lower maturity section often contain commercial accumulations of gas and gas condensate. Such is the case in many Canadian frontier basins (Powell and Snowdon, 1980). A particular case in point is the Mackenzie Delta–Beaufort Sea area in the Canadian Arctic. Here oil and gas condensate occurs in reservoirs at vitrinite reflectance levels below 0.6% R_0. Studies on the oil and condensate have suggested that liquid hydrocarbons have been generated at low levels of maturation (0.45–0.6% R_0) from terrestrial organic matter rich in resinite (Snowdon, 1980; Snowdon and Powell, 1982). By implication the gas must also have been generated within this maturation range. Other authors have also suggested that an early thermogenic phase of gas generation which is separate from the formation of biogenic gas, may be significant in forming accumulations of gas at low levels of maturity (Hitchon, 1963; Rumeau et al., 1972; Stroganov, 1973; Stahl, 1977; Connan and Cassou, 1980).

Several approaches are available to examine the processes of gas generation. One is to examine the distribution of carbon and hydrogen isotopes in natural gases and correlate them to maturation level (Stahl, 1977; Schoell, 1980). Another approach is to examine the gas yield during laboratory experiments (Harwood, 1977) while a third approach is to attempt to erect generation curves for gases utilizing analytical data on gas concentrations in sediments in much the same manner as has been done for liquid hydrocarbons. It is the latter approach which is used in this study, utilizing gas analyses which have been collected over a period of years in Canadian Arctic Basins. In order to eliminate the effects of lithology, organic matter type, and vertical migration, gas generation in this study has been followed in single lithostratigraphic units with uniform organic matter types of various maturation levels. Five stratigraphic units have been chosen. For Type III organic matter these are the Deer Bay (Cretaceous) and Van Hauen (Permian) Formations in the Sverdrup Basin, for Type II organic matter these are the Schei Point Formation (Triassic) in the Sverdrup Basin and Cape Phillips Formation (Ordovician to Silurian) in the Franklinian Geosyncline. The Boundary Creek Formation (Upper Cretaceous) in the Beaufort–Mackenzie Basin probably contains a mixture of these two organic matter types. Previous studies have documented the organic matter types present and the level of maturation of these formations (Snowdon and Roy, 1975; Powell, 1978; Snowdon, 1980; Creaney, 1980). The purpose of this paper is to compare the quantitative aspects of gas generation relative to oil generation and their relative order of occurrence for the different organic matter types in these formations.

METHODS AND SAMPLES

Methods

Cuttings gas data have been routinely collected for the majority of petroleum exploration wells to date in the Arctic Islands and for a substantial number of wells in the Beaufort–Mackenzie Basin. The procedure for cuttings gas analysis and organic carbon determination have been described by Snowdon and McCrossan (1972). Canned cuttings are received from the well site. A known volume of cuttings are homogenized with water in a gas-tight blender and a sample of head space is analysed for methane, ethane, propane and butanes. The concentration of gas is then calculated in parts per million (ppm) by volume on a rock basis. The organic carbon determination was done by combustion after acid digestion to remove carbonates. Samples are routinely analysed at intervals varying from 30 to 50 feet. It must be emphasized that the technique is at best semi-quantitative. Gas may be lost to the drilling mud during drilling and transport to surface. This is particularly true for permeable lithologies such as sandstones. Differences in degree of consolidation of the rock results in different behaviour during drilling. Relatively unconsolidated sediments may distintegrate more readily, losing more gas during drilling than their consolidated counterparts. These difficulties can be overcome by utilizing constant lithostratigraphic units and then only shales from these units. The wells and depth intervals used are listed in Table 1. Only data from continuous shale units were used. Where sandstones were interbedded with shales the analysis of samples containing sandstones were not used. In order to compare samples with differing organic carbon contents the total gas concentration was divided by the organic carbon content. The following parameters are compared in the discussion:

(1) Total gas/organic carbon (ppm by volume/per cent organic carbon, subsequently designated by the abbreviation 'U')
(2) Percentage of wet gas (ΣC_2–C_4/ ΣC_1–C_4) × 100.
(3) Isobutane to n-butane ratio (iC_4/nC_4).

Some vitrinite reflectance data were available from the work of Powell (1978) and have been supplemented by additional measurements for the Deer Bay and Van Hauen Formations using similar techniques.

Samples

The samples utilized are listed in Table 1. The Deer Bay Formation is an organic rich (up to 4% organic carbon) thick grey to black marine shale of Jurassic to Cretaceous age occurring in the Sverdrup Basin. It contains predominantly Type III kerogen (atomic H/C ~0.75 in the immature zone) (Powell, 1978) and is widespread throughout the Sverdrup Basin. Based on reconstruction of the burial history (Snowdon and Roy, 1975) its maximum depth of burial has ranged from 3000 to 13 000 feet representing a range of maturation from undermature to mature (Powell, 1978). Locally it becomes overmature due to intrusion by sills and dykes.

The Van Hauen Formation in the Sverdrup Basin consists of predominantly shales and siltstones with average organic carbon contents (1–1.5%). It occurs at the boundary of the Lower and Upper Permian. Data for this study were taken from the Panarctic et al. Drake D-68 well where the maximum depth of burial ranges 12 000 feet at the top of the formation to 17 000 feet at the base of the well. Again it contains Type III kerogen (Powell, 1978). This is based on lower hydrocarbon yields (< 30 mg per gram/organic carbon), in combination with kerogen atomic hydrogen to carbon ratios in the range 0.67 to 0.51. Data from immature Permian strata in the basis show kerogen atomic hydrogen to carbon ratios of ~0.82 and saturated hydrocarbons from

Table 1
Location of wells and formations.

Well name	Location Lat. N/Long. W	Interval depth (feet)	Burial correction (feet)
Sverdrup Basin *Deer Bay Formation*			
Panarctic Tenneco *et al.*, King Christian N-06	77°45'54"/101°02'19"	540–1560	7000
Panarctic Gulf, Helicoper J-12	78°41'33"/100°36'49"	4450–10 700	3000
Panarctic, Noice G-44	78°23'23"/104°21'39"	850–4150	6000
Bp *et al.*, Graham C-52	77°21'14"/90°51'25"	2790–3990	1000
Panarctic Dome Tenneco *et al.*, Dome Bay P-36	78°25'52"/103°47'54"	1400–4650	6000
Panarctic Gulf, Dumbells E-49	78°28'24"/100°24'12"	4150–8850	3500
Panarctic Dome Tenneco *et al.*, Louise O-25	78°44'57"/102°41'58"	100–3500	8000
BP *et al.*, Emerald K-33	76°42'43"/113°43'21"	2250–3300	2000
Panarctic Tenneco *et al.*, Kristoffer Bay B-06	78°15'18"/102°32'00"	1400–3600	5800
Sun KR Panarctic, Skybattle Bay C-15	77°14'12"/108°05'57"	4200–5100	500
Panarctic Hmstd. POR, North Sabine H-49	76°48'15"/108°45'11"	6800–9000	0
Elf, Cape Norem A-80	77°29'13"/110°27'05"	610–2650	3300
Panarctic *et al.*, Drake Point D-68	76°27'05"/108°55'43"	1650–3200	1500
Sverdrup Basin *Van Hauen Formation*			
Panarctic *et al.*, Drake Point D-68	76°27'05"/108°55'43"	10 850–15 200	1500
Sverdrup Basin *Schei Point Formation*			
Panarctic, Hecla J-60	76°19'37"/110°19'49"	3660–4050	1000
Elfex, Andreason L-32	77°11'37"/118°14'14"	2510–4070	est. 2500
Panarctic, Sandy Point L-46	76°25'38"/115°18'14"	2520–2640	1500
Panarctic, Fosheim N-27	79°36'54"/84°43'19"	60–2310	8500
Panarctic, Drake Point K-67	76°26'45"/108°55'13"	3920–4560	1200
Panarctic Tenneco *et al.*, Pollux G-60	79°09'23"/104°57'23"	1650–4650	est. 4500
Panarctic *et al.*, Brock C-50	77°49'00"/114°17'24"	100–1450	7000
Panarctic *et al.*, Drake Point D-68	76°27'05"/108°55'43"	3850–4600	1500
Elf, Cape Norem A-80	77°29'13"/110°27'05"	5200–7990	3300
Elf, Wilkins E-60	77°59'19"/110°21'45"	2530–3850	4400
Elf, Jameson Bay C-31	76°40'12"/116°43'45"	3260–3800	2000
Elf, Intrepid Inlet H-49	76°58'26"/118°45'03"	2360–3140	2500
BP *et al.*, Emerald K-33	76°42'43"/113°43'21"	4800–5400	2000
Panarctic Hmstd. POR, North Sabine H-49	76°48'15"/108°45'11"	10 150–11 900	0
Sun KR Panarctic, Skybattle Bay C-15	77°14'12"/108°05'57"	7080–9250	500
Franklinian Geosyncline *Cape Philepps Formation*			
Dome Panarctic Texex, Weatherall O-10	75°49'02"/108°31'50"	5850–7500	
Panarctic, Eldbridge Bay E-79	75°58'21"/109°29'38"	4350–5700	
Panarctic Dome, Dundas C-80	74°39'02"/113°22'59"	8500–9500	
Panarctic, Apollo C-73	75°32'00"/111°58'58"	6800–9200	
Panarctic Standard, Sabine Bay A-07	75°26'06"/110°00'49"	5700–7100	
Murphy *et al.*, Victoria Island F-36	72°45'18"/117°11'13"	4250–4600	
Beaufort Mackenzie Basin *Boundary Creek Formation*			
Shell, Ulu A-35	68°44'02"/135°52'57"	6240–6840	
Shell, Kugpik O-13	68°52'50"/135°18'15"	6320–7130	
Gulf Mobil, E. Reindeer G-04	68°53'16"/133°46'03"	5310–6320	
Dome Imp., Imnak J-29	69°08'41"/133°06'05"	7410–8760	
Imp Delta, Wagnark C-23	69°12'01"/133°21'45"	9690–9990	
Imp Dome, Louth K-45	69°54'32"/131°26'47"	5580–6270	
Imp Cigol, Kapik J-39	69°58'32"/130°08'10"	3360–3690	
Imp IOE, Kannerk G-42	70°01'24"/131°12'57"	6330–7140	

these immature rocks show evidence of terrestrial origin (Powell, 1978). In the Drake D-68 well, the Van Hauen Formation occurs in the mature and overmature zones and therefore the data complements that obtained from the Deer Bay Formation for Type III kerogen. Two igneous sills occur in the lower part of the Drake well but the section is already overmature due to regional catagenesis.

The Schei Point Formation is of Mid-Triassic age and in the western part of the Sverdrup Basin it consists of thin limestones, sandstones, bituminous shales and calcareous siltstones. The shale and limestone lithofacies contain Type II kerogen (atomic H/C ratios 1.1–1.2 at the immature stage) (Powell, 1978) and were selected for this study. The maximum depths of burial range from about 4000 to 12 000 feet and range from the onset of the marginally mature zone to the mature zone (Powell, 1978). Organic carbon values range up to 5% in the bituminous shales.

The Cape Phillips Formation is an organic rich (3–5%

organic carbon) graptolitic shale facies ranging in age from Upper Ordovician to Lower Devonian. It is encountered in wells in the Franklinian Geosyncline to the south of the Sverdrup Basin. Where mature, hydrocarbon yields and kerogen atomic hydrogen to carbon ratios indicate that the original organic matter is of Type II (Powell, 1978) but in many cases it is overmature. The maximum depths of burial are not known.

The Boundary Creek Formation in the Beaufort–Mackenzie Basin is an Upper Cretaceous organic rich (1.05–11.42% organic carbon) shale unit. The organic matter is extremely finely divided and frequently contains algal remains (Creaney, 1980). However, atomic hydrogen to carbon ratios of the kerogen rarely exceed 1.1 despite the fact that the formation is mostly immature or marginally mature (Snowdon, 1980). This data, in conjunction with distribution of saturated hydrocarbons in rock extracts, suggest that the organic matter is of mixed origin (Snowdon, 1980). The present burial depth of this formation ranges between 3000 and 10 000 feet.

RESULTS AND DISCUSSION

Samples containing Type III kerogen

The gas and reflectance data for the Deer Bay and Van Hauen Formations are plotted against maximum burial depth in Fig. 1. There is an increase in the proportion of wet gas in the cuttings to in excess of 60% at 4000 feet. This is the first indication of the onset of hydrocarbon generation from the kerogen and has been used to mark the onset of the marginally mature zone (Snowdon and Roy, 1975; Powell, 1978). Despite the change in gas composition at around 4000 feet, there is no significant increase in gas yield until depths of 7000 to 8000 feet. Gas yields at shallower depths show low values around 5000 units (U) whereas in the interval 7000 to 8000 feet there is a dramatic increase to 50 000 to 80 000 U. The possibility exists that the marked discrepancy in depth between the change in gas composition and the dramatic increase in gas yield, is an artifact due to differences in degree of consolidation between the shallower and deeper samples. The shallower, less consolidated samples may have disintegrated during drilling operations and lost their gas whereas the more consolidated samples retained their gas. This possibility is tested in Fig. 1, where the gas data are compared with the transit times determined from the sonic logs for the Deer Bay samples used in this study. A decrease in transit time (increase in sonic velocity) is usually observed with increasing depth in a given lithofacies. This is due to increasing consolidation brought about by compaction and cementation with increasing depth. If the increase in gas yield was due to preferential loss of gas from the shallower sediments then there should be a significant increase in degree of consolidation (decrease in transit

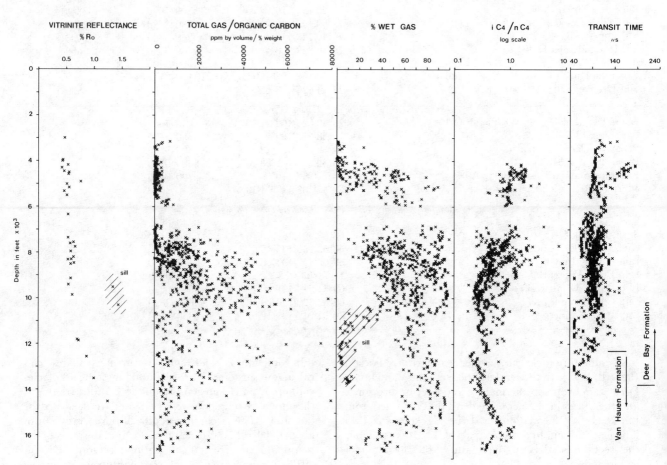

Fig. 1. Gas data, vitrinite reflectance, and transit time data for Deer Bay and Van Hauen Formations plotted against maximum burial depth.

time) across the transition zone from the low to high gas yields. The absence of a significant change indicates that the increase in gas yield must be attributed to maturation rather than an artifact. In fact, the main change in transit time occurs at shallower depths than the increase in gas yield.

The change in gas composition noted above occurs at vitrinite reflectance levels of 0.45 to 0.5% R_0, whereas the dramatic increase in gas yield occurs at reflectance levels of 0.55 to 0.65% R_0 which is at a somewhat lower level of maturation than in existing gas generation models (Harwood, 1977; Tissot *et al.*, 1974; Snowdon and Roy, 1975). Interestingly, the maximum gas yield is also reached at this reflectance level. The change in isobutane to *n*-butane ratio from approximately 1 to around 0.6 accompanies the significant change in gas yield and does not change at the point of onset of wet gas.

Below approximately 13 000 feet the gas yield is somewhat lower, at around 30 000 U with scattered values up to 50 000 U, even in the overmature zone. The reason for this is not clear. It perhaps could be attributed to migration or to the lower gas-producing capability of the organic matter in the Permian sediments as compared with the Deer Bay Formation. The transition from wet gas to dry gas occurs somewhat deeper than the decline in liquid hydrocarbon yields (Powell, 1978), nevertheless there is still no significant increase in gas yields even in excess of reflectance levels of 1.5% R_0.

The Deer Bay Formation in the central part of the Sverdrup Basin is intruded by sills and dykes (Powell, 1978). The effect is to cause overmaturity locally in the Helicopter J-12 and Louise Bay 0–15 wells. This is indicated by the low contents of wet gas and high reflectance levels (Fig. 1).

Samples containing Type II kerogen

Schei Point Formation (Sverdrup Basin). Unfortunately, it was not possible to obtain gas data from a single stratigraphic unit containing Type II kerogen over a wide maturation range. Three formations from different basins have been used to cover the maturation range. The gas data for the Schei Point Formation is illustrated in Fig. 2. The depth scale is directly comparable to that for the Deer Bay and Van Hauen Formations. Already at 4000 feet, there is a high content of wet gas in the cuttings gas. This parameter appears, therefore, to be a universal indicator of the first onset of hydrocarbon generation, providing vertical migration has not occurred (as in this case). The wide variation in percent wet values are, in part, attributable to the heterogeneity of this formation. Despite attempts to eliminate the effects of lithological variations it was not always possible in this case. The gas yield to a depth of 12 000 feet is generally below 15 000 U with occasional values up to 32 000 U from highly bituminous shales. These values are substantially lower than those obtained for Type III kerogen discussed above. The ratio of isobutane to *n*-butane decreases from 1 between 5000 and 6000 feet to 0.6–0.8 in the 7000 to 8000 foot range. Occasionally higher values are encountered at greater depths. The decrease in the isobutane to *n*-butane ratio coincides with the onset of liquid hydrocarbon generation in the Schei Point Formation (Powell, 1978).

Boundary Creek Formation (Beaufort–Mackenzie Basin). The gas data for the Boundary Creek Formation are shown in Fig. 3. There is a general increase in gas yield to 13 000 U in the depth interval

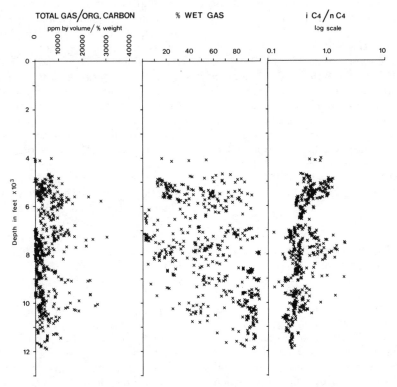

Fig. 2. Gas data for Schei Point Formation plotted against maximum burial depth.

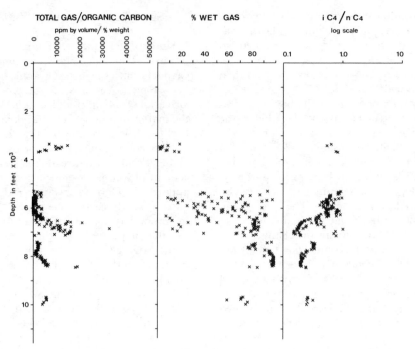

Fig. 3. Gas data for Boundary Creek Formation plotted against present burial depth.

6000 to 7000 feet. The onset of the mature zone at 5000 feet is indicated by the transition from below 60% wet gas to above 60% wet gas. The overall yields are similar to the Schei Point Formation in this maturation range but the depth separation of the increase in gas yield from the onset of wet gas is similar to the data for the Type III kerogen of the Deer Bay Formation. Again the change in isobutane to *n*-butane ratio coincides with the increase in gas yield as observed in the Deer Bay Formation. As noted above, the similarity in behaviour to the Deer Bay Formation can best be explained on the basis of the presence of a mixture of organic matter types.

Cape Phillips Formation. Gas data are available only for a few wells in this formation (Fig. 4). Only two wells (Eldridge Bay E-79 and Weatherall 0–10) contain the Cape Phillips Formation at the mature stage. The remainder of the Cape Phillips Formation is in the transition from mature to overmature or in the overmature zone. In the mature zone in Eldridge Bay E-79 and Weatherall 0–10, the gas yields are low at ~5000 U but increase in the overmature zone up to 40 000 U in Dundas C-80, 60 000 U in Apollo C-73, 150 000 U in Sabine Bay A-07, and up to 200 000 U in the Victoria Island F-36 well.

Comparison of gas generation and oil generation

The results for the various formations are compared in Fig. 5. The gas data are given in *μ*moles per gram of organic carbon, to facilitate comparison of gas data with data for extractable liquid hydrocarbons. The gas data were converted from a volume basis by supplying appropriate temperature and pressure factors and assuming a rock density of 2.5. Extractable hydrocarbon yields in milligrams per gram organic carbon, were

taken from previously published data (Powell, 1978; Snowdon, 1980) and converted to a molar basis by assuming an average molecular weight corresponding to a C_{22} saturated cyclic hydrocarbon. The curves were drawn up to represent the average maximum values at a given depth. The Sverdrup Basin data are plotted on a common depth scale and the vitrinite reflectance curve for the Deer Bay and Van Hauen Formations is given for comparison. Insufficient stratigraphic information is available to construct maximum burial depths for the Boundary Creek and Cape Phillips Formations. Instead the data are plotted relatively to a maturation datum. In the case of the Boundary Creek Formation this datum is represented by the onset of greater than 30% wet gas in the cuttings gas data and representing the transition from the undermature to marginally mature zones (Snowdon and Roy, 1975; Powell, 1978). In the case of the Cape Phillips Formation this datum is the onset of the overmature zone which is indicated in the cuttings gas by a decline in the proportion of wet gas from above 30% to below 30% (Snowdon and Roy, 1975; Powell, 1978).

It is immediately apparent that there is a marked difference in the timing of gas generation between the different organic matter types and between the amounts of gas that are generated at a given maturation stage. In the case of the Deer Bay Formation (Type III organic matter) significant gas generation commences at 6500 feet and at a reflectance level of 0.55% R_0, which is prior to the onset of liquid hydrocarbon generation. It reaches a maximum at the onset of liquid generation. In contrast, the amounts of gas generated from Type II kerogen at the marginally mature to mature stage (Schei Point Formation, Boundary Creek Formation) is only one-third of that generated from Type III kerogen. In the mature zone, the ratio of gas to liquid hydrocarbons is eight times higher for Type III kerogen than for Type II kerogen. The main phase of gas generation from Type

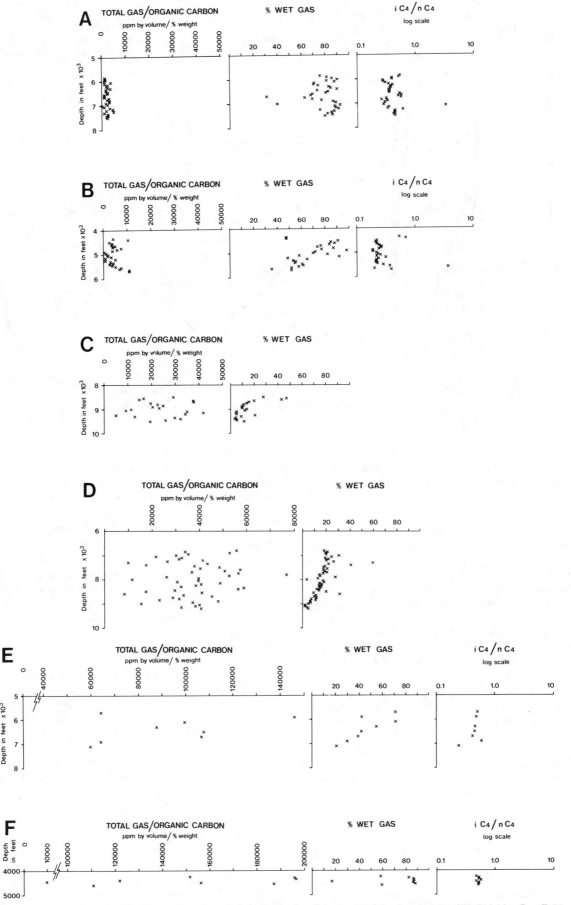

Fig. 4. Gas data for Cape Phillips Formation plotted on individual well basis: (A) Weatherall 0–10; (B) Eldridge Bay E-79; (C) Dundas C-80; (D) Apollo C-73; (E) Sabine Bay A-07; (F) Victoria Island F-36.

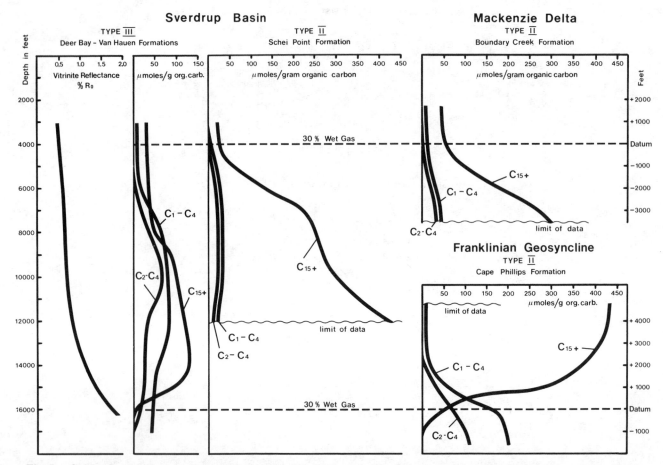

Fig. 5. Comparison of gas generation and liquid hydrocarbon generation for different organic matter types and formations. Depth scale for Sverdrup Basin is reconstructed maximum burial depth. Depth scale for Mackenzie Delta and Franklinian Geosyncline is relative to a datum at 30% wet gas at the onset of the marginally mature and overmature zones respectively.

II kerogen occurs in the overmature zone (Cape Phillips Formation) due to extensive cracking of the kerogen and liquid hydrocarbons. The yields of gas obtained are two to three times the maximum values obtained from Type III kerogen. No marked increase in gas yield occurred in the overmature zone for Type III kerogen. The reason for this is complex. If no loss of gas had occurred, then cracking of the liquid hydrocarbons in itself should cause an increase in gas yield, as occurs in the Cape Phillips Formation. At the same time, it can be argued that the amount of gas generated from Type III kerogen will be lower than that derived from Type II kerogen at this maturation stage. The reason for this is readily apparent from the atomic hydrogen to carbon ratios of kerogens from the mature zone for each type of organic matter. In the Van Hauen Formation, the atomic hydrogen to carbon ratio of the kerogen is ~0.55 and the liquid hydrocarbons available for cracking are of the order of 124 μmoles per gram organic carbon. In contrast, the atomic hydrogen to carbon ratios of kerogen from the Cape Phillips Formation in the mature zone (Weatherall 0–10 and Eldridge Bay E-79 wells) are still quite high at ~0.8 and the available liquid hydrocarbons are of the order of 400–425 μmoles per gram of organic carbon. Since hydrocarbon generation is dependent upon the availability of hydrogen it is apparent that there is still considerable potential for gas generation left in Type II organic matter at the mature

stage whereas the hydrogen content of Type III organic matter is already quite depleted at this stage. It must be concluded, however, that the failure to observe an increase in gas yield from the Van Hauen Formation in the overmature zone must be due to a deterioration of hydrocarbon generating capacity in these samples compared to the less mature samples or to unaccounted migration.

Evaluation of gas source potential

From Fig. 5 it can be seen that the maximum gas generation potential is reached early in the maturation history of Type III organic matter. This Type III organic matter can be a major source for thermogenic gas at reflectance levels as low as 0.6% R_0. In contrast the main phase of gas generation from Type II kerogen occurs in the overmature zone as extensive cracking of kerogen and liquid hydrocarbons occurs.

The gas yield obtained from cuttings gas analysis can be applied in a rough fashion to determine gas source potential. Values below 10 000 U (ppm volume/per cent organic carbon) are typical of background values and can be interpreted as having no or limited gas source potential. Values in excess of 25 000 U are typical of the maximum phase of gas generation in both Type II and Type III organic matter and can be considered to have excellent gas source potential. Values between 10 000 and 25 000 U are those that are typically encountered accompanying the main phase of oil generation from Type II kerogen and represent moderate gas source potential. It cannot be overemphasized, however, that these values must be applied in a discriminating fashion. They are unique to the system of analysis used and can only be used for discrete homogeneous shale units. Further, these values may be affected from basin to basin by the degree of consolidation of the sediments.

CONCLUSIONS

Because of the nature of the sampling process, the data obtained from cuttings gas analysis is at best semi-quantitative. However, by limiting the number of geological variables, it has been proven possible to draw some conclusions concerning the timing of gas generation and the relative amounts of gas generated by different organic matter types.

The existing gas generation model has been found to be adequate to predict the main phase of gas generation in respect of Type II organic matter but modifications have to be made in respect of gas generation from Type III organic matter.

Qualitative changes in cuttings gas composition (increase in proportion of C_2–C_4) preceed the main phase of gas generation and occur at a vitrinite reflectance level of about $0.45\% \, R_0$ and is independent of organic matter type. Changes in isobutane/n-butane ratios generally occur later than the onset of wet gas and accompany the initial increase in gas concentration in both Type II and Type III organic matter.

Significant gas generation from Type III organic matter commences at a reflectance level of $0.55\% \, R_0$ and has already reached a maximum by $0.7\% \, R_0$. In contrast, for Type II organic matter there is a slight increase in gas yield accompanying liquid hydrocarbon generation in the reflectance range 0.5 to $0.6\% \, R_0$ but a dramatic increase in gas yield only occurs in the late mature to overmature zones as liquid hydrocarbons are cracked to gas.

The amount of gas generated from Type III organic matter is three times that generated from Type II organic matter in the mature zone. The ratio of gas to liquids is eight times higher for Type III kerogen than for Type II kerogen. In the overmature zone, however, the amount of gas generated from Type II organic matter exceeds by a factor of three that generated from Type III organic matter in the case studied.

Threshold values have been erected for interpretation of gas source potential and are as follows: <10 000 U (ppm volume/per cent organic carbon), no or limited gas source potential; 10 000–25 000 U, moderate gas source potential; >25 000 U, excellent gas source potential. However, the utility of these values is confined to homogeneous shale units and by the analysis method. Adjustment of these values may be required in different basins.

Acknowledgements

The authors would like to thank K. Nairn for computer programming assistance and gratefully acknowledge the Swiss National Foundation of Scientific Research for providing F. Monnier with a research grant (No. 82.725.0.79).

REFERENCES

Connan, J. and Cassou, A. M. (1980) Properties of gases and petroleum liquids derived from terrestrial kerogen at various maturation levels. *Geochim. Cosmochim. Acta* **44**, 1–23.

Creaney, S. (1980) The organic petrology of the Upper Cretaceous Boundary Creek Formation, Beaufort–Mackenzie Basin. *Bull. Can. Pet. Geol.* **28**, 112–129.

Evans, C. R. and Staplin, F. L. (1980) Regional facies of organic metamorphism, Geochemical prospecting for petroleum and natural gas. *Can. Inst. Min. Metall.*, Special Vol. No. **11**, 517–520.

Harwood, R. J. (1977) Oil and gas generation by laboratory pyrolysis of kerogen. *Am. Assoc. Pet. Geol. Bull.* **61**, 2082–2102.

Hitchon, B. (1963) Geochemical studies of natural gas. *J. Can. Pet. Technol.* **2**, 60–76.

Powell, T. G. (1978) An assessment of the hydrocarbon source rock potential of the Canadian Arctic Islands. *Geological Survey of Canada*, Paper 78-12.

Powell, T. G. and Snowdon, L. R. (1980) Geochemical controls on hydrocarbon generation in Canadian sedimentary basins. *Facts and Principles of World Petroleum Occurrence*, ed. by Miall, A. D. Canadian Society of Petroleum Geologists, Memoir 6, 421–46.

Rumeau, J. L., Connan, J., Le Tran, K., van der Weide, B. and Coustau, H. (1972) Problèmes posés par les gisements de gas à faible profondeur et par l'hydrogène sulferé des gisements profonds. *Congrès A.T.G.* Paris, 1–12.

Schoell, M. (1980) The hydrogen and carbon isotopic composition of methane from natural gases of various origins. *Geochim. Cosmochim. Acta* **44**, 649–661.

Snowdon, L. R. (1980a) Resinite — A potential petroleum source in the Upper Cretaceous/Tertiary of the Beaufort–Mackenzie Basin. In *Facts and Principles of World Petroleum Occurrence*, ed. by Miall, A. D. Canadian Society of Petroleum Geologists, Memoir 6, 421–446.

Snowdon, L. R. (1980b) Petroleum source potential of the Boundary Creek Formation, Beaufort–Mackenzie Basin. *Bull. Can. Pet. Geol.* **28**, 46–58.

Snowdon, L. R. and McCrossan, R. G. (1973) Identification of petroleum source rocks using hydrocarbon gas and organic carbon content. *Geological Survey of Canada*, Paper 72-36.

Snowdon, L. R. and Powell, T. G. (1982) Immature oil and condensate. A modification to the hydrocarbon generation model for terrestrial organic matter. *Am. Ass. Pet. Geol. Bull.* **66**, 775–788.

Snowdon, L. R. and Roy, K. J. (1975) Regional organic metamorphism in the mesozoic strata of the Sverdrup Basin. *Bull. Can. Pet. Geol.* **23**, 131–148.

Stahl, W. J. (1977) Carbon and nitrogen isotopes in hydrocarbon research and exploration. *Chem. Geol.* **20**, 121–149.

Stroganov, V. P. (1973) On the main phase of generation of gaseous and liquid hydrocarbons and conditions of formation of zones of oil and gas accumulation. *Sov. Geol.* **9**, 65–75.

Tissot, B., Durand, B., Espitalié, J. and Combaz, A. (1974) Influence of nature and diagenesis of organic matter in formation of petroleum. *Am. Assoc. Pet. Geol. Bull.* **58**, 499–506.

Advances in Organic Geochemistry 1981, pp. 496–503
© *John Wiley & Sons Limited, 1983*

Molecular Measurements of Thermal Maturation of Cretaceous Shales from the Overthrust Belt, Wyoming, USA

A. S. Mackenzie∗, Li Ren-Wei[†], J. R. Maxwell

Organic Geochemistry Unit, University of Bristol, School of Chemistry, Cantock's Close, Bristol BS8 1TS, UK

J. M. Moldowan and W. K. Seifert

Chevron Oil Field Research Company, PO Box 1627, Richmond, California 94802, USA

Where present in the extracts of six Cretaceous shales from the Wyoming Overthrust Belt, the distributions of selected components in the alkane, aromatic hydrocarbon, and carboxylic acid fractions have been examined. Measurements indicative of the extent to which different reactions (isomerization at chiral centres, aromatization and carbon–carbon bond cleavage) have occurred, in a number of types of biological marker compounds have confirmed earlier studies of these samples by allowing maturity differences between all of them to be discerned. The extents of configurational isomerization in pristane and in the steranes of pyrolysates of the samples also confirm earlier studies of the hopanes, by showing that the rate of isomerization proceeds at a slower rate in kerogen than in the extract.

INTRODUCTION

Recent studies have indicated that the extent of thermal maturation of sedimentary rocks can be conveniently and accurately assessed by organic molecular measurements. These studies have used, in part, the extents of configurational isomerization (a) in the acyclic isoprenoid alkane, pristane (I, Patience *et al.*, 1978; Mackenzie *et al.*, 1980), (b) in the acyclic isoprenoid acids (e.g. II, Mackenzie *et al.*, 1982a), (c) at C-17, C-21 and C-22 in the hopanes (III, Ensminger *et al.*, 1977; Seifert and Moldowan, 1980), and (d) at C-14, C-17, C-20 and C-24 in the non-rearranged steranes (IV, Seifert and Moldowan, 1979, 1981; Mackenzie *et al.*, 1980). Other reactions are aromatization (Mackenzie *et al.*, 1981a) of monoaromatic steroid hydrocarbons (e.g. of proposed structural type V, Mackenzie *et al.*, 1982b; Seifert *et al.*, 1981 and this volume) to triaromatics (e.g. VI, Ludwig *et al.*, 1981; Mackenzie *et al.*, 1981a; Seifert *et al.*, 1981 and this volume), and cleavage of carbon–carbon bonds in aromatic steroid hydrocarbons (resulting in, e.g. VII, Seifert and Moldowan, 1978; Mackenzie *et al.*, 1981a), see diagram. In each case, the maturity assessment is based on devising a ratio of the concentrations of precursor and product(s) which measures the extent to

which the reaction has occurred. In all cases, the skeletons of the products are not found in significant relative amounts in the biosphere, and are not formed to any extent by the low temperature (<40 °C) processes associated with early diagenesis. Hence, the derived maturity measurements are thought to be independent of difference in original organic input.

This study reports the application of these types of measurements to the solvent extracts of a series of six Cretaceous shales from the Wyoming Overthrust Belt, although aspects of the measurements are also reported for the products of the temperature-programmed pyrolysis of four of the extracted shales (*cf.* Seifert, 1978). In the two least mature shales the pyrolysis yields were too low for analysis (Seifert and Moldowan, 1980).

EXPERIMENTAL

All procedures, including the computation of the ratios, have been reported previously (for alkanes, see Mackenzie *et al.*, 1980; for acyclic isoprenoid acids, see Mackenzie *et al.*, 1982a; for aromatic steroid hydrocarbons, see Mackenzie *et al.*, 1981a, b; for pyrolysis methodology, see Seifert, 1978).

RESULTS

The locations and stratigraphy of the shales are shown in Fig. 1. The proposed maturity order, derived from

---

∗ Present address: KFA-Jülich, ICH-5: Erdöl und Organische Geochemie, Postfach 1913, D-5170 Jülich 1, F.R.G.
† Present address: Institute of Geology, Academia Sinica, Peking, People's Republic of China.

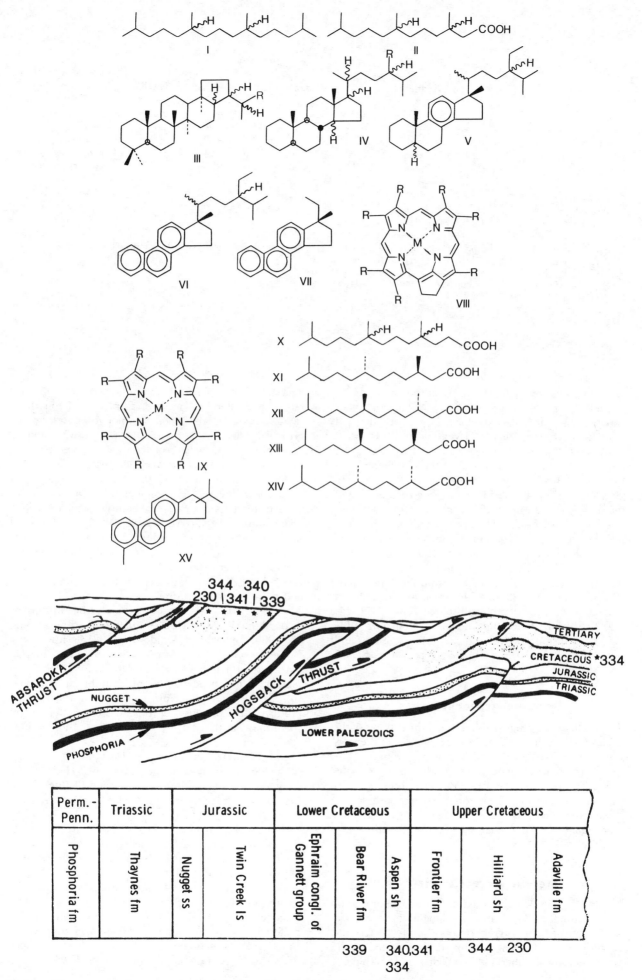

Fig. 1. Diagrammatical cross section and stratigraphic column to show the six sampling areas for Cretaceous shales from the Wyoming Overthrust Belt, and their geological ages.

Table 1

Vitrinite reflectance and stereochemistry of alkanes.

Sample[a]	R_0 (%)	Pristane % meso- E	P	% 20S[b] E	P	Steranes % $\beta\beta$[c] E	P	% 24S[d] E	Hopanes % 22S[e] E	NMR % Arom.[f] E	Sample equivalence[g]
U.Hilliard 230 (VI)	0.43	85	n.d.	9	n.d.	35	n.d.	60	28	10	Same as VI
L.Hilliard344 (V)	0.51	65	n.d.	22	n.d.	37	n.d.	n.d.	47	10	Part of V composite
Frontier 341 (IV)	0.41	50	60	23	11	23	low	n.d.	50	13	Shallower sample of IV core
Aspen 340 (II)	0.47	50	50	30	26	19	low	50	55	14	Same as III
Bear River 339 (II)	0.55	50	50	47	31	40	low	n.d.	59	23	Same as II
Mowry 334 (I)	0.80	50	50	55	65	72	60	n.d.	56	17	Similar to I

[a] In order of maturity from hopane stereochemistry and previous designation in brackets (Seifert and Moldowan, 1980).

[b] % (20S)- of (20R + 20S)-24-ethyl-5α(H), 14α(H), 17α(H)-cholestane.

[c] % 5α(H), 14β(H), 17β(H) of all identified non-rearranged C_{29} steranes.

[d] % (24S)/(24R + 24S)-(20R)-24-methyl-5α(H), 14α(H), 17α(H)-cholestane.

[e] % (22S)- of (22R + 22S)-17α(H), 21β(H)-hopanes (C_{31}-C_{34}).

[f] % Aromatic protons of all protons in the 90MH$_z$ ^{1}H NMR of the di- and triaromatic fractions. Original sample set published in Siefert and Moldowan (1980, 1981).

[g] With respect to Seifert and Moldowan (1980, 1981).

E = extract; P = pyrolysate; n.d. = not determined.

earlier work on the configurations of the hopanes (III) in extracts and pyrolysates (Seifert and Moldowan, 1980) and the configuration at C-20 in C_{29} non-rearranged steranes in extracts (Seifert and Moldowan, 1981), is 230 <344<341<340<339<334 (as listed in Table 1). Some samples are not identical to those of Seifert and Moldowan (1980, 1981). In general, the maturity sequence corresponds to increasing age because five of the shales are shallow (c. 20–40 m) cores from within a single thrust slice (Fig. 1). The exception is the most mature Mowry (334), obtained from a deep core of the Mowry shale (called Aspen in some locations), sampled at 2760–2763 m. The Mowry sample (334) is a more mature equivalent of sample 340, from the Aspen shale (Fig. 1). Samples 230 and 344 are from the Hilliard shale, but 344 is stratigraphically older (Lower Hilliard; Fig. 2). Vitrinite reflectance data are included in Table 1. The relevant gravimetric yields (extraction and pyrolysis) for similar samples were reported by Seifert and Moldowan (1980).

Pristane stereochemistry

The results are given in Table 1. Only the extracts of the Hilliard shales showed a preference (> 50%) of the meso-isomer (the biologically derived configuration). The alkane fractions of the extracts of all the other shales showed pristane to be fully isomerized (50% meso-pristane). In contrast, the pyrolysate of one of these four shales contained pristane with 60% of the meso-isomer. The other three pyrolysates contained the all-isomer mixture.

Sterane stereochemistry

Table 1 lists the Bristol results for the C-20 configuration of the extractable C_{29} steranes (analogous to, and in the same sequence as those reported previously, Seifert and Moldowan, 1981). New information is provided on the proportions of the thermodynamically more stable C_{29}

5α(H), 14β(H), 17β(H)-steranes to other C_{29} non-rearranged steranes in the extract and on both isomerization measurements for the pyrolysates. For U. Hilliard (230) and Aspen (340) it was also possible to determine the C-24 stereochemistry in the (20R)-24-methyl-5α(H), 14α(H), 17α(H)-cholestane (IV, 20R R = CH_3) in the extracts.

Although the analogous side chain isomerizations at C-22 in the hopanes (III) are complete by Aspen (see below and Seifert and Moldowan, 1980), isomerization at C-20 in the steranes continues until the most mature shale — Mowry (334). As in the case of pristane and the hopanes, isomerization at C-20 in the pyrolysate steranes lags behind the extractable equivalents (Table 1). The end point for isomerization at C-20 in the C_{29} 5α(H), 14α(H), 17α(H)-steranes has previously been proposed to be about 50% to 55% 20S/20R + 20S) (Mackenzie et al., 1980; Seifert and Moldowan, 1981). However, a value of 65% was measured for the most mature pyrolysate. It is not clear whether this value reflects (a) a temperature dependence of the equilibrium constant, (b) a different equilibrium constant for the steranes produced by pyrolysis of this mature shale, or (c) coelution of the 20S peak with an unidentified component.

The isomerization of C_{29} 5α(H), 14α(H), 17α(H)-steranes to their more stable 5α(H), 14β(H), 17β(H)-equivalents follows a more erratic trend (Table 1). For the extracts, the percentage of the latter falls between L. Hilliard and Aspen, then rises again to a value in Mowry shale approaching that seen in other mature samples (Mackenzie et al., 1980). The relative abundance of these compounds is only significant in the pyrolysate of the Mowry sample (Table 1).

Isomerization at C-24 shows analogies to earlier results for the Paris Basin (Mackenzie et al., 1980; Maxwell et al., 1980). The least mature shale shows a preference for the 24S isomer of (20R)-24-methyl-5α(H), 14α(H), 17α(H)-cholestane (cf. IV), whilst in Aspen shale this C_{28} sterane is fully isomeric at C-24.

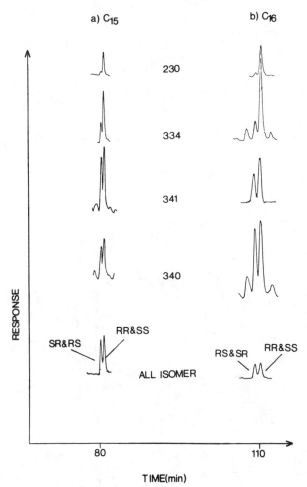

Fig. 2. Partial gas chromatograms of C_{15} and C_{16} isoprenoid acids (as methyl esters) from the four least mature Cretaceous shales from the Wyoming Overthrust Belt (230 is Upper Hilliard formation, 344 is Lower Hilliard, 341 is Frontier and 340 is Aspen), and all-isomer standard. Conditions: DEGS:PEGS (3:1, 0.6 μm, 100 m × 0.24 mm i.d., wall coated glass capillary; He carrier, 3 kg m^{-2}) programmed from 40–105 °C at 2 °C min^{-1}.

Hopane stereochemistry at C-22

The isomerization at C-22 in the hopanes of the extracts appears to be complete in Aspen shale, as reported previously (Seifert and Moldowan, 1980). Again (cf. isomerization at C-20 in the steranes) the L. Hilliard shale sample appears to be more mature than the corresponding L. Hilliard shale sample of Seifert and Moldowan (1980).

Acyclic isoprenoid acids

No compounds of this type were detected in the two most mature shales and all the pyrolysates. Only the C_{15} (II — 3,7,11-TMDD*) and C_{16} acids (X — 4,8,12-TMTD) were detected in all the other four shales. Sufficient material was present only in the Hilliard (230 and 344) shales to synthesize the (—)-menthyl esters. Only the relative

---

* Where 3,7,11-TMDD is 3,7,11-trimethyldodecanoic acid, etc.

---

configurations can therefore be compared over the four shales.

Gas chromatography resolves into doublets the methyl esters of the all-isomer standards (e.g. Fig. 2 and Ackman *et al.*, 1972). The first eluting peak contains the RS and SR (e.g. XI, XII) isomers[†], the second the RR and SS isomers (XIII, XIV). In general, the acids of immature shales comprise mainly the biological RR configuration (e.g. XIII, Mackenzie *et al.*, 1982a). Table 2 shows the proportion of the second eluting peak of the doublet as a percentage of the total for each acid (Fig. 2). Each acid in U. Hilliard (230) is dominated by the peak corresponding to the RR + SS isomers in the methyl ester standard, analysis of the (−)-menthyl esters showed the SS isomer to be absent. The relative abundance of the second eluting peak in the methyl esters decreases with increasing maturation. The (−)-menthyl esters showed that isomerization in the Hilliard shales (230 and 344) has occurred almost entirely at the chiral centre nearer the carboxylic acid group (Table 2).

Steroid hydrocarbon aromatization and side chain cracking

The ratio chosen to measure the extent of the aromatization process is the percentage of a C_{28} triaromatic VI (20*R* isomer, see Mackenzie *et al.*, 1981a, note added in proof; Ludwig *et al.*, 1981) to the combined abundance of the same C_{28} triaromatic and two C_{29} monoaromatics. The two monoaromatics have proposed structure type V, assigned by comparison of retention patterns in m/z 253 fragmentograms with synthesized C_{27} analogues (Mackenzie *et al.*, 1982b). The relevant peaks are arrowed in Fig. 3. Allowance is made for the contribution of a coeluting C_{28} monoaromatic to the earlier eluting of the two C_{29} monoaromatics (Mackenzie *et al.*, 1981a). Apparent side chain cracking is assessed from the percentage of the C_{20} triaromatic arrowed in Fig. 3 to the combined abundance of itself and the above C_{28} triaromatic (VI). The values are listed in Table 3.

No aromatic steroid hydrocarbons were detected in the pyrolysates. In the extracts the aromatization measurement shows a steady increase from the least mature sample (230) to the most mature sample (334), where the process is apparently complete. There is, however, little difference between Aspen (340) and Bear River (339). Only the two most mature samples, Bear River (339) and Mowry (334) showed significant relative abundances of the C_{20} triaromatic component. The latter sample had the higher value of the two (Table 3).

A C_{21} triaromatic compound (e.g. L. Hilliard 344 in Fig. 3) was observed in shallow samples. It has a longer retention time than the other C_{21} species which is prominent in Mowry shale (334). The mass spectra are similar and the later eluting component may be structure XV. This has been reported in recently deposited sediments and is thought to arise from an early diagenetic aromatization of plant triterpenoids (Spyckerelle, 1975; Wakeham *et al.*, 1980).

[†] In 3,7,11-TMDD, RS is the 3(R), 7(S) isomer, etc.

Table 2
Stereochemistry of acyclic isoprenoid acids.

Sample[a]	Relative configuration[b]		Stereoisomer composition (%)[c]							
	3,7,11-TMDD % RR + SS[d]	4,8,12-TMD % RR + SS[d]	3,7,11-TMDD				4,8,12-TMTD			
			RR	SR	RS	SS	RR	SR	RS	SS
230	84	90	83	15	tr	tr	90	10	0	0
344	72	80	76	16	12	2	80	20	0	0
341	56	53	n.d.				n.d.			
340	55	61	n.d.				n.d.			

[a] See Table 1.
[b] From GLC analysis on DEGS:PEGS (100 m × 0.24 mm i.d.) of methyl esters.
[c] From GLC analysis on DEGS:PEGS (100 m × 0.24 m i.d.) of (−)-menthyl esters.
[d] Both acids are resolved to doublets, the second eluting peak contains the RR isomer and its enantiomer (SS).
n.d. = not determined; tr = trace.

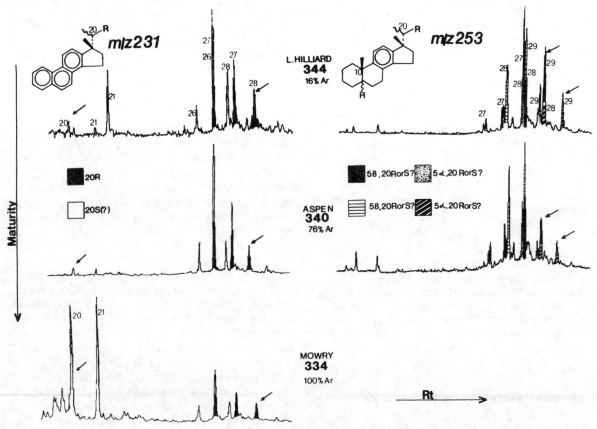

Fig. 3. Mass fragmentograms of m/z 231 and 253 for the aromatic fractions of three Cretaceous shales from the Wyoming Overthrust Belt.

Table 3
Aromatic steroid hydrocarbons — maturity measurements.

Sample[a]	'Aromatization' % C_{28} tri-Ar/ (C_{28} tri-Ar + C_{29} mono-Ar)[b]	'Cracking' % C_{20} tri-Ar/ (C_{20} tri-Ar + C_{28} tri-Ar)[b]
230	4	c. 5–10
344	16	c. 5–10
341	50	c. 5–10
340	76	c. 5–10
339	72	15
334	100	90

[a] See Table 1.
[b] Peaks shaded and arrowed in Fig. 3.

DISCUSSION

General

Overall, for the extracts, the extents of isomerization in pristane, the steranes (except the abundances of 5α(H), 14β(H), 17β(H)-C_{29} steranes, see below) and the hopanes confirm the maturity order proposed earlier for the same or similar samples (Seifert and Moldowan, 1980, 1981). The order is the same for the measured extent of isomerization of the C_{15} acyclic isoprenoid acid. The abundance of the later eluting peak of the C_{16} methyl ester shows a slight increase between Frontier (341) and Aspen (340). It is not known whether this difference reflects an apparent increase in the extent of isomerization for Frontier shale (341) or not, because only the relative configuration was measured (unlike the Hilliard shales 230 and 344), and two chiral centres are present. Apparent 'reversals' of maturity have been observed in the methyl esters from the Paris Basin Toarcian shales. These are not real when the isomer composition of the (−)-menthyl esters is examined (Mackenzie *et al.*, 1982a). With the exception of the similarity in the aromatization measurement for Aspen (340) and Bear River (339), the aromatization and cracking values confirm the maturity sequence and emphasize that Mowry (334) is by far the most mature.

Both Thermal Alteration Indices (TAI) (2.7–2.8 for 334), which measure the darkening of spore colours which occurs with increasing maturation (e.g. Burgess, 1975), and vitrinite reflectance measurements (Table 1), also show Mowry shale (334) to be by far the most mature. They do not, however, reveal the maturity gradation shown by the molecular measurements (Table 1; TAI for all other samples is *c.* 2.5).

The percentage of the protons of the extractable aromatic hydrocarbons which are aromatic protons can be measured by proton nuclear magnetic resonance spectroscopy (Alexander *et al.*, 1980). The PAP values show the gradual increasing maturity trend from U. Hilliard to Mowry shale. The anomalous value for Bear River shale seems out of line by comparison with other maturity parameters. A possible explanation is a difference in the environment of deposition between Bear River and Mowry/Aspen (e.g. see Fig. 5 and explanation below). The increases in PAP values are thought to arise by increased aromatization and increased cracking of alkyl substituents as thermal maturation progresses (Alexander *et al.*, 1980).

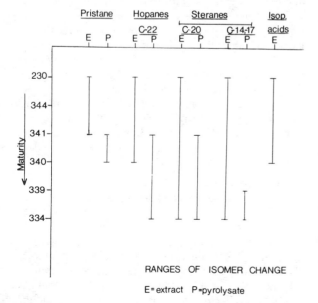

Fig. 4. Bar chart to show the ranges of change of configurational isomerization measurements for maturity assessment for the samples studied.

Isomerization at chiral centres

A schematic bar chart is shown in Fig. 4, which represents the sample range over which a change in each measurement was observed. In the extractable alkanes the order (for chiral centres not part of a ring system) in which the presumed equilibrium ratio is reached, corresponds to that observed previously in Paris Basin shales (Mackenzie *et al.*, 1980). The order is interpreted in terms of increasing steric hindrance of each centre.

The bar chart shows clearly that the isomerization at C-6 and C-10 in pristane and at C-22 in the hopanes occurs at a slower rate in the kerogen than in the extract. Epimerization of these carbon centres is still being observed in the pyrolysate alkanes beyond the point (in the maturity sequence) at which the corresponding changes in the extractable alkanes are complete. A similar behaviour is observed for the isomerization at C-20 in the steranes, except for sample 334 the percentage value of $20S/(20R + 20S)$ is lower for the pyrolysate. The high values for isomerization at C-14, C-17 and C-20 in the steranes of the extract and the pyrolysate of Mowry (334), but low values of $5\alpha(H)$, $14\beta(H)$, $17\beta(H)$-steranes in all samples but 334, provides further evidence for the large difference in maturity between Bear River (339) and Mowry (334).

That chiral centres of hopanoid moieties incorporated into kerogen (pyrolysate analysis) isomerize at a slower rate than their equivalent centres in the extract was proposed by Seifert and Moldowan (1980) to be the result of inductive effects arising from a functional group linkage of the moiety to the kerogen. Alternatively, the difference could result from effective catalysis without the kerogen matrix, that is, for the extract (if indeed the isomerizations are catalysed). It is also possible that the difference is the result of 'cage effects' in the kerogen, which could restrict the opportunity for one configuration to convert to another configuration.

Except for confirming that Mowry (334) is much more mature than the others, the proportions of extractable $5\alpha(H)$, $14\beta(H)$, $17\beta(H)$-steranes show no clear trends. The variations, for example: the anomalously high abundances in the two least mature shales, may reflect differing contributions of more mature reworked extractable material (*cf* Mackenzie *et al.*, 1980). On the other hand, such a large predominance of the $\beta\beta$-steranes over the $20S$ steranes, as in U. Hilliard (sample 230, Table 1), might not be expected to occur through the simple addition of mature material (*cf.* Fig. 10 in Seifert and Moldowan, 1981). Such a relatively high $5\alpha(H)$, $14\beta(H)$, $17\beta(H)$-sterane content suggests perhaps that some movement of lipids into the rock has occurred, creating a superimposed migration effect. Similar effects on the $\beta\beta$-sterane (C_{29}) abundances, attributed to migration, have been observed in some Overthrust Belt crude oils (Seifert and Moldowan, 1981).

Aromatization and side chain cracking in steroid hydrocarbons

It is noteworthy that, apart from ranking the samples in

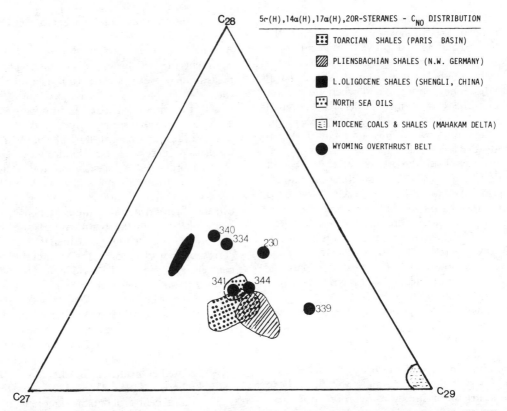

Fig. 5. Triangular diagram of the relative abundances (peak areas in *m/z* 217 fragmentograms) of 5α(H), 14α(H), 17α(H)-20R steranes (C_{27}–C_{29}) for a number of sample suites. Since the C_{27}–C_{29} sterol distributions of bottom sediments are dependent on the precursor organisms, the C_{27}–C_{29} distributions of the resultant steranes in ancient sediments and petroleums are expected to reflect variation in depositional environment. All of the sample suites shown other than the Overthrust Belt are thought to show only minor variation in depositional environment and cover quite restricted areas in the triangular diagram. The six Overthrust Belt samples are more spread out and therefore represent more diverse conditions than is the case *within* the other sample suites.

a maturity order, the aromatic steroid hydrocarbons were not present in the pyrolysates. They have been observed, however, in high relative abundance in the products from an immature Toarcian shale heated (*c.* 200–260 °C) in sealed tubes for periods up to a few weeks (Mackenzie *et al.*, 1981b). Under open conditions of pyrolysis (Seifert, 1980), the steroid species formed from the kerogen are removed rapidly from the system and cooled. Under the closed conditions of laboratory heating experiments in sealed tubes, steroid species, although containing initially no aromatic steroid hydrocarbon moieties of the type examined here, presumably have the opportunity to react further to form these compounds.

The low relative abundance of low molecular weight triaromatic steroid hydrocarbons in all of the samples except Mowry (334), supports the previous observation that the measurement of apparent side chain cracking is appropriate for a relatively late stage of thermal maturation, well beyond the onset of hydrocarbon generation. At this stage, most of the isomerization and aromatization measurements have gone to completion (Mackenzie *et al.*, 1981a).

Depositional environment

That there are differences in the deposition of environment between some of the samples is shown in Fig. 5. The diagram (based on the ideas of Huang and

Meinschein, 1979) is a triangular plot of C_{27} versus C_{28} versus C_{29} steranes, all with the 5α(H), 14α(H), 17α(H) 20R configuration. Within suites with proposed similar depositional environments, the samples tend to cluster (e.g. Late Oligocene shales from the Shengli Oilfield, and Miocene coals and shales from the Mahakam Delta), but the Overthrust Belt samples are more separated. The use of this diagram presumes that the carbon number distribution of sterols incorporated into a sediment during deposition reflects the composition of the contributing organisms. This relates to the depositional environment. The steranes of ancient sediments will inherit this distribution. Samples with similar depositional environments would be expected to plot together in Fig. 5 (e.g. Mahakam Delta samples), whilst different depositional environments may show more scatter.

Acknowledgements

ASM thanks the Science Research Council (SRC) for a studentship and the Natural Environment Research Council (NERC) for a Fellowship. L R-W thanks the Royal Society for help and support under an exchange scheme with the Chinese Academy of Sciences. We thank NERC for computerized GC–MS facilities (GR3/2951, GR3/3758). Dr D. M. Wilson assisted with 90 MHz NMR data. We are grateful to Mrs A. P. Gowar for technical assistance and to the management of

Chevron Oil Field Research Company, La Habra, California, for permission to publish.

REFERENCES

Ackman, R. G., Cox, R. E., Eglinton, G., Hooper, S. N. and Maxwell, J. R. (1972) Stereochemical studies of acyclic isoprenoid compounds. I. Gas chromatographic analysis of stereoisomers of a series of standard acyclic isoprenoid acids. *J. Chromatogr. Sci.* **10**, 392–401.

Alexander, R., Gray, M. D., Kagi, R. I. and Woodhouse, G. W. (1980) Proton magnetic resonance spectroscopy as a technique for measuring the maturity of petroleum. *Chem. Geol.* **30**, 1–14.

Burgess, J. D. (1975) Historical review and methods for determining thermal alteration of organic materials. In *Palynology: Proceedings of the Eighth Annual Meeting of the American Association of Stratigraphic Palynologists* **1**, pp. 1–7.

Didyk, B. M., Alturki, Y. I. A., Pillinger, C. T. and Eglinton, G. (1975) Petroporphyrins as indicators of geothermal maturation. *Nature* **256**, 563–575.

Ensminger, A., Albrecht, P., Ourisson, G. and Tissot, B. (1977) Evolution of polycyclic alkanes under effect of burial (Early Toarcian shales, Paris Basin). In *Advances in Organic Geochemistry 1975*, ed. by Campos, R. and Goni, J. Enadimsa, Madrid, pp. 45–52.

Huang, W.-Y. and Meinschein, W. G. (1979) Sterols as ecological indicators. *Geochim. Cosmochim. Acta* **43**, 739–745.

Ludwig, B., Hussler, G., Wehrung, P. and Albrecht, P. (1981) C_{26}–C_{29} triaromatic steroid derivatives in sediments and petroleums. *Tetrahedron Lett.* 3313–3316.

Mackenzie, A. S., Patience, R. L., Maxwell, J. R., Vandenbroucke, M. and Durand, B. (1980) Molecular parameters of maturation in the Toarcian shales, Paris Basin, France I. Changes in the configurations of the acyclic isoprenoid alkanes, steranes and triterpanes. *Geochim. Cosmochim. Acta* **44**, 1709–1721.

Mackenzie, A. S., Hoffmann, C. F. and Maxwell, J. R. (1981a) Molecular parameters of maturation in the Toarcian shales, Paris Basin, France III. Changes in aromatic steroid hydrocarbons. *Geochim. Cosmochim. Acta* **45**, 1345–1355.

Mackenzie, A. S., Lewis, C. A. and Maxwell, J. R. (1981b) Molecular parameters of maturation in the Toarcian shales, Paris Basin, France V Laboratory thermal alteration studies. *Geochim. Cosmochim. Acta* **45**, 2369–2376.

Mackenzie, A. S., Patience, R. L., Yon, D. A. and Maxwell, J. R. (1982a) The effect of maturation on the configutations of acyclic isoprenoid acids in sediments. *Geochim. Cosmochim. Acta.* **46**, 783–792.

Mackenzie, A. S., Lamb, N. A. and Maxwell, J. R. (1982b) Steroid hydrocarbons and the thermal history of sediments. *Nature* **295**, 223–226.

Maxwell, J. R., Mackenzie, A. S. and Volkman, J. K. (1980) Configuration at C-24 in steranes and sterols. *Nature* **286**, 694–697.

Patience, R. L., Rowland, S. J. and Maxwell, J. R. (1978) The effect of maturation on the configutation of pristane in sediments and petroleum. *Geochim. Cosmochim. Acta* **42**, 1871–1875.

Seifert, W. K. (1978) Steranes and terpanes in kerogen pyrolysis for correlation of oils and source rocks. *Geochim. Cosmochim. Acta* **42**, 473–484.

Seifert, W. K. and Moldowan, J. M. (1978) Applications of steranes, terpanes and monoaromatics to the maturation, migration and source of crude oils. *Geochim. Cosmochim. Acta* **42**, 77–92.

Seifert, W. K. and Moldowan, J. M. (1979) The effect of biodegradation on steranes and triterpanes in crude oils. *Geochim. Cosmochim. Acta* **43**, 111–126.

Seifert, W. K. and Moldowan, J. M. (1980) The effect of thermal stress on source rock quality as measured by hopane stereochemistry. In *Advances in Organic Geochemistry 1979*, ed. by Douglas, A. G. and Maxwell, J. R. Pergamon Press, Oxford, pp. 239–248.

Seifert, W. K. and Moldowan, J. M. (1981) Paleoreconstruction by biological markers. *Geochim. Cosmochim. Acta* **45**, 783–794.

Seifert, W. K., Carlson, R. M. K. and Moldowan, J. M. (1981) Geomimetic synthesis and structural assignment of monoaromatized petroleum steranes. *American Chemical Society, Division of Geochemistry, 182nd National Meeting, New York, August 1981.* Abstract No. 20.

Spyckerelle, C. (1975) Constituents aromatiques de sédiments. Thèse de Doctoratès-sciences, Université Louis Pasteur.

Wakeham, S. G., Schaffner, C. and Giger, W. (1980) Polycyclic aromatic hydrocarbons in Recent lake sediments II Compounds derived from biogenic precursors during early diagenesis. *Geochim. Cosmochim. Acta* **44**, 415–430.

Advances in Organic Geochemistry 1981, pp. 504–512
© *John Wiley & Sons Limited, 1983*

The Methylphenanthrene Index (MPI): A Maturity Parameter based on Aromatic Hydrocarbons

M. Radke and D. H. Welte

Institute for Petroleum and Organic Geochemistry (ICH-5) KFA-Jülich, PO Box 1913, D-5170 Jülich, F. R. Germany

Eighty core samples from North-West Germany, the Upper Rhine Graben and the Alps have been analysed for solvent-extractable aromatic hydrocarbons using semi-preparative high performance liquid chromatography (HPLC) and glass capillary gas chromatography with simultaneous flame ionization and sulphur-selective flame photometric detection. Evaluation of aromatic hydrocarbon distribution patterns has been focussed on tricyclic aromatics which showed pronounced changes with increasing thermal evolution of the organic matter. The Methylphenanthrene Index (MPI), which has been derived from the distribution of phenanthrene and the methylphenanthrene isomers, exhibited a good correlation with the mean vitrinite reflectance (R_m) within the oil window. A calculated mean reflectance (R_c) has been introduced for definition of the maturity levels in extracts which then have been compared to the measured maturity of source rocks as defined by R_m.

INTRODUCTION

Aromatic fractions from rock extracts are extremely complex mixtures of aromatic hydrocarbons, sulphur and oxygen heterocycles. In the past, conventional liquid and gas chromatographic techniques failed, in that they provided inadequate separation for the aromatics to be studied in greater detail (Brenneman and Smith, 1958; Rossini, 1960). At that time insight was gained into aromatic distributions mainly by mass spectrometry as applied to total aromatic fractions (Oudin, 1968). The mass-family approach revealed a striking constancy of the aromatic distribution pattern in recent sediments over a wide variety of depositional environments (Blumer and Youngblood, 1975; Youngblood and Blumer, 1975). More sophisticated analytical techniques, such as high performance liquid chromatography (HPLC), glass capillary gas chromatography and combined gas chromatography–mass spectrometry, are being used. This makes available more detailed information on aromatics composition e.g. depth profiles have been reported for the concentrations of various polycyclic aromatic hydrocarbons (PAH) in recent lake sediments (Wakeham *et al.*, 1980).

Little is known about the origin of PAH from unpolluted sediments. Forest fires may act as a common source for PAH in recent sediments (Blumer and Youngblood, 1975; Youngblood and Blumer, 1975). However, the distribution pattern of PAH may also have been controlled, after deposition, by microbiological processes which would impede the discovery of the

primary source (LaFlamme and Hites, 1978). The effect of leaching on PAH distributions, which has been postulated by Hites (1976), has not been verified by others (Lake *et al.*, 1979). The fate of PAH after deposition hence appears to be basically unknown. Obviously, the bulk of the PAH found in ancient sediments is derived from non-aromatic precursor molecules. It is generally accepted that a process of consecutive aromatization of steranes and triterpanes during diagenesis of sedimentary organic matter may contribute to the formation of PAH. This, however, is expected to end up with a very limited number of alkyl isomers only and may not account for the apparent multiplicity of alkyl homologues (Wakeham *et al.*, 1980).

Pyrolysis experiments by Ishiwatari and Fukushima (1979) and our previous studies on aromatics from rock and coal extracts have shown that the distribution of methylphenanthrene homologues is strongly controlled by the thermal maturation process (Radke *et al.*, 1982 a, b). Based on these observations, a Methylphenanthrene Index (MPI) has been developed which exhibits a close correlation with the vitrinite reflectance values. This paper reports data on aromatic-derived indices and shows how the MPI can be used to analyse and interpret the maturity of the soluble organic matter from sedimentary rocks.

EXPERIMENTAL

The analytical scheme is given in Fig. 1. The finely ground rock samples (<150 μm) were exhaustively

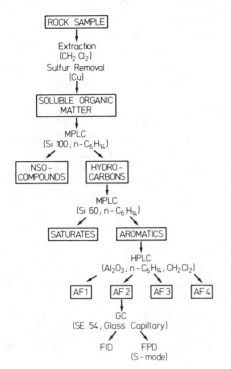

Fig. 1. Analytical scheme for the isolation and determination of tricyclic aromatics from a rock sample.

hydrocarbon fraction and an aromatic fraction (Radke *et al.*, 1980) using 40–63 μm silica gel Type 60 (E. Merck) as the stationary phase and *n*-hexane as the mobile phase. Polar NSO-compounds were retained on pre-columns packed with 63–200 μm silica gel Type 100 (E. Merck), which had been modified prior to use by heat treatment at 600 °C.

Aromatic fraction was further separated according to number of aromatic rings and molecular structure into four subfractions (AF1–AF4) by semi-preparative high performance liquid chromatography (Fig. 2). The HPLC-system was built up from two Model 740B pumps, a pressure monitor and a gradient programmer (Spectra-Physics). The spectrophotometric detector (SF 770, Schoeffel) was run at 270 nm (conditions: 2 columns, each of 250 mm length, 8 mm i.d., 3–6 μm irregular particles, Alumina Type N, Woelm, heated 4 h at 350 °C and then deactivated by addition of 3% w/w water). A flow rate of 16 ml min^{-1} was used with a stepwise gradient (% dichloromethane in *n*-hexane) of: 0% for AF1, 8% for AF2, 16% for AF3, 40% for AF4.

The aromatic subfractions were dissolved in xylene and analysed using a Varian 3700 gas chromatograph equipped with an inlet splitter, glass-lined outlet splitter, a flame ionization detector (FID), and a dual-flame flame photometric detector (FDP; 394 nm filter). Analysis time was reduced by application of the backflushing technique (Schaefer *et al.*, 1978). (Conditions: glass capillary column, two sections each of 50 m × 0.3 mm i.d., SE-54 silicone gum phase; temperature programmed 100 °C (2 min); 3 °C min^{-1} to 250 °C, hold 20 min; carrier gas helium 5 ml min^{-1}; split ratio inlet 1:10, outlet 1:1.) Splitter linearity and detector sensitivity were frequently checked by running test mixtures. Identification of PAH, oxygen and sulphur heterocycles was based on GC retention indices (Lee *et al.*, 1979; Willey *et al.*, 1981) and GC–MS

extracted with a mixture of redistilled dichloromethane and methanol (99:1, v/v) within 2 min using the modified 'flow-blending' method (Radke *et al.*, 1978). Extractions were carried out in a 1-L stainless steel centrifuge beaker into which the rotor–stator system was inserted. Elemental sulphur was removed during extraction by addition of copper powder. The hexane-soluble portion of the extract was separated by medium pressure liquid chromatography into a saturated

SEMI-PREPARATIVE HPLC
SAMPLE: 34mg ROCK EXTRACT - AROMATICS

5μm Al₂O₃

2 COLUMNS 250 x 8mm i.d.

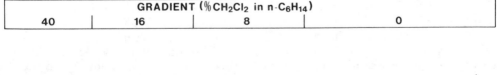

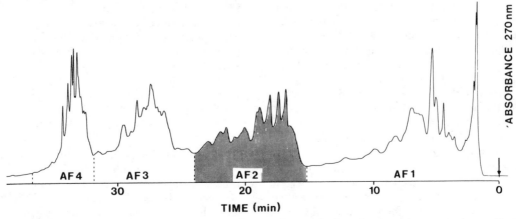

Fig. 2. HPLC fractionation of rock extract-aromatics on microparticulate alumina using a stepwise gradient.

analysis and was partly verified by comparison with reference materials.

Vitrinite reflectance (R_m — mean reflectivity) was measured on polished blocks of kerogen concentrates using oil immersion and a wavelength of 546 nm with a Zeiss MPM 01 microscope photometer.

GEOLOGIC SETTING AND SAMPLE MATERIAL

For this study, eighty core samples have been selected from fourteen wells drilled in various areas of Germany. The geologic description of the samples is presented in Table 1. All samples from NW Germany (Etzel Salt Dome, Hamburg Trough, Gifhorn Trough) are of Mesozoic age; with few exceptions these are Jurassic claystones, which were deposited in a marine environment. The sample series from the Upper Rhine Graben, SW Germany, is less homogeneous with respect to age and lithology. Samples are claystones and marls of Tertiary and Jurassic age. There is a greater variability of depositional environment which may be marine, brackish, evaporitic or limnetic. Samples from the Alps, S Germany, are mainly Mesozoic marls and limestones which were deposited in a marine environment.

Samples have been taken mainly from grey to dark-grey claystone and marl sections that were expected to represent potential source beds for hydrocarbons. Though all wells were dry, numerous oil stains indicated that oil may have been generated within these sections.

RESULTS AND DISCUSSION

Redistribution of C_{15+}-hydrocarbons

Previous work on aromatic-derived maturity parameters has been based on samples from wells where redistribution of C_{15+}-hydrocarbons has been shown to be negligible (Radke *et al.*, 1982 a, b). Only in the absence of migrated hydrocarbons will extract-derived maturity parameters be expected to correlate with the mean reflectivity of vitrinite (R_m). The measured reflectance, of course, has to be that of unaltered autochthonous vitrinite. The identification of the latter has been a serious problem mainly for the alpine limestone and marls which contain bituminous rather than coaly material, e.g. the very low reflectance of sample N-03 (Table 1) seems to have been measured on bituminite. A vitrinite reflectance decrease with depth, which otherwise would follow from the data, is unlikely. Though vitrinite reflectance has been used in this study to measure the maturity of sedimentary organic matter, a detailed discussion of problems inherent in the determination of this parameter would be outside the scope of this paper.

Redistribution (migration) of C_{15+}-hydrocarbons is an ubiquitous phenomenon which is associated with the hydrocarbon generation process (Asakawa and Fujita, 1979; Welte *et al.*, 1981) and the problem of detecting migrated C_{15+}-hydrocarbons is more complex than

generally has been realized. Very high organic-carbon-normalized C_{15+}-hydrocarbon yields (in excess of 150 mg g^{-1} C_{org}) are indicative of a major redistribution only. The relative abundance of C_{15+}-hydrocarbons in the extract, which shows a systematic increase from onset maturity up to the peak of the oil generation curve (Foscolos *et al.*, 1976; Powell *et al.*, 1978; Héroux *et al.*, 1979), may be used as a sensitive migration indicator within this maturity interval. Previous investigations indicate, that the relative abundance of non-migrated C_{15+}-hydrocarbons in the dichloromethane extract from clays, at a given maturation level, will show variations only within certain limits (Fig. 3, solid lines). A modified diagram is now tentatively applied to marls also (Fig. 3, broken lines). By using this approach the presence of migrated C_{15+}-hydrocarbons has to be assumed for a high percentage of the samples analysed. This is not evident from the organic-carbon-normalized C_{15+}-hydrocarbon yields, which may be less than 20 mg g^{-1} C_{org}. However, the presence of migrated C_{15+}-hydrocarbons has been verified indirectly in many cases, e.g. for samples from well K, Upper Rhine Graben (Table 1), which showed sporadic oil staining in the upper section.

Maturity parameters from aromatic hydrocarbons: basic concept

The development of an aromatic-derived maturity parameter has been based on the gas chromatographic determination of tricyclic aromatic hydrocarbons. The relevant part of a gas chromatogram obtained from the aromatic subfraction AF2 is presented in Fig. 4. The distribution pattern of the aromatic hydrocarbons has been corrected for coeluted sulphur heterocyclics using simultaneous flame ionization and flame photometric detection.

Three maturity-sensitive indices have been derived from the aromatics distribution, the Methyl-phenanthrene Indices (MPI 1 and MPI 2) which have been based on phenanthrene and four or three isomers of methylphenanthrene (for abbreviations and calculations see Appendix), and the Dimethyl-phenanthrene Index (DPI) which has been calculated from phenanthrene and two groups of dimethylphenanthrene isomers (Radke *et al.*, 1982a, b). Except for the first group of dimethylphenanthrene isomers (DMP 1–4) the peaks employed in index calculations have been shown to be major compounds of the aromatic subfraction AF2. Thus, precision of MPI determination was excellent whereas it was somewhat lower for the DPI.

Data from 25 bituminous coals and 56 Type III kerogen-containing rock samples evidenced a strong correlation between MPI 1 and R_m, which was positive within the oil window and negative at higher maturation levels (Fig. 5). The variability (standard deviation), which was very low within oil window, increased below the base of the oil window (Fig. 5, broken lines). These results demonstrate a general linear relationship between MPI 1 and R_m within the 0.6–1.3% R_m interval. This allows the calculation of mean vitrinite reflectance (R_c) from MPI 1 with a high degree of probability. The

Table 1

Geologic description of samples and analytical results.

Sample Desig-nation	Location	Depth (m)	Age	Formation	Lithology	Facies[a]	Org. carb. (wt%)	Hydro-carb. (wt%)[b]	Migr.[c]	R_m[d] (%)	R_c (%)	MPI 1	MPI 2	DPI
A-01	Etzel	1594	Jurassic	Lias zeta	clayst.	MSLB	2.0	61.1	+	0.53	0.62	0.36	0.41	0.23
A-02	Etzel	1618	Jurassic	Lias zeta	clayst.	MSLB	14.2	15.6	+	0.55	0.70	0.50	0.65	n.m.[e]
A-03	Etzel	1644	Jurassic	Lias zeta	clayst.	MSLB	2.4	49.0	+	0.44	0.59	0.32	0.37	0.22
A-04	Etzel	1673	Jurassic	Lias zeta	lime	MSLB	4.4	24.6	−	0.46	0.71	0.51	0.58	n.m.
A-05	Etzel	2009	Jurassic	Lias epsilon	clayst.	MSLB	4.1	21.1	+	0.64	1.07	1.12	0.83	n.m.
B-01	Etzel	1280	Jurassic	Dogger	clayst.	ML	1.5	44.8	−	0.62	0.65	0.42	0.47	0.33
C-01	Hamburg	1966	Cretaceous	U Albian	marl	MSL	0.2	54.5	−	0.78	0.80	0.66	0.72	n.m.
C-02	Hamburg	1997	Jurassic	Dogger gamma	clayst.	MSL	1.0	40.2	−	0.81	0.79	0.65	0.70	n.m.
C-03	Hamburg	2027	Jurassic	Dogger gamma	clayst.	MSL	0.9	58.4	(−)	0.74	0.77	0.61	0.69	0.64
C-04	Hamburg	2085	Jurassic	Dogger beta	clayst.	MSL	0.6	56.2	(−)	0.72	0.81	0.69	0.73	0.68
D-01	Hamburg	2040	Jurassic	Dogger beta	clayst.	MSL	1.1	60.5	+	0.59	0.57	0.29	0.30	0.27
D-02	Hamburg	2144	Jurassic	Dogger beta	clayst.	MSL	1.2	48.0	(−)	0.61	0.60	0.33	0.34	0.31
D-03	Hamburg	2168	Jurassic	Dogger beta	clayst.	MSL	1.2	46.3	(−)	0.62	0.66	0.44	0.43	0.52
E-01	Gifhorn	1547	Jurassic	Dogger beta	clayst.	MSL	0.7	67.6	+	0.71	0.72	0.53	0.61	0.95
E-02	Gifhorn	1551	Jurassic	Dogger beta	clayst.	MSL	0.5	33.8	(−)	(0.75)	0.71	0.51	0.55	0.60
E-03	Gifhorn	1554	Jurassic	Dogger beta	clayst.	MSL	1.1	33.4	(−)	(0.80)	0.78	0.63	0.69	0.72
E-04	Gifhorn	1582	Jurassic	Dogger beta	clayst.	MSL	1.5	20.2	+	(0.80)	0.79	0.65	0.72	0.72
E-05	Gifhorn	1586	Jurassic	Dogger beta	clayst.	MSL	1.5	37.3	(−)	0.84	0.74	0.56	0.58	0.70
E-06	Gifhorn	1587	Jurassic	Dogger beta	clayst.	MSL	1.3	50.4	−	0.83	0.81	0.68	0.63	0.88
E-07	Gifhorn	1588	Jurassic	Dogger beta	clayst.	MSL	1.3	62.5	−	0.82	0.78	0.63	0.59	0.92
F-01	Gifhorn	0	Jurassic	Lias epsilon	clayst.	MSL	3.8	16.4	−	0.42	0.64	0.40	0.49	0.29
G-01	Gifhorn	844	Cretaceous	M Barremian	clayst.	MSL	1.8	47.0	−	(0.69)	0.63	0.38	0.42	0.46
G-02	Gifhorn	941	Cretaceous	U Hauteriv.	clayst.	MSL	1.0	47.3	−	0.70	0.67	0.45	0.47	0.38
G-03	Gifhorn	1051	Cretaceous	U Valangin.	clayst.	MSL	0.8	60.7	(−)	0.71	0.70	0.50	0.51	n.m.
H-01	Gifhorn	1460	Jurassic	Dogger beta	clayst.	MSL	0.7	39.7	−	0.77	0.77	0.62	0.62	0.75
H-02	Gifhorn	1823	Jurassic	Lisa alpha	sandst.	ML	1.2	50.3	+	0.55	0.87	0.79	0.67	n.m.
H-03	Gifhorn	1851	Jurassic	Lias alpha	clayst.	MSL	0.6	22.9	(−)	0.70	0.71	0.52	0.49	0.65
I-01	Gifhorn	2068	Jurassic	Lias alpha	clayst.	MSL	0.6	32.8	−	0.70	0.78	0.63	0.63	0.72
J-01	Gifhorn	1635	Jurassic	Dogger beta	clayst.	MSL	0.6	34.4	−	0.68	0.69	0.49	0.52	0.73
J-02	Gifhorn	1640	Jurassic	Dogger beta	clayst.	MSL	0.6	44.5	−	0.65	0.67	0.45	0.40	0.72
K-01	U Rhine	596	Eocene	Pechelbronner S.	marl	MBRSL	0.7	32.0	+	(0.30)	0.63	0.38	0.41	0.34
K-02	U Rhine	618	Eocene	Pechelbronner S.	marl	MBRSL	0.6	35.1	+	0.30	0.67	0.45	0.51	0.48
K-03	U Rhine	795	Eocene	Pechelbronner S.	marl	MBRSL	0.7	37.1	+	0.36	0.66	0.43	0.49	0.35
K-04	U Rhine	841	Eocene	Pechelbronner S.	marl	MBRSL	2.1	36.5	+	0.43	0.85	0.75	0.83	0.93
K-05	U Rhine	953	Eocene	Pechelbronner S.	marl	MBRSL	0.2	39.3	+	(0.43)	0.70	0.50	0.56	0.57
K-06	U Rhine	1360	Eocene	Lymnaenmergel	clayst.	BRL	0.4	33.4	−	(0.57)	0.58	0.30	0.35	0.22
K-07	U Rhine	1566	Eocene	Lymnaenmergel	clayst.	BRL	0.8	47.2	−	0.64	0.78	0.63	0.71	0.69
K-08	U Rhine	1622	Eocene	Lymnaenmergel	clayst.	BRL	0.7	43.5	−	(0.66)	0.79	0.65	0.77	0.89
K-09	U Rhine	1628	Eocene	Lymnaenmergel	clayst.	BRLM	0.9	32.1	(+)	0.67	0.83	0.72	0.88	0.91
K-10	U Rhine	1784	Jurassic	Callovian	clayst.	MSL	0.7	44.6	−	0.58	0.57	0.29	0.32	0.30
K-11	U Rhine	1788	Jurassic	Callovian	clayst.	MSL	0.5	43.7	−	0.60	0.69	0.49	0.51	0.53
K-12	U Rhine	1792	Jurassic	Callovian	clayst.	MSL	0.5	45.9	−	0.61	0.72	0.54	0.51	0.54
L-01	U Rhine	1210	Oligocene	Cyrenenmergel	marl	BR	0.5	45.4	(+)	0.55	0.62	0.36	0.41	0.37
L-02	U Rhine	1338	Oligocene	Melettaschtn.	marl	MSL	0.7	44.8	(+)	0.54	0.62	0.36	0.43	n.m.
L-03	U Rhine	1405	Oligocene	Foraminiferenm.	marl	MSL	0.4	26.9	−	0.57	0.60	0.33	0.37	0.27
L-04	U Rhine	1776	Eocene	Pechelbronner S.	marl	MBRL	0.2	40.0	−	0.58	0.55	0.25	0.29	0.22
L-05	U Rhine	1931	Eocene	Pechelbronner S.	clayst.	MBRL	0.9	45.9	−	0.67	0.84	0.73	0.80	1.10
L-06	U Rhine	2171	Eocene	Lymnaenmergel	marl	BRLM	0.5	48.8	(+)	0.58	0.54	0.24	0.28	0.20
L-07	U Rhine	2246	Eocene	Lymnaenmergel	clayst.	BREV	0.5	68.2	+	0.63	0.87	0.79	0.92	1.11
L-08	U Rhine	2297	Eocene	Lymnaenmergel	clayst.	BREV	0.6	66.9	+	0.64	0.87	0.78	0.93	1.13
L-09	U Rhine	2362	Eocene	Lymnaenmergel	clayst.	BREV	0.5	68.0	+	0.65	0.89	0.81	0.95	1.13
M-01	U Rhine	930	Jurassic	Callovian	marl	MSL	0.5	50.0	(+)	0.62	0.61	0.35	0.37	0.33
M-02	U Rhine	1000	Jurassic	Bajocian	marl	MSL	0.7	58.5	+	0.65	0.87	0.79	0.87	1.35
M-03	U Rhine	1040	Jurassic	Dogger delta	marl	MSL	0.8	47.8	−	0.65	0.63	0.39	0.42	0.28
M-04	U Rhine	1057	Jurassic	Dogger gamma	marl	MSL	0.6	33.3	−	(0.66)	0.66	0.43	0.42	0.41
M-05	U Rhine	1060	Jurassic	Dogger gamma	marl	MSL	0.7	50.5	(+)	(0.66)	0.77	0.62	0.76	0.62
M-06	U Rhine	1063	Jurassic	Dogger gamma	marl	MSL	0.8	41.5	−	(0.66)	0.61	0.35	0.37	0.25
M-07	U Rhine	1073	Jurassic	Dogger beta	marl	MSL	0.8	34.0	−	(0.66)	0.63	0.36	0.41	0.27
M-08	U Rhine	1080	Jurassic	Dogger beta	clayst.	MSL	0.5	43.4	−	(0.66)	0.59	0.31	0.36	0.23

continued next page

Table 1 *continued*
Geologic description of samples and analytical results.

Sample Designation	Location	Depth (m)	Age	Formation	Lithology	Facies[a]	Org. carb. (wt%)	Hydro-carb. (wt%)[b]	Migr.[c]	R_m[d] (%)	R_c (%)	MPI 1	MPI 2	DPI
M-09	U Rhine	1111	Jurassic	Dogger beta	clayst.	MSL	1.3	62.0	+	0.67	0.75	0.58	0.59	n.m.
N-01	Alps	3473	Oligocene	Rupelian	marl	MSLB	0.5	35.4	+	0.47	0.69	0.49	0.53	0.70
N-02	Alps	3588	Eocene	Lattorfian	marl	MSLB	1.0	39.0	+	0.52	0.75	0.59	0.55	n.m.
N-03	Alps	3645	Eocene	Lattorfian	marl	ML	0.7	42.3	+	0.30	0.71	0.51	0.56	0.71
O-01	Alps	496	Cretaceous	Zementmergel S.	marl	MAB	0.2	37.4	−	n.m.	0.62	0.37	0.42	0.47
O-02	Alps	621	Cretaceous	Feuerstaetter D.	marl	MB	0.3	34.6	−	1.35	0.68	0.47	0.54	0.45
O-03	Alps	748	Cretaceous	Feuerstaetter D.	marl	MB	0.4	36.2	−	n.m.	0.72	0.54	0.61	0.46
O-04	Alps	856	Cretaceous	Feuerstaetter D.	marl	MB	0.3	34.5	−	1.65	0.68	0.46	0.52	0.37
O-05	Alps	969	Cretaceous	Feuerstaetter D.	marl	MB	0.3	58.7	−	1.65	0.76	0.60	0.91	0.56
O-06	Alps	1057	Cretaceous	Feuerstaetter D.	marl	MB	0.3	53.0	−	n.m.	0.86	0.76	0.88	0.86
O-07	Alps	1167	Cretaceous	Leist-Mergel	marl	MSL	0.2	43.3	−	n.m.	0.83	0.72	0.83	0.76
O-08	Alps	1260	Cretaceous	Seewen-Kalk	limest.	MSL	0.3	61.9	−	n.m.	0.89	0.82	0.95	0.92
O-09	Alps	1353	Cretaceous	Brisi-Sandst.	sandst.	MSL	0.3	56.5	−	1.72	0.86	0.76	0.88	0.86
O-10	Alps	1591	Cretaceous	Drusberg-S.	marl	MSL	0.2	48.0	−	n.m.	1.15	1.25	1.47	1.60
O-11	Alps	1896	Cretaceous	Valendis-Kalk	limest.	MSL	0.3	56.3	+	1.93	1.66	1.06	1.22	1.20
O-12	Alps	2063	Cretaceous	Valendis-Kalk	marl	MSL	0.7	55.3	(+)	n.m.	1.56	1.24	1.53	1.52
O-13	Alps	2212	Jurassic	Zementstein-S.	marl	MSL	0.4	54.2	−	n.m.	1.62	1.14	1.39	1.13
O-14	Alps	2317	Jurassic	Zementstein-S.	marl	MSL	0.7	37.9	−	1.89	1.65	1.09	1.39	0.81
O-15	Alps	2378	Jurassic	Quintner-Kalk	limest.	MSL	0.1	61.9	−	n.m.	1.98	0.54	0.62	0.35
O-16	Alps	2434	Jurassic	Quintner-Kalk	limest.	MSL	0.1	50.0	−	n.m.	1.83	0.78	0.92	0.66
O-17	Alps	2516	Jurassic	Quintner-Kalk	limest.	MSL	0.1	38.3	−	n.m.	1.81	0.82	0.98	0.52
O-18	Alps	2584	Jurassic	Quintner-Kalk	limest.	MSL	0.2	45.3	−	n.m.	2.13	0.29	0.31	n.m.

[a] AB — abyssal; B — bathyal; BR — brackish; EV — evaporitic; L — littoral; LM – limnetic; M — marine; SL — sublittoral; [b]of total dichloromethane extract; [c]Migr. — presence/absence of migrated C_{15+}-hydrocarbons indicated by $+/-$; [d]estimated values given in parentheses; [e]n.m. — not measurable.

idea is that the MPI 1 value determined for an extract indicates the vitrinite reflectance value (R_c) of the corresponding source rock unless the extract is not indigenous.

Application of basic concept

For data from wells A–N (Table 1) a plot of R_c v. R_m is given in Fig. 6. Points plotting close to the full line

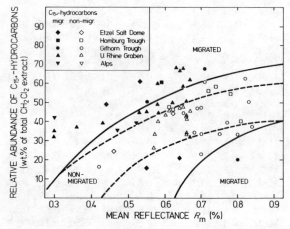

Fig. 3. Relative abundance of C_{15+}-hydrocarbons in total dichloromethane extract v. mean reflectance for core samples from various locations of West Germany.

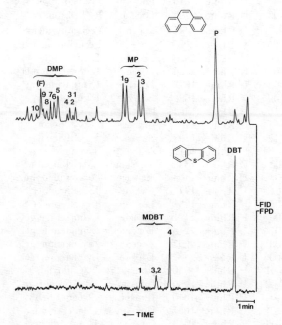

Fig. 4. Capillary gas chromatograms of the aromatic subfraction AF2 obtained from simultaneous flame ionization detection (FID) and sulphur-selective flame photometric detection (FPD). For identification of labelled peaks see Appendix.

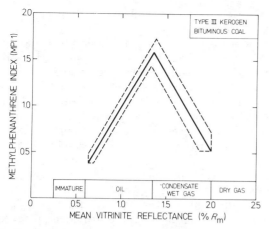

Fig. 5. Relationship between Methylphenanthrene Index (MPI 1) and mean vitrinite reflectance (% R_m) as based on previous data from Type III kerogen-bearing rock and bituminous coal samples.

indicate that the calculated values match the measured vitrinite reflectance data. The broken lines are spaced at $\pm S_{xy}$ from the full line where S_{xy} is the standard error estimate of x on y which had been obtained from statistical evaluation of previous data. Most values from non-impregnated samples plotted into the zone defined by the broken lines, proving the soundness of the basic concept.

In detail, a good agreement of R_c and R_m values has been observed for eleven samples from the Gifhorn Trough and five samples from the Hamburg Trough with their maturity ranging from 0.61 to 0.83% R_m. The correlation between R_c and R_m was good, as indicated by the correlation coefficient $r + 0.82$ for a total of 18 non-impregnated core samples from both troughs. There is only one R_c value which is significantly lower than the corresponding R_m value (E-05). Obviously, in this case, the mean vitrinite reflectance has been overestimated. Re-investigation of the histogram revealed a broad distribution with no clear maximum, which probably has been influenced by reworked vitrinite.

The samples from the Upper Rhine Graben were all fairly immature, as indicated by a vitrinite reflectance of less than 0.7% R_m. The kerogen was of Type III, which followed from Rock-Eval data. Only a part of the samples, so far tentatively described as non-migrated (Fig. 3), was found to plot in the above zone. A look into stratigraphy (Table 1) revealed that at least three of the samples (K-07, K-08, L-05) most probably have been influenced by migrated C_{15+}-hydrocarbons, though this was not evident from the gross composition of the extract. The distance of data points from the solid line (Fig. 6) in this particular case seems to be correlated with the degree of redistribution. This means that the migrated C_{15+}-hydrocarbons are derived from source beds which have reached a higher maturity level as compared to the impregnated zone, assuming that the aromatic distribution has not been changed on migration. It follows that the maturity of the source bed has not been lower than indicated by the actual R_c value, i.e. 0.8–0.9% R_m.

The effect of redistribution on aromatics composition is also demonstrated by samples from the NW Etzel Salt

Dome area where, in the past, a high sulphur asphaltic crude oil had been produced from a sandstone reservoir adjacent to the top of the Liassic bituminous shale section. A small asphalt deposit had been discovered at the opposite side, to the SE of the salt dome (Breyer, 1950). Kerogens from the Etzel shale samples were all of Type I–II. The very high maturity of aromatics from the lowermost sample (A-05) indicates a condensate injection. The addition of condensate to the reservoired oil could have produced the asphalt precipitate associated with the salt dome.

Dimethylphenanthrenes

Results from our earlier studies have shown, that the distribution pattern of dimethylphenanthrenes is controlled by the thermal maturation process (Radke *et al.*, 1982a, b). The characteristics of the Dimethyl-phenanthrene Index (DPI), which had been introduced to measure the changes of the dimethyl-phenanthrene distribution, have been re-evaluated in the present study. A plot of the DPI v. mean reflectance (R_m) for samples from wells A–N is presented in Fig. 7. A linear relationship between DPI and R_m is evident for the non-impregnated samples. The variation of data points about the regression line is greater than observed for the MPI 1. This was mainly due to the greater error inherent in the determination of the DMP 1–4 peaks which were only minor components. Obviously, the DPI data points of samples containing redistributed C_{15+}-hydrocarbons plot left from the regression line hence indicating a higher maturity for the migrated C_{15+}-hydrocarbons. The results which had been obtained by application of the MPI 1 were confirmed by DPI values.

A case history

Maturity evaluation of organic matter from an alpine marl–limestone sequence has tentatively been based on

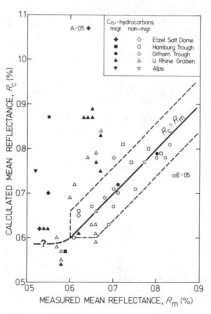

Fig. 6. Mean reflectance calculated from MPI 1 (R_c) v. mean reflectance from microscopic data (R_m) for core samples from various locations of West Germany.

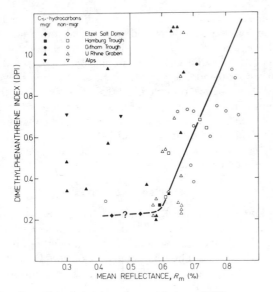

Fig. 7. Dimethylphenanthrene Index (DPI) v. mean reflectance (R_m) for core samples from various locations of West Germany.

the MPI 1 (well O, Table 1). Application of the Rock-Eval pyrolysis technique showed that the organic matter from core samples analysed was all of Type III, as indicated by the average Hydrogen Index of 30 mg hydrocarbons per gram of organic carbon. No clear maximum was obtained for the S_2 peak. Thus, the position of the S_2 peak maximum on the temperature scale could not be used as a maturity index in this

case. Most samples exhibited an organic carbon concentration of less than 0.5 wt % and the C_{15+}-soluble organic matter yield was generally less than 100 ppm. Potential source beds have not been discovered within the 500–2600 m depth interval. Indications of migrated hydrocarbons were obtained from sporadic oil stains.

Evaluation of the MPI 1 was carried out by gas chromatography of the total aromatics fraction since it showed a less complex distribution pattern than normal, with phenanthrene and methylphenanthrene homologues being the predominant components (Fig. 8). Maturity trends of single components such as the relative abundance increase of 2- and 3-methylphenanthrene with depth were evident. The thermal evolution of the dimethylphenanthrene distributions paralleled those of the methylphenanthrenes, i.e. the dimethylphenanthrene peaks 1–4 behaved much like the 2- and the 3-methylphenanthrene peaks. In summary, the thermal evolution of tricyclic aromatics was very similar to that previously observed in the Western Canada Deep Basin (Radke et al., 1982a).

Reflectance values (R_c) calculated from the MPI 1 are given in Fig. 9 along with the simplified stratigraphy and lithology of the well. A theoretical reflectance gradient has been established which showed a linear increase of 0.05% (absolute) per 100 m within the 500–1600 m depth interval, whereas it was approximately twice as high in the lower part of the well. Deviations from the trend line, which were observed for two impregnated samples from the Valanginian, indicated that the migrated C_{15+}-hydrocarbons have been derived from the Upper Jurassic section.

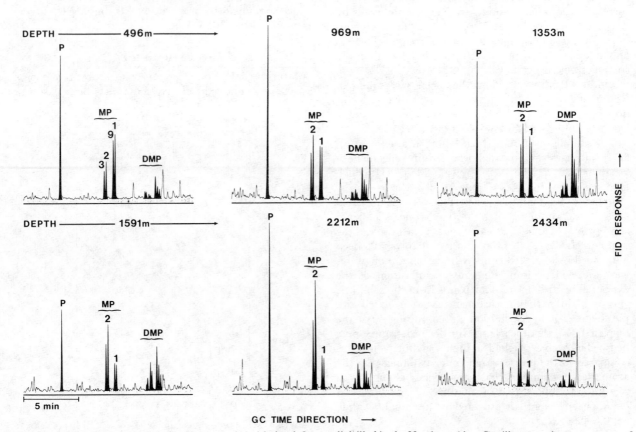

Fig. 8. Thermal evolution of tricyclic aromatics with depth for a well drilled in the Northern Alps. Capillary gas chromatograms of aromatics fractions from core sample-extracts. For identification of labelled peaks see Appendix.

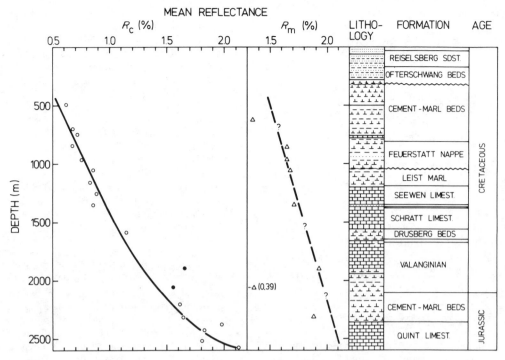

Fig. 9. Mean reflectance calculated from MPI 1 (R_c) and from microscopic data (R_m) v. depth for a well drilled in the Northern Alps. Presence of migrated C_{15+}-hydrocarbons is indicated by solid signature.

Measured vitrinite reflectance values for this well (Fig. 9), as in many carbonate–marl (and evaporitic) sequences, are not very reliable. Little coaly material was found and the identification of vitrinite was extremely difficult. The trend lines for R_c and R_m were found to be running nearly parallel over the 500–1600 m depth interval, the R_c values being approximately 1% (absolute) lower than the corresponding R_m values. At 2600 m depth the mean reflectance was 2.17% R_c, a value which was found to match the R_m trend line perfectly. A discrepancy between R_c and R_m values exists at shallower depths. The discrepancy is, however, not well-documented because of problems with the microscopical data.

In conclusion, it may be said that for this case study the calculated vitrinite reflectance values (as based on MPI 1) are a possible means to support or question actual measured microscopical data.

CONCLUSIONS

A general linear relationship has been shown to exist (within the oil window) for the maturity of the C_{15+}-soluble organic matter as defined by the Methylphenanthrene Index (MPI 1) and the maturity of the kerogen as defined by the mean vitrinite reflectance (R_m). Based on this relationship, maturity of rock extracts has been described in terms of calculated vitrinite reflectance (R_c). A good correlation between R_c and R_m values has been observed for non-impregnated samples. The apparent maturity of a sample bearing migrated C_{15+}-hydrocarbons, as given by R_c was always higher than the measured maturity of that sample. Thus, maturity of the C_{15+}-soluble organic matter from impregnated samples will be a good guide to the depth of burial of the corresponding source beds.

Acknowledgements

We thank the Preussag AG, Hannover, for providing the samples and the well descriptions. Technical assistance by the following members of KFA/ICH-5 is gratefully acknowledged: W. Laumer, F. Schlosser, M. Weiner and H. Willsch. Special thanks are due to C. Cornford and P. K. Mukhopadhyay for the vitrinite reflectance measurements and to U. Franz for the geological description of the samples. Financial support by the German Federal Ministry for Research and Technology (BMFT), Grant No. 3070 B, is gratefully acknowledged.

APPENDIX

Abbreviations and calculations

Compounds labelled on gas chromatograms (Fig. 4, 8)
P   phenanthrene
MP   methylphenanthrene (number indicates position of methyl group; 3-MP contains coeluted 1-MDBT)
DMP dimethylphenanthrene (number indicates order of elution from the GC column)
F   fluorene (contains coeluted DMP)
DBT   dibenzothiophene
MDBT methyldibenzothiophene (number indicates position of methyl group; 2- and 1-MDBT tentatively identified)

Methylphenanthrene Indices (MPI):

$$MPI\ 1 = \frac{1.5(2\text{-}MP + 3\text{-}MP)}{P + 1\text{-}MP + 9\text{-}MP}$$

$$MPI\ 2 = \frac{3(2\text{-}MP)}{P + 1\text{-}MP + 9\text{-}MP}$$

Dimethylphenanthrene Index (DPI):

$$DPI = \frac{4(DMP\ 1 + DMP\ 2 + DMP\ 3 + DMP\ 4)}{P + DMP\ 5 + DMP\ 6 + DMP\ 7}$$

Calculated mean reflectance (R_c):

$$R_c = 0.60\ MPI\ 1 + 0.40\ (\text{for } R_m < 1.35\%)$$

$$R_c = -0.60\ MPI\ 1 + 2.30\ (\text{for } R_m > 1.35\%).$$

REFERENCES

Asakawa, T. and Fujita, Y. (1979) Organic metamorphism and hydrocarbon generation in sedimentary basins of Japan. In *Proceedings of the Seminar on Generation and Maturation of Hydrocarbons in Sedimentary Basins.* COOP Techn. Publ. Ser. No. 6. Bangkok. pp. 142–162.

Brenneman, M. C. and Smith, P. V. (1958) The chemical relationships between crude oils and their source rocks. In *Habitat of Oil.* Ed. by Weeks, L. G. AAPG Publication. Tulsa, Oklahoma. pp. 818–849.

Blumer, M. and Youngblood, W. W. (1975) Polycyclic aromatic hydrocarbons in soils and recent sediments. *Science* **188**, 53–55.

Breyer, F. (1950) Der Salzstock von Etzel. *Erdöl-Kohle* **3**, 153–162.

Foscolos, A. E., Powell, T. G. and Gunther, P. R. (1976) The use of clay minerals and inorganic and organic geochemical indicators for evaluating the degree of diagenesis and oil generating potential of shales. *Geochim. Cosmochim. Acta* **40**, 953–966.

Héroux, Y., Chagnon, A. and Bertrand, R. (1979) Compilation and correlation of major thermal maturation indicators. *Bull. Amer. Ass. Petrol. Geol.* **63**, 2128–2144.

Hites, R. A. (1976) Sources of polycyclic aromatic hydrocarbons in the aquatic environment. In *Sources, Effects, and Sinks of Hydrocarbons in the Aquatic Environment.* American Institute of Biological Sciences. pp. 326–332.

Ishiwatari, R. and Fukushima, K. (1979) Generation of unsaturated and aromatic hydrocarbons by thermal alteration of young kerogen. *Geochim. Cosmochim. Acta* **43**, 1343–1349.

Laflamme, R. E. and Hites, R. A. (1978) The global distribution of polycyclic aromatic hydrocarbons in recent sediments. *Geochim. Cosmochim. Acta* **42**, 289–303.

Lake, J. L., Norwood, C., Dimock, C. and Bowen, R. (1979) Origins of polycyclic aromatic hydrocarbons in estuarine sediments. *Geochim. Cosmochim. Acta* **43**, 1847–1854.

Lee, M. L., Vassilaros, D. L., White, C. M. and Novotny, M. (1979) Retention indices for programmed-temperature capillary-column gas chromatography of polycyclic aromatic hydrocarbons. *Anal. Chem.* **51**, 768–774.

Oudin, J. L. (1968) Etude de la structure moléculaire d'hydrocarbures aromatiques extraits de roches. *Rev. Inst. Fr. Pet.* **23**, 850–856.

Powell, T. G., Foscolos, A. E., Gunther, P. R. and Snowdon, L. R. (1978) Diagenesis of organic matter and fine clay minerals: a comparative study. *Geochim. Cosmochim. Acta* **42**, 1181–1197.

Radke, M., Sittardt, H. G. and Welte, D. H. (1978) Removal of soluble organic matter from rock samples with a flow-through extraction cell. *Anal. Chem.* **50**, 663–665.

Radke, M., Willsch, H. and Welte, D. H. (1980) Preparative hydrocarbon group type determination by automated medium pressure liquid chromatography. *Anal. Chem.* **52**, 406–411.

Radke, M., Welte, D. H. and Willsch, H. (1982 a). Geochemical study on a well in the Western Canada Basin: relation of the aromatic distribution pattern to maturity of organic matter. *Geochim. Cosmochim. Acta* **46**, 1–10.

Radke, M., Willsch, H., Leythaeuser, D. and Teichmüller, M. (1982 b) Atomatic components of coal: relation of distribution pattern to rank. *Geochim. Cosmochim. Acta* **46** (in press).

Rossini, F. D. (1960) Hydrocarbons in petroleum *J. Chem. Education* **27**, 554–561.

Schaefer, R. G., Weiner, B. and Leythaeuser, D. (1978) Determination of sub-nanogram per gram quantities of light hydrocarbons (C_2–C_9) in rock samples by hydrogen stripping in the flow system of a capillary gas chromatograph. *Anal. Chem.* **50**, 1848–1854.

Wakeham, S. G., Schaffner, C. and Giger, W. (1980) Polycyclic aromatic hydrocarbons in Recent lake sediments. II Compounds derived from biogenic precursors during early diagenesis. *Geochim. Cosmochim. Acta* **44**, 415–429.

Welte, D. H., Yükler, M. A., Radke, M. and Leythaeuser, D. (1981) Application of organic geochemistry and quantitative basin analysis to petroleum exploration. In *Origin and Chemistry of Petroleum.* Ed. by Atkinson, G. and Zuckerman, J. J. Pergamon Press, Oxford. pp. 67–88.

Willey, C., Iwao, M., Castle, R. N. and Lee, M. L. (1981) Determination of sulfur heterocycles in coal liquids and shale oils. *Anal. Chem.* **54**, 400–407.

Youngblood, W. W. and Blumer, M. (1975) Polycyclic aromatic hydrocarbons in the environment: homologous series in soils and recent marine sediments. *Geochim. Cosmochim. Acta* **39**, 1303–1314.

Advances in Organic Geochemistry 1981, pp. 513–523
© *John Wiley & Sons Limited, 1983*

Phytol-containing Melanoidins and their Bearing on the Fate of Isoprenoid Structures in Sediments

S. R. Larter[1], H. Solli[2] and A. G. Douglas[3]

1. Exploration Research, Union Oil Company, Brea, California 92621, USA

2. Continental Shelf Institute, Hakon Magnussons Gt. 1B, 7001 Trondheim, Norway

3. Geology Department, Organic Geochemistry Unit, The University, Newcastle upon Tyne, NE 1 7RU, England

Melanoidins are acidic polymers which are produced by sugar/amino acid (or protein) condensation reactions. They have been shown to be capable of incorporating functionalized lipid molecules into their structures and, on artifical diagenesis, to develop some of the properties of kerogens. This work outlines studies which show that model melanoidin–lipid interactions are of value in studying natural geopolymers such as kerogen and humic substances. In these experiments, we have shown that phytol is incorporated into melanoidins as phytenyl esters and, possibly, through the formation of six membered carbocyclic systems, as benzene moieties. The uptake of phytol into the melanoidins, together with changes that occur during artificial diagenesis, was monitored using analytical pyrolysis techniques (py–gc–ms and py–ms). The relevance of these experiments to the origin of prist-1-ene in kerogen pyrolysates is also discussed.

INTRODUCTION

During the diagenesis of sedimentary organic matter complex, but poorly-defined, reactions take place which convert known kerogen precursors (carbohydrates, proteins, lignins, lipids etc.) to poorly-characterized heteropolycondensates. The combined effects of temperature and time on these polymers results in a material which may bear little chemical resemblance to the kerogen-forming components. It is therefore difficult to define the mechanisms, and source materials, which produce geopolymers by studying ancient kerogens alone. Instead, studies of ancient systems should be supported by simple model experiments in which it may be possible to follow changes in specific carbon skeletons occurring during the transformation of biolipids to geolipids: several relevant studies of model systems, and possible natural analogues, have been reported (Meuzelaar *et al.*, 1977; Hedges, 1978; Bracewell *et al.*, 1980; Larter and Douglas, 1980; Ioselis *et al.*, 1981).

The work of Maillard (1912) and Hoering (1973) suggested that melanoidins (dark coloured acidic polymers produced in carbohydrate/amino acid condensation reactions) have many of the properties of sedimentary humic substances. Recent work has shown that these synthetic materials can bind functionalized lipid molecules and, on artificial diagenesis, produce a material resembling some kerogens (Larter and Douglas, 1980).

In this communication, data are presented on the synthesis of phytol-containing melanoidins and their monitoring using pyrolysis–gas chromatography–mass spectrometry (py–gc–ms) and pyrolysis–mass spectrometry (py–ms). Also, after artificial diagenesis (heating to 220 °C or 350 °C), phytol-related skeletons in the remaining altered melanoidin, together with the bitumens produced, were analysed using Fourier transform infrared spectroscopy, (FT–IR), py–gc–ms and py–ms (polymer) and gc–ms (bitumen). The analytical scheme is outlined in Fig. 1.

The advantage of using model systems is that single lipids can be introduced under relatively controlled conditions, enabling effective study of the 'diagenesis' of individual carbon skeletons. This is more difficult with complex natural lipid systems. The advantage of analytical pyrolysis methods, over other degradative methods, is that pyrolysis techniques can provide a fast and reproducible means of characterizing complex materials (Meuzelaar and Kistemaker, 1973). These methods are not intended to supplant slower, but perhaps more fruitful, chemical degradation of the polymers, rather they should be regarded as rapid, qualitative methods.

This article provides results of model phyto-melanoidin studies, and attempts to integrate these results with data concerning the occurrence of isoprenoid moieties in natural kerogens. In particular, the relevance of these experiments to explaining the

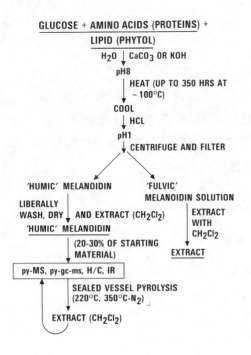

Fig. 1. Melanoidin synthesis.

dominance of the C_{14} and C_{19} isoprenoid alkenes in 'flash'* kerogen pyrolysates (Maters *et al.*, 1977; Larter *et al.*, 1979; Van de Meent *et al.*, 1980a) is discussed.

For example, Fig. 2 illustrates the differences in the pyrograms (600 °C) of a phytol-containing melanoidin (melanoidin-1, see experimental) and a typical, sapropelic kerogen, with respect to their contained acyclic isoprenoid skeletons. Thus, in contrast to the very simple isoprenoid hydrocarbon distribution in the kerogen pyrogram, the melanoidin pyrogram contains a complex mixture of C_{20} isoprenoids, together with lower homologues. It is clear that the isoprenoid moieties are bonded differently in the two materials and it is the nature, and significance, of these differences that are the subject of this paper.

EXPERIMENTAL

The general analytical scheme is outlined in Fig. 1, but further details are available elsewhere (Larter and

* This term is used to denote py–gc, py–gc–ms or py–ms analyses in which the kerogen is rapidly heated to a high temperature (e.g. 600 °C) and the pyrolysate is rapidly passed into the rest of the system.

A. PHYTOL CONTAINING MELANOIDIN

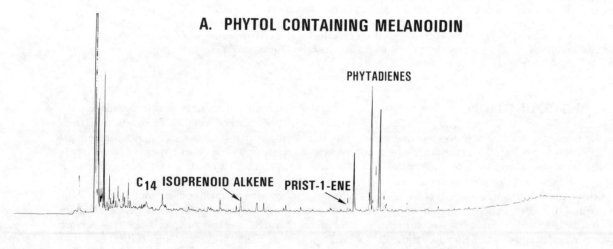

B. KEROGEN — MESSEL SHALE (EOCENE)

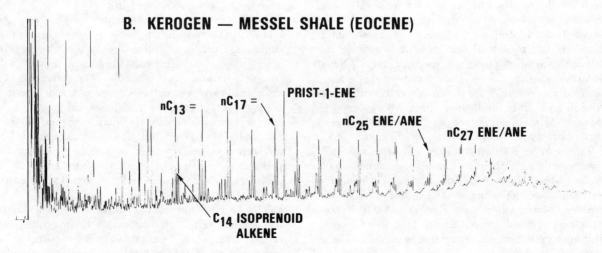

Fig. 2. Pyrograms (600 °C) of Messel kerogen and melanoidin 1. (cf Text for gas chromatographic pyrolysis conditions.)

Table 1

Melanoidin	1	2	3
Glucose[a]	12	12	12
Amino-acid mixture[a,b]	1	–	2
Casein[a]	–	2	–
Phytol[a]	1	1	1
Time (h)	100	240	240
Alkali	KOH[c]	CaCO$_3$	CaCO$_3$

a parts by weight
b Casein hydrolysate
c reaction maintained at pH8

Douglas, 1980). Three melanoidins (cf. Table 1) were synthesized in aqueous solution by boiling together glucose, a proetin or amino-acid mixture, and phytol. Solutions were maintained slightly alkaline by adding either potassium hydroxide or by boiling in the presence of excess calcium carbonate (cf. Table 1).

The reaction mixtures were cooled, acidified (pH 1, HCl), centrifuged and filtered (precipitate washed copiously with water), dried, washed and extracted (ultrasonically) with dichloromethane. The dried, acid-insoluble melanoidins, representing between 20% and 30% of the starting material, were analysed (a) for carbon, hydrogen and oxygen, (b) by py–gc–ms, py–ms and (c) by FT–IR.

Aliquots of the melanoidins (about 100 mg) were sealed, under nitrogen, in glass vials and heated at 220 °C or 350 °C for 18 h or 18 days. The vial contents were extracted (dichloromethane), and the recovered extracts fractionated using medium pressure liquid chromatography (MPLC) on silica gel columns: three fractions (aliphatic, aromatic and non-hydrocarbons) were collected. The altered melanoidins (after drying, and extraction with dichloromethane) were analysed in the same way as the untreated melanoidins (Fig. 1).

Pyrolysis experiments were conducted in two ways. Pyrolysis–gas chromatography and pyrolysis–gas chromatography–mass spectrometry were performed by pyrolysing (600 °C/1 sec) microgram quantities of extracted melanoidins using a CDS 120 Pyroprobe modified for use with capillary gc columns. The pyrolysis gases are passed through a glass-lined interface and 'split', dynamically, across the end of a fused silica (25 m × 0.2 mm I.D.) column coated with SP-2100. The flow of nitrogen (carrier gas) through the pyrolyser was maintained at 30 ml min^{-1} to minimise secondary reactions. The gc oven was programmed from 40 °C to 275 °C at 4 °C min^{-1}. Pyrolysis–gas chromatography–mass spectrometry was performed by interfacing the py–gc systems with either a VG-Micromass 12B or 7070 mass spectrometer. Gc–ms analyses of separated hydrocarbon fractions were obtained using a computer assisted Micromass 7070 instrument. Gas chromatographic conditions were similar to those used in the py–gc analyses.

Pyrolysis–mass spectrometry was performed using an apparatus similar to that described by Meuzelaar and Kistemaker (1973). Microgram quantities of the extracted melanoidins were pyrolysed (610 °C/10 sec) using a Curie-point pyrolyser: the pyrolysate was passed directly to the source of a rapid scanning quadrupole mass spectrometer. The integrated mass spectra of many scans (obtained at 11 eV) represent, dominantly, molecular ions with m/e values extending to about mass 180.

Fourier transform infrared spectra (FT–IR) of the melanoidins (KBr discs) were obtained on a Nicolet spectrometer. The melanoidin alteration experiments (artificial diagenesis) were performed at relatively low temperatures (220 °C and 350 °C) in a nitrogen atmosphere.

RESULTS AND DISCUSSION

Analytical pyrolysis of melanoidins

In an attempt to identify part structures in lipid-containing melanoidins, analytical pyrolysis techniques

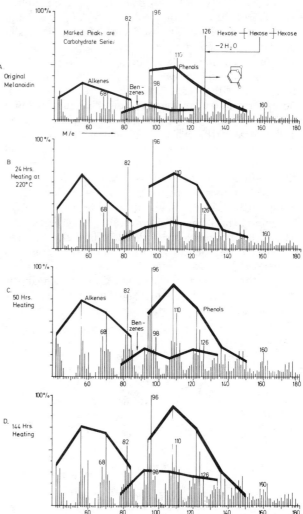

Fig. 3. Pyrolysis–mass spectra of melanoidin 1, (A) Unheated; heated (220 °C) for (B), 24 h; (C), 50 h; (D), 144 h. (cf. text for py–ms conditions).

have been employed previously (cf. Larter and Douglas, 1980). Both pyrolysis–gas chromatography and pyrolysis–mass spectrometry have been used to analyse untreated melanoidins, and also melanoidins that have been heated previously to 220 °C in a nitrogen atmosphere for periods ranging from 18 h to 18 days. A temperature of 220 °C was used for the 'artificial diagenesis' experiments since higher temperatures led to excess decomposition of the melanoidin, rather than to internal structure rearrangements.

Figure 3 shows pyrolysis mass spectra of the original and altered melanoidin. Although there are systematic changes in the spectra, with increasing heating times (24–144 h), the same compound group types are present in the original and heated materials. It has been noted previously that in the absence of corroborative py–gc–ms data, one should interpret low voltage parent peak, geopolymer py–ms data cautiously (Maters *et al.*, 1977; Larter, 1978; Van Gras *et al.*, 1980). However, in these experiments, knowledge of the starting materials allows more positive assignments to be made. Thus, for example, some authors have noted the presence of prominent ions with m/e ratios of 68, 82, 96, 98, 110, 126, in the pyrolysis–mass spectra of carbohydrates (Posthumus *et al.*, 1974; Meuzelaar *et al.*, 1977; Schulten and Gortz, 1978; Van de Meent *et al.*, 1980 and references therein). This series of abundant masses indicative of furan, furfural and furfuryl alcohol structures in the melanoidin spectra is considered evidence for the presence of intact carbohydrate fragments in these materials. The peak at m/e 126 is noteworthy in that an abundant ion at this mass is found in the pyrolysis–mass spectra of hexose sugars (Schulten and Gortz, 1978). This component is believed to be levoglucosenone, obtained by dehydration of levoglucosan, the monomer initially produced during the pyrolysis of hexose polysaccharides (Shafizadeh and Fu, 1973). Other compound groups similarly identified, and present in significant quantity in the spectra (Fig. 3), include phenols (ions with m/e values of 94, 108, 122, 136, 150), benzenes (m/e 78, 92, 106, 120, 134) and alkenes (m/e 42, 56, 70, 84): the last class was confirmed in parallel *py–gc–ms* studies (Larter, 1978).

All of the compound classes noted are present in the spectra shown in Fig. 3 which indicate that the relative abundance of each group changes with the severity of

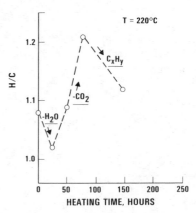

Fig. 5. Elemental analysis of melanoidin 1 heated in nitrogen.

artificial diagenesis. Thus, with increasing heating times each sample residue shows, on analysis by py–ms, a relatively greater proportion of alkenes and lower proportions of carbohydrate-related peaks. These changes are more clearly illustrated in Fig. 4 in which the fractional percentage of the ion current, recorded for each mass group over the mass range m/e 40–180 are plotted against heating time. This shows that the greatest changes in the abundance of different chemical types occurs in the initial heating periods. Accompanying the inversely-related changes in carbohydrate and alkene abundance, a general increase is observed for the benzenes after passing through a maximum (24 h): with increased heating the phenol content rises (24 h) and then falls to near initial values.

Figure 5 shows H/C atomic ratios for the original and heated melanoidin plotted as a function of heating time. From an initial value of 1.08 the H/C ratio drops, and then rises to a maximum of 1.21 before decreasing again. Since water and carbon dioxide are decomposition products of mildly-heated melanoidins (Larter, 1978) the initial drop in the H/C ratio is interpreted as water loss, the rise in the H/C ratio, with continued heating, suggests that reactions involving CO_2 loss now dominate. The final decrease in the H/C ratio is probably due to the loss of saturated hydrocarbon and alkyl-substituted molecules such as are found in the extractable bitumens (see later). These reactions may proceed concurrently so that changes in the H/C ratios reflect kinetic differences; that is, one or other reaction will control the changes in melanoidin chemistry at a different degree of artificial maturation.

The presence of carbohydrate-derived fragments is not surprising in view of the materials used to prepare the melanoidins, but they do suggest that intact carbohydrate molecules are present in the polymer. The decrease in carbohydrate abundance, with increased heating times, is not unexpected but their exact fate is at present unknown. The origin of the substituted benzenes and phenols in the pyrolysates can best be attributed to derivation from aromatic amino acids such as phenylalanine and tyrosine. The lipid components of the melanoidin, as represented by the alkenes in the py–ms (Fig. 3) may have a double origin, representing both the aliphatic chains of incorporated amino acids (cf. Ioselis *et al.*, 1981) with an additional minor component

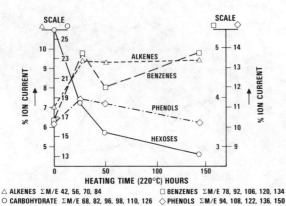

Fig. 4. Pyrolysis–mass spectra: data for compound types from heated melanoidin 1 (cf. text for py–ms data).

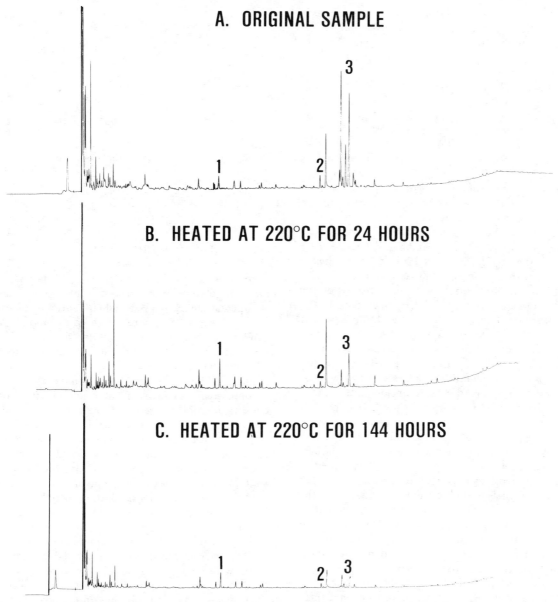

Fig. 6. Pyrolysis (600 °C) of unheated and heated (220 °C) melanoidin 1 (cf. text for pyrolysis and gas chromatographic conditions). Peak identifications: 1. C_{14} isoprenoid alkene; 2. prist-1-ene; 3. phytadienes.

resulting from pyrolytic fragmentation of the incorporated phytol.

The apparent relative increase in alkenes with increased artificial diagenesis might simply reflect a concentration effect, that is, loss of water and carbon dioxide during diagenesis must result in an increased relative content of other material. In the absence of data providing quantitative yields during pyrolysis (610 °C) it is generally unwise to place too much significance on apparent changes in the composition of pyrolysates. However, in this study, supportive H/C values (Fig. 5) do suggest that the py–ms data is providing a qualitatively valid picture of the changes that occur as the melanoidin is heated for increasing periods at 220 °C.

Since py–ms provided information restricted to the lower molecular weight products, py–gc was also used in these analyses. Using this method, the pyrograms shown in Fig. 6 were obtained; firstly from an unheated melanoidin, and then after heating for 24 h and 144 h at

220 °C respectively. These pyrograms show that much of the pyrolysate is of low molecular weight, as discussed above, but also that py–gc analyses are suited to the determination of higher molecular weight compounds. It is worth noting that while py–ms and py–gc analyses are carried out under different conditions there is data which suggests that the two techniques provide complementary, and parallel results (Maters *et al.*, 1977; Van de Meent *et al.*, 1980a; Van Gras *et al.*, 1980).

As noted earlier, pyrolysis of kerogens at elevated temperatures generally produces the one major isoprenoid component, prist-1-ene, with frequently a C_{14} isoprenoid alkene also present (Larter *et al.*, 1979; Van de Meent *et al.*, 1980a). In contrast, in phytol-containing melanoidin pyrograms, prist-1-ene is a minor component (Figs. 2 and 6). The major peaks in these pyrograms have been identified as phytadienes and pristenes; other isoprenoid olefins occur as minor components of the higher molecular weight fraction.

This complex distribution of isoprenoid hydrocarbons is not unlike that in recent kerogen (Philp *et al.*, 1978), chlorophyll, fluvial and recent lake sediment (Van de Meent *et al.*, 1980b) pyrolyses. The retention indices, and fingerprint, of the phytadienes produced during the py–gc of chlorophyll (Van de Meent *et al.*, 1980b) are very similar to those produced during melanoidin pyrolysis. This suggests that the bulk of the phytol in the melanoidin is present as phytenyl esters, since ester-bound alcohols undergo dehydration on pyrolysis to yield the corresponding unsaturated hydrocarbons (Levy and Paul, 1968; Larter, 1978; Van de Meent *et al.*, 1980b). The absence of a parent phytol peak in Figs. 2 and 6 confirms that free phytol is not present in the melanoidin (Larter and Douglas, 1980).

With increased heating times, the relative proportions of pristenes and phytadienes (2 and 3 in Fig. 6) decrease relative to the C_{14} alkene (peak 1). Data shown below indicate that this reduction of phytadienes in the more matured melanoidin pyrograms is accompanied by the production of free C_{20} isoprenoid hydrocarbons in the soluble reaction products, consistent with the view that cleavage of ester-bound phytol is occurring during heating. The relative increase in the abundance of the C_{14} isoprenoid alkene in the heated melanoidin pyrograms (Fig. 6) tentatively suggests that isoprenoid structures are also bound into the melanoidin by non-ester bonds: this view is discussed below. The important observation is that prist-1-ene is not a major peak in matured melanoidin pyrograms, indicating that this model system is not accurately duplicating natural isoprenoid diagenesis. Previous results, with melanoidin-bound saturated alcohols, tentatively suggests that artificial diagenesis of such systems could result in the formation of non-ester-bound alkyl groups, although no mechanisms were detailed (Larter and Douglas, 1980). This observation led to attempts to detect such a transformation with melanoidin-bound phytol but, as indicated above, no rearrangement to a prist-1-ene precursor has occurred during the artificial maturation of the melanoidin. It is now necessary to extend these experiments to include known, saturated, products of phytol diagenesis such as dihydrophytol, phytanic acid, etc. (de Leeuw *et al.*, 1974; Brooks and Maxwell, 1974). Results of such studies will be reported elsewhere.

Analysis of 'bitumens' extracted from artificially-matured melanoidins

Table 2 gives quantitative data for the soluble 'bitumen' and insoluble residue obtained when melanoidins 2 and 3 were each heated at 220 °C and 350 °C for 18 days and 18 h respectively.

The extractable bitumen from each experiment was separated into aliphatic, aromatic and non-hydrocarbon fractions. The volatile material produced (40% of starting material), included water, carbon dioxide and highly odiferous compounds which were not characterized.

Fourier transform infrared spectra (FT–IR) of the unheated melanoidins were characterized by amide (1640–1650 cm^{-1} and 1515 cm^{-1}), acid carbonyl (1710

Table 2

	Extractable[a] bitumens %	Aliphatic fraction ppm	Aromatic fraction ppm	H/C ratio of residue
Melanoidin 2[b]	4.4	433	263	1.21
	(6.8)	(2500)	(2000)	(0.98)
Melanoidin 3[b]	2.6	9233	2000	1.09
	(4.5)	(10200)	(8400)	(0.78)

Products obtained by heating protein-based melanoidin 2 and amino acid based melanoidin 3 at 220 °C for 18 days (350 °C for 18 h)
a Bitumens extracted with dichloromethane.
b H/C ratios of unheated melanoidins 2 and 3 were 1.50 and 1.35 respectively.
NB. All yields are related to the weight of starting materials.

cm^{-1}), carbohydrate CHO (1080 cm^{-1}) and C–H bands (Stephenson and Goh, 1971). On heating to 350 °C, weak absorption bands only were obtained, in a generally featureless spectrum; at this temperature the residues had markedly reduced H/C ratios (cf. Table 1). Whilst the spectra of both unheated melanoidins were similar, the protein-based melanoidin 2 had more intense amide bands than the amino acid melanoidin 3, whereas the latter had more intense carbohydrate bands. The weaker functional-group bands accompanying increased artificial maturation is consistent with the observed decrease in the solubility in alkali of heated melanoidins (Larter and Douglas, 1980). Whilst the composition of the hydrocarbons produced by heating the two melanoidins were qualitatively similar, the yields from the amino acid containing melanoidin were significantly greater. This, together with more intense (acid) carbonyl bands in the infrared spectrum of melanoidin 3 (as opposed to melanoidin 2) suggests that lipid-binding by a melanoidin is favoured when amino acids are present, since residual carboxyl groups are available to form ester bonds with the phytol. Undoubtedly some hydrolysis of the protein occurs during melanoidin synthesis, but the data suggests that lipid-binding sites are reduced. Since melanoidins 2 and 3 provided similar hydrocarbon data, representative examples only are given.

Chromatograms of the aliphatic hydrocarbon fractions obtained during the diagenesis of melanoidin 2 are shown in Fig. 7. Gc–ms data indicates that the major peaks in the chromatograms are isoprenoid alkenes and alkanes. At 200 °C phytenes are dominant, but at 350 °C phytenes, though still major components, are accompanied by shorter chain-length isoprenoid hydrocarbons: these are possibly secondary degradation products of C_{20} isoprenoid fragments. Comparison of the two chromatograms in Fig. 7 shows that the distribution of the C_{20} isoprenoid alkenes are qualitatively similar at both temperatures. The dominance of phytenes in these sealed vessel pyrolyses, as opposed to the dominance of phytadienes in the flash (600 °C) pyrograms (Fig. 2) merely reflects the different pyrolysis temperatures: that is, it is commonly observed that lower pyrolysis temperatures gives more saturated products. This may be related to the relative temperature dependence of the kinetics of hydrogen abstraction versus radical decomposition reactions during thermal decomposition of polymers. The

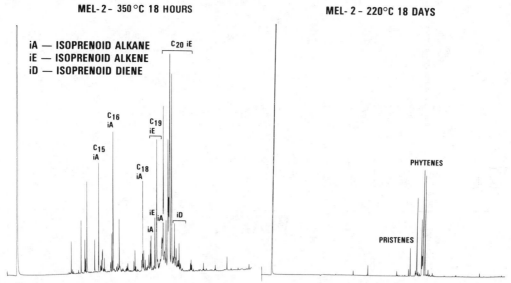

Fig. 7. Aliphatic hydrocarbons obtained by the artificial maturation of melanoidin 2 at 220 °C and 350 °C (cf. text for gas chromatographic conditions).

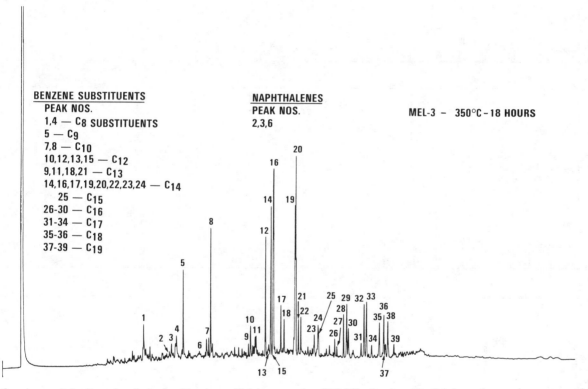

Fig. 8. Aromatic hydrocarbond obtained by the artificial maturation (350 °C) of melanoidin 3 (cf. text for gas chromatographic conditions).

reduction in the abundance of phytadienes in the matured melanoidin pyrograms (Fig. 6), and the production of phytenes in the sealed vessel bitumens, is consistent with the view that ester-bound phytol is being cleaved from the melanoidins during artificial diagenesis.

An aromatic hydrocarbon fraction was also obtained when the melanoidins were heated (350 °C 18 h^{-1}) as indicated by gc–ms data. This showed that while small amounts of diaromatic molecules were present, the major components of the fraction had base peaks, and

molecular ions, consistent with those of alkylbenzenes. The carbon numbers of the alkyl substituents are indicated in Fig. 8 (cf also Fig. 10). Since the gc fingerprints of the aromatic fractions from melanoidins 2 and 3 were very similar, the following discussion encompasses both.

The mass spectra (70e V) of some of the gc peaks of Fig. 8 are illustrated in Fig. 9. Many of the fragment ions in these spectra are due to alkylbenzenes (e.g. m/e 91, 105, 119, 133) and the abundance of certain fragments (e.g. m/e 147, 161, 175, 189 etc.) in many of the spectra

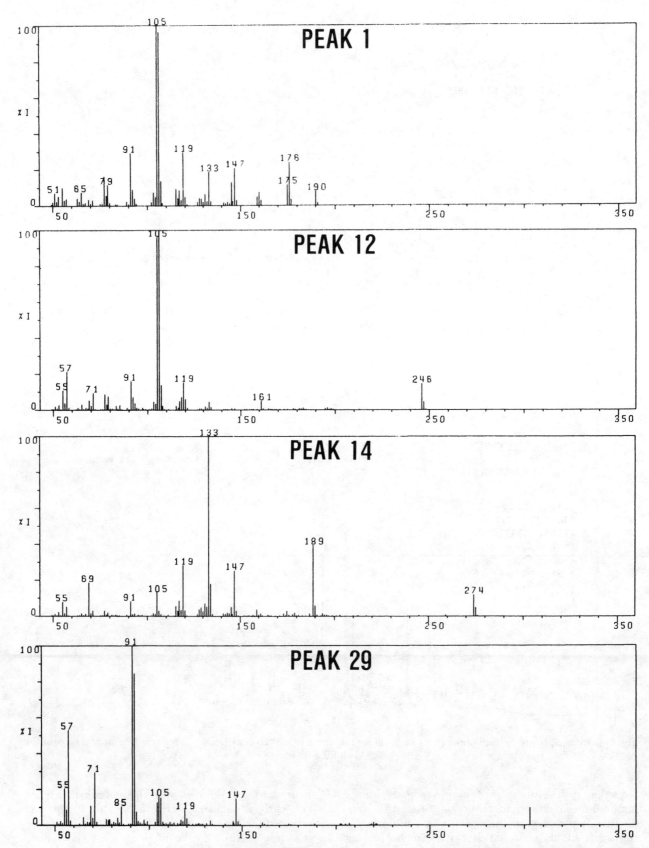

Fig. 9. Mass spectra of some aromatic hydrocarbons obtained during the artificial maturation (350 °C) of melanoidin 3. (Peak numbers refer to peaks in Fig. 8.)

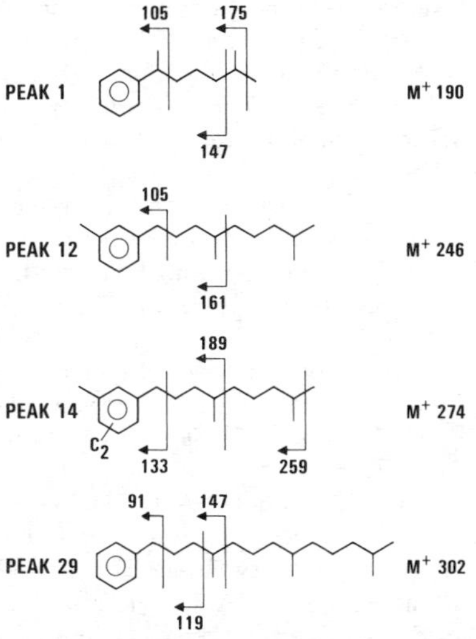

Fig. 10. Possible structures of aromatic hydrocarbons obtained by artificial maturation of melanoidin 3. (Peak numbers refer to those in Figs 8 and 9.)

suggests branched-chain alkyl substituents ranging from C_8 to C_{19}. These data suggest that the most abundant aromatic hydrocarbons formed during the thermal maturation of these melanoidins are branched chain alkylbenzenes. In the absence of standard compounds, it is impossible to establish unequivocally the identify of these compounds. However, since phytol was used in the formation of these melanoidins, it is not unreasonable to assume that the branched alkyl chains are isoprenoid: the suggested structures illustrated in Fig. 10 are compatible with the mass spectral data.

Alkylbenzenes containing two isoprenoid substituents have been reported in organic extracts of DSDP cores and from the low-temperature artificial diagenesis of phytol (de Leeuw *et al.*, 1977). These authors proposed that phytol reacts via a carbonium ion, to give phytadienes which, in turn, react via a Diels/Alder route to give cyclic molecules which may aromatize. Similar mechanisms are proposed to be involved in the production of melanoidin-bound isoprenoid substituted alkylbenzenes. Acid-catalysed carbonium ion and phytadiene formation from phytol may be followed by Diels/Alder reaction with unsaturated positions in the melanoidin, or its precursors. This suggestion is supported by the fact that unsaturated intermediates are reported to be important precursors to the pigmented melanoidins (McWeeny *et al.*, 1974). Ring aromatization during diagenesis, and β-cleavage of side chains on either side of the ring could produce both alkylbenzenes and shorter chain length ($< C_{20}$) aliphatic isoprenoid hydrocarbons: both of these are present in the bitumen extracts of the matured melanoidins. The possibility that phytol-derived isoprenoid structures can be incorporated into a melanoidin, other than via an ester bond, may explain the observed relative increase of the C_{14} isoprenoid alkene in the pyrograms of progressively heated melanoidins (Fig. 6). Isoprenoids bound into a polymer by strong C–C bonds are most likely to fragment (during thermolysis) by cleavage of the bond β to a methyl substituted carbon since the tertiary hydrogen atom is labile and easily abstracted

(Dougherty, 1974). Thus, for isoprenoid moieties bonded to a melanoidin by an aromatic (or other) ring, the most abundant high molecular weight isoprenoid in the pyrogram would be expected to be a C_{14} alkene. One might argue that the C_{14} and C_{19} isoprenoid alkenes have different origins, since their ratio in many kerogen pyrograms (Larter, unpublished) varies widely; that is, the C_{14} alkene is not, in general, a simple cracking product of longer chain isoprenoids. The factors controlling the relative abundance of these two compounds in kerogen pyrolysates are not understood at this time. Source control may be important in this respect in that the C_{14} alkene may sometimes represent an analogue of prist-1-ene, derived through similar routes from farnesyl as opposed to phytyl structures in the source organic matter.

The above discussion can be summarized by saying that experimental data suggests that phytol can be incorporated into melanoidins by at least two routes namely, as ester-bound phytyl (phytenyl) groups and as cyclic (including benzene) structures. A number of systems have been proposed for the bonding of isoprenoids in kerogens. Van de Meent *et al.* (1980b) have suggested that ester-bound phytanic acid moieties are responsible for the dominance of prist-1-ene in kerogen pyrograms. The ubiquity of pristene in ancient kerogen pyrolysates, including those that have been saponified, argues against dominantly ester bonding. This view is supported by the fact that prist-1-ene occurs in the pyrograms of kerogens whose rank is equivalent to 1.1% vitrinite reflectance, or more. The present study indicates that ester-bound phytenyl (phytyl) structures are probably unimportant in most ancient kerogens, although Van de Meent *et al.* (1980b) maintain that chlorophyll-bound (phytyl) esters are significant components of young kerogens.

Van der Berg *et al.* (1974) suggested, from ozonolysis studies, that olefinic isoprenoids were bound to kerogen via carbon/carbon bonds. Chappe *et al.* (1980) have suggested that ether bond isoprenoids, derived from archaebacteria, are significant components of some kerogens (e.g. Messel shale kerogen). The dominance of prist-1-ene and the C_{14} isoprenoid alkene in kerogen pyrolysates is consistent with their being bound into the polymer by strong C–C or C–O bonds in which the favoured decomposition route is controlled, as described earlier, by the facile removal of hydrogen atoms from tertiary positions in the isoprenoid chain. Fig. 11 shows how a C–C bound C_{20} isoprenoid might provide pristene. A radical mechanism (abstraction of a tertiary

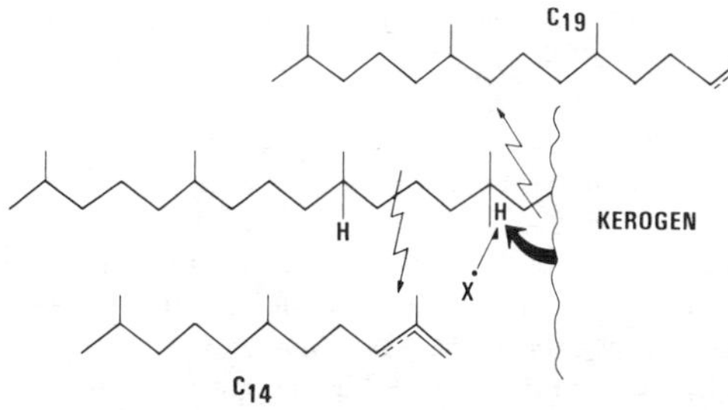

Fig. 11. A possible mechanism for the origin of the C_{14} and C_{19} isoprenoid alkenes commonly found in kerogen pyrograms.

hydrogen atom by radical X· followed by homolytic rupture of the C–C bond) is less favoured when a facile rearrangement at the tertiary-substituted carbon is possible (abstraction of H by a functional group on the kerogen, as shown by the heavy arrow).

It is not possible to identify the type of bonding unequivocally from the pyrolysis data alone, but strong C–C or C–O bonds are probable. The mechanism by which these bonds are formed from precursors is unknown at present, but model melanoidin experiments, as described here, may help to clarify the issue.

CONCLUSIONS

1. Phytol is incorporated into melanoidins both by the formation of phytyl (phytenyl) esters and also by the formation of six membered carbocyclic (including benzene) groups.
2. Artificial diagenesis of phytol-containing melanoidins results in the loss of functional groups and in the production of soluble aliphatic and aromatic hydrocarbons. Reactions of this type may be important in the early release of hydrocarbons and other biomarkers in Recent sediments.
3. Comparison of isoprenoid hydrocarbon distributions in melanoidin and kerogen pyrolysates suggests that (a) phytenyl esters are not important structures in most ancient kerogens, but may be so in some recent polycondensates and (b) strong kerogen-isoprenoid bonds (e.g. C–C, C–O) are consistent with the dominant presence of prist-1-ene in kerogen pyrograms.
4. The combination of melanoidin synthesis and pyrolysis techniques provides a facile, and rapid, method of investigating the uptake of lipids in protokerogen studies.

The present study suggests that phytol itself is not the direct source of isoprenoids derived from kerogens. Other phytol-derived molecules, such as dihydrophytol and phytanic acid are being investigated as alternative precursors. This type of study may prove of value in interpreting early diagenetic changes in cyclic and acyclic biomarker skeleton pools.

Acknowledgements

Greg Ovellette assisted with the melanoidin synthesis experiments.

REFERENCES

Brooks, P. W. and Maxwell, J. R. (1974) Early stage fate of phytol in recently deposited lacustrine sediments. In *Advances in Organic Geochemistry* 1973. Ed. by Tissot, B. and Bienner, F. Editions Technip, Paris. pp. 977–991.

Bracewell, J. M., Robertson, G. W. and Welch, D. I. (1980) Polycarboxylic acids as the origin of some pyrolysis products characteristic of soil organic matter. *J. Anal. Appl. Pyrolysis* **2**, 239–248.

Chappe, B., Michaelis, W. and Albrecht, P. (1980) Molecular fossils of archaebacteria as selective degradation products of kerogen. In *Advances in Organic Geochemistry* 1979. Ed. by Douglas, A. G. and Maxwell, J. R. Pergamon, London, pp. 265–274.

Douglas, A. G., Coates, R. C., Bowler, B. F. and Hall, K.

(1977) Alkanes from the pyrolysis of Recent sediments. In *Advances in Organic Geochemistry* 1975. Ed. by Campos, R. and Goni, J. Enadimsa, Madrid. pp. 357–374.

Dougherty, R. C. (1974) The relationship between mass spectrometric, thermolytic and photolytic reactivity. *Topics in Current Chem.* **45**, 93–138.

Hedges, J. I. (1978) The formation and clay mineral reactions of melanoidins. *Geochim. et Cosmochim. Acta* **42**, 69–72.

Hoering, T. C. (1973) A comparison of melanoidin and humic acid. *Carnegie Inst. Washington Yearb.* **72**, 682–690.

Ioselis, P., Rubinstein, Y., Ikan, R. and Peters, K. E. Pyrolysis of natural and synthetic humic substances. In *Advances in Organic Geochemistry* 1981. Ed. by Bjorøy, M. This volume.

Larter, S. R. (1978) Ph.D. Thesis, University of Newcastle upon Tyne, UK.

Larter, S. R., Solli, H., Douglas, A. G., DeLange, F. and De Leeuw, J. W. (1979) Occurrence and significance of prist-1-ene in kerogen pyrolysates. *Nature* **279**, 405–408.

Larter, S. R. and Douglas, A. G. (1980) Melanoidins — kerogen precursors and geochemical lipid sinks; a study using pyrolysis–gas chromatography (PGC). *Geochim. et Cosmochim. Acta* **44**, 2087–2095.

De Leeuw, J. W., Correia, V. A. and Schenck, P. A. (1974) On the decomposition of phytol under simulated geological conditions and in the top layer of natural sediments. In *Advances in Organic Geochemistry*, 1973. Ed. by Tissot, B. and Bienner, F. Editions Technip, Paris. pp. 993–1004.

De Leeuw, J. W., Simoneit, B. R., Boon, J. J., Rijpstra, W. I. C., De Lange, F., Van de Leeden, J. C. W., Correia, V. A., Burlingame, A. L. and Schenck, P. A. (1977) Phytol derived compounds in geosphere. In *Advances in Organic Geochemistry* 1975. Ed. by Campos, R. and Goni, J. Enadimsa, Madrid. pp. 61–79.

Maillard, L. C. (1912) Action des acides amines sur les sucres; formation des melanoidines par votre méthodiques. *C.R. Acad. Aci.* **154**, 66–68.

Maters, W. L., Van de Meent, P., Schuyl, P. J. W., De Leeuw, J. W. and Schenck, P. A. (1977) Curie point pyrolysis in organic geochemistry. In *Analytical pyrolysis*. Ed. by Jones, C. E. R. and Cramers, C. A. Elsevier, Amsterdam. pp. 203–216.

McWeeny, P. J., Knowles, M. E. and Hearne, J. F. (1974) The chemistry of non-enzymic browning in foods and its control by sulphites. *J. Sci. Food. Agric.* **25**, 735–746.

Meuzelaar, H. L. C., Haider, K., Nagar, B. R. and Martins, J. P. (1977) Comparative studies of pyrolysis–mass spectra of melanins, model phenolic polymers and humic acids. *Geoderma* **17**, 239–252.

Meuzelaar, H. L. C. and Kistemaker, P. G. (1973) A technique for fast and reproducible fingerprints of bacteria by pyrolysis–mass spectrometry. *Anal. Chem.* **45**, 587–590.

Philp, R. P., Calvin, M., Brown, S. and Young, E. (1978) Organic geochemical kerogen precursors in recently-deposited algal mats and oozes. *Chem. Geol.* **22**, 207–231.

Posthumus, M. A., Nibbering, N. N. M., Boerboom, A. J. H. and Schulten, H. R. (1974) Pyrolysis mass spectrometric studies of nucleic acids. *Biomed. Mass Spectrom.* **1**, 352–357.

Schulten, H. R. and Gortz, W. (1978) Curie point pyrolysis and field ionisation mass spectrometry of polysaccharides. *Anal. Chem.* **50**, 428–433.

Shafizadeh, F. and Fu, Y. L. (1973) Pyrolysis of cellulose. *Carb. Res.* **29**, 113–122.

Stevenson, F. J. and Goh, K. M. (1971) Infrared spectra of humic acids and related substances. *Geochim. et Cosmochim. Acta* **35**, 471–483.

Van der Berg, M. L. J., Mulder, G. J., De Leeuw, J. W. and Schenck, P. A. (1977) Investigations into the structure of kerogen — 1. Low temperature ozonolysis of Messel shale kerogen. *Geochim. et Cosmochim. Acta* **41**, 903–908.

Van Graas, G., De Leeuw, J. W. and Schenck, P. A. (1980) Analysis of coals of different rank by Curie point pyrolysis–mass spectrometry and Curie point pyrolysis–gas chromatography–mass spectrometry. In *Advances in Organic Geochemistry* 1979. Ed. by Douglas, A. G. and Maxwell, J. R. Pergamon, London. pp. 485–494.

Van de Meent, D., Brown, S. C., Philp, R. P. and Simoneit, B. R. T. (1980a) Pyrolysis high resolution gas chromatography and pyrolysis–gas chromatography–mass spectrometry of kerogens and kerogen precursors. *Geochim. et Cosmochim. Acta* **44**, 999–1013.

Van de Meent, D., De Leeuw, J. W. and Schenck, P. A. (1980b) Origin of unsaturated isoprenoid hydrocarbons in pyrolysates of suspended matter and surface sediments. In *Advances in Organic Geochemistry* 1979. Ed. by Douglas, A. G. and Maxwell, J. R. Pergamon, London. pp. 469–474.

Advances in Organic Geochemistry 1981, pp. 524–533
© *John Wiley & Sons Limited, 1983*

A Laboratory Study of Petroleum Generation by Hydrouspyrolysis

J. C. Winters, J. A. Williams and M. D. Lewan

Amoco Production Company Research Center, PO Box 591, Tulsa, Oklahoma 74102, USA

There have been many attempts to reproduce the natural generation of petroleum in the laboratory. However, because the low temperature natural transformation of kerogen into petroleum requires geologic time, it is impossible to use the natural time–temperature relationships for laboratory experiments. Fortunately, the rate of transformation approximately doubles for every 10 °C increase in temperature. For example, if the temperature is increased from 160 °C to 250 °C, the transformation will occur more than 1000 times faster. This makes real-time experiments possible. Prior to our publication of the hydrouspyrolysis procedure in 1979, published accelerated-rate experiments yielded a product consisting mostly of compounds not normally found in natural petroleum. Thus there has been some question about the validity of other conclusions drawn from these experiments. In contrast, the hydrouspyrolysis laboratory procedure replicates generation of crude oil, giving a product that closely resembles produced petroleum from a source rock of the same type and geologic age. As a result, we can now conduct detailed laboratory studies of petroleum generation which provide accurate incremental relationships of time, temperature, composition and yield. Thus, it is now possible to closely define the characteristics of a genuine immature, mature, or super-mature oil. By additional experimental procedures, mature oil in various stages of bacterial degradation can be produced for comparison with reservoired oils. This offers the opportunity to obtain a bottle of an oil before that oil is discovered by the drill, or perhaps even before nature has provided the conditions necessary for generation and expulsion of the oil from its source rock. Characteristics of immature, mature, and super-mature oils generated by hydouspyrolysis in the laboratory from Woodford (Devonian), Phosphoria (Permian) and Kimmeridge (Jurassic) source rocks are compared with their natural counterparts. In addition, a bacterially degraded mature oil is compared with an immature oil of the same genetic type. Similarities and dissimilarities between generated oils and the natural product at various stages of maturation are discussed.

INTRODUCTION

Ever since petroleum was observed seeping from the ground, man has speculated about the origin of this organic liquid and about the process that converted it into the liquid state. Theories about such topics reoccur in surprisingly similar form and in nearly predictable cycles. When inorganic theories seemed to fall short, organic origins of petroleum were offered.

Spielmann (1923) summarized the earlier theories very nicely when he said, 'In studying the subject it is sometimes almost pathetic to see so much application of effort and time to the working out of ideas which would at once have been modified or abandoned if their 'onlie begetters' had taken a wider view of what has to be accounted for. The effect of such mental blinkers will be seen almost at once in the summary of the positions of older ideas, and it is to be recognized down to the present moment'.

In more recent times, leaders in organic geochemistry such as Silverman (e.g. Silverman and Epstein, 1958), Hunt (e.g. Forsman and Hunt, 1958; Hunt, 1965) and Biederman (e.g. Biederman, 1965), using data published by Martin and coworkers (1963), have based sound theories on scientifically measured data. Then,

Philippi (1965) presented his landmark paper, consolidating the effects of time and temperature on transformation of organic matter in the earth. Outstanding publications of Durand and coworkers in France (e.g. Tissot *et al.*, 1974; Durand and Espitalié, 1972), Welte (1972) in Germany, Vassoevich and coworkers (1970), and Lopatin (1976) in Russia have clearly demonstrated the quality of the conclusions, the field work and the experimental work relating the thermochemical transformation of organic matter in source rocks to petroleum.

In the last two decades there have been many examples of good pyrolysis experiments, that — to varying degrees — tried to simulate the generation of petroleum from source rock (Bandurski, 1982; Douglas *et al.*, 1966; Eisma and Jurg, 1969; Khare *et al.*, 1978; Leventhal, 1976). However, all of these pyrolysis experiments either produced a product containing a majority of compounds rarely found in petroleum or used conditions that are never found in nature.

Then, in June 1977, while trying to experimentally reproduce most of the environmental conditions present during natural generation of petroleum, we produced an oil whose properties closely matched the crude oil produced naturally by a source rock of the same geologic

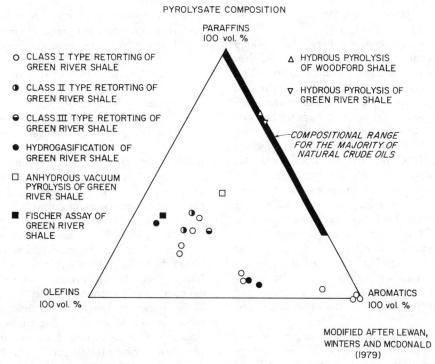

Fig. 1. Composition of pyrolysates from Green River shale and Woodford shale, using various pyrolysis and retorting methods, compared with composition of products from hydrouspyrolysis. Composition of natural crude oils is indicated along upper right side of the diagram.

age and type (Lewan *et al.*, 1979). It is impossible to reproduce exactly the natural environment of generation. However, we came so close that we felt we had direct experimental proof that petroleum is generated from kerogen, and that we could now quantitatively measure the effects of kerogen composition, time, and temperature on the generation of petroleum under controlled conditions in real time. Figure 1 shows the composition of pyrolysates generated by different pyrolysis and retorting methods, along with a band of compositions for natural crude oils. The composition of

products from hydrouspyrolysis coincides with the natural petroleum, having no detectable olefins and generally less aromatics than those from other methods.

A report of this, along with data, was submitted to *Science* in June 1978; it was published in March 1979 (Lewan *et al.*, 1979). The technique that we named hydrouspyrolysis was apparently noticed by only a few research people. The symposium-organizing committee requested that we give the hydrouspyrolysis technique more exposure.

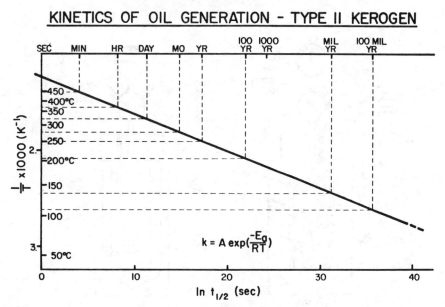

Fig. 2. Relationship between temperature and reaction rate for Type II kerogen. Rate approximately doubles for each 10 °C increase in temperature.

Hydrouspyrolysis

Effects of time and temperature   It has long been known that the rate of reaction increases dramatically with an increase in temperature. This relationship was expressed quantitatively by Arrhenius. Figure 2 shows the approximate relationship between the temperature and reaction rate of Type II kerogen (Tissot *et al.*, 1974) at millions of years, one year, one month, one day, etc. The rate of reaction approximately doubles for every 10 °C increase in temperature. This implies that we should be able to observe the same amount of reaction taking place in one month at 275 °C that would take 100 million years at 110 °C. Of course, no one knows whether this is rigorously correct; we do not have a way of conducting a hundred million year experiment. However, we can try to come as close to natural conditions as possible in the laboratory, except for exchanging temperature for time, and check the results against those that occurred in nature over geologic time to see if we are close to the same end result.

Basic conditions   When trying to reproduce experimentally the environment under which nature generates petroleum, we must immediately begin to compromise. There are many more differences than similarities. The following is a list of variables that we cannot reasonably reproduce.
1. Time.
2. Relative rates of reaction at low temperatures.
3. Relationship between diffusion and reaction rates.
4. Ratio between vertical and horizontal pressures.
5. Ratio of surface to volume.
6. Time reactants held in intimate contact with kerogen.
7. Secondary migration effects.
8. Low temperature adsorption effects.
9. Reaction of products with exogenous rock.
10. Solubility of organics in water.

There are conditions that we can reasonably approach.
1. Interchange of temperature for time.
2. Pressure to maintain most components as liquids.
3. Energy to complete all reaction stages.
4. Liquid water in intimate contact with organic phase.
5. Expulsion from shale.

This list might easily discourage one from attempting to mimic the natural generation environment. On the other hand, the alternative of dry pyrolysis in either a flowing inert gas or a vacuum could not be further from the natural conditions. We had the advantage of previous Amoco work (McCollum and Quick, 1976) on reactions between organic compounds and supercritical water that gave us some ideas about which of the variables might be the more important.

After looking at many experimental variables, we found that maintaining liquid water in the presence of both reactants and products overwhelms all other deficiencies in environmental replication. The presence of liquid water provides the most important of all environmental variables that allows reactions very similar to those occurring during natural generation of petroleum. Some other variables play a measurable but decidedly secondary role in obtaining the desired results. It seems hard to imagine why liquid water was not previously considered a primary requirement, except for the misguided thought that water is completely inactive. Whatever the reason, we have now identified most of the basic requirements for producing useful data for the study of petroleum generation.

EXPERIMENTAL

The hydrouspyrolysis apparatus can be simple. The only complexities are those dictated by strict observance of good safety practice when working with high pressure

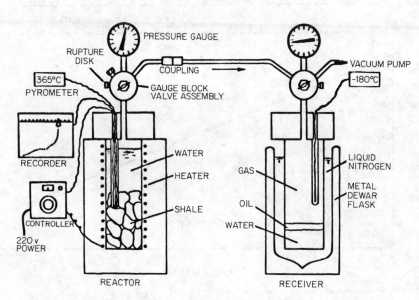

Fig. 3.   Diagram of apparatus used in hydrouspyrolysis experiments.

reactions. Figure 3 is a schematic of one apparatus configuration. In a simple form, only the reactor shown on the left-hand side would be used. The reactors are commercially available high pressure vessels, constructed of 316 stainless steel, with a 1000 cc volume. They may be heated by electrical coils, or alternatively by a fluidized sand bath if closer temperature control is needed.

Hydrouspyrolysis experiments can be done in reactors of almost any size. For these studies we chose the 1000 cc size because it has the lowest practical surface area to volume ratio and it holds enough shale and water to produce the oil and gas needed for all analyses as well as to provide data for a good weight balance.

In a typical experiment, 400 g of broken pieces or sawed cubes of shale are weighed and placed in the reactor. Distilled water is added to cover the shale. An accurate calculation must be made of the amount of water that will leave a minimum of vapor space after expansion at reaction temperature and yet contract to a level above the shale when the reactor is cooled. High-salinity water has been used but negligible effects on the results were observed. Distilled water is used for most experiments to reduce the serious corrosive effects of chloride ions on the stainless steel. If there is any uncertainty about expansion of the reactor contents, the reactor should be underfilled until experimental data on expansion are obtained. In many cases, a line will remain on the inside reactor wall, after shutdown, showing the maximum expansion level. Overfilling will result in either an unpleasant failure of pressure release devices or catastrophic failure of the pressure vessel.

The reactor is pressured several times with an inert gas to eliminate all molecular oxygen. After the final time, pressure is held at 2000 psi to test for leaks. If the reactor does not leak, the pressure is reduced to atmospheric. Helium is preferred for this test because it leaks more readily than most of the product gases, it can easily be detected and removed, but it does not seriously interfere with gas analysis if some remains in the reactor.

The temperature and time selected for an experiment will vary with the present maturity of the kerogen in the source rock and with the objectives of the experiment. Most experiments are likely to fall within 290–360 °C, 3000–5000 psi (20 000–35 000 kPa) and one to five days. Pure water has a supercritical temperature of about 374 °C; supercritical conditions for mixtures of water, oil,

gas, and dissolved inorganics cannot be predicted. If artifacts due to change of phase are to be avoided, operating temperatures below 360 °C are preferred.

Many modes of operation are possible. The choice will depend upon objectives of the experiment and the amount of equipment available. The simplest mode would use only the single pressure vessel shown on the left-hand side of Fig. 3. The vessel contents are heated to the desired temperature for the prescribed time and then cooled to ambient temperature. The pressure and temperature are recorded, and a gas sample is taken for analysis; the remaining gas is vented. When the reactor is opened, there should be a layer of oil on top of the water. Even though there will be a disturbance at the surface due to outgassing of carbon dioxide, hydrogen sulfide, and methane, a small sample of the oil usually can be obtained for gas chromatographic analysis of the low boiling components. After most of the oil is transferred to a weighed vial by a pipette, the liquids are poured into a Teflon separatory funnel and additional oil is recovered. The water can be recovered for dissolved organics and other analyses. The shale is then transferred into a funnel and the surface is rinsed with benzene to remove superficial oil. This wash is combined with the equipment wash and the solvent is removed to obtain the weight of oil. Gas yield is calculated from the pressure, volume, temperature and composition data. The shale is extracted in a Soxhlet extractor with an organic solvent to determine the bitumen content; it is then in condition for the full suite of normal geochemical analyses. Only hydrocarbon solvents are allowed to come into contact with the reactor parts, to avoid stress–crack corrosion effects of chlorides on stainless steel. This single-vessel type of experiment is called the batch method.

Another mode of operation consists of using the apparatus as shown in Fig. 3. The main part of the experiment is done identically, except that at the end of the reaction, the reactor is not cooled for sample recovery. An identical preconnected pressure vessel, that has been evacuated and cooled, is opened slowly to the hot reactor. The rate of transfer is controlled by a valve in the gauge block assembly to allow all of the water and other condensables to liquefy, thereby maintaining maximum pressure differential between the two vessels. The rate of transfer can be determined from a thermocouple taped to the outer wall of the transfer line.

Table 1

Sample identifications of shales used in hydrouspyrolysis experiments. Also shown are organic carbon and elemental analysis data for each sample

| | | | Organic carbon | Elemental analysis | | | |
| | Sample identification | | | | | | |
Formation	Age	Location	Wt %	H	C ·	O	N
Kimmeridge (sample 1, composite)	Jurassic	Dorset coast, England	11.2	8.0	75.8	14.1	2.2
Kimmeridge (sample II)	Jurassic	Dorset coast, England	25.2	9.3	79.3	9.5	2.0
Phosphoria	Permian	Beaverhead County Montana, USA	22.8	8.1	77.3	10.8	3.8
Woodford	Devonian	Carter County Oklahoma, USA	12.7	8.1	82.1	7.3	2.2

KIMMERIDGE I

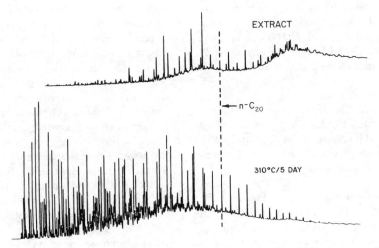

EXTRACT

← n-C$_{20}$

310 °C/5 DAY

Fig. 4. Gas chromatograms showing composition of a Kimmeridgian shale extract and a hydrouspyrolysis product of the same shale. 25 m × 0.25 mm i.d. open tubular glass capillary column coated with CP Sil 5, Chrompack, Middelburg, The Netherlands; initial temperature 30 °C for 3 min, programmed at 10° min⁻¹ to 325 °C and held for 30 min; Injector 360 °C, FID detector 360 °C, helium carrier gas; Hewlett Packard 5840A.

As the rate slows down, heat is removed from the reactor and as soon as the pressure differential approaches zero, the valves are closed and the transfer line is disconnected. Essentially all of the water, gas, and volatile products will have transferred to the receiver. The reactor is cooled and the receiver is warmed to room temperature. We call this mode the hot transfer method. All experiments with Kimmeridgian and Phosphoria shales were done by the hot transfer method; all Woodford experiments used the batch method.

The two methods of product recovery will give somewhat different results. The hot transfer mode is an excellent way to recover all volatile components, including very polar compounds, but it does not effectively transfer heavy resins and asphaltenes. The batch method will recover a broader boiling range of products with somewhat less polar content. There are many intermediate modes of operation and others requiring considerably more complex apparatus and operation. The choice will depend upon how closely one needs to mimic the exact environment of generation. The majority of useful petroleum geochemical experiments can be done in the simplest mode of operation.

RESULTS AND DISCUSSION

The formation, age, location, organic richness, and elemental analyses of the source rock samples are contained in Table 1. These represent a fairly wide range of richness, geological age, and carbonization, but they all contain the type II kerogen.

Figure 4 shows a gas chromatogram of a solvent extract of Kimmeridgian shale outcrop obtained from the Dorset Coast (Williams and Douglas, 1979). The low-boiling components are on the left and the high-boiling on the right. The gas chromatogram would show compounds over a range of 40 carbon numbers if they

were present. The vertical dashed line marks the 20 carbon n-alkane in this and all following figures. The extract contains a concentrate of the chemical fossils or biomarkers that would be expected from an immature kerogen in a source rock. The panel below the extract is a gas chromatogram of an early generation product produced by the hydrouspyrolysis method after five

KIMMERIDGE I

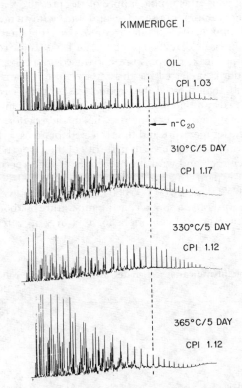

OIL

CPI 1.03

← n-C$_{20}$

310 °C/5 DAY

CPI 1.17

330 °C/5 DAY

CPI 1.12

365 °C/5 DAY

CPI 1.12

Fig. 5. Gas chromatograms showing composition of a produced North Sea crude oil derived from Kimmeridgian shale source, and three hydrouspyrolysis products obtained at indicated reaction conditions from a composite of Kimmeridgian shales. Gas chromatography conditions same as for Fig. 4.

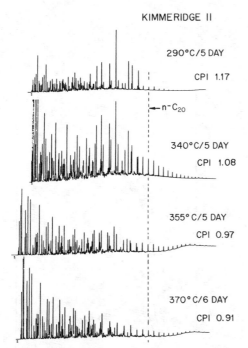

KIMMERIDGE II

290°C/5 DAY
CPI 1.17

←— n-C₂₀

340°C/5 DAY
CPI 1.08

355°C/5 DAY
CPI 0.97

370°C/6 DAY
CPI 0.91

Fig. 6. Gas chromatograms showing compositions of four hydrouspyrolysis products obtained at indicated reaction conditions from organic-rich zone in Kimmeridgian shale. Gas chromatography conditions same as for Fig. 4.

days at 310 °C. This product contains the original biomarkers, along with a complex mixture of early reaction products. Clearly, even under these mild conditions, many reaction products are generated that are not present in the original shale.

Figure 5 compares gas chromatograms of a natural North Sea oil from a Kimmeridgian source with those of hydrouspyrolysis products obtained from a composite of Kimmeridgian shale outcrops after five days at 310, 330, and 365 °C. Although detailed study of these chromatograms is needed to draw many conclusions, the product at 330 °C is approaching the natural oil and the one at 365 °C has been cracked to a thermal maturity stage approaching that of a condensate. For reference, Carbon Preference Index (CPI) values are included on this and subsequent figures showing gas chromatograms of hydrouspyrolysis products and produced oils. The CPIs were determined for the C_{24}–C_{30} range by the procedure reported by Bray and Evans (1961).

Figure 6 compares products from an especially rich zone of Kimmeridgian shale from the same location as the previous composite. The top panel shows the product recovered after five days at 290 °C. This product is similar to the solvent extract of the composite shale. It is mainly a hot water extract of the natural bitumen, along with a small amount of reaction product. The succeeding panels, showing reaction products at 340 and 355 °C for five days, and 370 °C for six days, show increasing maturation, but do not closely match the composition of the natural oil. This shale is hundreds of miles away from the source rock that generated the natural oil. These experiments show the effect of differences among kerogen precursors and the environments of deposition over many miles in a large basin. They also demonstrate that the products from a composite sample more closely resemble the natural oil than one isolated, very organic-rich zone. Thus, hydrous

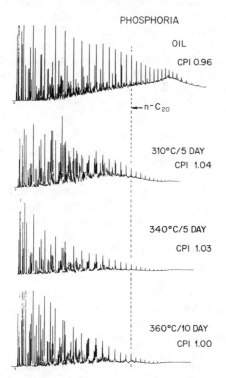

PHOSPHORIA

OIL
CPI 0.96

←— n-C₂₀

310°C/5 DAY
CPI 1.04

340°C/5 DAY
CPI 1.03

360°C/10 DAY
CPI 1.00

Fig. 7. Gas chromatograms showing compositions of a produced crude oil derived from a Phosphoria source, and three hydrouspyrolysis products obtained at indicated reaction conditions from Phosphoria shale. Gas chromatography conditions same as for Fig. 4.

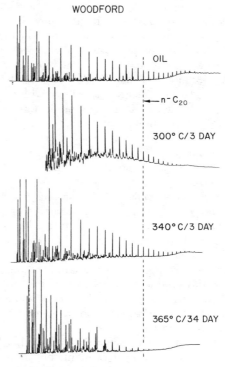

WOODFORD

OIL

←— n-C₂₀

300°C/3 DAY

340°C/3 DAY

365°C/34 DAY

Fig. 8. Gas chromatograms showing compositions of a produced oil derived from a Woodford source, and three hydrouspyrolysis products obtained at indicated reaction conditions from Woodford shale. Gas chromatography conditions same as for Fig. 4.

WOODFORD

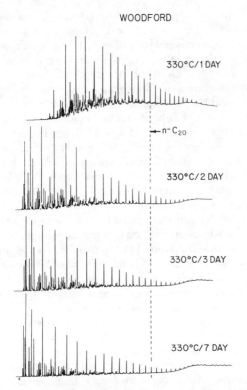

Fig. 9. Gas chromatograms showing compositions of four hydrouspyrolysis products from Woodford shale: all were run at 330 °C for indicated lengths of time. Gas chromatography conditions same as for Fig. 4.

EVOLUTION PATHS

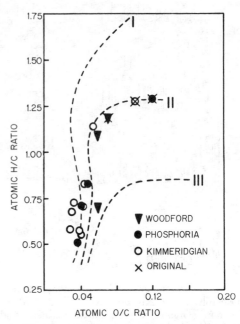

Fig. 10. Evolution paths of kerogens after hydrouspyrolysis of Woodford, Phosphoria and Kimmeridgian shales, shown by van Krevelen type diagram. Original kerogens before hydrouspyrolysis are indicated as being Type II.

pyrolysis is capable of demonstrating rather subtle differences among very similar kerogens.

Figure 7 shows a gas chromatogram of a natural Phosphoria oil from Wyoming in the United States. The panels below the oil show composition changes in products from hydrouspyrolysis of a Phosphoria shale after five days at 310 and 340 °C, and after ten days at 360 °C. The amount of unresolved material on the lower part of the gas chromatogram is reduced with time and temperature. The 340 °C five-day product approaches the composition of the natural product while the 360 °C ten-day product is considerably more thermally mature. The Phosphoria shale sample was obtained about 200 miles from the likely Phosphoria source rock for the natural oil.

Figure 8 shows similar results for products from a Devonian Woodford shale. The lower boiling components were lost from the immature 300 °C three-day product but the middle and high boiling oil are valid for comparison. The 340 °C three-day product approaches the composition of the natural crude and the 365 °C 34-day product is clearly past maturity for an oil and is becoming a condensate. This set of results shows the effects of temperature and a combination of temperature and time.

Figure 9 shows results using the same Woodford shale with the temperature held constant, but at different times of reaction. The composition of the product approaches that of the natural oil more closely with time, with the 330 °C three-day product and 330 °C seven-day product bracketing the composition of the natural oil.

Although the source rock shales used for these ex-

periments are from different geologic ages and widely different geographic locations, they all contain Type II kerogens as characterized by a van Krevelen diagram. Figure 10 shows the position of the three original kerogens on such a diagram. The Phosphoria sample is the least mature, the Kimmeridgian shale the next most mature, and the Woodford shale the most mature. As each shale was thermally matured during hydrouspyrolysis, the kerogen closely tracked the path predicted by the van Krevelen diagram for Type II kerogens. The spread of Kimmeridge data is produced by the difference between the composite sample and the single rich zone. All of the points are within the wide band usually shown on this type of diagram.

Table 2 shows the effect of increasing maturity more clearly than can be seen from the small-scale gas chromatograms. This table shows the increasing conversion of kerogen to oil and gas with increasing thermal exposure. In each set of experiments with Kimmeridgian shale, the last data line indicates a leveling of liquid generation and that the stage dominated by gas generation has been entered; on the second set some of the oil is being cracked to gas.

The results from the experiments with Phosphoria shale also demonstrate a leveling of oil generation, but continued generation of gas. The results are entirely consistent with those predicted by the position of the kerogen on the van Krevelen diagram at the end of each thermal period.

Table 3 shows similar results for the Woodford shale. However, in the first set, the long exposure at 365 °C for 34 days resulted in pronounced conversion of oil to gas,

Table 2

Yields of volatile hydrocarbon products from hydrouspyrolysis of Kimmeridgian and Phosphoria shales at indicated reaction conditions, using the hot transfer mode

| | Hydrouspyrolysis yields | | | | | |
| | | | | Yield, wt % o.m. | | |
Shale type	Temperature, °C	Time days	Organic matter, %	Liquid	Gas	Total
Kimmeridgian I	310	5	14.8	12.5	1.1	13.6
	330	5		25.3	2.6	27.9
	365	5		27.4	5.1	32.5
Kimmeridgian II	290	5	31.8	3.9	0.3	4.2
	340	5		21.5	1.8	23.3
	355	5		26.5	3.0	29.5
	370	6		25.9	4.6	31.0
Phosphoria	310	5	25.7	13.3	1.4	14.7
	340	5		24.6	2.8	27.4
	360	5		33.2	4.8	38.0
	360	10		33.9	6.4	40.3

Table 3

Yields of volatile hydrocarbon products from hydrouspyrolysis of Woodford shale at indicated reaction conditions, top; and at same temperature for different reaction times, bottom. Batch mode was used

| | Hydrouspyrolysis yields | | | | | |
| | | | | Yield, wt % o.m. | | |
Shale type	Temperature, °C	Time, days	Organic matter, %	Liquid	Gas	Total
Woodford	300	3	15.5	1.2	0.6	1.8
	340	3		13.4	2.4	15.8
	350	3		20.2	3.5	23.7
	365	34		11.4	7.7	19.1
Woodford	330	1	15.5	3.0	1.0	4.0
	330	2		4.1	1.4	5.5
	330	3		6.0	1.8	7.8
	330	7		14.3	2.6	16.9

with a loss of total soluble hydrocarbons to pyrobitumen and nonhydrocarbon gases. The second data set reflects the low temperature of reaction, with increasing yield of both liquid and gas throughout the series.

In general, other geochemical properties of kerogens and oils produced by hydrouspyrolysis follow the expected pathways, confirming that this method of simulating the natural generation of petroleum does follow a similar mechanism. Space limitations prevent discussing those properties in this paper, but they will be covered elsewhere at a later date.

Bacterial degradation of petroleum

Many analyses and interpretations of data have been made of heavy oils and bitumens found in nature since we first published evidence for microbial degradation of petroleum in reservoirs (Winters and Williams, 1969). However, since that time, many incorrect interpretations have been made of similar data applied to petroleum exploration. Many explorationists have participated in discussions about whether a heavy oil or

extract recovered from a North Sea core represents immature oil that has somehow escaped from the source rock and migrated to a reservoir or whether the heavy hydrocarbons are the residue of a microbially degraded mature oil. The implications of these interpretations span the extreme positions of pessimistic to optimistic in the search for oil. The ability to generate oils of known maturity by hydrouspyrolysis and compare them with mature oils microbially degraded in the laboratory should offer an answer to this dilemma.

The bottom left panel of Fig. 11 compares a natural Kimmeridge crude oil with an extract of immature Kimmeridgian shale (top left) and a relatively immature oil produced by hydrouspyrolysis at 310 °C for five days (middle left). We estimate that a natural oil corresponding to the stage of maturity of the 310 °C five-day product would still not have undergone primary migration from the source rock, but if it did, the composition of that oil would be represented by the product composition shown in the middle left panel.

For comparison, we microbially degraded the mature North Sea oil shown in the bottom left panel of Fig. 11 to mild, medium, and severe degradation stages. No stage

THERMAL IMMATURITY vs MICROBIAL DEGRADATION
KIMMERIDGE

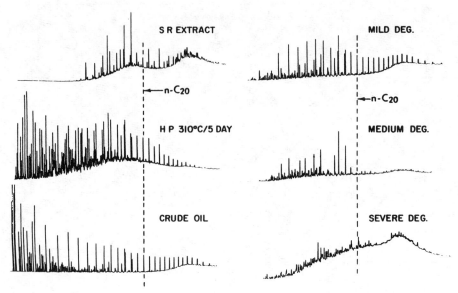

Fig. 11. Gas chromatograms showing compositions of a Kimmeridgian shale extract, hydrouspyrolysis product of Kimmeridgian shale, and a produced North Sea crude derived from a Kimmeridge source, at left; the same crude oil at mild, medium, and severe stages of microbial degradation, at right. Gas chromatography conditions same as for Fig. 4.

of microbial degradation resembles the immature oil produced by hydrouspyrolysis. There is a superficial resemblance between the medium stage of degradation and the source rock extract. However, every evidence indicates that the small amount of extract present in this shale could not migrate from the shale; furthermore, the kerogen is clearly in a pregeneration stage of maturity. If, however, we assume that there is some mechanism for migration of the heavy extract, comparison of the gas chromatograms of the extract with the microbially degraded crude oil show significant differences in composition. The immature extract contains *n*-alkanes with a marked odd–even preference in the C_{20}–C_{25} range; the medium-degraded product contains none. The immature extract has a concentration of biomarkers in the sterane–triterpane region; the degraded product contains very little. The ratios of isoprenoid compounds are different in a way that clearly reflects known maturity levels of the two samples. These are easily observed differences; detailed GC–MS analyses show even more. These results indicate that some heavy oils and core extracts have been mistakenly interpreted as migrating immature oil when in reality they are microbially degraded residues of mature oil.

CONCLUSIONS

We hope that this brief exposure to a few results from hydrouspyrolysis experiments has stimulated your interest in this approach. Our data show that it is a reasonable way to study the generation of petroleum in the laboratory under controlled time and temperature conditions, and eliminate the need for many of the secondary correlations that can only imply what might happen in the natural environment. Hydrouspyrolysis

methods lead to potentially useful practical applications in oil exploration. For example:

1. The use of originally immature source rock samples in oil to rock correlation work. This should be particularly helpful to GC–MS correlation studies.
2. The pursuit of advanced research in primary migration/oil expulsion studies.

Last, laboratory production of oil that resembles crude oil produced from the same type and age of kerogen in the natural environment provides the direct experimental proof for the origin of petroleum. We hope that this will strengthen the faith in and application of organic geochemistry to exploration.

Acknowledgements

Many of the hydrouspyrolysis experiments with Kimmeridgian and Phosphoria shales, calculations of results and the illustrations in this presentation are the result of efforts by Dr Marwin K. Kemp, Amoco Production Company consultant on leave from the University of Tulsa. From the beginning of the first hydrouspyrolysis experiments, Mr J. H. McDonald has made an unusual contribution to the success of the experimental work and Mr P. N. Vu has provided consistently high quality gas chromatographic and other analyses.

REFERENCES

Bandurski, E. (1982) Structural similarities between oil-generating kerogens and petroleum asphaltenes. *Energy sources* **6**, 47–66.

Biederman, E. W. Jr. (1965) Crude oil composition — a clue to migration. *World Oil*, Dec., 78–82.

Bray, E. E. and Evans, E. D. (1961) Distribution of n-paraffins as a clue to recognition of source beds. *Geochim. Cosmochim. Acta* **22**, 2.

Douglas, A., Eglinton, G. and Henderson, W. (1966) Thermal alteration of the organic matter in sediments. In *Advances in Organic Geochemistry 1966*, pp. 369–388.

Durand, B. and Espitalié, J. (1972) Formation and evolution of C_1 to C_{15} hydrocarbons and permanent gases in the Toarcian clays of the Paris basin. In *Advances in Organic Geochemistry 1972*. pp. 455–468.

Eisma, E. and Jurg, J. (1969) Fundamental aspects of the generation of petroleum in organic geochemistry. In *Organic Geochemistry*. Ed. by Eglinton, G. and Murphy, M. T. J. pp. 676–698.

Forsman, J. P. and Hunt, J. M. (1958) Insoluble organic matter (kerogen) in sedimentary rocks. *Geochim. Cosmochim. Acta* **15**, 170–182.

Hunt, J. M. (1965) Organic sediments. In *Encyclopedia of Earth Science*. Ed. by Fairbridge, R. W.

Khare, B. N., Sagan, C., Bandurski, E. L. and Nagy, B. (1978) Ultraviolet-photoproduced organic solids synthesized under simulated Jovian conditions: Molecular analysis. *Science* **199**, 1199–1201.

Leventhal, J. S. (1976) Stepwise pyrolysis–gas chromatography of kerogen in sedimentary rocks. *Chem. Geol.* **18**, 5–20.

Lewan, M. D., Winters, J. C. and McDonald, J. H. (1979) Generation of oil-like pyrolyzates from organic-rich shales. *Science* **203**, 897–899.

Lopatin, N. V. (1976) The determination of the influence of temperature and geologic time on the catagenic process of coalification and oil–gas formation. *Akad Nauk SSSR, Izdatel'stvo, 'Nauka'*, 361–366.

McCollum, J. D. and Quick, L. M. (1976) Process for upgrading a hydrocarbon fraction. *United States Patent 3,989,618*, November 2, 1976.

Martin, R. L., Winters, J. C. and Williams, J. A. (1963) Composition of Crude Oils by Gas Chromatography; Geological Significance of Hydrocarbon Distribution. *Proc. Sixth World Petroleum Cong.*, Sect V, Frankfurt, Germany. pp. 231–260.

Philippi, G. T. (1965) On the depth, time, and mechanism of petroleum generation. *Geochim. Cosmochim. Acta* **29**, 1021–1049.

Silverman, S. R. and Epstein, S. (1958) Carbon isotopic compositions of petroleums and other sedimentary organic materials. *Am. Ass. Petrol. Geol. Bull.* **42**, 998–1012.

Spielmann, P. E. (1923) *The Genesis of Petroleum*. Ernest Benn, Ltd. pp. 7–8.

Tissot, B., Durand, B., Espitalié, J. and Combaz, A. (1974) Influence of the nature and diagenesis of organic matter in formation of petroleum. *Am. Ass. Pet. Geol. Bull.* **58**, 499–506.

Vassoevich, N. B., Korchagina, Yu. I., Lopatin, N. V. and Chernischev, V. V. (1970) The main stage of petroleum formation. *Int. Geol. Rev.* **12**, 1276–1296.

Welte, D. H. (1972) Petroleum exploration and organic geochemistry. *J. Geochem. Explor.* **1**, 117–136.

Williams, P. V. F. and Douglas, A. G. (1979) A preliminary organic geochemical investigation of the Kimmeridgian oil shales. In *Advances in Organic Geochemistry 1979*. pp. 531–576.

Winters, J. C. and Williams, J. A. (1969) Microbial alteration of crude oil in the reservoir. *Preprint, Div. Petrol. Chem., Am. Chem. Soc.* **14**, E22–E31.

Advances in Organic Geochemistry 1981, pp. 534–545
© *John Wiley & Sons Limited, 1983*

Aromatic Structures in Coal Maceral Extracts and Kerogens

J. Allan* and S. R. Larter†

Esso Resources Canada Limited, 339–50 Avenue S.E. Calgary, Alberta, Canada T2G 2B3

†*Union Oil Company of California, Science and Technology Division, PO Box 76, Brea, California 92621, USA*

Solvent extracts and kerogens of a series of sporinite and vitrinite concentrates isolated from British Carboniferous coals (rank range 0.47–1.12% $\bar{R}_{max}$ of vitrinite) have been studied using a combination of chromatographic, pyrolytic and spectroscopic techniques. Aromatic hydrocarbon fractions of the extracts of both macerals are dominated by two and three ring compounds showing relatively simple alkyl substituents (C_1, C_2 and C_3). However, mass spectral compound type analysis has shown that long-chain alkylation is also present in all classes in the range Z–6 to Z–18. The general distributions of the extractable hydrocarbons appear to be largely maceral independent within a single coal, indicating that intra-seam homogenization of mobile organic compounds may be an active process. The maceral kerogens have been examined by analytical pyrolysis (610°C), and pyrolytic products of both types are composed primarily of similar ranges or aliphatic, alkylated phenolic and alkylated aromatic hydrocarbon fragments. The proportions of aliphatic products are greater in sporinites than in rank-equivalent vitrinites, and the apparent aliphaticity of both macerals decreases with increasing rank. Complimentary analyses by pyrolysis–gas chromatography (600 °C) have shown that short alkyl chains (C_1–C_3) are the predominant substituents on the alkylated phenols and aromatic hydrocarbons produced from both macerals. The data obtained in this study show that whereas differences exist in the overall aromaticities of the two maceral kerogens, degradable aromatic nuclei appear to be qualitatively similar in type. They are consistent with an aromatic/hydroaromatic structure for both macerals, although it is not possible to determine quantitatively what proportions of the two kerogens are represented by this structure.

INTRODUCTION

Coal is composed of many individual components, termed macerals, which are optically distinctive, and which represent both directly deposited particles (e.g. pollen, algae) and materials formed only after deposition of vegetal debris in the peat swamp (e.g. vitrinite, fusinite). The introduction of the atomic H/C v O/C diagram by Dormans *et al.*, (1957) showed in empirical terms that each of the three main maceral groups can be differentiated in terms of elemental composition, and that progressive coalification causes systematic changes in composition.

Conventionally, vitrinite and sporinite are regarded as chemically distinctive materials with individual molecular structures. Sporinite is more hydrogen-rich and contains a greater proportion of aliphatic material than a rank-equivalent vitrinite, at least to low-volatile bituminous rank. The biopolymer sporopollenin has been suggested as the main constituent of modern spore/pollen which survives early diagenesis (Brooks and Shaw, 1968), and is thereafter subject to dehydration and aromatisation during catagenesis (Brooks, 1971). In contrast, vitrinites are derived by complex diagenetic

processes involving the ligno–cellulosic woody tissues of plants to produce a mainly cyclic hydroaromatic/aromatic structure.

This paper presents the results of molecular analyses of extractable aromatic hydrocarbons from a limited rank range of vitrinites and sporinites. Additionally, results are presented discussing the aromatic structures produced during thermal degradation of the two maceral kerogens. The samples cover the rank range equivalent to vitrinite reflectances ($\bar{R}_{max}$) of 0.47–1.12%, and results are presented with reference to both maceral type and rank.

EXPERIMENTAL

Experimental details concerning sample identity, maceral concentration methods and solvent extraction have been published elsewhere (Allan *et al.*, 1977; Allan and Douglas, 1977). Aromatic hydrocarbons were separated from aliquots of total hydrocarbons by elution chromatography over activated silica gel, using dichloromethane as eluant, after first removing aliphatic hydrocarbons (pentane eluate). Hydrocarbon fractions isolated under these conditions were subsequently found to contain some sulphur and oxygen heterocyclic compounds.

Gas chromatographic analyses were carried out using a 25 m × 0.35 mm I.D. WCOT OV-101 glass capillary column, temperature programmed at 4 °C min^{-1} from 80 °C to 270 °C. Nitrogen carrier gas was used (1–2 ml min^{-1}) and the chromatograph was equipped with an FID detector.

Low ionizing voltage (11 eV) mass spectrometry was carried out using a CEC 103 mass spectrometer. Computer manipulation was used to produce carbon number distributions of Z-6 to Z-18 compound types from the molecular ion data.

Compound identifications were performed or supplemented by combined gas chromatography–mass spectrometry using an HP5930 gc–ms equipped with an Incos data system.

Pyrolysis–mass spectrometry was performed using a system similar to that described by Meuzelaar et al. (1978). Solvent-extracted, finely ground microgram size samples were pyrolyzed for 10 s at the wire Curie point (610 °C). The pyrolysate was monitored using low voltage (12 or 14 eV) electron impact ionization followed by rapid scan (10 scans sec^{-1}), quadrupole mass filtration and scan integration to give a whole pyrolysate mass spectrum. Under the conditions used, secondary pyrolysis reactions are minimal, and ions produced are dominantly molecular ions.

Pyrolysis–gas chromatography was performed using a CDS 120 filament pyroprobe connected via a glass-lined splitter to a 25 m × 0.2 mm ID WCOT SP2100 fused silica capillary column. A nitrogen carrier gas flow of 30 ml min^{-1} was maintained through the pyrolysis chamber to provide high sweep rates and minimize secondary reactions. Pyrolysis of extracted, microgram size samples was carried out at 600 °C for 1 s, and the effluent was analyzed by temperature-programmed gas chromatography (40–275 °C at 4° min^{-1}) using an FID detector. Peak identifications were made using a combination of retention time and pyrolysis–gas chromatography–mass spectrometry data (Larter et al., 1978).

RESULTS AND DISCUSSION

Extractable aromatic hydrocarbons

The yields of extractable aromatic hydrocarbons are shown in Fig. 1, plotted against rank. It can be seen that there is a general trend of increasing yield with increasing rank although there is considerable variability in yields between the lower rank samples. It is also apparent in Fig. 1 that sporinites always produced greater amounts of hydrocarbons than their rank-equivalent vitrinites. However, a more interesting observation is the remarkable parallelism of the yield trends from the two organic types which is an unexpected result considering the diverse origins of the materials under investigation. This observation is discussed below, as it will be shown that qualitative

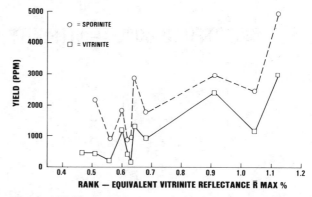

Fig. 1. Yield of soluble aromatic fractions as a function of rank.

similarities also exist along with the quantitative similarities.

The effect of progressive coalification on the gross molecular composition of the extractable aromatic hydrocarbons is clearly shown in Fig. 2 which shows high resolution gas chromatograms of the aromatic fractions isolated from three vitrinites covering the investigated rank range. Compound identifications shown in the figure are based on gas chromatographic–mass spectrometric analysis of the fractions, and comparison of mass spectra with the on-line data base and published data. The hydrocarbons occur as very complex mixtures but a shift to lower molecular weight compounds is noticeable as rank increases. This trend is similar to that observed in the aliphatic hydrocarbons isolated from these macerals and other coals (Allan and Douglas, 1977; Allan et al., 1977; Brooks and Smith, 1967; Leythaeuser and Welte, 1969; Radke et al., 1980). In the higher rank samples there is a clear relative increase in the proportions of simple alkylated naphthalenes and phenanthrenes, with perhaps the most prominent changes occurring in the relative abundance and isomeric distribution of monomethyl phenanthrenes. Radke and Welte (1981) have investigated the changes occurring in the amount of phenanthrene and its isomeric monomethyl derivatives, and have shown that progressive coalification induces systematic relative compositional changes in these compounds.

Although Fig. 2 shows gas chromatograms of vitrinite hydrocarbons, a similar trend is seen in sporinite hydrocarbons also. However, a most unexpected observation is that the detailed fingerprint distributions of the hydrocarbons from both macerals are very similar between maceral pairs at equivalent ranks. Two examples are shown in Fig. 3, which illustrate maceral-pair hydrocarbons at ranks of 0.51% and 0.91% $\bar{R}_{max}$ respectively. As extractable organic matter is derived both from indigenous sedimented molecules and the products of kerogen catagenesis the above result, coupled with the quantitative data shown in Fig. 1, are surprising observations given the diversity in origin of the two organic matter types under investigation. Reviewing previously published data on the aliphatic hydrocarbons from these macerals (Allan et al., 1977; Allan and Douglas, 1977), it is clear that strong compositional similarities are also evident in these fractions.

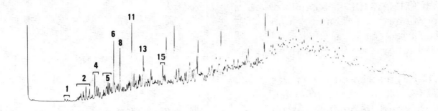

A.
WESTFIELD COAL — VITRINITE REFLECTANCE 0.47% R̄ MAX

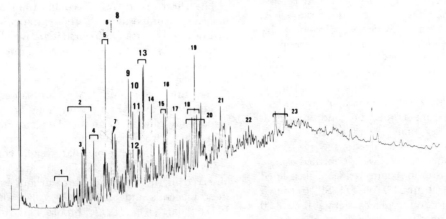

B.
HIGH HAZELS COAL — VITRINITE REFLECTANCE — 0.62% R̄ MAX

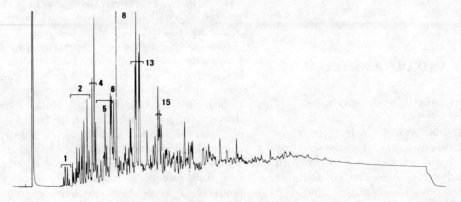

C.
PARKGATE COAL — VITRINITE REFLECTANCE — 1.12% R̄ MAX

Fig. 2. Representative gas chromatograms of extractable aromatic hydrocarbons isolated from vitrinites. GC conditions in text. Peak identities: 1. C_2-naphthalenes; 2. C_3-naphthalenes; 3. fluorene; 4. C_1-dibenzofurans + xanthene; 5. C_1-fluorenes; 6. 1-methyl, 7-isopropyl naphthalene (eudalene); 7. dibenzothiophene; 8. phenanthrene; 9. $C_{16}H_{14}$-tetracyclic hydroaromatic hydrocarbon?; 10. $C_{17}H_{16}$-tetracyclic hydroaromatic hydrocarbon?; 11. $C_{16}H_{18}$-substituted acenaphthene?; 12. 1,6-dimethyl, 4-isopropyl naphthalene (cadalene); 13. C_1-phenanthrenes; 14. $C_{17}H_{16}$-tetracyclic hydroaromatic hydrocarbon?; 15. C_2-phenanthrenes; 16. fluoranthene; 17. pyrene; 18. C_3-phenanthrenes; 19. 1-methyl, 7-isopropyl phenanthrene (retene); 20. C_1-pyrenes/fluoranthenes; 21. chrysene; 22. C_1-chrysene; 23. benzofluoranthenes/benzopyrenes.

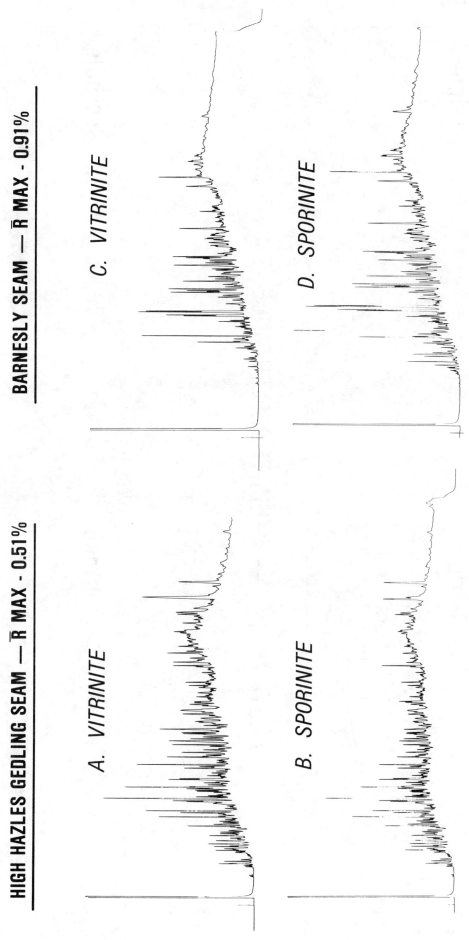

Fig. 3. Comparative fingerprint chromatograms of aromatic hydrocarbons. GC conditions in text.

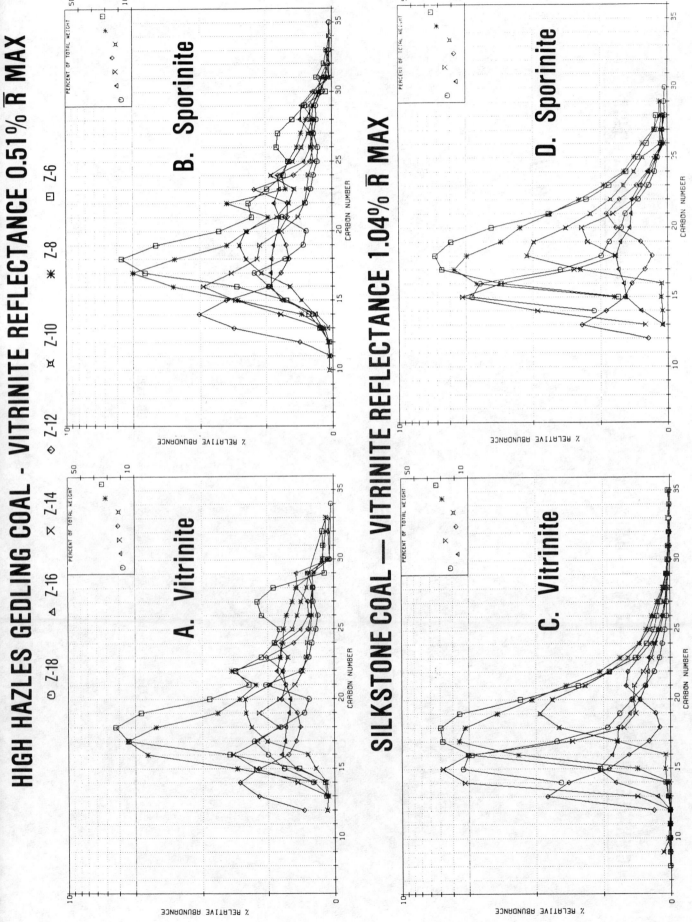

Fig. 4. Low voltage mass spectrometric aromatic group type analysis. MS conditions in text.

It can be hypothesized that as the hydrocarbons (aliphatic and aromatic) represent only a small proportion of the total organic material (less than 1% by wt), they may not be representative of the overall structures and could be derived from similar molecular precursors which are present in small amounts in both macerals. However, this explanation is difficult to accept for the rank range covered includes the phase of maximum hydrocarbon formation, and it is conceptually unsound to explain the above observations by preferred processes favouring selective and nonrepresentative portions of the two kerogens.

An alternative explanation, for which supportive data are given below, is that the extractable hydrocarbons isolated from the two sets of macerals in fact represent an average composition of compounds variously generated by all the labile macerals within the original coal seams and that these compounds are capable of a degree of migration within the body of the coal to the extent that homogenization occurs and specific type differences are submerged or obliterated. As internal pore sizes in coals are thought to be of the order of a few Angstroms only (van Krevelen, 1961), and hence too small to permit free movement of many of the identified hydrocarbons, the molecular homogenization concept necessarily requires that there exist some alternate pore or fracture system within the coals. One admittedly speculative possibility is that maceral grain boundaries may provide sufficient porosity for migration to occur due to differential volumetric changes within the variable macromolecular unit structures as catagenesis proceeds. Given the physical complexity and intimate intermixing of the component macerals within the Carboniferous coals, an extensive and pervasive porous network could exist.

Although the proposed mechanism is, as stated, highly speculative and argumentative, the actual concept of intra-seam homogenization of free molecules receives tentative support from some of the data. Referring back to Fig. 2, terpenoid-derived compounds such as cadalene, eudalene and retene were identified in both sporinite and vitrinite extracts and have been identified in other coals (Hayatsu *et al.*, 1978; Baset *et al.*, 1980; White and Lee, 1980). The latter two compounds are relatively prominent in the chromatograms of the lower rank samples, but become less so as rank increases. It is not possible at present to state whether their disappearance in the higher rank samples is relative or absolute. The important point is that the relative distributions of the two compounds, and their rate of decline of prominence in the chromatograms are similar in both maceral extracts. The commonality of occurrence supports the idea of a pervasive presence of these compounds throughout the coal, especially since retene is usually presumed to be derived from abietic acid in resinite (White and Lee, 1980; Baset *et al.*, 1980) and eudalene precursors also are associated with coniferous plants (White and Lee, 1980).

A second line of support for limited migration and molecular mixing is found in the mono- to triaromatic hydrocarbon portions of the extracts. These compounds were analyzed by compound class using low ionizing voltage (11 eV) mass spectrometry. Seven classes of hydroaromatic/aromatic compounds are identified by Z

numbers from Z-6 to Z-18, and examples of the data are shown in Fig. 4 which shows abundance versus carbon number plots of the seven compound classes isolated from lower and higher rank maceral pairs respectively. The analyses show that extended alkylation is present in each compound class with molecules with up to 35 carbon atoms being identified in the lower rank extracts. The significant points about the data are that rank-equivalent maceral pairs give broadly similar distributions of compounds within each class and that the relative abundances of each class within the whole analyses are very similar. Extensively alkylated aromatic hydrocarbons are not biosynthesized compounds *per se* but result from complex chemical restructuring of aromatic, hydroaromatic and aliphatic molecular moieties within the maceral kerogens during diagenesis and catagenesis. The molecular correlations apparent in these data are sufficient to imply a common source by standard geochemical practice, and this appears to be incompatible with individual derivation from the two differing kerogen types.

Aromatic hydrocarbons bearing extended alkyl substituents have been identified in numerous coal pyrolysis studies (Larter, 1978; Larter *et al.*, 1978; Baset *et al.*, 1980; Allan *et al.*, 1980; Gallegos, 1981), but infrequently in raw coal extracts (Hayatsu *et al.*, 1978; Gallegos, 1981). It is interesting to note that long alkyl chains are present on all the nuclear structures included in the compound classes (isomeric complexity prohibits specific identifications of individual nuclear structures and substituent configurations), and other data obtained extend this observation to heterocyclic aromatic compounds (Larter and Allan, unpublished results). Furthermore, reference to Fig. 4 shows that the number of carbon atoms in substituent groups decreases with increasing rank, presumably through degradative reactions similar to those invoked to explain the observed rank-dependent chain shortening in extractable aliphatic hydrocarbons (Allan *et al.*, 1977; Leythaeuser *et al.*, 1980).

The low ionizing voltage mass spectral analysis also provided quantitative data on the amounts of each compound class within the Z-6 to Z-18 fraction. These data show that within the seven classes, only the yields of Z-16 and Z-18 compounds show any apparent relationship with sample rank. While Z-18 compounds are much more abundant in the higher rank samples than in those of lower ranks, the reverse is true for the Z-16 compounds. If the two yields are expressed as the ratio Z-18/Z-16 then an excellent empirical relationship is apparent with sample rank (Fig. 5) for both maceral types. This is consistent with the concept of increasing aromaticity during progressive coalification although the data may not be used to indicate that Z-18 compounds are derived solely by dehydrogenation of Z-16 analogues. Nevertheless, the observation does comply in principle with the data of Hayatsu *et al.* (1978) and Gallegos (1978), who have demonstrated increasing relative abundances of tri- and tetracyclic aromatic units in coals of increasing rank.

Despite the identification of extended alkylation on extractable hydroaromatic/aromatic nuclei, the mass spectral data (Fig. 3) and the gas chromatograms (Fig.

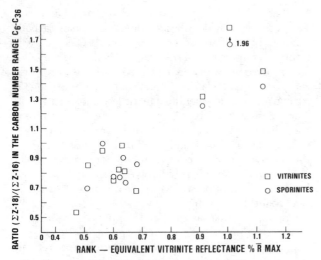

Fig. 5. Tricyclic aromatic species in coal maceral extracts.

2) show that simple substituents (i.e. C_1, C_2 and C_3) are much more predominant, which is consistent with data published on extracts of other coals (Hayatsu *et al.*, 1978; Gallegos, 1978; White and Lee, 1980; Philp and Saxby, 1980). While some of these compounds may be direct derivatives of precursor terpenoids (e.g. cadalene, eudalene, retene), it is thought that the bulk of the molecular species identified result from reactions occurring during kerogen diagenesis and catagenesis to give the mixture of compound types and isomers observed. Cleavage of C–C bonds β to aromatic nuclei is thought to be a favoured route of kerogen decomposition (Svob *et al.*, 1972) and so hydroaromatic structures and aromatic nuclei bearing alkyl substituents would both be expected to result in a predominance of methyl substituted aromatic products, as is observed.

Aromaticity and aromatic structures in kerogens

Various analyses have been carried out on the kerogens of the sporinites and vitrinites to assess the variability in chemical composition between the two organic types and to identify molecular changes incurred as a consequence of progressive coalification.

^{13}C Nuclear magnetic resonance spectroscopy
Several of the macerals used in this study have been examined by ^{13}C nuclear magnetic resonance spectroscopy, using the cross polarization/magic angle spinning technique. These data have been published by Zilm *et al.* (1981). It is not necessary to review that spectroscopic data in detail, but it is relevant to the preceding discussion to indicate that maceral types are clearly identifiable on the basis of both characteristic fine spectral details as well as overall aromaticity. As anticipated, the vitrinites contain greater proportions of carbon in aromatic structures than the sporinites and there are some molecular differences in the aliphatic C–H group distributions and oxygen functions.

Analytical pyrolysis
Analytical pyrolysis

(pyrolysis–mass spectrometry and pyrolysis–gas chromatography) has been applied extensively to the study of coals and individual macerals (Holden and Robb, 1958; Evans and Raphaely, 1964; Bricteaux, 1966; Romovacek and Kubat, 1968; Suggate, 1972; McHugh *et al.*, 1976; Larter and Douglas, 1978; Larter *et al.*, 1978; van Graas *et al.*, 1980; Larter and Douglas, 1980; Winans *et al.*, 1981).

In this study the sporinites and vitrinites have been compared on the basis of products identified in 610 °C Curie-point pyrolysates. The pyrolysates of both macerals are dominated by aliphatic, alkylated phenolic and alkylated aromatic components, as shown in Fig. 6. These fragment ion identifications are tentative but are based on complementary pyrolysis–gas chromatographic–mass spectrometric analyses of these samples. Other work (Maters *et al.*, 1977; Larter, 1978; van Graas *et al.*, 1980) has shown that whereas pyrolysis–mass spectrometry and pyrolysis–gas chromatography are carried out under quite different conditions (i.e. under vacuum and inert atmosphere respectively) there is good qualitative correspondence of the data obtained. The pyrolysates of sporinite and vitrinite differ in the relative abundances of aliphatic hydrocarbons compared to the alkylated phenolic and aromatic compounds, with greater amounts of aliphatic material being found in sporinites of any given rank, as would be expected. This is consistent with the above NMR data. Qualitatively, the two macerals produce similar pyrolytic fingerprints. However, while this observation must be interpreted cautiously as the proportions of the two macerals represented in the pyrolytic products may be small and variable (van de Meent *et al.*, 1980), it is nevertheless interesting that the thermally-labile structures (to 610 °C) can be degraded to similar molecular components. The effects of sample rank on pyrolysis products are shown for sporinites in Fig. 7 where a decline in phenolic constituents relative to benzenes and naphthalenes with increasing rank is most noticeable. This is consistent with the decreasing oxygen contents of coals with progressive coalification.

The analytical pyrolysis data indicate that mono- and diaromatic nuclei are the major aromatic hydrocarbon products of degradation. This is supported by other pyrolysis–gas chromatographic analyses on these samples (Larter *et al.*, 1978; Larter and Douglas, 1980; Solli *et al.*, 1980a, b) where it has also been shown that the proportions of alkylated benzenes and naphthalenes in pyrolysates increase with increasing rank. The simple alkylated compounds like toluene and xylenes are very prominent in the pyrograms (Fig. 8), and their abundance is probably due to the high stabilities of benzyl and methyl–benzyl radicals formed during pyrolysis (Svob *et al.*, 1972). They are interpreted as being derived from polycyclic hydroaromatic structures within the maceral kerogens (Larter and Douglas, 1978). Thus, the analytical pyrolysis data in general support a molecular model of the type proposed for vitrinite by Given (1961) where naphthalenic and dihydrophenanthrenic nuclei are common structural units, and they further extend the applicability of the model to bituminous-rank sporinite. These conclusions are necessarily restricted to those proportions of the two

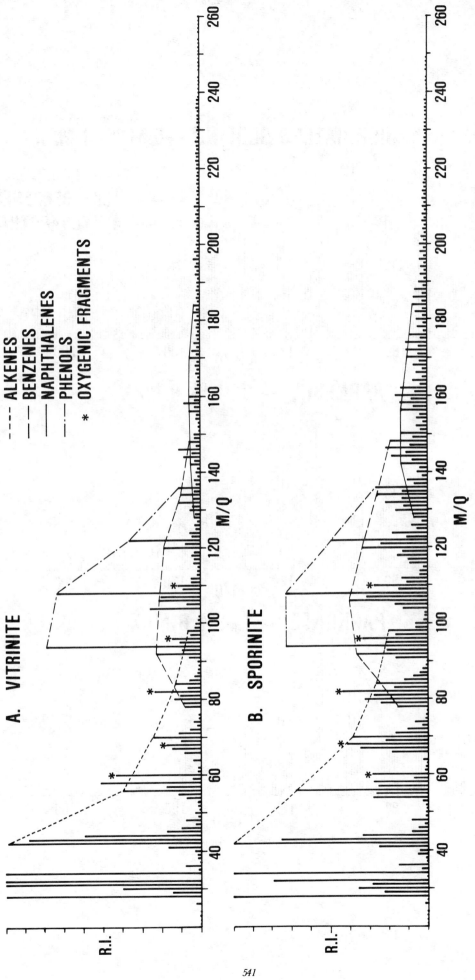

Fig. 6. 610 °C pyrolysis — mass spectra of coal macerals from the Shallow Coal Seam (Vitrinite $\bar{R}_{max}$ 0.56%). PMS conditions in text.

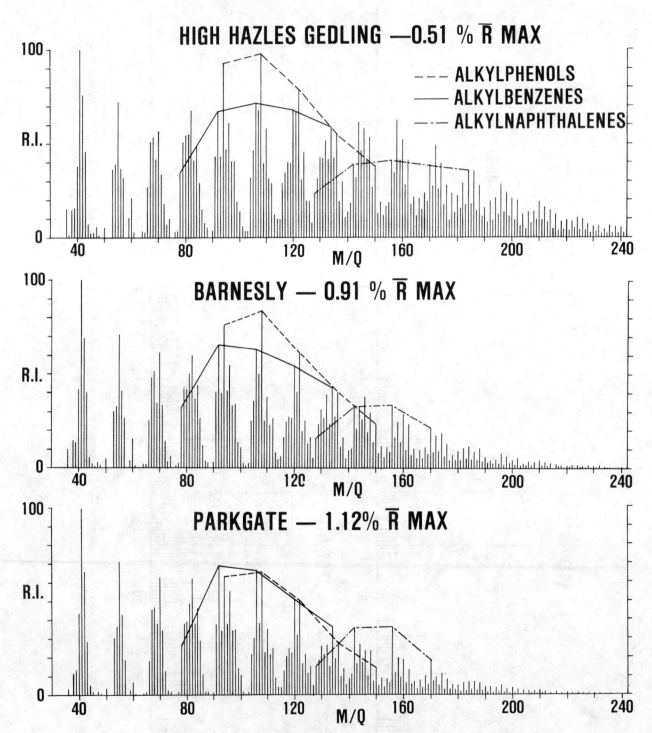

Fig. 7. 610 °C pyrolysis — mass spectra of sporinites. PMS conditions in text.

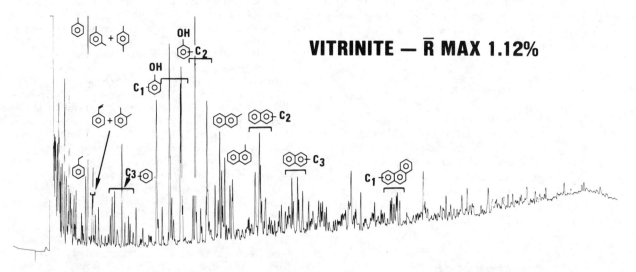

Fig. 8. 1 second 600 °C pyrogram of a high rank vitrinite (Parkgate coal). PGC conditions in text.

maceral structures which are degradable at ~600 °C, and such proportions are presently unknown.

The presence of phenols in vitrinite pyrolysates is consistent with a dominant lignin contribution to the vitrinite group, and the pyrolytic work shows that they are present to the highest rank examined (Fig. 8). The prominence of phenols in sporinite pyrolysates was not expected. Shaw and Yeadon (1966) stated that modern pollen contains some lignin-like material which may be the source of phenols, and other sources such as phenolic amino acids and proteins are possible (Larter *et al.*, 1980). Furthermore Dryden (1963) considers that sporinite oxygen is dominantly in hydroxyl or ether forms, which is not consistent with the present results. Neither is the predominance of phenols entirely consistent with the carotenoid ester polymer model of Brooks and Shaw (1968).

SUMMARY

Analysis of extractable hydrocarbons from sporinites and vitrinites has shown that a great deal of similarity exists in the amount and composition of these compounds. Conventionally, these two macerals are considered to be very different materials, at least at ranks below the second coalification break. Consequently, the compositional similarities in extractable hydrocarbons suggest that these compounds may not be representative of the individual maceral types, but rather represent average compositions resulting from homogenization of free molecules within coal seams. Other chemical (Winans *et al.*, 1981) and petrological work (Hutton, 1980) has led to the suggestion that vitrinite is capable of absorbing free molecules, but the present study of a rank series rather suggests that more complex processes of molecular interchange actually occur.

It has been further shown that aromatic hydrocarbons change consistently in composition with sample rank as a result of catagenetic processes, and that these changes are broadly similar to the well-documented trends established for aliphatic hydrocarbons.

Geochemical analyses of the maceral kerogens suggest that there are many structural similarities in the two materials, at least in a qualitative sense. In particular, simple alkylated benzenes, naphthalenes and phenols are predominant pyrolysis products of these proportions of the two kerogens which are susceptible to degradation at ~600 °C. These data support the two and three ring hydroaromatic/aromatic base structure which has been proposed for bituminous-rank vitrinites, but further suggest that this model is also applicable in part to sporinites. Unfortunately, the pyrolytic data are not quantitative and it is possible that different proportions of the two macerals are represented by the pyrolysis products.

In the past, bituminous-rank vitrinite and sporinite have been deduced to be different materials on the basis of differences in elemental analysis, aromaticity, functional group analysis, optical properties, etc. Their different botanical origins further lead to expectations of chemical variance, along with the fact that sporinite consists of sedimented entities while vitrinite is a diagenetic amorphous or cellular product of woody tissues. However, none of these data or observations have clearly established that sporinite and vitrinite consist of fundamentally different chemical structures. Observed chemical and physical differences could be explained as different molecular combinations of similar unit structures. The data presented in this paper do not provide equivocal answers to the problem, and although observable differences are sufficient to differentiate the two macerals, such differences are based on relative abundances of similar molecular fragments. It seems clear that this kind of comparative geochemistry needs to be extended to lower rank ranges to follow the molecular transformations occurring in the early stages of coalification. Further work is also required to quantitate analytical pyrolysis data, and to extend the range of analyses performed on these kerogens.

Acknowledgements

The authors wish to thank the staff of the Analytical Department of the Science and Technology Division of Union Oil Company of California who provided advice and analytical assistance in this work. We also thank Union Oil Company of California for permission to publish. Pyrolysis–mass spectra were provided through Dr K. Voorhees and Dr H. L. C. Meuzelaar. Technical assistance was provided by G. Ouellette and R. Husser.

REFERENCES

Allan, J., Bjorøy, M. and Douglas, A. G. (1977) Variation in the Content and Distribution of High Molecular Weight Hydrocarbons in a Series of Coal Macerals of Different Ranks. In *Advances in Organic Geochemistry* 1975. Ed. by Campos, R. and Goni, J. Enadimsa, Madrid. p. 633.

Allan, J., Bjorøy, M. and Douglas, A. G. (1980) A Geochemical Study of the Exinite Group Maceral Alginite Selected from Three Permo-Carboniferous Torbanites. In *Advances in Organic Geochemistry* 1979. Ed. by Douglas, A. G. and Maxwell, J. R. Pergamon Press, Oxford. p. 599.

Allan, J. and Douglas, A. G. (1977) Variations in the Content and Distribution of n-Alkanes in a Series of Carboniferous Vitrinites and Sporinites of Bituminous Rank. *Geochim. Cosmochim. Acta* **41**, 1223.

Baset, Z. H., Pancirov, R. J. and Ashe, T. R. (1980) Organic Compounds in Coal: Structure and Origins. In *Advances in Organic Geochemistry* 1979. Ed. by Douglas, A. G. and Maxwell, J. R. Pergamon Press, Oxford. p. 619.

Bricteaux, J. (1966) Pyrolyse-flash et Chromatographie en Phase Gazeuse. Application a l'étude des Houilles et de leur Dérives. *Annales Mines Belg.* **12**, 1543.

Brooks, J. (1971) Some Chemical and Geochemical Studies on Sporopollenin. In *Sporopollenin*. Ed. by Brooks, J., Grant, P. R., Muir, M., van Gijzel, P. and Shaw, G. Academic Press, London. p. 351.

Brooks, J. and Shaw, G. (1968) Chemical Structure of the Exine of Pollen Walls and a New Function for Carotenoids in Nature. *Nature* **219**, 532.

Brooks, J. D. and Smith, J. W. (1967) The Diagenesis of Plant Lipids During the Formation of Coal, Petroleum and Natural Gas — I. Changes in the n-Paraffin Hydrocarbons. *Geochim. Cosmochim. Acta* **31**, 2389.

Dormans, H. N. M., Huntjens, F. J. and van Krevelen, D. W. (1957) Chemical Structures and Properties of Coal Macerals (Vitrinite, Fusinite, Micrinite and Exinite). *Fuel* **36**, 321.

Dryden, I. G. C. (1963) Chemical Constitution and Reactions of Coal. In *Chemistry of Coal Utilization*, Supplementary Volume. Ed. by Lowry, H. H. J. Wiley and Sons Inc., New York. p. 232.

Evans, W. D. and Raphaely, P. B. (1964) A Comparison Between the Petrology and Pyrochromatography of an English and South African Coal. In *Advances in Organic Geochemistry* 1962. Ed. by Colombo, U. and Hobson, G. D. Pergamon Press, Oxford. p. 87.

Gallegos, E. J. (1978) Analysis of Five US Coals. In *Advances in Chemistry Series* **179**. Ed. by Uden, P. C., Siggia, S. and Jensen, H. B. ACS, Washington DC. p. 274.

Gallegos, E. J. (1981) Alkylbenzenes Derived from Carotenes in Coals by GC/MS. *J. Chromatogr. Sci.* **19**, 177.

Given, P. H. (1961) Dehydrogenation of Coals and its Relation to Coal Structure. *Fuel* **40**, 427.

van Graas, G., de Leeuw, J. W. and Schenck, P. A. (1980) Analysis of Coals of Different Ranks by Curie-Point Pyrolysis–Mass Spectrometry and Curie-Point Pyrolysis–Gas Chromatography–Mass Spectrometry. In *Advances in Organic Geochemistry* 1979. Ed. by Douglas, A. G. and Maxwell, J. R. Pergamon Press, Oxford. p. 485.

Hayatsu, R., Winans, R. E., Scott, R. G., Moore, L. P. and Studier, M. H. (1978) Trapped Organic Compounds and Aromatic Units in Coals. *Fuel* **57**, 541.

Holden, H. W. and Robb, J. C. (1958) Mass Spectrometry of Substances of Low Volatility. *Nature* **182**, 340.

Hutton, A. C. (1980) Problems of Vitrinite Reflectance of Oil Shales in Relation to Regional Rank. In *Oil Shale Petrology Workshop*. Ed. by Cook, A. C. and Kantsler, A. J. Keiraville Kopiers, Wollongong. p. 71.

van Krevelen, D. W. (1961) *Coal*. Elsevier, Amsterdam.

Larter, S. R. (1980) Ph.D. Thesis (unpublished), University of Newcastle upon Tyne, England.

Larter, S. R. and Douglas, A. G. (1978) Low Molecular Weight Aromatic Hydrocarbons in Coal Maceral Pyrolysates as Indicators of Diagenesis and Organic Matter Type. In *Environmental Biogeochem. and Geomicrobiol.* Ed. by Krumbein, W. E. Ann Arbor, Michigan. p. 373.

Larter, S. R. and Douglas, A. G. (1980) A Pyrolysis–Gas Chromatographic Method for Kerogen Typing. In *Advances in Organic Geochemistry* 1979. Ed. by Douglas, A. G. and Maxwell, J. R. Pergamon Press, Oxford. p. 579.

Larter, S. R., Solli, H. and Douglas, A. G. (1978) Analytis of Kerogens by Pyrolysis–Gas Chromatography–Mass Spectrometry Using Selective Ion Detection. *J. Chromatogr.* **167**, 421.

Leythaeuser, D., Hagemann, H., Hollerbach, A. and Schaefer, R. G. (1980) Hydrocarbon Generation in Source Beds as a Function of Type and Maturation of Their Organic Matter: A Mass Balance Approach. In *10th World Petr. Congr. Proc.* **2**, 31.

Leythaeuser, D. and Welte, D. H. (1969) Relation Between Distributions of Heavy n-Paraffins and Coalification in Carboniferous Coals from the Saar District, Germany. In *Advances in Organic Geochemistry* 1968. Ed. by Schenck, P. A. and Havenaar, I. Pergamon Press, Oxford. p. 429.

Maters, W. L., van de Meent, D., Schuyl, P. J. W., de Leeuw, J. W. and Schenck, P. A. (1977) Curie-Point Pyrolysis in Organic Geochemistry. In *Analytical Pyrolysis*. Ed. by Jones, C. E. R. and Cramers, C. A. Elsevier, Amsterdam. p. 203.

McHugh, D. J., Saxby, J. D. and Tardiff, J. W. (1976) Pyrolysis–Hydrogenation–Gas Chromatography of Carbonaceous Material from Australian Sediments. Part I. Some Australian Coals. *Chem. Geol.* **17**, 243.

van de Meent, D., Brown, S. C., Philp, R. P. and Simoneit, B. R. T. (1980) Pyrolysis–High Resolution Gas Chromatography and Pyrolysis–Gas Chromatography–Mass Spectrometry of Kerogens and Kerogen Precursors. *Geochim. Cosmochim. Acta* **44**, 999.

Meuzelaar, H. L. C., Kistemaker, P. G., Eshuis, W. and Boerboom, A. J. H. (1978) Automated Pyrolysis–Mass Spectrometry: Application to the Differentiation of Micro-Organisms. In *Adv. in Mass Spectrom. 76*. Ed. by Daly, N. R. Heyden and Sons Ltd., London. p. 1452.

Philp, R. P. and Saxby, J. D. (1980) Organic Geochemistry of Coal Macerals from the Sydney Basin (Australia). In *Advances in Organic Geochemistry* 1979. Ed. by Douglas, A. G. and Maxwell, J. R. Pergamon Press, Oxford. p. 539.

Radke, M., Schaefer, R. G., Leythaeuser, D. and Teichmüller, M. (1980) Composition of Soluble Organic Matter in Coals: Relation to Rank and Liptinite Fluorescence. *Geochim. Cosmochim. Acta* **44**, 1787.

Radke, M. and Welte, D. H. (1981) The Methylphenanthrene Index (MPI): A Maturity Parameter Based on Aromatic Hydrocarbons. This volume.

Romovacek, J. and Kubat, J. (1968) Characterization of Coal Substances by Pyrolysis–Gas Chromatography. *Anal. Chem.* **40**, 1119.

Shaw, G. and Yeadon, A. (1966) Chemical Studies on the Chemical Constitution of Some Pollen and Spore Membranes. *J. Chem. Soc. C.* **16**.

Solli, H., Larter, S. R. and Douglas, A. G. (1980a) Analysis of Kerogens by Pyrolysis–Gas Chromatography–Mass Spectrometry Using Selective Ion Monitoring — II Alkylnaphthalenes. *J. Anal. Appl. Pyrol.* **1**, 231.

Solli, H., Larter, S. R. and Douglas, A. G. (1980b) Analysis of Kerogens by Pyrolysis–Gas Chromatography–Mass Spectrometry — III Alkylbenzenes. In *Advances in Organic Geochemistry*. Ed. by Douglas, A. G. and Maxwell, J. R. Pergamon Press, Oxford. p. 591.

Suggate, R. P. (1972) Coal Rank from Pyrochromatography. *New Zealand J. Sci.* **15**, 601.

Svob, V., Deur-Siftar, D. and Cramers, C. A. (1972) Pyrolysis–Gas Chromatographic Analysis of Alkylbenzenes. *Chromatographia* **5**, 540.

White, C. M. and Lee, M. L. (1980) Identification and Geochemical Significance of Some Aromatic Components of Coal. *Geochim. Cosmochim. Acta* **44**, 1825.

Winans, R. E., Drykacz, G. R., McBeth, R. L., Scott, R. G. and Hayatsu, R. (1981) Characterization of Separated Coal Macerals. In *Inter. Conf. Coal Sci. Proc.* Dusseldorf 7–9.9.81. Verlag Gluckauf GmbH, Essen. p. 22.

Zilm, K. W., Pugmire, R. J., Larter, S. R., Allan, J. and Grant, D. M. (1981) Carbon-13 CP/MAS Spectroscopy of Coal Macerals. *Fuel* **60**, 717.

Advances in Organic Geochemistry 1981, pp. 546–553
© *John Wiley & Sons Limited, 1983*

Carbonization of Precambrian Kerogens*

K. W. Wedeking and J. M. Hayes

Precambrian Paleobiology Research Group, Department of Earth and Space Sciences, UCLA

and (permanent address)

Biogeochemical Laboratories, Departments of Chemistry and of Geology, Indiana University, Bloomington, Indiana 47405

As part of a systematic investigation of the extent to which Precambrian sediments have suffered thermal alteration, some forty different kerogenous residues have been isolated from cherts, carbonates, and shales 0.8 to 3.8 Ga in age and subjected to X-ray diffraction and elemental analyses. These specimens are representative of the least metamorphosed members of twenty-one major Proterozoic and Archean sequences. To aid in interpretation of the results obtained, a substantial amount of pertinent data has been drawn from the literature and included in this report. Specifically, study of the relationship between the ordering of aromatic layers (indicated by the graphite 002 reflection) and hydrogen abundance (atomic H/C ratio) in these primarily sub-graphitic materials has revealed that graphitization very probably proceeds in three distinct phases. During thermal maturation of natural kerogens, the width at half height of the 002 peak is not a smooth function of H/C ratio and may involve sudden 'jumps' or reversals (apparent retrocrystallization) within certain ranges of H/C. Possible mechanisms and physical conditions involved in the observed phases of development of crystalline order are discussed and seem to apply to a diversity of kerogen specimens. A consistent picture has emerged, leading to the conclusion that most (if not all) Precambrian materials have suffered severe alteration involving development of significant degrees of graphitic structure and extensive dehydrogenation. Barring the possibility that most of the materials analyzed represent recycled kerogen and that, therefore, they do not reflect the metamorphic history of their present sedimentary host, the chance that syngenetic chemical fossils can have survied in the Archean sediments analyzed appears near zero.

INTRODUCTION

While there has been considerable interest in the possible presence of chemical fossils in Precambrian sediments (see, for example, reviews by McKirdy, 1974; Hayes *et al.*, 1983), it is largely true that a study of Precambrian organic geochemistry involves most prominently the characterization of heavily altered kerogens (e.g. Dungworth and Schwartz, 1972, 1974; McKirdy and Powell, 1974; Leventhal *et al.*, 1975; Zumberge *et al.*, 1978; McKirdy *et al.*, 1980). The resolution and recognition of processes comprising the metagenetic and metamorphic alteration of kerogens and the correlation of those processes with the corresponding post-depositional histories of the host sediments are, accordingly, principal goals of Precambrian organic

geochemistry. It is of special interest to determine whether the bulk physical and chemical properties of the abundant kerogen component of Precambrian sediments are consistent with the presence of syngenetic chemical fossils and, therefore, whether analytically complex analyses of traces of extractable organic material are useful for the characterization of ancient ecosystems.

In the present work, X-ray diffraction and elemental analyses have been applied to 38 kerogen samples isolated from specimens of varying lithology collected from 21 major Precambrian sequences, 0.8–3.8 Ga in age. Particular attention is given to matters of general geochemical interest:

1. the utility of X-ray diffraction analyses in the determination of levels of metagenetic alteration of kerogens;
2. correlations between inorganic and organic metamorphism; and
3. possible mechanisms and separable stages of graphitization.

---

* These analyses have been carried out in connection with the work of the Precambrian Paleobiology Research Group (for a complete account of the work of this group, see Schopf, 1983). A more detailed discussion of experimental procedures and a presentation of related analytical results will appear elsewhere (Wedeking *et al.*, 1983; Hayes *et al.*, 1983).

EXPERIMENTAL

Isolation of carbonaceous material

Samples were ground to less than 100 μm. The first dissolution step employed 60% HF if the rock was a carbonate-poor chert or shale, 37% HCl for a carbonate, or a 5:2 (v/v) mixture for carbonate-bearing cherts or shales. Rock powder was slowly added to and stirred with the acid solution while the temperature was held below 60 °C. The resulting slurry was allowed to stand with intermittent stirring for 12 h at 25 °C. The solid residue was isolated by settling or centrifugation and washed with approximately 1 l of distilled water. The acid treatment was repeated using the HF–HCl mixture and the water-washed residue was analyzed by X-ray diffraction in order to determine whether minerals susceptible to acid dissolution had survived. If such minerals were present, acid digestion was continued until these species were no longer detectable.

Neoformed fluorides (Durand and Nicaise, 1980) were removed using a solution of aluminum chloride (Grew, 1974; Wedeking et al., 1983). Fluoride-containing samples, previously rinsed to neutrality, were shaken with approximately 200 ml of 1.2 M AlCl$_3$ (prepared by dissolving 250 g of AlCl$_3$·6H$_2$O in 750 g water) for 24 h at 25 °C, after which the aqueous phase was removed and discarded. The resulting carbonaceous residue was washed and analyzed by X-ray diffraction, the AlCl$_3$ washing being repeated (up to five times) until no detectable fluoride remained. Usually, three such treatments were effective in complete removal of the typically encountered quantities of fluoride complexes. Samples were washed with distilled water and dried in vacuo.

After drying, the residues were weighed, and, based on the previously determined organic carbon content of the starting material (Wedeking et al., 1983) and the amount initially digested, an estimate of carbon content (and therefore maximal ash content) of each kerogen residue was obtained. X-ray diffraction and transmitted light microscopy revealed that pyrite was the only significant mineral phase remaining in these samples, and was present in amounts $\leqslant 50\%$ by weight. Pyrite produced no reflections in the region of the graphite 002 peak, therefore its presence in some samples did not represent an interfering species.

Elemental analyses

The H/C and N/C ratios of the isolated materials were determined using an adaptation (Wedeking et al., 1983) of a technique (Frazer, 1962; Frazer and Crawford, 1963; Frazer and Crawford, 1964) involving combustion of samples in quartz bombs (with CuO as oxidant), followed by separation and measurement of the N$_2$, CO$_2$ and H$_2$O produced (H$_2$O being converted to H$_2$ over uranium metal at 800 °C before measurement). Replicate analyses of individual kerogen samples and of pure compounds with known elemental compositions (Wedeking et al., 1983) indicated that the accuracy of these H/C measurements was better than $\pm 15\%$ (95% confidence interval) and that the accuracy of the N/C measurements was better than $\pm 12\%$ (95% confidence interval).

X-ray diffractometry

The technique employed was similar to that of Griffin (1967). A small amount of dry sample was evenly dispersed using a few drops of water within a $1 \times 2 \times 0.05$ cm depression in an aluminum slide. Samples were allowed to dry and were then scanned using nickel-filtered CuK$_\alpha$ radiation at a rate of $1°$ ($2\,\theta$) min^{-1}, beginning at $10°$ and continuing to at least $40°$. The aluminum (111) reflection at $38.47°$ provided a convenient internal standard for peak position. Strip-chart recordings of the X-ray diffraction patterns were used to measure both the position (measured at peak centroid in degrees $2\,\theta$, converted to d_{002} in Å) and peak width at half height (measured in degrees $2\,\theta$ at half the centroid peak height) of the developing graphite (002) reflections.

The peak centroid was located using a commonly employed geometrical technique, as illustrated in Fig. 1. Width at half height was always measured parallel to the diffractogram baseline. Replicate slide preparations and analyses (Wedeking et al., 1983) showed that the uncertainty (95% confidence level) in peak position (converted to d spacing by the Bragg equation) was ± 0.01 Å and was $\pm 0.4''$ ($2\,\theta$) for width at half height.

RESULTS AND DISCUSSION

Representative diffractograms obtained in this work are shown in Fig. 1, which demonstrates that the diffraction pattern characteristic of the kerogen is far more readily apparent when aluminum (Griffin, 1967), as opposed to the commonly employed glass, is used to carry the sample. Reflections other than the 002 line were not well developed in the majority of samples examined, and the present study has, thus, been restricted to consideration of variations in the position and shape of the 002 reflection. The broad X-ray diffraction peak characteristic of glass is very similar to that of an immature kerogen (Fig. 1). The problem can be largely overcome if care is taken to apply a considerable thickness (~ 1 mm) of kerogen to the glass substrate (e.g. French, 1964), but the problem need not be faced at all if the aluminum slides described above are used in place of glass. While most workers have reported diffraction peak position at the intensity maximum rather than at the centroid location, it has been found in the present work that, for the broad peaks characteristic of these carbonaceous phases, centroid values of peak position can be determined with considerably greater reproducibility (see Fig. 1) and yield significantly better correlations of $w_{1/2}$ with d_{002}.

Results of the X-ray and elemental analyses are shown in Table 1. Comparable results gleaned from the literature are summarized in Table 2, which includes all reports that allow correlations between at least three of the four tabulated parameters (in some cases one or both

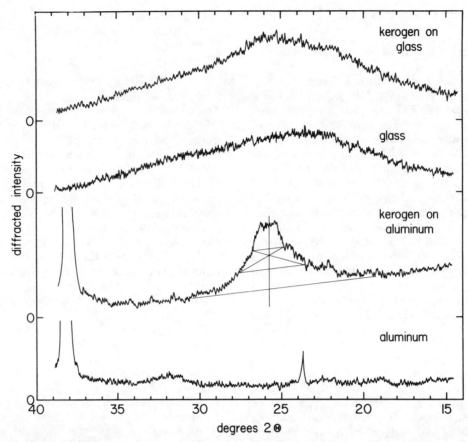

Fig. 1. Representative X-ray diffractograms of a subgraphitic kerogen (Bungle–Bungle Fm. chert–carbonate with $w_{1/2} = 2.90°$ (2θ), see Table 1) and blank mounting substrates. From top to bottom: sample on glass substrate, blank glass slide, kerogen on aluminum slide (geometrical construction for locating 002 peak centroid shown), and blank aluminum plate.

of the X-ray parameters was estimated from illustrations in the original publications). A graphic summary of the results is shown in Fig. 2, the first portion of which illustrates the relationship between apparent interplanar spacing and the width of the peak measured at half the centroid height. It can be seen that $w_{1/2}$ and d_{002} are linearly correlated over a wide range, and that the relationship between these parameters is similar for the kerogen specimens of this report and for those studied by other workers. It appears, therefore, that this correlation is quite general. Figure 2a includes some points from Table 2, specifically those for which it has been possible to determine with reasonable accuracy both the peak width and its precise location. When necessary, the centroid location has been estimated from the relationship:

$$d_{002} \text{ (centroid)} = d_{002} (I_{\max}) + 0.04 \text{ Å}, [d_{002}(I_{\max}) \geqslant 3.45 \text{ Å}].$$

$$d_{002}(\text{centroid}) = d_{002}(I_{\max}), [d_{002}(I_{\max}) \text{ Å} < 3.45 \text{ Å}].$$

This empirical relationship summarizes the results of the present study and is assumed to be applicable to all similar materials. The second portion of Fig. 2 graphically summarizes the relationship between

diffraction peak widths and H/C ratios, including all entries from Table 2 for which both parameters are tabulated.

Ross (1968) has pointed out that interpretation of widths of diffraction peaks strictly in terms of average crystal subunit thickness perpendicular to the diffracting planes is not straightforward and involves complex theoretical calculation when the material under study contains crystal subunits with varying interplanar distances. If interplanar distance were constant, application of the Scherrer equation (Scherrer, 1918) would allow calculation of average subunit thickness (as done by Griffin, 1967). That this condition is not met in the case of subgraphitic kerogens is confirmed by electron microscopic studies (Landis, 1971; Oberlin *et al.*, 1980) showing that interplanar spacings in kerogens and sub-graphitic carbons vary widely. Considering such cases, Ross (1968) has shown that *broad diffraction peaks can represent varying interplanar spacings* as well as — or, rather than — thin crystal subunits. This unusual relationship must clearly be borne in mind in the interpretation of the present results.

Figure 2b shows $w_{1/2}$ values plotted versus corresponding H/C ratios. It is apparent that orderly stacking increases rapidly ($w_{1/2}$ decreases) during the early phase of maturation corresponding to a range in H/C from ~1.2 to ~0.5. This decrease in $w_{1/2}$ is probably best understood in terms of the 'turbostratic' structural model first proposed by Blayden *et al.* (1944).

Table 1

Analyses of Precambrian carbonaceous phases.

Rock Unit[a]	Age[a]	Metamorphism[a]	Lithology[b]	$W_{1/2}$, °2θ	d_{002}, Å	H/C
				X-ray Diffraction		
Skillogallee Dolomite	0.8	lower greenschist	C	4.25	3.52	0.17
Bitter Springs Fm.	0.9	unknown	C	3.31	3.48	0.34
Roper River Grp.	1.5	'little or none'	S	3.2	3.6	0.79
			S	4.06	3.58	0.48
			Q	3.23	3.51	0.40
Bungle-Bungle Fm.	1.6	unknown	C	2.78	3.47	0.31
			S	1.65	3.47	0.45
			AC	2.68	3.45	0.38
			AC	2.90	3.48	0.39
Earaheedy Fm.	1.8	lower than greenschist	A	4.45	3.55	0.27
Wyloo Gp.	2.0	pumpellyite–epidote	C	3.8	3.5	0.32
		pumpellyite–actinolite	A	3.50	3.52	0.15
Rove Fm.	2.0	'subgreenschist'	S	2.44	3.48	0.41
Mistassini Grp.	2.1	greenschist	A	4.29	3.52	0.14
Belcher Supergrp.	2.1	'subgreenschist'	CA	4.88	3.57	0.26
Transvaal Dolomite	2.2	'subgreenschist'	A	4.33	3.49	0.14
			A	4.96	3.56	0.21
Hamersley Grp.	2.6	prehnite–pumpellyite	SA	4.96	3.53	0.14
		pumpellyite–actinolite	S	3.70	3.52	0.11
		greenschist	S	5.24	3.53	0.11
Steeprock Grp.	2.6	to greenschist	C	3.23	3.52	0.17
Ventersdorp Grp.	2.64	greenschist	C	4.09	3.53	0.14
Belingwe Greenstone Belt	2.64	upper greenschist	C	3.58	3.48	0.13
Bulawayan Limestone	2.64	greenschist	A	3.46	3.48	0.098
Fortescue Grp.	2.77	pumpellyite-epidote	C	5.12	3.55	0.25
		pumpellyite-actinolate	S	4.38	3.52	0.14
Pongola Supergrp.	3.0	greenschist	S	1.38	3.39	0.11
Gorge Creek Grp.	3.4	greenschist	S	4.57	3.57	0.086
Warrawoona Grp.	3.52	lower greenschist	C	4.21	3.58	0.16
			C	3.66	3.52	0.30
Swaziland Supergrp.	3.54	greenschist	C	3.70	3.52	0.12
			C	4.02	3.53	0.13
			C	3.57	3.50	0.096
			C	3.49	3.48	0.085
			C	3.03	3.48	0.16
		unknown	S	<0.8	3.38	0.019
Isua Supracrustal Grp.	3.77	amphibolite	B	<0.8	3.39	0.016
			H	<0.8	3.38	0.012

[a] For detailed information on sample locations, ages, and metamorphism, see Walter (1983).
[b] A = carbonate, B = banded iron formation, C = chert, H = schist, Q = sandstone, S = shale; combined symbols indicate mixtures.

Investigation of developing graphite structure by electron microscopy (Oberlin *et al.*, 1980) indicates that, structurally, kerogen begins (at H/C ~1.2) as a poorly ordered matrix, consisting of stacks of two or three aromatic layers having diameters of less than 10 Å. These small structural subunits have varied interplanar spacings, are associated in a mosaic-like structure, are crosslinked by aliphatic moieties, and are interspersed with non-aromatic material. Their association forms larger, irregular, wrinkled layers about 200 Å in diameter. During pregraphitization ($\leqslant$2000 °C in artificial heating experiments), the major change is probably an increase in the number of aromatic layers per subunit from two or three to more than forty (Oberlin *et al.*, 1980) with little change in the diameter of associated parallel layers. The X-ray diffraction results of Fig. 2b are consistent with the possibility that expulsion of hydrocarbons (petroleum, gas) or other relatively mobile phases allows stacking of aromatic layers to form larger (thicker) subunits in the H/C range ~1.2 to ~0.5.

From H/C ~0.5 to ~0.1, it is evident (Fig. 2b) that $w_{1/2}$ actually *increases* with decreasing H/C. This trend is consistent with observations of Diamond (1959) as summarized by van Krevelen (1961), in which layer packing deteriorates (with a resulting increase in average d spacing) before graphitization proceeds to completion. Disruption of aliphatic crosslinks between (and possibly within) individual subunits may lead to either, or both, (i) an increased range of interlayer spacings, (ii) an increased average interlayer spacing. Given the diversity of samples studied and the clear trend towards higher $w_{1/2}$ in the H/C range ~0.5 to ~0.1, the present results suggest that this structural progression occurs regardless of kerogen type (source) or the physico-chemical conditions that prevailed during maturation.

The diffuse broken line in Fig. 2b crudely represents the trends noted and discussed above, with $w_{1/2}$ decreasing as H/C decreases from ~1.2 to ~0.5, then

Table 2

Correlations between graphite crystallinity and other indicators of maturity and metamorphism. Entries are arranged in order of increasing alteration

Entry number	X-ray diffraction parameters[a]		Correlative parameters		
	$W^c_{1/2}$ °2θ	d_{002}, Å	H/C atomic ratio	metamorphic indicators	Reference[b]
1	>10*	>4*	1.0		1
2	20*	3.6–3.9	0.7–0.8		2
3	12	3.8	1.0–1.2	coal ranks lignite; sub-bituminous A, B	3
4	11*	3.5–3.8		zeolite facies, prehnite–pumpellyite facies	4
5	7–12*	3.5–3.7	0.6–0.9		5
6	7*	3.5–3.6		250 < T < 270 °C, lawsonite zone, lawsonite–albite facies	6
7	8*	3.4–3.6		lawsonite–epidote pumpellyite zone, lawsonite–albite–chlorite facies; pumpellyite–actinolite facies	4
8	6.5*	3.4*	0.6		1
9	5.1–6.8	3.55–3.61	0.8–0.9	coal ranks high-volatile bituminous A, B, C	3
10	5–7*	~3.5		iron fm. with siderite, ankerite, chamosite, grunerite and calcite	7
11	4.5	3.54	0.7	coal ranks low- and medium-volatile bituminous	3
12	4–5*	3.4–3.5	0.3–0.5		5
13	3.5–5*	3.5–3.6	0.2–0.3		2
14	5*	3.4–3.5		270 < T < 320 °C, lawsonite zone, lawsonite–albite facies	2
15	5.6	3.6	0.075	chlorite zone, greenschist facies	8
16	~5*	3.37–3.52	0.11–0.25	chlorite zone, greenschist facies	9
17	2–4*	3.43		as entry 10, but with iron pyroxenes	7
18	3.6	3.51	0.61	coal rank semi-anthracite	3
19	3.9*	3.4*	0.6		1
20	2.4*	3.4*	0.5		1
21	5.1	3.55	0.4	coal rank anthracite	3
22	<4*	3.36–3.40		320 < T < 370 °C, lawsonite–ferroglaucophane zone, lawsonite–albite facies	6
23	1.5*	3.37–3.44		as entry 7 and in chlorite zone, greenschist facies and blueschist facies	4
24	<1.2	3.39–3.40	0.05–0.1		2
25	0.6–1.3	3.37–3.42	0.05	chlorite zone, greenschist facies	8
26	<1*	3.36		iron pyroxenes, grunerite, calcite	7
27	0.7*	3.37–3.39		biotite zone, greenschist facies	10
28	0.5–0.7	3.37–3.38	0.01–0.03	chlorite–biotite zone, greenschist facies	8
29	1.5*	3.35–3.38		biotite zone, greenschist facies, blueschist facies	4
30	0.6	3.36	0.09	coal rank meta-anthracite	3
31		3.36–3.40	0.01–0.11	biotite zone and higher	9
32	0.3–0.5	3.36	0.01–0.04	garnet zone	8
33	0.3	3.36	0.01	staurolite zone	8
34	0.2*	3.35		andalusite–staurolite zone, amphibolite facies	10
35		3.35–3.36		amphibolite facies	4
36	3.36			390 < T < 440 °C, epidote zone, amphibolite facies	6
37	0.2–0.3	3.36	0.00–0.01	sillimanite zone, amphibolite facies	8
38	0.2*	3.36		sillimanite zone, amphibolite facies	10

[a] Asterisk (*) indicates value estimated from figure in publication.

[b] Reference: 1. Powell et al. (1975); 2. Izawa (1968); 3. Griffin (1967); 4. Landis (1971); 5. Long et al. (1968); 6. Diessel et al. (1978); 7. French (1964); 8. Grew (1974); 9. McKirdy et al. (1975); 10. Diessel and Offler (1975).

[c] Indicates width at half height of the 002 reflection of graphite or graphitic material.

increasing as H/C decreases to values near 0.1. There is clearly a great deal of scatter when results from so wide a variety of samples and localities are considered, but it seems worth noting that this general pattern of development, with $w_{1/2}$ first decreasing, then increasing as dehydrogenation proceeds, is found in all the sample series investigated. Specifically, least-squares calculations indicate that a positive slope for $w_{1/2}$ v. H/C is found in the range 1.2 > H/C > 0.5 for the series of samples (n = 9) investigated by Griffin (1967), for the series (n = 18) investigated by Blayden et al. (1944) and for the

relevant samples (n = 6) in Table 2. Similarly, a negative slope is found in the range 0.5 > H/C > 0.1 for the relevant samples (n = 30) in Table 1 and (n = 5) Table 2 and for the series of samples (n = 9) investigated by Blayden et al. (1944). Like the correlation observed in Fig. 2a, therefore, it appears that this pattern of development is quite generally observed.

Finally, it appears (Fig. 2b) that there is a marked discontinuity in the graphitization of natural kerogens in the range of H/C ratios below 0.1. Numerous workers have noted that graphitization does not proceed

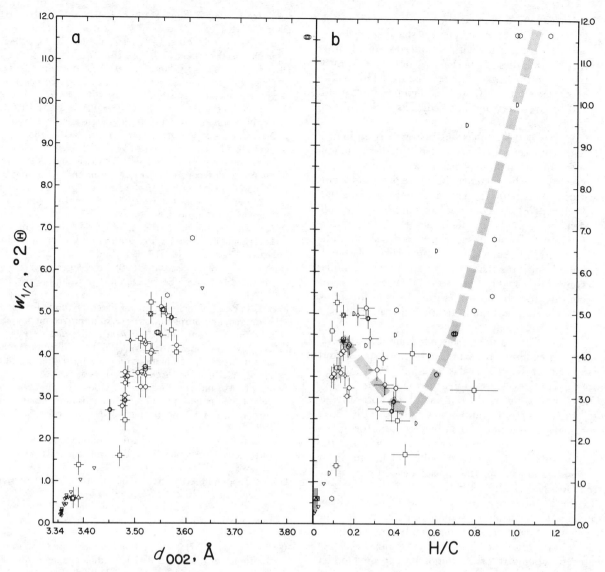

Fig. 2. (a) Peak widths, $w_{1/2}$ (degrees 2θ) versus corresponding interplanar spacing (for all samples listed in Table 1 and for entries 3, 9, 11, 15, 18, 21, 25, 28, 30, 32, 33, and 37 in Table 2). Symbols with uncertainties indicated represent results of this study, with circles denoting cherts, squares shales, diamonds carbonates, and combinations mixtures. Hexagons represent the results of Griffin (1967) and triangles the results of Grew (1974). Interplanar spacings are in Ångströms (Å), calculated from the Bragg equation. While Table 2 reports d values calculated from peak maxima, the figure plots d values corresponding to centroid locations (see text). (b) Peak width versus corresponding hydrogen elemental abundance (as atomic H/C ratio) for samples of Tables 1 and 2. Symbols are as in Fig. 2a, with half circles denoting additional entries from Table 2.

smoothly and continuously, but can involve sudden changes above a certain degree of crystallinity close to that of true graphite (Goma and Oberlin, 1980; Inagaki *et al.*, 1975; Landis, 1971; McKirdy *et al.*, 1975; Oberlin *et al.*, 1980; van Krevelen, 1961). This behaviour very probably occurs after breakage of covalent crosslinked structure is complete, resulting in rapid development of parallel structure associated with increased mobility of crystallites. Evidently, when an H/C ratio of ~0.1 is reached, most (if not all) crosslinked structure is lost and graphitization proceeds to completion. Other factors such as elimination of sorbed gases or pi-bonded metal ions may play an important role in the graphitization 'jump'. Figure 2b shows clearly that when a certain degree of crystallinity is attained, corresponding to a range of $w_{1/2}$ from ~5° to ~3° (2 θ) regardless of sample origin, the development of well ordered graphitic

structure is sudden and virtually complete (in agreement with the transition noted by McKirdy *et al.*, 1975).

The discontinuities observable in Fig. 2a and b are suggestive of a change in activation energy for the graphitization process, reflecting the transition from crosslink disruption to three dimensional ordering. Fig. 2a indicates that a natural break occurs at a d_{002} value of ~3.42 Å. Significantly, Inagaki *et al.* (1975) mention that 3.42 Å represents an important point of transition, involving both an activation energy change (associated with the change from elimination of tilt/twist defects to three dimensional ordering) and changes in physical properties such as Hall coefficient and magneto-resistance.

The present results and interpretation indicate that graphite crystallinity can be an ambiguous indicator of kerogen maturity. The evidence is consistent with three distinct phases of graphitization.

1. $1 > H/C > 0.5$. An initial phase of stacking aromatic layers; associated with expulsion of hydrocarbons/volatiles (perhaps not covalently bonded to the kerogen superstructure). This phase takes place during catagenesis. Temperatures up to 150 °C are probably involved (Tissot and Welte, 1978).

2. $0.5 > H/C > 0.1$. A phase of apparent *increase* in $w_{1/2}$ with decreasing H/C, associated with disruption of covalent crosslinks between mosaic elements of the pregraphitic kerogen matrix. These processes occur during metagenesis and metamorphism (Tissot and Welte, 1978) and continue to a temperature cutoff defined by the beginning of phase 3.

3. $H/C < 0.1$. Rapid onset of well ordered graphite structure. The correlations summarized in Tables 1 and 2 indicate that this 'jump' in crystallinity coincides roughly with the disappearance of chlorite and the transition from low- to medium-grade metamorphism at temperatures in the range 350–400 °C.

Metamorphism to the greenschist facies can thus be linked with extensive dehydrogenation of kerogen and consequent gross structural alteration. Well-ordered graphite is not developed under these conditions, X-ray diffraction parameters do not vary monotonically or with great reproducibility, and H/C ratios are, accordingly, better indicators of levels of maturity. X-ray diffraction does, however, clearly indicate the development of well-ordered graphite and does furnish a sharp indication of metamorphism beyond the upper greenschist facies.

In the Precambrian generally and in the Archean especially, metamorphism to the greenschist facies is the rule, not the exception. The consistently observed levels of dehydrogenation indicate clearly that the survival of syngenetic chemical fossils cannot be expected under these conditions.

Acknowledgements

We appreciate the assistance of our colleagues in the Precambrian Paleobiology Research Group, particularly J. W. Schopf, I. R. Kaplan, M. R. Walter, and H. J. Hofmann. G. Stummer and K. Hayes provided invaluable assistance with the X-ray diffraction analyses, and U. Matzigkeit carried out many of the chemical analyses. We appreciate useful criticisms of an earlier version of this manuscript by Profs. A. Oberlin and R. P. Wintsch. The work was supported by the National Aeronautics and Space Administration (grants NGR 15-003-118 to JMH and NSG 7489 to JWS *et al.*) and by the National Science Foundation (grant DEB 77-22518 to JWS).

REFERENCES

Blayden, H. E., Gibson, J. and Riley, H. L. (1944) An X-ray study of the structure of coals, cokes, and chars. In *Proceedings of a Conference on the Ultra-fine Structure of Coals and Cokes*. Cheney & Sons, Banbury Pub. pp. 176–231.

Diamond, R. (1954) A study of some carbonized coals using new X-ray techniques. In *Proceedings of the Third Conference on Carbon*. Pergamon Press. pp. 367–375.

Diessel, C. F. K. and Offler, R. (1975) Changes in physical properties of coalified and graphitised phytoclasts with grade of metamorphism. *N. Jb. Miner. Mh. 1975*, 11–26.

Diessel, C. F. K., Brothers, R. N. and Black, P. M. (1978) Coalification and graphitization in high-pressure schists in New Caledonia. *Contrib. Mineral. Petrol.* **68**, 63–78.

Dungworth, G. and Schwartz, A. W. (1972) Kerogen isolates from the Precambrian of South Africa and Australia: analysis for carbonized microorganisms and pyrolysis gas–liquid chromatography. In *Advances in Organic Geochemistry 1971*. Ed. by von Gaertner, H. R. and Wehner, H. Pergamon Press. pp. 609–706.

Dungworth, G. and Schwartz, A. W. (1974) Organic matter and trace elements in Precambrian rocks from South Africa. *Chem. Geol.* **14**, 167–172.

Durand, B. and Nicaise, G. (1980) Procedures for kerogen isolation. In *Kerogen*. Ed. by Durand, B. Technip, Paris. pp. 35–54.

Frazer, J. W. (1962) Simultaneous determination of carbon, hydrogen, and nitrogen. Part II. An improved method for solid organic compounds. *Mikrochem. Acta 1962*, 993–999.

Frazer, J. W. and Crawford, R. W. (1963) Modifications in the simultaneous determination of carbon, hydrogen, and nitrogen. *Mikrochim. Acta 1963*, 561–566.

Frazer, J. W. and Crawford, R. W. (1964) The handling of volatile compounds for the simultaneous determination of carbon, hydrogen, and nitrogen. *Mikrochim. Acta 1964*, 676–678.

French, B. M. (1964) Graphitization of organic material in a progressively metamorphosed Precambrian iron formation. *Science* **146**, 917–918.

Goma, J. and Oberlin, M. (1980) Graphitization of thin carbon films. *Thin Solid Films* **65**, 221–232.

Grew, E. S. (1974) Carbonaceous material in some metamorphic rocks of New England and other areas. *J. Geol.* **82**, 50–73.

Griffin, G. M. (1967) X-ray diffraction techniques applicable to studies of diagenesis and low rank metamorphism in humic sediments. *J. Sed. Petrol.* **37**, 1006–1011.

Hayes, J. M., Kaplan, I. R. and Wedeking, K. W. (1983) Precambrian organic geochemistry, preservation of the record. In *The Origin and Evolution of the Earth's Earliest Biosphere*. Ed. by Schopf, J. W. Princeton University Press.

Inagaki, M., Oberlin, A. and Noda, T. (1975) Structural changes of graphitizing carbons during graphitization — Review. *Tanso (Japan)* **81**, 68–72.

Izawa, E. (1968) Carbonaceous matter in some metamorphic rocks in Japan. *J. Geol. Soc. Japan* **84**, 427–432.

Landis, C. R. (1971) Graphitization of dispersed carbonaceous material in metamorphic rocks. *Contr. Mineral. and Petrol.* **30**, 34–45.

Leventhal, J., Suess, S. E. and Cloud, P. (1975) Nonprevalence of biochemical fossils in kerogen from pre-Phanerozoic sediments. *Proc. Nat. Acad. Sci.* **72**, 4706–4710 (1975).

Long, G., Neglia, S. and Favretto, L. (1968) The metamorphism of the kerogen from Triassic black shales, southeast Sicily. *Geochim. Cosmochim. Acta* **32**, 647–656.

McKirdy, D. M. (1974) Organic geochemistry in Precambrian research. *Precamb. Res.* **1**, 75–137.

McKirdy, D. M. and Powell, T. G. (1974) Metamorphic alteration of carbon isotopic composition in ancient sedimentary organic matter: new evidence from Australia and South Africa. *Geology* **2**, 591–595.

McKirdy, D. M., Sumartojo, J., Tucker, D. H. and Gostin, V. (1975) Organic, mineralogic, and magnetic indications of metamorphism in the Tapley Hill Formation, Adelaide

Geosyncline. *Precamb. Res.* **2**, 345–373.

McKirdy, D. M. and Kantsler, A. J. (1980) Oil geochemistry and potential source rocks of the Officer Basin, South Australia. *Aust. Petrol. Explor. Assn. J.* **20**, 68–86.

Oberlin, A., Boulmier, J. L. and Villey, M. (1980) Electron microscopic study of kerogen microtexture. Selected criteria for determining the evolution path and evolution stage of kerogen. In *Kerogen.* Ed. by Durand, B. Technip, Paris. pp. 191–241.

Powell, T. G., Cook, P. J. and McKirdy, D. M. (1975) Organic geochemistry of phosphorites: relevance to petroleum genesis. *Am. Assoc. Petrol. Geol. Bull.* **59**, 618–632.

Ross, M. (1968) X-ray diffraction effects by non-ideal crystals of biotite, muscovite, montmorillonite, mixed-layer clays, graphite, and periclase. *Z. Kristallogr.* **126**, 1–3.

Scherrer, P. (1918) Bestimmung der Gröss und derinneren Struktur von Kolloidteilchen mittels Röntgenstrahlen. *Nachrichten Akad. Wiss. Göttingen, Heft.* **1**, 98–100.

Schopf, J. W. (1983) (Ed.) *The Origin and Evolution of the Earth's Earliest Biosphere.* Princeton University Press.

Tissot, B. P. and Welte, D. H. (1978) *Petroleum Formation and Occurrence.* Springer-Verlag, Heidelberg.

van Krevelen, D. W. (1961) *Coal.* Elsevier.

Walter, M. R., Hofmann, H. J. and Schopf, J. W. (1983) Appendix I: geographic and geologic data for processed rock samples. In *The Origin and Evolution of the Earth's Earliest Biosphere.* Ed. by Schopf, J. W. Princeton University Press.

Wedeking, K. W., Hayes, J. M. and Matzigkeit, U. (1983) Appendix IV: Procedures of organic geochemical analysis. In *The Origin and Evolution of the Earth's Earliest Biosphere.* Ed. by Schopf, J. W. Princeton University Press.

Zumberge, J. E., Sigleo, A. C. and Nagy, B. (1978) Molecular and elemental analyses of the carbonaceous matter in the gold and uranium bearing Vaal Reef carbon seams, Witwatersrand Sequence. *Minerals Sci. Eng.* **10**, 223–246.

Advances in Organic Geochemistry 1981, pp. 554–560
© *John Wiley & Sons Limited, 1983*

Nature of Kerogen from the Green River Shale based on the Character of the Products of a Forty-Step Alkaline Permanganate Oxidation

A. Amblès*, M. V. Djuričić, Lj. Djordjević and D. Vitorović

*Institute of Chemistry, Faculty of Science, University of Belgrade, PO Box 550, YU-11001, Belgrade, and
Institute of Chemistry, Technology and Metallurgy, Belgrade, Yugoslavia*

A careful, forty-step alkaline permanganate degradation of the Green River shale kerogen concentrate was carried out. A very high total yield of oxidation products was obtained ($c.$ 81% based on original organic matter). The ether-soluble acids ($c.$ 15% of oxidation products) were found to consist of saturated unbranched α,ω-dicarboxylic acids (C_6–C_{17}), saturated branched dicarboxylic acids (C_9–C_{15}) and isoprenoid acids (C_{14}–C_{17}); saturated unbranched monocarboxylic acids (C_{10}–C_{18}), three series of alkane-tricarboxylic acids (C_7–C_{14}; C_{10}–C_{16} and C_9–C_{10}), alkane-tetracarboxylic acids (C_9–C_{13}), keto-acids (C_9–C_{11}) and aromatic acids were also found but in small concentrations. ^{13}C NMR investigation of precipitated acids ($c.$ 83% of oxidation products) suggested that they consisted mainly of long-chain aliphatic structures. The acids obtained by further controlled permanganate degradation of precipitated acids were found to consist of unbranched α,ω-dicarboxylic acids (C_6–C_{29}), saturated unbranched monocarboxylic acids (C_9–C_{32}), saturated branched dicarboxylic acids (C_9–C_{14}), alkane-tricarboxylic acids (C_8–C_{13}), alkane-tetracarboxylic acids (C_9–C_{14}) and isoprenoid acids (C_{16}–C_{20}, except C_{18}). On the basis of experimental evidence it is suggested that the Green River shale kerogen is predominantly of an open-chain, cross-linked aliphatic structure, with subordinate, isolated elements of alicyclic and heterocyclic structure.

INTRODUCTION

The kerogen from the Green River Formation shale (USA) is one of the most extensively studied kerogens. Nevertheless, a controversy still exists concerning the proportion of alicyclic to linear saturated structures in this kerogen (Vitorović, 1980).

Several authors (Burlingame *et al.*, 1969; Simoneit and Burlingame, 1974; Djuričić *et al.*, 1971; Tissot *et al.*, 1978) suggested that kerogen from the Green River Formation shale contained predominantly aliphatic chains with subordinate saturated cyclic material.

On the other hand, a number of authors (Robinson *et al.*, 1961, 1963, 1969, 1976; van den Berg, 1975; Yen, 1976; Young and Yen, 1977) suggested that the Green River shale kerogen contained predominantly alicyclic and heterocyclic structures with smaller amounts of straight-chain and aromatic structures. Young and Yen (1977) proposed that only *ca.* 2–4 carbon atoms out of every 10 in the Green River shale kerogen were in the form of straight-chain aliphatic structures which are longer than C_4.

In this paper an attempt was made to contribute to the clarification of this controversy. A stepwise oxidative degradation approach was chosen. In order to obtain maximum yields of identifiable products (which still

retain structural relationship to the kerogen) a careful, forty-step alkaline permanganate degradation of a kerogen concentrate from the Green River shale was carried out.

The examination of the products, obtained in a very high total yield (*ca.* 81% based on original organic matter), consisted of:

1. Capillary GC–MS analysis of the methyl esters of ether-soluble acids;
2. ^{13}C NMR investigation of precipitated, ether-insoluble acids; and
3. Further careful stepwise alkaline permanganate oxidation of precipitated, ether-insoluble acids, followed by GC–MS analysis of the ether-soluble acids thus obtained.

EXPERIMENTAL

A sample of Green River shale was obtained from the U.S. Bureau of Mines test mine near Rifle, Colorado. The kerogen concentrate was prepared by the method as described by Markey (1968) and contained 23.8% ash (inorganic material), with the organic portion consisting of 70.9% carbon, 9.4% hydrogen, and 1.9% nitrogen. The same sample had been investigated in some of our previous studies (Djuričić *et al.*, 1971).

The kerogen concentrate (6.5 g, containing 4.9530 g

---

* Present address: Department of Chemistry, Faculty of Science, University of Poitiers, Poitiers, France.

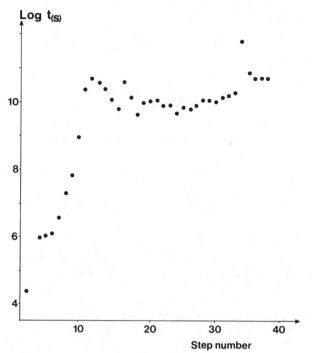

Fig. 1. Duration of single degradation steps (log t_s = log time in seconds).

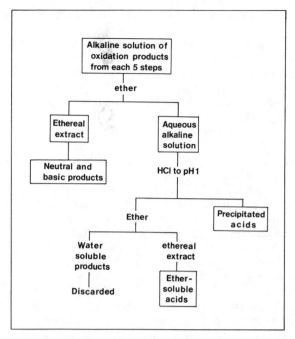

Fig. 2. Isolation of oxidation products.

organic matter) was oxidized in 39 steps with a very small amount of $KMnO_4$ (0.5 g) per step in 100 cm³ of 1% KOH according to the degradation scheme as described by Amblès *et al.* (1981). The permanganate–hydroxide ratio assured an excess of alkali in each oxidation step. Prior to addition of each portion of permanganate (0.5 g in 10 cm³ of aqueous solution), the mixture of kerogen concentrate (or partially degraded kerogen concentrate) and alkali solution was heated to the reaction temperature of 75 °C.

After reduction of each portion of reagent (the end of reaction was established by disappearance of the violet and green colours), the remaining kerogen concentrate plus MnO_2 was separated by centrifugation and washed thoroughly, mixing it three times with 66 cm³ of 0.5% KOH in order to quantitatively remove oxidation products.

The first few portions were reduced in a relatively short period of time. The reduction periods increased in successive steps, being approximately the same (6–9 h) in most of the middle steps (Fig. 1). The last, thirty-ninth portion of reagent was not fully reduced even after 36 h, indicating final oxidation of the kerogen.

Following every five steps, the MnO_2 was removed by treating the solid residue with an excess of a solution of oxalic acid. The residue was then thoroughly rinsed with distilled water and the remaining kerogen concentrate was treated further with the next aliquot of permanganate. The last oxidation mixture, which contained the remaining potassium permanganate and MnO_2, was treated in a similar way. The washed solid residue was dried and analysed for organic matter. The products from each five steps were collected and 8 portions of products (marked 1–8) were thus obtained. These eight fractions were separately worked up according to the scheme as outlined in Fig. 2. Three

types of products were isolated from each of the eight fractions; neutrals and bases, ether-soluble acids, and precipitated acids.

A blank procedure was carried out for 48 h with total amounts of reagents ($KMnO_4$ and KOH) corresponding to five steps. Following the reduction of excess $KMnO_4$ and MnO_2, the products from blank experiment were isolated and analysed in the same way as kerogen oxidation products.

Investigation of soluble acids

The soluble acids were methylated with ethereal diazomethane. The esters wree analysed by capillary gas chromatography (GC), and identified by gas chromatography–mass spectrometry (GC–MS). The capillary gas chromatographic separations were performed in a gas chromatograph Packard Model 427, using two types of capillary columns, OV-17 (25 m) and SE-30 (25 m), coupled to an integrator–calculator Spectra Physics 'System 1'. The temperature of the column was programmed from 100 to 300 °C at 2° min⁻¹ or from 80 to 300 °C at 2° min⁻¹.

The GC–MS analyses were performed with a system consisting of a gas chromatograph (Perkin Elmer Sigma 3) coupled to a mass spectrometer (Kratos MS 25). The components were separated in the gas chromatograph using an SE-30 capillary column (25 m). This column was also temperature-programmed from 100 to 300 °C (or from 70 to 300 °C) at 2° min⁻¹, and had a He (carrier gas) flow rate of 1 cm³ min⁻¹. Mass spectra were recorded for all the main separated components. In most cases, identifications of individual components were accompanied by comparison of the mass spectra obtained with available mass spectra of authentic compounds.

Investigation of precipitated acids

The precipitated acids were analysed by ^{13}C NMR spectroscopy. ^{13}C NMR is very useful for general characterization of complex mixtures of compounds. Even if identification of individual compounds is not possible, data on general molecular features may be obtained.

The main goal in this paper was a qualitative ^{13}C NMR analysis of kerogen oxidation products. Usual precautions (Joseph and Wong, 1980) were taken, in order to avoid missing some absorptions as a consequence of unfavourable experimental conditions and a poor signal/noise ratio. Besides, the possibility of estimation of relative proportions of molecular species in the samples was also taken into consideration.

A Bruker SXP-100 NMR spectrometer with 10 mm probe and B-NC 12 computer (8 K memory for 'free induction decay' (FID) accumulation) was used in the Fourier transform mode to obtain ^{13}C spectra at 22.63 MHz. A 5000 Hz spectral width with 100 μs dwell time and 0.819 s acquisition time was used in all spectra. The spectra of model substances were taken in $CDCl_3$ solutions and the spectra of kerogen oxidation products, i.e. precipitated acids, in C_5D_5N solutions. The solvent, C_6D_5N, to which a small quantity of TMS (internal standard) was added, also served the purpose of an internal deuterium lock. A relaxation agent, $Cr(ac\,ac)_3$, was used in a concentration of 50 mg g^{-1} of sample. The FIDs were accumulated at various pulse widths (30–90 °C), with 1–5 s delay between the end of data acquisition and the beginning of the next pulse. Accumulations were usually taken overnight for >50 000 pulses. A 5.0 W decoupling power was applied in broad band proton noise decoupling mode.

Further oxidation of precipitated acids

Following NMR investigations, the precipitated acids were recovered from their corresponding solutions and an aliquot of 2.6243 g was oxidized in 20 steps with small amounts (0.5 g) of $KMnO_4$ per step in 100 cm³ of 1% KOH. Prior to addition of each new portion of permanganate (0.5 g in 10 cm³ of aqueous solution), the acids were dissolved in the alkali solution, which was heated to the reaction temperature of 75 °C.

After reduction of each portion of the reagent, the solid residue (MnO_2) was separated by centrifugation and washed thoroughly with 1% KOH to remove oxidation products. The MnO_2 was reduced, as described earlier, after the 5th, 13th and 20th steps. The alkali solution from each degradation step, containing the oxidation products, was worked up according to a scheme similar to the scheme presented in Fig. 2. The precipitated acids thus obtained were always further oxidized, in the next step, with a new portion of permanganate. The last oxidation mixture (20th step) was treated in the same way. The precipitated acids obtained in the last step (the oxidation had not yet been completed) were rinsed and dried.

The soluble acids from 1–13th and 14–20th steps were collected and these two portions of soluble acids (marked I and II) were methylated with ethereal diazomethane and analysed by GC and GC–MS in the same way as the soluble acids obtained in the degradation of the kerogen concentrate.

RESULTS

Kerogen concentrate degradation

The rate of permanganate oxidation, based on one gram of kerogen, was approximately linear up to 150 hours (30 steps), and increased slowly thereafter. Thirty-nine steps were necessary for complete degradation of the kerogen in approximately 260 h, and a total amount of 19.5 g $KMnO_4$ was consumed (3.94 g per gram of kerogen).

The yields of products in the eight oxidation stages are shown in Fig. 3. The yields of neutrals and bases, ether-soluble acids, and precipitated acids, were 1.86%, 11.74%, and 67.95%, respectively, relative to original organic matter (the total yield being 81.55%). The solid residue obtained in the final step (0.4936 g) contained 0.0366 g organic matter (0.74% relative to original organic matter).

In the blank experiment, 15.5 mg of ether-soluble extract were obtained. GC analysis of this product showed a large number of minor components, none of which was a major constituent. Phthalates, a common contaminant, were not found in any significant amount.

Ether-soluble acids

Investigation of the ether-soluble acids from all the eight steps, in the form of their methyl esters, was reported elsewhere (Amblès et al., 1981). The GC–MS analyses of the same eight fractions were repeated under improved analytical conditions which enabled more detailed investigation of the ether-soluble acids. The GC–MS analysis revealed the presence of saturated normal α,ω-dicarboxylic acids (C_6–C_{17}), saturated branched dicarboxylic acids (C_9–C_{15}) and isoprenoid acids (C_{14}–C_{17}); saturated normal monocarboxylic acids (C_{10}–C_{18}), three series of alkane-tricarboxylic acids (C_7–C_{14}, C_{10}–C_{16} and C_9–C_{10}), alkane-tetracarboxylic acids (C_9–C_{13}), keto-acids (C_9–C_{11}) and aromatic acids were also found but in small concentrations. There was no marked difference in the compositions of the ether-soluble acids from various oxidation stages.

NMR investigation of precipitated acids

The selected experimental ^{13}C NMR conditions were checked with the following model substances: heneicosanic and n-nonadecanoic acids, cholestanone, lithocholic acid and methyl ester of deoxycholic acid, which were, hypothetically, extreme representative structures expected in kerogen oxidation products. Chemical shift values showed quite close agreement when compared with standard reference sources.

The main problem involved in ^{13}C investigation of the precipitated acids was their poor solubility in solvents

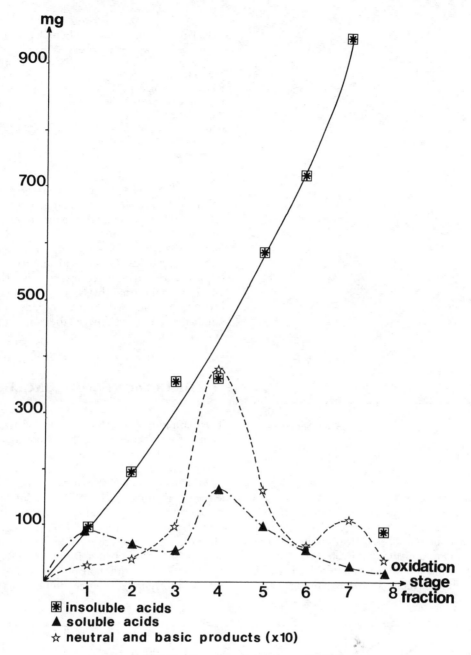

Fig. 3. Yields of products in various oxidation stages.

usually applied in NMR measurements. Even the solubility in C_5D_5N, which was shown to be the most powerful of all solvents examined, was not such as to produce spectra with a good signal/noise ratio. Ultrasonic treatment and mild heating did not help much. However the following conclusions are considered valid.

The spectra of all eight samples subjected to NMR analysis were very similar and showed strong resemblance to the spectra of straight-chain, saturated aliphatic acids, consisting of approximately 20 C-atoms. Typical spectra consisted of a large methylene peak at 29.6 ppm, surrounded asymmetrically by two pairs of peaks. Peaks at *ca.* 37.5 and 25.3 ppm were from carbons in positions 2 and 3 relative to carboxylic group, and at 23.3 and 34.6 ppm from carbons next and second to the methyl group. Small trace peaks centred around 175.6

and 15 ppm were also observed. They obviously originated from carboxylic and methyl-groups. No aromatic carbons were detected.

Oxidation products from precipitated acids

The rate of permanganate oxidation of precipitated acids, based on one gram of the acids, was approximately linear up to 120 min (13 steps), with a lower rate of oxidation thereafter. Twenty steps were not sufficient for a complete degradation of 2.6243 g of precipitated acids. The total duration of the twenty steps was 260.5 min and the total amount of $KMnO_4$ consumed was 10 g (3.81 g per gram of precipitated acids). The duration of individual oxidation steps did not differ much, as illustrated in Fig. 4. One noticeable change in the

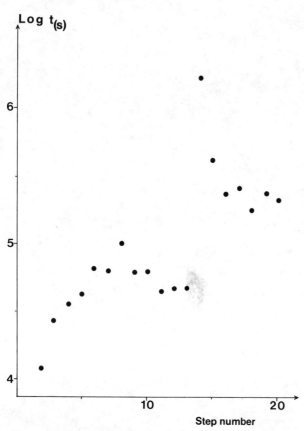

Fig. 4. Duration of single oxidation steps in the degradation of precipitated acids (log t_s = log time in seconds).

Table 1

Oxidation products obtained from the precipitated acids

	g	%
precipitated acids	2.6243	100
ether-soluble acids	1.1577	44.11
neutrals and bases	0.0710	2.71
solid residue*	0.5400	20.58
difference (loss at CO_2, etc)	0.8556	32.60

* unoxidized

Fig. 6. The GC–MS analysis of these two fractions revealed the presence of normal α,ω-dicarboxylic acids (C_6–C_{29}, C_7–C_{15} being the main components, with a maximum at C_9 and C_{10}), saturated unbranched monocarboxylic acids (C_9–C_{32}), saturated branched dicarboxylic acids (C_9–C_{14}), alkane-tricarboxylic acids (C_8–C_{13}), and alkane–tetracarboxylic acids (C_9–C_{14}); isoprenoid acids (mainly C_{16}–C_{20} except C_{18}), were also present, but in small concentrations. There was no significant difference between the compositions of acids I and II.

DISCUSSION AND CONCLUSIONS

The main aim of this study was to contribute to solving the controversy concerning the proportion of open-chain to alicyclic structures in the kerogen from the Green River shale.

As in our previous structural study of the same kerogen (Djuričić et al., 1971), oxidative degradation method was used. Thanks to a careful, forty-step degradation, a very high yield of oxidation products was obtained, ca. 81% based on the original organic matter. This is the highest yield so far reported for Green River shale kerogen degradation products. Moreover, a high ratio of precipitated v. ether-soluble acids was achieved

duration was observed after the 13th step. Approximate duration of individual steps suggested a relatively uniform structure of precipitated acids. The yields of products obtained in the 20-step degradation of the precipitated acids are presented in Table 1.

Gas chromatograms of the ether-soluble acids I and II in the form of their methyl esters are shown in Fig. 5 and

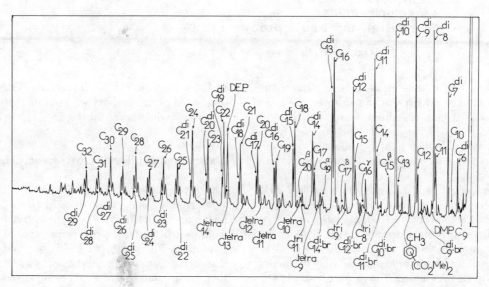

Fig. 5. Gas-chromatogram of ether-soluble acids I, in the form of methyl-esters, obtained by oxidation of precipitated acids. C_x^{di} denotes saturated normal dicarboxylic acids; C_x^{di}br, saturated branched dicarboxylic; C_x^i, isoprenoid; C_x^o, keto-acids; C_x^{trn}, alkane-tricarboxylic; and C_x^{tetra}, alkane-tetracarboxylic acids. DMP and DEP denote dimethyl- and diethylphthalate, respectively.

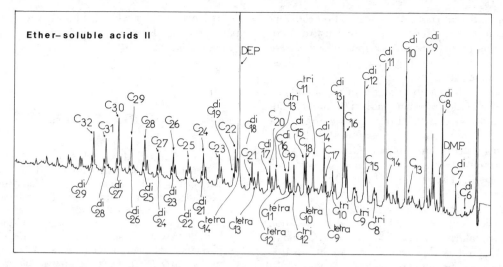

Fig. 6. Gas chromatogram of ether-soluble acids II, in the form of methyl-esters, obtained by oxidation of precipitated acids. (Denotations are the same as in Fig. 5).

(5.8:1). Since precipitated acids retained more structural relationship to the kerogen than the lower molecular mass ether-soluble acids, the distribution of oxidation products obtained in this study may be considered advantageous.

Which types of acids could have been expected as kerogen oxidation products? Any organic matter — consisting predominantly of alicyclic and heterocyclic structures — should yield as intermediate oxidation products (in a stepwise alkaline permanganate degradation) in addition to lower molecular mass dicarboxylic acids up to C_6 (adipic) acid, dicarboxylic acids of higher molecular mass involving saturated cyclic and/or heterocyclic, isolated or condensed structures, as well as alkane-tri- and/or other polycarboxylic acids. Long-chain unbranched or branched dicarboxylic acids, saturated unbranched or branched monocarboxylic, isoprenoid, and some other similar types of acids should be expected as major oxidation

Table 2

Acids identified as oxidation products of kerogen from Green River shale.

	ether-soluble acids	precipitated acids*
n-diacids	C_6–C_{17}	C_6–C_{29}
branched diacids	C_9–C_{15}	C_9–C_{14}
n-monoacids	C_{10}–C_{18}	C_9–C_{32}
isoprenoid acids	C_{14}–C_{17}	C_{16}, C_{17}, C_{19}, C_{20}
	a. C_7–C_{14}	
series of	b. C_{10}–C_{16}	a. C_8–C_{13}
triacids	c. C_9; C_{10}	
tetracids	C_9–C_{13}	C_9–C_{14}
other structures	D.M.P., D.E.P.	
	aromatics	D.M.P., D.E.P.†
	ketoacids:	aromatic (1)
	C_9–C_{11}	

* oxidation products of P. acids
† D.M.P. (D.E.P.): dimethyl(ethyl)-phthalate

products of kerogens of aliphatic-type structure. Aromatic-type organic matter should yield aromatic carboxylic acids as final oxidation products. The major components, identified as ether-soluble acids and acids obtained as products of further controlled oxidation of precipitated acids, are summarized in Table 2.

The major components in the fraction of ether-soluble acids (11.7% yield) were found to be saturated unbranched α,ω-dicarboxylic acids (C_7–C_{17}) (Amblès et al., 1981). Saturated branched dicarboxylic and isoprenoid acids were less important but still significant components. The saturated branched dicarboxylic acids were not identified in our previous studies of the same kerogen concentrate. The quantity of other types of identified acids such as saturated unbranched monocarboxylic acids, alkane-tricarboxylic acids and alkane-tetracarboxylic acids, keto-acids and aromatic acids was smaller in this fraction.

On the basis of evidence obtained from ether-soluble acids, predominance of saturated unbranched dicarboxylic acids of higher molecular mass ($> C_7$), together with smaller but significant yields of branched dicarboxylic and isoprenoid acids, it was suggested that the Green River shale kerogen was predominantly of an open-chain, cross-linked aliphatic structure. However, since ether-soluble acids represented maximum up to 20% of the kerogen, the validity of such a conclusion depended on the structure elucidation of the major oxidation product, the precipitated acids.

The results of ^{13}C NMR investigation of the precipitated acids suggested that linear saturated long-chain aliphatic structures prevailed in the precipitated, ether-insoluble oxidation products from Green River shale. However, further proof was sought in the GC–MS examination of the products of further careful stepwise degradation of the precipitated acids.

The lower molecular mass acids, obtained in high yields as oxidation products of precipitated acids, were also shown to consist predominantly of unbranched α,ω-dicarboxylic acids. Moreover, straight-chain, saturated monocarboxylic acids were found to be the second most abundant class of acids in this case. Branched dicarboxylic and isoprenoid acids were also relatively significant components. Hence, the major constituents of the degradation products of the precipitated acids were shown to be similar to the ether-soluble kerogen degradation products.

Therefore — taking into account on one hand the high yields of oxidation products and, on the other hand, their prevailing saturated aliphatic structure — a predominantly open-chain, cross-linked aliphatic structure is suggested for the sample of Green River shale kerogen examined. Such an assumption supports the previously suggested kerogen structure (Djuričić et al., 1971; Murphy et al., 1971).

However, various series of alkane-tri- and tetracarboxylic acids were found in the oxidation products, particularly in those of the precipitated acids' degradation products. Various series of alkane-tricarboxylic acids and tetracarboxylic acids presented a novelty in kerogen oxidation products. Identification of this type of acids may indicate that isolated alicyclic and/or heterocyclic rings were involved in long-chain aliphatic structure, yielding alkane-tri- and/or tetracarboxylic acids at one stage of controlled, progressive oxidative degradation. Nevertheless, according to the amount of these acids in the oxidation products, the proportion of alicyclic/heterocyclic structures in the examined kerogen is not of prime significance.

According to Robinson (1976), the Green River shale kerogen appears to be predominantly a saturated 'macro' cyclic material, consisting of linear networks of cyclic rings of methylene groups, with or without hetero-groups (to which some long chains and aromatic structures are associated) with the entire system being held together by short methylene interconnections and cross-links of oxygen bridges. Young and Yen (1977) proposed that only 20–40% carbon atoms in the Green River shale kerogen were in the form of straight-chain aliphatic structures longer than C_4.

Our experiments indicated that the high molecular mass open-chain products obtained in very high yields under controlled oxidative degradation of the kerogen could only be considered as fragments of the original complex kerogen structure.

It seems quite possible, however, that one of the main reasons for the controversial conclusions concerning the structure of the kerogen from Green River shale could be a consequence of the differences in the provenance of the shale samples that were investigated by different authors: differences in the properties of kerogens from different stratigraphic and geographic locations are well known.

Acknowledgements

The authors are grateful to Prof. J. C. Jacquesy and Dr R. Jacquesy, Maître de Recherche (CNRS), University of Poitiers, France, for their interest in the work, as well as to Dr W. E. Robinson, Laramie Energy Center, USA who kindly provided the sample of Green River shale used in this experiment. The technical assistance of Mrs S. Bajc, Mrs. O. Cvetković, Miss B. Janković and Mrs J. Joffre is greatly appreciated. This work was supported in part by the Research Fund of the S.R. Serbia (Yugoslavia).

REFERENCES

Amblès, A., Djuričić, M. V. and Vitorović, D. (1981) Nature of kerogen from the Green River shale based on the character of the products of a forty-step alkaline permanganate oxidation. Evidence from soluble acids. Bull. Soc. Chim. Beograd. 46, 275–283.

Burlingame, A. L., Haug, P. A., Schnoes, H. K. and Simoneit, B. R. (1969) Fatty acids derived from the Green River Formation oil shale by extractions and oxidations — a review. In Advances in Organic Geochemistry 1968. Ed. by Schenck, P. A. and Havenaar, I. Pergamon Press, Oxford. pp. 85–129.

Djuričić, M. V., Murphy, R. C., Vitorović, D. and Biemann, K. (1971) Organic acids obtained by alkaline permanganate oxidation of kerogen from the Green River (Colorado) shale. Geochim. Cosmochim. Acta 35, 1201–1207.

Joseph, J. T. and Wong, J. L. (1980) Distribution of aliphatic and aromatic carbons in H-Coal liquids by quantitative ^{13}C FT-n.m.r. spectroscopy. Fuel 59, 777–781.

Markey, S. P. (1968) Structure elucidation of organic compounds in complex mixtures by mass spectrometry. PhD Thesis, Massachusetts Institute of Technology.

Murphy, R. C., Biemann, K., Djuričić, M. V. and Vitorović, D. (1971) Acids obtained by alkaline hydrolysis of kerogen from the Green River (Colorado) shale. Bull. Soc. Chim., Beograd 36, 281–287.

Robinson, W. E. (1969) Kerogen of the Green River Formation. In Organic Geochemistry Methods and Results. Ed. by Eglinton, G. and Murphy, M. T. J. Springer Verlag, Berlin. pp. 619–637.

Robinson, W. E. (1976) Origin and characteristics of Green River oil shale. In Oil shale. Ed. by Yen, T. F. and Chilingarian, G. V. Elsevier, Amsterdam. pp. 61–79.

Robinson, W. E. and Lawlor, D. L. (1961) Constitution of hydrocarbon-like materials derived from kerogen oxidation products. Fuel 40, 375–388.

Robinson, W. E., Lawlor, D. L., Cummins, J. J. and Fester, J. I. (1963) Oxidation of Colorado oil shale. U.S. Bureau of Mines, Rep. Invest. 6166, 1–33.

Simoneit, B. R. and Burlingame, A. L. (1974) Ketones derived from the oxidative degradation of Green River Formation oil shale kerogen. In Advances in Organic Geochemistry 1973. Ed. by Tissot, B. and Bienner, F. Editions Technip, Paris. pp. 191–201.

Tissot, B., Deroo, G. and Hood, A. (1978) Geochemical study of the Uinta Basin: Formation of petroleum from the Green River Formation. Geochim. Cosmochim. Acta 42, 1469–1485.

van den Berg, M. L. J. (1975) Some investigations on the chemical nature of kerogen. PhD Thesis, Technische Hogeschool, Delft.

Vitorović, D. (1980) Structure elucidation of kerogen by chemical methods. In Kerogen, Insoluble Organic Matter from Sedimentary Rocks. Ed. by Durand, B. Editions Technip, Paris. pp. 301–338.

Yen, T. F. (1976) Structural aspects of organic components in oil shales. In Oil Shale. Ed. by Yen, T. F. and Chilingarian, G. V. Elsevier, Amsterdam. pp. 129–148.

Young, D. K. and Yen, T. F. (1977) The nature of straight-chain aliphatic structures in Green River kerogen. Geochim. Cosmochim. Acta 41, 1411–1417.

Advances in Organic Geochemistry 1981, pp. 561–567
© John Wiley & Sons Limited, 1983

Geochemistry of the Marine 'Katharina' Shale in the Coal-bearing Upper Carboniferous Strata of the Ruhr District, F.R. Germany: Source-Controlled versus Migration-related Effects

A. M. Altebäumer, D. Leythaeuser and R. G. Schaefer

Institute of Petroleum and Organic Geochemistry (ICH-5), KFA-Juelich, PO Box 1913, D-5170 Juelich, FRG

The organic content of an organic-rich shale unit from the Upper Carboniferous of the Ruhr District has been examined to study the effects of changes in paleoenvironment from marine to brackish to non-marine. Discussion of organic matter type is restricted to insoluble kerogen, since the soluble organic matter yields of all samples studied suggest severe depletion by primary migration. Shales associated with a brackish paleoenvironment appear in general to contain a better quality kerogen (richer in hydrogen) than the shales associated with the other two environments. The brackish shales also seem to be the most affected by migration processes, which result in a depletion of hydrocarbons.

INTRODUCTION

During the Upper Carboniferous about 3800 m of coal-bearing sediments ranging in age from Namurian C to Westphalian C were deposited in the Subvariscan foredeep. Although predominantly terrestrial, the stratigraphic sequence contains numerous thin marine intercalations. Some of these marine transgressions were geographically widespread. A major marine incursion at the beginning of Westphalian B deposited a thin, organic-rich shale unit on the top of the 'Katharina' coal seam. Figure 1 gives an E–W striking schematic cross-section through the 'Katharina' coal seam and overlying shales. The 'Katharina' shale decreases in thickness from the east of the Ruhr area to the west. The majority of the rocks are unfossiliferous with only a few bedding-planes yielding a modest fauna. The amount of fossils in this shale unit is even smaller towards the west.

The faunal associations, particularly in the east, suggest a distinct facies pattern. Lingulids and foraminifera indicate a brackish paleoenvironment, goniatites, pterinopectinids and conodonts a marine paleoenvironment. The overlying non-marine shales are exemplified by non-marine bivalves. Changes of paleoenvironment were observed within the stratigraphic section as well as within the lateral distribution of the layers. For example, a rapid change from marine to non-marine paleoenvironment was observed in the western part of the Ruhr area, whereas a brackish shale sequence is observed between the marine and non-marine sequences in the East. In the western marginal part, shales of a marine paleoenvironment were not proved. Samples deposited in brackish, marine and non-marine paleoenvironments were available. Geochemical investigations of these samples should give information about the origin of organic detritus and the influence of paleoenvironment on the organic matter deposited. Especially, it was

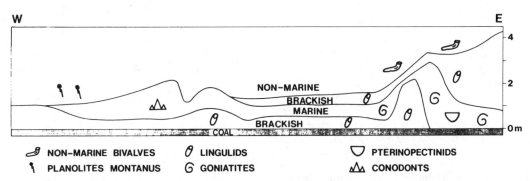

Fig. 1. Schematic E–W cross-section of the 'Katharina' coal seam and overlying 'Katharina' shales. Facies subdivision was based on geochemical data and the fossil assemblages present.

intended to examine to which degree migration processes have altered the original hydrocarbon yield and composition resulting from generation.

SAMPLES AND METHODS

The 'Katharina' coal seam and the overlying 'Katharina shale' were selected because the widespread occurrence of these stratigraphic units and the homogenous lithology of the shales appeared well suited for geochemical investigations of facies-related changes. The 'Katharina' shale unit consists of dark coloured, fine grained shales ranging in thickness from about 1 to 4 m. Therefore, within a narrow interval the influence of different paleoenvironments could be studied, ranging from marine to brackish, and then to non-marine. Fresh, unweathered samples were collected from ten mines and four deep core holes of the northern Ruhr District. They cover a maturity interval from 0.83 to 1.4% mean vitrinite reflectance.

The samples were analysed by the following geochemical techniques, which have been described in detail elsewhere: organic carbon analysis, extraction of C_{15+}-soluble organic matter with dichloromethane for shales and a mixture of redistilled chloroform, acetone, and methanol (47:30:23) for coals using the 'flow-blending' method (Radke et al., 1978); fractionation of extracts by medium-pressure liquid chromatography (Radke et al., 1980) and gas chromatography of the C_{15+}-saturated hydrocarbons. The evaluation of all gas chromatograms was done by a chromatography-data system (Datachrom II, Kratos-Instem Ltd., Stone, England). Absolute concentrations of each n-alkane and

isoprenoid alkane in μg/g of organic carbon were obtained by calibrating each chromatogram with n-pentadecane as an external standard. Characterization of kerogen-type by pryolysis yield measurements of whole-rock samples was done according to the Rock-Eval technique (Espitalié et al., 1977). Mean vitrinite reflectance values ($\%R_m$) were measured at 546 nm wavelength on polished sections of coals and kerogen concentrates.

RESULTS AND DISCUSSION

Despite their lithologically homogenous appearance, the 'Katharina' shales show significant variations in total organic carbon content between 0.6 and 13.4%. A general trend of decreasing organic carbon content with increasing distance from the coal seam was observed.

The kerogen of all shale samples can be classified as **hydrogen lean type III kerogen (Durand and Espitalié, 1973; Tissot et al., 1974).** The organic matter of type III kerogens originates from land–plant derived organic detritus. Figure 2 shows the hydrogen index for all shale **samples plotted against mean vitrinite reflectance.** A general trend of decreasing hydrogen index with increasing maturity can be ascertained. Furthermore, the samples shown in Fig. 2 can be subdivided according to hydrogen index into three groups. This subdivision reflects the influence of the paleoenvironment. The samples with the best quality, i.e. hydrogen-richest kerogens and highest organic carbon contents (1.9 to 13.4%, mean 6.3%) were deposited in the brackish environment. Shales deposited in the marine environment exhibit lower hydrogen index and lower carbon

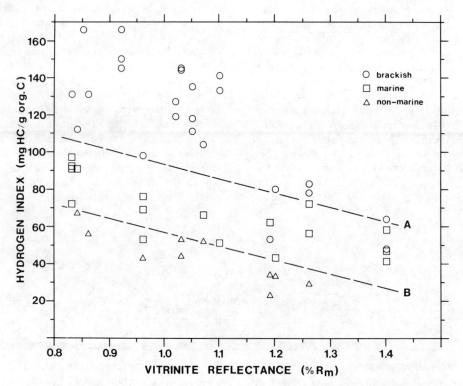

Fig. 2. Kerogen quality of samples from the 'Katharina Horizont' and overlying non-marine beds. Relation between hydrogen index and mean vitrinite reflectance. Lines A and B separate the fields of different hydrogen index values which are thought to reflect differences in paleoenvironment.

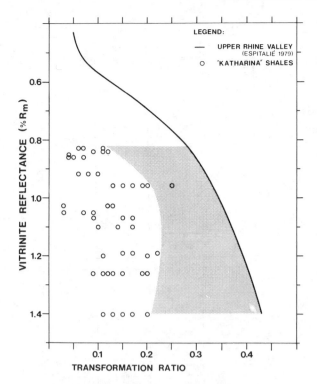

Fig. 3. Transformation ratio of 'Katharina' shales as a function of maturity in comparison with data from a Tertiary series from the Upper Rhine Valley (Espitalié, 1979). The shaded field indicates the degree of depletion of the 'Katharina' shales.

contents (1.0 to 3.5%, mean 2.0%). Shales of non-marine paleoenvironment show the lowest values for the hydrogen index and organic carbon contents below 1.0% (mean 0.9%).

The degree of evolution of the organic matter and any possible migration effects were evaluated on the basis of so called 'transformation ratio' (Espitalié *et al.*, 1977). The 'transformation ratio' is the ratio of hydrocarbons already formed by the kerogen (S_1: oil and gas) to the total amount of hydrocarbons ($S_1 + S_2$) that the kerogen is capable of generating. The transformation ratio is thought to be independent of changes in kerogen quality. Figure 3 shows the trend of increasing transformation ratio as a function of maturity for a Tertiary series from wells in the Upper Rhine Valley (Espitalié, 1979). This trend reflects generation of hydrocarbons in source rocks with little or no effects due to expulsion or accumulation of hydrocarbons. Most of the Rhine Valley samples are of similar kerogen quality to the samples investigated in this study. Obviously, the transformation ratios for the shales overlying the 'Katharina' coal seam are significantly lower than the values for the Tertiary samples. Therefore, for each of the Carboniferous shale samples the difference between the measured transformation ratio and the transformation ratio measured at the corresponding maturation level by Espitalié (1979), is interpreted to indicate the amount of hydrocarbon expelled during primary migration. According to this concept, the expulsion efficiency is calculated based on the ratio between the computed and the

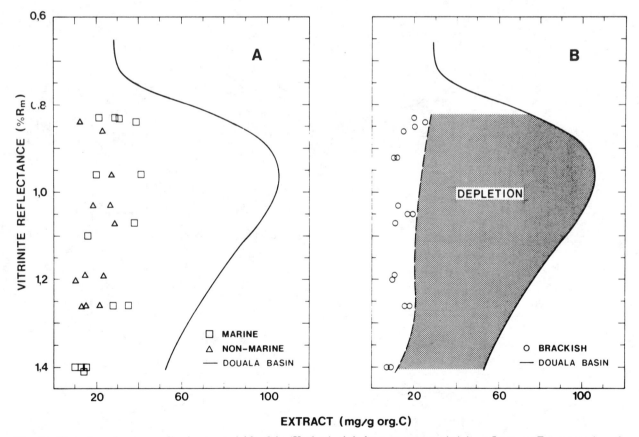

Fig. 4. Organic carbon-normalized extract yields of the 'Katharina' shales versus mean vitrinite reflectance. For comparison the trend line for Upper Cretaceous shales from the Douala Basin (Albrecht *et al.*, 1976) is shown. A and B display samples from different paleoenvironments for the 'Katharina' shales.

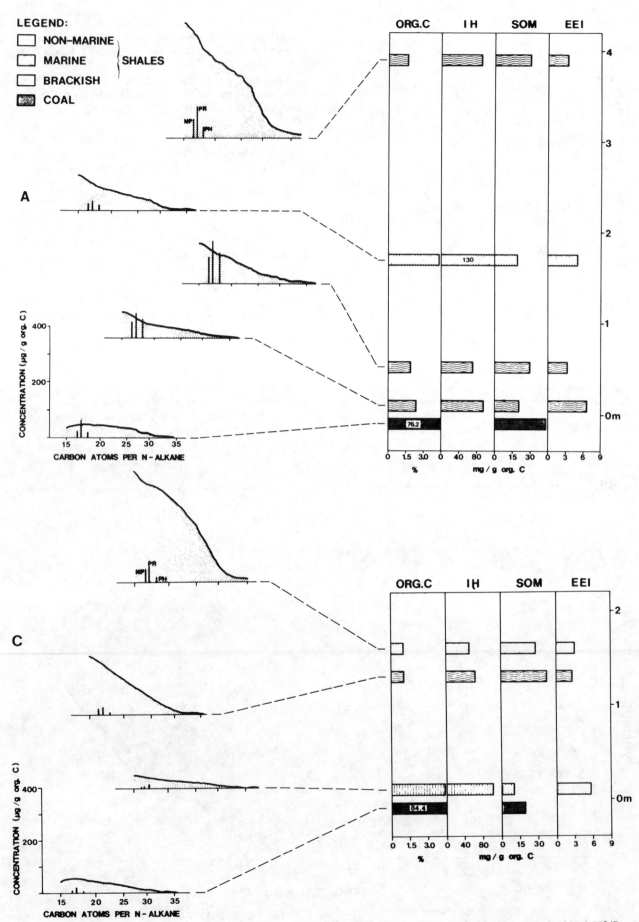

Fig. 5. Absolute carbon-normalized concentrations of *n*-alkanes (C$_{15}$-C$_{35}$) for selected sections of different rank (A = 0.83%R$_m$; B = 0.96%R$_m$; C = 1.07%R$_m$; D = 1.26%R$_m$) from the Ruhr district. In addition, data are shown for organic carbon-normalized extract yields and expulsion efficiency index.

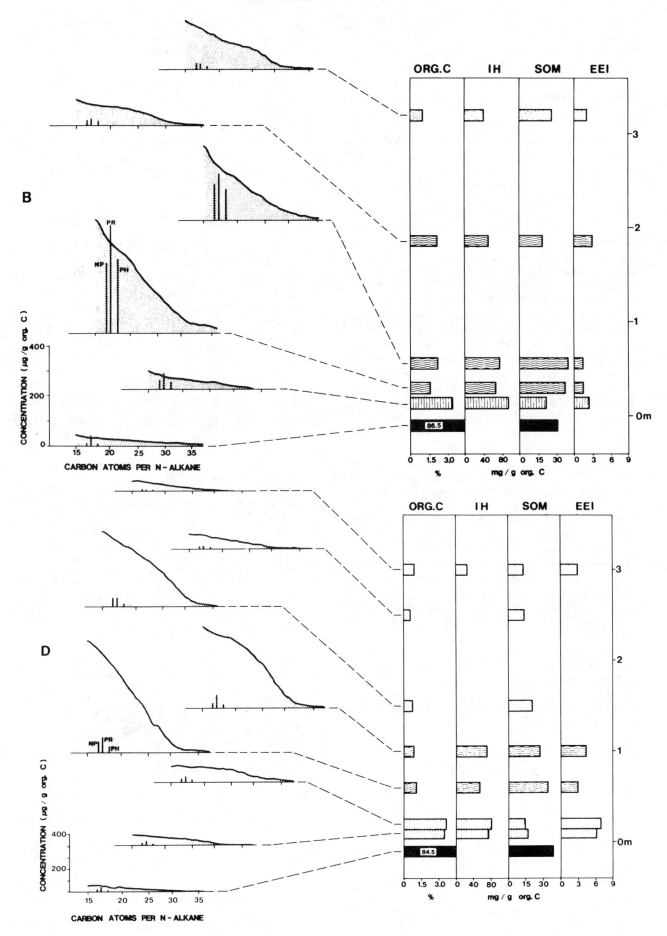

measured S_1 peaks. This new ratio is called the 'expulsion efficiency index' (EEI).

Rocks of unmodified organic composition, unaffected by migration processes will have an EEI of about 1, if accumulation occurs the index will become less than 1. Conversely, if the index exceeds 1, expulsion must be assumed. For the Carboniferous shales the EEI varies between 1.5 and 6.7 for marine shales, between 3.5 and 21.0 for brackish shales, and for non-marine shales from 1.5 to 4.0. This result is illustrated with selected examples in Fig. 5. The variation in EEI leads to the conclusion that different degrees of expulsion of hydrocarbon have occurred.

The amount of extractable organic matter shows no regular trend as a function of increasing maturity. It is noteworthy that shales of inferior kerogen quality yield, in part, even higher extracts than brackish shales of best kerogen quality. Figure 4 shows the relationship between organic carbon-normalized soluble organic matter and vitrinite reflectance for Upper Cretaceous shales from the Douala Basin, West Africa (Albrecht *et al.*, 1976). A comparison is also made with the corresponding values from the Carboniferous shales. The latter show significantly lower extract yields, especially the brackish shales, which contain kerogen of a similar quality to that of the Douala Basin samples. This difference in extractable hydrocarbon yields is interpreted as depletion due to primary migration. The highest degree of hydrocarbon expulsion is as high as 75 to 95% in some of the brackish shales.

In Fig. 5, organic carbon-normalized absolute concentrations of *n*-alkanes and isoprenoid alkanes from selected vertical sections through the 'Katharina Horizont' are shown along with kerogen and extract data. The EEI is also shown. Some striking features are observed, which are best explained by an assumption of extensive redistribution by migration of hydrocarbons. For most samples there is a striking discrepancy between the value for the absolute concentrations of C_{15+}-*n*-alkanes and the kerogen quality: Samples with hydrogen lean kerogens often show higher concentrations of C_{15+}-*n*-alkanes, than do those with a higher hydrogen index. Particularly low concentrations of C_{15+}-*n*-alkanes occur for all samples immediately above the 'Katharina' coal seam, irrespective of their facies type and location. Different samples of a similar facies type which contain kerogen of a similar quality can show significant differences in the carbon-normalized concentrations of their C_{15+}-*n*-alkanes (Fig. 5).

CONCLUSIONS

The effect of changes in paleoenvironment on the nature of sedimentary organic matter has been studied in a thin stratigraphic sequence from the Upper Carboniferous of the Ruhr District, containing marine, brackish and non-marine shales.

Rock-Eval pyrolysis results and microscopic investigations suggested, that all three types of sediment studied contain a similar type of organic matter, dominated by terrestrial plant remains. Furthermore, it has been shown, that the shales deposited in brackish depositional environment contain kerogens with the highest hydrogen index, followed by that of the marine shales. The non-marine shales contain the poorest quality kerogens.

Comparison with data of Tertiary series from the Upper Rhine Valley and Upper Cretaceous shales from the Douala Basin, which contain kerogens of a similar quality, suggest that significant depletion of petroleum-range hydrocarbons has occurred during primary migration. In the case of the brackish water 'Katharina' shales expulsion has been estimated to be as high as 75 to 95%.

Acknowledgements

We are indebted to Ruhrkohle AG, Essen, FRG for supplying sample material.

Assistance with the experimental work by W. Benders, U. Disko, K. Otterberg, H. Pooch, F. Leistner, B. Schmidl, F. Schlosser, H. Willsch is gratefully acknowledged.

REFERENCES

Albrecht, P., Vandenbroucke, M. and Mandengué, M. (1976) Geochemical studies on the organic matter from the Douala Basin (Cameroon): I. Evolution of the extractable organic matter and the formation of petroleum. *Geochim. Cosmochim. Acta* **40**, 791–799.

Durand, B. and Espitalié, J. (1973) Évolution de la matière organique au cours de l'enfouissement des sédiments. *C.R. Acad. Sci.* 2253–2256.

Durand, B. and Espitalié, J. (1976) Geochemical studies on the organic matter from the Douala Basin (Cameroon): II. Evolution of kerogen. *Geochim. Cosmochim. Acta* **40**, 801–808.

Espitalié, J. (1979) Charakterisierung der organischen Substanz und ihres Reifegrades in vier Bohrungen des mittleren Oberrhein-Graben sowie Abschätzung der paläogeothermischen Gradienten. *Fortschr. Geol. Rheinl. Westfalen* **27**, 87–96.

Espitalié, J., Laporte, J. L., Madec, M., Marquis, F., Leplat, P., Paulet, G. and Boutefeu, A. (1977) Méthode rapide de caractérisation des roches meres, de leur potential pétrolier et de leur degré d'évolution. *Rev. Inst. Fr. Pet.* **32**, 23–42.

Hunt, J. M. (1979) *Petroleum Geochemistry and Geology*, Freeman, San Francisco.

Leythaeuser, D., Hagemann, H. W., Hollerbach, A. and Schaefer, R. G. (1980) Hydrocarbon generation in source beds as a function of type and maturation of their organic mass: A mass balance of approach. In *Proceedings of the 10th World Petroleum Congress*, Heyden and Son, London, Vol. 2, pp. 31–41.

Powell, T. G., Douglas, A. G. and Allan, J. (1976) Variations in the type and distribution of organic matter in some Carboniferous sediments from Northern England. *Chem. Geol.* **18**, 137–148.

Rabitz, A. (1966) Der marine Katharina-Horizont im Ruhrrevier und seine Fauna. *Fortschr. Geol. Rheinl. Westfalen* **13**, 125–194.

Radke, M., Sittardt, H. G. and Welte, D. H. (1978) Removal of soluble organic matter from rock samples with a flow-through extraction cell. *Anal. Chem.* **50**, 663–665.

Radke, M., Willsch, H. and Welte, D. H. (1980) Preparative hydrocarbon group type determination by automated medium pressure liquid chromatography. *Anal. Chem.* **52**, 406–411.

Teichmüller, M. (1979) Die Diagenese der kohligen Substanzen in den Gesteinen des Tertiärs und Mesozoikums des mittleren Oberrhein-Graben. *Fortschr. Geol. Rheinl. Westfalen.* **27**, 19–49.

Tissot, B. P., Durand, B., Espitalié, J. and Combaz, A. (1974) Influence of nature and diagenesis in formation of petroleum. *AAPG Bull.* **58**, 499–506.

Tissot, B. P. and Welte, D. H. (1978) *Petroleum Formation and Occurrence*, Springer-Verlag, Heidelberg.

Advances in Organic Geochemistry 1981, pp. 568–575
© *John Wiley & Sons Limited, 1983*

The Effects of Lithologic Variation on Organic Geochemistry in the Kimmeridge Clay of Britain

P. F. V. Williams and A. G. Douglas

Organic Geochemistry Unit, University of Newcastle, Newcastle upon Tyne NE1 7RU, UK

Many Jurassic successions are characterized by alternating sequences of bituminous shale, clay and limestone, and much discussion has centred on the origin of these sedimentary rhythms. It was considered possible that comparable variations in the organic geochemistry of the major lithotypes would also be observed, and that results on the nature and extent of such variations could be employed towards a better understanding of the problem. This paper presents the results of an organic geochemical examination of sequences of shale, clay and limestone of Kimmeridgian age. Microscopical examination (reflected and transmitted light), Fischer Assay, bitumen extraction and chromatography, capillary gas chromatography of saturated hydrocarbon fractions, and GCMS examination of cyclic hydrocarbon fractions indicated no major qualitative differences between the three sedimentary units, but major variations in quantity of organic matter were observed: shales contained greater proportions than either the clays or limestones. This was ascribed to a combination of mineralogical dilution of kerogen and sedimentary preservation effects. That no major qualitative differences were observed in organic geochemistry suggests that the source of the organic detritus remained reasonably constant throughout the sedimentation of the three lithological units. Minor variations in sterane content were observed between shales and limestones, but available evidence suggested a carbonate-catalysed diagentic mechanism to account for the observations.

INTRODUCTION

Lithology is determined primarily by the nature of the sediment input, and by the conditions of deposition. The depositional environment of the northwestern European Juarssic is characterized by alternations between a shallow water, near-shore facies, and one in which deeper water, more fully marine conditions were developed, and dominated by periodic marine transgressions (Arkell, 1933; Arkell, 1956). During the shallow water phases of deposition limestones predominated, whilst the deeper water facies produced more argillaceous deposits. Although the Jurassic system as a whole shows large scale rhythmic variations between shales and limestones, lithologic variations are also evident on a smaller scale within either of the two dominant lithologies. The major deeper water phases of deposition, during which argillaceous deposits were formed, occurred in the Lias, Callovian and Kimmeridgian; in all three small scale rhythmic variations between shale, limestone and clay are observed (Hallam, 1960; Duff, 1975).

The question of variable lithology was examined by Hallam (1964) in relation to the Blue Lias of southern Britain. He concluded that, for this particular sequence of rhythmically banded shales and limestones, variations in water depth provided an initial differentiation into more clay-rich or carbonate-rich horizons, but secondary diagenetic solution and reprecipitation of calcite also occurred, causing more lithological segregation.

The British Kimmeridgian succession in particular is characterized by sequences displaying a rhythmic alternation between three dominant lithologies, bituminous shale, limestone and clay (e.g. Gallois and Cox, 1974). If these lithologic differences are the result of variable sedimentation and/or depositional conditions, then it is possible that these variations may also influence the nature of the organic matter found within the sediments. In particular, changes in the primary organic input associated with sediment variation, and differences in post-depositional diagenetic conditions associated with varying depositional environments may be observed. Thus an examination of the organic matter from such rhythmic sequences might be expected to show variability for the above reasons. The results of such an examination may, in turn, allow a greater understanding of the causes of variable lithology in these sediments: they may also be of interest in oil exploration, where the oil-producing potential of variable sequences is under examination.

In this paper we report the results of organic geochemical and microscopical examination of selected clay/shale/limestone sequences in an attempt to clarify this problem.

SAMPLES

At two of the three localities studied, the Kimmeridge Clay succession provides interbedded sequences of bituminous shales, clays and carbonates allowing the

Table 1
Sample details

Sample no.	Locality	Lithology	Zone
KM 16	Marton, North Yorkshire	Coccolith limestone (The Whitestone Band)	*pectinatus*
KM 15	Marton, North Yorkshire	Bituminous shale	*hudlestoni*
KM 14	Marton, North Yorkshire	Grey clay	*hudlestoni*
KM 9	Marton, North Yorkshire	Bituminous shale	*hudlestoni*
KM 8	Calcareous mudstone	Hudlestoni	*hudlestoni*
KB 2	Kimmeridge Bay, Dorset	Bituminous shale	*autissiodorensis*
KB 1	Kimmeridge Bay, Dorset	Oil shale	*autissiodorensis*
KB 3	Kimmeridge Bay, Dorset	Cementstone (Maple Ledge stoneband)	*autissiodorensis*
KS 82	Swindon[a]	Grey clay	*eudoxus*

[a] IGS Borehole, Swindon, Wiltshire, SU 1413 8349.

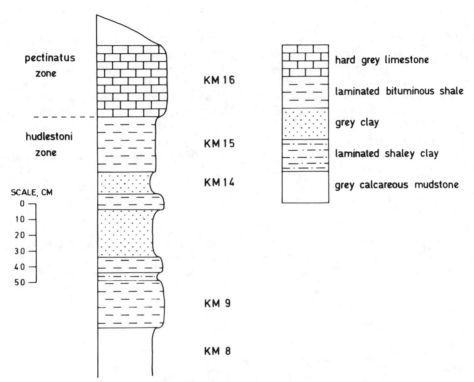

Fig. 1. Detail of section exposed at Marton, North Yorkshire and position of beds sampled.

evaluation of any lithology-related variation in the organic geochemistry of the sediments. In both sections the close proximity of the samples ensures that effects due to differential maturation are minimized.

Outcrop samples were obtained from sections at two localities, Kimmeridge Bay, Dorset, and Golden Hill brickpit, Marton, North Yorkshire. In addition, to provide further data for clay lithologies, a sample was obtained from the Swindon borehole drilled by the Institute of Geological Sciences (Swindon borehole, Wiltshire, SU 1413 8349, Gallois, 1976a), (Table 1). The relative disposition of lithologies studied at Marton is shown in Fig. 1. The coccolith limestone KM16 can be correlated with the Whitestone band of Dorset (Gallois and Medd, 1979). At Kimmeridge Bay, Dorset (Gallois and Cox, 1981), the Maple Ledge stone band occurs as a 35 cm thick band of limestone, of which the upper 17.5 cm was sampled, immediately overlain by a thin, very fissile oil shale (KB1) 3 cm in thickness. Above this is a

series of bituminous shales, of which the lowest 8.5 cm was sampled (KB2).

EXPERIMENTAL

Most relevant experimental details are reported elsewhere (Williams and Douglas, 1980; Williams and Douglas, 1981a). Thin layer chromatographic separations were conducted on silica gel plates containing 10% silver nitrate as in Williams and Douglas (1981a). The carbonate content was determined quantitatively by treatment of the solvent-extracted rock powder with HCl; the kerogen content was determined quantitatively by digestion of the residue from the carbonate determinations with HF. Elemental analyses were performed on a Carlo Erba 1106 elemental analyser.

RESULTS

Microscopical analysis and petrographic description

In general, reflected light microscopy of the samples under oil immersion reveals a sparsity of recognizable coal macerals. Of these, the inertinite group is most abundant, with occasional particles of reworked vitrinite. In all cases primary vitrinite is rare, the bulk of the organic matter being represented by structureless low reflecting amorphous material (bituminite). Due to its low reflectance, this organic matter is better observed with an air objective, employing polarization colours to enhance the subject. Pyrite is common throughout the samples studied, occurring mainly as framboids. Bituminous shales have the highest concentrations, while clays and carbonates contain less.

The bituminous shales from Yorkshire are somewhat coarse grained, whilst those from the Dorset section show a fine grained texture. In the three organic-rich shales KM15, KM9 and KB1, the structureless organic matter (kerogen) is prominent, and occurs rhythmically interlaminated with fine grained clay minerals. Occasional coarse calcite grains are also present, and in some areas, notably in KM9, rhythmic couplets of kerogen and calcite are present in addition to the more usual kerogen/clay laminations. In the oil shale KB1, the calcite is more fine grained and dispersed within the clay matrix. The kerogen in bituminous shale KB2 is more thinly laminated and generally less prominent, with the clay matrix containing fine grained calcite and occasional coarser calcite which is concentrated in planes parallel to those of the main lamination.

Whilst calcite is the most noticeable mineralogical component of the three calcareous lithologies, laminated organic matter is still apparent. Coarse grained calcite is the dominant component of the coccolith limestone KM16 groundmass, but thin laminae of amorphous organic matter are also observed: this rhythmic lamination of kerogen/calcite is observable throughout the total thickness of this individual bed. Elongated lenses of coccolith debris are also dispersed in the matrix.

Thin bands of laminated kerogen are again apparent in the Maple Ledge cementstone (KB3) and extensive dolomitization of the calcite is observed. The calcareous mudstone shows a much finer texture with an extensive groundmass of calcite and clay minerals containing some discontinuous laminae of organic matter. Granular calcite is also apparent.

The Swindon and Marton clays both show fine grained texture with a dominantly clay mineral groundmass, although some kerogen is also present, showing discontinuous lamination. Some larger calcite is observed, but is only developed locally.

Similar petrographic characteristics are revealed by transmitted light microscopy of the three lithologies prepared as thin sections. In the bituminous shales the yellow–brown structureless kerogen is prominent, and the laminated character well displayed, with finer grained clay minerals interlaminated. Calcite grains are sparingly distributed throughout the matrix of KM15, but are more common in the Dorset oil shale KB1. In the poorly bituminous Dorset shale KB2, structureless organic matter is less abundant, but still appears as discontinuous laminations in a fine grained clay/calcite groundmass.

Yellow–brown laminated kerogen is again apparent

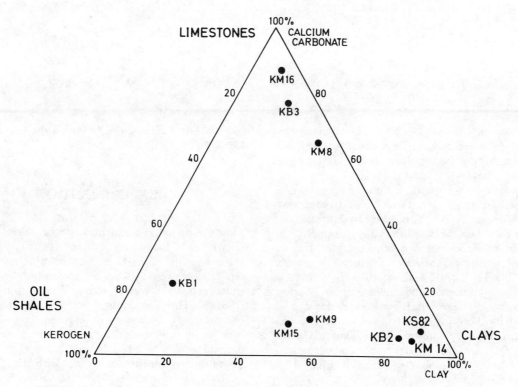

Fig. 2. Composition of samples plotted in terms of kerogen, calcium carbonate and clay.

Table 2
Variation of Organic Geochemical Parameters with lithology.

Sample no.	Lithology	Soluble bitumen wt% whole rock	Kerogen pyrolysis yield, wt% whole rock	Kerogen atomic H/C ratio
KB 1	Oil shale	2.00	13.8	1.35
KM 9	Bituminous shale	1.50	11.7	ND[a]
KM 15	Bituminous shale	2.10	10.1	1.17
KB 2	Bituminous shale	0.51	3.4	ND
KM 16	Coccolith limestone	0.19	1.4	1.18
KB 3	Cementstone	0.40	2.8	1.37
KM 8	Calcareous mudstone	0.35	1.4	ND
KM 14	Clay	0.20	Trace	ND
KS 82	Clay	0.15	0.5	ND

[a] ND = not determined.

in the carbonate lithologies although it is generally patchy and discontinuous. The calcite groundmass of the coccolith limestone KM16 is fine grained, but occasional coarser elongated lenses of calcite also occur. The Maple Ledge cementstone shows well laminated brown kerogen and coarse grained dolomite. A much coarser texture is found in the calcareous mudstone KM8, with a greater proportion of clay minerals and coarse calcite. Brown organic matter is patchy, but still displays a discontinuous laminated orientation.

The two clays KS82 and KM14 are fine grained with clay minerals dominating the groundmass. Coarse calcite grains are not common, but again yellow–brown kerogen is present and shows discontinuous lamination.

Isolated kerogen strew mounts in transmitted light are composed primarily of structureless amorphous organic matter, light brown in colour, with very occasional particles of brown wood. Black wood is observed occasionally, but is generally very rare.

Mineralogical and organic geochemical analysis

Kerogen, carbonate and clay contents of the samples are presented in Fig. 2, no attempt being made to quantify the pyrite content. General organic geochemical parameters are presented in Table 2, related to sample lithology. Elemental (atomic H/C) analyses for isolated kerogens are also appended for four samples.

It is observed that the four bituminous shales contain higher quantities of soluble bitumen, and produce noticeably higher levels of kerogen pyrolysate than the carbonate or clay lithologies, the values obtained generally following the trend of the kerogen contents. A difference in hydrogen content of the kerogens is observed, with a lower atomic H/C ratio being found for the Yorkshire samples. This could be the result of increased maturity which has been observed for the northern part of the British onshore Kimmeridgian succession (Williams and Douglas, 1981). In both areas the carbonate lithologies show a small but reproducibly higher atomic H/C ratio. (A more aliphatic nature for these kerogens is also suggested by preliminary pyrolysis gas chromatographic examination, but further analysis is needed to confirm this.)

Table 3
Bitumen analysis by column chromatography. Aliphatic and alicyclic hydrocarbons are eluted in the petrol fraction, aromatic hydrocarbons in the DCM fraction, and NSO compounds in the methanol fraction.

Sample no.	Weight % crude bitumen		
	Petrol eluate	Dichloromethane eluate	Methanol eluate
KM 15	10.1	12.8	36.2
KM 9	9.9	13.1	32.2
KB 1	8.1	21.7	33.3
KB 2	15.8	12.2	41.0
KM 16	12.7	18.0	42.0
KB 3	10.0	16.9	46.4
KM 8	15.4	16.9	40.4
KM 14	5.9	8.2	49.5
KS 82	4.8	9.3	42.8

Whilst lithology-related variations are observable in the above results, no such correlations can be seen in the results obtained by column chromatography of the bitumens (Table 3). Bitumen composition is dominated by polar NSO compounds which are generally more than twice as abundant as the aromatic hydrocarbons. Aliphatic and alicyclic hydrocarbons are found in low concentrations and in most cases are subordinate to the aromatic hydrocarbons. These values are similar to those previously obtained for other British Kimmeridgian bitumens (Williams and Douglas, 1980; Williams and Douglas, 1981a).

Capillary gas chromatographic examination of saturated hydrocarbon mixtures, separated from the extracted bitumens reveals no distinction between the three lithologies, and representative chromatograms are shown in Fig. 3. The major features of the aliphatic hydrocarbon distributions are comparable for all samples, showing n-alkane maxima at nC_{17}, together with a large peak at nC_{23} (Williams and Douglas, 1980). Samples from Kimmeridge Bay show high CPI values (nC_{20}–nC_{30}) whilst those of the Marton samples are lower due to their greater maturity. The isoprenoid hydrocarbons pristane and phytane are prominent, with

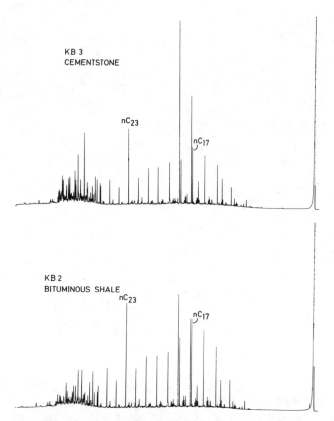

Fig. 3. Capillary gas chromatograms of saturated hydrocarbons isolated from extracted bitumens obtained from bituminous shales and cementstones. GC conditions: 25 m fused silica capillary column coated with OV 101, hydrogen carrier gas, temperature programmed from 40 to 260 °C at 4 °C min^{-1}, Carlo Erba 4160 chromatography.

phytane dominant over pristane in all samples except the clay and calcareous mudstone samples from Marton (KM14 and KM8) where the order is reversed. Finally, the higher molecular weight region of the gas chromatograms is dominated by a complex series of peaks due to polycycloalkanes. Analysis of this complex group of compounds by GC and GC–MS allows a differentiation into two series, pentacyclic triterpanes and steranes. Relative cycloalkane fraction compositions are presented in Table 4, together with details of relative

sterane composition. Representative capillary gas chromatograms of cycloalkane fractions are shown in Fig. 4, and major peaks assigned by mass spectrometry.

DISCUSSION

The similarity in microscopical appearance of the organic matter from the three lithologies studied suggests that these units can be described in terms of three major petrographic components common to all samples, namely kerogen, carbonate and clay. Fig. 2 shows the relationship between the three lithologies and petrographic composition described in the above terms. Limestones are characterized by a dominance of calcite, clays by clay minerals and oil shales by kerogen. The relationship between the samples studied can be examined in these terms, and compositions are plotted in Fig. 2. The observed variation in organic matter may then be considered simply in terms of quantity. For example, the oil shale KB1 and the bituminous shale KM9 are related by a decrease in kerogen content, while the difference between the coccolith limestone KM16 and the calcareous mudstone KM8 is one of increasing clay content at the expense of carbonate. Thus the lithology-related variation in quantity of organic matter can be regarded partly as one of dilution of the sediment by either clay or carbonate at the expense of kerogen.

This observed variation in quantity of organic matter is again displayed by the analytical results in Table 2: as suggested by microscopical analysis, shales contain much greater quantities of kerogen and soluble bitumen. These quantitative variations are not paralleled by significant differences in either kerogen or bitumen composition, although elemental analysis suggests that the kerogens from carbonate facies are slightly more marine. This difference is, however, very small.

Bitumens from the three distinct facies show similar compositional characteristics, and the comparability of aliphatic hydrocarbon distributions suggests that significant differences in the composition of the biological input to each sedimentary unit were limited. This implies that the source of the organic detritus remained broadly constant not only during deposition of

Table 4
Composition of cycloalkane fraction.

	Fraction composition		Sterane composition			
Sample no.	Pentacyclic triterpanes (%)	Steranes (%)	5α,24 Ethyl cholestane (%)	5α,cholestane (%)	5β,24 Ethyl cholestane (%)	Ratio 5α cholestane/ 5α,24 ethyl cholestane (%)
KM 16	41.6	58.4	9.2	19.2	2.5	2.08
KM 15	34.6	65.4	14.7	17.6	4.0	1.19
KM 14	39.3	60.7	8.4	10.4	2.5	1.23
KM 9	39.5	60.5	9.2	12.2	3.3	1.32
KM 8	37.8	62.7	13.8	15.2	3.6	1.10
KB 1	26.9	73.1	6.9	19.1	1.4	2.76
KB 2	21.3	78.7	9.6	16.2	3.6	1.68
KB 3	20.3	79.7	7.3	16.9	2.1	2.31

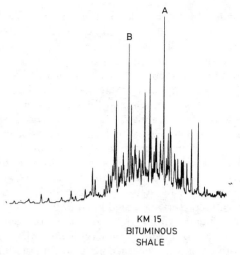
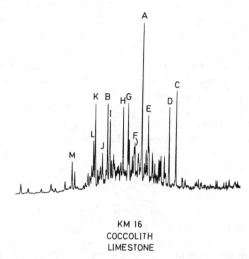

KM 15
BITUMINOUS
SHALE

KM 16
COCCOLITH
LIMESTONE

Fig. 4. Capillary gas chromatograms of cycloalkanes (urea non-adducts) isolated from bitumens extracted from bituminous shales and coccolith limestones. GC conditions as Fig. 3 except temperature programmed from 150 to 280 °C at 4 °C min⁻¹. Peak assignments (mass spectrometry) A, 5α cholestane; B, 5α, 24-ethyl cholestane; C and D, diasteranes; E, 5β cholestane; F, 17α (H) trisnorhopane; G, co-eluting mixture of 17β (H) trisnorhopane and unidentified sterane; H, 5α, 24-methyl cholestane; I, 17α (H), (H) norhopane; J, 17β (H), 21α (H) normoretane; K, 17α (H), 21β (H) hopane; L, 17β (H), 21α (H) moretane (tentative); M, 17α (H), 21β (H) homohopane (tentative).

a sequence of variable lithology at one locality, but also at a site of deposition some 300 km distant. However, regional correlation of fauna and lithology suggests similar ecological environments for much of the Kimmeridgian, at least in southern Britain (Gallois, 1976).

Whilst a major difference in organic geochemical composition is not apparent, minor variations are observed. In all three facies steranes are more abundant than pentacyclic triterpanes in the cycloalkane fractions (Table 4), and variations in molecular composition are noticeable. Specific ion mass chromatograms (m/z 217) of steranes from both carbonate and bituminous shale facies are shown in Fig. 5, whilst qualitative

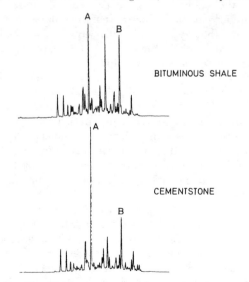

BITUMINOUS SHALE

CEMENTSTONE

Fig. 5. Specific ion mass chromatograms, m/z 217, of cycloalkanes (urea non-adducts) isolated from bitumens extracted from shales and cementstones. Peak assignments as for Figure 4. Conditions: 20 m OV 101 glass capillary column coupled directly to the source of a VG 12F mass spectrometer at 280 °C, helium carrier gas, temperature programming 150–275 °C at 2 °C min⁻¹, 70 eV, 100 μA trap current.

compositions are very similar, variations in quantity of specific molecular structures are apparent (peaks A and B, Fig. 4).

In the cementstone, peak A, identified by mass spectrometry as 5α cholestane, is enhanced relative to the bituminous shales. Comparison of cycloalkane gas chromatograms (Fig. 4) again suggests that in limestones the 5α cholestane peak is enhanced. Reference to Table 4 however suggests that depletion of peak B (5α, 24-ethyl cholestane) has occurred in the carbonate facies. Since only relative compositions are measured, it cannot be established whether these results represent a decrease in the actual quantity of 5α, 24-ethyl cholestane in the carbonates, or an increase in the content of 5α cholestane. However, the ratio of peak A to peak B, presented in Table 4 underlines the difference between shales, clays and limestones. When contributions from all major C_{27} and C_{29} steranes are compared, limestones, showing a higher $C_{27}:C_{29}$ ratio appear to be enriched in C_{27} and/or depleted in C_{29} steranes (Table 5).

Sterane hydrocarbons in the geological environment are derived diagenetically from steroids of biological origin (e.g. Dastillung and Albrecht, 1977; Lee *et al.*, 1977) and are thus a reflection of the steroid composition of the organisms responsible for the organic matter found in the sediment. Steroid distributions are known to vary

Table 5
Ratio of C_{27} to C_{29} steranes in cycloalkane fraction.

Sample no.	Lithology	$C_{27}:C_{29}$ Sterane ratio
KM 16	Coccolith limestone	2.16
KB 3	Cementstone	2.40
KM 15	Bituminous shale	1.25
KM 14	Clay	1.34
KM 9	Bituminous shale	1.41
KM 8	Calcareous mudstone	1.18
KB 2	Bituminous shale	1.54

from marine to terrestrial organisms, and their distributions can be used to indicate the source of sedimentary organic matter (Huang and Meinschein, 1976). In an examination of sterols from oceanic and coastal environments, Lee *et al.* (1979) observed large amounts of C_{29} sterols in river and coastal sediments, derived from land plant sources. Farther from areas of terrestrial influence, deep ocean sterols were found to be dominated by the C_{27} members. Thus the presence of C_{27} sterols could be used as an indicator of marine organic matter whilst C_{29} sterols, derived mainly from β sitosterol indicate terrestrial sources. Huang and Meinschein (1979) have utilized these distributions as ecological indicators, plotting the relative quantities of C_{27}, C_{28} and C_{29} sterols on a ternary diagram: they can recognize marine planktonic and higher land plant contributions together with a range of transitional environments.

Thus the increased $C_{27}:C_{29}$ sterane ratio found for the coccolith limestone KM16 suggests a somewhat more marine origin for the organic matter in this sample. Considering the significant proportion of marine coccolith debris found in this sediment (in its lateral equivalent in Dorset, the bed contains over 30% of recognizable coccoliths (Gallois and Medd, 1979)) this observation is not surprising. However, the Maple Ledge stoneband in Dorset also shows a high $C_{27}:C_{29}$ ratio. The correlation of high $C_{27}:C_{29}$ sterane ratios with the demonstrated coccolith origin of the Marton Whitestone band is acceptable, but a similar correlation applied to the Maple Ledge stoneband is less favourable. This particular limestone is not of coccolith origin but a post-depositional diagenetic example (Irwin *et al.*, 1977). Two explanations are possible to acount for the similar sterane distributions in limestones of different origin. Either the significant quantity of inorganic coccolith debris in the Marton limestone is not associated with a significant input of coccolith-derived organic matter, or that the high $C_{27}:C_{29}$ sterane ratios are chemically produced as a result of pre- or post-depositional carbonate interactions. It is unlikely that the large influx of inorganic coccolith debris was also not accompanied by a significant quantity of organic detritus, and thus the latter, chemical explanation is more feasible. It is possible that carbonate-catalysed diagenetic effects have influenced some part of the sterol–sterane transformation pathway producing the observed results. This hypothesis receives support from the apparent correlation of the $C_{27}:C_{29}$ ratio with carbonate content for the three calcareous samples KM16, KB3 and KM8. For samples with lower carbonate contents however, the relationship is not valid.

The quantitative variability of the organic matter is more difficult to rationalize. We state above that the dilution effect of clay or carbonate can, in part, account for this observation; an argument also suggested by Dunn (1974) to account for variable lithology in certain Kimmeridge sections. If the hypothesis is regarded as plausible, then it becomes necessary to rationalize the variability in clay/carbonate sedimentation.

We propose a model that explains this variable sedimentation, one which also serves to provide further

reason for the observed kerogen variability. Changes in primary biological productivity would explain the differences in kerogen content, but sedimentary preservation of organic matter is a further factor warranting consideration. Whilst it is feasible to explain the small scale rhythmic variations between kerogen and clay on the basis of seasonal fluctuations in biological productivity (e.g. algal blooms, Gallois, 1976b; Dickman and Artuz, 1979; Degens and Stoffers, 1980) this explanation seems less satisfactory when applied to the larger scale variability of the three distinct lithologic units. It is suggested that this seasonal fluctuation of biological productivity is continuous, and that differential preservation modifies the quantity of organic matter found within the particular sediment. The particular sedimentary environments that favour deposition of clay or carbonate are those that are unfavourable towards the preservation of organic matter. These sedimentary environments are discussed in detail elsewhere (Williams and Douglas, 1981b).

CONCLUSIONS

The significant observations arising from this investigation can be summarized as follows:

1. The most noticeable lithology-related variation is one of organic matter quantity contained within the sediment, being highest for bituminous shales and lowest for clays.
2. The general character of organic matter in sediments from each of the three facies shows no major lithology-related difference in composition.
3. Carbonate horizons show an increase in the ratio of $C_{27}:C_{29}$ steranes.

From the above observations, several important conclusions can be deduced. It is concluded that the resulting lithology of a particular stratigraphic unit is determined by the dominance of one of three major petrographic components, which are themselves the result of a balance between particular depositional conditions. Limestones are dominated by carbonates, oil shales by kerogen, and clays and poorly bituminous shales by clay minerals. Whilst organic matter is found in all three lithologies its quantity is determined partly by a dilution effect of either clay or carbonate, and partly by differential preservation, a consequence of the particular environmental conditions operational at the time of deposition.

Uniformity in the broad character of the organic matter in any of the three sedimentary facies implies an unchanging biological source, and indicates that major variations in sediment source were also limited. Minor but significant variations in sterane compositions are likely to be diagenetic in origin. It is considered that transformation pathways of sterol precursors to steranes are modified by the presence of carbonate, producing the observed results.

It is thus possible to reconstruct a situation in which a broadly constant organic input is introduced into a varying sedimentary environment along with clays or carbonates. The extent of dilution of the organic matter and its preservation, which will ultimately determine the resultant quantity of organic matter in the rock, being determined by the specific environmental conditions operational at the time of deposition. Subsequently, during diagenesis, differential alteration of the organic matter occurs in sediments rich in carbonates.

In this particular sequence of Jurassic rocks, organic matter type remains broadly independent of lithology, and only quantity is affected by sedimentary facies. It is possible that other sequences showing similar lithological characteristics, e.g. the Toarcian or Callovian, could also display similar organic geochemical characteristics. In oil exploration studies, the significance of mixed shale/carbonate/clay sequences dominated by generally uniform organic geochemistry is obvious.

Acknowledgements

We thank the Institute of Geological Sciences for the Swindon borehole sample, and we thank Crossley Building Products for permission to visit Golden Hill brickpit, Marton. Mr Taylor provided valuable comment on the Golden Hill pit, and we thank Paula Cassidy for technical assistance. Financial support from NERC (GR3/3298) is gratefully acknowledged.

REFERENCES

Arkell, W. J. (1933) In: *The Jurassic System in Great Britain*, Clarendon Press, Oxford, 681 pp.

Arkell, W. J. (1956) *Jurassic Geology of the World*, Oliver and Boyd, Edinburgh, 800 pp.

Dastillung, M. and Albrecht, P. (1977) Δ^2 Sterenes as diagentic intermediates in sediments. *Nature*, **269**, 678–679.

Degens, E. T. and Stoffers, P. (1980) Environmental events recorded in quaternary sediments of the Black Sea. *J. Geol. Soc. London* **137**, 131–138.

Dickman, M. and Artuz, I. (1978) Mass mortality of photosynthetic bacteria as a mechanism for dark lamina formation in sediments of the Black Sea. *Nature*, **275**, 191–195.

Duff, K. L. (1975) Palaeoecology of a bituminous shale — the lower Oxford Clay of central England. *Palaeontology*, **18**, 443–482.

Dunn, C. E. (1974) Identification of sedimentary cycles through Fourier analysis of geochemical data. *Chem. Geol.*, **13**, 217–232.

Gallois, R. W. (1976a) Kimmeridge Clay oil shale project. In: *IGS Boreholes* 1975. Rep. Inst. Geol. Sci. 76/10, 21–24.

Gallois, R. W. (1976b) Coccolith blooms in the Kimmeridge Clay and origin of North Sea Oil. *Nature*, **259**, 473–475.

Gallois, R. W. and Cox, B. M. (1974) Stratigraphy of the upper Kimmeridge Clay of the Wash area. *Bull. Geol. Surv. Gt. Br.*, **47**, 1–28.

Gallois, R. W. and Medd, A. W. (1979) Coccolith rich marker bands in the English Kimmeridge Clay. *Geol. Mag.*, **116**, 247–334.

Gallois, R. W and Cox, B. M. (1981) The stratigraphy of the Kimmeridge Clay of the Dorset type area and its correlation with other Kimmeridge sequences. *Rep. Inst. Geol., Sci.*, 80/4.

Hallam, A. (1960) A sedimentary and faunal study of the Blue Lias of Dorset and Glamorgan. *Phil. Trans. R. Soc.*, **B 243**, 1–44.

Hallam, A. (1964) Origin of the limestone-shale rhythms in the Blue Lias of England: a composite theory. *J. Geol.*, **72**, 157–169.

Huang, W.-Y. and Meinschein, W. G. (1976) Sterols as source indicators of organic materials in sediments. *Geochim. Cosmochim. Acta*, **40**, 323–330.

Huang, W.-Y. and Meinschein, W. G. (1979) Sterols as ecological indicators. *Geochim. Cosmochim. Acta*, **43**, 739–745.

Irwin, H., Curtis, C. and Coleman, M. (1977) Istotopic evidence for source of diagenetic carbonate formed during burial of organic-rich sediments. *Nature*, **269**, 209–213.

Lee, C., Gagosian, R. B. and Farrington, J. W. (1977) Sterol diagenesis in recent sediments from Buzzards Bay Massachusetts. *Geochim. Cosmochim. Acta*, **41**, 985–992.

Lee, C., Farrington, J. W. and Gagosian, R. B. (1979) Sterol geochemistry of sediments from the Western North Atlantic Ocean and adjacent coastal areas. *Geochim. Cosmochim. Acta*, **43**, 35–46.

Williams, P. F. V. and Douglas, A. G. (1980) A preliminary organic geochemical investigation of the Kimmeridgian oil shales. In: *Advances in Organic Geochemistry* 1979 (ed. by Douglas, A. G. and Maxwell, J. R.) Pergamon, Oxford, 531–545.

Williams, P. F. V. and Douglas, A. G. (1981a) Kimmeridge Oil Shale, A study of organic maturation. In: *Organic Maturation Studies and Fossil Fuel Exploration* (ed. by Brooks, J.), Academic Press, London, 255–269.

Williams, P. F. V. and Douglas, A. G. (1981b) in preparation.

Advances in Organic Geochemistry 1981, pp. 576–587
© *John Wiley & Sons Limited, 1983*

The Distribution of Cyclic Alkanes in Two Lacustrine Deposits

P. B. Hall

Continental Shelf Institute, Hakon Magnussons Gt. 1B, 7001 Trondheim, Norway

A. G. Douglas

Organic Geochemistry Unit, Geology Department, The University Newcastle-upon-Tyne, England, NE1 7RU

The soluble bitumens of a number of rock samples from two lacustrine sedimentary sequences were analysed by gas chromatography and gas chromatography–mass spectrometry. The kerogens of the same samples were analysed by reflected light microscopy and gas chromatography of shale oils obtained by pyrolysis in a modified Fischer Assay-type apparatus. The deposits investigated were the oil shales of Autun from France (Permian) and the bituminous flagstones from Caithness in northern Scotland (Devonian). The depositional environments of these two sequences have some common features; a semi-arid climate (at least during part of their depositional history), intermontane fault-bounded depositional basins and a presumed, large algal input (Feys and Greber 1964; Wolf, 1966; Elsass, 1977; Doubinger and Elsass 1979; Westoll, 1937; and Donovan, 1980). Particular emphasis, in this investigation, was placed on the distribution of cyclic alkanes in the saturated hydrocarbon fraction of the soluble bitumens. Values for extractable organic matter (EOM), total organic carbon (TOC), aromatic and saturated hydrocarbon contents, are tabulated. Reflected light microscopy was done in both ultra violet and white light to obtain some measure of the ratio of recognizable organic to amorphous organic matter. Variable amounts of terpanes, steranes and carotenoid hydrocarbons were identified by GC—MS, and selective ion monitoring at m/z 191, 217. The occurrence of terpanes, steranes and carotenoid hydrocarbons is discussed in relation to environmental conditions. The occurrence of carotane and some tetra-alkylated cyclohexanes, believed to be derived from carotenoids, was a feature common to certain samples from both deposits. The normal alkane distributions are also similar. The relative amounts of normal alkanes and carotenoid hydrocarbons varies from sample to sample and is roughly correlated with the phytoclast types observed in reflected light microscopy, particularly for the Autun samples. An origin for the carotenoid hydrocarbons is suggested.

INTRODUCTION

Evidence for the organic matter in sediments being of biological origin includes the discovery of organic compounds in sediments which have chemical structures close to, or the same as, those produced by plants and animals. These 'biological markers' (biomarkers, chemical fossils), retain enough of the original chemical structure to allow them to be related to compounds produced by common organisms.

The search for biomarkers in sediments and sedimentary rocks has led to the detailed examination of a number of organic-rich shales. A few shales have been investigated in very great detail, including: the Tertiary Green River shales (U.S.A) (for example, Murphy *et al.* 1967; Anders and Robinson, 1971; Gallegos, 1971, 1973; Tissot *et al.*, 1978) and the Toarcian (Lower Jurassic) of the Paris Basin (France) (for example, Tissot *et al.*, 1971, 1974; Rubinstein and Albrecht, 1975; Mackenzie *et al.*, 1980, 1981).

A variety of compounds have been identified in these and other deposits including numerous steranes and hopanes (Kimble *et al.*, 1974; van Dorsselaer *et al.*, 1977; Seifert and Moldowan, 1978; Ourisson *et al.*, 1979; Mackenzie *et al.*, 1980). The variation in distribution and the absolute and relative amounts of these and related unsaturated and oxygenated compounds have been used to indicate the predominant input, and to trace the probable reactions which occur during deposition and burial of the organic matter in sediments.

Many other interesting compounds have been identified in ancient sediments and crude oils. Numerous compounds of probable bacterial origin including head to head and tail to tail acyclic isoprenoid alkanes have been identified (Albaiges *et al.*, 1978; Seifert and Moldowan, 1979; Albaiges, 1980) including squalane (Gardner and Whitehead, 1972; McKirdy and Kantsler, 1980), Branched alkanes such as Botryococcane (Moldowan and Seifert, 1980) and cyclic alkanes such as carotane (Murphy *et al.*, 1967; Anders and Robinson, 1971; Hunt, 1979; Rullkötter and Philp, 1981) are thought to be of algal origin. Lycopane, a fully reduced compound derived from lycopene, has been identified in Messel shale (Kimble *et al.*, 1974) and may be derived from a higher plant pigment. A variety of bicyclic and tricyclic terpanes have been identified in oil shales, crude oils, coals and bitumens. They are thought to be derived in part from higher plant material (Bendoraitis, 1974; Seifert and Moldowan, 1978; Philp *et al.*, 1981).

This report describes, briefly, some aspects of the organic geochemistry of two ancient lacustrine deposits; the Lower Permian Autun shales from France and Devonian shales and flagstones from north–east Scotland. This includes identification of certain cyclic alkanes including terpanes, steranes, alkylated cyclohexanes and carotane.

Geology

Ten oil shale samples from the Permian Autun sequence were collected, namely; three from the Igornay formation (C2, C6, C7) which are thought to be Stephanian to Lower Autunian in age, one from a shale in the Lally sandstones (C1), one shale from the Muse beds (C5) which are both of Lower Autunian age. In the Upper Autunian succession; two from the Surmoulin beds (C8 and C8a), one from Telot formation (C9) and two from the Boghead group (C3, C4). The stratigraphic location and ages of those samples is based on the work of Doubinger and Elass (1979). These shales are all dark grey to brown–black shales. The samples from the Devonian of north–east Scotland were also collected. Five samples are discussed here. Four come from horizons rich in fossil fish remains. One of these, the Achanarras limestone, is considered to be very extensive. Two samples collected from fish bed horizons in Nairnshire at Clava (D3), and on the north coast near Dounreay (D10) are thought to be from approximately the same horizon (Donovan *et al.*, 1978). Another sample from near Achanarras at Spital (D7) is higher in the succession than the Achanarras limestone. These are all from the Middle Devonian (Richardson, 1965;

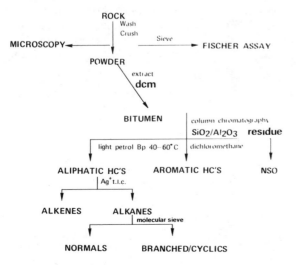

Fig. 1. Experimental, procedure — flow diagram.

Donovan *et al.*, 1978). One sample from the Lower Devonian or basal Middle Devonian (Donovan *et al.*, 1978) is from the Spa beds at Strathpeffer. These shales are associated with beds containing stromatolite structures (Donovan *et al.*, 1978). The Middle Devonian sediments are considered to have been deposited in thermally stratified lakes (Donovan, 1980). There are indications that the climate was semi-arid, with periods when the lakes dried up (Westoll, 1937) and sometimes hypersaline conditions were developed (Michie, 1979). The Autun deposit is interesting because it includes a sequence with predominantly coal swamp floras in the Stephanian and Lower Autunian which are replaced in the Upper Autunian by dry climate floras including some of the early gymnosperms (Doubinger and Elsass, 1979).

EXPERIMENTAL

Flow diagram

The procedures described in this section are summarized in Fig. 1. The samples were ground in a centrifugal mill to a particle size smaller than 125 μm and extracted for 24 h in a Soxhlet apparatus with dichloromethane (DCM). The DCM extract was evaporated under a nitrogen flow to remove the solvent and to determine the total amount of extractable organic matter (EOM). The EOM was then separated by column chromatography into aliphatic hydrocarbons, aromatic hydrocarbons and residue using *n*-hexane and DCM as eluants. Each eluate was evaporated and weighed. The aliphatic hydrocarbon fraction was purified by silver ion thin-layer chromatography to produce a total alkane fraction, which was further separated into normal and branched/cyclic components by treatment with 5A molecular sieve. The saturated hydrocarbon fraction was analysed by glass capillary gas chromatography and combined gas chromatography–mass spectrometry (GC–MS).

The gas chromatographic analyses were performed on a Perkin–Elmer F17 chromatograph fitted with a 20 × 0.25 mm glass capillary column coated with OV-101; using hydrogen carrier gas (flow rate 1 ml min^{-1}). The oven was programmed from 60 to 280 °C at 4 °C min^{-1}, and the samples were injected in the split mode (20:1). Ten saturated hydrocarbon fractions were analysed by selected ion monitoring (SIM) and sequential scanning using a VG-Micromass 12B or 7070 mass spectrometers coupled directly to a Varian 1400 or 3400 gas chromatograph respectively, via an all glass line. A 20 m × 0.3 mm i.d. glass capillary column coated with OV-1 was temperature programmed from 60 °C to 280 °C at 4 °C min^{-1} with helium carrier gas at a flow rate of 1 ml min^{-1}. Data aquisition was carried out in part by a VG-Data Systems 'Multispec' data system. The sequential scanning was performed at 1 s/decade and SIM recording at 200 ms dwell time per ion. The ion at m/z 191 was monitored for triterpanes, and those at m/z 217 and 218 for steranes.

Organic carbon values were determined using a Aminco carbon analyser. Pyrolysis was carried out on

Table 1

Ages, extraction data, CPI and pristane/phytane values of samples

Sample	Age	TOC %	EOM ppm w/w	EOM mg g⁻¹ TOC	Sat. HC mg g⁻¹ TOC	Aromatic HC mg g⁻¹ TOC	CPI $nC_{23}-nC_{33}$	Prist. phyt. ratio
D1		0.6	1187	197.8	68.3	93.7	1.20	1.8
D3		1.0	2210	221.0	71.0	109.3	1.20	1.4
D7	Devonian	0.7	2155	307.9	71.4	160.6	1.00	1.0
D8	north-east Scotland	5.1	3120	61.2	11.6	23.4	0.96	0.6
D10		5.2	2934	72.6	25.1	26.5	1.08	1.1
C1		13.4	9577	71.5	—	—	1.20	1.6
C2		15.6	5128	32.8	—	—	0.98	1.2
C3		10.7	4450	41.6	9.2	16.7	1.11	1.9
C4		7.3	4178	57.2	17.5	23.8	1.12	2.2
C5	Permian	10.1	6308	62.5	17.7	22.0	1.30	2.6
C6	(Autun)	15.7	4978	31.7	—	—	1.15	2.2
C7		7.0	2550	36.3	12.0	11.4	1.15	1.7
C8		13.0	11974	92.1	20.7	49.6	1.12	1.9
C8a		6.6	5109	77.4	—	—	—	2.2
C9		18.4	8148	44.3	16.5	30.9	1.10	1.3

100 mg aliquots of freshly crushed samples using a Rock–Eval instrument. The vitrinite reflectance measurements were taken on whole rock samples. The whole rock samples were also pyrolysed in air using a small, modified Fischer type retort (Stanfield and Frost, 1949).

A few grams of whole rock (20 mesh size) were heated to 500 °C in a small retort at a heating rate of 10 °C min⁻¹, and then held at 500 °C for 15 min. The oils produced were gas chromatographed directly.

Table 2a.

Vitrinite reflectance, and spore fluorescence data.

Sample	Vitrinite reflectance	Spore fluorescence
D1	–	Nil
D3	–	Nil
D7	–	Nil
D8	–	Nil
D10	–	Mid-orange
C1	0.44(47)	Yellow–orange
C2	0.41(24)	Yellow–orange
C3	0.44(33)	Yellow–orange
C4	0.36(32)	Yellow, yellow–orange
C5	0.39(28)	Yellow, yellow–orange
C6	0.46(27)	Yellow–orange
C7	0.45(29)	Yellow–orange
C8	0.38(25)	Yellow, yellow–orange
C8a	0.38(39)	Yellow, yellow–orange
C9	0.40(8)	Yellow, yellow–orange

RESULTS AND DISCUSSION

Microscopy, extraction and isolation of alkane fraction

The fifteen samples analysed varied considerably in the amount of total organic carbon (TOC). The organic carbon content of the Devonian samples varied from 0.6 to 5.2% and the Permian samples from 6.6 to 18.4%. The concentration of EOM (in mg g⁻¹ of TOC) is much higher for the Devonian samples, particularly those with the lowest TOC values (Table 1).

Although vitrinite reflectivity measurements were not obtained for the Devonian sediments, the lack of fluorescence in the Devonian samples (except for D10) suggests that the kerogens are probably mature, high rank. The Permian samples show yellow and yellow–orange fluorescence in ultra violet light and vitrinite

Table 2b

Rock-Eval pyrolysis data

Sample	S1 (mg HC g⁻¹ rock)	S2 (mg CO₂ g⁻¹ rock)	S3	TOC (%)	Hydrogen index	Oxygen index	Oil and gas content S_1+S_2 (kg HC/ton rock)	Production index $\dfrac{S_1}{S_1+S_2}$	$T_{(max)}$ (°C)
D8	0.14	1.63	0.47	5.1	32	9	1.77	0.08	434
D10	1.53	34.71	0.41	5.2	668	8	36.24	0.04	441
C6	1.23	65.82	3.00	15.7	419	19	67.05	0.02	438
C8a	2.31	33.09	1.80	6.6	501	27	35.40	0.07	420
C9	4.33	101.89	1.47	18.4	554	8	106.22	0.04	440

Table 3
Hopane compounds identified by GC–MS

Peak number	Carbon number	Compound name
1.	C_{27}	17α(H) 22,29,30-trisnorhopane
3.	C_{29}	17α(H) 21β(H) 30-norhopane
5.	C_{30}	17α(H) 21β(H) hopane
8. and 9.	C_{31}	17α(H) 21β(H) 22R and 22S homohopane
12. and 13.	C_{32}	17α(H) 21β(H) 22R and 22S bishomohopane
15. and 16.	C_{33}	17α(H) 21β(H) 22R and 22S trishomohopane
4.	C_{29}	17β(H) 21α(H) 30-normoretane
7.	C_{30}	17β(H) 21α(H) moretane
11.	C_{31}	17β(H) 21α(H) homomoretane

Table 4
Sterane compounds identified by GC–MS

Peak code	Carbon number	Compound name
A.	C_{27}	5β(H)14α(H)17α(H) Cholestane 20R (Coprostane 20R)
B.	C_{27}	5α(H)14α(H)17α(H) Cholestane 20R (Cholestane 20R)
C.	C_{28}	5β(H)14α(H)17α(H) 24-methylcholestane 20R
E.	C_{28}	5α(H)14α(H)17α(H) 24-methylcholestane 20R
G.	C_{29}	5β(H)14α(H)17α(H) 24-ethylcholestane 20R
I.	C_{29}	5α(H)14α(H)17α(H) 24-ethylcholestane 20R
	C_{28}	$5\alpha14\alpha17\alpha20S$ methylcholestane
	C_{29}	$5\alpha14\alpha17\alpha20S$ ethylcholestane
	C_{28} C_{28}	$5\alpha14\beta17\beta20R$ and S 24-methylcholestanes
	C_{29} C_{29}	$5\alpha14\beta17\beta20R$ and S 24-ethylcholestanes

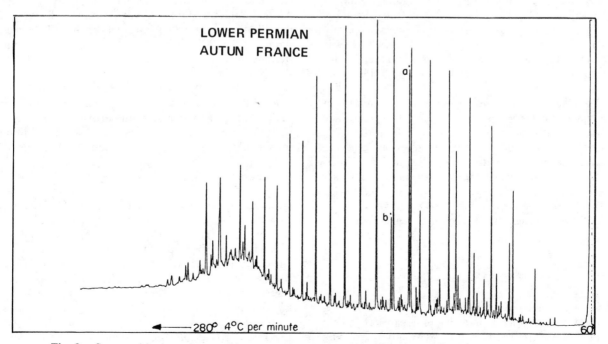

Fig. 2. Saturated hydrocarbon gas chromatogram of sample C5, Lower Autunian, Muse, Autun, France.

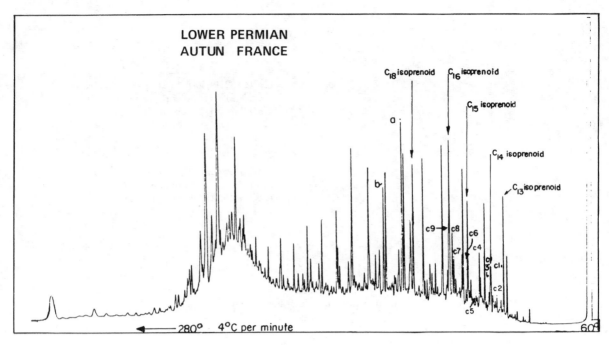

Fig. 3. Saturated hydrocarbon gas chromatogram of sample C4, Upper Autunian, Millery, Autun, France.

reflectances between 0.36 and 0.46% which indicates that the kerogens are immature (Table 2a).

Examination in reflected light indicates that roughly 10% by volume of the Autun samples consists of microscopically recognizable material. This material consists of a few wisps and small blocky fragments of vitrinite, scattered fragments of highly reflecting inertinites, but mostly of red–brown to dull grey spores and algal bodies of the Botryococcus type which fluoresce in ultra violet light yellow–orange and bright yellow respectively. Large spores and/or pollen grains are particularly prominent in the Muse shale (C5) from the Lower Autunian and the Upper Autunian samples (particularly C8, C8a). In most of the Devonian samples, there was very little microscopically recognizable organic matter. In D10 however, there was abundant light-to mid-orange fluorescent material with no obvious structures interlaminated with inorganic mineral matter.

The alkanes of these two deposits vary considerably in amount and composition (Figs 2–5, 12). The percentage of saturated hydrocarbons varies roughly from 20 to 40% with no correlation between the maturity and the amounts of saturated hydrocarbons. The n-alkane distributions are similar for all samples, except for D8, which has an even predominance of 0.77 between $nC_{13}–nC_{23}$. Otherwise the n-alkane distributions ranging from $nC_{12}–nC_{33}$ show only slight odd carbon preference (between 1 and 1.3).

GC–MS analysis

A selected number of samples were analysed by GC–MS, partly by selected ion monitoring of hopanes (m/z 191) and steranes (m/z 217 and 218) and partly by identification of single compounds from their mass spectra. Analyses were done on branched and cyclic alkanes, or saturated hydrocarbon fractions.

A series of hopanes and steranes were identified and although the samples analysed contained the same hopane components (Table 3) a large variation in the relative concentrations of these compounds was found. Only partial identification of some of the steranes (Table 4) was made, the concentration of steranes relative to the hopanes varies considerably. Most of the Autun samples are rich in hopanes and relatively poor in steranes. For example, Figs 2 and 3 showing gas chromatograms of samples C5 and C4. The gas chromatograms of the Devonian samples are much more complex than the Autun samples, and it is difficult to compare the relative contribution of steranes and triterpanes. However, samples D7 and D8 (Figs 6 and 7) appear to be rich in steranes.

Hopanes The $17\alpha(H),21\beta(H)$-hopanes with carbon numbers from C_{29} to C_{33} together with the $17\beta(H)$ $21\alpha(H)$ moretanes with carbon numbers from C_{29} to C_{31} were identified in most samples. In addition the C_{27} $17\alpha(H)$-trisnorhopane was identified (Table 3).

Steranes Two series of steranes were identified in samples D7 and D8 (Table 4). In these two Devonian samples the prominent components are C_{28} and C_{29} compounds with base peaks at m/z 218 indicative of isocholestanes $5\alpha(H)$, $14\beta(H)$, $17\beta(H)$, $20R$ and $20S$ which have only been identified in crude oils and mature ancient sediments (Seifert and Moldowan, 1979; Mackenzie et al., 1980). The C_{27} isocholestanes are present but are minor components in comparison with the C_{28} and C_{29} compounds (see Figs 6 and 7, mass fragmentograms m/z 217 and 218). C_{28} and C_{29} $5\alpha(H)$, $14\alpha(H)$, $17\alpha(H)$, $20R$ and $20S$ compounds have been identified (see Figs 6 and 7).

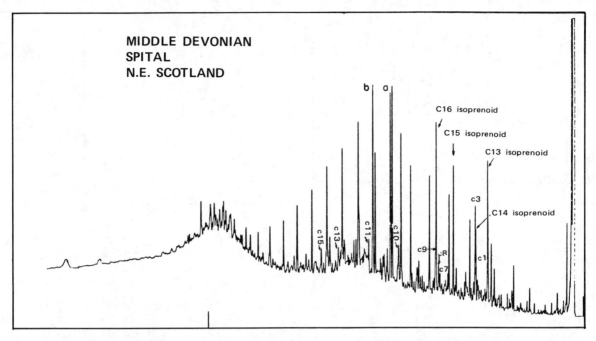

Fig. 4. Saturated hydrocarbon gas chromatogram of sample D7, Mid-Devonian, Spital, Caithness, Scotland.

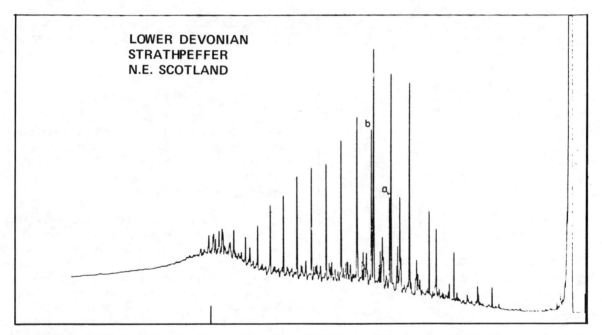

Fig. 5. Saturated hydrocarbon gas chromatogram of sample D8, Lower Devonian, Strathpeffer, Cromarty, Scotland.

Carotane, and related compounds A variety of other compounds were tentatively identified from mass spectra only (Table 5). These include: carotane and a series of tetra-alkyl substituted cyclohexanes, 3 tricyclic terpanes, a tetracyclic compound and 3 bicyclic compounds. Mass spectra of the $C_{22}H_{32}$ tetra-alkyl substituted cyclohexane compound, a $C_{21}H_{38}$ tricyclic terpane, and $C_{23}H_{40}$ tetracyclic compound and a C_{15} bicyclic compound are shown in Fig. 8.

Pyrolysis

Rock–Eval pyrolysis of the Devonian sample D10 and

Permian samples C9, C6 and C8a indicates that they are type I or II kerogens. The hydrogen index of the Devonian sample is high indicating that it is a type I kerogen. Low T_{max} and production index values indicate that the Autun samples and D10 are immature-to-early-mature, based on the classification used by Espitalié *et al.* (1977) (see Table 2b).

Gas chromatogram 'fingerprints' of the shale oils produced from heating samples of the shale in a small retort were obtained. Pyrolysis–gas chromatography has been used to distinguish the 'fingerprints' of a number of natural products including; coal macerals, lignites and recent sediments (Larter *et al.*, 1978, 1980; van de

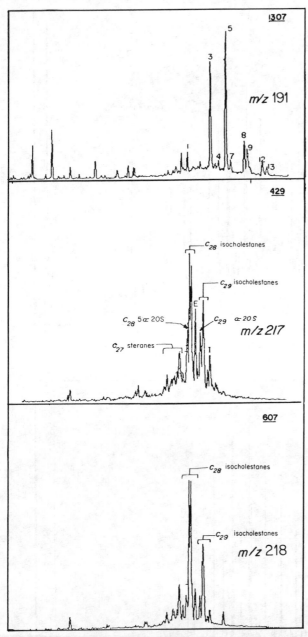

Fig. 6. Mass fragmentograms of *m/z* 191, 217 and 218, of sample D7; branched and cyclic alkanes.

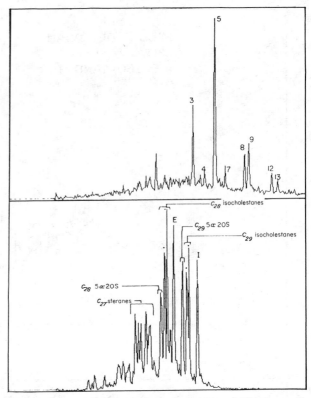

Fig. 7. Mass fragmentograms of *m/z* 191 and 217 of sample D8; saturated hydrocarbons.

DISCUSSION

Carotenoids are ubiquitous in nature and these pigments have been found, either intact or as recognizable derivatives (Baker and Louda, 1980). Conjugated unsaturated compounds such as β-carotene and lycopene survive in marine and freshwater sediments for thousands of years, particularly in highly reducing environments (Schwendiger and Erdman, 1963; Watts and Maxwell, 1977; Didyk *et al.*, 1978). In a recent paper, Watts *et al.* (1977) discuss the use of carotenoids as environmental indicators in recent sediments. They relate, in an approximate fashion, the types and quantities of carotenoids with three types of environment namely, marine anoxic waters (e.g. Cariaco Trench), sub-tropical algal mat (e.g. Shark Bay algal mat — Australia) and temperate eutrophic lake (e.g. Rostherne Mere). Watts and co-workers consider that the use of carotenoids as environmental indicators is limited to a life span of these compounds of only several thousand years.

Study of the Cariaco Trench sediments has shown that the diagenesis of carotenoids in reducing conditions can preserve the structure and it is traceable over geological time spans of 50 000 to 350 000 years (Watts and Maxwell, 1977). Diagenesis in a reducing environment, entailing a progressive hydrogenation of carotenoids might explain the findings of carotane in various ancient sediments (Baker and Louda, 1980). Simoneit and Burlingame (1971) identified a number of unsaturated carotenoid hydrocarbons in some Tertiary sediments and suggested that they were derived from terrestrial

Meent *et al.*, 1980). Study of the shale oil chromatograms reveal that many of the Lower and Upper Autunian shale oils are rich in straight chain compounds, these consist mostly of *n*-alkanes and alk-1-enes e.g. C5 (Fig. 9), the only exception is sample C8a (Fig. 10) which has little or no *n*-alkanes and alk-1-enes. The saturated hydrocarbon gas chromatogram of the soluble bitumen from this sample is also poor in *n*-alkanes and consists mostly of branched and cyclic alkanes including carotane (Fig. 12). One gas chromatogram of the shale oil of the Devonian sample D10 was obtained, it has a pronounced unresolved hump but *n*-alkane and alk-1-ene homologies, are also prominent (Fig. 11).

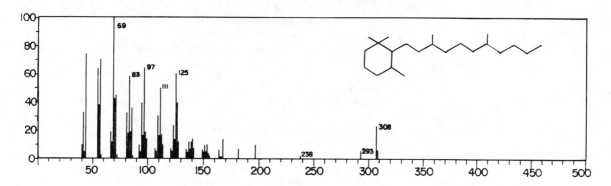

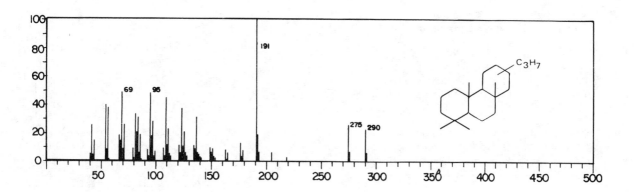

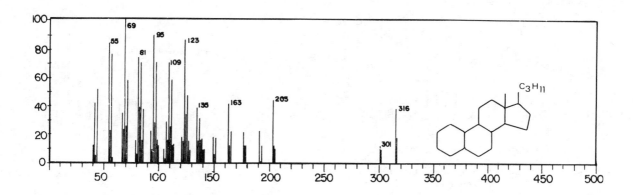

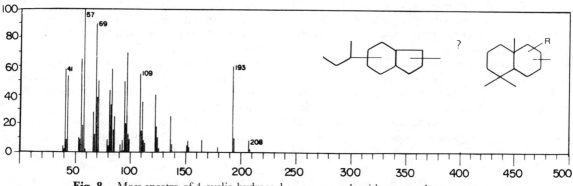

Fig. 8. Mass spectra of 4 cyclic hydrocarbon compounds with proposed structures.

Table 5a

Carotenoid products identified by GC–MS

Peak	Carbon number	Compound name
c1.	C_{13}	1,1,3,trimethyl-2-(butyl) cyclohexane
c3.	C_{14}	1,1,3,trimethyl-2-(3-methylpentyl) cyclohexane
c6.	C_{15}	1,1,3,trimethyl-2-(3-methylhexyl) cyclohexane
c9.	C_{16}	1,1,3,trimetyl-2-(3-methylheptyl) cyclohexane
c10.	C_{18}	1,1,3,trimethyl-2-(3-methylnonyl) cyclohexane
c11.	C_{20}	1,1,3,trimethyl-2-(3,7,dimethylnonyl) cyclohexane
c13.	C_{22}	1,1,3,trimetyl-2-(3,7,dimethylundecyl) cyclohexane
c15.	C_{24}	1,1,3,trimethyl-2-(3,7,dimethyltridecyl) cyclohexane
c19.	C_{40}	1,1,3,trimethyl-2-(3,7,12,16,24 hexamethylpentasyl cyclohexane

Table 5b.

Other cyclic hydrocarbons identified by GC–MS

Peak	Carbon number	Compound name
C7	C_{15}	Bicyclic Terpane
C8	C_{15}	Bicyclic Terpane
C12	C_{20}	Tricyclic
C14	C_{21}	Tricyclic
C16	C_{23}	Tricyclic
C17	C_{23}	Tetracyclic
C20	C_{40}	Carotane

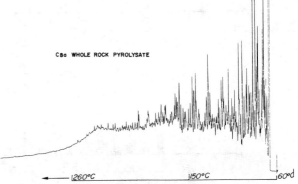

Fig. 10. Gas chromatogram of shale oil produced on pyrolysis of sample C8a.

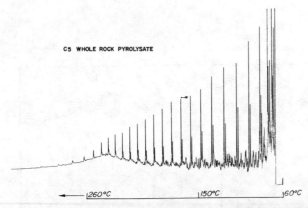

Fig. 9. Gas chromatogram of shale oil produced on pyrolysis of sample C5.

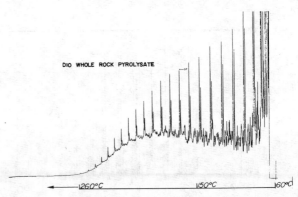

Fig. 11. Gas chromatogram of shale oil produced on pyrolysis of sample D10.

plant matter. The most ancient intact carotenoid pigment has been isolated from a Miocene sediment in the Blake-Bahama basin, western North Atlantic (Baker and Louda, 1980). However, unsaturated carotenoids are converted to the reduced forms over geological time, and only the fully reduced compounds, such as carotane have been found in pre-Tertiary ancient sediments, e.g. the Permian Irati shale (Hunt, 1979) and a Silurian dolomite (Rullkötter and Philp, 1981).

Erdman (1961) amongst others, studied the degradation of β-carotene under mild thermal conditions (110 °C), and reported the formation of several percent of certain aromatic compounds e.g. toluene, m-xylene and 2,6 dimethylnaphthalene. These would be expected products if cyclization of the isoprenoid chain occurs. The remainder of the material

produced was a colourless oil which, he suggested, contained compounds with 'naphthenic and aromatic rings with attached hydrocarbon chains of varying length'. Anders and Robinson (1971) and Gallegos (1971) have identified carotane, and a number of naphthenic and aromatic hydrocarbons with attached hydrocarbon chains which appear to be associated with the occurrence of carotane, in the soluble bitumen of Green River oil shale.

Anders and Robinson (1971) identified 52 cyclic alkanes in Green River oil shale bitumen. Twenty-one compounds displayed fragmentation patterns indicative of a series of tetra-alkyl substituted cyclohexanes. Fourteen compounds including a series of tetracyclic

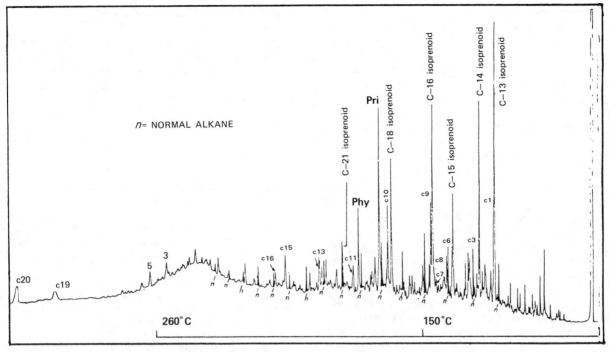

Fig. 12. Saturated hydrocarbon gas chromatogram of sample C8a Surmoulin, Autun, France.

compounds were considered to have originated from plant steroids, the rest were terpanes including 6 tricyclic terpanes which were suggested to be derived from pentacyclic triterpenes, or from diterpenes of the agathic or sclareol variety. Gallegos (1971) identified ten tricyclic terpanes in soluble bitumen from the Green River shale; 5 pairs of isomers from $C_{20}H_{36}$ to $C_{26}H_{48}$ (excluding the C_{22} compounds, and only one C_{24} compound).

Some of the same compounds were tentatively identified in the soluble bitumen from the two deposits discussed in this paper (see Table 5). The precursors for carotenoids may be either algal, fungal, bacterial or higher plant pigments (Maxwell and Watts, 1977; Watts *et al.*, 1977). Indeed, the origin of carotane in the Green River shale has been ascribed to an algal source (Tissot *et al.*, 1978). The samples analysed in this report can be divided into two groups, those containing carotane and C_{13}–C_{24} tetra-alkyl substituted cyclohexanes e.g. D1, D3, D7, D10, C3, C4, C8, C8a and those without e.g. D8, C2, C5, C6, C7.

The Permian Autun samples C1, C2, C5, C6 and C7 come from the Lower Autunian which consists of a few thin shales in a mainly sandstone sequence, thought to have been deposited in a coal swamp environment (Elsass, 1977; Doubinger and Elsass, 1979). The other Autun samples, C3, C4, C8, C8a and C9 are shales from the Upper Autunian, and are thought to have been deposited in a lacustrine environment. During the Autunian the climate became gradually drier, and the predominant types changed from coal swamp species such as Calamites to early gymnosperm floras (Doubinger and Elsass, 1979). Certain species at this stage were probably types capable of resisting periodic dry spells such as the modern *Ephedra* (Elsass, 1977). The changes in environment and plant species in the Lower

and Upper Autunian thus coincide with the major change in the saturated hydrocarbon composition.

The carotenoid-related compounds are found in the Upper Autunian but are absent in the Lower Autunian. It is tempting to relate the appearance of carotenoid hydrocarbons with this change in input. However, the microscopically recognizable material constitutes only about 10% by volume of the whole rock in these samples. The remaining material is amorphous, some of which appears in ultra violet light as dull yellow flecks or lamellae, the rest fluoresces dull brown. To relate this to any particular input is impossible and it is necessary to resort to chemical techniques to obtain some measure of the predominant structures in this amorphous material. Gas chromatography of the shale oils indicates that straight chain material predominates in all the Autun samples except C8a. All the Autun samples contain some algal bodies of the Botryococcus type except C8a. Pyrolysis–gas chromatography of Botryococcus-rich shales yields a product rich in *n*-alkanes and alkenes (Allan *et al.*, 1980; Larter *et al.*, 1978, 1980). The conclusion from this is that algae of the Botryococcus type have not contributed to this sample. Terrestrial debris, including spores, is probably the main source of the kerogen in the C8a sample. The carotenoid hydrocarbons which are particularly prominent in C8a are probably derived from the terrestrial material present in the sample.

The carotenoid hydrocarbons are also found in the Devonian samples, particularly the Achanarras Limestone horizon (samples D1, D3 and D10). It has been suggested that the source of the organic matter in the Devonian sediments is of algal origin (Donovan *et al.*, 1980). Microscopical examination of the kerogen in the samples analysed in this report give little indication of the origin of the kerogen. Only D10 was rich in an exinite component which fluoresces light- to mid-orange in ultra violet light. However, the origins of this material is not clear since no obvious structure could be seen. A gas chromatogram of the shale oil from this sample shows it to be rich in straight chain material (Fig. 11) and a high Rock–Eval hydrogen index indicates a type I kerogen. Whether all allochthonous terrestrial or autochthonous algal input is responsible for the carotenoid hydrocarbons in the Devonian samples is impossible to decide, on the basis of the evidence available.

It is interesting that there are many similarities in the proposed depositional environments of the Permian and Devonian deposits and that of the Green River shales. The climate, at least part of the time, was semi-arid and the lake basins periodically dried up (Bradley, 1973; Eugster and Surdam, 1973; Elsass, 1977; Doubinger and Elsass, 1979; Westoll, 1937; Donovan *et al.*, 1978, 1980). There were periods in which hypersaline conditions developed, particularly in the Green River and Devonian deposits (Bradley, 1973; Eugster and Surdam, 1973; Fannin, 1969; Michie, 1979). The stratified lake model has been proposed for both the Devonian and Green River deposits (Bradley and Eugster, 1969; Donovan *et al.*, 1980). Algal remains are abundant in all three deposits, although the types of algae were probably different. Blue–green algae are reported to be the probable source for the Green River shale kerogens (Bradley, 1970). Stromatolites are found in the Devonian sediments and indicate that blue–green algae may have contributed to the kerogens (Donovan *et al.*, 1978, 1980). In the Permian shales, Botryococcus algae are present and presumably are a major source of the organic matter in this deposit. It would appear from this that the presence of carotane and related hydrocarbons is related to a specific input which develops in the particular environmental conditions mentioned. At least for the Autun deposit it is probably not of algal origin.

Another feature, in certain samples from these deposits, is the co-occurrence (with carotenoids), of di- and tricyclic compounds (see Table 5); the tricyclic compounds do not occur, significantly, in the other shales analysed.

The relationship between di- and tricyclic compounds and the carotenoid-related compounds may be coincidental. These compounds could be derived from steroid or di- and triterpenoid compounds. Di- and triterpenoids have been suggested as sources of dicyclic and tricyclic hydrocarbons found in a number of sediments (Anders and Robinson, 1971; Bendoraitis, 1974; Barrick and Hedges, 1981; Philp *et al.*, 1981). However, cyclization, fragmentation and hydrogenation during diagenesis may be an alternative route to the tricyclic compounds.

The distributions of hopanes and steranes are not discussed in detail. There are considerable variations in the relative amounts of hopanes and steranes which may be related to environmental and/or input differences. Further work is in progress, on these aspects. However, it is noteable that the sterane-rich samples are from Devonian sediments that have been deposited in waters where salinities varied from fresh to hypersaline, for example the sedimentary sequence from which D8 was collected was probably deposited in hypersaline waters (Donovan *et al.*, 1978).

Acknowledgements

Financial support of the Natural Environment Research Council (NERC). Particularly thanks go to M. Bjorøy and the Continental Shelf Institute (IKU) Trondheim, Norway. Thanks also go to Keith Hall, for help in the GC–MS work.

REFERENCES

Albaiges, J. (1979) Identification and geochemical significance of long chain acyclic isoprenoid hydrocarbons in crude oils. *Advances in Organic Geochemistry 1979*. Ed. by Douglas, A. G. and Maxwell, J. R. Pergamon, Oxford. pp. 19–28.

Albaiges, J., Borbon, J. and Salgre, P. (1978) Identification of a series of C_{25}–C_{40} acyclic isoprenoid hydrocarbons in crude oils. *Tetr. Lett.* 595–598.

Allan, J., Bjorøy, M. and Douglas, A. G. (1980) A geochemical study of the exinite group maceral alginite, selected from three Permo–Carboniferous torbanites. *Advances in Organic Geochemistry 1979*. Ed. by Douglas, A. G. and Maxwell, J. R. Pergamon, Oxford. pp. 599–618.

Anders, D. E., Doolittle, F. G. and Robinson, W. E. (1973) Analysis of some aromatic hydrocarbons in a benzene soluble bitumen from the Green River Shale. *Geochim. Cosmochim. Acta* **37**, 1213–1228.

Anders, D. E. and Robinson, W. E. (1971) Cycloalkane constituents of the bitumen from the Green River Shale. *Geochim. Cosmochim. Acta* **35**, 661–678.

Baker, E. W. and Louda, J. W. (1980) Organic geochemistry: Highlights in the deep-sea drilling project. *Advances in Organic Geochemistry 1979*. Ed. by Douglas, A. G. and Maxwell, J. R. Pergamon, Oxford. pp. 295–320.

Barrick, R. C. and Hedges, J. I. (1981) Hydrocarbon geochemistry of the Puget Sound region II. Sedimentary diterpenoid, steroid and triterpenoid hydrocarbons. *Geochim. Cosmochim. Acta* **45**, 381–392.

Bendoraitis, J. G. (1974) Hydrocarbons of biogenic origin in petroleum — aromatic triterpenes and bicyclic sesquiterpenes. In *Advances in Organic Geochemistry 1973*. Ed. by Tissot, B. and Bienner, F. Editions Technip, Paris. pp. 209–224.

Bradley, W. H. (1970) Green River Oil Shale — Concept of origin extended. *Geol. Soc. Am. Bull.* **81**, 985–1000.

Bradley, W. H. (1973) Oil shale formed in desert environment: Green River Formation, Wyoming. *Geol. Soc. Am. Bull.* **84**, 1121–1124.

Bradley, W. H. and Eugster, H. P. (1969) Geochemistry and palaeolimnology of the trona deposits and associated authigenic minerals of the Green River Formation of Wyoming. *U.S. Geol. Survey* Prof. Paper 496-B.71.

Cardoso, J. N., Wardroper, A. M. K., Watts, C. D., Barnes, P. J., Maxwell, J. R., Eglinton, G., Mound, D. G. and Speers, G. C. (1978) Preliminary organic geochemical analysis. Site 391, Leg 44 of the Deep Sea Drilling Project. In *Initial Reports of the Deep Sea Drilling Project*. Ed. by Benson, W. E., Sheridan, R. E. *et al.* Vol. 44. U.S. Government Printing Office, Washington D.C. pp. 617–623.

Didyk, B. M., Simoneit, B. R., Brassel, S. C. and Eglinton, G. (1978) Organic geochemical parameters of palaeoenvironmental conditions of sedimentation. *Nature (London)* **272**, 216–222.

Donovan, R. N. (1980) Lacustrine cycles, fish ecology and stratigraphic zonation in the Middle Devonian of Caithness. *Scott. J. Geol.* **16**, 35–72.

Donovan, R. N., Peacock, J. D. and Mykura, W. (1978) *Devonian of Scotland, the Welsh Borderland and South Wales*. Ed.

by Friend, P. F. and Williams, B. P. J. 106 pp.

Doubinger, and Elsass, F. (1979) Le Bassin Permo-Carbonifère d'Autun. Nouvelles données stratigraphiques et palynologiques. *Soc. d'Hist. Nat. Amis Mus d'Autun* No. 91, September 1979, 9–25.

Elsass, F. (1977) Les 'schistes bitumineux' du basin d'Autun. Pétrographie–Mineralogie–Cristallochimie–Pyrolyse– Thèse Docetur–Ingénieur, University of Paris.

Ensminger, A., Albrecht, P., Ourisson, G. and Tissot, B. (1977) Evolution of polycyclic alkanes under the effect of burial. (Early Toarcian Shales, Paris Basin.) In *Advances in Organic Geochemistry.* Ed. by Campos, R. and Goni, J. Enadimsa, Madrid. pp. 45–52.

Erdman, J. G. (1961) Some chemical aspects of petroleum genesis as related to the problem of source bed recognition. *Geochim. Cosmochim. Acta* **22**, 16–36.

Espitalié, J., Madec, M., Tissot, B., Leplat, P. and Menning, J. J. (1977) Source rock characterization method for petroleum exploration. *Rev. Inst. Fr. Pétr.* (Ref. 24843).

Eugster, H. P. and Surdam, R. C. (1973) The depositional environment of the Green River Formation of Wyoming: A preliminary report. *Geol. Soc. Am. Bull.* **84**, 115–1120.

Feys, R. and Greber, Ch. (1964) Bassin Carbonifère et Permien d'Epinac et d'Autun. *5ᵉ Congr. Intern. Strat. Géol. Carbon. Paris, 1963,* C.R.I., 45–51.

Fortey, N. J. and Michie, U. M. (1979) Aegirine of possible authigenic origin in Middle Devonian sediments in Caithness, Scotland. *Mineralog. Mag.* **42**, 439–442.

Gallegos, E. J. (1971) Identification of new steranes, terpanes and branched paraffins in Green River Shale by GC/MS. *Anal. Chem.* **43**, 1151–1160.

Gardner, P. M. and Whitehead, E. V. (1972) The isolation of squalane from a Nigerian Petroleum. *Geochim. Cosmochim. Acta* **36**, 259–263.

Hunt, J. (1979) *Petroleum Geochemistry and Geology.* Freeman.

Kimble, B. J., Maxwell, J. R., Philp, R. P., Eglinton, G., Albrecht, P., Ensminger, A., Arpino, P. and Ourisson, G. (1974) Tri- and tetraterpenoid hydrocarbons in the Messel oil shale. *Geochim. Cosmochim. Acta* **38**, 1165–1181.

Larter, S. R. and Douglas, A. G. (1978) Low molecular-weight aromatic hydrocarbons in coal maceral pyrolysates as indicators of diagenesis and organic matter type. In *Environmental Biogeochemistry and Geomicrobiology.* Ed. by Krumbein, W. E. Ann Arbor Sc. Publ., Ann Arbor. pp. 373–386.

Larter, S. R. and Douglas, A. G. (1980) Characterisation and typing of kerogens by pyrolysis capillary gas chromatography. In *Advances in Organic Geochemistry (1979).* Ed. by Douglas, A. G. and Maxwell, J. R. Pergamon Press, Oxford. pp. 579–584.

Mackenzie, A. S., Patience, R. L., Maxwell, J. R., Vandenbroucke, M. and Durand, B. (1980) Molecular parameters of maturation in the Toarcian shales, Paris Basin. France I. Changes in the configurations of acyclic isoprenoid alkanes, steranes and triterpanes. *Geochim. Cosmochim. Acta* **44**, 1709–1721.

Mackenzie, A. S., Hoffman, C. F. and Maxwell, J. R. (1981) Molecular parameters of maturation in the Toarcian shales: Paris Basin, France III. Changes in aromatic steroid hydrocarbons. *Geochim. Cosmochim. Acta* **45**, 1345–1358.

McKirdy, D. M. and Kantsler, A. J. (1980) Oil geochemistry and potential source rock of The Officer Basin, South Australia, *A.P.E.A. J.* **20**, 68–86.

Michie, U. M. (1979) Aegirine of possible authigenic origin in Middle Devonian sediments in Caithness, Scotland.

Moldowan, J. M. and Seifert, W. K. (1980) First discovery of Botryococcane in petroleum. *J. Chem. Soc. Chem. Commun.,* 912–914.

Murphy, M. T. J., McCormick, A. and Eglinton, G. (1967) Perhydro-β-carotane in the Green River shale. *Science* **157**, 1040–1042.

Ourisson, G., Albrecht, P. and Bohmer, M. (1979) The hopanoids, palaeochemistry and biochemistry of a group of natural products. *Pure Appl. Chem.* **151**, 709–729.

Philp, R. P., Gilbert, T. D. and Friedrich, J. (1981) Bicyclic sesquiterpenoids and diterpenoids in Australian crude oils. *Geochim. Cosmochim. Acta* **45**, 1173–1180.

Richardson, J. B. (1965) Middle Old Red Sandstone spore assemblages from the Orcadian Basin, North–East Scotland. Palaeontology, **7**, 559–605.

Rubinstein, I. and Albrecht, P. (1975) The occurrence of nuclear-methylated steranes in a shale. *J. Chem. Soc. Chem. Comm.* 957–958.

Rullkötter, J. and Philp, R. P. (1981) Extended hopanes up to C_{40} in Thornton bitumen. *Nature (London)* **292**, 616–618.

Schwendiger, R. B. and Erdman, J. G. (1963) Carotenoids in sediments as a function of environment. *Science* **141**, 808–810.

Seifert, W. K. and Moldowan, J. M. (1978) Applications of steranes, terpanes, and mono-aromatics to the maturation, migration and source of crude oils. *Geochim. Cosmochim. Act.* **42**, 77–95.

Seifert, W. K., Moldowan, M. J. (1979) The effect of biodegradation on steranes and terpanes in crude oils. *Geochim. Cosmochim. Acta* **43**, 111–126.

Simoneit, B. R. and Burlinghame, A. L. (1971) Preliminary organic analyses of the DSDP (JOIDES) cores, Legs V–IX. In *Advances in Organic Geochemistry.* Ed. by Gaertner, H. R. V. and Wehner, H. Pergamon Press, Oxford. pp. 189–229.

Stanfield, K. E. and Frost, I. C. (1949) Method of assaying oil shale by a modified Fischer retort. *U.S. Bur. Mines Rep. Invest.* 4477.

Tissot, B., Califet-Debyser, Y., Deroo, G. and Oudin, J. L. (1971) Origin and evolution of hydrocarbons in early Toarcian shales, Paris Basin, France, *Am. Ass. Petrol. Geol. Bull.* **55**, 2177–2193.

Tissot, B., Durand, B., Espitalié, J. and Combaz, A. (1974) Influence of the nature and diagenesis of organic matter in formation of petroleum. *Am. Ass. Petrol. Geol. Bull.* **58**, 499–506.

Tissot, B., Deroo, G. and Hood, A. (1978) Geochemical study of the Uinta Basin: formation of petroleum from the Green River Formation. *Geochim. Cosmochim. Acta* **42**, 1469–1486.

van de Meent, D., Brown, S. C., Philp, R. P. and Simoneit, B. R. T. (1980) Pyrolysis–high resolution gas chromatography and pyrolysis–gas chromatography–mass spectrometry of kerogens and kerogen precursors. *Geochim. Cosmochim. Acta* **44**, 999–1013.

Watts, C. D. and Maxwell, J. R. (1977) Carotenoid diagenesis in a marine sediment. *Geochim. Cosmochim. Acta* **41**, 493–497.

Watts, C. D., Maxwell, J. R. and Kjosen, H. (1977) The potential of carotenoids as environmental indicators. In *Advances in Organic Geochemistry 1975.* Ed. by Campos, R. and Goni, J. Enadimsa, Madrid. pp. 391–414.

Westoll, T. S. (1937) Old Red Sandstone Fishes of North of Scotland. *Proc. Geol. Assoc.,* **48**, 13–45.

Wolf, M. (1966) Observations pétrographiques sur les schistes boghead d'Autun. *Sci. de la Terre* **11**, 7–18.

Advances in Organic Geochemistry 1981, pp. 588–596
© John Wiley & Sons Limited, 1983

Vitrinite Reflectance and the Derivation of Heat Flow Changes with Time

D. J. Toth, I. Lerche, D. E. Petroy, R. J. Meyer and C. G. St. C. Kendall

Gulf Science and Technology Company, PO Drawer 2038, Pittsburgh, Pennsylvania 15230, USA

Vitrinite reflectance has been modelled for wells in the North Sea by assuming that reflectance changes as a result of first order chemical reactions. The Arrhenius-type equation is used to relate changes in the first order rate constant to temperature and is modified by including a term that allows the rate of a chemical reaction to double for every T_D increase in temperature. The approach treats time and temperature as knowns, deduced from thermal modelling and burial history, and tries to minimize the difference between calculated and measured reflectances by stepping through various values for the activation energy, E_a, scaling temperature, T_D, and time-varying heat flow, $Q(t)$, using a non-linear least squares technique. As a consequence of the modelling, we conclude that vitrinite reflectance can be modelled using an activation energy and scaling temperature of about $0.05 \text{ K cal mol}^{-1}$ and $438 \pm 140 \text{K}$ respectively. The model allows the prediction of depths and timing for oil generation in areas where the temperature history is known. Conversely, and significantly, an inverse approach can be taken and paleo-heat flow can now be deduced from reflectance measurements. Applying this inverse approach in the North Sea suggests that its spatially varying heat flux has not changed by more than a few per cent over the last 100 My or so.

INTRODUCTION

The purpose of this paper is to illustrate a method for determining both the spatial and temporal variation of temperature for a basin. Temperature is an essential variable in any hydrocarbon maturity calculation. When coupled with time, temperature governs the rate at which organic material is altered and also the amount of hydrocarbons and hydrocarbon-like products generated. An awareness of the temperature history of an area would greatly assist explorationists in determining the maturity of potential source rocks and the geologic timing (i.e. prior to or after trap development) for the onset of oil and/or gas generation. It also would provide an independent check on the numerous geologic models used for the prediction of temperature.

At present, there are three different approaches to handling paleotemperatures. The first and simplest assumes that the thermal gradient has been constant through time and invokes either present day values or an average value for ancient gradients (as in Tissot and Welte, 1978). The second approach assumes that the heat flux, and consequently the temperature, was higher in the past. Heat flow equals the product of the geothermal gradient and the thermal conductivity of a sedimentary section and is directly proportional to the temperature if the sediments in an area have similar thermal conductivities.

This approach for deriving paleotemperatures assumes one of the numerous geologic models for basin formation, such as the crustal stretching model of McKenzie (1978), the dike intrusion model of Royden *et al.* (1980), or the thermal expansion models of Sleep (1971) and Keen (1978). All these models relate basement subsidence to thermal contraction and cooling. As a consequence, these models predict that the heat flux, and consequently the temperature, decreases with time.

The third approach is also based on a geologic model for basin formation. However, unlike the second approach, this model assumes that initial subsidence is due to deep crustal metamorphism caused by a heating period followed by cooling (Falvey, 1974; Falvey and Middleton, 1980; Middleton, 1980). The model predicts that heat flow first increases linearly with time and then decreases.

The above geologic models are based on continuously subsiding basins. They neglect periods of uplift, volcanism, extensive orogenic activity, or major breaks in sedimentation. They predict heat flow changes in one direction, or at best, allow for only one change (increase to decrease) in the heat flow. They are also based on *hypothetical ideas* for basin formation.

In contrast, the method we have developed allows for many perturbations or changes in heat flow and basin geology, and it is primarily based on *measured values* of vitrinite reflectance, which maintain an irreversible record of the time–temperature history of rocks. Only major unconformities or periods of erosion are not included at this time, although we propose to handle these in the future.

With this in mind, we modelled the behaviour of vitrinite reflectance from 30 wells in the Norwegian and 6 wells in the UK sector of the North Sea. This paper presents the results of that modelling.

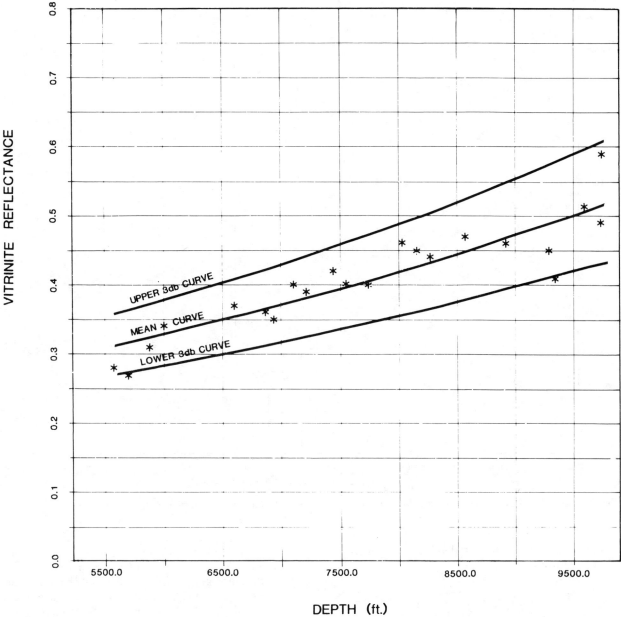

Fig. 1. Example of mean, upper, and lower error curves (referred to as 3 db) used to fit measured reflectance data.

MODEL

The procedure we followed first models the change in vitrinite reflectance with depth. As a consequence of errors inherent in vitrinite measurements, we approximated the increasing trend of measured vitrinite values with depth by fitting an exponential curve through them (Fig. 1). To assess the errors in using this mean curve, we also bounded the measured reflectance values by fitting upper and lower curves to them. Henceforth, all further discussion of reflectance values refers to these smoothed curves.

We assumed reflectance to change as a result of first order chemical reactions and used an *Arrhenius-type* equation to relate changes in the first order rate constant to temperature. Since it is possible for the rate of a reaction to be more dependent on temperature than is represented by the classical Arrhenius equation, we

allowed for this possibility by including a temperature term in the rate 'constant'. The equation we used is:

$$k = A \exp(-E_a/RT + T/T_D)$$

where k is the first order rate 'constant', A is a constant, R is the ideal gas constant, T is temperature in K, and E_a and T_D are *scaling* parameters. For convenience, we refer to E_a and T_D as an activation energy and scaling temperature respectively, in order to draw as close a parallel as seems warranted with conventional chemical nomenclature. In the classical Arrhenius equation, $k = A \exp(-E_a/RT)$, k is a function of temperature. In the above expression, this dependence is represented by $\exp(T/T_D)$.

Our model treats the maturation of vitrinite as a function of time and temperature; the effect of pressure is not included. Time is handled as a known parameter and is deduced from the burial history of each well.

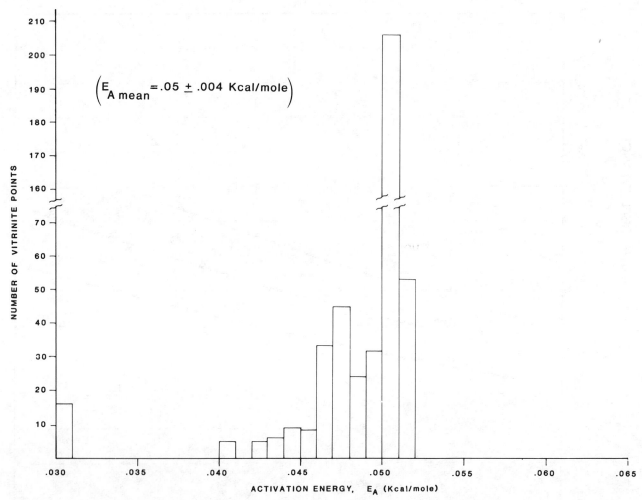

Fig. 2. Spread of activation energies, E_a, obtained from modelling all 36 North Sea wells. Weighted mean $E_a = 0.05 \pm 0.004$ Kcal mol^{-1}.

Temperature, T (in K), at depth z and time, t, is calculated from:

$$T = T_s + \int_{z=0}^{z} \frac{Q(t) \cdot dz}{K(t, z)}$$

where T_s is the temperature at the sediment surface, $Q(t)$ is the time varying heat flux, and $K(t, z)$ is the thermal conductivity. K is a function of lithology, depth and time and is calculated from the relationship between porosity and conductivity discussed in Sclater and Christie (1980).

The effect of time and temperature on the maturation of vitrinite are combined in a mathematical expression called the time–temperature integral. The unknowns in this expression are E_a, T_D, and the time-varying heat flux, $Q(t)$. A non-linear least squares procedure was used to solve for these unknowns. The method involves specifying initial values for E_a, T_D, and $Q(t)$ and then minimizing the difference between measured and calculated values by stepping through various values for the unknowns. Initially $Q(t)$ is set at its present day value, as calculated from bottom hole temperature (BHT) measurements, and we solved for first approximations to E_a and T_D. Then we allowed the program to pick the best value for *all* variables, i.e. for $Q(t)$, E_a, and T_D. A

check on the results was provided by making a basin-wide comparison on the calculated E_a and T_D values. The values of E_a and T_D for all wells should be consistent, since they are chemical parameters, independent of the geology. Another check was provided by comparing our best fit and calculated values (from BHT measurements) for present day values of the heat flux. If the difference between the two was greater than 20%, our best fit values were discarded as unacceptable and the well was not used. This method necessitates at least 10 or more reflectance values, roughly uniformly spaced with depth, for good results. It also requires that the reflectance values lie between major unconformities.

RESULTS

The weighted mean values for E_a and T_D determined from modelling vitrinite values from 36 North Sea wells are 0.05 ± 0.04 Kcal mol^{-1} and 438 ± 140 K respectively. Figures 2 and 3 illustrate the distributions obtained for these values normalized to the number of vitrinite points. The spreads for E_a and T_D are large, primarily because of the quality of the reflectance data, and the number and spacing of reflectance values per well. Some of the wells contained fewer than 10

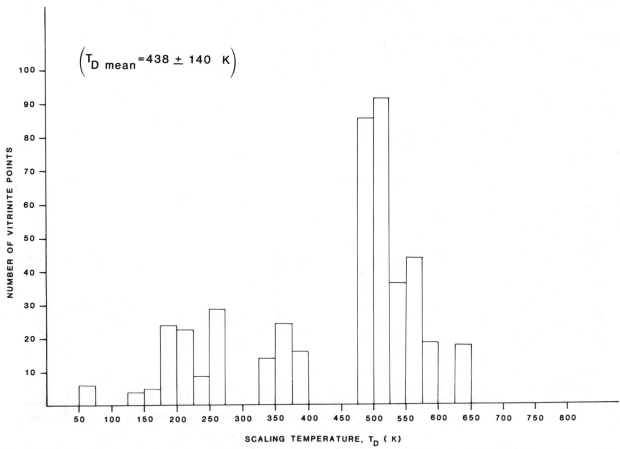

Fig. 3. Distribution of scaling temperatures, T_D, obtained from modelling all 36 North Sea wells. Weighted mean $T_D = 438 \pm$ 140 K.

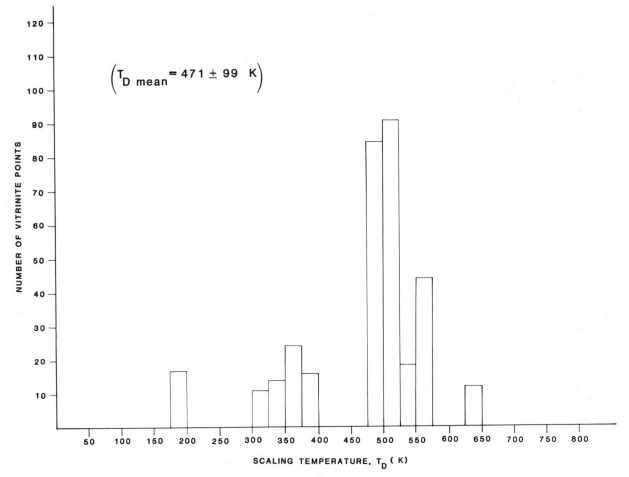

Fig. 4. Distribution of scaling temperatures, T_D, obtained from modelling the mean reflectance curve in Fig. 1 for wells with 10 or more reflectance measurements. Weighted mean $T_D = 471 \pm 99$ K.

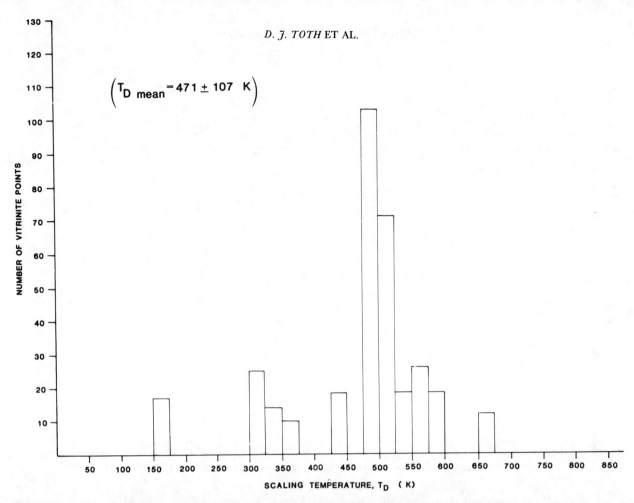

Fig. 5. Distribution of scaling temperatures, T_D, obtained from modelling the upper 3 db reflectance curve (Fig. 1) for wells with 10 or more reflectance measurements. Weighted mean $T_D = 471 \pm 107$ K.

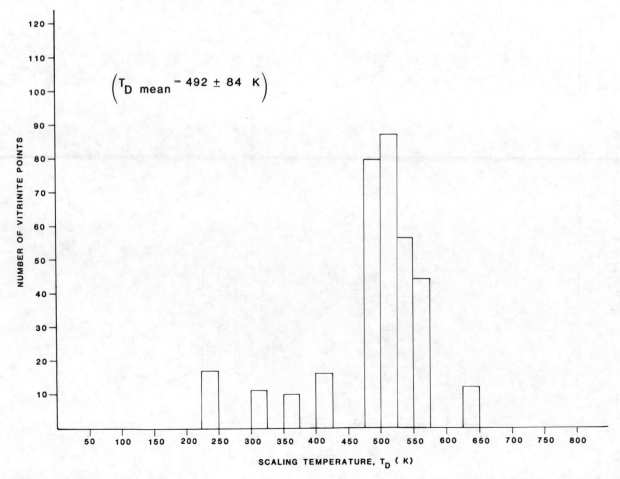

Fig. 6. Distribution of scaling temperatures, T_D, obtained from modelling the lower 3 db reflectance curve (Fig. 1) for wells with 10 or more reflectance measurements. Weighted mean $T_D = 492 \pm 84$ K.

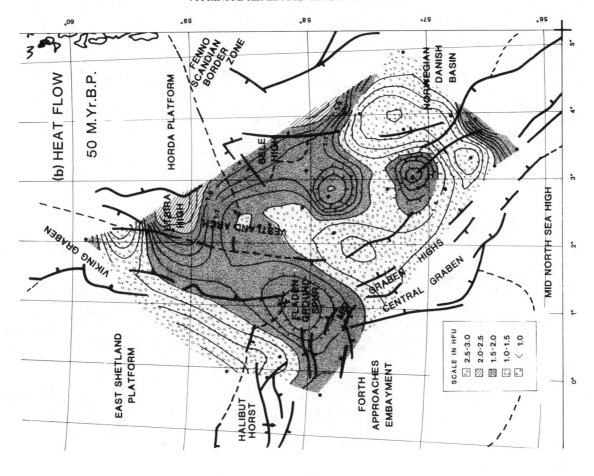

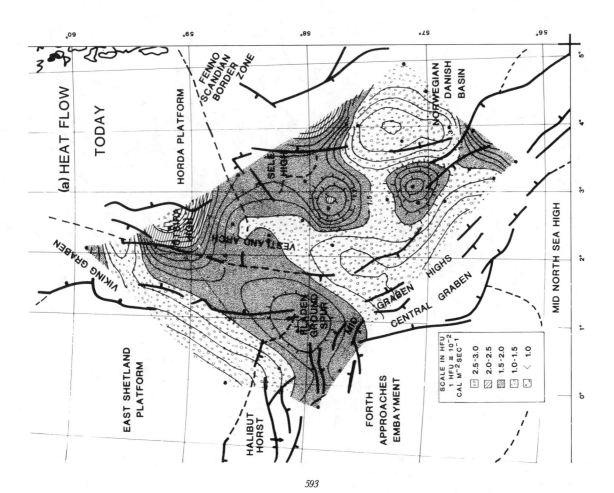

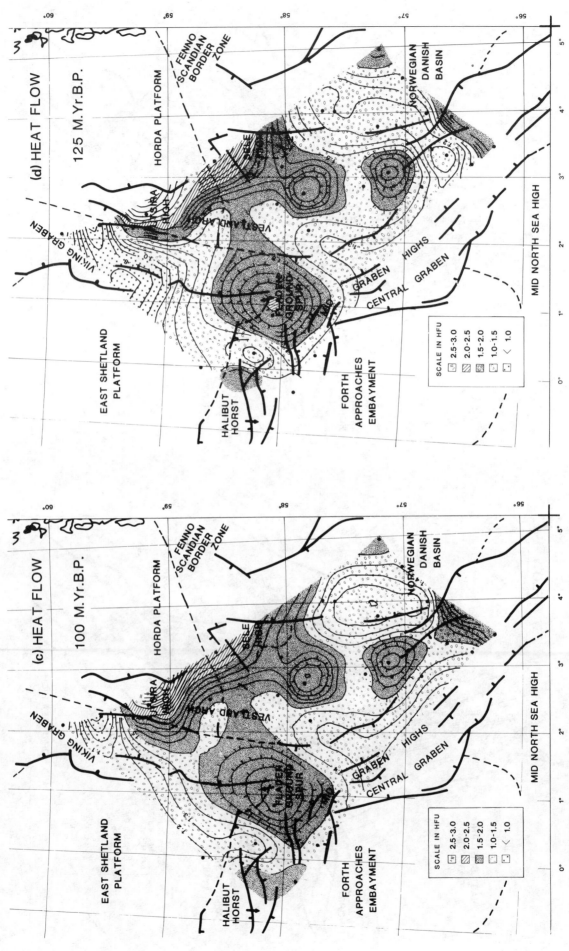

Fig. 7. Heat flow map for the northern North Sea for: (a) today, (b) 50 My b.p., (c) 100 My b.p. and (d) 125 My b.p.

reflectance values, in contrast to the requirement for greater than 10 for good results. The distributions are reduced in width when wells with 10 or more reflectance points are used (compare Figs 3 and 4).

Figures 5 and 6 also illustrate the distribution of T_D obtained when either the upper or lower 3 db curve (Fig. 1) is used to approximate reflectance values with depth for wells with 10 or more vitrinite measurements. The distributions are quite similar and cluster around 475–575 K. Despite the larger scatter in T_D values, the weighted mean T_Ds obtained using all three curves is remarkably similar: T_D (mean) $=471 \pm 99$K, T_D (lower) $=492 \pm 84$K, T_D (upper) $=471 \pm 107$K; and are within the uncertainty in T_D (438 ± 140K) obtained for all 36 wells. All three curves also yield similar activation energies and time-varying heat flows. Further discussion will be based on the results obtained from modelling the mean reflectance vs. depth curve. This includes all 36 wells, not just those with 10 or more data points.

Equivalent values of E_a and T_D (*without any quoted error bars*) extracted from the experimental data of Ting (1975), as recorded by Hunt (1979), for heated woody lignite ($E_a=0.2$, $T_D=320$ K), and Bostick (1971) for vitrinite ($E_a=0.02$, $T_D=464$ K) and for liptinite ($E_a=0.5$, $T_D=203$ K), provide corroborative support for the values for E_a and T_D obtained above. Additional modelling of reflectance in Cretaceous and Tertiary age sediments from the NW shelf of Australia provides additional verification for these parameters. In this case E_a was set at 0.05 and a value of 312 ± 87K was obtained for T_D.

The small value for E_a implies that the changes responsible for an increase in reflectance do not require a large energy, in fact the energy is less than 100 cal mol^{-1}. Chemical changes that require very little energy are the breaking of weak van der Waals bonds and hydrogen bonds.

The value for T_D implies that the processes governing reflectance changes do not increase very rapidly with temperature. In fact, viewed in the light of transition-state theory, T_D represents a transition temperature. It is the temperature corresponding to a minimum in the change in entropy, represented as $\Delta S^\dagger$, between reactant and activated complex.*

The optical properties of vitrinite change from isotropic to anisotropic for reflectance values above about 0.5 to 0.6. This transition is governed by a combination of both time and temperature. T_D may represent the temperature for this change.

HEAT FLOW VARIATIONS THROUGH TIME

Figure 7(a–d) illustrated how the heat flow has changed in the northern North Sea for the past 125 My. The

*This conclusion is reached by equating the pre-exponential constant in the Arrhenius equation above (given by $A = \beta \exp(T/T_D)$ where β is a constant) and that from transition state theory ($A = kT/h \exp \Delta S^\dagger/R$), where k and h are Boltzmann' and Planck's constants respectively) to obtain:
$\Delta S^+ = R((C + T)/T_D - \ln T)$; C is a constant $= \ln \beta h/k$.

Differentiating ΔS^+ with respect to T at constant p yields:
$$(\partial \Delta S^+ T)_p = R/T_D - R/T$$
which is zero when $T = T_D$.

contours on these maps are dependent upon our well control and may be in error north of 59°30′ N latitude and west of 2°30′ E longitude where there are only two wells.

Comparison of Fig. 7(a–c) suggests that the heat flow has not changed appreciably for the past 100 My. The greatest change in Q appears to occur around 125 million years ago (compare Figs 7c and 7d). This age corresponds with the time of the last major rifting phase in the North Sea. This rifting occurred during Late Cimmerian time (Jurassic–Cretaceous boundary).

The North Sea rift system became inactive in the early Tertiary and subsidence dominated basin evolution during the Tertiary (Ziegler, P. A., 1975; Ziegler, W. H., 1975). Our heat flow maps are in accord with this geologic picture of basin evolution.

Figure 7 also allows a comparison to be made between our calculated heat flows and the structural provinces of the North Sea. Examination of these figures suggest that the East Shetland Platform, the western edge of the Norwegian Danish basin, and the northern boundary of the Central Graben are cool, with heat flows of 1.0–1.5 HFU; the Viking Graben, Sele High, and Fladen Ground Spur have intermediate heat flows of 1.5–2.0 HFU; and the Utsira High is hot, with a heat flow of 2.5–3.0 HFU. Only the Sele High and Fladen Ground Spur were appreciably hotter 125 My ago, with heat flows as high as 2.5–3.0 and 2.0–2.5 HFU respectively. The increased heat flow for these regions implies that structural changes at depth were responsible for their evolution. In contrast, the Utsira High has a high heat flow today which was maintained in the past. The processes responsible for its heat flow are still operative today.

REFERENCES

Bostick, N. H. (1971) Thermal alteration of clastic organic particles as an indicator of contact and burial metamorphism in sedimentary rocks. *Geoscience and Man* **3**, 83–92.

Day, G. A., Cooper, B. A., Andersen, C., Burgers, W. F. J., Ronnevik, H. C. and Schöneich, H. (1981) Regional seismic structure maps of the North Sea. In *Petroleum Geology of the Continental Shelf of North-West Europe*, ed. by Illing, L. V. and Hobson, G. D. Heyden & Son Ltd, London, pp. 98–103.

Falvey, D. A. (1974) The development of continental margins in plate tectonic theory. *Aust. Petrol. Explor. Ass. J.* **14**, 95–106.

Falvey, D. A. and Middleton, M. F. (1980) Passive continental margins: Evidence for a prebreakup deep crustal metamorphic subsidence mechanism (unpublished).

Hunt, J. M. (1979) *Petroleum Geochemistry and Geology.* W. H. Freeman and Company, San Francisco.

Keen, C. E. (1978) Thermal history and subsidence of rifted continental margins — Evidence from wells on the Nova Scotian and Labrador shelves. *Can. J. Earth Sci.* **16**, 505–522.

McKenzie, D. (1978) Some remarks on the development of sedimentary basins. *Earth Planet. Sci. Lett.* **40**, 25–32.

Middleton, M. F. (1980) A model of intracratonic basin formation, entailing deep crustal metamorphism *Geophys. J. Roy. Astr. Soc.* **62**, 1–14.

Royden, L., Sclater, J. G. and von Herzen, R. P. (1980) Continental margin subsidence and heat flow: Important parameters in formation of petroleum hydrocarbons. *AAPG Bull.* **64**, 173–187.

Sclater, J. G. and Christie, P. A. F. (1980) Continental stretching: An explanation of the Post-Mid-Cretaceous subsidence of the Central North Sea Basin. *J. Geophys. Res.* **85**, 3711–3739.

Sleep, N. H. (1971) Thermal effects of the formation of Atlantic continental margins by continental breakup. *Geophys. J. Roy. Astr. Soc.* **24**, 325–350.

Ting, T. C. (1975) Reflectivity of disseminated vitrinites in the Gulf Coast region. In *Pétrographie de la matiere organique des sediments relations avec la paléotempérature et le potentiel pétrolier* ed. by Alpern, B. Centre National de la Recherche Scientifique, Paris.

Tissot, B. P. and Welte, D. H. (1978) *Petroleum Formation and Occurrence: A New Approach to Oil and Gas Exploration.* Springer-Verlag, Berlin, pp. 516–520.

Ziegler, P. A. (1975) North Sea basin history in the tectonic framework of North-Western Europe. In *Petroleum and the Continental Shelf of North-West Europe*, ed. by Woodland, A. W. Vol. 1. John Wiley and Sons, New York, pp. 131–150.

Ziegler, P. A. (1975) Outline of the geological history of the North Sea. In *Petroleum and the Continental Shelf of North-West Europe*, ed. by Woodland, A. W., Vol. 1. John Wiley and Sons, New York, pp. 165–190.

Advances in Organic Geochemistry 1981, pp. 597–606
© *John Wiley & Sons Limited, 1983*

Hydrocarbon Potential of Kerogen Types by Pyrolysis-Gas Chromatography

J. R. Gormly and P. K. Mukhopadhyay

Institute of Petroleum and Organic Geochemistry (ICH-5) KFA-Jülich, PO Box 1913, F. R. Germany

Kerogens (defined by maceral analysis and Rock-Eval measurements as either type II or type III) were subjected to pyrolysis-gas chromatography (PGC) to determine if a fingerprint pattern exists. No unique pattern was observed although pyrolysis of type II kerogens typically produced more *n*-alkanes/alkenes than did that of type III kerogens. Kerogens fractionated by various density solutions produced different PGC patterns when the relative maceral concentrations were different. After pyrolysis, liptinite tends to be converted into inertinite. The reflectance of vitrinite associated with type III kerogen increased more than that associated with type II kerogen after the same heating event. PGC identified a potential oil source rock that, on the basis of hydrogen index and maceral analysis, might otherwise have been considered as a potential gas source rock.

INTRODUCTION

The bulk of petroleum hydrocarbons are generated by the natural thermal maturation of kerogen. The nature of these hydrocarbons depends, to a large extent, on the nature of the kerogen from which they came. Kerogen can be characterized by elemental analysis (Tissot *et al.*, 1974), composition and reflectance–fluorescence of the macerals (van Gijzel, 1981; Dow, 1977) and C_{15+} hydrocarbon concentrations and distributions (e.g. Philippi, 1965; Leythaeuser *et al.*, 1980). Pyrolysis has been employed in recent years to define kerogen types and maturities (Gransch and Eisma, 1970; Claypool and Reed, 1976; Espitalié *et al.*, 1977). Pyrolysis–gas chromatography (PGC) has been used to distinguish kerogen types by comparing amounts of certain aromatic and aliphatic compounds (Larter and Douglas, 1978, 1980; Leventhal, 1976) and by comparing relative amounts of pyrolysate fractions distilling over certain temperature ranges (Larter *et al.*, 1977). The influence of minerals on pyrolysis has been studied by Horsfield and Douglas (1980), Espitalié *et al.* (1980) and Monin *et al.* (1980).

In this study 11 kerogens of different type (defined by detailed maceral analysis) and maturity (defined by vitrinite reflectance) were subjected to PGC to determine if kerogen types could be distinguished by fingerprint patterns of the hydrocarbons generated. In addition, the chromatograms of kerogen fractions separated by density centrifugation were compared to see if differences existed among the fractions. The kerogens were examined both before and after pyrolysis to determine the effect of the programmed temperature pyrolysis on the macerals.

ANALYTICAL PROCEDURE

The organic matter was concentrated from the inorganic matrix by 4N HCl and heavy liquid (ZnI_2 at specific gravity 1.95) centrifugation. The kerogen concentrates thus obtained were later fractionated by the heavy liquid at three specific gravity levels (1.35, 1.60 and 1.95) in order to concentrate bituminite/alginite in the 1.35 fraction, vitrinite/particulate liptinite in the 1.60 fraction and inertinite in the 1.95 fraction. This procedure was modified from those of van Krevelen (1961), Welte *et al.* (1975) and Allan and Douglas (1977). Due to the small amount of sample material resulting from heavy liquid centrifugation, some of the fractions were not recovered. The different kerogen fractions were later treated with 48% HF to remove most of the silicate matrix from the kerogen fabric. The kerogens (before and after pyrolysis) were later embedded in a transoptic powder and polished according to the normal procedure followed at our institute '(Bendes *et al.*, 1979). Maceral analysis was carried out using transmitted and normal fluorescence reflected light microscopy. Reflectance of vitrinite was measured on both non-pyrolysed and pyrolysed kerogens using Zeiss Standard Universal Microscope under standard conditions (ICCP, 1971). Both reflectance of vitrinite and maceral analysis were automatically recorded in a PDP-11 computer simultaneously.

The terms for the macerals used in this text are either from ICCP (1971) or are modified slightly from those used by Teichmüller (1974), Teichmüller and Ottenjann (1977), Robert (1981) and van Gijzel (1981).

Because different names are given to the same

macerals in the literature, the following descriptions are given:

1. Bituminite I is similar to Amorphinite A as described by van Gijzel (1981), Bituminite I according to Teichmüller and Ottenjann (1977), Alginite B described by Hutton et al. (1979) and sapropelic groundmasses according to Robert (1981). In fluorescent light it is whitish–yellow (R_m ~0.5%). It is assumed to be the degraded product of algal material; it is sometimes grainy and sometimes shows the relict algal material.

2. Bituminite II is similar to Amorphinite B according to van Gijzel (1981) and Bituminite II as described by Teichmüller and Ottenjann (1977) or Bituminite by Robert (1981). In fluorescent light it is organge to reddish–brown (R_m~0.5%), mostly grainy and without any shape. This is assumed to be the degraded product of either phyto- and zooplankton/benthos or bacterially altered products of plant lipids.

3. Bituminite III is slightly different from Amorphinite C of van Gijzel (1981) and Bituminite III of Teichmüller and Ottenjann (1977). In fluorescent light it is greyish–brown to grey in colour (R_m~0.5%), grainy, sometimes with the relict tissue of telinite or sporinite, etc. It is assumed to be the degraded products of humic matter and higher plant liptinites.

Aliquots of the whole-rock samples were analysed by a Rock–Eval instrument (Espitalié et al., 1977) modified for detection of S_1 and S_2 by FID only. Pyrolysis–gas chromatography (PGC) utilizing a Chemical Data Systems (CDS) 820GS instrument was performed on solvent-extracted whole-rock and whole-kerogen or fractions thereof. Whole-rock samples of 10–30 mg and kerogen samples of 0.5–4.5 mg were placed in quartz tubes (15 mm × 4 mm), the material held in by quartz wool and the tube placed in a desorber probe. A thermocouple in the desorber probe was inserted directly into the sample and the probe was then installed in the pyrolysis interface. Helium gas flushed the interface chamber for 1 min, the interface being rapidly heated from 50 to 290 °C and remaining at 290 °C for 6 min. This procedure produced a small S_1 peak. The sample was then pyrolysed at 25 °C min^{-1} to 600 °C. Two Tenax GC (60/80 mesh) traps, which hold hexane and larger compounds at room temperature, can be switched in and out of the gas flow to trap selected peaks, or portions thereof. Subsequently, a trap was heated to 300 °C and the material was flushed to the dual column CDS gas chromatograph. The columns were 3 m × 2 mm stainless steel, packed with Dexsil 300 GC coated on Gas-Chrom Q, 80/100 mesh. The oven temperature was programmed from 70 to 290 °C at 4 °C min^{-1}. The FID response of S_1 and S_2 and the gas chromatograms were plotted and integrated with a Varian Vista 401. Peaks were identified by co-injecting a standard periodically.

RESULTS

Pyrolysis

Table 1 shows the details of maceral analysis and vitrinite reflectance of 9 kerogens and 2 coal samples before and after the pyrolysis experiments. Several of the kerogens have been fractionated into 2 or 3 fractions depending on the availability of the kerogen concentrates.

The kerogens and 2 sapropelic coals classified as type II (Tissot and Welte, 1978) show a wide variation in maceral composition and maturity. Lias epsilon and the Kimmeridge Clay Formation (sample no. 2558, R_m = 0.58%) contain mostly bituminite I or II with alginite. In the Messel shale a complex combination of algal and higher-plant lipid from a terrestrial source and some brackish-water, degraded phytoplankton (bituminite II) is encountered. A hydrogen index of 660 indicates a type II kerogen which results from a mixture of types I and III. The Cretaceous limestone (sample no. 11440) from the Gulf of Suez contains an equal mixture of bituminite II and III. The mature Kimmeridge Clay (sample no. 3919, R_m = 1.1%) is composed of residual micrinite and red-fluorescent to non-fluorescent bituminite II. The micrinite is a product of the maturation of the amorphous bituminites. The sapropelic Venezuelan coal contains mostly Botryococcus algae, resinite/fluorinite (Teichmüller, 1974) and bituminite II, while the coal from Westfalian B, F.R. Germany, contains mostly sporinite, resinite, bituminite II and only minor amounts of alginite.

Of the four type III kerogens analysed (Indonesia, sample no. 12294; Paleocene W. Greenland, sample no. 1302; Lias delta, F.R. Germany, sample no. 9826 and Cretaceous W. Canada, sample no. 10899), the Indonesian sample is resinite-rich, while the Canadian sample, no. 10899, shows sporinite/vitrinite with some fish remains. In all the samples vitrinite (telocollinite and desmocollinite) is the major maceral.

As Table 1 shows the density separation procedure permits an enrichment of maceral types in specific fractions, but it does not allow a purification of maceral types. Repeated density separations would increase the enrichment, however. The liptinite content was always highest in the less dense fraction than it was in a more dense fraction and the opposite tended to be true for inertinite. Vitrinite was not always enriched in the middle density fraction.

Organic carbon levels were determined for the whole-rock samples and for the kerogens and fractions where possible (Table 1). The only sample for which data are available on all fractions was the Kimmeridge Clay Formation (sample no. 2558). The three density fractions separated after the HCl treatment and those obtained after subsequent HF treatment contained decreasing amounts of organic carbon with increasing density. The HF-treated fractions, naturally, had higher organic carbon concentrations than their corresponding HCl-only treated fractions. The relatively low values of organic carbon (as low as 45%) even after HF treatment, are due apparently to large amounts of pyrite and possible detrital heavy minerals such as rutile or fluorides formed during HF treatment (Forsman and Hunt, 1958).

Hydrogen index values would have been calculated for the kerogen and fractions except for two reasons. First, the small amounts of kerogen required in the Rock–Eval and the CDS instruments (0.5–5.0 mg) cause problems with weighing accuracy. Second, the kerogens

Table 1

Sample details and results of kerogen analyses. (Alg. = alginite; Bit. I, II, III = bituminite I, II, III; Inertodet. = inertodetrinite; Micri. = micrinite; Res. = resinite; Desmocol. = desmocollinite; Part. = particulate; Lip. = liptinite; Spor. = sporinite; Telo. = telocollinite; Recyc. = recycled; Vit. = vitrinite; Inert. = inertinite)

Sample	Org. Carb. (%)	Hydr. Index (mg HC g^{-1} C$_{org}$)	Mean reflect. (% R_m)	Maceral comp. volume (%) Vit.	Inert.	Lip.	Kerogen type	Major maceral type
1) Messel shale, Germany, Eocene (11328)								
whole-rock	35	660	0.32[a] (—)[b]	26 (—)	3 (—)	71 (—)	II	Bit. II
Kerogen 1.35–HCl	—	—	0.34 (1.90)	15 (2)	7 (96)	78 (2)	II	Bit. II (Inertodet. + micri.)
Kerogen 1.35-HF	65		—	—	—	—		
Kerogen 1.60-HCl	—	—	—	16 (4)	20 (94)	64 (2)	II	Bit. II (Inertodet. + micri.)
Kerogen 1.60-HF	63		—	—	—	—		
Kerogen 1.95-HCl	—	—	0.32	28 (—)	15 (—)	57 (—)	II	Bit. II + III
2) Lias *epsilon* shale, Germany, Jurassic (9063)								
whole-rock	9.7	495	0.47	8	15	77	II	Bit. II + I
wh.-kerogen-HF	79	230		—	—	—		
Kerogen 1.35-HCl	—	—	—	0 (—)	0 (—)	100 (—)	I	Bit. I + Alg.
Kerogen 1.60-HCl	—	—	0.47 (1.71)	6 (1)	16 (80)	78 (19)	II	Bit. II + I (Inertodet + micri.)
3) Coal Venezuela (13123)								
whole-rock	80	464	0.51 (2.11)	—	—	—		
wh.-kerogen-HCl	77	—	—	27 (25)	17 (75)	56 (0)	II	Bit. II + Alg. (micri.)
Kerogen-HF	80	—	—	—	—	—		
4) Kimmeridge Clay Formation, North Sea, Jurassic (2558)								
whole-rock	22	541	—	—	—	—		
wh.-kerogen-HCl	37		0.58	8	4	88	II	
wh.-kerogen HF	66		—	—	—	—		
Kerogen 1.35-HCl	40		0.58 (1.80)	5 (4)	9 (85)	86 (11)	II	Bit. II (micri.)
Kerogen 1.35-HF	63		—	—	—	—		
Kerogen 1.60-HCl	37		—	5 (2)	13 (89)	82 (9)	II	Bit. II (micri.)
Kerogen 1.60-HF	58		—	—	—	—		
Kerogen 1.95-HCl	34		—	2 (0)	19 (90)	79 (10)	II	Bit. II (micri.)
Kerogen 1.95-HF	45		—	—	—	—		
5) Limestone, Gulf of Suez, Cretaceous (11440)								
whole-rock	2.2	430	0.60 (1.78)	—	—	—		
wh.-kerogen-HCl	—	—	—	8 (2)	22 (75)	70 (23)	II	Bit. II + III (micri.)
6) Kimmeridge Clay Formation, North Sea, Jurassic (3919)								
whole-rock	8.3	137	1.12	9 (—)	62 (—)	31 (—)	Residual Type II	Micri.
Kerogen 1.35-HCl	—	—	—	0 (—)	54 (—)	46 (—)		Bit. II + micri. (micri.)
Kerogen 1.60-HCl	—	—	1.04 (2.10)	23 (13)	37 (83)	40 (4)	Residual Type II	Bit. II (micri. + Inertodet.)
Kerogen 1.95-HCl	—	—	1.10 (2.10)	16 (6)	52 (93)	31 (1)		Bit. II (micri. + Inertodet.)

continued next page

Table 1 *continued*

Sample details and results of kerogen analyses. (Alg. = alginite; Bit. I, II, III = bituminite I, II, III; Inertodet. = inertodetrinite; Micri. = micrinite; Res. = resinite; Desmocol. = desmocollinite; Part. = particulate; Lip. = liptinite; Spor. = sporinite; Telo. = telocollinite; Recyc. = recycled; Vit. = vitrinite; Inert. = inertinite)

| Sample | Org. Carb. (%) | Hydr. Index (mg HC g^{-1} C$_{org}$) | Mean reflect. (% R_m) | Maceral comp. volume (%) | | | Kerogen type | Major maceral type |
				Vit.	Inert.	Lip.		
7) Indonesia shale (12294)								
whole-rock	1.04	116	—	—	—	—		
wh.-kerogen-HCl	—	—	0.52	59	2	39	III	Res. + desmocol.
			(2.15)	(46)	(51)	(3)		(micri. + Inertodet.)
8) Lias *delta*, Germany, Jurassic (9826)								
whole-rock	1.14	142	0.57	32	32	36	III	Part. Lip.
				(—)	(—)	(—)		
Kerogen 1.60-HCl	—	—	0.57	21	26	53		Part. Lip.
			(2.11)	(21)	(77)	(2)		(Inertodet. + micri)
Kerogen 1.95-HCl	—	—	0.56	23	46	31		Part. Lip.
			(2.17)	(12)	(76)	(12)		(Inertodet. + micri)
9) Coal, Germany (13124)								
whole-rock	63	259	—	—	—	—		
wh.-Kerogen-HCl	78	—	0.74	50	13	37	II–III	Res. + Spor.
			(2.18)	(46)	(54)	(0)		(micri. + Telo.)
wh.-Kerogen-HF	80	—	—	—	—	—		
10) Shale W Canada, Cretaceous (10899)								
whole-rock	1.0	95	0.74	28	59	11	III–IV	Recyc. Vit. + Telo.
				(—)	(—)	(—)		(micri. + Telo.)
Kerogen 1.35-HCl	—	—	0.72	72	15	13	III	Recyc. Vit. + Telo.
			(1.92)	(44)	(56)	(0)		(micri. + Telo.)
Kerogen 1.60-HCl	—	—	0.72	50	38	12	III	Recyc. Vit. + Telo.
			(2.21)	(35)	(65)	(0)		(micri. + Telo.)
Kerogen 1.95-HCl	—	—	0.72	34	53	13	III–IV	Recyc. Vit. + Telo.
			(2.20)	(19)	(78)	(3)		(micri. + Inertodet.)
11) Shale W Greenland, Paleocene (1302)								
whole-rock	10.0	110	1.02	36	55	9	III–IV	Recyc. Vit. + Telo.
				(—)	(—)	(—)		(micri. + Inertodet.)
Kerogen 1.60-HCl	—	—	0.98	27	64	9	III–IV	Recyc. Vit. + Telo.
			(2.60)	(18)	(79)	(3)		(micri. + Inertodet.)
Kerogen 1.95-HCl	—	—	0.98	14	81	5	IV	Recyc. Vit. + Telo.
			(2.31)	(21)	(88)	(0)		(micri. + Inertodet.)

[a] Before pyrolysis.
[b] After pyrolysis.

which were treated with HCl only and subsequently were subjected to ZnI$_2$ solutions for separation, could have higher hydrogen index values than in fact they should. Even though the kerogens were washed after the heavy liquid centrifugation, traces of the ZnI$_2$ may still be present. ZnI$_2$ produces a significant FID signal at temperatures used in normal pyrolysis (Gormly, unpublished). Because possibly misleading conclusions could be drawn, no hydrogen indices for the kerogens are reported here.

After pyrolysis most of the bituminites I, II and III have been transformed into micrinite. Most of the particulate liptinites and alginite have been converted to inertodetrinite which, in some cases, retain their original skeletal structure. Most of the vitrinites (telocollinites, desmocollinites) either show a surface pitted with micrinite (the micrinite being derived from small amounts of liptinitic maceral that are in the vitrinite pores) or large hollow circular pits in the vitrinite surface, suggesting removal of liquid/gaseous hydrocarbons within the vitrinite structure (similar to semi-coke structure). Figure 1 shows the general shift in the maceral composition toward inertinites.

Pyrolysis causes modification not only in maceral composition but also in vitrinite reflectance. In this study, a distinct trend emerges in which the type II kerogens have consistantly lower R_m values then those of the type III after pyrolysis (Fig. 2). Figure 3 shows a histogram of the *increase* in % R_m with pyrolysis for these 11 samples. Type II kerogens have increases in % R_m of 1.1 to 1.2%, while type III kerogens have 1.5 to 1.6% increases. Included with the type III kerogens are the

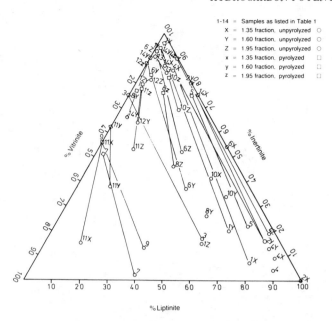

Fig. 1. Change in maceral composition of kerogens after pyrolysis. Numbers refer to sequential sample numbers in Table 1.

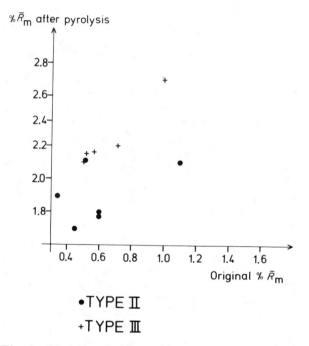

Fig. 2. Vitrinite reflectance of kerogens before and after pyrolysis.

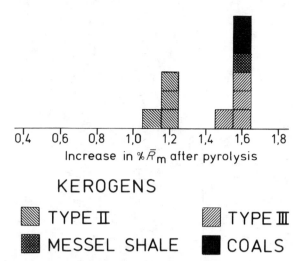

Fig. 3. Histogram depicting the % increase in vitrinite reflectance of kerogens after pyrolysis.

reflectance of the same maceral, vitrinite. According to these results, type III kerogens and coals show a higher response with respect to vitrinite reflectance for a given time–temperature event than do type II kerogens. These pyrolysed samples were not extracted after pyrolysis before $\% R_m$ was measured. The difference of 0.3 to 0.4% between the vitrinite associated with type III and that associated with type II may be due to impregnation of bitumins in the type II kerogens which lower the real reflectance values (Mukhopadhyay, unpublished). The differences observed in reflectance should not be due to anisotropy since in all cases the mean random vitrinite reflectance of unpolarized light was determined.

Pyrolysis–gas chromatography

In this study 6 whole-rock and kerogen samples (sample no. 1–6) defined by maceral composition as hydrogen-rich type II kerogens were analysed to study the 'fingerprint' pattern by PGC. Although several of the kerogens produced similar chromatograms, others were sufficiently different that no 'typical' or unique pattern characterizes type II kerogens.

The chromatograms of samples from the Lias *epsilon*, the Cretaceous limestone and the mature Kimmeridge Clay Formation (sample no. 3919) are similar in that they are mainly *n*-alkanes/alkenes with peak size decreasing as a function of increasing carbon number (Fig. 4). These chromatograms, in which paraffins predominate, correspond to those of marine sediments (Giraud, 1970) and to those from pyrolysed alginite (Larter and Douglas, 1978). The less-mature Kimmeridge Clay Formation (sample no. 2558) produced a chromatogram that is somewhat different, in that there are other compound types present (perhaps naphthalenes) in addition to the significant amounts of paraffins (Fig. 6a). The chromatogram of the Venezuela coal (sample no. 13123) contains primarily paraffins but has a maximum at C_{23} (Fig. 8a). The Messel shale produces not only a large amount of

two coal samples and the Messel shale, a sample with strong terrestrial input. The pyrolysis temperature and the rate of heating and subsequent cooling was the same for all samples, suggesting this variation is due to the nature of the kerogens. This is an unexpected observation since in all cases we were measuring

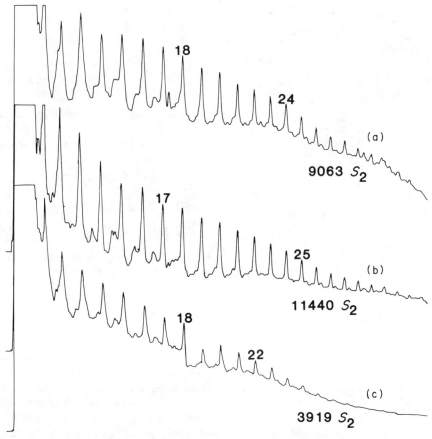

Fig. 4. PGC of type II kerogens in whole rocks; a. Lias *epsilon*; b. Cretaceous limestone; c. Kimmeridge Clay Formation (sample no. 3919).

paraffins but also other unidentified compounds which reflect the mixed marine and terrestrial sources (not shown). The pyrolysis of type II kerogens does not produce a unique 'fingerprint' chromatogram but there are significant amounts of paraffinic compounds in all 6 of the type II kerogens analysed. All of the type II kerogens have bituminite II as their major maceral type, suggesting that the degraded products of phyto- and zooplankton (bituminite II) produce, upon pyrolysis, primarily *n*-alkanes/alkenes. The exact distribution of these hydrocarbons, however, is difficult to predict, and is based on relative pyrolytic volatility of individual components in the kerogens (Larter and Douglas, 1980).

Figure 5 shows the chromatograms for the type III kerogens and the first three (a, b, c) are typical for terrestrial-source organic matter, with much non-*n*-alkanes/alkenes and compounds between C_{27}–C_{35}. These results are similar to those by Giraud (1970) which showed 'aromatic' pyrolysates from terrigenous material and those of Larter and Douglas (1978, 1980) which showed that pyrolysed vitrinite produced less straight chain hydrocarbon in relation to aromatics than that of sporinite or alginite.

The sample from W Greenland Paleocene (sample no. 1302) gives an interesting result (Fig. 5d). Although having only 9% liptinite and a hydrogen index of 110 mg HC g^{-1} C_{org} at a maturity of 1.04% R_m, the PGC result shows a distribution of mainly *n*-alkanes/alkenes. Based on maceral composition, vitrinite reflectance and hydrogen index, this shale would not be considered as a

potential source rock for oil. However, because of the high level of organic carbon and the results of PGC, this formation could be considered a potential oil source rock. In terms of pyrolysis yield (mg HC g^{-1} whole rock), this sample produces as much as an acknowledged good source rock which has 2% organic carbon and a hydrogen index in excess of 500 mg HC g^{-1} C_{org}. In this example PGC helps identify a potential oil source rock that might otherwise be overlooked.

One purpose of this study was to see if any significant differences existed in the PGC 'fingerprint' between the various density fractions. Because of problems in isolation of sufficient quantities of individual fractions, the only sample for which data are available on all fractions is the Kimmeridge Clay Formation (sample no. 2558). Only slight differences can be seen for the chromatograms produced by pyrolysis of the whole rock and the density fractions of the kerogens (Fig. 6a–d). The percent liptinite in the kerogen fractions ranges from 79% in the 1.95 density fraction to 86% in the 1.35 fraction. Since the fractions are relatively uniform it is not surprising that the 'fingerprints' are similar. On the other hand the 1.6 and 1.95 fractions of the Lias *delta* sample (no. 9826) show significant differences in the PGC (Fig. 7). The 1.6 fraction contains a reasonable amount of *n*-alkanes/alkenes and compares favorably with the whole-rock sample (Fig. 5b), while the 1.95 fraction contains no *n*-alkanes. The 1.95 fraction has an unresolved envelope in the range from C_{15} to C_{22}, which can be seen somewhat as a background also in the 1.6

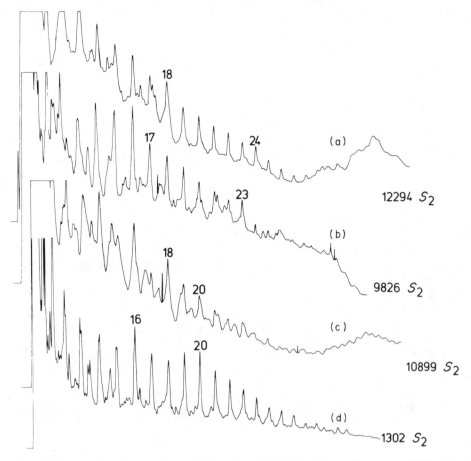

Fig. 5. PGC of type III kerogens in whole rocks; a. Indonesia shale; b. Lias *delta*; c. Cretaceous W Canada; d. Paleocene W Greenland.

fraction. The only obvious significant difference between the two fractions is the relative amount of inertinite and liptinite, the amount of vitrinite being constant. The difference in the PGC results is presumably due to the relative amounts of macerals.

The two sapropelic coals provide an opportunity to determine if kerogens which are classified as being different type produce different chromatograms after pyrolysis. The Venezuela coal (sample no. 13123), with an R_m of 0.51%, contains type II kerogen with 56% liptinite (mostly *Botryococcus* alginite) and 27% vitrinite. On the other hand, the German coal (sample no. 13124), with an R_m of 0.74%, contains 50% vitrinite and only 37% liptinite and is classified as type II–III. In spite of the difference in maturity and type, the pyrolysis–gas chromatograms look very similar (Fig. 8). Both have a smooth distribution of *n*-alkanes/alkenes with a maximum at *n*-C_{22} or *n*-C_{23}. The more-mature, and vitrinite-rich coal has peaks (aromatics?) that can be seen slightly separated from the *n*-C_{11} to *n*-C_{16} peaks, while the less-mature, liptinite-rich coal seems to have only *n*-alkanes/alkenes. Of the material monitored between C_6 and C_{35}, 47% is C_6–C_{10} in the mature coal while 27% is C_6–C_{10} in the less-mature sample. Although C_1–C_6 could not be monitored, the higher amount of C_6–C_{10} in the German coal suggests its higher maturity. Of the 56% liptinite in the Venezuelan coal the proportion of bituminite II:resinite:sporinite/cutinite:alginite is 37:10:33:20 while that of the 37% liptinite in the

German coal is 50:31:19:1, respectively. The similarity in the distributions of the PGC of the two coals may derive from the equivalent absolute amounts of bituminite II (18–20%). However, this completely ignores any effects by the other macerals in the coals.

These results point out the problems of kerogen classification, whether it is by maceral analysis, hydrogen index or PGC-'fingerprint'. The predominately *n*-alkanes/alkenes nature of the chromatogram of the German coal (sample no. 13124) suggests it is a type II kerogen. The maceral analysis indicates a type II–III while the hydrogen index would also suggest a type II–III, particularly when one considers the maturity (0.74% R_m). What this underscores is the oft-stated need to characterize kerogens by as many parameters as possible. Further studies are required on specific purified macerals to establish their individual 'fingerprint' (if one exists). Relative contributions of hydrocarbons and their distribution from specific macerals to the hydrocarbons generated from a whole rock or kerogen could then be estimated.

GENERAL OBSERVATIONS AND CONCLUSIONS

The amount of C_6–C_{10} compounds produced by PGC tends to be greater for whole-rock than for separated

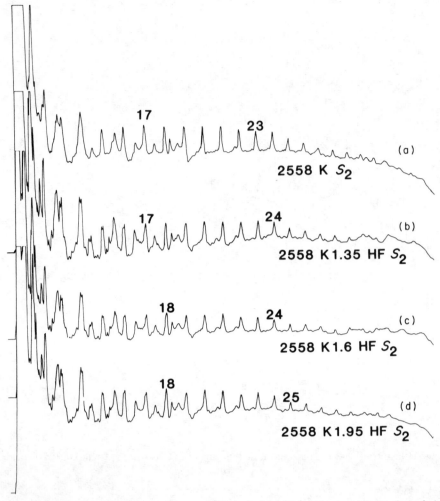

Fig. 6. PGC of Kimmeridge Clay Formation; a. whole-rock; b. 1.35 fraction; c. 1.6 fraction; d. 1.95 fraction.

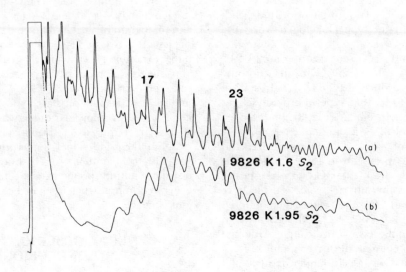

Fig. 7. PGC of Lias *delta* fractions; a. 1.6 fraction; b. 1.95 fraction.

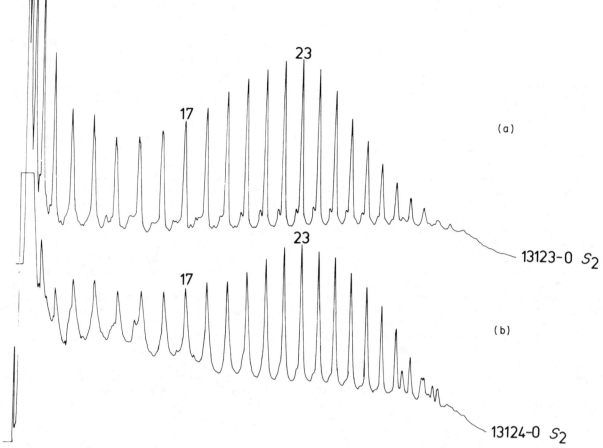

Fig. 8. PGC of 2 sapropelic coals. a. Venezuela, $R_m = 0.51\%$; b. W Germany, $R_m = 0.74\%$.

kerogen. This is similar to the gasification effect observed by Horsfield and Douglas (1980) in which the concentration of C_5–C_7 compounds was greater in the presence of silicate minerals.

The kerogens in which the silicate minerals have been removed frequently generate pyrolysis products having more n-alkanes/alkenes than those rock samples which have been subjected only to HCl treatment. Likewise, both the HF-treated kerogens and the HCl-only-treated kerogens generate pyrolysis products having less unresolved background (more alkanes/alkenes) than those which are still associated with the silicate (comparisons not shown). It may be that the minerals function as catalysts to create a large variety of compounds when the organic matter is pyrolysed. Another possible explanation is that the unresolved material is physically trapped in the mineral matrix and is not released until high temperature pyrolysis, perhaps undergoing cracking or rearranging. If the inorganic matrix is destroyed by HCl and/or HF, this material is subsequently removed in the S_1 peak and not seen at all in the thermal degradation products in peak S_2. Since HCl and HF treatments both give less unresolved background in the pyrogrammes, this particular 'matrix effect' occurs with both silicates and carbonates.

After pyrolysis, the reflectance of vitrinite associated with type III kerogen has increased by 0.3 to 0.4% more than that associated with type II kerogen. This difference may be due to impregnation of bitumen in the

type II kerogen which would lower the real reflectance values. Sapropelic coal behaves as type III kerogen in this regard, even though it is classified as a type II kerogen based on maceral composition and hydrogen index.

No unique 'fingerprint' pattern could be seen for pyrolysis products of either type II or type III kerogens, although some samples had similar chromatograms within each group. In most cases, type II kerogens produced pyrograms which had more n-alkanes/alkenes than did type III kerogens. However, two sapropelic coal samples, one having type II kerogen and one having type II–III kerogen, produced nearly identical chromatograms dominated by n-alkanes/alkenes. Differences in the chromatograms of the pyrolysis products of the various density fractions of kerogens can be significant when the relative concentrations of macerals are different.

PGC identified a potential oil source rock that, on the basis of hydrogen index and maceral analysis, might otherwise have been considered as a potential gas source rock.

PGC can be a useful method for characterizing kerogens but further research is needed on purified macerals, preferably of different maturities, to determine the possible hydrocarbon distribution patterns. This, coupled with detailed maceral analysis and improved GC resolution would be helpful in predicting expected hydrocarbon distributions of source rocks.

REFERENCES

Allan, J. and Douglas, A. G. (1977) Variations in the content and distribution of *n*-alkanes in a series of carboniferous vitrinites and sporinites of bituminous rank. *Geochim. Cosmochim. Acta* **41**, 1223–1230.

Benders, W., Flekken, P., Jacobs, I. (1979) Anleitung zur Herstellung von präparaten für die organisch-petrologische Untersuchung, KFA/ICH-5 Bericht Nr. 500874.

Claypool, G. E. and Reed, P. R. (1976) Thermal analysis technique for source rock evaluation, quantitative estimate of organic richness and effects of lithologic variation. *Am. Assoc. Petrol. Geol.* **60**, 608–626.

Dow, W. (1977) Kerogen studies and geological interpretations. *J. Geochem. Explor.* **7**, 79–100.

Espitalié, J., Laporte, G. C., Madec, M., Marquis, F., Leplat, D., Paulet, G. and Boutefeu, A. (1977) Méthode rapide de caractérization des roches mères de leur potential petrolier et de leur degré d'évolution. *Rev. Inst. Fr. Petr.* **33**, 23–42.

Espitalié, J., Madec, M. and Tissot, B. (1980) Role of mineral matrix in kerogen pyrolysis: influence on petroleum generation and migration. *Am. Ass. Petrol. Geol. Bull.* **64**, 59–66.

Forsman, G. and Hunt, J. M. (1958) Insoluble organic matter (kerogen) in sedimentary rocks. *Geochim. Cosmochim. Acta* **15**, 170–182.

Gallegos, E. J. (1979) Pyrolysis gas chromatography. In *Chromatography in Petroleum Analyses* Vol. 11. Ed. by Altgelt, K. H. and Gouw, T. H. Chromatographic Science Service, Marcel Dekker, Inc., New York, pp. 163–184.

Giraud, A. (1970) Application of pyrolysis and gas chromatography to the geochemical characterization of kerogen in sedimentary rocks. *Am. Assoc. Petr. Geol. Bull.* **54**, 439–455.

Gransch, J. A. and Eisma, E. (1970) Characterization of the insoluble organic matter of sediments by pyrolysis. In *Advances in Organic Geochemistry 1968*. Ed. by Hobson, G. D. and Speers, G. C. Pergamon Press, Oxford. pp. 407–426.

Horsfield, B. and Douglas, A. G. (1980) The influence of minerals on the pyrolysis of kerogens. *Geochim. Cosmochim. Acta* **44**, 1119–1131.

Hutton, A. C., Kantsler, A. J., Cook, A. C. and McKirdy, D. M. (1980) Organic matter in oil shales. *Austr. Petrol. Explor. Ass. J.* **20**, 44–67.

Ikan, R., Baedecker, M. J. and Kaplan, I. R. (1975) Thermal alteration experiments on organic matter in recent marine sediments II. Isoprenoids. *Geochim. Cosmochim. Acta* **39**, 187–194.

International Committee of Coal Petrology (1971) *International Handbook of Coal Petrology*, supplement to second edition. Centre Nat. de la Rech. Scientifique, Paris.

International Committee of Coal Petrology (1975) *International Handbook of Coal Petrography*, second supplement to second edition. Centre. Nat. de la Rech. Scientifique, Paris.

Larter, S. and Douglas, A. G. (1978) Low molecular weight aromatic hydrocarbons in coal maceral pyrolysates as indicators of diagenesis and organic matter type. In *Environmental Biogeochemistry and Geomicrobiology*. Ed. by Krumbein, W. E. Ann Arbor Science, Ann Arbor. pp. 373–386.

Larter, S. and Douglas, A. G. (1980) A pyrolysis–gas chromat-

ographic method for kerogen typing. In *Advances in Organic Geochemistry 1979*. Ed. by Douglas, A. G. and Maxwell, J. R. Pergamon Press, Oxford. pp. 579–583.

Larter, S. R., Horsfield, B. and Douglas, A. G. (1977) Pyrolysis as a possible means of determining the petroleum generating potential of sedimentary organic matter. In *Analytical Pyrolysis, Proceedings of the Third International Symposium on Analytical Pyrolysis, Amsterdam, 1976*. Ed. by Roland-Jones, C. E. and Cramers, C. A. Elsevier, Amsterdam. pp. 189–202.

Leventhal, J. S. (1976) Stepwise pyrolysis gas chromatography of kerogen in sedimentary rocks. *Chem. Geol.* **18**, 5–20.

Leythaeuser, D., Hagemann, H. W., Hollerbach, A. and Schaefer, R. G. (1980) Hydrocarbon generation in source beds as a function of type and maturation of their organic matter: a mass balance approach. In *10th World Pet. Cong. Proc. Bukarest 1979*, Vol. 2, pp. 31–41.

Monin, J. C., Durand, B., Vandenbroucke, M. and Huc, A. Y. (1980) Experimental simulation of the natural transformation of kerogen. In *Advances in Organic Geochemistry 1979*. Ed. by Douglas, A. G. and Maxwell, J. R. Pergamon Press, Oxford. pp. 517–530.

Philippi, G. T. (1965) On the depth, time and mechanism of petroleum generation. *Geochim. Cosmochim. Acta* **29**, 1021–1049.

Robert, P. (1981) Classification of organic matter by means of fluorescence; application to hydrocarbon source rocks. *Int. J. Coal Geol.* **1**, 101–137.

Saint-Paul, C., Monin, J. C. and Durand, B. (1980) Méthode de caractérisation rapide des hydrocarbures de C_1 à C_{25} contenus dans les roches sédimentaires et dans les huiles. *Rev. Inst. Fr. Petr.* **35**, 1065–1078.

Scrima, D. A., Yen, T. F. and Warren, P. L. (1974) Thermal chromatography of Green River shale I. Bitumen and kerogen. *Energy Sources* **1**, 321–336.

Solli, H., Larter, S. R. and Douglas, A. G. (1980) The analysis of kerogens by pyrolysis gas chromatography–mass spectrometry using selective ion monitoring. *J. Anal. Appl. Pyrol.* **1**, 231–241.

Teichmüller, M. (1974) Entstehung und Veränderung bituminöser Substanzen in Kohlen in Bezeihung zur Entstehung und Umwandlung des Erdöls. *Fortschr. Geol. Rheinld. u. Westf.*, 65–112.

Teichmüller, M. and Ottenjann, K. (1977) Art und Diagenese von Liptiniten und lipiden Stoffen in einem Erdölmuttergestein. *Erdöl-Kohle* **30**, 387–398.

Tissot, B., Durand, B., Espitalié, J. and Combaz, A. (1974) Influence of the nature and diagenesis of organic matter in the formation of petroleum. *Bull. Am. Ass. Petrol. Geol.* **58**, 499–506.

Tissot, B. and Welte, D. (1978) *Petroleum Formation and Occurrence*, Springer Verlag, Berlin.

van Gijzel, P. (1981) Applications of the geomicrophotometry of kerogen, solid hydrocarbons and crude oils to petroleum exploration. In *Organic Maturation Studies and Fossil Fuel Exploration*. Ed. by Brooks, J. Academic Press, New York. pp. 351–377.

van Krevelen, D. W. (1961) '*Coal*'. Elsevier Publication Co., Amsterdam. p. 113.

Welte, D. H., Hagemann, H. W., Hollerbach, A., Leythaeuser, D., Stahl, W. (1975) Correlation between petroleum and source rock. *Proc. 9th World Pet. Congr.* Col. 2, pp. 179–191.

Advances in Organic Geochemistry 1981, pp. 607–612
© *John Wiley & Sons Limited, 1983*

Characteristics and Diagenesis of Kerogens associated with Clay Fractions of Mudstone

N. Suzuki† and K. Taguchi‡

Institute of Mineralogy, Petrology and Economic Geology, Faculty of Science, Tohoku University, Sendai, Miyagi, 980, Japan

Eight kerogen fractions obtained by the size-fractionation of the siltstone from the Haizume Formation of Pliocene age, Niigata Prefecture, Japan were examined by elemental analysis, and infrared (IR) and electron spin resonance (ESR) spectrometry. The kerogens from coarse fractions were relatively rich in aromatic structures, and they indicated characteristics similar to the fusinite maceral of coal, showing low g-value (2.0029), narrow line width (2.62G) and high spin density. On the other hand, the kerogens from fine fractions were rich in functional groups and aliphatic structure, were composed of amorphous kerogen and showed similar properties to humic acid from marine muds. Kerogens associated with clay-size fractions obtained from thirteen core samples from the Nishiyama Oil Field, were investigated for diagenetic change. A systematic change of kerogen properties with burial was recognized, particularly in the ESR properties though all the investigated samples were immature in the degree of organic alteration, and the variation of ESR line width changed from gradual increase to rapid decrease all within the early stage of diagenesis. It is suggested that the kerogen analysis by such a size-fractionation as in this study provides more detailed information about the diagenetic change than analysis of unfractionated rocks.

INTRODUCTION

The distribution of organic matter in a sediment can in many cases be related to inorganic constituents or sedimentary fractionation (Trask, 1939; Weiss, 1969; Theng, 1979). Kerogen, dispersed organic matter which consists of a great variety of discrete organic particles such as identifiable phytoclasts and unidentifiable organic debris, is considered to have a close relationship with particle size distribution and inorganic constituents (clay minerals) (Kodama and Schnitzer, 1971; Maximov *et al.*, 1975). On the other hand, it has been reported that diagenetic parameters obtained from such kerogens give a poor correlation with other depth-dependent geothermal parameters (Morishima and Matsubayashi, 1978). However, there have been a few studies which investigated the distribution of organic matter associated with particular size fractions of a sediment (Thompson and Eglinton, 1978; Tanoue and Handa, 1979).

This paper investigates the properties of kerogen obtained from different size fractions of mudstone. The diagenetic changes of kerogen associated with the clay-size fraction were also examined.

† Present address: Department of Geology, Faculty of Science, Shimane University, Matsue, Shimane, 690, Japan
‡ Correspondence.

EXPERIMENTAL

The eight fractions from a marine siltstone sample from the Haizume Formation of Pliocene age and thirteen core samples of marine mudstones from UMEDA R-1, Nishiyama Oil Field, Japan (Fig. 1 and Table 1) were chosen for study.

The rock sample was carefully cleaned and then was crushed into fragments of about 3–5 cm in diameter. After dryness was completed, the piecement was soaked and frozen in liquid nitrogen for 5 min. The frozen piece was disintegrated by use of 0.1% solution of sodium pyrophosphate (30 °C) and the dispersed samples were agitated in the shaker for 7 h to promote the dispersion more and to remove the alkaline soluble organic matter. After dispersion had been completed, the material was washed through a 47 μm sieve to remove particles coarser than that dimension. The coarse fraction was dried, separated into three size grade fractions and weighed. The material smaller than 47 μm was separated into five fractions by centrifuging.

The fractions above 47 μm were examined under the microscope for mineral identification. The fractions under 47 μm were examined by X-ray diffraction. Organic material in each sample was analyzed for total organic carbon, extractable organic matter, and *n*-alkane and kerogen composition according to the procedure shown in Fig. 2. Kerogen samples from each

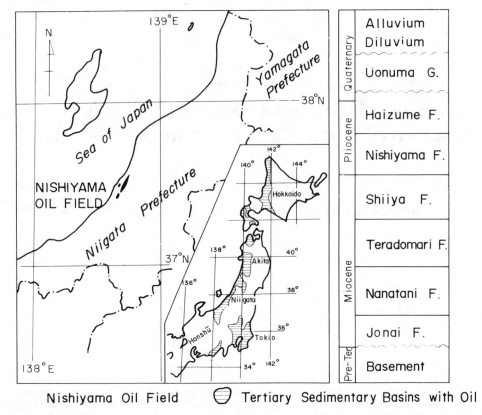

Fig. 1. Location map and generalized stratigraphic column for Nishiyama Oil Field, Japan.

fraction were analyzed to determine electron spin resonance (ESR) and infrared (IR) spectra using a Jeol PE-3 X-band spectrometer and Hitachi 260-50 Infrared Spectrophotometer respectively. Organic carbon and hydrogen determinations were made by the Pregel method with a Shimazu Universal Organic Micro-analyzer UM-3. The hydrocarbons were analyzed on a Hitachi–Perkin Elmer F6D Gas Chromatograph fitted with a 2 m × 3 mm SUS column coated with 2% Apiezone L on Chromosorb W AW DMCS.

RESULTS AND DISCUSSION

Inorganic and organic compositions in each size fraction from a siltstone of the Haizume Formation

Inorganic compositions The microscopic obser-vation showed that the most abundant minerals in the coarse size fractions were quartz and feldspar. On the other hand, X-ray diffraction (Fig. 3) showed that clay minerals such as illite, montmorillonite and chlorite are abundant in the finer fractions (<7 μm). The clay fraction (finer than 3 μm) contains mostly montmorillonite with a small amount of illite and chlorite.

Organic composition Total organic carbon (TOC), extractable organic matter (EOM) and n-alkane CPI are listed in Table 1. ESR properties and elemental compositions of kerogens obtained from each fraction are shown in Table 2. The amounts of TOC decreases from the coarse (74–105 μm) to the fine (47–62 μm) size fractions, but markedly increases from silt-size fraction toward the clay-size fraction. The variation of EOM amounts also shows a similar tendency though the amounts of two size fractions were not determined. A similar observation in recent lacustrine and marine sediments has been reported by Thompson and Eglinton (1978), and Tanoue and Handa (1979) respectively. As most of the organic carbon in the sedimentary rocks exists as insoluble organic matter (kerogen), the

Table 1

Haizume siltstone fractions: organic carbon and extractable organic matter contents, and n-alkane CPI. —, not determined. The CPI values were obtained from the combined extracts.

Fraction size (μm)	Frequency (%)	Organic carbon (mg/g)	Extractable organic matter (mg/g)	n-Alkane CPI (C_{24}–C_{34})
1–3	1.1	18.2	–	
3–7	8.8	16.1	0.94	} 4.6
7–15	17.1	13.0	0.35	
15–30	23.7	6.6	0.17	} 3.1
30–47	19.1	4.2	0.09	
47–62	14.6	1.3	0.06	
62–74	6.2	1.8	0.08	} 1.8
74–105	4.5	5.6	–	

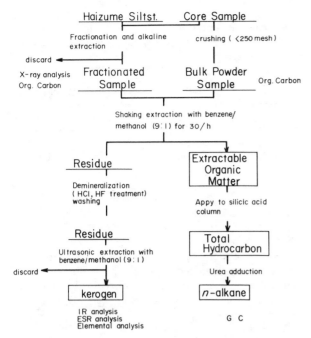

Fig. 2. Flow-chart of the analytical procedure.

variation of organic carbon content with particle size may be attributed to the kerogen content in each fraction. On the other hand, it is evident that kerogens in the coarse fractions are composed mostly of organic detritus visible during microscopic observation, while kerogens in the finer than silt-size fractions are composed of organic matter closely associated with clay minerals as seen in Fig. 3. Therefore, the high organic carbon content in the finer fractions may be attributed to the existence of the amorphous kerogen as discussed later.

A parallel variation of TOC and EOM contents with the particle size appears to be in accord with the observation that normally the amounts of EOM are proportional to TOC content of the rocks (Taguchi, 1962, 1974; Schrayer and Zarrella, 1966). Of course, EOM ratio may be affected by burial on petroleum generation and rather type of organic matter. However, as in this study, in a case of the sample immatured and composed predominantly of marine organic matter, probably those effects can be ignored. It is also suggested that the high yield of EOM from the clay fraction is due to the increased TOC values, although part of the cause may be due to the adsorption of organic material on the mineral surfaces (Thompson and Eglinton, 1978).

n-Alkanes Odd/even preference of the *n*-alkane components, expressed as the Carbon Preference Index (CPI) shows a progressive increase from the coarse (47–105 μm) fraction to the finer (1–7 μm) fraction (Table 1). It is noted that this is completely contrary to the result obtained from recent sediments by Thompson and Eglinton (1978). These authors found that the CPI decreased from the coarse to the fine fractions and they presented two reasons for this decrease:
1. recycled geolipid material (matured material) is apt to get into the finer fractions;
2. the coarser fractions mostly consist of higher plant detritus, while the finer fractions consist of bacterial lipids.

However, it has also been reported that coarse sediments of Pliocene age in a Japanese oil field have a low CPI (1.0) (Taguchi, 1968; Taguchi *et al.*, 1981). On the other hand, Palacas *et al.* (1972) reported that most sand samples in an estuarine environment have a low CPI of 2.0 or less, while mud samples in the same environment have a high CPI of about 8. Consequently, at the present time, we cannot give a definite answer to this problem: further investigation is necessary.

Kerogen Electron spin resonance (ESR) properties, elemental compositions and IR spectra of kerogens in the eight size fractions are given in Table 2 and Fig. 4. The amount of hydrogen (%) and the H/C atomic ratio of kerogens in each size fraction show an increase from the coarse (15–30 μm) to the fine fractions (Table 2). The IR spectra show characteristic absorption bands (Robin and Rouxhet, 1976) of: aliphatic C–H stretching near 2900 cm^{-1} and C=O stretching of carbonyl and carboxyl groups at 1710 cm^{-1} in the finer size fractions, and C=O stretching of quinone functions and C=C of olefins and aromatic structures at 1630 cm^{-1}, and aromatic C–H stretching near 800 cm^{-1} in the coarse fractions.

Analytical results of ESR give relatively broader line width and higher g-value in the finer fractions than the coarse fractions. The spin concentration gives the minimum value in the 30–47 μm fraction and becomes higher toward both the coarse and the fine size fractions. As is evident from the above results, the kerogens from the coarse fractions are relatively rich in aromatic structure, and they indicate characteristics similar to fusinite maceral of coals (Austin *et al.*, 1966; Retcofsky *et al.*, 1968), showing low g-value, narrow line width and high spin density in the ESR properties. On the other hand, the kerogens from the fine fractions are rich in functional groups and aliphatic structure, and they

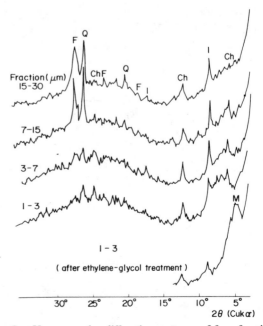

Fig. 3. X-ray powder diffraction patterns of four fractions finer than 30 μm Q: quartz, F-feldspar, I: illite, Ch: chlorite, **M**: montmorillonite.

Table 2

ESR properties and elemental compositions of kerogens in each size fraction obtained from Haizume siltstone. ([a]: dry ash free, -: not determined, Δ Hmsl: peak to peak height, Ns: spin concentration per g organic carbon of kerogen).

Size fraction (μm)	ESR properties			Elemental compositions[a]		
	ΔHmsl (G)	g-value	Ns (10^{18} spins/g C)	C (%)	H (%)	O+N+S (%)
1–3	4.31	2.00326	1.57	60.4	6.9	32.7
3–7	4.56	2.00320	1.28	60.5	6.5	33.0
7–15	4.40	2.00326	0.82	66.4	5.4	28.2
15–30	3.56	2.00297	0.79	69.2	4.2	26.6
30–47	3.91	2.00297	0.67	—	—	—
47–62	2.97	2.00291	1.97	—	—	—
62–74	3.07	2.00291	1.66	—	—	—
74–105	2.62	2.00288	1.79	—	—	—

indicate characteristics similar to humic acid found in DSDP samples (Sato, 1980). The above results seem to indicate that most of the kerogens from finer fractions consist of the 'amorphous kerogen', and little recycled geolipid materials and higher plant detritus, that is, they are mostly derived from 'melanoidins' which are considered to be dark coloured acidic polymeric products of sugar/amino acid condensation reactions with many of the properties of humic acids. From this viewpoint, the diagenetic change of the kerogens from finer fractions was examined as stated in the following section.

Diagenetic change of the kerogens in clay-size fraction

Table 3 shows the vertical distribution of organic carbon, extractable organic matter and total hydrocarbon contents, and the CPI of unfractionated core samples from UMEDA R-1. Fig. 5 presents the depth-dependent change of ESR properties and IR spectra of kerogens obtained from the clay fractions in the core samples. Table 3 indicates that studied samples are still immature in the degree of organic alteration and have not reached the level of 'principal zone of oil generation'. Although the ESR–kerogen method for the determination of the maximum paleotemperature has been used by many workers since Pusey's study (1973), it has been pointed out that the ESR parameters observed for isolated kerogens or coaly particles show a poor correlation with geothermal history (Morishima and Matsubayashi, 1978). However, as seen in Fig. 5, ESR parameters of kerogens obtained from the clay fraction show a systematic change with burial depth, i.e. geothermal history. Spin concentration shows a remarkable increase with burial depth and g-value shows no distinct change at shallower depth, but a rapid decrease near about 1400 m depth. Line width (ΔHmsl) shows a gradual increase down to approximately 1400 m depth and then rapid decrease with depth. IR spectra also clearly show the successive decrease of absorption bands of aliphatic C–H near 2900 cm^{-1} and C=O stretching of carbonyl and carboxyl groups at 1710 cm^{-1} with burial depth.

It is noteworthy that the ESR line width showed the change from gradual increase to rapid decrease at a certain depth within the immature stage of organic alteration. It may be related to the chemical composition of the kerogens and to a possible catalytic role of clay minerals associated preferentially with the clay-size fraction. Consequently, it is suggested that the kerogens have changed their chemical composition even at this immature stage of organic alteration.

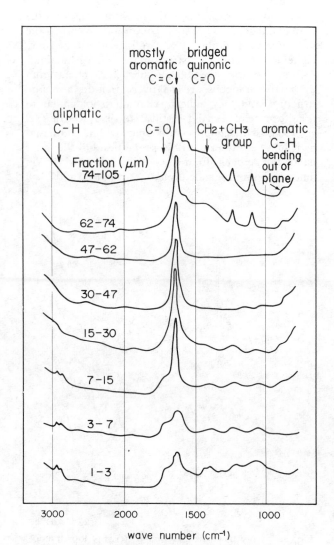

Fig. 4. Comparison of infrared spectra of kerogens in each size fraction.

Table 3

Organic carbon, extractable organic matter and total hydrocarbon concentration and CPI of unfractionated samples from UMEDA R-1. OC: organic carbon, EOM: extractable organic matter, THy: total hydrocarbon, -: not determined. 212–387 m: Haizume F., 503–927 m: Nishiyama F., 1107–1355 m: Shihiya F., 1448–1801 m: Teradomari F

Sample (Depth) (m)	OC (%)	EOM (ppm)	THy (ppm)	EOM/OC EOM/OC	THy/OC THy/OC	CPI (C_{24}–C_{34})
212	0.56	734	71	0.13	0.013	5.58
387	0.58	820	98	0.14	0.017	3.95
503	0.67	710	57	0.11	0.024	4.89
819	0.96	1255	166	0.13	0.017	3.73
927	0.78	1100	179	0.14	0.023	5.05
1017	0.71	1250	95	0.18	0.013	5.00
1237	0.62	928	136	0.15	0.022	3.75
1355	0.34	588	45	0.17	0.013	—
1448	0.87	982	51	0.11	0.006	3.21
1529	0.93	1037	208	0.11	0.022	2.83
1657	0.65	556	91	0.09	0.014	2.27
1762	0.62	886	106	0.14	0.017	1.48
1801	0.51	1303	87	0.26	0.017	1.21

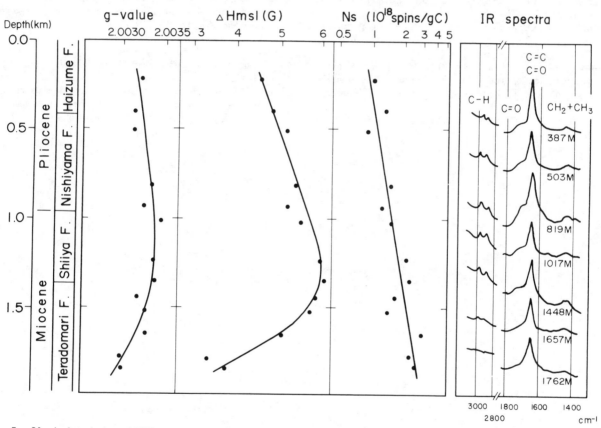

Fig. 5. Vertical variation of ESR properties and IR spectra of kerogens in clay-size fraction obtained from UMEDA R-1 core samples. No unconformities and intrusive or volcanic rocks were observed in the sequences studied. The scatter in measured values is mainly due to experimental error.

Acknowledgements

The authors wish to thank Mr T. Asakawa and Dr S. Sato of Technology Research Center, Japan Petroleum Development Corporation, Tokyo for performing ESR analyses; and Mr Y. Yoshida of Japan Petroleum Exploration Co., Ltd for providing the core samples. The authors also gratefully acknowledge Dr C. Cornford of the British National Oil Corporation, who has improved the manuscript as a reviewer.

REFERENCES

Austin, D. E. G., Ingram, D. J. E., Given, P. H., Binder, C. R. and Hill, L. W. (1966) Electron spin resonance study of pure macerals. In *Coal Sci.* Ed. by Gould, R. F. American Chemical Society. pp. 344–362.

Kodama, H. and Schnitzer, M. (1971) Evidence for inter-lamellar adsorption of organic matter by clay in a Podzol soil. *Can. J. Soil Sci.* **51**, 509–512.

Maximov, S. P., Kalinko, M. K., Botneva, T. A., Radionova, K. F., Larskaya, Ye. S. and Chetveridova, O. P. (1975) Facial-genetic types of dispersed organic matter, their chemical and physical characteristics, specific features and amount of generated hydrocarbons. In *Advances in Organic Geochemistry 1975*. Ed. by Campos, R. and Goni, J. pp. 487–492.

Morishima, H. and Matsubayashi, N. (1978) ESR diagram: A method to distinguish vitrinite macerals. *Geochim. Cosmochim. Acta* **42**, 537–540.

Palacas, J. G., Love, A. H. and Gerrild, P. N. (1972) Hydrocarbons in estuarine sediments of Choctawhatchee Bay, Florida, and their implications for genesis of petroleum. *Am. Ass. Petrol. Geol. Bull.* **56**, 1402–1418.

Pusey, W. C. (1973) How to evaluate potential gas and oil source rocks. *World Oil*, April, 71–73.

Retcofsky, H. L., Stalk, J. M. and Friedel, R. A. (1968) Electron spin resonance in American Coals. *Anal. Chem.* **40**, 1699–1704.

Robin, P. L. and Rouxhet, P. G. (1976) Contribution of molecular water in the infrared spectra of kerogens and coals. *Fuel* **55**, 177–183.

Sato, S. (1980) Organic geochemical study on the core samples from Japan Trench (DSDP Leg 57). *Technical Report of Technology Research Center, J.N.O.C.* **21**, 1–59.

Shrayer, G. J. and Zarrella, W. M. (1966) Organic geochemistry of shales II. Distribution of extractable organic matter in the siliceous Mowry shale of Wyoming. *Geochim. Cosmochim. Acta* **30**, 415–434.

Taguchi, K. (1968) Problems on *n*-paraffin hydrocarbons from the viewpoint of origin of oil — with special reference to Carbon Preference Index. *Jour. Japan Petrol. Inst.* **11**, 414–423 (in Japanese).

Taguchi, K. (1962) Basin architecture and its relation to the petroleum source rocks development in the region bordering Akita and Yamagata Prefectures and the adjoining areas, with special reference to the depositional environment of petroleum source rocks in Japan. *Sci. Rept. Tohoku Univ. Sendai, 3rd Ser.* **7**, 293–342.

Taguchi, K. (1974) Some considerations on the time of formation of petroleum deposits in the Neogene Tertiary basins, northeastern Japan. *Report, Geological Survey of Japan*, No. 250–2, 175–200 (in Japanese with English abstract).

Taguchi, K., Kano, T., Suzuki, N. and Ikehara, Y. (1981) Organic diagenesis of the Neogene Tertiary along Oashizawa river, Shinjo Oil Field, Japan. In *Studies on Diagenesis of Sedimentary Rocks*. Ed. by Taguchi, K. Tohoku Univ. Sendai. pp. 67–78 (in Japanese).

Tanoue, E. and Handa, N. (1979) Differential sorption of organic matter by various sized sediment particles in recent sediment from the Bering Sea. *J. Oceanogr. Soc. Japan* **35**, 199–208.

Theng, B. K. G. (1979) *Formation and properties of clay-polymer complexes*. Elsevier, Amsterdam. pp. 283–326.

Thompson, S. and Eglinton, G. (1978) The fractionation of a recent sediment for organic geochemical analysis. *Geochim. Cosmochim. Acta* **42**, 199–207.

Trask, P. D. (1939) Organic content of recent marine sediments. In *Recent Marine Sediments — A Symposium*. Ed. by Trask, P. D. Am. Assoc. Petr. Geol., Tulsa, Oklahoma. pp. 428–453.

Weiss, A. (1969) Organic derivatives of clay minerals, zeolites and related minerals. In *Organic Geochemistry, Method and Results*. Ed. by Eglinton, G. and Murphy, M. T. J. Springer–Verlag, Berlin. pp. 737–781.

Advances in Organic Geochemistry 1981, pp. 613–619
© *John Wiley & Sons Limited, 1983*

Continuous Infrared Analysis of Temperature Programmed Pyrolysis Products of Laboratory Oxidized Kerogens and Borehole Samples

Leplat, P., Paulet, J. and Melotte, M.

Petrofina Exploration Dept., Research Centre, Rue de la Loi 33 1040, Brussels, Belgium

A study of the chemical nature and structure of kerogens has been undertaken by monitoring, with infrared detection, the CO_2 evolved during programmed pyrolysis of oxidized model kerogen, containing samples. The model study is used as a reference when studying core and cuttings from a borehole of about 1000 m depth. This borehole provides information on CO_2 evolution from a variety of sedimentary environments which range from pelagic clays and turbidites deposited in a marine environment, to fluviatile deposits. Also studied by the programmed pyrolysis CO_2 technique were samples of marine Posidonie (seawed) leaves and roots, and recent and sub-recent sediments. Results from other physico–chemical analyses, vitrinite reflectance measurements, head space analysis, together with kinetic calculations, are reported.

INTRODUCTION

Stepwise permanganate oxidation has been described by a number of investigators (e.g. Khalifeh *et al.*, 1961) for comparison of source rocks. A modified Rock–Eval apparatus has been designed to analyse the organic material remaining after each oxidation step. The modification, shown in Fig. 1, comprises the replacement of the device for trapping CO_2 by an infrared analyser.

Without changing the operating procedure or the analysis cycle of the pyrolysis equipment, the evolved hydrocarbons and CO_2 are quantified and graphically plotted.

The major objective of this study was to investigate quantitatively the evolution of CO_2 from untreated as well as from oxidized rock samples during pyrolysis using the modified Rock–Eval for the analysis of organic matter contained in rock samples.

EXPERIMENTAL AND RESULTS

Pyrolysis methods

We utilized four methods:
1. The first method is based on a home-made apparatus in which a horizontal oven is directly connected to a 'Cosma Rubis 3000' Infrared analyser. The oven temperature, controlled by a temperature programmer, allows the sample to be heated in a boat in an inert atmosphere (helium) up to 450 °C at a rate of 6 °C min^{-1}.

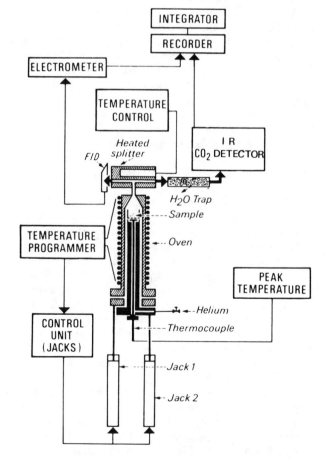

Fig. 1. Operational flowsheet of the modified Rock–Eval apparatus.

2. The second method involved is the Rock–Eval Pyrolysis which has been described by Espitalié *et al.* (1977).

3. The third method involves a 'modified' Rock–Eval Pyrolysis apparatus, the CO_2 trap being replaced by an Infrared 'Cosma Rubis 3000' Gas analyser (Fig. 1). The sample is heated at a rate of 25 °C min^{-1}.

4. The fourth method is also based on a home-made apparatus, comprising a horizontal micropyrolysis oven, with heating controlled by a temperature programmer, in which the sample is heated in a hydrogen flow of 6 ml min^{-1}. The oven is connected to a trap which is connected in turn to a Carlo Erba Fractovap FID chromatograph. During thermovaporization of S_1 the trap is cooled in liquid nitrogen. The trap is then heated to 300 °C and S_1 flushed onto the gas chromatography (gc). The cycle is repeated for the pyrolysis of S_2.

The gc column length 25 m, internal diameter 0.5 mm, and coated in OV 101, is run with a carrier gas of hydrogen at 6 ml min^{-1} and bypass helium at 24 ml min^{-1}. The column temperature is programmed from 40 °C to 230 °C at a rate of 2 °C min^{-1}.

Head space gas chromatography

Head space analysis is carried out with an automatic sampler (Carlo Erba 250) water thermostatted at 60 °C (syringe at 85 °C) and an injection split of 1/3 onto a 24 m SE 52 column of internal diameter 0.3 mm and film thickness of 4 μm. The chromatograph is a Carlo Erba 2900 using hydrogen carrier gas at 2 ml min^{-1}, with column temperature programmed from 30 °C to 60 °C at a rate of 3 °C min^{-1} and then to 80 °C at a rate of 2 °C min^{-1}.

Oxidation methods

Oxidation was carried out using the potassium permanganate stepwise process described by Khalifeh and Louis (1961). The reduction power (PR) Trask method represents theoretically the quantity of oxygen consumed for the complete oxidation of the organic matter to CO_2 and H_2O. This is not in practice the case, other products such as benzene carboxylic acids also being formed. The PR falls during stepwise oxidation because cyclic molecules are more resistant to oxidative attack. The ratio PR/total organic carbon (PR/CO) is a truer measure of the oxidation of the organic matter: oxidation steps are continued until 90% of the organic matter is oxidized. Results are expressed as curves with axes PR/CO and % of non-oxidized organic carbon (% CO non-oxidized, Fig. 4).

The Khalifeh and Louis method is time consuming and costly which is the reason why we set up a rapid oxidation method. This rapid oxidation method was devised to monitor quickly the products of oxidation. 0.2 g of rock sample were placed in a 10 ml glass vial with increasing quantities of potassium permanganate. The vials were immediately sealed with a rubber teflon coated cap and an aluminium ring, and placed in a water bath at 60 °C for 6 h.

Samples

Leaves and roots (*Pos-L* and *Pos-R* respectively) of the Mediterranean seaweed *Posidonie* were sampled along with sediments from 0–15 cm and 150–165 cm below the seaweed beds.

Samples from borehole B are of Quaternary age and samples from borehole C are of Tertiary age. Type I, II, III kerogens are known classical model samples, as are the coal and lignite samples.

DISCUSSION

Study of the evolution of CO_2 during pyrolysis at 6 °C min^{-1} using a home-made pyrolysis apparatus connected to an infrared detector for the analysis of 'as received' samples

As can be seen from Fig. 2 the quantity and rate of evolution of CO_2 changes with depth. In Fig. 2a we give an example of CO_2 evolved from marine *Posidonie* leaves, roots and from two recent sediment samples taken just underneath the *Posidonie* roots at 0–15 cm and 150–165 cm depth. In Fig. 2b we show the evolution of the CO_2 from sub-recent sediments taken from cores between 33

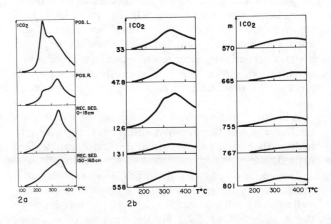

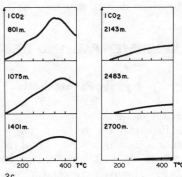

Fig. 2. Posidonie seaweeds. a. Evolved CO_2 from borehole B of about 1000 m depth. c. Evolved CO_2 from borehole C of about 2000 m depth. Intensity of CO_2 released (ICO_2).

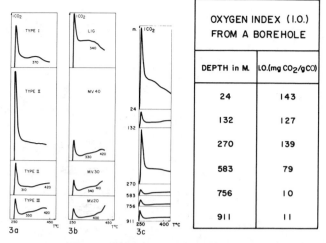

OXYGEN INDEX (I.O.) FROM A BOREHOLE	
DEPTH in M.	I.O.(mg CO₂/gCO)
24	143
132	127
270	139
583	79
756	10
911	11

Fig. 3. a. Intensity of CO_2 released (ICO_2). b. Evolved CO_2 of reference samples. c. Evolved CO_2 from borehole B.

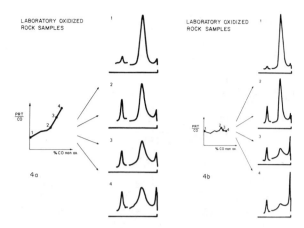

Fig. 4. (a) Source rock; (b) Non-source rock.

m and 801 m depth in a borehole B. Finally we show in Fig. 2c the evolution of the CO_2 evolved from sediments from cores taken between 801 m and 2700 m depth in a borehole C. The changes in the pattern of CO_2 evolution with depth suggests that the technique may be a useful exploration tool to define sediment maturity.

The evolution of CO_2 during pyrolysis using the modified Rock–Eval for the quick analysis of organic matter contained in unprocessed rock samples (Fig. 3)

Here we examined several standard samples containing type I, II and III kerogens (Fig. 3a) and samples of lignite and coal (Fig. 3b). The CO_2 evolution profile for the sample at 24 m, in the borehole (Fig. 3c) has the same shape as the lignite reference (Fig. 3b). We know from independent studies that the sample taken at 24 m depth was of terrestrial origin, the sedimentary environment being swamp or fluviatile, and consequently oxygenated. Table 1 gives the oxygen index (IO) calculated from evolved CO_2 of borehole B samples (Fig. 3c) using the modified Rock–Eval apparatus.

Laboratory oxidized samples

Further investigations were carried out in the laboratory to monitor the oxidation by fingerprinting the 'generated' organic matter of model oxidized samples using the unmodified Rock–Eval apparatus. With these results we hoped to gain a better understanding of the stages of oxidation that the sediments have reached in nature. The procedure has been carried out on a number of samples, two of which are shown in Fig. 4a and 4b. The rock sample (Fig. 4a) with an ascending curve is a petroleum source rock: the other with a more or less descending curve (Fig. 4b) is a non-source rock. The generated organic matter from the kerogen is clearly shown by the increasing S_1 peak, which rises at the expense of the falling S_2 peak. As can be seen the evolution of the shape of the S_2 peak for a source rock is completely different from the evolution of the shape for a

non-source rock. Figure 5 gives the detailed gas chromatographic analysis of S_1 and S_2 peaks using an OV 101 column; Fig. 3a shows the S_1 and S_2 peaks of the original oxidized sample, and Fig. 3c the S_1 and S_2 peak from the fourth oxidation step. From these analyses it appears that oxidation has solubilized a part of the kerogen. The two S_1 detailed analyses were carried out with the same sample quantities and sensitivity levels. Figure 3b shows the cumulative S_1 carbon number curves, the slope of which indicates whether the products are like crude oil, or not, as proposed by Price (1979). Figures 4a and 4b show that S_3 peak is also increasing with oxidation.

In Fig. 6a the continuous infrared analysis of the evolved CO_2 from a laboratory step-oxidized sample is shown. The temperature for the maximum production of CO_2 increases with oxygen index (Fig. 6b).

A more detailed kinetic study is impossible with the unmodified Rock–Eval because the CO_2 is trapped on a molecular sieve during the programmed heating interval. At the end of the temperature programming, the trap is reheated for the desorption of the CO_2 which is then drawn to a Porapak column and detected as one peak by a thermal conductivity detector. However, the modified Rock–Eval allows analysis of the rate of evolution of CO_2. Figure 7b shows the results of a calculation as proposed by Coats and Redfern (1964) and Feeman and Carrol (1958). For example with the modified Rock-Eval pyrolysis apparatus the decomposition of siderite gives an approximately first order curve. In addition calculation of the energy of activation deduced from the Coats and Redfern equation as well as from the Freeman and Carrol method, gives a value of about 34 Kcal M^{-1}. This value is in good agreement with values obtained by other workers. As you can see in Fig. 7b the table gives the calculated figures of the energy of activation of the sample taken at 801 m depth, in Fig. 7a. The value is about 8.5 Kcal M^{-1} showing a good agreement between the two calculation methods. The information presented here indicates that a worthwhile preliminary use of the Coats and Redfern and Freeman and Carrol equations may serve as a convenient means of comparing the relative thermal stabilities of a series of substances.

The rapid oxidation method seems very promising using Head Space gas chromatography for the study of

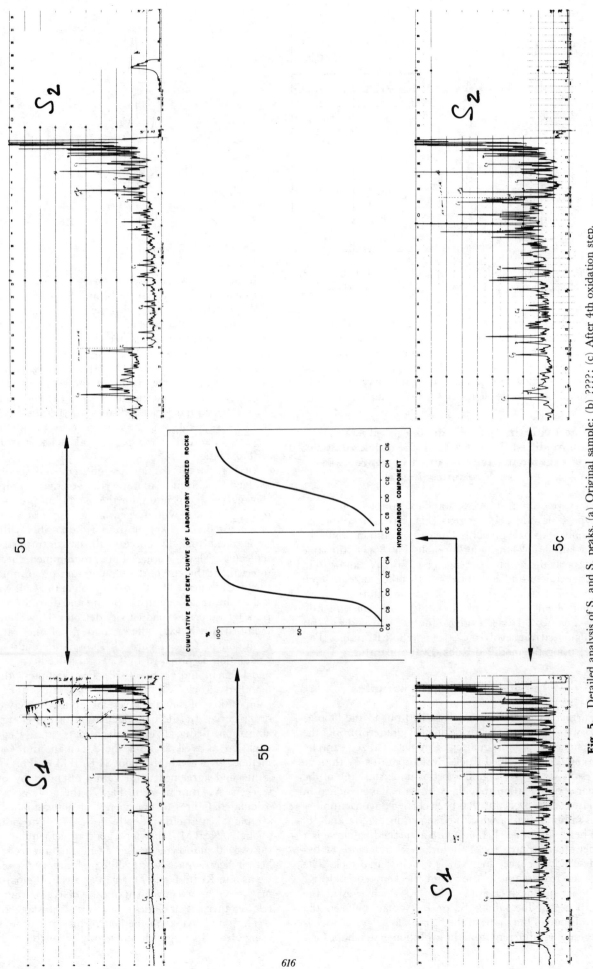

Fig. 5. Detailed analysis of S_1 and S_2 peaks. (a) Original sample; (b) ????; (c) After 4th oxidation step.

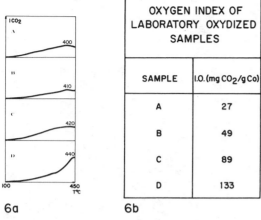

OXYGEN INDEX OF LABORATORY OXYDIZED SAMPLES	
SAMPLE	I.O.(mg CO₂/gCo)
A	27
B	49
C	89
D	133

6a 6b

Fig. 6. a. Intensity of CO_2 released (ICO_2). b. Evolved CO_2 of Laboratory oxidized samples.

light hydrocarbons generated in the gas phase. Based on the quick oxidation method followed by head space gas chromatography fingerprinting and quantification we are able to distinguish the three model kerogen samples type I, II and III (Fig. 8).

The oxidation method permits rapid monitoring of the products of oxidation. Using this method allows definition of the oxidation rates of the samples.

CONCLUSIONS

1. Rock–Eval pyrolysis apparatus was modified for continuous infrared analysis of the evolved CO_2. This permits visualization of the patterns of CO_2 evolution and quantification of the rate of CO_2 evolution with temperature.

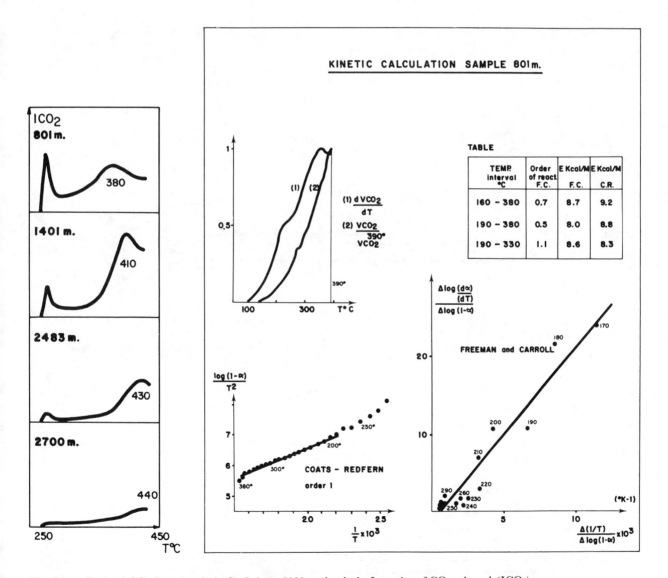

Fig. 7. a. Evolved CO_2 from borehole C of about 2000 m depth. b. Intensity of CO_2 released (ICO_2).

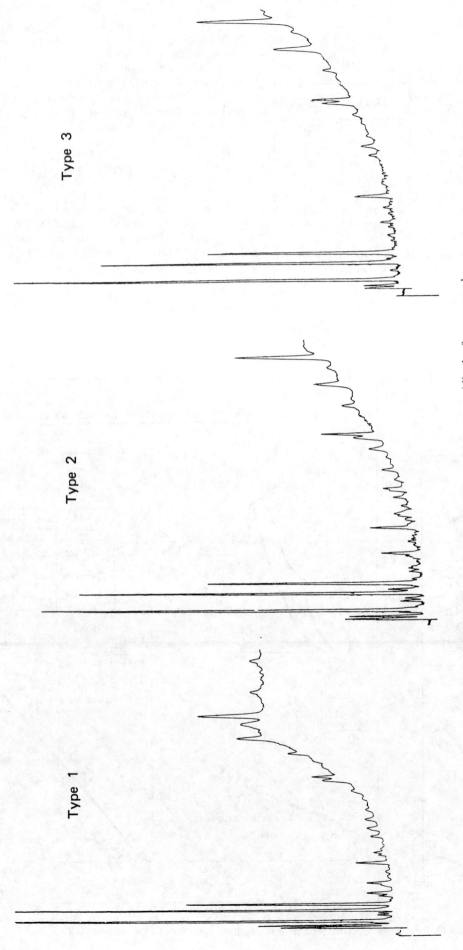

Fig. 8. Head space gas chromatography of laboratory oxidized reference samples.

2. Stepwise permanganate oxidation followed by the modified Rock–Eval analysis permits a rapid evaluation of the most promising oxidation step for a further detailed study.

3. Fingerprinting model oxidized samples and kinetic calculation may contribute to a better understanding of the stage of maturation of organic matter in rock samples.

4. Head space gas chromatography fingerprinting and quantification of the gas phase from oxidized samples is a very convenient and easy way for studying oxidation rates of organic matter in rock samples.

5. Our conclusions are necessarily tentative at this stage and further work is needed. Studies in this direction are now in progress in our laboratory.

Acknowledgements

We thank Mr G. Fortems, manager of Petrofina Exploration and Mr P. Rousseau for the permission to publish this paper. We are grateful for extremely helpful reviews of the manuscript by Mr C. Corfort, B.N.O.C.

REFERENCES

Coats, A. W. and Redfern, J. P. (1964) Thermogravimetric analysis: A review. *Analyst* **28**, 906.

Espitalié, J., Laporte, J. L., Madec, M., Marquis, F., Leplat, P., Paulet, J. and Boutefeu, A. (1977) Méthode rapide de caractérisation des roches mères, de leur potentiel pétrolier et de leur degré d'évolution. *Rev. Inst. Fr. Pétr.* **32**, 23.

Freeman, E. S. and Carrol, B. (1958) The application of the thermo–analytical techniques to reaction kinetics: the thermogravimetric evaluation of the kinetics of decomposition of calcium oxalate monohydrate. *J. Phys. Chem.* **62**, 394.

Khalifeh, Y. and Louis, M. (1961) Etude de la matière organique dans les roches sédimentaires. *Geochim. Cosmochim Acta* **22**, 50.

Applied Headspace gas chromatorgaphy. Ed. by Kolb, 1980. Heyden and Son Ltd.

Leplat, P. Contribution à la prospection géochimique du pétrole, Thèse Doctorat, 1972, Université de Louvain, Belgique.

Price Mabre Maness, J. G. W. (1979) Well formation characterization by residual hydrocarbon analysis *J. Petr. Technol.* **118**.

Advances in Organic Geochemistry 1981, pp. 620–627
© John Wiley & Sons Limited, 1983

Structural Investigation of Aleksinac Shale Kerogen by Chemical and Spectroscopic Methods

D. Vitorović, P. A. Pfendt and V. D. Krsmanović

Department of Chemistry, Faculty of Sciences, University of Beograd, Studentski trg 16, PO Box 550, 11001 Beograd, Yugoslavia

In the first part of this paper, data obtained in the bromination of kerogen concentrates (e.g., the amount of bound bromine and hydrogen bromide evolved) were correlated with several peak areas in the IR spectra of the corresponding sedimentary kerogens viz: Estonian Kukersite (Ordovician), Australian Torbanite (Permian–Carboniferous), Kimmeridge shale, Dorset, England (Jurassic), Colorado Green River shale (Eocene), and Aleksinac shale, Yugoslavia (Oligocene–Miocene). A relationship was found between the behaviour of the corresponding shale kerogens towards bromine and selected peak areas (3660–3580, 3040–3010, 3000–2800, 1800–1740, 1740–1700, 1725–1690, 1690–1640, 1640–1600 and 1600–1500 cm^{-1}) of the IR spectrum. The second part of the paper reports an investigation of various factors influencing alkaline permanganate degradation of Aleksinac shale kerogen. Effects of reaction temperature and of periodic removal of primary degradation products were estimated from the compositions of partially degraded kerogen concentrates, and on the basis of the time necessary for complete reduction of the added permanganate. The results were compared with evidence obtained from the degradation of model substances (cholestanol and cholesterol) carried out under similar experimental conditions.

Part I:

Kerogen structural studies, correlation of bromine consumption and IR spectra

In previous studies it was shown that by bromination of shale kerogen concentrates it was possible to obtain some new indications concerning the structure of kerogen as well as determining several basic differences in the chemical nature of kerogens from different shales (Vitorović and Pfendt, 1974a; Pfendt and Vitorović, 1973; Pfendt, 1975; Vitorović *et al.*, 1977; Pfendt and Vitorović, 1977). However, by the use of the bromination method alone, interpretation of the nature of kerogen is limited because of the complexity of its structure and the high reactivity of bromine.

The use of quantitative IR spectroscopy, particularly combined with other physical methods, was shown to be successful in following the maturation of kerogen (Espitalié *et al.*, 1973; Radchenko *et al.*, 1975; Rouxhet *et al.*, 1980). However, small qualitative differences in the IR spectra of various kerogens as well as the fact that some absorption bands involve several different structural types, suggested a combination of IR spectra evidence with the results of chemical investigations

would be a more useful means of kerogen characterization.

In the first part of this paper, the relationship between several absorption bands in the quantitative IR spectra of kerogens and data based upon bromination is reported. The correlation basis was related to the known behaviour of individual classes of compounds towards bromine.

EXPERIMENTAL

Kerogen concentrates of the following shales were examined: Estonian Kukersite (Ordovician), Australian Torbanite (Permian–Carboniferous), Kimmeridge shale, Dorset, England (Jurassic), Colorado Green River shale (Eocene), and Yugoslav Aleksinac shale (Oligocene–Miocene).

Preparation of kerogen concentrates

Powdered shale samples were treated with 2M HCl on a steam bath and then filtered, washed, dried at 80 °C and extracted with benzene in a Soxhlet apparatus. The concentrates were separated using standard DIN-sieves. Three samples of each concentrate were investigated: the total unsieved sample and two fractions i.e. the

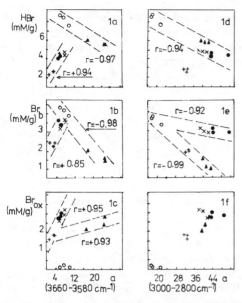

Fig. 1. Correlation of evolved hydrogen bromide (HBr), bound bromine (Br$_b$) and amount of bromine consumed by oxidation reactions (Br$_{ox}$) with band intensities in the 3660–3580 and 3000–2800 cm^{-1} regions (Estonian Kukersite ×; Australian Torbanite +; Kimmeridge shale ○; Green River shale ●; Aleksinac shale ▲).

$-0.050+0.040$ mm fraction and the -0.040 mm fraction.

The kerogen content in the concentrates was determined according to the method described by Jovanović and Vitorović (1952) and the values obtained were corrected for the contents of silicate crystalline water. Kerogen contents of the concentrates were as follows (%):

Kukersite	76.89	79.80	76.65
Torbanite	81.73	79.71	77.26
Kimmeridge shale	61.69	62.79	52.42
Green River shale	39.04	42.78	34.24
Aleksinac shale	28.44	30.26	29.04

Bromination

The concentrates were brominated and the kerogen behaviour towards bromine was evaluated according to procedures described earlier (Pfendt and Vitorović, 1973; Pfendt, 1975).

IR spectra

Quantitative IR spectra of kerogen concentrates were obtained on a Perkin Elmer 337 IR spectrometer using a KBr disc technique described in a previous paper (Pfendt and Vitorović, 1977).

The contents of specific structures absorbing in various regions ('band intensities') were expressed in the form of numerical values which were calculated in the following way:

$$a = \frac{\text{area} \times 10^2}{\text{transmission} \times \text{kerogen content (\%)}}$$

DISCUSSION

The contents of individual specific structures were correlated graphically with data such as the amount of bound bromine, the amount of liberated hydrogen bromide, the maximum amount of addable bromine or the amount of bromine which may be involved in oxidation reactions (Pfendt, 1975; Vitorović et al., 1977).

3660–3580 cm^{-1} region

Experiments with kerogens have shown (Espitalié et al., 1973; Saxby, 1976; Rouxhet et al., 1980) that absorptions in the 3600–2700 cm^{-1} region were derived from various types of hydroxyl structures, from molecular water and NH-groups. In the spectra of defined compounds, Bellamy (1954) ascribed the 3650–3590 cm^{-1} region to the free hydroxyl group, which gives a sharp peak of varying intensity.

In these studies, the liberated hydrogen bromide, the bound bromine and the bromine consumed in oxidation reactions were correlated with the intensity of the band in the 3660–3580 cm^{-1} region.

Correlation with the amount of liberated hydrogen bromide (Fig. 1a) showed that kerogens from different shales behaved quite differently. A positive linear correlation $(r = 0.94)$ obtained for kerogens from Torbanite, Green River shale and Kukersite showed that, with these kerogens, the absorptions derived primarily from alcoholic and phenolic hydroxyl groups. Negative coefficients of high absolute value obtained for Aleksinac and Kimmeridge kerogens $(r = -0.97)$ showed that, with these kerogens, hydroxyl structures unreactive towards bromine, such as carboxylic hydroxyl groups, were involved.

Similar, but less pronounced, evidence was obtained from the correlation with bound bromine (Fig. 1b): the participation of structures absorbing in the 3660–3580 cm^{-1} region was smaller in binding bromine than in formation of hydrogen bromide. This was confirmed by the intersection on the Br$_b$ and HBr axes (3.934 and 1.679, respectively) for $a = 0$.

Finally, correlations with the maximum amount of bromine most likely used in oxidation reactions (Fig. 1c) showed that with all kerogens investigated, with the exception of the Kimmeridge shale concentrate, structures were involved which may be oxidized by bromine e.g. primary and secondary alcohols and phenols. With Kimmeridge shale kerogen, structures absorbing in this region do not bind bromine, nor do they take part in oxidation reactions involving liberation of hydrogen bromide. These structures are probably carboxylic hydroxyls. An exception was found with Aleksinac shale kerogen whose absorptions seem to derive both from carboxylic hydroxyl as well as from other hydroxylic structures.

3040–3010 cm^{-1} region

In defined compounds, this region corresponds to stretching vibrations of olefinic bonds, vinyl- and R_1R_2C

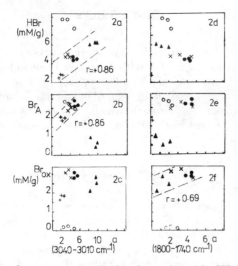

Fig. 2. Correlation of evolved hydrogen bromide (HBr) and the amounts of bromine consumed by addition reactions (Br_A) or by oxidation reactions (Br_{ox}), with the band intensities in the 3040–3010 and 1800–1740 cm^{-1} regions (Estonian Kukersite ×; Australian Torbanite +; Kimmeridge shale ○; Green River shale ●; Aleksinac shale ▲).

$= CHR_3$ structures (Bellamy, 1954). Moreover, at approximately 3030 cm^{-1} aromatic structures also give a sharp peak. In kerogens, this region is included in the wide range band 3600–2700 cm^{-1} which is ascribed to hydroxyl groups (Espitalié *et al.*, 1973; Saxby, 1976; Rouxhet *et al.*, 1980).

If this absorption region involves hydroxyl structures which are reactive towards bromine, a positive correlation should be obtained with the amount of liberated hydrogen bromide as well as with the maximum amount of bromine involved in oxidation reactions. A good correlation with the amount of liberated hydrogen bromide would indicate the presence of aromatic structures, and a positive correlation with the amount of addable bromine could be ascribed to olefinic structures.

According to structures absorbing in this region, the kerogens investigated differed substantially (Fig. 2a–2c). All kerogens, with the exception of Kimmeridge shale kerogen, probably involve hydroxyl structures which react by substitution and oxidation (Fig. 2a, 2c) and, with the Torbanite, Green River shale and Kukersite, it is possible that some absorptions are due to structures which may take part in addition reactions (Fig. 2b). With Kimmeridge shale kerogen, these absorptions probably derive from carboxylic hydroxyl groups and groups taking part in oxidation reactions.

3000–2800 cm^{-1} region

According to the literature (Espitalié *et al.*, 1973; Saxby, 1976; Rouxhet *et al.*, 1980) this is the region of aliphatic CH absorptions. Correlations of the relative intensities of bands of individual kerogens with bound bromine (Fig. 1e), liberated hydrogen bromide (Fig. 1d) and the amount of bromine which may be involved in oxidation reactions (Fig. 1f), showed that structures absorbing in this region were not an important factor in the reactions

with bromine. The Aleksinac shale kerogen was, however, shown to be rather different as it seems that aliphatic structures in this kerogen are related to structures which may be oxidized by bromine (Fig. 1f) and whose content increases with the increase of the content of aliphatic structures in the kerogen.

In order to investigate in more detail the 1800–1700 cm^{-1} absorption range which is ascribed to various carbonyl structures, the areas of absorption bands from the 1800–1740 cm^{-1} and 1740–1700 cm^{-1} ranges were examined separately.

1800–1740 cm^{-1} region

In this region, absorptions can be due to the following structures: five-membered ring cyclic ketones, vinyl groups, five-membered ring lactones, saturated esters, α-halogen-ketones, vinyl-esters, acid halides, anhydrides, etc. (Bellamy, 1954; Luther, 1960). Poor correlation with the amount of liberated HBr (Fig. 2d) suggested that the absorptions may be derived from structures which do not react with bromine such as saturated esters, vinyl-esters, halogen-esters, halogen-ketones, acid halides and anhydrides. On the other hand, a relatively good correlation with the amount of bromine most likely involved in oxidation reactions indicated that lactones or some other by bromine-oxidizable structure may be present (Fig. 2f). No correlation with the amount of bromine which may be involved in addition reactions indicated an absence of olefinic structures absorbing in this region (Fig. 2e).

1740–1700 cm^{-1} region

A very large number of carbonyl structures absorb in this region (Bellamy, 1954) some of which react, and some of which do not react, with bromine under the conditions used in these studies. In kerogens, absorption in the 1745–1700 cm^{-1} range is usually ascribed to different carbonyl structures (Saxby, 1976) with a maximum at approximately 1710 cm^{-1} (Rouxhet *et al.*, 1980) or 1700 cm^{-1} (Espitalié *et al.*, 1973).

Relatively poor correlations with the amount of liberated HBr (Fig. 3a), bound bromine (Fig. 3b), and addable bromine (Fig. 3c) showed that, in the kerogens investigated, different absorbing carbonyl structures were both reactive and non-reactive towards bromine. The relative average abundance of structures absorbing in this range, with the exception of Torbanite, was found to be approximately the same viz: Torbanite 1.0; Aleksinac shale kerogen 9.7; Kukersite 10.2; Colorado shale kerogen and Kimmeridge shale kerogen 10.4.

1725–1690 cm^{-1} region

In kerogens, the absorption range 1745–1680 cm^{-1} is ascribed to different carbonyl structures. With defined compounds, various carbonyl and aromatic structures absorb in this range e.g. ketones, aldehydes, 1,2 and 1,4-diketones, saturated and α,β-unsaturated acids, α-halogen-carboxylic acids, alkyl- and aryl-esters, amino-acids, γ-lactones etc. (Bellamy, 1954).

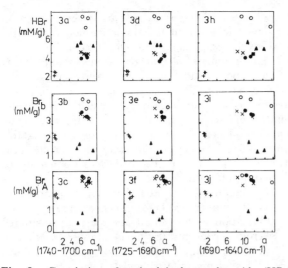

Fig. 3. Correlation of evolved hydrogen bromide (HBr), bound bromine (Br$_b$) and amount of bromine consumed by addition reactions (Br$_A$) with band intensities in the 1740–1700, 1725–1690 and 1690–1640 cm^{-1} regions (Estonian Kukersite ×; Australian Torbanite +; Kimmeridge shale ○; Green River shale ●; Aleksinac shale ▲).

Results obtained for the various kerogens (Figs. 3d–3f) showed that, generally, there was no correlation between the content of structures absorbing in this region and the amount of bound bromine, liberated HBr and the maximum amount of addable bromine. With all kerogens, a reverse proportionality was found between the content of these structures and the amount of bound bromine. The same was observed for the amount of liberated HBr, except for the Torbanite and Green River shale kerogens. These results indicated that in this absorption region, various structures non-reactive towards bromine were probably prevailing. With the two mentioned kerogens, structures reacting by substitution may also be present.

1690–1640 cm^{-1} region

In the IR spectra of kerogens, this region is also related to a wide range of carbonyl structures. In defining compounds, the following compounds absorb in this range: alkyl-substituted olefins, unsaturated aldehydes and unsaturated ketones, diaryl-ketones, aromatic acids, thioesters, amides, primary and secondary amines, nitrogen heterocyclic compounds, polycyclic aromatic structures, quinones (Bellamy, 1954). Among these compounds, there are structures which, under the condition used in these studies, react with bromine by substitution, addition or oxidation. However, the results obtained (Figs. 3h–3j) showed that there was no positive correlation between the kerogen structures absorbing in this region and their behaviour towards bromine. Hence, in this region it may also be assumed that absorptions were mainly due to structures unreactive towards bromine e.g. carboxylic, amide, graphite etc. An exception may be the kerogen from Green River shale, which probably predominantly contains structures which may be involved in substitution

reactions, e.g. ketones, aromatic and heterocyclic structures.

1640–1600 cm^{-1} region.

In kerogens, absorption in this region is not completely understood. Rouxhet *et al.* (1980) believe that absorptions in the 1630–1600 cm^{-1} range may be derived from molecular water, quinones, olefins, aromatic rings, polyaromatic nuclei and from coaly particles. Espitalié et al. (1973) ascribe to these structures the wider absorption range from 1625 to 1575 cm^{-1}, and Saxby (1976) a band from 1650–1580 cm^{-1}. According to Radchenko *et al.* (1975) absorptions in the 1660–1570 cm^{-1} range are due to quinone structures conjugated with aromatic structures. However, Bellamy (1954) ascribes the 1640–1600 cm^{-1} region to tropolones, phenols with carbonyl groups, 1,3-diketones, aromatic nuclei and –CO·C=C– structures.

With the exception of Kimmeridge kerogen, a good correlation exists between the content of structures absorbing in this region and the a,ount of liberated HBr (r = 0.95) (Fig. 4a). On this basis, it may be assumed that kerogens, particularly from Green River shale and Torbanite, with structures which react with bromine in substitution reactions, are absorbing in this region.

Because of a pronounced reverse proportionality with the maximum amount of addable bromine (Fig. 4c) it may also be assumed that an absorption deriving from quinones, or other structures which may be involved in addition reactions, is less probable. This is supported by a negative correlation with the amount of bound bromine (Fig. 4b).

1600–1500 cm^{-1} region

This region is also not well understood. Rouxhet *et al.* (1980) succeeded in eliminating the 1520 cm^{-1} band in

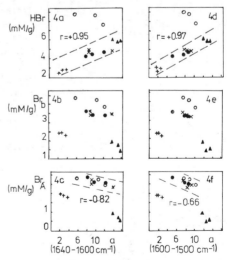

Fig. 4. Correlation of evolved hydrogen bromide (HBr), bound bromine (Br$_b$) and amount of bromine which can be consumed by addition reactions (Br$_A$) with band intensities in the 1640–1600 and 1600–1500 cm^{-1} regions (Estonian Kukersite ×; Australian Torbanite +; Kimmeridge shale ○; Green River shale ●; Aleksinac shale ▲).

kerogens by bromination. On the basis of this result, they concluded that the absorption was due to aromatic structures. The following defined compounds absorb in this region: aromatic structures, 1,3-diketones, tropolones, primary and secondary amines, secondary amides, nitrogen heterocyclic compounds. These structures react with bromine by substitution liberating HBr. Some of them do not react with bromine under the conditions used in these studies e.g. sec. amides and some nitrogen heterocyclic compounds. Taking into account the positive correlation of the intensities of the bands in this region with the amount of liberated HBr, it may be concluded that absorptions derive primarily from structures which are substituted by bromine whilst addition reactions are much less probable.

Part II:

Alkaline permanganate degradation

INTRODUCTION

During the degradation of kerogen concentrates with alkaline permanganate a number of reactions may occur. On the basis of experimental data (Vitorović *et al.*, 1974b; Vitorović *et al.*, 1977) a general scheme involving the main degradation reactions can be outlined (Fig. 5). Several reaction sequences and many parallel single reactions may occur concurrently. The actual situation in the reaction mixture is even more complex, as most single symbols in the general scheme correspond to a number of compounds. For example, the

symbol ESA (Fig. 5) represents several types of carboxylic acids (aromatic, aliphatic, monocarboxylic, dicarboxylic, isoprenoid acids etc.) which can contain different numbers of carbon atoms. Some other reactions, not included in the general scheme, are also possible e.g. further oxidation of ether-soluble and precipitated acids to the same type of acids with smaller numbers of C-atoms, conversion of neutral products into acidic products, direct formation of non-isolatable products from kerogen concentration etc. In spite of the diversity of possible reactions, they can generally be divided into five groups:

1. Oxidation of the initial kerogen concentrate to partially degraded kerogen concentrate;
2. Oxidation of the initial and partially degraded kerogen concentrates to isolatable degradation products (neutral and basic products, ether-soluble acids and precipitated acids);
3. Oxidation of isolatable degradation products to carbon dioxide, water and other products which cannot be determined by the procedure used (non-isolatable products);
4. Conversion of primary degradation products to other isolatable products (the main reaction in this group is the oxidation of precipitated acids to ether-soluble acids);
5. Oxidation of pyrite to sulphate and ferric hydroxide.

In this aspect of the structural studies, the main aim was to find out how the yields of various isolatable degradation products and the duration of degradation steps depended on degradation temperature and periodic removal of degradation products. More precisely, the aim was to estimate the influence of the above-mentioned factors on various reactions and, consequently, on yields of the different degradation

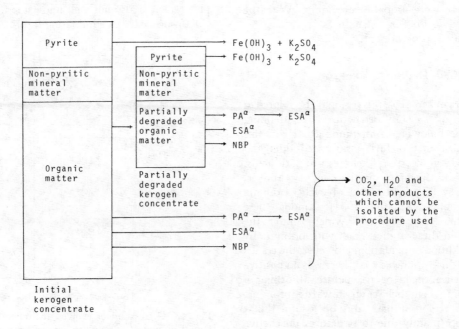

$^{\alpha}$ Potassium salts of all acidic products are present in the reaction mixture.

Fig. 5. General scheme for degradation of kerogen concentrates (NBA = neutral and basic products; ESA = ether-soluble acids; PA = precipitated acids).

Table 1

Degradation of Aleksinac kerogen concentrate with alkaline permanganate — experimental details and results.

		Experiments without periodic removal of degradation products		Experiments with removal of degradation products after each five steps	
Temperature (°C)		20	75	20	75
Amount of oxidized organic matter (g)[a]		0.2784	0.1401	0.3497	0.2039
Oxidized organic matter (% of organic matter in initial kerogen concentrate)		34.8	17.5	43.7	25.5
Total yield of isolatable degradation products (g)		0.0339	0.1072	0.2995	0.1858
Yield of isolatable degradation products (g)	Neutral and basic products	0.0034	0.0061	0.0069	0.0155
	Ether-soluble acids	0.0095	0.0406	0.0251	0.0663
	Precipitated acids	0.0210	0.0605	0.2675	0.1040
Total yield of isolatable degradation products (%)[b]		12.2	76.5	85.6	91.1
Losses (%)[b]		87.8	23.5	14.4	8.9

[a] Difference between the amount of organic matter in the initial and in the partially degraded kerogen concentrate.
[b] Based on the amount of the oxidized organic matter.

products. In order to decrease the number of possible reactions (Fig. 5) a pyrite-free kerogen concentration was used. This enabled more precise interpretation of experimental results to be achieved.

EXPERIMENTAL

A kerogen concentrate was prepared from powdered Aleksinac shale (−100 mesh, Tyler) by successive treatment with benzene (72 h), 1M hydrochloric acid, benzene (36 h), potassium hydroxide in methanol (24 h), 1M hydrochloric acid, water and benzene–methanol (1:1, 3 × 72 h). Pyrite was removed according to procedure described by Lawlor et al. (1963). 13 g of kerogen concentrate and 4 g of LiAlH$_4$ were used and the resulting kerogen concentrate was extracted with benzene–methanol mixture (1:1, 3 × 36 h) and dried at 80 °C. The final kerogen concentrate consisted of 64.35% of non-pyritic mineral matter and 35.65% of organic matter (by difference).

Cholestanol or cholesterol (0.002 moles) adsorbed on silica gel ('Merck' silica gel 60 extra pure for column chromatography, 70–230 mesh ASTM) were also used as model substances in degradation experiments. The amounts of cholestanol (0.7774 g) and cholesterol (0.7733 g) were very similar to the amount of organic matter in the samples of kerogen concentrate subjected to degradation (0.7796 g). Cholestanol or cholesterol were dissolved in 3 cm³ of ethanol-free chloroform, added to 5 g of silica gel and left at room temperature for at least 24 hours to allow evaporation of the chloroform.

The degradation of kerogen concentrates was carried out under different experimental conditions (Table 1). 2.2429 g of kerogen concentrate was dispersed in 50 cm³ of 3.2% KOH and degraded by portionwise addition of powdered KMnO$_4$ (22.9 mg per step, 25 steps). An additional amount of permanganate was added only when the previous one has been used up. Addition was controlled by measuring the electromotive force between a Pt-electrode and a saturated calomel electrode, both immersed in the reaction mixture (Vitorović et al., 1977). Degradation products and partially degraded kerogen concentrates were isolated

according to the procedure outlined by Krsmanović et al. (1978).

Model substances i.e. cholesterol and cholestanol, were degraded with ten 22.9 mg portions of KMnO$_4$. The degradation was carried out at 20 and 75 °C, without removal of degradation products.

RESULTS AND DISCUSSION

The results obtained by partial degradation of pyrite-free kerogen concentrate with alkaline permanganate under different experimental conditions are shown in Table 1. The effect of reaction temperature and of periodic removal of primary degradation products was estimated on the basis of changes in the partially degraded kerogen concentrates, changes in total yields of isolatable degradation products, changes in yields of major degradation products (precipitated acids and ether-soluble acids) and their relative ratios.

In an experiment without removal of degradation products at 20 °C, the kerogen was oxidized to a smaller extent (lower % of oxidized organic matter, Table 1) indicating an increased oxidation of primary degradation products (compared with periodic removal of the latter) which were protecting oxidation of the kerogen. This conclusion was confirmed by the apparently low yield of isolatable degradation products (12.2% compared with 85.6%, Table 1). Such a low yield, and consequently high losses indicated that degradation to non-isolatable products was more favoured than the conversion of primary degradation products to other isolatable degradation products (Fig. 5).

Similar results were obtained in degradation experiments at 75 °C (Table 1), but the difference in total yield of isolatable degradation products was smaller (76.5% c.f. 91.1%).

In all experiments, the increase of degradation temperature from 20° to 75 °C promoted further oxidation of degradation products compared to kerogen i.e. it lowered the percent of oxidized organic matter (Table 1). As the losses were also smaller at 75 °C, conversion of primary degradation products to other

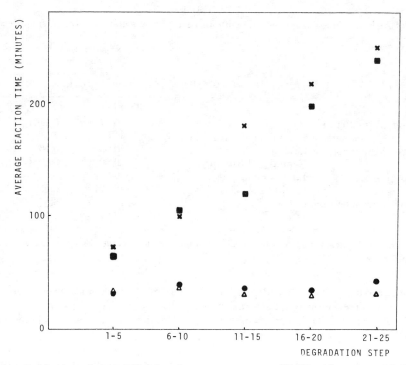

Fig. 6. Average reaction time for degradation of Aleksinac kerogen concentrate (20 °C, without removal of degradation products ■; 20 °C, with removal of degradation products ×; 75 °C, without removal of degradation products ●; 75 °C, with removal of degradation products △).

isolatable degradation products e.g. precipitated acids to ether-soluble acids, should be more favoured than their oxidation to non-isolatable products (Fig. 5). The previous suggestion was confirmed by the decrease in the ratio of the yield of precipitated acids and ether-soluble acids (2.2 and 1.5 in the experiment without removal of degradation products and 10.7 to 1.6 in the experiment with removal of degradation products), which indicated oxidation of precipitated acids to ether-soluble acids. The overall effect of higher temperature was increase of the total yield of isolatable degradation products.

Changes of average reaction time (mean value of reaction duration for five degradation steps) strongly supported the conclusions based on yields of isolatable degradation products and yields of partially degraded kerogen concentrates. At 20 °C average reaction times were practically the same in both experiments during the first ten steps (Fig. 6). In the later steps (11–25), they were lower in the experiment where there was no removal of degradation products indicating the latter's easier oxidation compared with kerogen. The average reaction times at 75 °C were practically constant, and nearly the same in both experiments (Fig. 6). These results suggested that structures susceptible to oxidation with permanganate were present in sufficient amounts during all twenty five degradation steps. That was not the case in experiments at 20 °C, as average reaction times increased towards the later steps. Such changes of average reaction times at 20 °C may be attributed to the increased selectivity of permanganate (Lee, 1969) and the depletion of structures susceptible to oxidation. At higher temperatures (75 °C) the cleavage of carbon–

carbon bonds is possible and, consequently, there are more structures susceptible to oxidation. For this reason, their depletion should not be expected during the partial degradation of kerogen concentrate. On the other hand, their abundance resulted in nearly constant average reaction times during the degradation steps (Fig. 6).

The two model substances viz. cholestanol and cholesterol adsorbed on silica gel, were subjected to oxidation with alkaline permanganate under similar experimental conditions in order to examine the dependence of the rate of $KMnO_4$ consumption on the structure of the corresponding organic substance. Beside the 3β-hydroxy group present in both steroids, cholesterol also has a double bond at the 5,6-position. In all experiments, average reaction times for the oxidation of cholesterol were lower than those for cholestanol (Table 2). The corresponding higher rates of permanganate consumption could be attributed to the presence of the reactive carbon–carbon double bond in the cholesterol molecule.

Table 2

Average reaction time (minutes) needed for degradation of model substances.

	20 °C		75 °C	
	Degradation step		Degradation step	
	1–5	6–10	1–5	6–10
Cholesterol	595	1426	128	173
Cholestanol	1176	1736	168	290

CONCLUSIONS

Alkaline permanganate degradations

Pyrite-free kerogen concentrates of Aleksinac shale were degraded with alkaline permanganate under different experimental conditions in order to investigate the influence of a number of factors on various degradation reactions and, consequently, on yields of the different degradation products.

1. By periodic removal of degradation products, yields of the latter increased considerably as a result of preferred oxidation of kerogen. The effect was more pronounced at lower temperature e.g. at 20 °C, the total yield of degradation products increased from 12.2 to 85.6%.
2. Increase of degradation temperature from 20 °C to 75 °C promoted further oxidation of degradation products (compared to kerogen). Their degradation to non-isolatable products was less favoured than some other reactions e.g. degradation of precipitated acids to ether-soluble acids, so that overall yields of isolatable degradation products were higher at 75 °C.
3. Conclusions based on the yields of degradation products and the partially degraded kerogen concentrates were supported by average duration of degradation steps. Moreover, it was found that oxidation of the degradation products was faster than the degradation of the kerogen at 20 °C, whilst these rates were approximately the same at 75 °C.
4. Degradation experiments with model substances (cholestanol and cholesterol), under similar experimental conditions, clearly indicated that the duration of the degradation steps was a function of the structure of the corresponding organic substance.

REFERENCES

Bellamy, L. J. *The infrared spectra of complex molecules.* Methuen & Co. Ltd., London, 1954.

Espitalié, J., Durand, B., Roussel, J. C. and Souron, C. (1973) Etude de la matiére organique insoluble (kérogène) des argiles du Toarcian du basin de Paris. *Rev. Inst. Franc. Pétrole* **28**, (1), 37–66.

Jovanović, S. LJ. and Vitorović, D. (1952) Contribution to the study of oil shales from Aleksinac. *Bull. Soc. chim. Belgrade* **17**, 347–360.

Krsmanović, V. D., Ercegovac, M. and Vitorović, D. (1978) Parallel micropetrographic and chemical studies of the solid degradation products from stepwise alkaline permanganate oxidation of a kerogen concentrate. *Org. Geochem.* **1**, 85–88.

Lawlor, D. L., Fester, J. I. and Robinson, W. E. (1963) Pyrite removal from oil-shale concentrates using lithium aluminium hydride. *Fuel* **42**, 239–244.

Lee, D. G. (1969) Hydrocarbon oxidation using transition metal compounds. In *Oxidation*, Vol. 1. Ed. by Augustine, R. L. Marcel Dekker Inc., New York. p. 5.

Luther, C. (1969) Physikalisch-chemische Prüfungen. In *Mineralöle und verwandte Produkte*. Ed. by Zerbe, C. Springer-Verlag, Berlin, Heidelberg, New York, Erster Teil. pp. 177–238.

Pfendt, P. A. (1975) Ein Studium der chemischen Natur des Kerogens auf Grund Bromierungsreaktionen. Dissert. Univ. Beograd.

Pfendt, P. A. and Vitorović D. (1973) Untersuchung der Struktur des Aleksinacer Oelschieferkerogens mittels modifizierter Jodzahlmethoden. II. Der Einfluss des Bromwasserstoffs. *Erdöl u. Kohle* **26**, 143–148.

Pfendt, P. A. and Vitorović, D. (1977) Vergleichende Untersuchung der chemischen Natur der unlöslichen organischen Substanz einiger alter Sedimente auf Grund ihres Verhaltens gegenüber Brom. 8th International Congress on Organic Geochemistry, Moscow. Abstracts, Vol. 1, 126–127.

Radchenko, O. A., Parpanova, G. M., Lebedev, B. A., Zhukova, A. M., Faizullina, E. M. and Shaks, I. A. (1975) Ob osobennostiach ugleifikatsii sapropelevyh uglei, goriuchih slantsev i rasseiannogo organicheskogo veshchestva porod. In *Organicheskoe veshchestvo v geologicheskih protsessah. Trudy VSEGEI nov. ser.* **261**, (122), 21–38.

Rouxhet, P. G., Robin, P. L. and Nicaise, G. (1980) Characterization of kerogens and their evolution by infrared spectroscopy. In *Kerogen, insoluble organic matter from sedimentary rocks.* Ed. by Durand, B. Edition Technip, Paris. pp. 163–190.

Saxby, J. D. (1976) Chemical separation and characterization of kerogen from oil shales. In *Oil Shale.* Ed. by Yen, T. F. and Chilingarian, G. V. Elsevier, Amsterdam, Oxford, New York. p. 118.

Vitorović, D., Krsmanović, V. D. and Pfendt, P. A. (1977) Eine Untersuchung der Struktur des Aleksinacer Oelschieferkerogens mittels verschiedener chemischer Methoden. In *Advances in Organic Geochemistry* 1975. Ed. by Campos, R. and Goni, J. Enadisma, Madrid. pp. 717–734.

Vitorović, D. K. and Pfendt, P. A. (1974a) Effect of bromine on Aleksinac shale kerogen — a source of data for better understanding of its chemical nature. *An. Acad. Brasil. Ciênc.* **46**, (1), 49–55.

Vitorović, D., Djuricić, M. V. and Ilić, B. (1974b) New structural information obtained by stepwise oxidation of kerogen from Aleksinac (Yugoslavia) shale. In *Advances in Organic Geochemistry* 1973. Ed. by Tissot, B. and Bienner, F. Edition Technip, Paris. pp. 179–189.

Advances in Organic Geochemistry 1981, pp. 628–634
© *John Wiley & Sons Limited, 1983*

The Distribution of Fatty Acids in Coal Precursors in the Okefenokee Swamp, Georgia

D. J. Casagrande and A. Ferguson*

Exxon Production Research Company, PO Box 2189, Houston, TX, USA

*Governors State University, Park Forest South, IL, USA

The Okefenokee Swamp, Georgia, includes open marsh and swamp environments. The botanical similarities of the Okefenokee relative to the precursors of various lignites and brown coals allows the peat-forming systems in the Okefenokee to serve as a suitable environment to study organic geochemical changes. The distribution of saturated, unsaturated and branched fatty acids in *Taxodium*-dominated and *Nymphaea*-dominated sub-environments of the Okefenokee were compared; this report focuses on a peat profile found in the *Taxodium* Swamp area known as Minnie's Lake. In the core studied, the upper metre of peat was derived from *Taxodium*, while the lower two metres were derived from *Nymphaea*. *Taxodium* samples showed a dominance of C_{16}, with modest amounts of unsaturated acids (16.1, 18.1, 18.2, 20.1, 20.3, 22.1). While C_{16} dominated the $<C_{20}$ group in the peat profile, C_{22} and C_{24} dominated the $>C_{20}$ group. In the peat profile, total concentrations of fatty acids ranged from 1.5 to 7.2 mg g^{-1} of organic matter. In the upper levels of the peat profile, the signature of fatty acids showed that *Taxodium* roots were giving rise to the peat, thus confirming results from paleobotanical studies. Unsaturated acid concentrations declined rapidly in the first metre of peat. Iso and anteiso acids found in the topmost layers of peat would indicate that bacteria were significant contributors. As a function of peat depth, the $>C_{20}$ acids predominate although the concentration of total fatty acids decreases. The levels of peat derived from *Nymphaea* have a distribution of fatty acids that (1) was not as complex as found in the *Nymphaea* living plant and (2) showed a dominance of the C_{22}, C_{24}, C_{26} and C_{28} fatty acids.

INTRODUCTION

The geochemical interest in fatty acids stems from their distribution in living organisms and chemical stability in sedimentary environments. Considerable research has been accomplished on the distribution of fatty acids in the marine environment (Cooper and Blumer, 1968; Parker, 1969; Cooper, 1971; Farrington and Quinn, 1971; Brown *et al.*, 1972; Aizenshtat *et al.*, 1973; Johnson and Calder, 1973; Lytle 1973; Boon *et al.*, 1975; Brooks *et al.*, 1976). Matsuda and Koyama (1977 a, b), Cranwell (1978) and Meyers *et al.* (1980) concentrated on freshwater lake deposits. In most cases, little was known about the biological source of the sedimentary materials. Perry *et al.* (1979) and Volkman *et al.* (1980) demonstrated the importance of fatty acid distributions in determining the biological source inputs to marine sediments.

This report will document the early changes in fatty acid distributions in the sequence, living higher plant →sediment, where the sediment is:

1. highly organic ($>95\%$ on dry basis);
2. freshwater-derived;
3. autochthonous;
4. anaerobic (<-100 mV at 3 cm from the surface);
5. derived from plant materials that are extant; and
6. recognized as a precursor of coal.

SAMPLING SITES

The Okefenokee Swamp in southeastern Georgia, USA is a paludal region of swamps and marshes of approximately 1700 km². Two major peat-forming environments are recognized: (1) a swamp environment in which *Taxodium* (cypress) is the dominant vegetation; and (2) a marsh environment in which *Nymphaea odorata* (white water lily) is dominant. The interest in the Okefenokee stems from its vegetational and geologic similarity to ancient sedimentary environments that have given rise to coal (Spackman *et al.*, 1974). Cohen (1974a,b) has demonstrated that the vegetation of the Okefenokee has changed substantially over the 6500 years of peat accumulation. These changes in vegetation have caused variations in the source of organic material at various depths of the peat profile. The Minnie's Lake area of the Okefenokee is presently covered by *Taxodium* vegetation; however, the peat profile shows that *Nymphaea* gave rise to the peat below 80 cm (Fig. 1).

EXPERIMENTAL

The technique used for fatty acid analysis was similar to that developed by Farrington and Quinn (1971). Details

Present Vegetation On Surface	*Taxodium*
Core Depth	300 cm
Water Cover	Intermittent
Eh	
overlying water (when present)	+300 mv
5 cm	-40 mv
15 cm	-100 mv
pH	2.5 → 4.5
Sulfur Content (Mean of 12 peat levels, dry basis)	0.25%
Metals Content (Mean of 12 peat levels, dry basis)	2959 PPM
Conductivity Of Pore Water	50 μmho
Temperature In July (below 20 cm)	25°C
Organic Fractions (Mean of four levels, % of total organic matter)	
Water Soluble	
Water Soluble	2.1%
Benzene Methanol Soluble	7.3%
Humic Acids	27%
Fulvic Acids	11.6%
Humin	50%
Age Of Peat At Maximum Depth	4000 yrs. B. P.
Basal Material	Quartz Sand

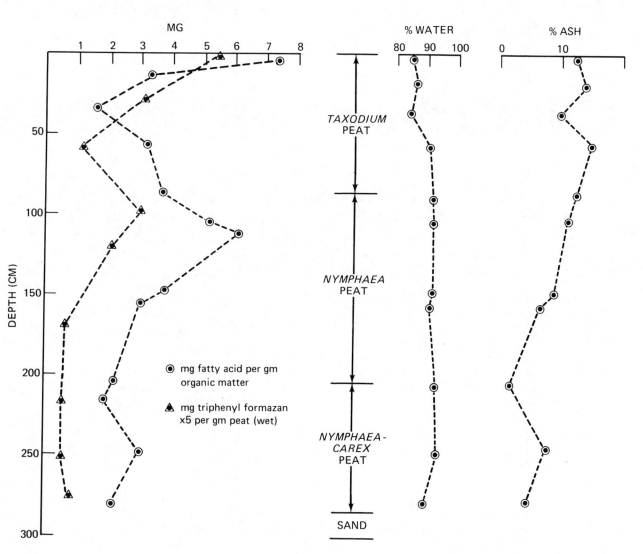

Fig. 1. Geochemical parameters associated with Minnie's Lake coring site.

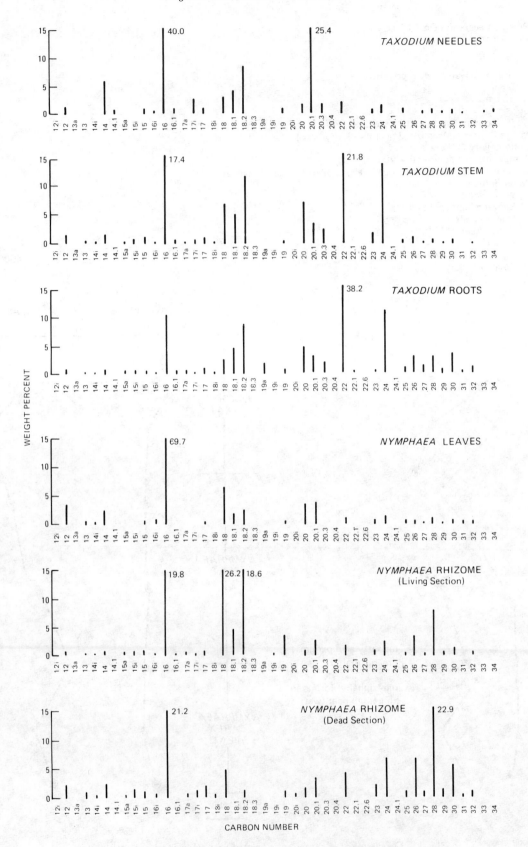

Fig. 2. Distribution of fatty acids in plants from Minnie's Lake coring site.

of the technique are presented elsewhere (Casagrande et al., 1979), however, the salient aspects of the procedure include the following:

1. saponification of the sediment with alcoholic KOH after the addition of a C_{21} standard;
2. acidification of the extract followed by a hexane wash to remove fatty acids;
3. esterification with 12% BCl_3-methanol;
4. silica gel chromatography with petroleum ether, then 97% petroleum ether/3% ethyl ether;
5. silver-nitrate-impregnated silica gel column chromatography to separate the saturated from unsaturated fatty acids; and
6. gas–liquid chromatographic analysis of the C_{12}–C_{34} saturates on 6 ft × 2 mm i.d. column packed with, 10% SP 2330, on 100/120 mesh Chromosorb W, A/W.

A separate chromatographic run was done for the unsaturated fatty acids. Additional confirmation was done on a 6 ft × 2 mm i.d. column of 10% FFAP on 80/100 mesh Chromosorb W, AW.

RESULTS AND DISCUSSION

Figure 1 shows some geochemical data that have been obtained from the peat profile in the Minnie's Lake coring site. The peat in the 300 cm core profile is reducing, a few centimetres from the surface. The overlying waters are oxidizing and have a pH of 4. The low conductivity of the overlying water and relatively low sulphur content of the sediment indicates that the waters are fresh. Considerable information has been published on the sulphur distributions in this peat (Casagrande et al., 1977; Casagrande and Siefert, 1978; Casagrande, 1979) and the distribution of organic matter in the various solvent fractions (Casagrande and Erchull, 1976; Casagrande et al., 1980). Dehydrogenase enzyme content, which is a measure of the bacterial activity in a sediment or soil (Casida et al., 1964), decreases with depth. This test utilized triphenyltetrazolium chloride which is reduced to triphenylformazan by dehydrogenase-H complex formed by bacteria. The surface peat has a bacterial activity similar to that found in fertile farm soils. Total fatty acid concentration as a function of depth in the peat profile is somewhat erratic, but does appear to reflect changes in source plant materials. The spike at 100 cm is relatively close to the Taxodium/Nymphaea interface. It should be noted that the interface does not represent an abrupt change, but rather a gradual transition from one peat to another; thus the fatty acid distribution will reflect this change. The sediment is > 85% water and has variations in the ash content; the Taxodium-derived material routinely has more inorganic material associated with it than Nymphaea-derived peats (Casagrande and Erchull, 1976) and is a reflection of water regimes, plant uptake differentials between the two sedimentary environments, the influx of any quartz sand at high water, and the influence of fires in the swamp.

Figure 2 is a series of histograms which depict the weight percent distribution of fatty acids in the anatomical parts of Taxodium and Nymphaea, the source plants for the upper and lower levels of peat, respectively. Even carbon numbered acids are dominant in all samples. While C_{16} is an important contributor to all the plant samples, C_{22} and C_{24} are important contributors to Taxodium stem and roots, but not living Nymphaea components. Taxodium root, which is the principal ingredient of Taxodium-derived peat (Cohen, 1974a), has more $> C_{20}$ acids than the other anatomical parts of Taxodium. Nymphaea rhizome, the principal anatomical contributor to Nymphaea peat, also has considerable $> C_{20}$ acids relative to Nymphaea leaves. Furthermore, the dead Nymphaea rhizome has a distribution of fatty acids skewed in the $> C_{20}$ direction (Gunther et al., 1979). In general, unsaturated acids such as $C_{16.1}$, $C_{18.1}$, $C_{18.2}$, $C_{20.1}$ are important contributors to the fatty acid distribution in the living plant materials; however, the distribution in the dead rhizome from the intact plant shows that unsaturated acids are quickly degraded or changed. Very little iso and anteiso acids are obvious in the fatty acid distribution of the living plant material, but considerably more is evident in the dead rhizome component of the Nymphaea. The decrease in unsaturation and increase in iso/anteiso acids is a reflection of bacterial activity (Rhead et al., 1971; Matsuda and Koyama, 1977a,b) in the dead rhizome component. It should be noted that generally all histograms of living plant components show two to four fatty acids, dominating the distribution. Thus, 65% of the fatty acid weight in Taxodium needles is due to C_{16} and $C_{20.1}$, 70% of the fatty acid weight in Nymphaea rhizome is C_{16} and 58% of the fatty acid weight in Taxodium root is due to $C_{16} + C_{22} + C_{24}$.

Figure 3 contains a series of histograms which show the weight percent distribution of fatty acids at various depths of peat in the Minnie's Lake core profile. The upper layers of peat (0–7.5 cm, 15–23 cm, 30–38 cm) show a more uniform distribution of fatty acids so that $< C_{20}$ components are more evident than that seen in Taxodium source materials (especially roots). Even carbon numbered fatty acids are dominant, unsaturated fatty acids such as $C_{16.1}$, $C_{18.1}$ and $C_{18.2}$ are present and iso/anteiso fatty acids are prevalent. Iso and anteiso fatty acids of C_{15}, C_{17}, C_{19}, etc. are known for their occurrence in bacteria (Erwin, 1973) and the quantitative importance of these acids complements the high bacterial activity as measured by dehydrogenase enzyme concentration. Bacterial contributions to the peat fatty acid pool would be primarily in the $< C_{20}$ fatty acids, while waxes of higher plants would give rise to many of the $> C_{20}$ fatty acids. This is one reason why a bimodal distribution of fatty acids (i.e. $C_{12} \rightarrow C_{20}$ and $C_{20} \rightarrow C_{34}$) is observed. Cooper (1971), Kvenvolden (1970), Brown et al. (1972), Nissenbaum et al. (1972), Eglinton et al. (1974), and Brooks et al. (1976) observed a bimodal distribution of fatty acids in other sedimentary environments. Taxodium roots, which are the principal source material for these core levels, have a fatty acid distribution with $C_{22} + C_{24} + C_{26} + C_{28} + C_{30}$ fatty acids accounting for more than 65% of the fatty acid weight. This distribution undoubtedly impresses a $> C_{20}$ signature on the fatty acid distributions in the peat, much like bacteria impress a signature in the $< C_{20}$

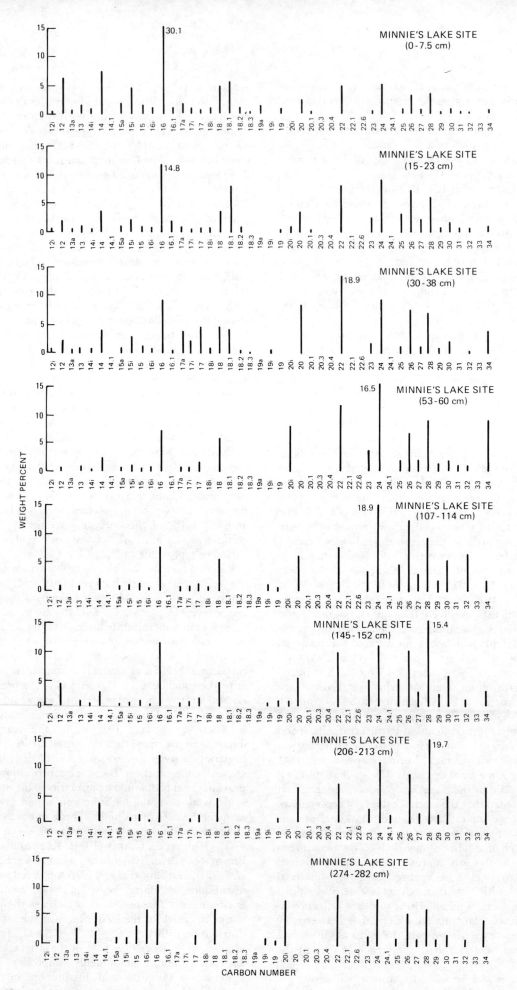

Fig. 3. Distribution of fatty acids at various levels in the peat profile at the Minnie's Lake coring site.

range with their iso/anteiso acid contributions to the sediment.

The last member of the three sample sequence discussed above (30–38 cm) begins to show the first sign of a trend toward distribution domination by the $>C_{20}$ acid range. The increased weight percents of $>C_{20}$ acids in the samples below 60 cm are probably a consequence of at least the following aspects:

1. $<C_{20}$ acids are known to be more liable to bacterial attack than $>C_{20}$ acids (Matsuda and Koyama, 1977a,b); and
2. there is a vegetation source material change at 100 cm from *Taxodium* to *Nymphaea* and as seen in Fig. 2, the distribution of fatty acids in dead *Nymphaea* rhizome shows a trend toward a fatty acid distribution in favor of the $>C_{20}$ range.

In the latter case, unsaturated fatty acids have disappeared in the dead rhizome sample and this will certainly be reflected in the weight percent of those acids such as the $>C_{20}$ which are quantitatively significant, even in the presence of unsaturated acids.

Unsaturated fatty acids play a significant quantitative role in living plants. This is reflected in the upper three levels of sediment that were studied. However, even at very early stages (such as the 0–7.5 cm sample) unsaturated fatty acids contribute significantly less on a weight percentage basis to the fatty acid distribution, when compared to living plants. By 60 cm no unsaturated fatty acids were detected. This rapid, elimination of unsaturated fatty acids may be due to two processes:

1. a chemical/biological process that involves hydrogenation of the unsaturated fatty acids and their conversion to their saturated analogues (Rhead *et al.*, 1971); and
2. a microbially mediated degradation of the unsaturated fatty acids that results in the generation of shorter carbon numbered fatty acids and/or hydrocarbons.

The unsaturated fatty acids appear to undergo differential degradation in that $C_{18.3}$ and $C_{18.2}$ degrade more readily than $C_{18.1}$ or $C_{16.1}$. This is probably due to an increased tendency of the multi-unsaturated acids to undergo microbially mediated oxidation.

The very last histogram shows a distribution of fatty acids quite unlike those above it. No fatty acid appears to show a dominant weight percent. Furthermore, this particular level is at the peat–sand interface. When dehydrogenase measurements have been made at this type of interface in other cores, considerable bacterial activity has been discovered. This increased bacterial activity, which may result from water flow and nutrient availability in the sand, appears to be reflected in the increased amounts of $<C_{20}$ fatty acids. Also, Cohen (1974a) has indicated that there is a time discontinuity between the peat (≈ 4000 years B.P.) and basal sand ($>250\,000$ years B.P.). At this time interval, considerable change was likely in the environments of deposition, alternating between *Taxodium*, fire, *Carex* and *Nymphaea* cycles. This could also be reflected in the fatty acid distribution observed.

While distributions of fatty acids are changing with depth, it should be noted that Fig. 1 showed the absolute

quantity of fatty acids to be decreasing from 7.2 to 1.5 mg g^{-1}. One should not expect a uniform decrease in the quantity of fatty acids with depth since source vegetation has changed and environmental conditions at the time of deposition are certainly not uniform. The trend toward decreasing amounts of fatty acids in the peat profile may be due to:

1. decreasing amounts of fatty acids that are exuded by roots of living plants and serve to replenish fatty acid pools;
2. the bacterial degradation and utilization of fatty acids; and
3. the incorporation of fatty acids into the structures of kerogen and humic acids (Schnitzer and Khan, 1972; Van Vleet and Quinn, 1979) in such a way as to make associated fatty acids non-extractable.

In summary, the peat-forming systems of the Okefenokee offer an opportunity to combine petrographic control with geochemical information. There are substantial changes in the distribution of fatty acids in the living plant→dead plant→peat profile system. Plants imprint a type of signature on the fatty acid distribution of peats they produce. Various anatomical parts of the plant contribute differentially to the peat; hence, needles with their large $C_{20.1}$ component do not appear to contribute significantly to the peat since little $C_{20.1}$ is seen in the topmost layers of peat. On the other hand, petrographic analysis and the skewed distributions towards $>C_{20}$ fatty acids in the sediment appear to favour *Taxodium* roots and *Nymphaea* rhizome as major source components to the peat. Unsaturation in fatty acids diminishes rapidly with depth. The quantity of fatty acids in the peat profile is a reflection of a number of factors:

1. amount and distribution in exudates of living plants and bacteria and their dead counterparts in the peat profile;
2. the degradation of fatty acids by bacteria and the incorporation of original or degraded fatty acids in humic acids, kerogen etc.,
3. the change in source plant material and hence environment of deposition in the peat profile; and
4. the inherent geochemical stability of fatty acids in an environment of differential sedimentation with associated aerobic sequences.

Acknowledgements

The authors wish to thank the National Science Foundation Geochemistry Section and Governors State University for supporting this work. Dr Peter Gunther is thanked for his help in the collection of peat and plant samples and for many useful discussions. Mr John Eadie; Okefenokee Refuge Manager and his staff are thanked for their cooperation and help during the field endeavours.

REFERENCES

Aizenshtat, Z., Baedecker, M. J. and Kaplan, I. R. (1973) Distribution and diagenesis of organic compounds in

JOIDES sediment from the Gulf of Mexico and Western Atlantic. *Geochim. Cosmochim. Acta* **37**, 1881–1898.

Boon, J. J., DeLeeuw, J. W. and Schenck, P. A. (1975) Organic geochemistry of Walvis Bay diatomaceous ooze: I Occurrence and significance of the fatty acids. *Geochim. Cosmochim. Acta* **39**, 1559–1565.

Brooks, P. W., Eglinton, G., Gaskell, S. J., McHugh, D. J., Maxwell, J. R. and Philip, R. P. (1976) Lipids of recent sediments: I Straight chain hydrocarbons and carboxylic acids of some temperate lacustrine and sub-tropical/tidal flat sediments. *Chem. Geol.* **18**, 21–38.

Brown, F. S., Baedecker, M. J., Nissenbaum, A. and Kaplan, I. R. (1972) Early diagenesis in a reducing fjord, Saanich Inlet, British Columbia: III. Changes in organic constituents of sediment. *Geochim. Cosmochim. Acta* **36**, 1185–1203.

Casagrande, D. J. (1979) The origins of sulfur in low sulfur coal. Presentation at the 9th International Congress on the Carboniferous. Urbana, Illinois.

Casagrande, D. J. and Erchull, L. D. (1976) Metals in Okefenokee peat-forming environments: Relation to constituents found in coal. *Geochim. Cosmochim. Acta* **40**, 387–393.

Casagrande, D. J. and Siefert, K. (1978) A new form of sulfur in peat: Implications to coal. *Science* **195**, 675–676.

Casagrande, D. J., Ferguson, A., Boudreau, J., Predny, R. and Folden, C. (1979) Organic geochemical investigations in the Okefenokee Swamp, Georgia: The fate of fatty acids, amino sugars, cellulose and lignin. Proc. IX International Congress on Carboniferous Stratigraphy and Geology. To be published in *Compte Rendu*.

Casagrande, D. J., Gronli, K. and Sutton, N. (1980) Incorporation of sulfur into coal precursors. *Geochim. Cosmochim. Acta* **44**, 23–33.

Casagrande, D. J., Siefert, K., Berschinski, C. and Sutton, N. (1977) Sulfur in peat-forming systems of the Okefenokee Swamp and Florida Everglades. Origins of sulfur in coal. *Geochim. Cosmochim. Acta* **41**, 161–167.

Casida, L. E., Klein, A. and Santoro, T. (1964) Soil dehydrogenase activity. *Soil Sci.* **98**, 371–376.

Cohen, A. D. (1974a) Possible influences of sub-peat topography and sediment type upon the development of the Okefenokee Swamp of Georgia. *Southeastern Geol.* **15**, (3), 141–151.

Cohen, A. D. (1974b) Petrology and paleoecology of Holocene peats from the Okefenokee Swamp of Georgia. *Sed. Petrol.* **44**, 716–726.

Cooper, W. J. (1971) Geochemistry of lipid components in peat-forming environments of the Florida Everglades. M.Sc. Thesis, The Pennsylvania State University.

Cooper, W. J. and Blumer, M. (1968) Linear, iso and anteiso fatty acids in recent sediments of the North Atlantic. *Deep-Sea Res.* **15**, 535–540.

Cranwell, P. A. (1978) Extractable and bonded lipid components in a freshwater sediment. *Geochim. Cosmochim. Acta* **42**, 1523–1532.

Eglinton, G., Maxwell, J. R. and Philip, R. P. (1974) Organic geochemistry of sediments from contemporary aquatic

sediments. In *Advances in Organic Geochemistry*. Ed. by Tissot, B. and Bienner, F. Editions Technip. pp. 941–961.

Erwin, J. A. (1973) *Lipids and Biomembranes of Eukaryotic Microorganisms*. Academic Press, New York.

Farrington, J. W. and Quinn, J. G. (1971) Comparison of sampling and extraction techniques for fatty acids in recent sediments. *Geochim. Cosmochim. Acta* **35**, 735–741.

Gunther, P., Casagrande, D., Chipman, M. and Considine, R. (1979) The rhizome as a model of subsurface peat formation in the Okefenokee Swamp. Proc. IX International Congres on Carboniferous Stratigraphy and Geology. To be published in *Compte Rendu*.

Johnson, R. W. and Calder, J. A. (1973) Early diagenesis of fatty acids and hydrocarbons in a salt marsh environment. *Geochim. Cosmochim. Acta* **37**, 1943–1955.

Kvenvolden, K. (1970) Evidence of transformations of normal fatty acids in sediments. In *Advances in Organic Geochemistry*. Ed. by Hobson, G. and Speers, G. Pergamon Press, Oxford. pp. 335–366.

Lytle, T. F. (1973) A geochemical study of a marsh environment. *Gulf Coast Res. Lab. Rept.* **4**, 214–232.

Matsuda, H. and Koyama, T. (1977a) Early diagenesis in lacustrine sediments: I. Identification and distribution of fatty acids in recent sediments from a fresh water lake. *Geochim. Cosmochim. Acta* **41**, 777–783.

Matsuda, H. and Koyama, T. (1977b) Early diagenesis of fatty acids in lacustrine sediments: II A statistical approach to changes in fatty acid composition from recent sediments and some source materials. *Geochim. Cosmochim. Acta* **41**, 1825–1834.

Meyers, P. A., Bourbonniere, R. A. and Tukeuchi, N. (1980) Hydrocarbons and fatty acids in two cores of Lake Huron sediments. *Geochim. Cosmochim. Acta* **44**, 1215–1221.

Nissenbaum, A., Baedecker, M. J. and Kaplan, I. R. (1972) Organic geochemistry of Dead Sea sediments. *Geochim. Cosmochim. Acta* **36**, 709–727.

Parker, P. L. (1969) Fatty acids and alcohols. In *Organic Geochemistry*. Ed. by Eglinton, J. and Murphy, T. M. Springer-Verlad. pp. 357–373.

Perry, G. J., Volkman, J. K., Johns, R. B. and Bavor Jr, H. J. (1979) Fatty acids of bacterial origin in contemporary marine sediments. *Geochim. Cosmochim. Acta* **43**, 1715–1725.

Rhead, M. M., Eglinton, G., Draffan, G. H. and England, P. J. (1971) Conversion of oleic acid to saturated fatty acids in Severn Estuary sediments. *Nature (London)* **232**, 327–330.

Schnitzer, M. and Khan, S. U. (1972) *Humic Substances in the Environment*. Marcel Dekker, Inc.

Spackman, W., Cohen, A., Given, P. and Casagrande, D. (1974) The comparative study of the Okefenokee Swamp and the Everglades Swamp/Marsh complex of Southern Florida: *Preconvention Field Guide Book, GSA Annual Meeting, Miami Beach*.

Van Vleet, E. S. and Quinn, J. G. (1979) Early diagenesis of fatty acids and isoprenoid alcohols in estuarine and coastal sediments. *Geochim. Cosmochim. Acta* **43**, 289–304.

Volkman, J. K., Johns, R. B., Gillan, F. T. and Perry, G. J. (1980) Microbial lipids of an intertidal sediment I. Fatty acids and hydrocarbons. *Geochim. Cosmochim. Acta* **44**, 1133–1143.

Biomarkers

Advances in Organic Geochemistry 1981, pp. 637–649
© *John Wiley & Sons Limited, 1983*

Fatty Acids in some Biodegraded Petroleums. Possible Origins and Significance

A. S. Mackenzie*, G. A. Wolff and J. R. Maxwell

Organic Geochemistry Unit, University of Bristol, School of Chemistry, Cantock's Close, Bristol BS8 1TS,
England

The distributions of the 'free' fatty acids in eighteen oil and tar sand samples, showing varying extents of biodegradation (as deduced from the alkane distribution), have been examined by GC and GC–MS, along with the 'bound' acids in one of the sample suites (six crudes from the Bell Creek field, Montana). The presence of high relative abundances of 'free' C_{16} and C_{18} saturated acids, of 'free' C_{18} mono- and diunsaturated acids, and of 'bound' fatty acids in a number of the Bell Creek samples is taken as evidence of present day or recent microbial activity. In other cases, the low concentrations of acids are explicable in terms of the absence, or virtual absence of biodegradation (E. Benekat and Limau crudes, Sumatra), or of biodegradation in the past having ceased (Athabasca tar sand). In the six Mission Canyon crudes of Saskatchewan, unlike the crudes from the Bell Creek field, the concentrations of 'free' acids bear no relationship to the extent of biodegradation, suggesting differential water washing. The positions and stereochemistry of the double bond(s) in the C_{18} unsaturated acids (where present) tentatively suggest an origin from bacteria using the aerobic pathway of biosynthesis, or using mainly the aerobic pathway with a minor contribution from the anaerobic pathway. In the few oils where phytanic acid was present, the stereochemistry suggests a recent origin. The configuration of the pristane, where present, shows that effective stereoselective biodegradation does not occur in the reservoir for this isoprenoid alkane.

INTRODUCTION

Krejci-Graf (1932) stated that the shallow heavy naphthenic petroleums of Rumania were the result of 'an influence working down from the surface'. It is now widely accepted that this influence is in-reservoir biodegradation and Demaison (1977), for example, believes it has had a world-wide effect on many pooled crude oils, reducing in many cases their economic value. Winters and Williams (1969) noted, for the Bell Creek Field (Montana), the main features of subsurface biodegradation, namely decrease in *n*-alkane concentration and °API gravity, and an increase in specific rotation; these were most pronounced where the reservoir temperature and dissolved oxygen content were highest. For the Mission Canyon crudes of Saskatchewan, Bailey *et al.* (1973a) proposed that an increased extent of water washing, causing an increasing freshness of formation waters, enhanced the extent of biodegradation by creating more favourable conditions for the microbial population.

To date, detection of subsurface biodegradation by examination of the distributions of petroleum constituents has relied on an observed decrease in the relative abundances of readily utilised components. Many authors have proposed a sequence, based on both field and laboratory studies, of ease of uptake of different alkane types (e.g. Bailey *et al.*, 1973a, b; Deroo *et al.*,

1974; Claret *et al.*, 1977; Rubinstein *et al.*, 1977; Higgins and Gilbert, 1978; Connan *et al.*, 1980). Normal alkanes are removed first, followed by branched alkanes; in extreme cases steroid and triterpenoid alkanes appear to be attacked (Seifert and Moldowan, 1979). Less information is available about the effect of biodegradation of the aromatic hydrocarbons but it appears that alkylbenzenes are readily removed and that the rate of uptake decreases with increasing number of aromatic rings (e.g. Walker *et al.*, 1975; Aldridge *et al.*, 1977; Rubinstein *et al.*, 1977). In addition, some evidence exists for the presence of bacteria in the formation waters of biodegraded crudes using both the aerobic (Bell Creek; Winters and Williams, 1969) and anaerobic (Davis, 1967; Bailey *et al.*, 1973a) pathways. Recently, electron microscope evidence has been presented (Sassen, 1980) for the presence of bacteria in a biodegraded crude.

Carboxylic acids are major microbial lipids (e.g. Shaw, 1974) and products of hydrocarbon biodegradation (e.g. Higgins and Gilbert, 1978) which can be conveniently separated from crude oils (e.g. Ramijak *et al.*, 1977). Such components generally form a very minor proportion of petroleums (e.g. Seifert, 1975; Schmitter *et al.*, 1978), although there are exceptions (e.g. Seifert and Howells, 1969).

In the present study, the fatty acid composition of eighteen crude oil and oil sand samples from five different basins showing varying degrees of hydrocarbon depletion (and therefore indirect evidence of biodegradation) have been studied. Evidence of microbial marker compounds (e.g. Perry *et al.*, 1979) or

* Present address: Institut fur Chemie 5 (Erdöl und Organische Geochemie) der Kernforschungsanlage-Jülich, ICH-5, Postfach 1913, D-5130 Jülich 1, Federal Republic of Germany.

activity has been sought, using a method of extraction described previously (Schmitter *et al.*, 1978). In most cases, the alkane distributions of the samples have been reported previously, and biodegradation postulated. The samples were six oils from the Bell Creek field (Montana; cf. Winters and Williams, 1969) and six from different fields of the Mississippian Mission Canyon carbonates (Saskatchewan; cf. Bailey *et al.*, 1973a), all showing varying *n*-alkane losses; two Tertiary Sumatran crudes, one possibly a slightly biodegraded version of the other (G. C. Speers, personal communication); three samples comprising one crude and two oil sands from Alberta (Lloydminster, Cold Lake and Athabasca; Vigrass, 1968; Deroo *et al.*, 1974; Rubinstein *et al.*, 1977) and a sample of Moonie oil (Queensland, Australia; Powell and McKirdy, 1972, 1976).

EXPERIMENTAL

Alkanes

Alkane fractions were isolated from the neutral fraction of a sedimentary rock extraction and were analysed as described previously (Mackenzie *et al.*, 1980).

Isolation

The crude 'free' acid fraction was isolated from each oil (15–25 g) using a recycling column of silica (150 g) impregnated with KOH (McCarthy and Duthie, 1962; Ramijak *et al.*, 1977; Schmitter *et al.*, 1978). Methylation (CH_2N_2, Brooks *et al.*, 1976), followed by column (10 cm Al_2O_3; hexane/Et_2O 90:10 v/v, 100 ml) and thin layer chromatography (TLC; SiO_2G, 0.25 mm; hexane/Et_2O, 95:5 v/v) gave a monomethyl ester fraction (Rf = methyl palmitate). 'Bound' mono acids of the Bell Creek samples were obtained after removal of the 'free' acids, by hydrolysis (8 h, reflux; satd. *i*-PrOH/KOH, c. 100 ml) of the residue, acidification (6 M HCl to pH = 1) and extraction (Et_2O, 3×100 ml), followed by the methods outlined above.

The free mono acids (as Me esters) of the Bell Creek and Sumatran crudes were separated further by TLC (10% Ag^+/SiO_2, 0.25 mm; hexane/Et_2O 95:5 v/v) into saturated (Rf = methyl palmitate) and unsaturated fractions. The saturated fraction was separated into straight and branched chain components by urea adduction (Brooks *et al.*, 1976).

Gas chromatography (GC)

Samples were analysed using a Carlo Erba FTV 2150 chromatograph (FID detector), fitted with either an OV-1 or SE-52 (c. 0.1 μm) wall-coated open tubular glass column (WCOT c. 20 m $\times$ 0.25 mm i.d.) with N_2 or He as carrier (inlet pressures c. 1.0–2.0 kg cm^{-2}; flow rate c. 2 ml min^{-1}), with injector and detector temperatures of 300 °C. Double bond posititional and stereoisomers of unsaturated fatty acids were determined by GC (with reference to standards) using the above

conditions but with a Carbowax 20M WCOT (c. 0.1 μm) glass column (20 m $\times$ 0.25 mm i.d.) and using a modified Perkin Elmer F-17 chromatograph fitted with a split/splitless injector, and with a diethylene glycol succinate (DEGS)/polyethylene glycol succinate (PEGS) (3:1, w/w; 0.06 μm) WCOT glass column (100 m $\times$ 0.24 mm i.d.). For the DEGS/PEGS column the back pressure was 2.5 kg cm^{-2} (He carrier; c. 4–5 ml min^{-1}). Programming was typically from 50 to 180 °C (DEGS:PEGS) to 220 °C (Carbowax 20M) and to 260 °C (OV-1 and SE-52) at 4–6°C min^{-1}.

Gas chromatography–mass spectrometry (GC–MS)

This was carried out on the Finnigan 4000 system described previously (Mackenzie *et al.*, 1980) using an OV-1 WCOT glass capillary column of the same type and under the programme and flow conditions described above. The mass spectrometric conditions were: electron energy 40 eV, filament current 350 μA, accelerating voltage c. 2 kV and source temperature 250 °C. The spectrometer was interfaced to two data systems. For the earlier work, a DEC PDP 8/e (32 K) computer was used and spectra and fragmentograms were plotted using a Calcomp 565 plotter. This allowed a spectral scan time of c. 2.5 s. Later work (Mission Canyon suite) used a Finnigan INCOS 2000 series data system with shorter scan times (1.0 s^{-1}).

Structural assignments

The alkanes were assigned as described previously (Mackenzie *et al.*, 1980). The acids (Me esters) were assigned on the basis of retention data and/or GLC coinjection (SE-52 or OV-1, Carbowax 20M, DEGS:PEGS) with authentic standards, and also by comparison of mass spectra with those of standard compounds.

Quantitation

Flame ionisation response factors (ng/peak height) for the compounds quoted were determined from comparison with solutions of standards. For some oils where the mixtures were very complex, quantitation was carried out from the base peak intensity (m/z 74 for saturated *n*-acids; m/z 101 for phytanic acid) or from the intensity of a diagnostic ion (e.g m/z 264 in $C_{18:1}$) measured from mass fragmentograms, and comparison with standardised mixtures.

RESULTS

General

The oils were analysed as four groups (Bell Creek, E. Benekat and Limau, Alberta, Mission Canyon and Moonie, respectively). A blank analysis was carried out before and after examination of each group, the reagents and solvents being from the same batch as used for the group. Weights and types of chromatographic phases and solvent volumes were identical for both blank and actual analyses. Thus, in total, eight blank runs were carried out; in five of these, three individual fatty acids were detected (n-$C_{14:0}$, n-$C_{16:0}$, and n-$C_{18:0}$). The distribution was similar in each blank and for the samples only concentrations of individual acids $> \times 2$ the more contaminated blank are quoted (Tables). The considerably greater amounts of fatty acids isolated from most of the oils, up to c. 10^3 times the highest concentration in the blanks, clearly rules out contamination from the work up as the source of acids.

Bell Creek oils (Montana: Cretaceous)

'Free' acids   These samples compare with those of Winters and Williams (1969) for other oils of the same field. The 'free' acids are conveniently defined as those obtained from the SiO_2/KOH column. It should be noted, however, that when a mixture of three phospholipids (lecithin, lysolecithin and phosphatidyl ethanolamine, c. 1 mg each, previously extracted with aqueous base) was subjected to the full analytical procedure, a small extent (c. 10%) of hydrolysis occurred. A similar effect was also observed for butter triglycerides in contact with SiO_1/KOH (Stark *et al.*, 1976). The 'free' acids of the Bell Creek samples therefore probably contain a proportion contributed from the 'bound' acids. Representative gas chromatograms of the 'free' monoacids (Me esters) are shown in Fig. 1. Many components in the oils were not fully characterised, but it is apparent that straight chain fatty acids are the major components with C_{16} and C_{18} species predominating. The amounts of certain components are shown in Table 1. Unsaturated acids were detected in five out of six samples. Phytanic acid was detected in significant amounts in two oils (31829 and 31833).

The summed amounts of major 'free' n-acids are greatest for the three most degraded oils (as suggested by other information in Table 1). Figure 2 shows the GC distributions of a saturated adduct (31833) and a non-adduct (31829). The predominance of $C_{16:0}$ and $C_{18:0}$ in 31833 is evident, together with an approximately gaussian distribution of the other C_{15}–C_{28} n-acids, again with a slight even over odd preference. Phytanic acid is the major branched acid of 31829 (Fig. 2, Table 1). Pentacyclic triterpenoid acids of the hopane type are also present, including C_{31}–C_{33} components with the less stable $17\beta(H)$, $21\beta(H)$-stereochemistry (as observed in other oils by Schmitter *et al.*, 1978). The only other oil containing triterpenoid acids was 31833, again with the three stereoisomeric types present. Although the 'free' acid distributions for the oils are fairly similar, there is some variation. In general, oils with a similar pristane:n-C_{17} alkane ratio (e.g. 31833 and 31831) have similar distributions.

'Bound' acids   A significant proportion of the total fatty acids of micro-organisms and sediments can exist in esterified or 'bound' forms (e.g. Davis, 1964; Douglas *et*

al., 1970; Farrington and Quinn, 1973). Accordingly, after the 'free' acids were extracted, the neutral/basic fractions of all six oils were hydrolysed and the resulting acids isolated. GC analysis on DEGS/PEGS and Carbowax was useful for assigning the stereochemistry and positions of the double bonds in both the 'free' and 'bound' acid fractions and a partial chromatogram of the 'bound' acids for sample 31834 is shown in Fig. 3 as an example; the concentrations of the major C_{16} and C_{18} components are listed in Table 2. In general, for the 'bound' acids the mixtures were less complex than the 'free' acids, with the variation in distribution between oils being less, and the even/odd predominance higher. The diunsaturated C_{18} acid was not detected in 31829 and 31833 and the Δ^9 mono-unsaturated C_{18} acid in 31830; these components were not found in the corresponding 'free' acids. The 'bound' acids were specially concentrated in the most biodegraded oil (31832).

Mission Canyon oils (Saskatchewan; Mississippian)

The concentrations of the C_{16} and C_{18} 'free' fatty acids and phytanic acid are given in Table 3. Although each sample represents an individual field (as opposed to different parts of a single field, as for the Bell Creek suite), the range of extents of biodegradation as measured by the pristane:n-C_{17} ratio is less. Bailey *et al.* (1973a) have reported detailed studies of the alkanes, and of the gross compositions of six oils from the area and of their formation waters. Five of those studied here are from the same fields as those previously investigated (names used by Bailey *et al.* are underlined in Table 3). The total 'free' monoacid fraction was in some cases more complex than those of the Bell Creek samples, the major n-acids being less obvious. In addition to the methods used for the Bell Creek acids, mass fragmentography was used where the concentrations were low (Shell, Husky, Grizzly) to determine the distribution of saturated straight chain acids (m/z 74). Distributions of identified acids were similar within the suite, and to the Bell Creek samples, and again C_{16}, C_{18} acids were major components (Table 3). However, $C_{18:1}\Delta^9$ and $C_{18:2}$ were only detected in Bedford and the amounts of acids decreased with increasing extent of biodegradation (as the oils are thought to be of similar maturity and source, the pristane:n-C_{17} ratio should be valid for comparison within the suite, Bailey *et al.*, 1973a).

Other samples

Limau and East Benekat (Tertiary)   These two Sumatran crudes are thought to have a similar source (British Petroleum, unpublished results). The amounts of n-alkanes $< C_{18}$ are slightly lower in Limau and since the concentration of benzene is the same in both oils, this is interpreted (British Petroleum, unpublished results) as resulting from very mild biodegradation. Very low concentrations of acids were present in the Limau crude (Table 4), whilst none were detected above blank levels in the East Benekat sample.

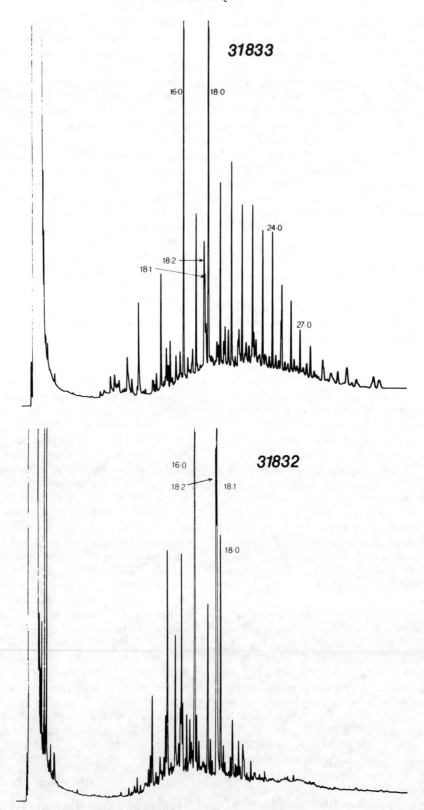

Fig. 1. Representative gas chromatograms (20 m × 0.25 mm i.d. SE-52) of total 'free' fatty acids (Me esters) of two Bell Creek crudes (31833 and 31832). For conditions see text.

Alberta suite (Lloydminster crude, Cold Lake and Athabasca tar sands; Cretaceous) Extensive biodegradation is though to have converted the Lower Cretaceous pooled oils (e.g. Lloydminster) into the tar sands of Alberta (Vigrass, 1968; Deroo *et al.*, 1974). The detailed petroleum geology and geochemistry of the area

have been reviewed by Deroo *et al.* (1977). The hydrocarbons of these three samples have been studied in detail (Rubinstein *et al.*, 1977); *n*-alkanes have been totally removed from all three and many branched, cyclic and aromatic components have been attacked. The extents of sterane and triterpane degradation in

Table 1

Alkane ratios, specific activity and concentrations of certain 'free' fatty acids in Bell Creek crudes

Sample	$\dfrac{iC_{14}-C_{20}}{n\text{-}C_{15}-C_{30}}$ [a]	$\dfrac{Pr}{n\text{-}C_{17}}$ [b]	Sp. Activity[c] $[\alpha]^{25}_{400}$	Major 'Free' Acids[d] 16:0	18:0	$18:1\Delta^9$	$18:1\Delta^{11}$	$18:2\Delta^{9,12}$	Total	Pf
31830	0.27	0.5	0.43	250	80	—	—	—	330	—
31829	0.34	1.0	0.70	310	430	43	—	—	783	310
31833	0.47	2.5	0.90	230	210	35	—	—	475	140
31831	0.93	2.5	0.83	340	275	460	52	310	1437	trace
31834	0.97	4.5	0.96	220	525	510	130	310	1695	—
31832	1.09	4.5	0.88	580	190	280	190	320	1560	—
Blank ('worst' of 2)[e]	—	—	—	3	0.5	—	—	—	3.5	—

(Left side bracket: Increasing Biodegradation)

[a] i — Isoprenoid; from GC.
[b] Pr = Pristane; from GC.
[c] Supplied by Chevron Oil Field Research Co.
[d] ppb of oil, all double bonds *cis*.
[e] Using materials for 20 g of oil.
[f] Phytanic acid.
— Not detected.

these samples have been reassessed herein (see below). The results for the acids are given in Table 4; the amounts are small when compared to the Bell Creek suite and comparable to the amounts seen in the more degraded members of the Mission Canyon suite. No acids were produced by hydrolysis of Lloydminster crude.

Moonie oil (Queensland, Australia; Jurassic) The 'free' mono acids of this oil have been previously analysed (van Hoeven *et al.*, 1969). However, this is repeated here for another sample for the following reasons: (i) the earlier work showed phytanic acid as the most abundant component and determination of its configuration was thought to be of interest here (see below), and (ii) recent evidence not available to van Hoeven *et al.* (1969) suggests biodegradation has been active in the petroleum-bearing basin where the oil is found and may, indeed, have affected parts of the Moonie field (Powell and McKirdy, 1972, 1976; Hunt, 1979; J. D. Saxby, personal communication). Again, n-$C_{18:0}$, n-$C_{16:0}$ and phytanic acid were identified as the major components (280, 85 and 90 ppb respectively), although the relative concentration of the latter was less than that reported by van Hoeven *et al.* (1969) in another sample; n-C_{13} to n-C_{27} acids (excluding C_{16}, C_{18}) with a slight even over odd preference were also detected. This straight chain distribution is similar to, and the concentrations slightly less than, the less degraded Bell Creek crudes (Fig. 1; Table 1, cf. 31833). Blank analyses produced no monoacids.

Phytanic acid

Phytanic acid was identified in appreciable concentrations only in the 'free' acids of five oils — Bell Creek (31829 and 31833), Mission Canyon (Bedford and Anadarko) and the Moonie oil. Using the techniques described by Mackenzie *et al.* (1982) the stereochemistry was examined.

GC analysis (DEGS:PEGS) of the methyl esters was attempted for three samples (relative stereochemistry: 31829; Bedford and Moonie) and of the (–)-menthyl esters of the Bedford oil (absolute stereochemistry, Fig. 4). The phytanic acid of Bedford is only one isomer — 3(R), 7(R), 11(R), and the methyl esters of the other two show a strong preference for the peak containing this isomer.

Alkanes

The configuration of pristane was examined for all of the oils, and in addition, four of the Californian oils reported by Seifert and Moldowan (1979) which include members with no n-alkanes. Those Californian oils where both the steranes and triterpanes have apparently been attacked (Seifert and Moldowan, 1979) did not contain pristane. No pristane was present in the Athabasca tar sand sample. In all 20 cases examined, the pristane appeared to be present in an all-isomer mixture.

The sterane distributions in the C_{27}–C_{30} region for Lloydminster crude and Cold Lake tar samples (m/z 217) are typical of those seen in mature sediments and oils (Fig. 5), but the Athabasca tar sample showed markedly lower relative concentrations of total steranes, especially of the non-rearranged components (Fig. 5). The triterpane distributions in the three samples were all very similar, particularly when the minor components were considered, as would be expected from their proposed common origin (Rubinstein *et al.*, 1977).

DISCUSSION

Origin of oil fatty acids

Rationalising the origins and distributions in the Bell Creek and Mission Canyon suites is difficult because they presumably reflect the combination of many

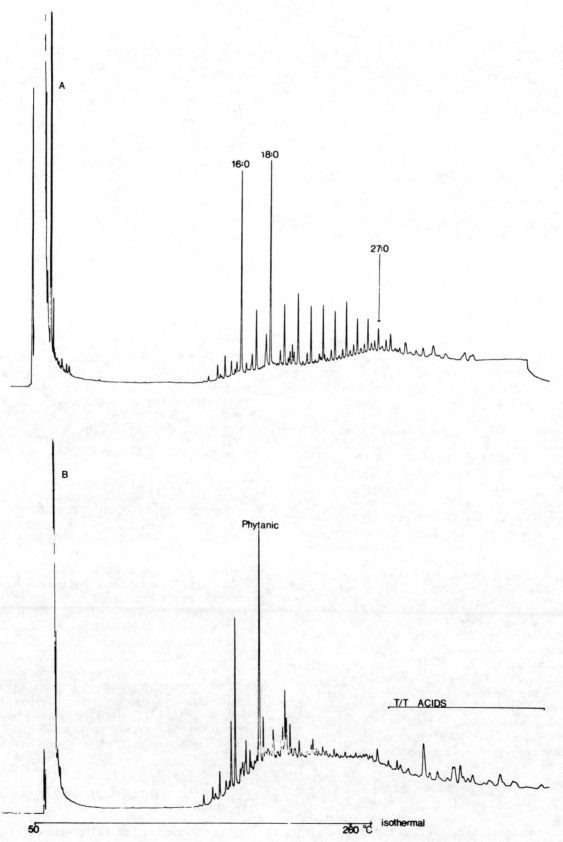

Fig. 2. Representative gas chromatograms (20 m × 0.25 mm i.d., SE-52) of 'free' saturated fatty acids (Me esters) from Bell Creek crudes. A: urea adduct of 31833. B: urea non-adduct of 31829. For conditions see text.

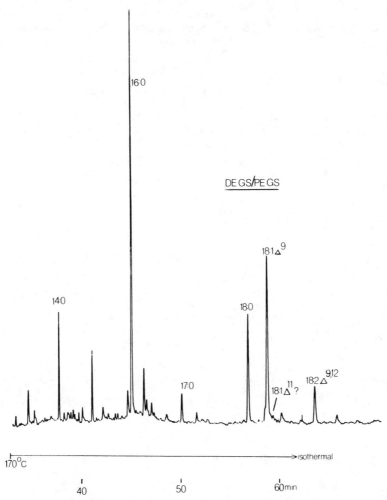

Fig. 3. Representative partial gas chromatogram (100 m × 0.24 mm i.d., DEGS/PEGS) of total 'bound' fatty acids (Me esters) of Bell Creek crude 31834. For conditions see text.

Table 2

Concentrations of major C_{16} and C_{18} 'bound' acids in Bell Creek crudes

	Sample	'Bound' Fatty Acids[a]					Total 'Bound'
		16:0	18:0	$18:1\Delta^9$	$18:1\Delta^{11}$	$18:2\Delta^{9,12}$	
Increasing Biodegradation	31830	460	210	360	—	—	1030
	31829	825	330	180	—	30	1365
	31833	220	105	30	—	10	365
	31831	110	30	5	—	5	150
	31834	160	70	120	—	30	380
	31832	2580	500	2830	—	1660	7571
	Blank	1	2	—	—	—	—

[a] ppb Oils, all double bonds *cis*.

processes. If microbes are utilising an oil at present as a carbon source, then certain hydrocarbons will continuously be converted to acids, then further via acetyl-CoA to biosynthesised acids, including 'bound' and 'free' components. Therefore, the acids of the crude oils could contain: (i) the original acids of the source rock, (ii) acids arising from biodegradation of the oil, and (iii) acids biosynthesised *de novo* by the organisms. These acids will be continuously removed relative to the remaining oil by the processes of water washing, further

biodegradation and thermal alteration. In the 'free' acids of the samples of the two major suites (e.g. Figs. 1 and 2), the broad envelope of saturated *n*-acids (where present) with a small even over odd preference in the higher components ($> C_{18}$) might possibly, therefore, represent in part intermediate products of biodegradation of a smooth distribution of *n*-alkanes. Alternatively, these components could represent, in part, a smooth distribution of indigenous *n*-acids.

Superimposed on these will be the products of *de novo*

Table 3

Pristane/n-C_{17} alkane ratios and concentrations of C_{16}, C_{18} and phytanic acids in Mission Canyon biodegraded crudes (Mississippian, Saskatchewen)

	Sample	Pr/n-C_{17}[a]	16:0	18:0	18:1Δ^9	18:1Δ^{11}	18:2$\Delta^{9,12}$	Ph[c]	Total
					Free Fatty Acids[b]				
Increasing Biodegradation	Anadarko Stoughton	0.40	3400	1460	1030	—	—	305	5890
	Bedford Browning	0.43	1280	610	65	5	20	3070	1980
	Grizzly Forget	0.47	56	32	60	—	—	—	148
	Husky Horsehill	0.50	10	6	8	—	—	—	24
	Shell Innes Griffin	0.53	50	29	4	—	—	7	83
	Mohawk Creelman	0.56	—	—	—	—	—	—	—

No acids detected in blank
[a] Pr = pristane
[b] ppb of oil, all double bonds *cis*.
[c] Ph = phytanic acid.
— Not detected.

Table 4

Concentrations of saturated mono acids in crude oils

	Sample Sumatra	14:0	16:0	18:0	20:0	22:0	24:0	26:0	Total
					Free Fatty Acids[a]				
Increasing Biodegradation	E. Benekat	—	—	—	—	—	—	—	—
	Limau	—	NAB	5	1	2	2	1	11
	Alberta								
	Lloydminster	13	21	65	4	3	—	—	106
	Cold Lake	NAB	NAB	96	8	33	—	—	137
	Athabasca	NAB	NAB	5	14	15	5	1	78
	Blank ('worst' of 2)	0.5	5	1	—	—	—	—	6.5

[a] ppb of oil
NAB Not above blank.

synthesis, including $C_{16:0}$ and $C_{18:0}$, unsaturated equivalents, and low concentrations of the other even acids to give a small even over odd preference in the higher homologues. A recent origin for some of the acids must therefore be envisaged, as strongly suggested by the enhancement of $C_{16:0}$ and $C_{18:0}$, not generally seen in ancient sediments (Douglas et al., 1970; Kvenvolden, 1967) and the persistence of mono- and di-unsaturated components. Unsaturated acids such as $C_{18:1}$ rapidly disappear in recently deposited sediments (Rhead et al., 1971; Farrington and Quinn, 1973), although Perry et al. (1979) suggest that intracellular bacterial components may be more protected from alteration. Continual biosynthesis and biodegradation must be necessary, to maintain measurable quantities of unsaturated acids in the oil. Thermal degradation at the temperatures of most reservoirs will be expected to remove acids preferentially, and unsaturated species would be expected to be especially labile. Water washing will also preferentially remove fatty acids relative to other oil constituents.

Although C_{16} and C_{18} straight chain acids, both saturated and mono-unsaturated, are frequently the major components of most strains of bacteria (e.g. Oliver and Colwell, 1973; Fulco, 1974), these compounds are not sufficiently definitive to assign their presence as arising from bacterial activity (Perry et al., 1979). Yeasts (Cook et al., 1973), fungi (Perry and Cerniglia, 1973) and algae (Walker et al., 1975) are known to biodegrade oils in a similar manner to bacteria. Since these types of micro-organisms can biosynthesise saturated and monounsaturated fatty acids dominated by C_{16} and C_{18} components, clear definition of the type of petroleum biodegrading micro-organism is difficult.

Tentative evidence for a bacterial origin for the fatty acids is given, however, by the diunsaturated acid present in some of the oils, and by the distribution of the two positional isomers of $C_{18:1}$. Romero and Brenner (1966) isolated a bacterium, *Pseudomonas aeruginosa*, from a petroleum contaminated soil and grew it with *n*-hexadecane as sole carbon source. $C_{18:1}$ and $C_{18:2}$ were identified as the major fatty acids with the dienoic acid comprising 35% of the triglyceride fraction. The dienoic acid has also been found in bacteria by a number of other researchers (e.g. Hunter and James, 1963; Cho and Salton, 1966; Tornabene et al., 1967; Oliver and Colwell, 1973; Yano et al., 1971). Furthermore, in some of these studies, hydrocarbons were used as sole carbon source (e.g. Yano et al., 1971). These studies show that the once held belief that bacteria could not synthesise polyunsaturated fatty acids (Erwin and Bloch, 1964) is no longer valid, and the presence of $C_{18:2}$ in some of the

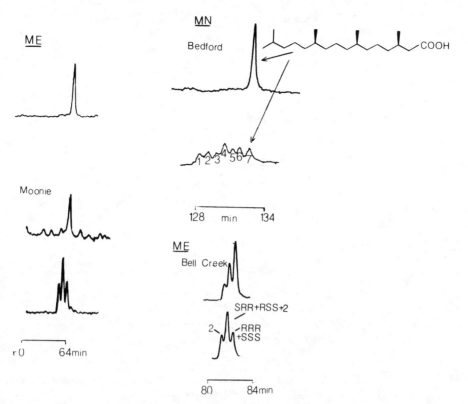

Fig. 4. Partial gas chromatograms (100 m × 0.24 mm i.d., DEGS/PEGS) of phytanic acid (Me or (-)-menthyl esters) in three crudes (Bedford, Browning, Bell Creek 31829 and Moonie), and all-isomer standard. For conditions see text.

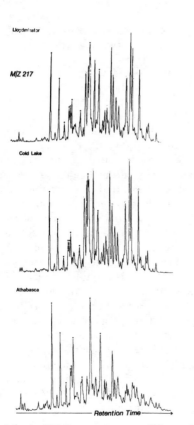

Fig. 5. Partial *m/z* 217 fragmentograms (20 m × 0.25 mm i.d., OV-1) of total alkanes of a biodegraded heavy crude (Lloydminster) and two tar sand samples (Cold Lake and Athabasca) from Alberta. For conditions see text. Key: ● = representative rearranged steranes; O = non-rearranged steranes.

oils could arise from bacteria. The other types of possible hydrocarbon utilisers (listed above) usually produce this acid (Erwin, 1973). With these microorganisms desaturation of C_{18} acids is, however, continued (to give for example $C_{18:3}$, Erwin and Bloch, 1964), but acids with more than two double bonds were not detected herein in the crudes. Unfortunately, studies with standards have shown that $C_{18:3}$ acid is degraded by the work-up procedure; also, c 70% of $C_{18:2}$ and c. 30% of the $C_{18:1}$ acids were also degraded, suggesting these components are present in even greater amounts in the crudes than reported here.

Volkman and Johns (1977) and Perry *et al.* (1979) have used the presence of significant amounts of *cis*-vaccenic acid ($C_{18:1}\Delta^{11}$) to show a bacterial input to recently deposited sediments, given its higher relative concentration in bacteria than in other organisms. This acid has been detected in some of the Bell Creek oils (Table 1). It is thought to result mainly from bacteria using the anaerobic biosynthetic pathway (Erwin and Bloch, 1964), via the *β*- and *γ*-dehydration of medium chain *β*-hydroxy acids and subsequent chain elongation of the resulting 3-enoates (Scheuerbrandt and Bloch, 1961).

The other major isomer, $C_{18:1}\Delta^9$, oleic acid, arises from oxidative desaturation (aerobic pathway) by alteration of the corresponding saturated long chain fatty acid ($C_{18:0}$). This pathway is oxygen dependent and is probably also used by bacteria to synthesise diunsaturated acids such as $C_{18:2}$. since this acid cannot be produced by the anaerobic pathway (Fulco, 1974). Sklan *et al.* (1972) and Sklan and Budowski (1972) reported aerobic biosynthesis of $C_{18:2}$ by aerobic bacteria

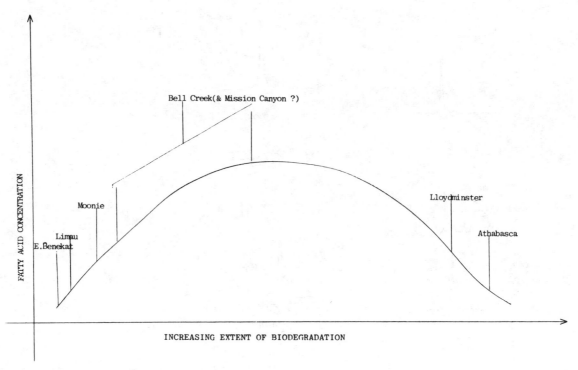

Fig. 6. Proposed schematic of variation in concentration of fatty acids with extent of biodegradation in crudes (excluding effects of differential water washing).

in calf rumen liquor and rat colon contents. More recently, Johns and Perry (1977) also attributed polyunsaturated fatty acids in the marine bacterium, *Flexibacter polymorphus* to oxidative desaturation.

In summary, it can be said that the aerobic pathway in bacteria will lead initially to *cis*-Δ^9 monoenoic acids of varying even carbon number, and further desaturation of $C_{18:1}$ *cis*-Δ^9 gives rise to the $C_{18:2}$ acid (*cis,cis*-$\Delta^{9,12}$). Alternatively, synthesis via the anaerobic pathway gives only monounsaturation, with a mixture of positional isomers (Δ^9,Δ^{11}, etc.) produced, the major $C_{18:1}$ isomer being, however, *cis*-Δ^{11} (Bloch *et al.*, 1961). The results from the oils therefore suggest, as a working hypothesis, that bacteria utilising the aerobic pathway of fatty acid biosynthesis are involved. The significant amounts of $C_{18:1}$ *cis*-Δ^{11} occurring in some oils (see above) could be due to aerobic biosynthesis via chain elongation of $C_{16:1}$ *cis*-Δ^9 (produced by oxidative desaturation of $C_{16:0}$) to $C_{18:1}$ *cis*-Δ^{11}. This has been postulated for algae (Johns *et al.*, 1979) and for aerobic bacteria (Russell and Volkman, 1980) but has never been proved. At present, therefore the C_{16} and C_{18} acids are best explained by an origin from bacteria using solely or mainly the aerobic pathway of biosynthesis. The ideas of Jobson *et al.* (1979) that (in the reservoir) the hydrocarbon degradation is aerobic, and that anaerobes can utilise the oxygenated products of the degradation fit well here.

Of course, the above discussion presupposes that the C_{16} and C_{18} acids are associated with the degradation and are not artefacts of bacteria 'contamination' during storage or production. The wide range (c. 10^3) of concentrations of acids in the crudes tends to argue against the latter hypothesis.

Concentrations of 'free' fatty acids

Whilst concentrations generally increase with increasing extent of biodegradation in the Bell Creek crudes (Table 1), the opposite is true for the Mission Canyon suite (Table 3). Other oils (except the Moonie oil) have lower amounts of acids than the average for the Bell Creek and Mission Canyon suites (cf. Tables 1, 3 and 4). In the case of the Bell Creek suite, an increase in extent of biodegradation resulting in greater concentrations of microbially-derived lipids is a possible explanation for the results. In the case of the Mission Canyon suite, the wide differences in the concentrations of 'free' acids may be the result of an additional process, such as differential extents of water washing. It is noteworthy in this context that the three most biodegraded crudes are from the northwestern fields (Horsehill, Griffin and Creelman) of the area (Table 3). Here, the formation waters are thought to have a recent meteoric origin (Bailey *et al.*, 1973a); presumably an increased proportion of meteoric water results in an increased extent of water washing which could remove the acids selectively. In the area of the southwestern fields (Stoughton, Browning and Forget), the formation waters have a higher salinity so presumably water washing is less effective here, where the acid concentrations are higher (e.g. Anadarko, Table 3).

Figure 6 is an attempt to explain the concentrations of fatty acids in relation to extent of biodegradation. In the absence of biodegradation or where it is minimal, the concentrations (derived from biosynthesis or biodegradation) would be expected to be low. As biodegradation proceeds, the amounts would rise as the readily biodegradable hydrocarbons (e.g. *n*-alkanes) are utilised (cf. Bell Creek suite). The effects of water washing will be superimposed on these trends and may distort them if the effects are differential (cf. Mission Canyon).

At the later stages of degradation, the rate of alkane depletion and therefore of acid production will slow. This will result in a decrease in acid concentrations since those produced from earlier activity will be removed by further biodegradation, water washing and thermal degradation.

The acid concentrations will be a reflection not only of present-day conditions but also of the timing of biodegradation. If the biodegradation has ceased, then acids will no longer be produced, and those from the degradation in the past will be gradually removed, resulting in a net decrease in concentration. This may be the case in the Alberta suite. If the Athabasca tar sand is a degradation 'end point', as claimed by Rubinstein *et al.* (1977), little or no acids are being produced at present, and those produced in the past will have been removed.

It is difficult to comment on the results for the Moonie oil in the absence of any related oils for comparison of alkane distributions. There is no evidence in the alkanes of significant biodegradation (pristane/*n*-C_{17} alkane $= 0.2$) but the 'free' acid concentrations suggest some bacterial activity. Such activity might be expected from the relative freshness of the formation water (500 ppm NaCl; from Beddoes, 1973), the low reservoir temperature (68 °C; Beddoes, 1973) and from the fact that degradation has occurred elsewhere in the basin where the oil is found (Powell and McKirdy, 1972, 1976).

'Bound' acids The hydrolysis releases additional acids from the Bell Creek oils suggests many are present in a bound form, possibly as triglycerides, phospholipids and wax esters commonly found in bacteria (e.g. Davies, 1964; Oliver and Colwell, 1973a; Russell and Volkman, 1980). The absence of 'bound' acids in the Lloydminster crude further suggests active present day bacterial biosynthesis is not occurring in the reservoir.

Phytanic acid (Fig. 4)

The strong stereopreference in certain oils suggests a recent origin, as isomerisation at the chiral centres with increasing maturation in the source rock would have been expected to give rise to a less stereospecific mixture of isomers (Mackenzie *et al.*, 1981). If this is the case, two sources can be envisaged: (i) from the stereoselective biodegradation of phytane, or (ii) from the lipids of microorganisms. The first explanation is unlikely since stereoselective biodegradation of isoprenoid alkanes is not suspected (see below) and also phytanic acid is the only isoprenoid acid present.

Alkanes

The presence of pristane as an all-isomer mixture indicates that effective stereoselective biodegradation

does not occur in the reservoir, although stereoselectivity has been observed in the laboratory over a short time period using a pure culture (Cox *et al.*, 1974).

In the Alberta suite, the increase in the relative abundance of rearranged steranes to non-rearranged steranes in the most severely biodegraded sample (Athabasca), and thus their presumed greater resistance to biodegradation, agrees with the results of Seifert and Moldowan (1979) for Californian and Gulf Coast crudes, but apparently contradicts the findings of Rubinstein *et al.* (1977) for another sample from the Athabasca tar sands, which was reported to have a similar sterane distribution to Lloydminster and Cold Lake crudes.

The decrease in the sterane/hopane ratio over the three samples shows the greater resistance of the hopanes to biodegradation, as found previously for other oils (Seifert and Moldowan, 1979).

SUMMARY

Assuming that the fatty acids in the oils containing the highest concentrations are not contaminants (see above), then circumstantial evidence has been obtained for recent bacterial activity in these oils. It appears, therefore, that biodegradation is occurring at present in the Bell Creek oils and certain of the Mission Canyon oils. Although a simple model of increasing acid concentration, followed by a decrease with increasing extent of biodegradation, has been proposed (Fig. 6), the concentrations cannot be used as a measure of the extent of this process. The results for the Mission Canyon oils indicate the influence of other factors, such as variation in rate of water washing within related oils, which distort this trend. Clearly, laboratory simulations are required to confirm the model.

In short, the factors affecting the fatty acid concentrations in crudes are complex, and although the presence of bacteria may be detected, the absence of the necessary acids does not mean biodegradation has not occurred in the past and/or is continuing to occur. The degradation may indeed have stopped or other factors may have removed acids as quickly as they were produced.

Acknowledgements

We gratefully acknowledge Dr J. K. Volkman for help and advice with this work, and Mrs A. P. Gowar for aid in running samples on GC–MS. Samples were kindly provided by Dr W. K. Seifert of Chevron Oil Field Research Company (Bell Creek), Dr C. W. D. Milner of Esso Resources Canada Ltd. (Mission Canyon), Dr I. Rubinstein of the University of Alberta (Alberta), Mr G. K. Speers of British Petroleum Company Ltd. (Indonesia), and Dr R. P. Philp of CSIRO, Australia (Moonie). A.S.M. and G.W. also thank the Science Research Council for Studentships. GC–MS facilities were provided by the Natural Environment Research Council (GR3/2951 and GR3/2758).

REFERENCES

Aldridge, A. K., Brooks, P. W., Eglinton, G. and Maxwell, J. R. (1977) The analysis of the hydrocarbons of petroleum. In *The Genesis of Petroleum and Microbial Means for its Recovery.* Proc. Inst. of Petrol. Microbiol. Grp Symp., Oct. 1976. pp. 4–21.

Bailey, N. J. L., Krouse, H. R., Evans, G. R. and Rogers, M. A. (1973a) Alteration of crude oil — evidence from geochemical and isotope studies. *Petr. Geol. Bull.* **57**, 1276–1290.

Bailey, N. J. L., Jobson, A. M. and Rogers, M. A. (1973b) Bacterial degradation of crude oil, comparison of field and experimental data. *Chem. Geol.* **11**, 203–221.

Beddoes, L. R. (1973) Ed. *Oil and Gas Fields of Australia, Papua New Guinea, and New Zealand.* Tracer Petroleum and Mining Publications Ltd., Sydney.

Bloch, K., Baronowsky, P., Goldfine, H., Lennarz, W. J., Light, R., Norris, A. J. and Scheuerbrandt, G. (1961) Biosynthesis and metabolism of unsaturated fatty acids. *Fed. Proc.* **20**, 921–927.

Brooks, P. W., Eglinton, G., Gaskell, S. J., McHugh, D. J., Maxwell, J. R. and Philp, R. P. (1976) Lipids of recent sediments, Part 1. Straight-chain hydrocarbons and carboxylic acids of some temperate lacustrine and subtropical lagoonal/tidal flat sediments. *Chem. Geol.* **18**, 21–38.

Cho, K. Y. and Salton, M. R. J. (1966) Fatty acid composition of bacterial membrane and wall lipids. *Biochim. Biophys. Acta* **116**, 73–79.

Claret, J., Tchikaja, J. B., Tissot, B., Deroo, G. and Van Dorsselaer, A. (1977) Un example d'huile biodegradée à basse teneur en soufre: le gisement d'Emeraude (Congo). In *Advances in Organic Geochemistry* 1975. Ed. by Campos, R. and Gõni, J. Enadimsa. pp. 509–522.

Connan, J., Restle, A. and Albrecht, P. (1980) Biodegradation of crude oil in the Aquitaine Basin. In *Advances in Organic Geochemistry* 1979. Ed. by Douglas, A. G. and Maxwell, J. R. Pergamon, Oxford. pp. 1–18.

Cook, W. L., Massey, J. K. and Ahern, D. G. (1973) The degradation of crude oil by yeasts and its effect on *Lesbistes reticulatus.* In *Microbial Degradation of Oil Pollutants.* Ed. by Ahern, D. G. and Mayers, S. P. Centre for Wetland Resources, Louisiana State University, Baton Rouge, LA, USA. pp. 279–282.

Cox, R. E., Maxwell, J. R., Ackman, R. G. and Hooper, S. N. (1974) Stereochemical studies of acyclic isoprenoid compounds IV — microbial oxidation of 2,6,10,14-tetramethylpentadecane (pristane). *Biochim. Biophys. Acta* **360**, 166–173.

Davis, J. B. (1964) Microbial incorporation of fatty acids derived from *n*-alkanes into glycerides and waxes. *Appl. Microbiol.* **12**, 210–214.

Davis, J. B. (1967) *Petroleum Microbiology.* Elsevier. p. 110.

Demaison, G. T. (1977) Tar sands and supergiant oil fields. *Bull Am. Ass. Petr. Geol.* **61**, 1950–1961.

Deroo, G., Tissot, B., McCrossan, R. G. and Der, F. (1974) Geochemistry of the heavy oils of Alberta. *Can. Soc. Petrol. Geol. Mem.* **3**, 148–167, 186–189.

Douglas, A. G., Douraghi-Zadeh, K., Eglinton, G., Maxwell, J. R. and Ramsey, J. N. (1970) Fatty acids in sediments including the Green River shale (Eocene) and Scottish Torbanite (Carboniferous). In *Advances in Organic Geochemistry* 1966. Ed. by Hobson, G. D. and Speers, G. C. Pergamon, Oxford. pp. 315–334.

Erwin, J. (1973) Comparative biochemistry of fatty acids in eukaryotic microorganisms. In *Lipids and Biomembranes of Eukaryotic Microorganisms.* Ed. by Erwin, J. Academic Press. pp. 41–143.

Erwin, J. and Bloch, K. (1964) Biosynthesis of unsaturated fatty acids in microorganisms. *Science* **143**, 1006–1012.

Farrington, J. W. and Quinn, J. G. (1973) Biogeochemistry of fatty acids in recent sediments from Narragansett Bay, Rhode Island. *Geochim. Cosmochim. Acta* **37**, 259–268.

Fulco, A. J. (1974) Metabolic alterations of fatty acids. *Ann. Rev. Biochim.* **43**, 215–241.

Higgins, J. and Gilbert, P. D. (1978) The biodegradation of hydrocarbons. In *The Oil Industry and Microbial Ecosystems.* Ed. by Chater, K. W. A. and Somerville, H. J. Heyden & Son, London. pp. 80–117.

Hunt, J. M. (1979) *Petroleum Geochemistry and Geology.* Freeman.

Hunter, G. D. and James, A. T. (1963) Lipoamine acids from *Bacillus megaterium Nature* **198**, 789.

Krejci-Graf, K. (1932) Rule of density of oils. *Bull. Am. Ass. Petr. Geol.* **16**, 1038.

Kvenvolden, K. A. (1967) Normal fatty acids in sediments. *J. Am. Oil. Chem. Soc.* **44**, 628–636.

Jobson, A. M., Cook, E. D. and Westlake, D. W. S. (1979) Interaction of aerobic and anerobic bacteria in petroleum biodegradation. *Chem. Geol.* **24**, 355–365.

Johns, R. B. and Perry, G. J. (1977) Lipids of the marine bacterium *Flexibacter polymorphus. Arch. Microbiol.* **114**, 267–271.

Johns, R. B., Nichols, P. D. and Perry, G. J. (1979) Fatty acid composition of ten marine algae from Australian waters. *Phytochem.* **18**, 799–802.

Macarthy, R. D. and Duthie, A. H. (1962) Separation of free fatty acids from other lipids. *J. Lipid Research* **3**, 117–119.

Mackenzie, A. S. (1980) Applications of biological marker compounds to subsurface geological processes. PhD Thesis, University of Bristol.

Mackenzie, A. S., Patience, R. L., Maxwell, J. R., Vandenbroucke, M. and Durand, B. (1980) Molecular parameters of maturation in the Toarcian shales, Paris Basin, France — I. Changes in the configurations of acyclic isoprenoid alkanes, steranes and terpanes. *Geochim. Cosmochim. Acta* **44**, 1709–1721.

Mackenzie, A. S., Patience, R. L., Yon, D. A. and Maxwell, J. R. (1982) The effect of maturation on the configurations of acyclic isoprenoid acids in sediments. *Geochim. Cosmochim. Acta* **46**, 783–792.

Oliver, J. D. and Colwell, R. R. (1973) Extractable lipids of gram negative bacteria: fatty acid composition. *Internatn. J. Syst. Bact.* **23**, 442–458.

Perry, J. J. and Cerniglia, C. E. (1973) Studies on the degradation of petroleum by filamentous fungi. In *Microbial Degradation of Oil Pollutants.* Ed. by Ahern, D. G. and Meyers, S. P. Center for Wetland Resources, Louisiana State University, Baton Rouge, LA, USA. pp. 89–94.

Perry, G. J., Volkman, J. K., Johns, R. B. and Bavor, H. Jr. (1979) Fatty acids of bacterial origin in contemporary marine sediments. *Geochim. Cosmochim. Acta* **43**, 1715–1725.

Powell, T. G. and McKirdy, D. M. (1972) The geochemical characterisation of Australian crude oils. *The APEA Journal*, 125–131.

Powell, T. G. and McKirdy, D. M. (1976) Geochemical character of crude oils from Australia and Papua, New Guinea. In *Economic Geology of Australia and Papua, New Guinea 3 — Petroleum.* Ed. by Leslie, R. B., Evans, H. J. and Knight, C. L. Australian Institute of Mining and Metallurgy Monograph Series No. 7. pp. 18–29.

Ramijak, Z., Solc, A., Schmitter, J. M., Arpino, P. and Guiochon, G. (1977) Separation of acids from asphalts. *Anal. Chem.* **49**, 1222–1224.

Rhead, M. M., Eglinton, G., Draffan, G. H. and England, P. J. (1971) Conversion of oleic acid to saturated fatty acids in Severn Estuary sediments. *Nature* **232**, 327–340.

Romero, E. M. and Brenner, R. R. (1966) Fatty acids synthesised from hexadecane by *Pseudomonas aeruginosa. J. Bact.* **91**, 183–188.

Rubinstein, I., Strausz, O. P., Spyckerelle, C., Crawford, R. S. and Westlake, D. W. S. (1977) The origin of the oil sand bitumen of Alberta, a chemical and microbiological simulation study. *Geochim. Cosmochim. Acta* **41**, 1341–1353.

Russell, N. J. and Volkman, J. K. (1980) The effect of growth temperature on wax ester composition in the psychrophilic bacterium *Micrococcus cryophilus* ATCC 15174. *J. Gen. Microbiol.* **118**, 131–141.

Sassen, R. (1980) Biodegradation of crude oil and mineral deposition in a shallow Gulf Coast salt dome. *Org. Geochem.* **2**, 153–166.

Scheuerbrandt, G. and Bloch, K. (1961) Unsaturated fatty acids in microorganisms. *J. Biol. Chem.* **237**, 2064–2068.

Schmitter, J. M., Arpino, P. and Guiochon, G. (1978) Investigation of high molecular weight carboxylic acids in petroleum by different combinations of chromatography (gas and liquid) and mass spectrometry (electron impact and chemical ionisation). *J. Chromatogr.* **167**, 149–158.

Seifert, W. K. (1975) Carboxylic acids in petroleum and sediments. In *Progress in the Chemistry of Organic Natural Products* **32**. Springer. pp. 1–49.

Seifert, W. K. and Howells, W. G. (1969) Interfacially active acids in a Californian crude oil. Isolation of carboxylic acids and phenols. *Anal. Chem.* **41**, 554–562.

Seifert, W. K. and Moldowan, J. M. (1979) The effect of biodegradation on steranes and terpanes in crude oils. *Geochim. Cosmochim. Acta* **43**, 111–126.

Shaw, N. (1974) Lipid composition as a guide to classification of bacteria. *Adv. Appl. Microbiol.* **17**, 63–109.

Sklan, D. and Budowski, P. (1972) Formation of linoleic acid in the rat colon. *Brit. J. Nutr.* **28**, 457–462.

Sklan, D., Budowski, P. and Volcani, R. (1972) Synthesis *in vitro* of linoleic acid by rumen liquor of calves. *Brit. J. Nutr.* **28**, 239–248.

Stark, W., Urbach, G. and Hamilton, J. S. (1976) Volatile compounds in butter oil IV. Quantitative estimation of free fatty acids and free δ-lactones in butter oil by cold finger molecular distillation. *J. Dairy Res.* **43**, 469–477.

Tornabene, T. G., Bennette, O. and Oro, J. (1967) Fatty acid and aliphatic hydrocarbon composition of *Sarcina lutea* grown in three different media. *J. Bact.* **94**, 344–348.

Tornabene, T. G., Gelpi, E. and Oro, J. (1967) Identification of fatty acids and aliphatic hydrocarbons in *Sarcina lutea* by gas chromatography and combined gas chromatography–mass spectrometry. *J. Bact.* **94**, 333–343.

van Hoeven, W., Maxwell, J. R. and Calvin, M. (1969) Fatty acids and hydrocarbons as evidence of life processes in ancient sediments and crude oils. *Geochim. Cosmochim. Acta* **39**, 877–881.

Vigrass, L. W. (1968) Geology of the Canadian heavy oil sands. *Bull. Am. Ass. Petr. Geol.* **52**, 1984–1999.

Volkman, J. K. and Johns, R. B. (1977) The geochemical sugnificance of positional isomers of unsaturated acids from an intertidal zone sediment. *Nature* **267**, 693–694.

Walker, J. D., Cowell, R. R. and Petrakis, L. (1975) Microbial petroleum degradation:application of computerised mass spectrometry. *Can. J. Microbiol.* **21**, 1760–1767.

Walker, J. D., Colwell, R. R., Vaituzis, Z. and Meyer, S. A. (1975) Petroleum-degrading achlorophyllous algae, *Prototheca zopfii. Nature* **254**, 423–424.

Winters, J. C. and Williams, J. A. (1969) Microbial alteration of crude oil in the reservoir. *Am. Chem. Soc. (Div. Petr. Chem. Prep.)* Sept. 1969, pp. E21–E31.

Yano, I., Furukawa, Y. and Kusunose, M. (1971) Fatty acid composition of *Arthrobacter simplex* grown on hydrocarbons. Occurrence of α-hydroxy fatty acids. *Eur. J. Biochem.* **23**, 220–228.

Advances in Organic Geochemistry 1981, pp. 650–658
© *John Wiley & Sons Limited, 1983*

Crude Oil Biodegradation under Simulated and Natural Conditions

N. S. Goodwin, P. J. D. Park and A. P. Rawlinson

BP Research Centre, Chertsey Road, Sunbury-on-Thames, Middlesex

A major problem in petroleum geochemistry is to relate oils from differing stratigraphic levels within a basin to their probable source rocks. This problem is made more acute when the crude oil is highly biodegradaed or otherwise altered. One method of attempting this correlation, which is highly favoured by a number of geochemists, is the correlation of the sterane and pentacyclic triterpane fingerprints. This approach is advocated by research geochemists who have attempted to simulate biodegradation of crude oils in laboratory experiments and have consistantly noted that the steranes and pentacyclic triterpanes remain unaltered. On the other hand, several petroleum exploration geochemists have noted that many naturally biodegraded oils, which according to all known data, must be related to other non-degraded oils within the basin have exhibited highly altered sterane and pentacyclic triterpane distributions. As a continuation of our work at BP, in trying to identify specific biodegradation markers and effects an examination of many biodegraded oils, both from laboratory-simulated experiments and natural occurrences, has been conducted. In our laboratory experiment, oils originally collected from a bund spillage at BP Kent Refinery, have had their naturally occurring biological activity aided by the addition of a nutrient medium (mineral salts) and continual agitation at a constant temperature. After several months it has been observed that a substantial alteration of the sterane and triterpane composition has occurred. The C_{27} regular and rearranged steranes have been severely reduced in relative concentration, and this has been followed by a reduction of the higher molecular weight (C_{35}) $\alpha\beta$ hopanes. There is also evidence to suggest that ($22R$) epimers of naturally occurring extended hopanes are degraded at a slightly faster rate than the related ($22S$) epimers.

INTRODUCTION

Together with the extensive study of source rocks (their potential and maturity), the exploration geochemist must undertake extensive efforts to find if a relationship exists between any hydrocarbons found within a sedimentary basin and, if possible, their proposed source rocks. Such correlations form an integral part of any exploration assessment of a basin, since it enables the exploration geochemist to ascertain whether more than one mature source rock exists and if hydrocarbons found at differing stratigraphic horizons are related.

Such correlations are particularly pertinent when the known source rock data comes from mainly immature sediments taken from wells drilled on stratigraphic highs or are derived from highly weathered immature outcrops collected from basin margins. Very often such oil source rock correlation studies have revealed that the most potentially prolific source within an area does not contribute to oils found in that area (an example being the Cretaceous sediments on the North Slope of Alaska, which are too immature to be a major contributor to the North Slope Crude oils (Seifert *et al.*, 1978)). Early attempts to oil–oil correlation were undertaken using bulk properties such as API gravities, sulphur content etc. These correlations have been considerably

improved by the extensive use of biological markers, the distributions of which are related in both crude oil and the extractable material from mature source rocks. Such an approach has concentrated on the distributions of *n*-alkanes, acyclic isoprenoids and, in particular, the steranes and pentacyclic triterpanes (van Dorsselaer *et al.*, 1978; Seifert and Moldowan, 1978).

A major difficulty associated with these correlation studies comes when the reservoired oils have undergone post-accumulation changes. Such changes include the thermal maturation of the oil, the associated effects of gravity segregation, deasphalteing etc, and the extensive alterations associated with water-washing and biodegradation. This latter phenomenon is widespread, and explorationally highly significant, since over 10% of the known crude oil reserves have probably been affected and a predicted loss of a further 10% has probably occurred (Hunt, 1979). The large reserves of heavy oil in Western Canada and Eastern Venezuela alone, which most likely result from biodegradation, exceed the entire reserves in the Middle East (Demaison, 1977).

Because of the importance of biodegradation to oil exploration, BP Geochemistry Branch at Sunbury has spent some time studying the problems of biodegradation in an attempt to find specific

Table 1
Bacterial Counts. N.D. = not determined,

	Sample no	1	2	3	4	5	6	7	8	9	10	11	12
After 4½ months	Bacteria	1.8×10^5	$<10^4$	$<10^2$	1.3×10^6	3×10^6	1.2×10^7	2.2×10^6	4.9×10^6	5.3×10^6	3×10^7	5.7×10^6	1.5×10^6
	Yeast	3×10^3	1.7×10^5	2×10^3	1.3×10^4	3×10^3	2.1×10^4	1.4×10^4	$<10^3$	2×10^3	3×10^3	$<10^3$	1×10^3
After 7½ months	Bacteria	8.2×10^3	N.D.	N.D.	N.D.	N.D.	6.6×10^6	1.4×10^2	N.D.	N.D.	1.8×10^7	1.8×10^6	N.D.
	Yeast	<100					100	100			<100	100	

biodegradation markers or, more specifically, compounds which show that biodegradation has occurred and the affects on the composition of the oil.

Many workers have published on the pattern of crude oil biodegradation e.g. Winters and Williams (1969) and Bailey *et al.* (1973), showing that the first compounds to be removed from a crude oil by aerobic bacteria are *n*-alkanes followed by alkyl cyclic alkanes, aromatics and acyclic isoprenoids. A review of this work has been made by Milner *et al.* (1977) and fair agreement exists between workers in this field about the relative rates of removal of these compounds. However, disagreement has arisen as to whether the biological marker compounds steranes and pentacyclic triterpanes are degraded. Reed (1977) and Siefert and Moldowan (1979) concluded from their studies of reservoired oils that these families of compounds are degraded by bacteria, whilst Rubinstein *et al.* (1977) and later Connan *et al.* (1979) reported that the steranes and pentacyclic triterpanes were unaffected in either reservoirs or laboratory experiments. Connan *et al.* (1979) studied oils from the Aquitane basin (SW France) and showed that they could microbially degrade crude oils from this region in the laboratory to match heavy oils found in the Aquitane Tar belt region. The pentacyclic triterpanes and the steranes were exactly similar in the laboratory-degraded and reservoired oils.

Despite the results of Connan and Rubenstein, the petroleum geochemist is still left with the dilemma that, in many basins, degraded and non-degraded oils exist which must be related but in which considerable alteration of these multicyclic compounds has occurred. The experiments reported here were undertaken in an attempt to answer some of these ambiguities.

EXPERIMENTAL

Sample origin

During 1979, a set of 12 crude oil samples were collected from a tank bund at BPs Kent Refinery, Isle of Grain, in which a contained spillage had occurred some weeks before. Examination of aliquots of each sample by liquid chromatography followed by gas chromatography (GC) and gas chromatography–mass spectrometry (GC–MS) showed that each sample could be regarded as identical in type analysis, *n*-alkanes, acyclic isoprenoidal alkanes, steranes and pentacyclic triterpane distributions.

Table 2
Cultures present in Sample 7 after 4½ months biodegradation Bacteria 2.2×10^6 per gm made up 4 types all Gram Negative S Rods.

Type 1. Colony 1–2 mm dia., round smooth glossy, opaque yellow
Type 2. Colony of slightly bigger than Type 1, round smooth glossy, 3–4 mm dia. flat grey/brown.
Type 3. 2 mm dia., round smooth glossy, white with transparent margin.
Type 4. 1–2 mm dia., round smooth glossy, opaque white.
Also present: Yeast 1.4×10^4 per gm, and some sulphide-producing bacteria.

Laboratory biodegradation

In vitro biodegradation of the oil samples collected from Kent, was carried out in flat-bottomed baffled culture vessels. These were fitted with an air condenser permitting entry of air to the flasks without loss of hydrocarbons by evaporation. Each of the samples (3 ml aliquots) was added to 200 ml of a mineral salts solution (Omori *et al.*, 1975) in separate flasks and incubated with shaking at 30 °C.

Analysis

No additional inoculum of organisms was added, the oil sample from the field providing both inoculum and carbon source for the growth of bacteria and/or yeasts.

After periods of 4½, 7½ and 11½ months, about 1 ml of each oil was extracted from the flask using a pipette. A small portion of each oil was put aside for bacterial counts. Counts were made (Table 1) on the moleculum and subsequent cultures for aerobic bacteria, yeasts and moulds. Counts of aerobic bacteria were made using a dropcount technique, on Plate Count Agar incubated at 30 °C for 48 h. Counts of hydrocarbon-utilising bacteria were made using a modification of Walker and Colwell's Oil Salts Agar (Walker and Colwell, 1976) incubated at 30 °C for 7 d. Counts of yeasts and moulds were made on Rose Bengal Chlorotetracycline Agar (Jarvis, 1973) incubated at 30 °C for 5 d.

The oil in the remaining part of the sample was extracted, by first adding 1 ml of N/10 hydrochloric acid and then extracting several times with 25 ml portions of redistilled methylene chloride. The methylene chloride was removed using a rotary evaporator with the water bath at 50 °C. The extracted oils were separated into saturated alkanes, aromatics and polar material by

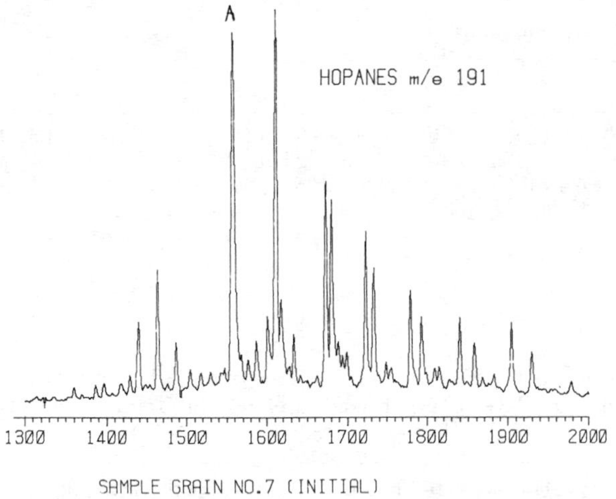

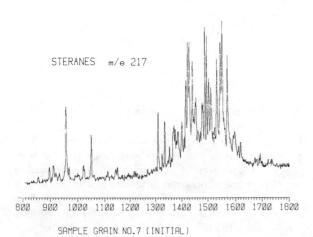

Fig. 1. Sample Grain No. 7 (Initial) *m/e* 191 hopanes.

STERANES *m/e* 217

SAMPLE GRAIN NO.7 (INITIAL)

Fig. 2. Sample Grain No. 7 (Initial) *m/e* 217 steranes.

liquid chromatography using activated silica gel columns and heptane solvent to remove the saturated alkanes and aromatic fractions.

Gas chromatographic analysis was undertaken on the saturated alkane fractions using a Carlo Erba gas chromatograph with an FID detector and a 20 m × 0.3 mm glass capillary column coated with OV1 (Jaeggi). Analysis conditions were injector temperature 360 °C; detector 360 °C; carrier gas helium 1–1.5 ml min^{-1}; temperature programmed 70 °C–280 °C (4 °C min^{-1}) after initial hold at 70 °C of 5 min and a final hold at 280 °C of 20 min. Prior to any GC or GC–MS run, a standard sample containing *n*-alkanes in the region C_{11}–C_{36} was run through the instruments to check that no front- or back-end losses occurred.

The GC conditions for the Varian Mat 44S GC–MS were the same as above. Scans were repeatedly taken over the whole GC run using a scan rate of 1.0 s between 510 and 50 mass units. The source temperature was 210 °C, ionisation voltage 70 eV and interface lines 320 °C. Data was stored on the SS200 data system and mass fragmentograms were reconstructed from the total collected spectra.

RESULTS AND DISCUSSION

Laboratory experiments

All of the twelve original oil samples showed very similar properties. The *m/e* 191 pentacyclic triterpanes and *m/e* 217 sterane fragmentograms were identical and are presented in Figs. 1 and 2 respectively for sample 7. It can be seen from these figures that all the normal (17αH, 21βH) hopanes and C_{27}, C_{28} and C_{29} regular and rearranged steranes are present. The concentration of the C_{27} steranes is relatively low compared with the C_{28} and C_{29} compounds and this is thought to be due to the oil coming from a source with a high terrestrial input. Unfortunately the actual origin of this spilled oil was unknown.

The first of the biodegraded samples was taken from each of the sample flasks after $4\frac{1}{2}$ months of laboratory-cultivation. The results showed a wide variation in the degree of biodegradation. Three of the samples showed little or no indication that biodegradation had occurred. GC analysis of all of these samples showed the *n*-alkanes were still present. Five of the remaining samples showed that biodegradation had occurred, but there was still evidence of *n*-alkanes and/or acyclic isoprenoidal alkanes being present. Samples 6, 7, 10 and 11 all showed identical patterns of biodegradation with the *n*-alkanes and acyclic isoprenoids removed. Figures 3 and 4 show the *m/e* 191 and *m/e* 217 traces for one of these oils (sample 7) although all four samples were considered to be identical. It is evident from a comparison of Figs. 1 and 3 that the (17αH, 21βH) hopanes have been biodegraded. Certainly the $22R/22S$ ratio of the C_{31}–C_{35} epimers has been considerably altered, and there is an apparent increase in the concentration of moretanes relative to the hopanes. The degradation of the steranes indicated by Figs. 2 and 4 and, in particular, the C_{27} steranes looks even more pronounced with an apparent complete loss of these compounds.

The mass fragmentograms of sample 7 after $11\frac{1}{2}$ months' biodegradation are presented in Figs. 5 and 6. From a comparison of Figs. 1 and 5 it is obvious that the (17αH, 21βH) hopanes have been considerably

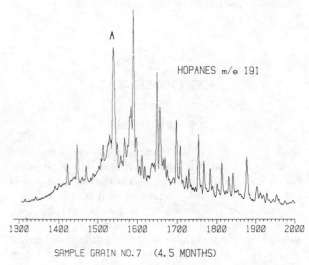

Fig. 3. Sample Grain No. 7 ($4\frac{1}{2}$ months) *m/e* 191 hopanes.

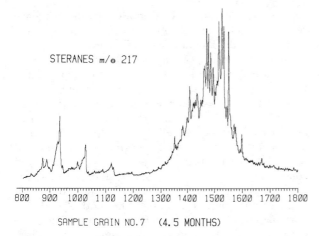

STERANES m/e 217

SAMPLE GRAIN NO.7   (4.5 MONTHS)

Fig. 4.   Sample Grain No. 7 ($4\frac{1}{2}$ months) m/e 217 steranes.

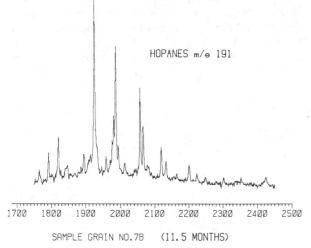

HOPANES m/e 191

SAMPLE GRAIN NO.7B   (11.5 MONTHS)

Fig. 5.   Sample Grain No. 7B ($11\frac{1}{2}$ months) m/e 191 hopanes.

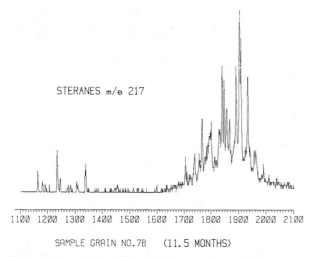

STERANES m/e 217

SAMPLE GRAIN NO.7B   (11.5 MONTHS)

Fig. 6.   Sample Grain No. 7B ($11\frac{1}{2}$ months) m/e 217 steranes.

degraded. This is very evident if one considers peak A, the (1.7αH, 21βH)-30-norhopane in comparison with the higher homologues. It is worth noting that the increased relative intensity of the moretanes noted after $4\frac{1}{2}$ months' biodegradation no longer appears to be apparent. The reason for this is not obvious, but could be

due to the fact that the moretanes are degraded but at a slightly slower rate than the hopanes.

Extensive studies of the m/e 163, 177 and 205 mass fragmentograms did not reveal a series of (17αH, 21βH) (A/B ring) nor methyl hopanes as reported by Seifert and Moldowan. The evidence for the preferential degradation of ($22R$) over ($22S$) is more pronounced in this $11\frac{1}{2}$ month sample.

After $11\frac{1}{2}$ months, the sterane distribution does not, at first sight, seem to have changed when compared with the $4\frac{1}{2}$ months situation. However, closer examination of Fig. 6 shows that the C_{27}–C_{29} steranes are considerably weaker in intensity. There is also strong evidence that the regular steranes are being biodegraded at a considerably faster rate than the rearranged compounds. This can best be seen by comparing the Chemical Ionisation Spectra (Methane gas) of the pseudo-molecular ions for the C_{27}, C_{28} and C_{29} steranes. Initial distributions are shown in Figs. 7, 8 and 9 and, after $11\frac{1}{2}$ months, in Figs. 10, 11, 12. The reduction in the C_{29} 5α sterane Peak B is very evident.

The conclusions from the series of laboratory-biodegraded samples examined are that both regular and rearranged steranes can be affected, the relative rates being regular > rearranged and $C_{27} > C_{28} > C_{29}$.

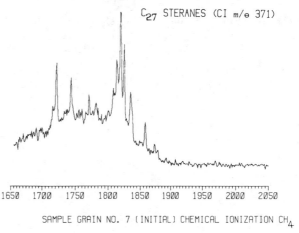

C_{27} STERANES (CI m/e 371)

SAMPLE GRAIN NO. 7 (INITIAL) CHEMICAL IONIZATION CH$_4$

Fig. 7.   Sample Grain No. 7 (initial) chemical ionization CH$_4$ m/e 371 C_{27} steranes.

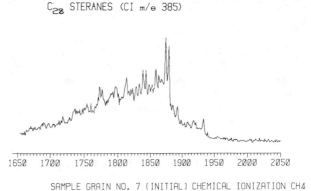

C_{28} STERANES (CI m/e 385)

SAMPLE GRAIN NO. 7 (INITIAL) CHEMICAL IONIZATION CH4

Fig. 8.   Sample Grain No. 7 (initial) chemical ionization CH$_4$ m/e 385 C_{28} steranes.

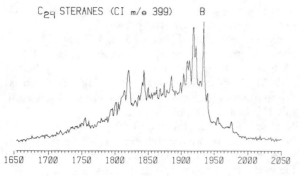

Fig. 9. Sample Grain No. 7 (initial) chemical ionization CH_4 m/e 399 C_{29} steranes.

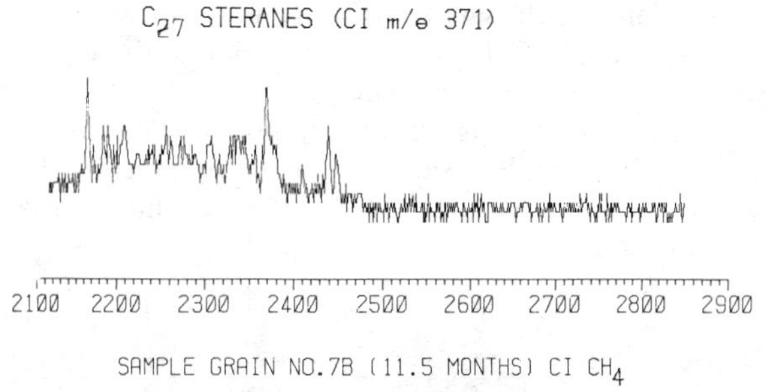

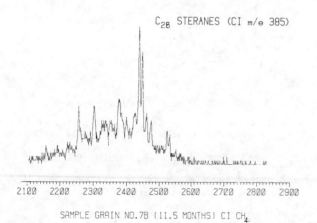

Fig. 10. Sample Grain No. 7B ($11\frac{1}{2}$ months) chemical ionization CH_4 m/e 371 C_{27} steranes.

Fig. 11. Sample Grain No. 7B ($11\frac{1}{2}$ months) chemical ionization CH_4 m/e 385 C_{28} steranes.

($17\alpha H$, $21\beta H$) hopanes and moretanes are biodegraded, hopanes slightly faster than the moretanes. The ($22R$) hopanes apparently undergo biodegradation at a faster rate than the corresponding ($22S$) epimers, and, in these experiments, there is an apparent preference for the higher molecular weight molecules.

Naturally degraded field samples

Many of the previous laboratory observations have already been noted by Seifert and Moldowan (1979) in naturally occurring biodegraded samples. However in general, the naturally biodegraded crude oils have reached a higher degree of degradation of the hopanes than seen in the laboratory experiment.

Similar results to those reported above have been seen in degraded oils from the Geneva area of Switzerland. Swiss sample 6 is a medium degraded oil found as a seep in a tunnel. The *n*-alkanes are present and the m/e 191 and m/e 217 fragmentograms shown in Figs. 13 and 14 are normal for this type of oil. A few metres away, sample 5 was collected. Here a highly degraded oil is observed with no normal alkanes or acyclic isoprenoids, and considerably altered steranes and pentacyclic triterpanes (see Figs. 15 and 16). The only dominant hopane remaining in the sample is the ($17\alpha H$, $21\beta H$)-30-norhopane and the only steranes remaining are the rearranged C_{27}, C_{28} and C_{29} compounds. Nearly all of the regular steranes have apparently been totally degraded. It is interesting to note that the tricyclic terpanes appear unaffected. A similar observation was noted by Seifert and Moldowan (1979) in their study. An outcrop sample (Swiss sample 1) taken from just a few hundred metres north of the previous two samples again contained a highly biodegraded oil. However in

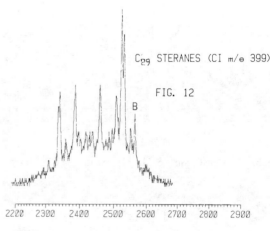

Fig. 12. Sample Grain No. 7B ($11\frac{1}{2}$) chemical ionization CH_4 m/e 399 C_{29} steranes.

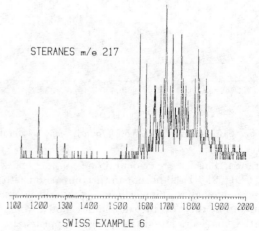

Fig. 13. Swiss example 6 m/e 217 steranes.

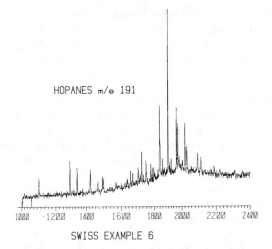

Fig. 14. Swiss example 6 *m/e* 191 hopanes.

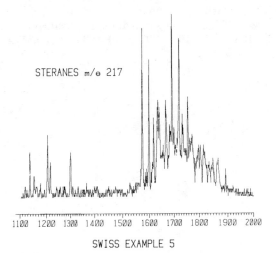

Fig. 15. Swiss example 5 *m/e* 217 steranes.

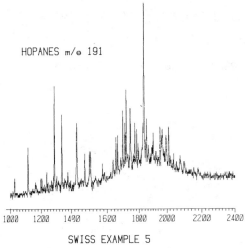

Fig. 16. Swiss example 5 *m/e* 191 hopanes.

section). It therefore appears likely that the rate of biodegradation of the different molecular types is not constant and can obviously depend on the prevailing environmental conditions.

Seifert *et al.* (1979) observed the existence of a series of (A/B ring) normethylhopanes (base peak *m/e* 177) in some of their degraded samples. This series was not observed in the laboratory studies or the naturally occurring Swiss degraded samples. Members of this series do, however, appear to be present in a highly biodegraded oil from the North Sea. Figs. 19 and 20 give the *m/e* 217 and *m/e* 191 mass fragmentograms of an oil found at 860 m in the Eocene in block 14 of the North Sea. This was a very heavy oil with an API gravity of 10.6, and containing no *n*-alkanes, but with a stable carbon isotopic ratio δ^{13}PDB $- 28.7$ per mil suggesting a source similar to the Jurassic oil found in this area. As can be seen from Fig. 19, the C_{27}–C_{29} steranes (both regular and rearranged) have been considerably degraded, as have the (17αH, 21βH) hopanes (Fig. 20). If one plots the *m/e* $149 + 163 + 177 + 191 + 205 + 219 + 733 + 247$ summation fragmentograms (Fig. 21), it can readily be seen that there are three main components in the hopane region. All of these components have been identified as having *m/e* 177 as the base peak. Components 1 and 2 have a molecular ion of

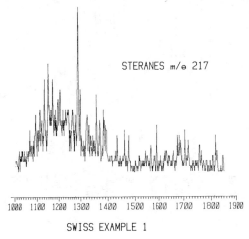

Fig. 17. Swiss example 1 *m/e* 217 steranes.

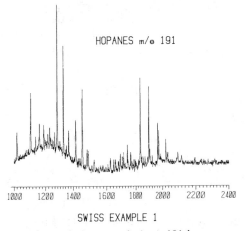

Fig. 18. Swiss example 1 *m/e* 191 hopanes.

this case, although the regular and rearranged steranes had been totally degraded (Fig. 17), not all of the (17αH, 21βH) hopanes had been removed (Fig. 18). The pattern observed was, in fact, very similar to the $11\frac{1}{2}$ month laboratory-degraded sample (see previous

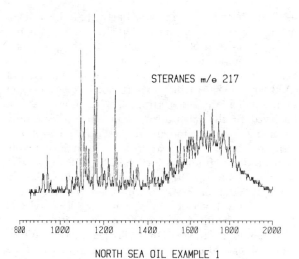

Fig. 19. North Sea example 1 ,/e 217 steranes.

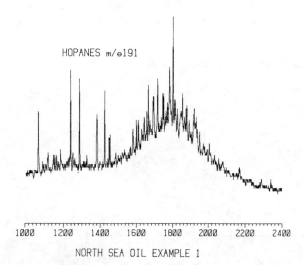

Fig. 20. North Sea example 1 *m*/*e* 191 hopanes.

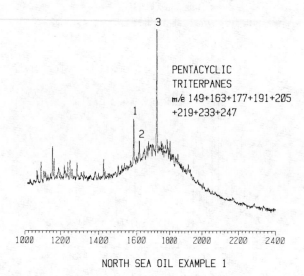

Fig. 21. North Sea example 1 *m*/*e* 149 + 163 + 177 + 191 + 205 + 219 + 233 + 247 pentacyclic triterpanes.

356, an abundant *m*/*e* 149 and are tentatively assigned as the (A/B ring) demethylated homologue of (18αH) 22, 29, 30 trisnorneohopane (Ts) and 17αH) 22, 29, 30, trisnorhopane (Tm). The third peak (component 3) also has a base peak of *m*/*e* 177, and the spectrum is shown in Fig. 22. This spectrum is the same as the norhopane first seen in biodegraded samples by Reed (1977) and also observed by Seifert and Moldowan (1979). The methyl group has been lost from the A/B ring position 10 according to Rullkötter (personal communication), and Bjorøy and Rullkötter (1980). No other members of this series were observed. Similar results were obtained for a highly degraded oil in block 3 close to the Ninian field. Here again the same 25-norhopane was observed but not a compound series.

However, in an Alaskan North Slope oil reservoired in the Upper Cretaceous, a very high degree of biodegradation was observed with *n*-alkanes, acyclic isoprenoids and C_{27}–C_{29} steranes absent (Fig. 23). In the *m*/*e* 191 mass fragmentograms only one peak was observed (Fig. 24). The summation fragmentograms *m*/*e* 149 + 163 + 177 + 191 + 205 + 219 + 233 + 247 indicates

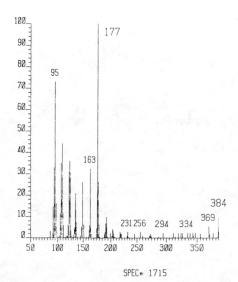

SPEC⊕ 1715

Fig. 22. Mass spectrum of large component in Fig. 21.

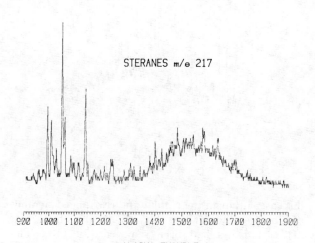

ALASKA EXAMPLE 1

Fig. 23. Alaska example 1 *m*/*e* 217 steranes.

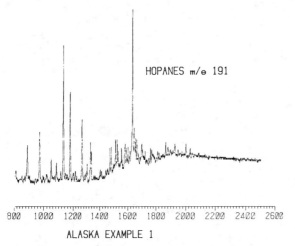

Fig. 24. Alaska example 1 *m/e* 191 hopanes.

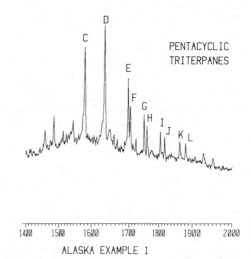

Fig. 25. Alaska example 1 pentacyclic triterpanes *m/e* 149 + 163 + 177 + 191 + 205 + 219 + 233 + 247.

Table 3

	Relative Intensity *m/e* %								
	149	163	177	191	205	219	384	398	412
GC peak									
C	19	28	100	0	2	2	6	N/A	N/A
D	35	52	60	100	7	0	0	8	N/A
E	72	74	83	16	100	5	0	0	13
G	72	77	98	0	0	100	0	0	0

Table 4
Retention index Jaeggi OV1.

CN	*CN	Tentative identification (based on mass spectra)	Occurence
27.84	28.01	(18αH) 22,29,30-Trisnorneohopane	C
28.13	28.30	(17αH) 22,29,30-Trisnorhopane	C
28.46	28.63	25,30-Bisnorhopane	A
29.33	29.50	25-Norhopane	A
29.54	29.71	(17αH, 21βH)-30-Norhopane	C
30.40	30.57	(1st) 25-Nor-30-methylhopane	A
30.45	*30.62	(17αH, 21βH) hopane	C
30.52	30.69	(2nd) 25-Nor-30-methylhopane	A
31.28	31.45	(1st) 25-Nor-30-ethylhopane	A
31.44	31.61	(2nd) 25-Nor-30-ethylhopane	A
31.45	31.62	22S-(17αH, 21βH)-30-methylhopane	C
31.59	31.76	22R-(17αH, 21βH)-30-methylhopane	C
32.29	32.46	(1st) 25-Nor-30-*n*-propylhopane	A
32.32	32.49	22S-(17αH, 21βH)-30-ethylhopane	C
32.47	32.64	(2nd) 25-Nor-30-*n*-propylhopane	A
32.51	32.68	22R-(17αH, 21βH)-30-ethylhopane	C
33.27	33.44	(1st) 25-Nor-30-*n*-butylhopane	A
33.28	33.45	22S-(17αH, 21βH)-30-*n*-propylhopane	C
33.51	33.68	22R-(17αH, 21βH)-30-*n*-propylhopane	C
33.55	33.72	(2nd) 25-Nor-30-*n*-butylhopane	A
34.26	34.43	(1st) 25-Nor-20-*n*-pentylhopane	A
34.27	34.44	22S-(17αH, 21βH)-30-*n*-butylhopane	C
34.61	34.78	22R-(17αH, 21βH)-30-*n*-butylhopane	C
34.67	34.84	(2nd) 25-Nor-30-*n*-pentylhopane	A
35.37	35.54	22S-(17αH, 21βH)-30-*n*-pentylhopane	C
35.73	35.90	22R-(17αH, 21βH)-30-*n*-pentylhopane	C

C = common   A = Alaskan

in the hopane region a complete series (Fig. 25) which closely resembled the normal (17αH, 21βH) hopanes. However, the relative retention times are different (see Table 4). Further examination of these peaks indicates that they are a series with the base peak increasing by 14 from 177 (Peak C). The spectral details given in Table 3 correspond to peaks C, D, E and G respectively. From the spectral data of compounds E and G etc. it would at first appear that the series is one of normoretanes, the methyl group missing from the A/B ring giving rise to a dominant 177 peak. In E a slight dominance of the D/E ring fragment (m/e 205) can be seen whilst in G, the same situation is observed for the m/e 219 fragment. As the molecular weight increases the dominance of the D/E ring base fragment is reduced, and is no longer observed. In a recent publication Rullkötter has shown that in the mass spectra of 25-nor(17αH) hopanes the intensity of the A/B and D/E ring fragments are approximately equal as in the (17β21α) moretane spectra. This new evidence would suggest that the demethalated compounds observed in the Alaskan North Slope oils are 25-nor-(17α)-hopanes. Peaks C and D are regarded as (17αH)25-norhopanes, although it is impossible to distinguish hopanes from moretanes in this molecular weight range and on the basis of mass spectra alone. It should be noted that Peak C is mass spectrometrically identical and has the same retention on an OV1 capillary column as the compound in the North Sea samples above. On this basis, it is assigned as the (17αH, 21βH)-25-norhopane already proposed (Seifert and Moldowan, 1979).

It is not yet proven that these 25-norhopanes are a product of biodegradation, they may be present in crudes in low concentration. Similarity in retention time to the normal (17αH, 21βH) hopanes may result in them not being observed until these normal hopanes are removed via biodegradation etc.

CONCLUSIONS

Laboratory experiments have shown that steranes and pentacyclic triterpanes can be biodegraded. The rates of biodegradation of steranes appears to be regular $>$rearranged and $C_{27} > C_{28} > C_{29}$. The rates of biodegradation of pentacyclic triterpanes is $(22R)$ $> (22S)$ and $C_{35} > C_{34} > C_{33} > C_{32} > C_{31} > C_{30} > C_{29}$. Tricyclic terpanes do not appear to be biodegraded.

A series of (17αH)25-norhopanes has been found in North Slope Alaskan biodegraded crude oil. It is believed that this series can also be biodegraded but in many highly biodegraded oils the lower members of this series can still be found.

The relative rates of degradation of steranes and pentacyclic triterpanes are probably dependent on a range of complex environmental factors which, in turn, affect microbial utilisation of these hydrocarbons.

Acknowledgements

We wish to thank the management of the British Petroleum Co. Ltd for the support of this project and permission to publish.

REFERENCES

Bailey, N. J. L., Jobson, A. M. and Rodgers, M. A. (1973) Bacterial degradation of crude oil: comparison of experimental data. *Chem. Geol.* **11**, 203–221.

Bjorøy, M. and Rullkötter, J. (1980) An unusual C_{27} triterpane 25,28,30-Trisnormoretane. *Chem. Geol.* **30**, 27–34.

Connan, J., Restle, A. and Albrecht, P. (1979) Biodegradation of crude oil in the Aquitaine Basin. In *Advances in Organic Geochemistry 1979.* Ed. by Maxwell, J. R. and Douglas, A. G. pp. 1–17.

Demaison, G. T. (1977) Tar sands and supergiant oil fields. *AAPG Bull.* **61**, 1950–1961.

Hunt, J. M. (1979) *Petroleum Geochemistry and Geology.* W. H. Freeman & Co.

Jarvis, B. (1973) Comparison of an improved Rose Bengal Chlorotetracycline Agar with other media for the selective isolation and enumeration of moulds and yeasts in food. *J. Appl. Bact.* **36**, 723–727.

Milner, C. W. D., Rodger, M. A. and Evans, C. R. (1977) Petroleum transformation in reservoirs. *J. Geochem. Explor.* **7**, 101–153.

Omori, T., Jigami, Y. and Minoda, Y. (1975) Isolation identification and substrate assimilation specificity of some aromatic hydrocarbon utilising bacteria. *Agr. Biol. Chem. (Japan)* **39**, 1775–1779.

Reed, W. E. (1977) Molecular compositions of weathered petroleum and comparison with its possible source. *Geochim. Cosmochim. Acta* **41**, 237–247.

Rubinstein, I., Strausz, O. P., Spyckerelle, C., Crawford, R. J. and Westlake, D. W. S. (1977) The origin of the oil sand bitumens of Alberta. *Geochim. Cosmochim. Acta* **41**, 1341–1353.

Rullkötter, J. (1982) Gas chromatography/mass spectrometry of degraded triterpanes in fossil organic matter. Proc. 9th International Mass. Spec. Conf. Vienna. Elsevier (in press).

Seifert, W. K., Moldowan, J. M. and Jones, R. W. (1978) Application of biological marker chemistry to petroleum exploration. *Proc. 10th World Petrol. Conf.* Vol. 2. Heyden & Son.

Seifert, W. K. and Moldowan, J. M. (1979) The effects of biodegradation on steranes and terpanes in crude oils. *Geochim. Cosmochim. Acta* **43**, 111–126.

van Dorsselaer, A., Schmitter, J. M., Albrecht, P., Claret, J. and Connan, J. (1978) Use of biological markers in correlation problems. *8th Internat. Congr. Org. Geochem. (Moscow).*

Walker, J. and Colwell, R. (1976) Enumeration of petroleum-degrading micro-organisms. *Appl. Env. Microbiol.* **31**, 198–207.

Winters, J. C. and Williams, J. A. (1969) Microbiological alteration of crude oil in the reservoir. Symposium on petroleum transformations in geochemical environments. *Am. Chem. Soc. Div. Petroleum Chem.* New York. 7–12 Sept.

Advances in Organic Geochemistry 1981, pp. 659–667
© *John Wiley & Sons Limited, 1983*

Occurrence and Formation of Tricyclic and Tetracyclic Terpanes in Sediments and Petroleums

F. R. Aquino Neto*, J. M. Trendel*, A. Restle*, J. Connan† and P. A. Albrecht*

Institut de Chimie, Université Louis Pasteur, 1, rue Blaise Pascal 67008 Strasbourg, France

†*Centre Micouleau, Société Nationale Elf-Aquitaine, 64001 Pau, France*

Two series of tricyclic and tetracyclic terpanes previously reported by several authors have been studied in about forty crude oils and rocks from various environments and ages. The tricyclic series extends from C_{19} to C_{30} with a constant ring system and an isoprenoid side chain of variable length, suggesting a yet unknown tricyclohexaprenane precursor skeleton 8. The tetracyclic series (17,21-secohopanes) extends from C_{24} to C_{27} (tentative evidence up to C_{35}) and is closely related to the pentacyclic hopanoids of microbial origin, by cleavage of the 17(21) bond during early diagenesis or maturation. These considerations are based on data obtained by computerized gas chromatography–mass spectrometry, as well as on the conclusive identifications of several members of both series (three tricyclics: C_{19}, C_{20}, 1–3, and four tetracyclics, C_{24}–C_{27}, 4–7) by comparison with synthesized standards. Both series are apparently absent in recent sediments and very resistant towards biodegradation. In ancient sediments and crude oils they are almost ubiquitous, implying most probably a microbial or algal origin. Several variations in the distribution of these compounds were observed in our samples, but depend for their understanding upon a clearer knowledge of their biological precursors. Thermal alteration experiments carried out *in vitro* on a crude oil and on crude oil fractions indicate a neoformation of both series from the polar fractions (resins, asphaltenes), a conclusion reached previously by other authors in the case of the tricyclics. With increasing maturation both series show a stronger increase, as compared with the pentacyclic hopanes.

INTRODUCTION

The polycyclic alkanes which occur as a significant part of the organic matter of sediments and petroleums are the saturated counterparts of functionalized precursors from living organisms. They may be formed during early diagenesis or at further stages of maturation in the subsurface, and their identification can give useful information on their origin and on the chemical reactions which take place in the geological environment (Didyk *et al.*, 1978; Ourisson *et al.*, 1979). Furthermore they find an increasing use as correlation parameters between various geological organic matters (crude oils; source rocks) (Seifert and Moldowan, 1978). Most of the effort during the last decade has been concerned with the characterization of the steranes and of the pentacyclic triterpanes, the latter being mainly composed of the various hopane series of microbial origin (Ourisson *et al.*, 1979). However tri- and tetracyclic terpanes are also present in sediments and crude oils, often in amounts of the same order of magnitude as the steranes and the triterpanes, as has been noticed by several research groups during recent years (Anders and Robinson, 1971; Reed, 1977 and references therein; Vorobieva *et al.*,

1978; Seifert and Moldowan, 1979; Scholefield and Whitehurst, 1980; Simoneit and Kaplan, 1980; Connan *et al.*, 1980; Rullkötter and Philp, 1981; Zumberge, 1982). The major tricyclic terpanes belong to a series which seems to be relatively widespread in geological samples, whereas the tetracyclic series has been less frequently observed.

We have now firmly established the structural elucidation of several members of these tri- and tetracyclic series, allowing new considerations of their origin. Indeed we have conclusively identified three low molecular weight (C_{19}, C_{20}) members of the tricyclic series, 1–3, as well as four homologues (C_{24}–C_{27}; 17,21-secohopanes) of the tetracyclic series 4–7 (Fig. 1).

These results were first reported at the Tenth International Meeting on Organic Geochemistry (Bergen, Norway) and the details of the identifications by comparison with synthesized reference compounds have been published elsewhere (Trendel *et al.*, 1982; Aquino Neto *et al.*, 1982). We would like here to report on the distribution of the tri- and tetracyclic terpane series in about forty crude oils and sediments of various origins and ages, as well as on their neoformation by thermolysis in the case of a crude oil. Finally we have added the results from heating experiments carried out

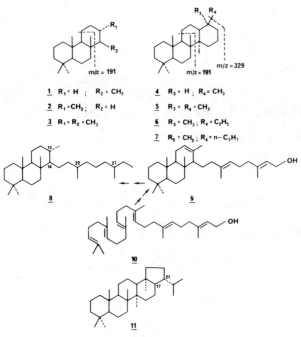

Fig. 1. Tricyclic (C_{19}, C_{20}; 1–3) and tetracyclic (C_{24}–C_{27}: 4–7) terpanes conclusively identified in sediments and crude oils. Tricyclohexaprenol 9 (from cyclization of hexaprenol 10) as possible precursor of tricyclohexaprenane 8 (C_{30}). 11: (17αH, 21βH) hopane (C_{30}).

on fractions from another crude oil, which show indeed that the tri- and tetracyclic alkanes can be generated from the polar fractions of the petroleum, confirming a finding first presented at the Bergen meeting in the case of the tricyclics by another research group (Ekweozor and Strausz, 1982; see below, Note added in proof).

EXPERIMENTAL

The total alkanes were obtained from the sediment extracts and the deasphaltened crude oils by silica gel chromatography and the *n*-alkanes were removed by using 5 Å molecular sieves, as previously described (Albrecht *et al.*, 1976). The unsaturated hydrocarbons formed in the heating experiments were separated on silica gel impregnated with silver nitrate (10%). After elution of the 'aromatic' fraction with benzene, the resins were obtained by exhaustive elution with methanol.

The asphaltenes of the crude oils were precipitated with pentane and redissolved in chloroform before being

reprecipitated in pentane; this last operation was repeated twice.

The heating experiments were carried out in glass vessels in a nitrogen vacuum. The heated fractions were extracted with chloroform.

The analysis of the alkanes was done by capillary column gas chromatography (CCGC) and by CCGC coupled with computerized mass spectrometry (SE-30 or OV-1, 25 m × 0.3 mm; LKB 9000S or Finnigan 1015). The mass fragmentograms were obtained by computerized GC–MS or, in the cases where high sensitivity was required, by single ion fragmentometry using a UV chart. The latter technique was always used in the identification work for the coelution with the reference compounds (Aquino Neto *et al.*, 1982; Trendel *et al.*, 1982) on phases of various polarities.

RESULTS AND DISCUSSION

General aspects

The identification of four homologues of the tetracyclic series (C_{24}–C_{27}; Fig. 2) showed an obvious relationship between these 17,21-secohopanes and the ubiquitous pentacyclic hopane triterpanes. However further work is needed in order to decide whether the cleavage of the 17(21) bond of the pentacyclic hopanoids leading to these tetracyclic degradation products (or their functionalized counterparts) takes place during maturation or is microbially induced during early diagenesis (Trendel *et al.*, 1982). The mass spectra of these compounds are shown in Fig. 3. Noteworthy is the fragment at $m/z = 329$, corresponding to the loss of the side chain in the C_{25}–C_{27} components. By using the specific $m/z = 329$ mass fragmentogram we indeed obtained preliminary evidence for the extension of this tetracyclic series up to C_{35}, despite the fact that the higher homologues fall in the elution range of the major pentacyclic hopanes, which precluded the use of the $m/z = 191$ fragmentogram for their study.

The tricyclic series extends in most samples from $C_{19}H_{34}$ to at least $C_{30}H_{56}$ (Figs. 2 and 6). Gas chromatographic and mass spectrometric considerations were compatible with a constant ring system and an isoprenoid side chain of varying length. The complete structural elucidation of three members (C_{19}, C_{20} 1–3) of this series and the synthesis of several isomers excluded in this case a formation from hopanoid precursors. It rather pointed towards a formation from another pre-

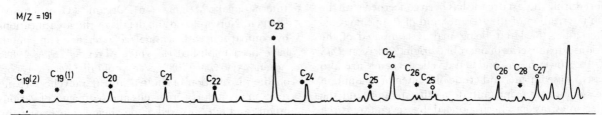

Fig. 2. Single ion mass fragmentogram ($m/z = 191$) of the total alkanes of a biodegraded petroleum (Lembeye 1, Aquitaine basin, France). Conditions: SE 30, 25 m × 0.3 mm, 100–290 °C, 3 °C min^{-1}. ✳, Tricyclic terpanes, O, Tetracyclic terpanes.

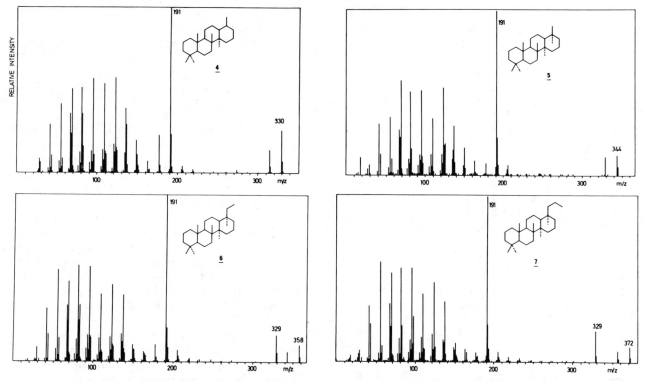

Fig. 3. Mass spectra (70 eV) of authentic tetracyclic terpane standards: C_{24}–C_{27} (4–7).

cursor based on a yet unknown C_{30} tricyclic hexaprenane skeleton 8, which could be formed *in vivo* by the cyclization of the regular hexaprenol 10, a universal cell constituent (Fig. 1). From the molecular architecture of the plausible tricyclic hexaprenol precursor 9, we assumed that this compound could play a role in membranes of micro-organisms similar to that of the pentacyclic hopanoids, a prediction which awaits confirmation (Aquino Neto *et al.*, 1982).

The mass spectra of the reference compounds 1–3 are shown in Fig. 4. The spectra of the two C_{19} compounds show major differences. In the spectrum of compound 2, which results from the cleavage of the side chain at C-14 of the assumed precursor skeleton 8, there is only a small $m/z = 191$ fragment. In compound 1, which corresponds to the loss of the methyl group at C-13 and the partial loss of the side chain, the ion at $m/z = 191$ is the base peak despite the fact that the C-14 position on the cyclic system is only monosubstituted.

Distribution of the tri- and tetracyclic terpanes in sediments and crude oils

The tri- and tetracyclic terpanes usually occur in geological samples in complex mixtures of alkanes. Their distributions are best studied in coupled gas chromatography–mass spectrometry by monitoring the $m/z = 191$ ion, which, except for compound 2, is the major fragment in these terpane series. Typical $m/z = 191$ mass fragmentograms are shown in Figs. 2 and 6.

About forty crude oils and ancient sediments from France (Aquitaine basin, Lodève basin), Guatemala, Iraq, Libya, Tunisia, USA and Western Africa (Congo), ranging in age from Jurassic to Tertiary have been

analysed for the tri- and tetracyclic terpane series described above. Although tetracyclic terpenes, in particular related to the lupane triterpane series, have been described and identified in some cases in recent sediments (Corbet *et al.*, 1980), these novel series are apparently absent, or present in very low amounts, in this type of sediment, which suggests their formation in a later stage of maturation. Our samples mostly comprised sediments and petroleums from carbonate basins, but also marine petroleums from other environments, as well as one terrestrial crude oil. They included several biodegraded petroleums.

Table 1 shows typical distributions of the tri- and tetracyclic terpanes in a selection of samples. The tricyclic series was present in all the samples which we have analysed, except in the terrestrial oil from New Zealand. This series always showed a maximum at C_{23} and minima at C_{22} and C_{27}, characteristics which are in agreement with methyl substituents at the corresponding positions of the precursor skeleton 8. The broadened peak at C_{25} and the occurrence of doublets at each of the higher carbon numbers (e.g. C_{26} and C_{28}), again observed in all cases, most probably correspond to mixtures of diastereomers at position C-22. Such positions may indeed epimerize in the conditions prevailing in the subsurface, as shown in the case of the hopanes and steranes (Ourisson *et al.*, 1979; Ensminger *et al.*, 1978; Mackenzie *et al.*, 1980). The higher homologues of the series (C_{29}, C_{30}) were usually less easily distinguished in the $m/z = 191$ mass fragmentograms, mainly because they fall in the elution range of the pentacyclic hopanes. They were better analysed by using the corresponding molecular mass fragmentograms ($m/z = 402$; 416). Only the C_{19}

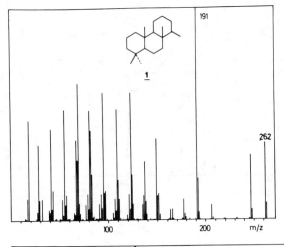

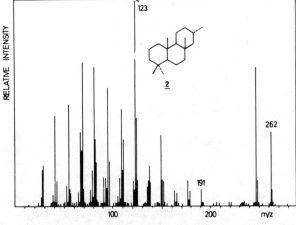

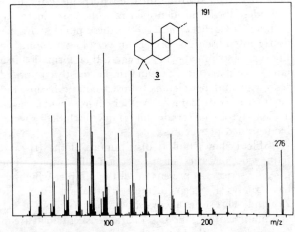

Fig. 4. Mass spectra (70 eV) of authentic tricyclic terpane standards: C_{19} (1, 2) and C_{20} (3).

compound 1 has been systematically considered; it is relatively small in most cases. In a few samples, however, the distributions of both 1 and 2 have been studied by using their molecular mass fragmentogram ($m/z = 262$). In some cases (carbonate basins) both compounds occur in similar amounts, whereas in others, such as the Emeraude oil field (Congo), the compound 2, which corresponds to the complete loss of the side chain, is by far the most predominant. In most crude oils and rocks from carbonate basins the higher homologues of the tricyclic series (above C_{26}) are relatively small and often not significantly represented, whereas in samples from

other environments the $C_{26}-C_{30}$ compounds are of the same order of magnitude as the lower members as shown in the case of the Emeraude crude oils (Claret et al., 1977) (Figs. 5 and 6).

The tetracyclic terpane series was also present in all samples, except again in the terrestrial crude oil where it was very weak. The C_{24} homologue was always the major component of this series. In many carbonate samples the higher homologes ($C_{25}-C_{27}$) were present in significant amounts, whereas these compounds were usually small in samples from other environments.

Both the tri- and the tetracyclic series seem to be at first unaffected by biodegradation, which mostly alters the straight and branched alkanes (Connan et al., 1980). Quite resistant towards bacteria (Reed, 1977; Seifert and Moldowan, 1979; Goodwin et al., 1982) they even undergo a concentration effect during this process, making the biodegraded petroleums most suitable for their detailed study (cf. Fig. 5). However in heavily degraded asphalts these compounds have been greatly altered, like the steranes and the pentacyclic hopanes (Restle, 1981).

The variations in the distributions of the tri- and tetracyclic terpane series which we have observed cannot be clearly interpreted at the present stage, either in terms of source, palaeoenvironment or maturation. A better knowledge of the biological precursors, especially of the tricyclic series, would be quite helpful for the understanding of these results.

Effect of *in vitro* thermal maturation of a crude oil (Aquitaine basin, France) on the distribution of the tri- and tetracyclic terpanes

A heavy immature petroleum from the Aquitaine basin (Grenade) was heated at 300 °C for periods of time ranging from 2 to 24 weeks. The amounts of total alkanes increased with heating time in the deasphaltened fraction, as expected (Table 2). The $m/z = 191$ mass fragmentogram of the branched and cyclic alkanes showed only low concentrations of the tri- and tetracyclic terpanes, as compared to the pentacyclic hopanes, in the unheated sample, and the usual predominance of the C_{23} tricyclic and the C_{24} tetracyclic homologues (Fig. 7). With increasing heating time a progressive increase in the tri- and tetracyclic terpanes took place, with a shift towards the lighter members of the tricyclic series, a feature which may be interpreted in terms of a thermal cleavage of the side chain attached to the tricyclic ring system. The distribution of the pentacyclic hopanes remained almost unaltered after 8 weeks, but was significantly changed after 24 weeks of heating: the homologues above C_{30} became very weak and the more stable rearranged C_{27} trisnorhopane (neohopane) reached the same magnitude as its $17\alpha(H)$ isomer. Due to the lack of absolute quantitation, it was not possible to decide between two hypotheses: (a) a neoformation of tri- and tetracyclic terpanes from the more polar fraction of the petroleum, since this fraction of crude oils has been well recognized as a potential precursor of hydrocarbons (e.g. Connan, 1972; Spyckerelle et al., 1979; Tissot and Welte, 1978), or (b) a

Table 1

Distribution of tricyclic and tetracyclic terpanes in a selection of geological samples. The data were obtained from $m/z = 191$ mass fragmentograms normalized to the major terpane peak.[a] $C_{19}(I)$, tr: traces.

Location of samples	Age	Characteristics	C_{19}[a]	C_{20}	C_{21}	C_{22}	C_{23}	C_{24}	C_{25}	C_{26}	C_{27}	C_{28}	C_{29}	C_{30}	C_{24}	C_{25}	C_{26}	C_{27}
						Tricyclics									Tetracyclics		
Cagnotte 101 (Aquitaine, France)	Cretaceous	Biodegraded oil. Carbonate basin (Connan et al., 1980)	15	20	30	20	100	40	25	15	tr	tr	tr	tr	80	10	30	30
Pecorade 3 (Aquitaine, France)	Cretaceous	Crude oil. Carbonate basin (Connan et al., 1980)	10	25	20	10	55	20	15	10	tr	tr	tr	tr	100	10	35	25
Ashtart 1 (offshore Tunisia)	Eocene	Crude oil. Carbonate basin	12	25	50	tr	100	70	50	30	tr	30	20	30	50	tr	tr	tr
Emeraude 1 (Congo)	Cretaceous	Biodegraded oil (Claret et al., 1977)	tr	30	70	10	100	75	50	65	tr	65	60	50	15	tr	tr	tr
Asphalt Ridge (Utah, USA)	Eocene	Native bitumen Uinta basin	tr	50	90	20	100	35	50	50	tr	45	25	25	55	tr	tr	tr
New Zealand	Eocene	High wax oil in sandstones	0	0	0	0	0	0	0	0	0	0	0	0	tr	0	0	0
St-Privat shale (Lodève basin, France)	Permian	Source rock of St-Privat bitumen	20	50	90	20	100	70	40	40	tr	45	20	20	35	tr	tr	tr
St-Privat bitumen (Lodève basin, France)	Permian	Biodegraded solid bitumen in baryte veins	tr	35	90	30	100	85	50	55	tr	50	40	45	30	tr	tr	tr

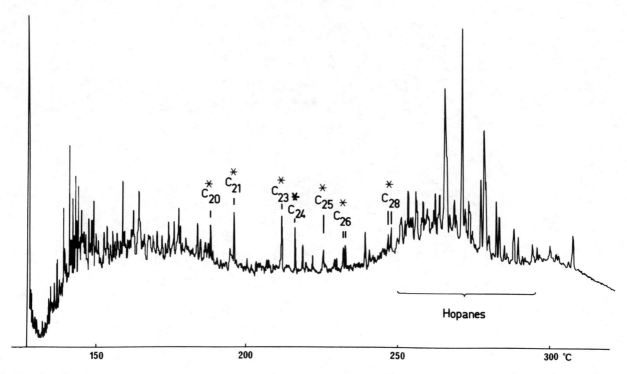

Fig. 5. Gas chromatogram of the total alkanes of a petroleum from the Emeraude oil field (Congo), enriched in tricyclic terpanes ($+$) by biodegradation. Conditions: SE 30, 25 m × 0.3 mm, 120–300 °C, 3 °C min^{-1}.

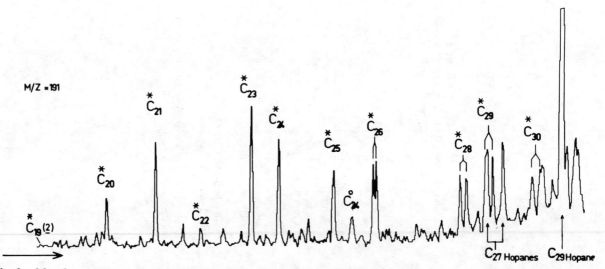

Fig. 6. Mass fragmentogram ($m/z = 191$) of the alkanes of a petroleum from the Emeraude oil field (Congo; see gas chromatogram on Fig. 5) showing the complete tricyclic terpane series. ✳ Tricyclic terpanes, O Tetracyclic terpanes. Conditions as in Fig. 2.

Table 2

Compositional changes in Grenade crude oil (Aquitaine basin, France) by artificial thermal maturation at 300 °C. n = normal; BC = branched and cyclic.

Heating time (weeks)	Residue insoluble in chloroform %	Composition of chloroform extract			
		Asphaltenes %	Alkanes %	Aromatics %	Alkanes n/BC
0	0	13	6	20	0.7
2	0	27	10	31	1.1
8	6	32	16	27	1.1
24	30	19	26	28	1.7

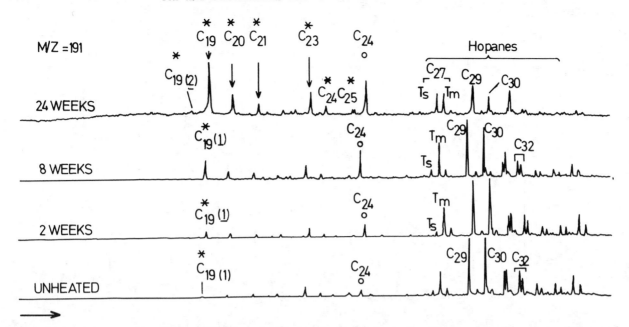

Fig. 7. Mass fragmentograms ($m/z = 191$) of branched and cyclic alkanes illustrating the changes in the patterns of terpanes by thermal treatment of a crude oil (2–24 weeks, 300 °C; Grenade, Aquitaine basin, France). ∗ Tricyclic terpanes, O Tetracyclic terpanes $T_s = 18\alpha(H)$ Trisnorhopane II (neohopane), $T_m = 17\alpha(H)$ Trisnorhopane (Seifert and Moldowan, 1978). Conditions OV1, 25 m $\times$ 0.3 mm, 100–300 °C, 3 °C min^{-1}.

better thermal stability of these terpanes, as compared to the hopanes. In both cases a preferential thermal cleavage of the higher homologues of these series would take place. Both explanations may contribute to some extent to the observed transformations.

Note added in proof

At the Bergen meeting another approach aiming at the identification of the tricyclic terpane series occurring in the Athabasca oil sand bitumen was reported (Ekweozor and Strausz, 1982). From chromatographic and spectroscopic data these authors came to similar structural conclusions as ours and proposed in particular an identical tricyclic precursor skeleton 8 for this series. They furthermore presented first evidence for the neoformation of tricyclic terpanes during the thermal alteration of the resins and the asphaltenes of the bitumen.

These results led us to reexamine several fractions obtained from unpublished thermal maturation experiments carried out previously on a biodegraded asphalt (Cagnotte, Aquitaine basin, Connan *et al.*, 1978). In these experiments the alkanes, resins and asphaltenes of the crude oil were subjected to 300 °C for 3 months. After this period. the alkanes which could be isolated from the various fractions represented respectively 85.4%, 3.9% and 2.2% of the starting alkanes, resins and asphaltenes. The thermal treatment had little effect on the original polycyclic alkanes which remained unchanged (Fig. 8), showing the thermal stability of these compounds when heated alone, in the absence of functionalized components. The resins and the asphaltenes generated new series of tri-, tetra- and pentacyclic terpanes, the relative proportion of the tri- and tetracyclics being more important as compared to pentacyclic hopanes (Fig. 8). In the tetracyclic series

only the C_{24} compound was neoformed in significant amounts and reached the same order of magnitude as the hopanes. In the tricyclic series the lower homologues (C_{19}–C_{24}) were predominant, the C_{19} homologue being greater in the experiment with the resins. The distribution of the tri- and tetracyclic terpanes, especially in the experiment with the resins, showed a high resemblance to that observed after 24 weeks from the Grenade oil (Fig. 7). The distribution of the pentacyclic hopanes generated from the resins and asphaltenes closely resembled that of the original alkanes, with the exception of an almost total lack of the rearranged C_{27} neohopane. Although only qualitative, these results confirm the conclusions previously reached on the tricyclic terpanes by Ekweozor and Strausz (1982). They indicate that a significant part of the tricyclic, but also of the tetracyclic terpanes, can be neoformed from the resins and the asphaltenes, implying the presence of functionalized precursors in these fractions. In addition to the polycyclic alkanes, a neogenesis of homologous series, including iso-, anteiso-, cyclohexyl-, methylcyclopentylalkanes has been clearly recognized from both resins and asphaltenes. These classes of compounds were completely lacking in the original asphalt due to intensive biodegradation. This *de novo* genesis clearly confirms that the polar fractions of crude oils contain precursors of various families of alkanes as stated previously.

Further studies on the molecular mass fragmentograms of the tricyclic series recently showed preliminary evidence for an extension of the isoprenoid side-chain beyond a C_{30} skeleton, at least up to C_{36} in the case of the Emeraude crude oil (Ocampo and Albrecht, unpublished results). A similar observation was also made independently by another research group who detected the series up to C_{39} in a California petroleum (Seifert and Moldowan, personal communication).

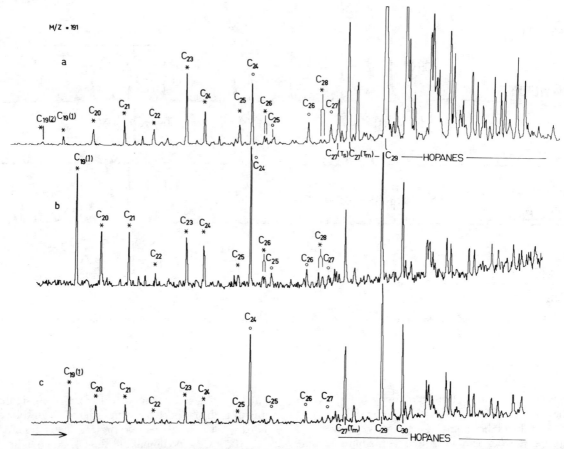

Fig. 8. Mass fragmentograms ($m/z = 191$) of the branched and cyclic alkanes neoformed by thermal treatment (24 weeks, 300 °C) of the resins (b) and asphaltenes (c) from a biodegraded crude oil (Cagnotte 101, Aquitaine basin, France). Fragmentogram (a) corresponds to the original alkanes, unaffected by this thermal treatment. * Tricyclic terpanes, O Tetracyclic terpanes. Conditions as Fig. 2.

CONCLUSIONS

Two tricyclic and tetracyclic terpane series often observed in geological samples have been studied in about forty crude oils and sediments of various environments and ages.

The tricyclic series extended from C_{19} to C_{30} and comprised a constant ring system with an isoprenoid side chain of variable length. From the data obtained by computerized gas chromatography–mass spectrometry and the synthesis of authentic standards, three lower members (C_{19}, C_{20}) of this series were conclusively characterized. Their identification suggests a yet unknown tricyclic hexaprenane precursor skeleton, which could be derived *in vivo* from the cyclization of a regular hexaprenol. The tricyclic terpane series was observed in all the studied samples, with the exception of one terrestrial petroleum. In carbonate samples the higher homologues were often relatively weak, whereas they could be of the same order of magnitude as the other members of the series in samples from other environments. The ubiquity of this series in geological samples almost certainly implies a microbial or algal origin.

The tetracyclic terpane series was completely identified between C_{24} and C_{27} by the same criteria as above. Preliminary evidence obtained from the specific

$m/z = 329$ mass fragmentogram, corresponding to the loss of the side chain, suggested that this series extends up to C_{35}. These tetracyclics are clearly related to the pentacyclic hopanoids of microbial origin, from which they could derive by cleavage of the 17(21) bond during early diagenesis (e.g. microbial oxidation of hop-17(21)-enes, often detected in recent and immature ancient sediments) or during maturation. This series was again observed in all the samples, the C_{24} member being always by far the most predominant. In carbonates the higher homologues were often present in significant amounts, which was not the case in the other environments. In the terrestrial oil, only the C_{24} compound could be detected in trace amounts.

Both terpane series are apparently absent in recent sediments, implying their formation during maturation at later stages. They are furthermore quite resistant towards microbial degradation.

Several thermal alteration experiments carried out *in vitro* on a crude oil or on crude oil fractions showed that both series can be neoformed from the polar fractions (resins, asphaltenes), confirming the results obtained previously by Ekweozor and Strausz (1982) in the case of the tricyclic terpanes of the Athabasca oil sand bitumen.

The variations in distributions of these novel series cannot be clearly interpreted at the present stage. A better knowledge of the biological precursors of these compounds, especially of the tricyclic series, would be very helpful for their understanding in terms of source, palaeoenvironment or maturation. It would also increase the value of these series as correlation parameters (e.g. Zumberge, 1982).

Acknowledgements

This study was supported by the Centre National de la Recherche Scientifique, France. We thank the Société Nationale Elf-Aquitaine for financial support and supply of samples. We also thank A. K. Aldridge, Masspec Analytica., P. Gryczka, R. Hueber and G. Teller for mass spectrometrical data, R. Ocampo and Professor G. Ourisson for helpful discussions. One of us, F.R.A.N., on leave from the Universidade Federal do Rio de Janeiro, thanks the Conselho Nacional de Desenvolvimento Cientifico Tecnologico (CNPq, Brazil) for a research grant.

REFERENCES

Albrecht, P., Vandenbroucke, M. and Mangengue, M. (1976) Geochemical studies on the organic matter from the Douala basin (Cameroon) I. Evolution of the extractable organic matter and the formation of petroleum. *Geochim. Cosmochim. Acta* **40**, 791–799.

Anders, D. E. and Robinson, W. E. (1971) Cycloalkane constituents of the bitumens from Green River shale. *Geochim. Cosmochim. Acta* **35**, 661–678.

Aquino Neto, F. R., Restle, A., Connan, J., Albrecht, P. and Ourisson, G. (1982) Novel tricyclic terpanes (C_{19}, C_{20}) in sediments and petroleums. *Tetrahedron Lett.* **23**, 2027–2030.

Claret, J., Tchikaya, J. B., Tissot, B., Deroo, G. and Van Dorsselaer, A. (1977) Un exemple d'huile biodegradée à basse teneur en soufre: le gisement d'Emeraude (Congo). In *Advances in Organic Geochemistry 1975*. Ed. by Campos, R. and Goni, G. Enadimsa, Madrid. pp. 509–522.

Connan, J. (1972) Laboratory simulation and natural diagenesis I. Thermal evolution of asphalts from the Aquitaine basin (SW France). *Bull. Centre Rech. Pau — SNPA* **6**, 195–214.

Connan, J. and Van der Weide, B. M. (1978) Thermal evolution of natural asphalts. In *Bitumens, Asphalts and Tar sands*. Ed. by Chilingarian, G. V. and Yen, T. F. Elsevier, Amsterdam. pp. 27–55.

Connan, J., Restle, A. and Albrecht, P. (1980) Biodegradation of crude oil in Aquitaine basin. In *Advances in Organic Geochemistry 1979*. Ed. by Douglas, A. G. and Maxwell, J. R. Pergamon, Oxford. pp. 1–17.

Corbet, B., Albrecht, P. and Ourisson, G. (1980) Photochemical or photomimetic fossil triterpenoids in sediments and petroleums. *J. Am. Chem. Soc.* **101**, 1171–1173.

Didyk, B. M., Simoneit, B. R. T., Brassel, S. C. and Eglinton, G. (1978) Organic geochemical indicators of palaeoenvironmental conditions of sedimentation. *Nature* **272**, 216–222.

Ekweozor, C. M. and Strausz, O. P. (1982) Tricyclic terpanes in the Athabasca oil sands: their geochemistry. In *Advances in Organic Geochemistry 1981*, this volume.

Ensminger, A., Joly, G. and Albrecht, P. (1978) Rearranged steranes in sediments and crude oils. *Tetrahedron Lett.* **18**, 1575–1578.

Goodwin, N. S., Park, P. J. D. and Rawlinson, A. P. (1982) Crude oil biodegradation under simulated and natural conditions. In *Advances in Organic Geochemistry 1981*, this volume.

Mackenzie, A. S., Patience, R. L., Maxwell, J. R., Vandenbroucke, M. and Durand, B. (1980) Molecular parameters of maturation in the Toarcian shales, Paris basin, France I. Changes in the configurations of acyclic isoprenoid alkanes, steranes and triterpanes. *Geochim. Cosmochim. Acta* **44**, 1709–1721.

Ourisson, G., Albrecht, P. and Rohmer, M. (1979) The hopanoids. *Pure and Appl. Chem.* **51**, 709–729.

Reed, W. E. (1977) Molecular compositions of weathered petroleum and comparison with its possible source. *Geochim. Cosmochim. Acta* **41**, 237–247.

Restle, A. (1981) Unpublished results.

Rubinstein, I., Spyckerelle, C. and Strausz, O. P. (1979) Pyrolysis of asphaltenes: a source of geochemical information. *Geochim. Cosmochim. Acta* **43**, 1–6.

Rullkötter, J. and Philp, P. (1981) Extended hopanes up to C_{40} in Thornton bitumen. *Nature* **292**, 616–618.

Scholefield, D. and Whitehurst, J. S. (1980) Organic geochemistry of some Georgia–South Carolina Clays: C_{19}–C_{28} isoprenoids and the possible presence of a sesterterpene derived hydrocarbon. *J. Chem. Soc. Chem. Commun.*, 135–136.

Seifert, W. K. and Moldowan, J. M. (1978) Applications of steranes, terpanes and monoaromatics to the maturation, migration and source of crude oils. *Geochim. Cosmochim. Acta* **42**, 77–95.

Seifert, W. K. and Moldowan, J. M. (1979) The effect of biodegradation on steranes and terpanes in crude oils. *Geochim. Cosmochim. Acta* **43**, 111–126.

Simoneit, B. R. T. and Kaplan, I. R. (1980) Triterpenoids as molecular indicators of palaeoseepage in recent sediments of the Southern California Bight. *Mar. Environ. Res.* **3**, 113–128.

Tissot, B. P. and Welte, D. H. (1978) Petroleum formation and occurrence. Springer, Berlin.

Trendel, J. M., Restle, A., Connan, J. and Albrecht, P. (1982) Identification of a novel series of tetracyclic terpene hydrocarbons (C_{24}–C_{27}) in sediments and petroleums. *J. Chem. Soc. Chem. Commun.*, 304–305.

Vorobieva, N. S., Ziemskova, E. K. and Petrov, A. A. (1978) Polycyclic hydrocarbons (C_{14}–C_{26}) of *in situ* petroleums. *Neftekhimiia* **18**, 855–863. (In Russian).

Zumberge, J. E. (1982) Tricyclic diterpane distributions in the correlation of Paleozoic crude oils from the Williston basin. In *Advances in Organic Geochemistry 1981*. This volume.

Advances in Organic Geochemistry 1981, pp. 668–674
© *John Wiley & Sons Limited*, 1983

Petroporphyrin Fingerprinting as a Geochemical Marker

A. J. G. Barwise and P. J. D. Park

BP Research Centre, Chertsey Road, Sunbury-on-Thames, Middlesex

The discovery by Treibs, almost fifty years ago, that porphyrins are present in petroleum, shales and coals, led to the realization that the latter have a biogenic origin. However, the lack of a good analytical technique for the separation and identification of complex petroporphyrin mixtures has resulted in a limited understanding of their composition. Petroporphyrins are usually too involatile to be analysed by gas chromatography but, with the recent advances in high performance liquid chromatography (HPLC), porphyrins can now be successfully analysed. We have developed a new solvent system for the HPLC of petroporphyrins which allows us to use petroporphyrin distributions as a source of geochemical information. In order to characterize the HPLC fingerprint, porphyrins from Gilsonite and Marl Slate were separated to give high concentrations of individual components which were then characterized by mass spectrometry. The use of porphyrin distributions as a geochemical parameter for sample maturity is discussed, as well as their possible use as an oil–oil or oil–source rock correlation parameter.

INTRODUCTION

The discovery of alkyl porphyrins in petroleum, coals, shales and bitumens by Treibs (1934, 1936) was one of the first indications of the biogenic origin of petroleum. Despite this discovery almost 50 years ago, relatively little was known until recently about their exact chemical composition, because of difficulties encountered in the isolation and analysis of petroporphyrins.

Petroporphyrins were shown (e.g. Baker *et al.*, 1967; Yen *et al.*, 1969) to consist mainly of nickel and vanadyl complexes of deoxophylloerythroetioporphyrins (DPEP, Fig. 1a), and etioporphyrins (etio, Fig. 1b), which are all thought to have been derived from chlorophylls (e.g. chlorophyll α Fig. 1c). Other minor porphyrin types have been observed (e.g. Baker *et al.*, 1967; Barwise and Whitehead, 1980) and proposed structure types are Di-DPEP (Fig. 1d), Rhodo-Etio (Fig. 1e), and Rhodo-DPEP (Fig. 1f). These porphyrin-types consist of pseudohomologous series ranging in carbon number from 25 to as many as 50 carbons or more (Barwise and Whitehead, 1980; Quirke *et al.*, 1980), and although these series can be observed by mass spectrometry (e.g. Baker *et al.*, 1967), little is known about their chemical structures.

One major drawback to determining petroporphyrin composition is that under normal conditions they are too involatile to be analysed by gas chromatography. Recently, the increasingly powerful technique of high performance liquid chromatography (HPLC) has been applied to the analysis of complex petroporphyrin mixtures (Hajibrahim *et al.*, 1978). This technique separates structural isomers which are undetected by mass spectrometry and much structural information has been gathered recently on the chemical composition of individual porphyrin components (e.g. Quirke *et al.*, 1979, 1980a, b; Quirke and Maxwell, 1980). The ease of analysis by HPLC has led to an interest in using porphyrin distributions as a geochemical indicator of sediment maturity (Mackenzie *et al.*, 1980). Thus, with increasing thermal stress, the initially predominant DPEP-type derived from chlorophyll is believed to crack thermally to produce the etio-type, and hence a measure of percentage DPEP in a porphyrin mixture should be related to the thermal history of the sediment. Laboratory-simulation experiments (Didyk *et al.*, 1975) and examination of sediment extracts (e.g. Baker *et al.*, 1978; Mackenzie *et al.*, 1980) have shown that there is indeed a conversion of DPEP to etio and also other changes were noted such as a decrease in average carbon number and an increase in relative abundance of vanadyl to nickel porphyrins with maturity.

In this study, we have examined the porphyrins from Gilsonite (a natural asphalt, Eocene, Lake Uinta Basin, USA) and Marl Slate (a sediment, Permian, Co. Durham, England), and have developed an improved HPLC solvent system. A correlation has been attempted between vitrinite reflectance values for a set of sediments and the percentage DPEP-type in a porphyrin mixture for each sediment. Examples of attempted oil–oil porphyrin correlations are shown.

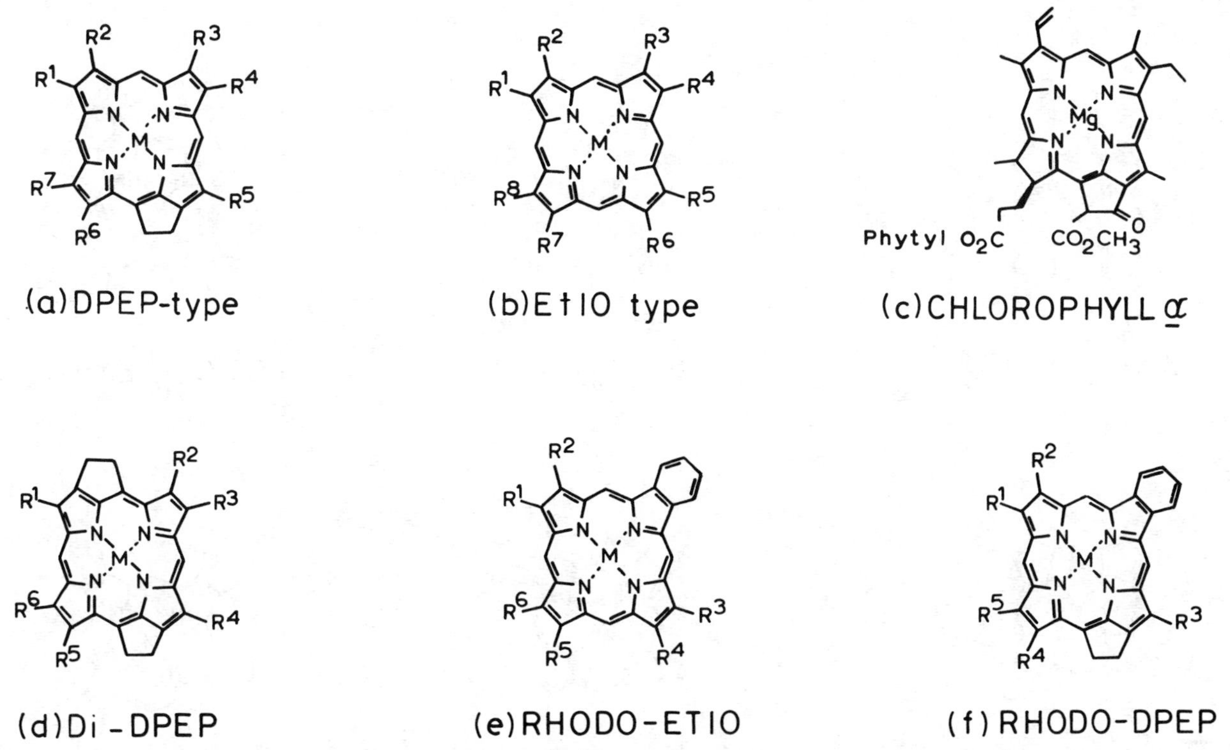

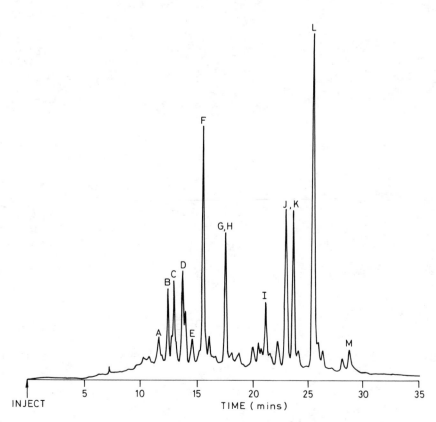

(a)DPEP-type
(b)EtIO type
(c)CHLOROPHYLL a
(d)Di-DPEP
(e)RHODO-ETIO
(f)RHODO-DPEP
Phytyl O2C
CO2CH3

Fig. 1. Porphyrin structures.

A
B
C
D
E
F
G,H
I
J , K
L
M
INJECT
5
10
15
20
25
30
35
TIME (mins)

Fig. 2. HPLC chromatogram Gilsonite.

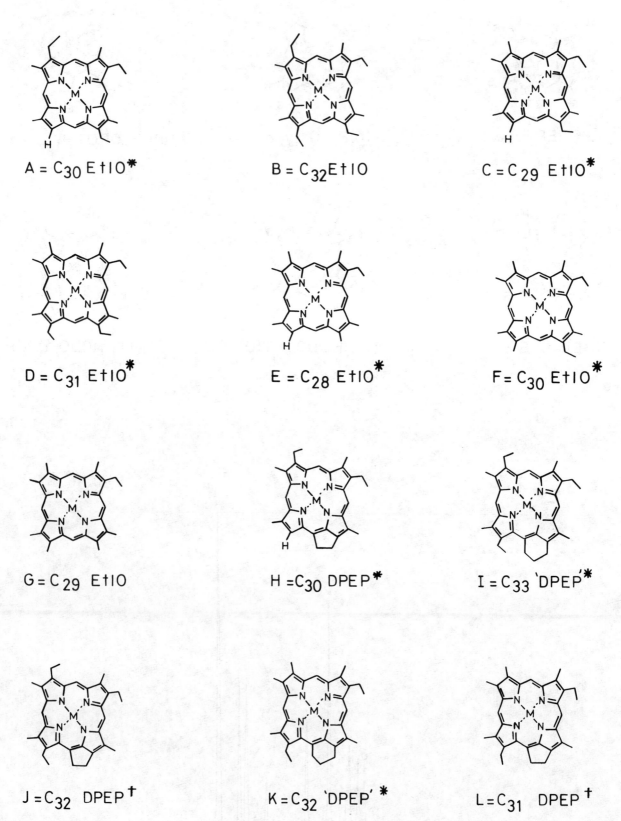

$A = C_{30} EtIO^*$

$B = C_{32} EtIO$

$C = C_{29} EtIO^*$

$D = C_{31} EtIO^*$

$E = C_{28} EtIO^*$

$F = C_{30} EtIO^*$

$G = C_{29} EtIO$

$H = C_{30} DPEP^*$

$I = C_{33}\ 'DPEP'^*$

$J = C_{32}\ DPEP^†$

$K = C_{32}\ 'DPEP'^*$

$L = C_{31}\ DPEP^†$

Fig. 2a. Postulated structures for Gilsonite porphyrins (m = nickel) (* several isomers possible); († a limited number of isomers possible).

EXPERIMENTAL

Sediments were extracted with dichloromethane and the soluble extract separated into saturates, aromatics, an NSO fraction and asphaltenes. When present, the nickel porphyrins were found predominantly in the aromatics fraction and the vanadyl porphyrins in a combined NSO and asphaltene fraction. Porphyrins were demetallated with methane sulphonic acid using a standard procedure (Erdman, 1965). The concentration of porphyrins in a sediment extract was estimated by visible absorption spectrophotometry at 550 nm for nickel porphyrins and 575 nm for vanadyl porphyrins. Demetallated porphyrins were analysed by high performance liquid chromatography (HPLC), which consisted of a Waters System Controller, two Waters M6000 HPLC pumps, a Rheodyne 7125 sample injection valve, three 25 cm $\times$ 0.5 mm i.d. 5 μm Spherisorb silica columns joined in series, and a Perkin–Elmer LC55 detector at 400 nm. The chromatographic data were recorded onto a Hewlett–Packard 3354 laboratory data system, which measured peak area by integration. Relative areas of etio and DPEP porphyrin-types were measured by summation, but were not corrected for differences in extinction coefficients as pure standards were not available.

Porphyrins from both Gilsonite and Marl Slate were trapped from the HPLC eluant and characterized by mass spectrometry. Co-injection experiments confirmed the identity of components in unknown mixtures, and assignments from the Gilsonite petroporphyrins were cross-checked with the available published data (e.g. Quirke *et al.*, 1979). Many components were only characterized by their molecular ions from mass spectrometry and their relative retention times from HPLC, hence it is fully acknowledged that much structural identification needs to be carried out. Vitrinite reflectance measurements were made at Newcastle University.

RESULTS AND DISCUSSION

HPLC distributions

An example of the resolution of the HPLC system is shown by the chromatogram of the demetallated Gilsonite porphyrins (Fig. 2). The chromatogram shows that there are at least two types of etio-porphyrins and three types of DPEP-porphyrins. The major etio-type has a fully alkylated porphyrin nucleus (Fig. 2a — B, D, F, G) and the pseudohomologous series is presumably derived via conversion of ethyl substituents to methyl substituents. The C_{32} compound (B) has been rigorously proved to be etioporphyrin-III (Quirke and Maxwell, 1980), the molecule predicted from the Treibs hypothesis. The minor etio-types (A, C, E) have been shown (Quirke *et al.*, 1979) to have one unsubstituted β-pyrrolic position and the pseudohomologous series probably begins at C_{30} (A). The other members of the series (C, E) are again probably derived from A via conversion of ethyl groups to methyl groups. A

postulated structure for A is shown in Fig. 2a, and these porphyrins may be diagenetically derived from chlorophyll via complete loss of the propionic side chain. However, this structure and diagenetic pathway need to be confirmed by full structural elucidation and synthesis of standard compounds.

The major DPEP components (J, L, M) are the fully alkylated species consistent with an origin from chlorophyll-α, and the structures of the C_{32}-DPEP (J) and C_{31}-DPEP (L) compounds have been shown to be probably those depicted in Fig. 2a (Quirke *et al.*, 1980). A second DPEP type (I, K) has been shown to contain an unusual six-membered isocyclic ring (Maxwell, personal communication) possibly with the structure shown in Fig. 2a. This porphyrin type has not been observed in any other sample in as high a concentration as found in Gilsonite and may relate to some unusual porphyrin input in the Lake Uinta Basin. A third DPEP type must be present for the C_{30}-DPEP component (H) which co-elutes with G under these conditions. Normally a decrease in molecular weight increases the polarity of the molecule, resulting in an increased retention-time under normal phase conditions. However, H elutes before J, the normal C_{32}-DPEP, and this behaviour can only be explained if the C_{30}-DPEP contains an unsubstituted β-pyrrole position since this chromatographic behaviour is observed for the two etio series. Thus, a proposed structure-type for H is shown in Fig. 2a, and it is further postulated that H is the diagenetic precursor of the minor etio series, via cleavage of the isocyclic ring. As only compounds B and C have been fully characterized, much work remains in the identification of the remaining porphyrins.

Marl slate porphyrins

Gilsonite is thought to have had a relatively mild thermal history and yet its porphyrin distribution is rather unusual in our experience. A more typical distribution for an immature sediment is seen from the Marl Slate petroporphyrins. This sediment is thought to have been deposited in an anoxic restricted marine environment (Dungworth, 1972; Gibbons, 1978) and is rich in marine algal material. It is also extremely abundant in both nickel and vanadyl porphyrins and we have examined sections of a core of this material to examine how porphyrin distributions change upon input rather than with thermal maturity. Adjacent sections were extracted and the yields of porphyrins are shown in Table 1. A large variation in yields of vanadyl porphyrins was observed with smaller fluctuations in yields of nickel porphyrins. Thus the nickel/vanadium (Ni/V) ratios varied greatly over core sections only centimetres apart, and this raises some doubt as to the usefulness of Ni/V ratios as a correlation parameter. The reasons for such fluctuations are unclear but may point to a different source input for nickel or vanadyl porphyrins. There is some evidence that nickel porphyrins are often more terrestrially derived and the vanadyl porphyrins often more marine derived (Louda and Baker, 1981). There were differences noted in the demetallated porphyrins from the separated nickel and

Table 1

Yield of porphyrins from core sections of marl slate

Core section	Yield soluble extract, (%)	Yield nickel[a] porphyrins	Yield vanadium[a] porphyrins	Ni/V ratio	Porphyrin in extract, (%)
A	0.20	3.3	1.2	2.8	2.2
B	0.35	5.8	3.4	1.7	2.6
C	0.46	6.4	4.6	1.4	2.4
D	0.32	4.6	1.8	2.6	2.0
E	0.28	4.1	2.2	1.8	2.2

[a] mg porphyrin per 100 g sediment.

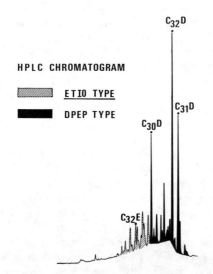

Fig. 3. Marl Slate: demetallated nickel porphyrins.

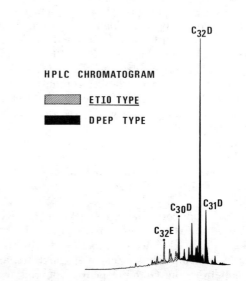

Fig. 4. Marl Slate: demetallated vanadyl porphyrins.

vanadyl fractions (Figs. 3, 4). The nickel porphyrins contained relatively more etio-porphyrins than the vanadyl porphyrins and this was consistently observed for each core section examined. This difference has been reported previously in a sequence of sediments covering a wide range of maturity (Mackenzie *et al.*, 1980) and although it may be explained by differences in the thermal stabilities of metalloporphyrins (in that case), it may also be explained by a different source input (as indicated by the Marl Slate results). Despite these differences, the overall distributions were similar, with both nickel and vanadyl fractions containing abundant C_{32}-DPEP, C_{31}-DPEP and the C_{30}-DPEP with an unsubstituted β-pyrrolic position. The abundance of this latter porphyrin is a common feature of porphyrin distributions from immature sediments (Barwise, unpublished) and indicates that its formation is probably due to a low temperature chemical process rather than a thermal process.

Porphyrins as an indicator of maturity

Sediments from various locations were extracted and the demetallated porphyrin distributions determined for each sediment extract. The percentage DPEP components were estimated via peak integration of the HPLC chromatogram, and a graph plotted for vitrinite reflectance (R_o) against percentage DPEP (Fig. 2). Immature sediments contained mostly DPEP-

porphyrins but, with increasing maturity, the relative content of etio-porphyrins increased and finally became dominant. Overall, a reasonably good correlation between R_o and % DPEP was observed, which indicates that porphyrins are a very sensitive maturity parameter in the range 0.3 to 0.7% R_o vitrinite reflectance. One problem is that algal-rich sediments abundant in porphyrins are usually lacking in vitrinite particles, making reflectance values relatively difficult to measure. However, it is exactly under these circumstances that an alternative maturity parameter is required, and porphyrins may provide a useful alternative in the range $\% R_o = 0.3$ to 0.7.

Porphyrins as a correlation parameter

From Fig. 5 it can be seen that the porphyrin distributions are very sensitive to thermal maturity and hence it would be difficult to relate mature oils to immature source rocks using porphyrin distributions. When attempting oil–oil correlations, the distributions are again very sensitive to maturity-effects and must be used with care. For example, four oils were examined which were known to have been generated from the same source but were reservoired at different depths. The shallower oils were also extensively biodegraded but the porphyrin distributions (Fig. 6) seem unaffected, as the distributions are similar to those from non-biodegraded oils at the same level of maturity. The

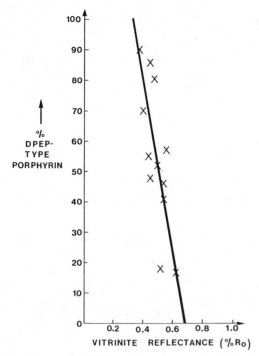

Fig. 5. Percentage DPEP versus percentage R_o for sediments.

relative concentration of the DPEP components decreases (Fig. 6) and consequently measurement of % DPEP in a porphyrin mixture is an excellent indicator of the thermal maturity of an oil.

CONCLUSIONS

Porphyrins, when present in sediment samples, are useful indicators of thermal maturity, and are sensitive to changes in temperature. A good, reproducible high resolution HPLC system has been developed which permits a rapid analysis of petroporphyrins leading to a much greater knowledge of their composition and diagenetic pathways.

Acknowledgements

We would like to thank the management of BP for permission to publish this paper. We would also like to thank Dr M. Gibbons and Dr G. Dungworth for providing cores of Marl Slate, and for very helpful discussions concerning its geology and geochemistry.

REFERENCES

Baker, E. W., Yen, T. F., Dickie, J. P., Rhodes, R. E. and Clark, L. F. (1967) Mass spectrometry of porphyrins II. Characterisation of petroporphyrins. *J. Am. Chem. Soc.* **89**, 3631–3639.

Baker, E. W., Palmer, S. E. and Huang, W. Y. (1978) Intermediate and late diagenetic tetrapyrrole pigments, Leg 41: Cape Verde Rise and Basin. In *Initial Reports of the Deep Sea Drilling Project*. Ed. by Lancelot, Y., Siebold, E., et

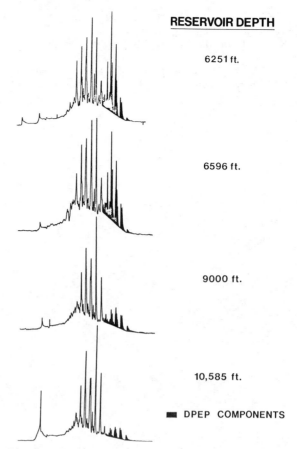

RESERVOIR DEPTH

6251 ft.

6596 ft.

9000 ft.

10,585 ft.

■ DPEP COMPONENTS

Fig. 6. Variation of percentage DPEP with reservoir depth.

al. Vol. 41. U.S. Government Printing Office, Washington. pp. 832–832.

Barwise, A. J. G. and Whitehead, E. V. (1980) Separation and Structure of petroporphyrins. In *Advances in Orgsnic Geochemistry 1979*. Ed. by Maxwell, J. R. and Douglas, A. G. Pergamon Press, Oxford. pp. 181–192.

Didyk, B. M., Alturki, Y. I. A., Pillinger, C. T. and Eglinton, G. (1975) Petroporphyrins as indicators of geothermal maturation. *Nature (London)* **256**, 563–565.

Dungworth, G. (1972) PhD Thesis, University of Newcastle.

Erdman, J. G. (1965) Process for removing metals from a mineral oil with an alkyl sulphonic acid. *U.S. Patent* 3,190,829.

Gibbons, M. (1978) PhD Thesis, University of Newcastle.

Hajibrahim, S. K., Tibbetts, P. J. C., Watts, C. D., Maxwell, J. R., Eglinton, G., Colin, H. and Guiochon, G. (1978) Analysis of carotenoid and porphyrin pigments of geochemical interest by high performance liquid chromatography. *Anal. Chem.* **50**, 549–553.

Louda, J. W. and Baker, E. W. (1981) Geochemistry of tetrapyrrole, carotenoid and perylene pigments from the San Miguel Gap (Site 467) and Baja California Border (Site 471), *DSDP/IPOD Leg 63*. In press.

Mackenzie, A. S., Quirke, J. M. E. and Maxwell, J. R. (1980) Molecular parameters of maturation in the Toarcian Shales, Paris Basin, France II. Evolution of metalloporphyrins. In *Advances in Organic Geochemistry 1979*. Ed. by Maxwell, J. R. and Douglas, A. G. Pergamon Press, Oxford. pp. 239–248.

Quirke, J. M. E., Eglinton, G. and Maxwell, J. R. (1979) Petroporphyrins I. *J. Am. Chem. Soc.* **101**, 7693–7697.

Quirke, J. M. E. and Maxwell, J. R. (1980) Petroporphyrins III. *Tetr. Lett.* **36**, 3453–3456.

Quirke, J. M. E., Shaw, G. J., Soper, P. D. and Maxwell, J. R.

(1980a) Petroporphyrins II. *Tetr. Lett.* **36**, 3261–3267.

Quirke, J. M. E., Maxwell, J. R., Eglinton, G. and Saunders, J. K. M. (1980b) Petroporphyrins Iv. *Tetr. Lett.* **21**, 2987–2990.

Treibs, A. (1934) Chlorophyll und Häminderivate in bituminösen Gesteinien, Erd ölen, Erdwachsen und Asphalten. *Ann. Chem.* **510**, 42–62.

Treibs, A. (1936) Chlorophyll und Häminderivate in organischen Mineralstoffen. *Angew.* **49**, 682–686.

Yen, T. F., Boucher, L. J., Dickie, J. P., Tynan, E. C. and Vaughan, G. B. (1969) Vanadium complexes and porphyrins in asphaltenes. *J. Inst. Pet. (London)* **55**, 87–99.

Advances in Organic Geochemistry 1981, pp. 675–683
© *John Wiley & Sons Limited, 1983*

Triterpanes in a number of Far-Eastern Crude Oils

P. J. Grantham, J. Posthuma and A. Baak

Koninklijke/Sheel Exploratie en Produktie Laboratorium, Rijswijk, The Netherlands

To date, the triterpanes 18αH oleanane and compound 'J' (Hills and Whitehead, 1966) have been reported to occur only in Nigerian crude oils. This paper presents evidence that these compounds are also present in crude oils from Indonesia, Brunei and Sabah which have been derived from source rocks containing land-plant organic matter. Evidence is based on mass spectral and Kovats retention data equivalence of oleanane and compound 'J' in a triterpane concentrate isolated from Nigerian crude with that of the compounds in the examined crudes. In addition to oleanane and 'J', some of the analysed crudes have been shown to contain three unusual compounds. These hydrocarbons appear to be derived from plant resins since they can be generated from a fossilized land-plant resin from Brunei in the laboratory. The hypothesis of a resin origin of these hydrocarbons is also supported by the presence of resin in a source rock which contains the hydrocarbons. The presence of oleanane, 'J' and the resin-derived hydrocarbons in a crude oil appears to indicate the presence of mixtures of different types of land-plant organic matter in the source rock of the crude.

INTRODUCTION

The earliest research (1966) on the structure of steranes and triterpanes in crude oils and sediments is, for many research workers in this field, synonymous with the work of E. V. Whitehead and his colleagues at British Petroleum. They identified, amongst other triterpanes, 18αH-oleanane in a Nigerian crude oil (Hills and Whitehead, 1966; Whitehead, 1970; Hills *et al.*, 1970). These, and other workers, have suggested that the oleanane could have originated from a land–plant-derived triterpenoid precursor (Hills *et al.*, 1970; Fowell

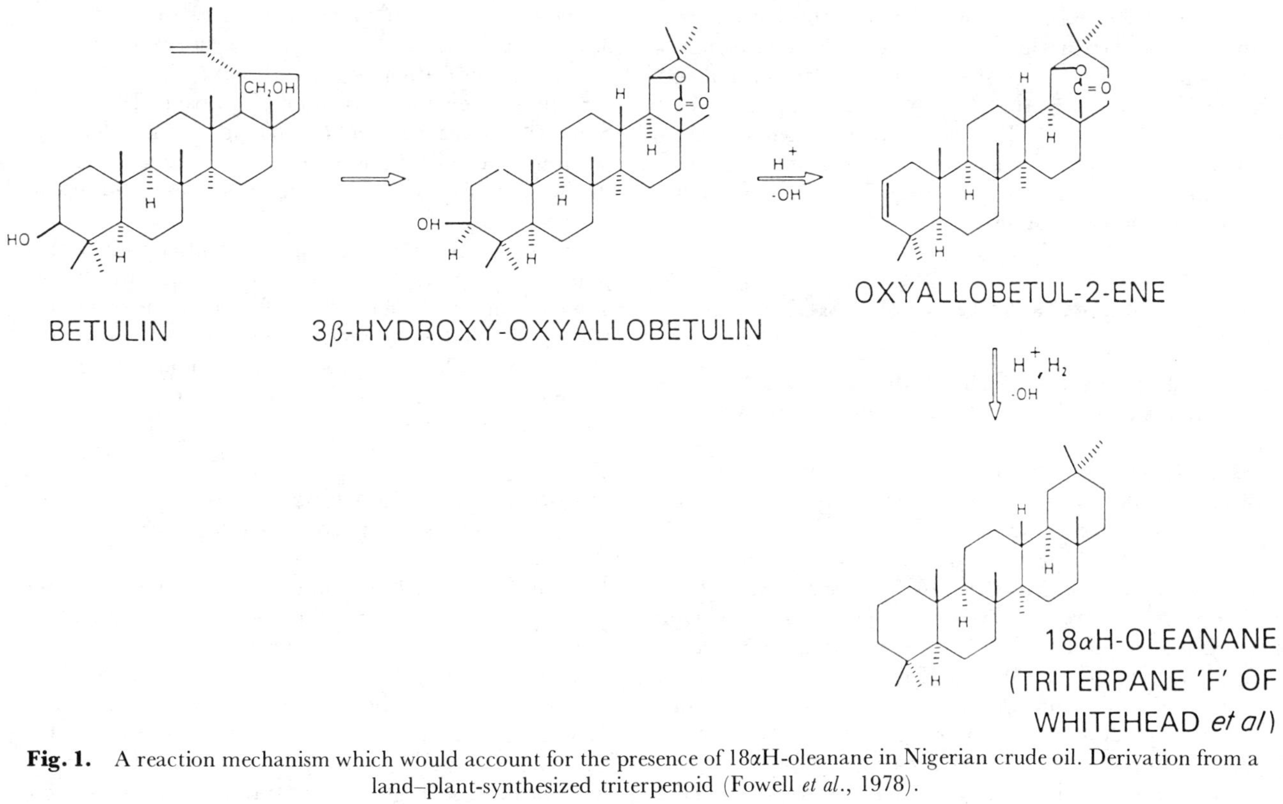

Fig. 1. A reaction mechanism which would account for the presence of 18αH-oleanane in Nigerian crude oil. Derivation from a land–plant-synthesized triterpenoid (Fowell *et al.*, 1978).

Table 1
Geochemical data of crude oils which contain 18αH- oleanane and compound 'J'

Crude oil	C$_{15}$-ring distribution[a]			C$_{30}$-ring distribution[a]			Type of crude oil as revealed by gas chromatogram of saturates	Pristane
	1-ring	2-ring	3-ring	3-ring	4-ring	5-ring		*n*-C$_{17}$
South Sumatra, W. Prabumulih-3	11	69	19	5	23	72	Strongly waxy	2.1
South Sumatra, Gunung Kemala-1	15	69	16	4	20	76	Strongly waxy	1.7
South China Sea, crude A	14	63	23	12	21	67[b]	Strongly waxy	1.3
South China Sea, crude B	24	56	20	6	25	69	Moderately waxy	1.0
South China Sea, crude C	19	62	19	8	23	70	Moderately waxy	2.0
West Irian, Wasian	42	43	14	26	34	40	Waxy	0.5
West Irian, Jaya	36	47	17	17	34	49	Moderately waxy	1.4
Nigeria, Imo River-14	29	55	16[c]	10	37	53	Moderately waxy	1.1
Nigeria, Benin West-1	36	49	15	23	37	40	Waxy	0.9
Nigeria, Umuechem-5	45	46	9	14	37	49	Moderately waxy	0.8

[a] Normalized to 100%.
[b] C$_{30}$-ring distribution of a second crude from the same well.
[c] C$_{15}$-ring distribution of another Nigerian crude oil from well Apara-4.

et al., 1978). The subsequent discovery of an intermediate compound (olean-13(18)-ene) of the proposed reaction mechanism (see Fig. 1) in an immature shale of the Agbada Formation in the Niger Delta (Ekweozor *et al.*, 1979a,b) supports this hypothesis. The mechanism is also attractive since it only requires commonly occurring geochemical reactions such as dehydration, acid-catalysed molecular rearrangements and reduction. The hypothesis of a land–plant precursor is also in line with evidence for a deltaic, land–plant-containing source rock of Nigerian crudes (Evamy *et al.*, 1978).

This article describes the finding of 18αH-oleanane and the compound 'J' of Hills and Whitehead (1966) in a number of Far-Eastern crude oils, thereby indicating that these triterpanes are not restricted to Nigerian crude oils. The article also describes the discovery of a number of previously unreported C$_{30}$ five-ring compounds in Indonesian crude oils. Evidence is presented that these hydrocarbons (the structures of which are as yet unknown) have been generated on the thermal degradation of fossil resins.

RESULTS AND DISCUSSION

Occurrence of 18αH-oleanane and compound 'J' in Far-Eastern crude oils

Seven Far-Eastern and three Nigerian crude oils have been analysed in order to determine their triterpane composition (see Table 1).

Amongst the ubiquitous (17αH, 21βH) hopanes, the analysis has revealed that 18αH-oleanane and the compound 'J' are also present in these crudes. Their presence has been established by equivalence of mass spectra (Figs. 2 and 3) and Kovats retention indices (Table 2) of the compounds investigated with those of the compounds in a triterpane concentrate from Nigerian crude (Hills and Whitehead, 1966). There is, moreover, equivalence of the mass spectra of 18αH-

oleanane in our samples with published mass spectra (Kimble, 1972).

There is fairly strong evidence that the analysed crude oils were all derived from land–plant-containing source rocks. This can be concluded from the following crude oil properties which are summarized from Table 1:
1. The crudes contain varying amounts of *n*-C$_{25+}$ waxy hydrocarbons. Their distributions are typical of land–plant waxes (Hedberg, 1968).
2. The crudes display predominances of C$_{15}$ 2-ring and C$_{30}$ 5-ring compounds as indicated by Field Ionization–Mass Spectrometric analysis. Lijmbach *et al.* (this volume) have shown that such predominances are typical of crudes derived from land–plant-resin-containing source rocks.
3. The pristane:*n*-C$_{17}$ ratios of the crudes are generally high, indicating a bacteriostatic (peat swamp) environment of deposition (Lijmbach, 1975).

Since 18αH-oleanane and compound 'J' only appear to occur in crude oils of this type, further weight is added to the hypothesis that these triterpanes are land–plant-derived.

Finally, although Nigerian crude oil contains other noteworthy triterpanes in addition to 18αH-oleanane and compound 'J', an example of which is the triterpane 'E' (1(10→5) abeo-3β-methyl-24β-nor-18αH-oleanane; Hills *et al.*, 1968), no specific search for these less-prominent triterpanes in the analysed Indonesian crude oils has been undertaken.

Resin-derived C$_{30}$ 5-ring compounds in Far-Eastern crudes and an extract

In addition to 18αH-oleanane and 'J' we have evidence of the presence of at least three unusual compounds in some of the samples investigated.

The compounds have been arbitrarily labeled W, T and R (see Fig. 7). Their mass spectra are shown in Fig. 4. The parent ion at *m/e* 412 indicates that they are C$_{30}$ five-ring compounds, although the absence of an intense base peak at *m/e* 191 demonstrates that they are not

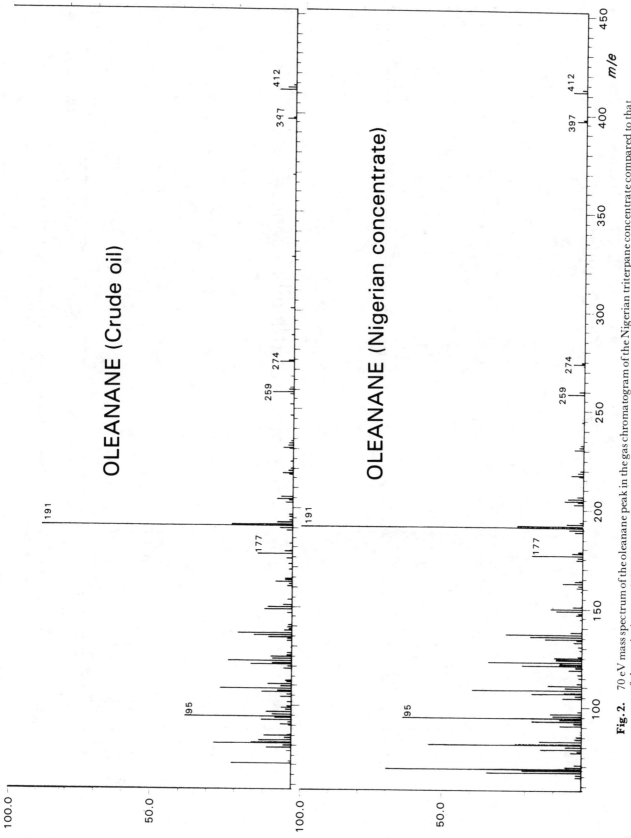

Fig. 2. 70 eV mass spectrum of the oleanane peak in the gas chromatogram of the Nigerian triterpane concentrate compared to that of the equivalent peak in the chromatogram of one of the investigated crude oils (South China Sea, crude A).

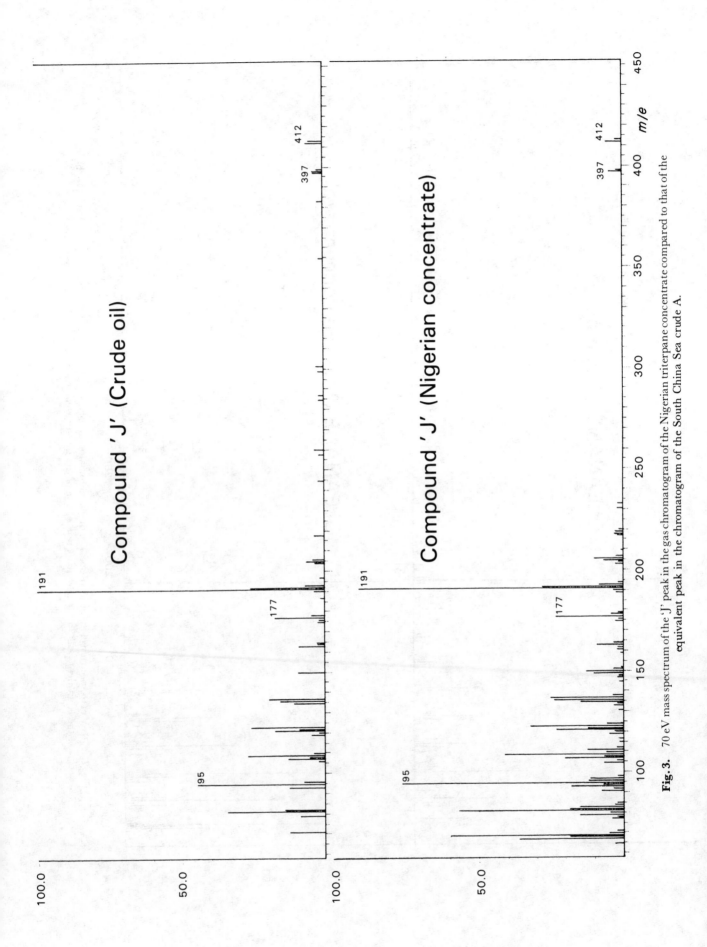

Fig. 3. 70 eV mass spectrum of the 'J' peak in the gas chromatogram of the Nigerian triterpane concentrate compared to that of the equivalent peak in the chromatogram of the South China Sea crude A.

Table 2.

Summary — Kovats retention indices.

	3 Nigerian and 10 Indonesian crude oils	Triterpane concentrate Nigerian crude ex BP
SE-30 230 °C isothermal		
18αH-oleanane	3016	3019
Compound 'J'	3021	3023
17αH, 21βH hopane	3029	3031
Carbowax 20m 230 °C isothermal		
18αH-oleanane	3413	3416
Compound 'J'	3427	3422
17αH, 21βH-hopane	3431	3432

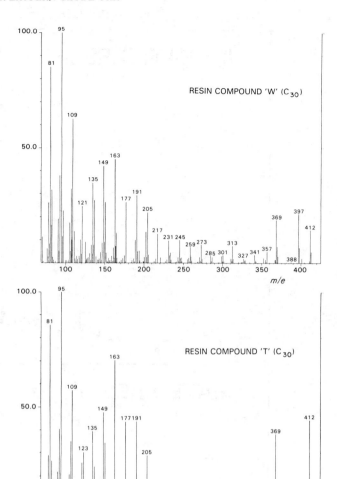

pentacyclic triterpanes with methyl substituents at both C-8 and C-14 (Kimble, 1972). The spectrum of compound W shows parent-15 and parent-43 fragment ions indicating loss of CH_3 and C_3H_7. The spectra of T and R however indicate loss of C_3H_7 ions in preference to CH_3. In all spectra the peak at m/e 313 implies loss of a C_7H_{15} fragment, whilst the prominent ion at m/e 163 is indicative of a $C_{12}H_{19}$ (C_nH_{2n-5}) fragment.

These mass spectral features appear to be consistent with triterpanes containing a cyclopropane ring, a side chain at least seven carbon atoms long and easily removable methyl and isopropyl groups. However, the spectra of W, T and R do not compare well with the published spectra of triterpanes which would fit this description such as cycloartane and cycloeucalane (Kimble, 1972; Kimble *et al.*, 1974; Wardroper *et al.*, 1977) and as yet there are no further indications of the identity of these compounds.

Since the fragment ions m/e 191 and 217 are present in the mass spectra of all three compounds and since the compounds are present in relatively large concentrations in some of our samples, their peaks appear in triterpane and sterane fragmentograms based on these ions. These compounds may therefore be the same as the ones which produce intense peaks in the sterane fragmentograms shown by Schoell *et al.* (this volume) for rock extracts and crude oils from the Mahakam Delta, Kalimantan.

The compounds W, T and R have also been found in the extract of a heated sample of a fossil resin outcropping in Tertiary sediments — in general well known for their content of angiosperm-derived fossil resins (Frondel, 1967; Langenheim, 1969) — at Lumapas in Brunei (see Fig. 5). Since these compounds are not present in the saturated hydrocarbon fraction isolated from the unheated resin (Fig. 5) it seems likely that they are generated by the thermal breakdown of resinous material.

Furthermore, these same compounds are also present in a sediment from a well in South Sumatra (East Benakat) which has been shown by maceral analysis to contain resins (see Fig. 6). It is interesting to note that the chromatographic distribution of W, T and R in the sediment is almost identical with that of the heated fossil resin (compare Figs. 5 and 6).

Since it would appear that these compounds are thermally generated from the above-described variety of

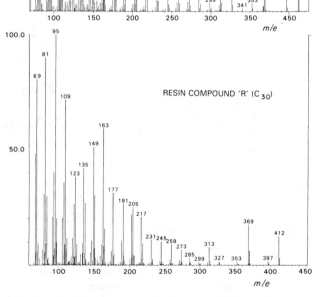

Fig. 4. 70 eV mass spectra of compounds W, T and R in the South China Sea crude A.

fossil resin, their presence in a crude oil must indicate that the source rocks of the crudes contained this variety of land–plant resin.

It should be noted that the compound W is present in much greater concentration, relative to T and R, in the crude oils than it is in the heated resin or the sediment

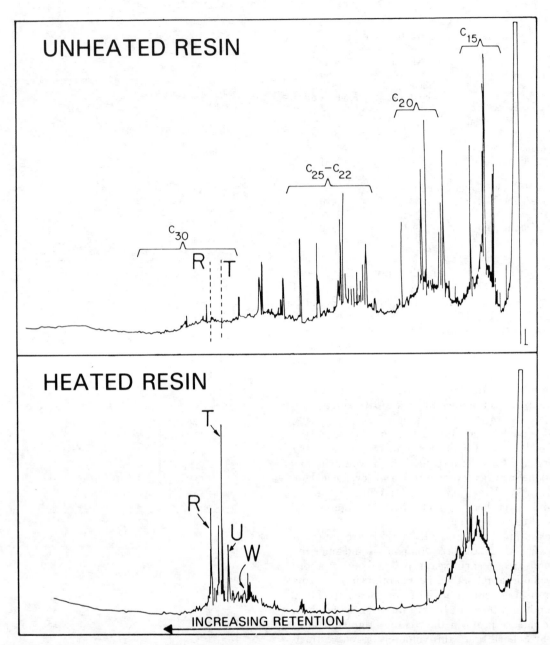

Fig. 5. Gas chromatograms of the saturated branched/cyclic fractions isolated from unheated and heated samples of Brunei Lumapas resin.

(compared Figs. 5, 6 and 7). As yet we have no explanation for this phenomenon.

Variations in the relative content of land–pland-derived triterpanes

In a number of crude oils, the triterpanes oleanane and 'J' and the compounds W, T and R are present together whilst in Nigerian crudes only oleanane and J are present. Table 3 lists the crudes and gives the relative proportions of the ubiquitously present (17αH, 21βH) hopane together with W + T and oleanane + 'J'.

The variations in the relative proportions of W and T and oleanane and 'J' in the examined crude oils are probably due to variations in the land–plant organic

matter composition of the source rocks. Figure 7 shows the gas chromatograms of triterpane concentrates of three crudes chosen as examples. The South China Sea, crude oil A (Fig. 7A) contains predominantly W and T whilst oleanane, 'J' and the hopane are relatively minor components. Hence, in this case, land–plant resins of the Lumapas type appear to have been relatively major components of the land–plant material in the source rock. The South China Sea crude oil B is an intermediate case (Fig. 7B), containing relatively less W and T and more oleanane and 'J'. Finally, the West Irian, Jaya crude is an example (Fig. 7C) of crudes with more oleanane and 'J' compared to W and T. This indicates that the source rock contained larger amounts of the possibly resin-derived precursors of oleanane and 'J' compared to the Lumapas type of land–plant resin.

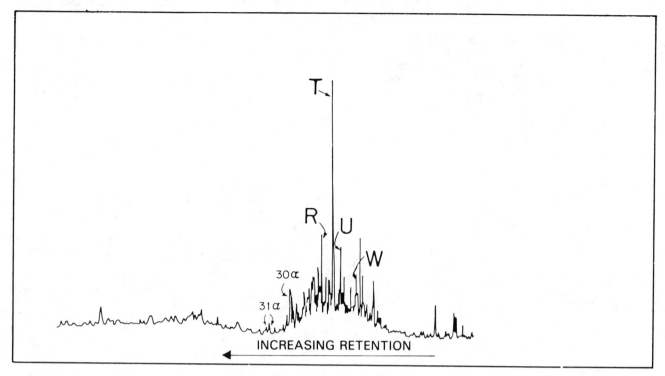

Fig. 6. Gas chromatogram of the saturated branched/cyclic fraction isolated from a source rock, well East Benakat, S Sumatra.

Table 3.

Relative content of triterpanes in Far-Eastern and Nigerian crude oils (normalized to 100%).

Crude oil	W + T	Oleanane + compound 'J'	$17\alpha H$, $21\beta H$ hopane
South Sumatra			
W Prabumulih-3	82	8	10
Gunung Kemala-1	88	4	7
South China Sea			
Crude A	89	5	6
Crude B	56	17	27
Crude C	19	46	34
West Irian			
Wasian	10	29	61
Jaya	33	40	27
Nigeria			
Imo River-14	–	38	62
Benin West-1	–	26	74
Umuechem-5	–	25	75

CONCLUSIONS

The following conclusions can be drawn from this study:
1. The presence of oleanane and compound 'J' is not restricted to Nigerian crude oils.
2. The presence of oleanane and compound 'J' in a sample can be related to the presence of land–plant-derived organic matter in the source rock.
3. The compounds W, T and R originate from a specific type of Tertiary land–plant fossil resin.

4. Mixtures of oleanane, 'J', W, T and R in a crude oil indicate the presence of mixtures of different types of land–plant organic matter in the source rock.

Acknowledgements

We are indebted to E. V. Whitehead of British Petroleum (BP) for his kind donation of a triterpane concentrate from Nigerian crude oil. The Directors of the Shell International Petroleum Company are also thanked for their permission to publish this article.

REFERENCES

Ekweozor, C. M., Okogun, J. I., Ekong, D. E. V. and Maxwell, J. R. (1979a) Preliminary organic geochemical studies of samples from the Niger Delta (Nigeria) I. Analyses of crude oils for triterpanes. *Chem. Geol.* **27**, 11–28.

Ekweozor, C. M., Okogun, J. I., Ekong, D. E. V. and Maxwell, J. R. (1979b) Preliminary organic geochemical studies of samples from the Niger Delta (Nigeria) II. Analyses of shale for triterpenoid derivatives. *Chem. Geol.* **27**, 29–37.

Evamy, B. D., Haremboure, J., Kamerling, P., Knaap, W. A., Molloy, F. A. and Rowlands, P. H. (1978) Hydrocarbon habitat of Tertiary Niger Delta. *Bull. Am. Ass. Petrol. Geol.* **62**, 1–37.

Fowell, D. T., Melsom, B. G. and Smith, G. W. (1978) The crystal and molecular structures of 18-α(H)-oleanane, $C_{30}H_{52}$. *Acta. Cryst.* **B34**, 2244–2250.

Frondel, J. W. (1967) X-Ray diffraction of Fossil Elemis. *Nature (London)* **215**, 1360–1361.

Hedberg, H. D. (1968) Significance of high-wax oils with respect to genesis of petroleum. *Bull. Am. Ass. Petrol. Geol.* **52**, 736–750.

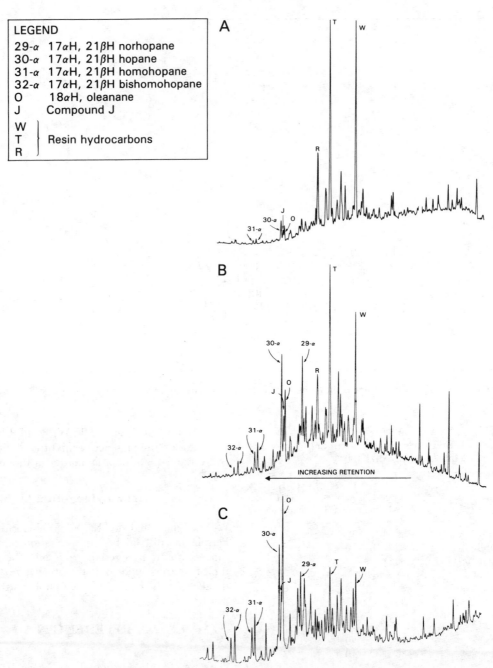

Fig. 7. Gas chromatograms of triterpane concentrates isolated from crude oils. (A) South China Sea, crude A; (B) South China Sea, crude B; (C) West Irian, Jaya. Gas chromatographic conditions: 25 m × 0.25 mm i.d. glass capillary column coated with CP Sil-5. Temperature programmed from 100 to 280 °C at 1 °C min⁻¹. Helium flow rate 0.8 ml min⁻¹.

Hills, I. R. and Whitehead, E. V. (1966) Triterpanes in optically active petroleum distillates. *Nature (London)* **209**, 977–979.

Hills, I. R., Smith, G. W. and Whitehead, E. V. (1968) Optically active spirotriterpane in petroleum distillates. *Nature (London)* **219**, 243–246.

Hills, I. R., Smith, G. W. and Whitehead, E. V. (1970) Hydrocarbons from fossil fuels and their relationship with living organisms. *J. Inst. Petrol.* **56**, 127–137.

Kimble, B. J. (1972) The geochemistry of triterpenoid hydrocarbons. PhD Thesis, University of Bristol.

Kimble, B. J., Maxwell, J. R., Philp, R. P. and Eglinton, G. (1974) Identification of steranes and triterpanes in geolipid extracts by high resolution gas chromatography and mass spectrometry. *Chem. Geol.* **14**, 173–198.

Langenheim, J. H. (1969) Amber: A botanical inquiry. *Science* **163**, 1157–1169.

Lijmbach, G. W. M. (1975) On the origin of petroleum. *Proceedings of the World Petroleum Congress*, Special Paper 1, 357.

Wardroper, A. M. K., Brooks, P. W., Humberston, M. J. and Maxwell, J. R. (1977) Analysis of steranes and triterpanes in geolipid extracts by automatic classification of mass spectra. *Geochim. Cosmochim. Acta* **41**, 499–510.

Whitehead, E. V. (1970) Molecular evidence for the biogenesis of petroleum and gas. *Proceedings of a Symposium on Hydrogeochemistry and Biogeochemistry*. Volume II (Biogeochemistry). Ed. by Ingerson, E. Clarke Co., Washington. pp. 158–211.

Question

Had the GC-MS RIC's shown (during the presentation in Bergen) been computer reprocessed in order to enhance the apparent chromatographic separations?

Answer

During the course of research into steranes and triterpanes using GC-MS we have used both computer-enhanced and non-computer-enhanced chromatograms. At the time of the presentation it was believed that non-enhanced chromatograms were being shown although this was not the case.

Gas chromatograms shown in this article have not been computer enhanced.

Advances in Organic Geochemistry 1981, pp. 684–697
© *John Wiley & Sons Limited, 1983*

Steroids and Triterpenoids in Deep Sea Sediments as Environmental and Diagentic Indicators

S. C. Brassell and G. Eglinton

Organic Geochemistry Unit, University of Bristol, School of Chemistry, Cantock's Close, Bristol BS8 1TS, UK

The extractable lipids of deep sea sediments, ranging from Quaternary to Creaceous age, from the Japan and Middle America Trenches, the Walvis Ridge and the Moroccan and Angolan Basins have been examined by computerized gas chromatography–mass spectrometry. Comparison of the lipid distributions, in particular the steroid and triterpenoid components, provides new information for the characterization of depositional environments and lipid transformations during diagenesis. Autochthonous inputs of organic matter are reflected in the occurrence of marine sterols such as C_{21} to C_{24}, C_{30} and C_{31} components, and sterol ethers, whereas 3-oxytriterpenoids and their degraded derivatives are indicators of terrigenous lipid sources. The prominence of hopanoids and fernenes in the extracts emphasizes the importance of bacterial contributions to, and/or activity in, deep sea sediments. The steroidal lipid distributions of Japan Trench samples suggest that $5\beta(H)$-steroids may derive from cholest-4-en-3-one which is itself contributed as a direct input to the sediment. In these sediments conversion of Δ^5-stenol to $5\alpha(H)$-stanols is not apparent, whereas sterol dehydration in certain sediments is supported by sterol carbon number distributions. The survival of lipid signatures in deep sea sediments is discussed and the important of understanding diagenetic and evolutionary changes in lipid compositions warrants further study. The marked similarity of certain lipid distributions from diverse sediments suggests some uniformity of inputs, depositional environments or diagenetic processes between specific samples.

INTRODUCTION

The opportunity to study various facets of the accumulation and fate of organic matter in the oceanic system is presented by the sediments recovered by the Deep Sea Drilling Project (DSDP). The potential and value of the overall DSDP programme and the scope for future drilling are described elsewhere (Eglinton *et al.*, this volume), but three advantages of DSDP samples pertinent to this paper warrant specific mention. First, by deep drilling on ocean margins the Glomar Challenger has recovered ancient sediments from areas of low geothermal gradient which are immature and therefore retain much of their original environmental lipid signatures. Second, the scope of the drilling programme permits the selection of samples that enable the comparison and contrasting of sediments of dominantly autochthonous or allochthonous material, permitting an evaluation of the validity of using lipid markers to assess sediment inputs. Third, DSDP samples bridge the sampling gap between the shallow cores of sediments retrieved by conventional piston, gravity or box coring and the deeper drilling of mature sediments by the petroleum industry. They thereby provide an important link in the understanding of the diagenetic processes that transform bio- into geolipid distributions.

The wide range of sediments from sites drilled in areas of low or high geothermal gradient also offer the chance to compare and contrast slow and rapid rates of lipid diagenesis, respectively.

In general, our investigations of the lipid constituents of DSDP sediments are focused on two themes; the elucidation and assessment of (i) depositional environments and (ii) diagenetic processes. Within these broad themes this paper addresses four aspects of the lipid geochemistry of deep sea sediments. First, the use of steroidal and triterpenoidal compounds as biological markers of sediment inputs. Second, the survival of lipid signatures under diagenesis coupled with the problems associated with the recognition and distinction of differences in lipid distribution patterns arising from evolutionary changes. Third, selected aspects of sterol diagenesis and, finally, the remarkable similarity that occurs between certain lipid distributions of geographically and temporally diverse sediments.

EXPERIMENTAL

The examples cited in this paper include results from the analysis of DSDP samples of various ages from several different areas (Table 1; Fig. 1). The procedures used in

Table 1

Basic descriptions of samples

Leg	Location[a]	Ages	Dominant lithologies	Reference(s)
56/57	Japan Trench	Pleistocene–Miocene	Diatomaceous oozes	Brassell, 1980; Brassell *et al*, 1980b, c
66/67	Middle-America Trench	Quaternary	Biogenic oozes	Brassell *et al*, 1981b
75	Walvis Ridge	Pleistocene–Pliocene	Biogenic oozes	
64	Gulf of California	Quaternary	Diatomaceous ooze	Thomson *et al*, in press
62	Hess Rise	Albian	Finely laminated limestone	Comet *et al*, 1981
75	Angola Basin	Cenomanian	Black shale	—
48	Bay of Biscay	Albian/Aptian	Carbonaceous marly chalks	Barnes *et al*, 1979; Wardroper, 1979
50	Moroccan Basin	Valanginian	Turbidites	Brassell *et al*, 1980a

[a] see Fig. 1.

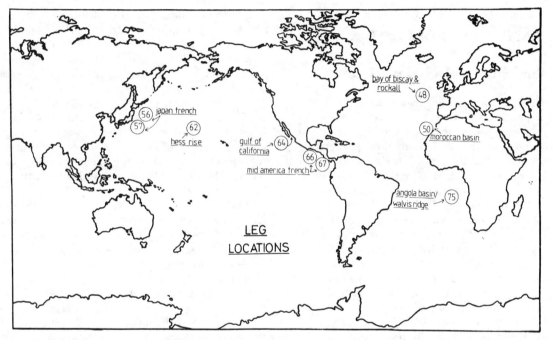

Fig. 1. Drilling areas of the Legs that recovered the sediments discussed in this paper (cf. Table 1).

the extraction, fractionation and analysis of their lipid components have been extensively documented elsewhere (Barnes *et al.*, 1979; Brassell *et al.*, 1980a, d). In brief, these methods involve ultrasonic extraction of the wet sediment, fractionation according to functionality by thin-layer chromatography followed by analysis of individual lipid fractions by capillary gas chromatography (GC) and computerized gas chromatography–mass spectrometry (C-GC–MS). In the latter technique extensive use is made of mass fragmentograaphy (MF) to aid compound recognition and quantitation (cf. Brassell *et al.*, 1980d).

Individual components are recognised using C-GC–MS from their mass spectra, by comparison with standard or published spectra, or from their MF response given the aid of values for standard compounds or from the literature for GC retention times. Some identifications are tentative, being mainly based on mass spectral interpretations. The assignments of several of the lipids discussed herein (e.g. fernenes) have been confirmed by GC or C-GC–MS coinjections with standard compounds (cf. Brassell *et al.*, 1980d). The absolute quantitation of individual components was based on the GC response relative to that of standard mixtures of alkanes of known concentrations. Alternatively, quantitation was made either from the RIC or from MF of specific ions by relating the abundance of a given peak to that of a chosen compound quantitated directly from its GC response. These quantitation procedures do not make allowance for the variable GC response of different lipid classes (e.g. alcohols as TMS ethers v. ketones v. alkanes). Accurate quantitation remains a major problem in the lipid analysis of DSDP samples, since the total concentrations of certain lipid classes is of the order of ng g^{-1} dry sediment weight. Hence, the quantitation of several of the lipid classes discussed herein is relative rather than absolute.

Table 2

Estimated values of steroids as biological markers of sediment inputs[a]

Steroidal class	Algal/Marine	Bacterial	Terrigenous higher plant
Sterols	+ + +[b]	?	+
4-Methylsterols	+ +	+ +?	–
Sterones	+	+?	+
Steryl ethers	+ + +?	–	–
Steryl esters	+	–	+
Steroidal acids	?	+?	+?

[a] For further description see text.
[b] The ratings provide an estimate of the value of the steroidal classes as markers of inputs from the respective sources (– unknown, ? uncertain).

RESULTS AND DISCUSSION

Concept of biological markers

An important key in the understanding of past and present depositional environments is the origin of sedimentary organic matter. The specificity of lipid structures and stereochemistry makes them particularly sensitive indicators of the sources of organic matter in that such features are inherited, either directly or in modified form, from the biolipids biosynthesized by organisms. In considering immature sediments the thermal stability of a given biological marker is of secondary importance to its value as an indicator of sediment inputs. Indeed, many of the compounds of greatest utility in the elucidation of the source of sedimentary organic matter contain functionalities, notably hydroxyl and carbonyl groups, that do not survive extensive diagenesis. The recognition of marker compounds in immature sediments can provide evidence of inputs from marine, terrestrial and bacterial sources and, in some instances, from specific classes or families of organisms. For example, the presence of dinosterol (4α,23,24-trimethyl-5α(H)-cholest-22-en-3β-ol, VIIq) denotes sediment contributions from dinoflagellates (Boon et al., 1979). From the wide range of biolipids that are useful markers of sediment inputs two broad structural types, steroids and triterpenoids are discussed herein.

Steroids as biological markers

The value of various classes of steroids as indicators of inputs from organisms to sediments are estimated in Table 2. Sterols are particular useful markers of organic matter of marine origin and can also provide evidence of terrestrial higher plant inputs. Bacteria are not thought to synthesize 4-desmethyl sterols (e.g. Ourisson et al., 1979), but they can effect the hydrogenation of Δ^5-stenols to 5α(H)- and 5β(H)-stanols (Gaskell and Eglinton, 1975) and thus potentially, can leave their imprint on sedimentary sterol distributions. The utility of sterols as marine marker lipids stems from a number of factors. First, sterols act as rigidifiers of biomembranes

and are therefore ubiquitous components of eucaryotic organisms. Second, there exists extensive literature on the sterol compositions of marine organisms, although many of these biota cannot be regarded as major, or even significant, contributors of sedimentary organic matter. Third, there is a remarkable variety in the sterol structures of marine organisms (e.g. Schmitz, 1978; Djerassi et al., 1979; Djerassi, 1981), notably in the size, alkylation pattern, stereochemistry and unsaturation of their side chains. Indeed, it is the desire to understand the biochemical role and the biosynthesis of unusual steroids that has prompted much of the research which now provides such a wealth of information on their occurrence in marine biota. Several sterol side chains appear to be restricted to specific classes of organisms and can therefore serve as markers for such classes in the assessment of sediment inputs (e.g. Mackenzie et al., 1982). Others occur more widely, but are useful in ascribing inputs from a broader range of organisms, for example 24(R)-ethyl sterols mainly originate from terrigenous higher plants.

In previous studies, marine and terrestrial contributions to sediments have been assessed using the relative proportion of cholest-5-en-3β-ol(IIg) and 24-ethylcholest-5-en-3β-ol(IIu), respectively (Huang and Meinschein, 1976) and, as an extension of this approach, a triangular plot of C_{27}, C_{28} and C_{29} steroids has been suggested as a basis for differentiating between ecological systems (Huang and Meinschein, 1979). This latter proposal is, however, unsatisfactory in the evaluation of sediments with complex sterol distributions for various reasons. In particular, (i) the C_{29} components include 23,24-dimethylsterols that are of marine rather than terrestrial origin (e.g. Volkman et al., 1980), and (ii) 4-methylsterols are not considered, although they are often dominant sterol components (cf. Fig. 2). Here, inputs to Japan sediments are assessed from the sterol markers for specific inputs found among their highly complex sterol distributions (Fig. 2, sterol assignments are given in Table 3). First, the sterol components possessing short side chains ($<C_{25}$; a–h) and the 24-propylidenesterols (a′–d′), denoted by 1 in Fig. 2, are probably derived from sponges (Ballantine et al., 1977; Carlson et al., 1978; Delseth et al., 1978; Brassell et al.,

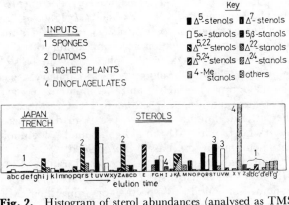

Fig. 2. Histogram of sterol abundances (analysed as TMS ethers) in Section 440B-3-5, a Pleistocene diatomaceous ooze, from the Japan Trench. Sterol assignments are given in Table 3. Some of the sterols thought to be markers of specific inputs to the sediment are marked as such.

Table 3

Sterols identified in Japan Trench sediment (Section 440B-3-5)

Peak (Fig. 2)	Assignment[a]	Structure	Peak (Fig. 2)	Assignment[a]	Structure
a	unknown C_{21} sterol	—	E	24-methylenecholest-5-en-3β-ol	IIc
b	5α(H)-pregnan-3β-ol?	Ia	F	24-methylene-5α(H)-cholestan-3β-ol	Io
c	20-methyl-5α(H)-pregnan-3β-ol?	Ib	G	24-methylcholest-5-en-3β-ol	IIp
d	unknown C_{22} sterol	—	H	24-methyl-5α(H)-cholestan-3β-ol	Ip
e	unknown C_{22} Δ^5-sterol		I	4α,24-dimethyl-5α(H)-cholest-22-en-3β-ol[d]	VIIn
f	24-norchol-5-en-3β-ol?	IIc	J	23,24-dimethylcholesta-5,22-dien-3β-ol	IIq
g	24-nor-5α(H)-cholan-3β-ol?	Ic	K	23,24-dimethyl-5α(H)-cholest-22-en-3β-ol	Iq
h	5α(H)-cholan-3β-ol?	Id	L	24-ethylcholesta-5,22-dien-3β-ol	IIr
i	24-norcholesta-5,22-dien-3β-ol	IIe	M	24-ethyl-5α(H)-cholest-22-en-3β-ol	Ir
j	24-nor-5α(H)-cholest-22-en-3β-ol	Ie	N	24-methyl-5α(H)-cholest-7-en-3β-ol	VIp
k	24-nor-5α(H)-cholestan-3β-ol	If	O	unknown C_{29} steradienol	—
l	5β(H)-cholestan-3β-ol	IIIg	P	unknown C_{29} 5α(H)-stanol	—
m	5β(H)-cholestan-3α-ol	IVg	Q	23,24-dimethylcholest-5-en-3β-ol	IIs
n	unknown C_{27} stera-5,22-dien-3β-ol[b]	IIh?	R	24(E)-ethylidenecholest-5-en-3β-ol	IIt
o	unknown C_{27} 5α(H)-ster-22-en-3β-ol[c]	Ih?	S	23,24-dimethyl-5α(H)-cholestan-3β-ol	Is
p	27-nor-24-methylcholesta-5,22(E)-dien-3β-ol[c]	IIi	T	24-ethylcholest-5-en-3β-ol	IIu
q	cholesta-5,22(E)-dien-3β-ol	Ii	U	24(E)-ethylidene-5α(H)-cholestan-3β-ol	It
r	5α(H)-cholest-22(E)-en-3β-ol	IIj	V	24-ethyl-5α(H)-cholestan-3β-ol	Iu
s	unknown C_{27} 5α(H)-stan-3β-ol[b]	Ij	W	24(Z)-ethylidenecholest-5-en-3β-ol	IIv
t	cholest-5-en-3β-ol	IIg	X	24(Z)-ethylidene-5α(H)-cholestan-3β-ol	Iv
u	5α(H)-cholestan-3β-ol	Ig	Y	4α,23,24-trimethyl-5α(H)-cholest-22(E)-en-3β-ol	VIIq
v	27-nor-24-methyl-5α(H)-cholestan-3β-ol	Il	Z	24-ethyl-5α(H)-cholest-7-en-3β-ol	VIu
w	cholesta-5,7-dien-3β-ol	Vg	a′	24(E)-propylidenecholest-5-en-3β-ol	IIw
x	unknown C_{28} 5α(H)-stan-3β-ol	—	b′	24(E)-propylidene-5α(H)-cholestan-3β-ol	Iw
y	cholesta-5,24-dien-3β-ol	IIm	c′	24(Z)-propylidenecholest-5-en-3β-ol	IIx
z	24-methylcholesta-5,22(E)-dien-3β-ol	IIn	d′	24(Z)-propylidene-5α(H)-cholestan-3β-ol	Ix
A	24-methyl-5α(H)-cholest-22(E)-en-3β-ol	In	e′	4α-methyl-24-ethyl-5α(H)-cholest-8(14)-en-3β-ol	VIIIu
B	5α(H)-cholest-7-en-3β-ol	VIg	f′	4α,22,23-trimethyl-5α(H)-cholestan-3β-ol[e]?	VIIy
C	unknown C_{28} ster-22-en-3β-ol	—	g′	4α,23,24-trimethyl-5α(H)-cholestan-3β-ol[f]	VIIz
D					

? Tentative assignments based solely on spectral interpretation and GC retention times.

[a] Assignments, unless stated otherwise, are made by comparison with reference or literature spectra of sterol TMS ethers (e.g. Wardroper et al., 1978; Wardroper, 1979; Boon et al., 1979; Lee et al., 1979; Brassell, 1980; Brassell and Eglinton, 1981) and by consideration of GC elution orders, for example 24(E) isomers of $\Delta^{24(28)}$-sterols elute prior to their 24(Z) counterparts (Idler et al., 1976).

[b] Components may be 26,27-bisnor-23,24-dimethylcholesteroids (IIh, Ih and Ik, respectively; see Brassell and Eglinton, 1981).

[c] Assignment substantiated by coinjection with authentic standard, although coelution of cholesta-5,22(Z)-dien-3β-ol (IIz), which possesses a similar mass spectrum, cannot be excluded.

[d] The prominence of m/z 69 in the mass spectrum of the sterol TMS ether suggests C-24 (n) rather than C-23 (aa) methylation.

[e] May possess a 22,24-dimethyl (ab) rather than a 22,23-dimethyl (y) side chain; neither compound is available as a reference standard for comparison.

[f] Identification substantiated by coinjection of an authentic standard with other sedimentary sterol distributions (J. K. Volkman, personal communication).

1980c), assignments supported by the abundance of sponge spicules in the samples (Langseth *et al.*, 1980). Second, the presence of C_{27} and C_{28} $\Delta^{5,22}$ sterols (r and A numbered 2 in Fig. 2) may reflect inputs from diatoms (e.g. Rubinstein and Goad, 1974; Volkman *et al.*, 1981), as might be expected in diatomaceous oozes, although these compounds could also originate from coccolithophores. Third, the 24-ethylsterols (T and V numbered 3 in Fig. 2) probably represent higher plant inputs, given that they are markedly more abundant in terrigenous higher plants than in algae, and the hemipelagic nature of the sediments (Langseth *et al.*, 1980). In the absence of stereochemical evidence regarding the C-24 configuration of the 24-ethylsterols (cf. Maxwell *et al.*, 1980), this supposition that they represent higher plant inputs remains tentative. Indeed, it has been suggested (Lee *et al.*, 1980) that 24-ethylcholest-5-en-3β-ol in Namibian shelf sediments originates from diatoms.

Dinosterol (4α,23,24-trimethyl-5α(H)-cholest-22-en-3β-ol, VIIq; component Y, numbered 4, in Fig. 2) is the principal sterol of dinoflagellates (Shimizu *et al.*, 1976; Alam *et al.*, 1979a, b) and a marker for contributions from these organisms to sediments (Boon *et al.*, 1979). In addition, 4α,24-dimethyl-5α(H)-cholestan-3β-ol (VIIn, component I, numbered 4, in Fig. 2) occurs in dinoflagellates (Withers *et al.*, 1979) and may be derived from these organisms. Dinoflagellates may also be the source of other sedimentary 4α-methylstanols; for example, the presence of 4α-methylgorgostanol (22,23-methylene-4α,23,24-trimethyl-5α(H)-cholestan-3β-ol, VIIac) in a sediment from the Japan Trench (Brassell, 1980; Brassell and Eglinton, 1981) may reflect inputs from dinoflagellates, since this unusual C_{31} sterol has been identified in such organisms (Withers *et al.*, 1979; Alam *et al.*, 1979b). Also, 4α,23,24-trimethyl-5α(H)-cholestan-3β-ol (VIIs) has recently been identified in dinoflagellates (Alam *et al.*, 1981). 4,4-Dimethyl and 4-methyl sterols (Bird *et al.*, 1971; Bouvier *et al.*, 1976) have been identified in the methanotrophic bacterium *Methylococcus capsulatus*, hence the suggestion that the latter compounds in sediments are derived from bacteria (Dastillung *et al.*, 1980b), as reflected in Table 2. Present evidence, however, argues against such bacterial sources as major contributors of 4-methylsterols in marine sediments on two counts. First, the 4-methylsterols of *M. capsulatus* possess unsaturated steroidal skeletons, whereas those found in sediments are dominantly ring saturated. Also, the 4α-methyl sterol with an unsaturated ring system identified in the sediments if a C_{30} compound, 4α-methyl-24-ethyl-5α(H)-cholest-8(14)-en-3β-ol (VIIIn; peak e′ in Fig. 2), previously recognized in dinoflagellates (Kokke *et al.*, 1981a), whereas only C_{28} 4α-methyl $\Delta^{8(14)}$-steroids have been found in bacteria (Bouvier *et al.*, 1976). Second, the recognition of dinosterol (VIIq) in sediment traps (Wakeham *et al.*, 1980) indicates that 4-methylsterols can originate from pelagic sources, which are principally algal rather than bacterial.

The value of steroidal ketones as indicators of sediment inputs (Table 2) stems partly from their side chain specificity, like the sterols, but such assessments are hindered by the scarcity of reports of these compounds as constituents of organisms. One compound that is an exception to this constraint is dinosterone (4α,23,24-trimethyl-5α(H)-cholest-22-en-3-one, IXq), which has been identified as a component of dinoflagellates (Withers *et al.*, 1978), and therefore, like its sterol counterpart, reflects sediment inputs from these organisms. Various sources of cholest-4-en-3-one (Xg), which has been identified in both lacustrine (Gaskell and Eglinton, 1975) and marine (Brassell, 1980) sediments, are possible. In the former instance it is a diagenetic product derived from microbial oxidation of cholest-5-en-3β-ol (Gaskell and Eglinton, 1975), whereas in the latter it probably represents direct sediment inputs from sponges (Delseth *et al.*, 1978, 1979) or other organisms, including pelagic species (Schmitz, 1978). The recognition of cholest-4-en-3-one in sediment trap particulates (Wakeham *et al.*, 1980) confirms that this compound can originate from pelagic sources, although it is not apparent whether it is derived directly from an organism or is formed as a microbial transformation product of cholest-5-en-3β-ol in the water column. Other products of microbial oxidation of cholest-5-en-3β-ol include 5α(H)- and 5β(H)-stan-3-ones (XI and XII, respectively, which are intermediates in the conversion of Δ^5-stenols to 5α(H)- and 5β(H)-stanols (Gaskell and Eglinton, 1975). It is this intermediacy of stanones in the microbiological degradation of stenols to stanols in sediments (Gaskell and Eglinton, 1975; Gagosian and Smith, 1979) that suggests their possible use as markers of bacterial activity (Table 2; Brassell *et al.*, 1980c), although it remains open whether 5α(H)- and 5β(H)-stanones, like dinosterone and cholest-4-en-3-one, may also be direct biological inputs to sediments. As microbial degradation products they do, however, retain the side chain of their precursor stenols and may therefore indicate specific sediment inputs on that basis. For example, 24-ethylcholestan-3-ones (XIu and XIIu) might be expected to reflect terrestrial higher plant inputs, like their Δ^5-stenol counterpart (IIu; see above).

The origin of steryl ethers (e.g. XIIIa) in sediments is unclear, but their occurrence in diatomaceous oozes dominated by autochthonous inputs (Boon and de Leeuw, 1979; Brassell *et al.*, 1980b, c) suggests that they originate from marine algal, or possibly bacterial, sources (Table 2). The discrepancies between the distributions of the steroidal skeletal moieties of the steryl ethers and those of their co-occurring sterols suggest that the former are not diagenetic products. In addition, the size of the alkyl moieties of the steryl ethers (C_8–C_{11}; Boon and de Leeuw, 1979; Brassell, 1980; Brassell *et al.*, 1980b, c) are unusual and have no obvious source from other sediment lipids.

Steryl esters (e.g. XIIIb) are components of various algae (e.g. Orcutt and Richardson, 1970; Mercer *et al.*, 1974; Rohmer *et al.*, 1980) and of higher plants (Kemp and Mercer, 1968) so that their presence in sediments may reflect inputs from either of these categories of organism (Table 2). In general, the sterol moieties of the steryl esters of an organism are qualitatively similar to its free sterols and may therefore provide an indication of their source. Hence, the steryl esters of a Recent lacustrine sediment that possess 24-ethylcholest-5-en-3β-ol (IIu) as their dominant sterol moiety represent inputs

Table 4

Estimated values of triterpenoids as biological markers of sediment inputs

Triterpenoid class	Algal/ marine	Bacterial	Terrigenous higher plant
Hopanoids	+ [a]	+ + +	—
Fernenes	—	+ + +	+ + ?
'Oleanoids'[b]	—	—	+ +
A-ring degraded 3-oxytriterpenoids	—	+ + ?	+ +
'Gammaceroids'[c]	?	—	?

[a] The ratings provide an estimate of the value of the triterpenoidal classes as markers of inputs from the respective sources (— unknown, ? uncertain).

[b] Includes lipids possessing oleanane, ursane, glutane, friedelane and lupane skeletons.

[c] Includes gammacerane and tetrahymanol.

from higher plants (Cranwell and Volkman, 1981). In contrast, the steryl esters found in sediment trap particulates appear to derive from algal sources (Wakeham *et al.*, 1980).

At present the origin of steroidal acids (e.g. $5\alpha(H)$-cholanic acid, XIV) in sediments is uncertain (Boon *et al.*, 1978), which diminishes their use and value as biological markers of inputs (Table 2). They may be derived directly from higher plants (Mandava *et al.*, 1974) or be formed as bacterial degradation products of sterols (Charney and Herzog, 1967). The sedimentary distributions of steroidal acids, however, are different from those expected from this bacterial oxidation degradative pathway (Boon *et al.*, 1978). In addition, the end product of the oxidation process ia a 17-oxysteroid (Charney and Herzog, 1967) which has yet to be recognized in sediments.

In summary, steroids provide a means of assessing the sources of immature sediment lipids through the use of biological marker compounds, although the origin and significance of some of the steroidal classes is at present unclear.

Triterpenoids as biological markers

The values of various classes of triterpenoids in assessing direct sediment inputs from organisms are estimated in Table 4. Of these classes the hopanoids are the most abundant in sediments (e.g. Ourisson *et al.*, 1979) and appear, principally, to reflect bacterial inputs. In particular all extended hopanoids (alkanes, alkenes, alkanoic and alkenoic acids, alkanols and alkanones) are thought to derive from precursor poly-hydroxybacteriohopanes (XVe, Rohmer and Ourisson, 1976) and indicate sediment inputs from prokaryotes (Ourisson *et al.*, 1979), which in the marine environment are dominantly bacteria rather than blue–green algae (Brassell *et al.*, 1980c). The diagenetic processes that generate the wide variety of hopanoids found in immature sediments (e.g. Dastillung *et al.*, 1980a, b; van Dorsselaer *et al.*, 1974; Brassell *et al.*, 1980b) from tetrahydroxy precursors are uncertain.

Among the variety of C_{30} hopenes that occur in sediments hop-17(21)-ene (XVII) and $17\beta(H), 21\beta(H)$-

hop-22(29)-ene (XVb), like $17\beta(H), 21\beta(H)$-hopane (XVa) itself, are known constituents of bacteria (De Rosa *et al.*, 1971, 1973), wherease neohop-13(18)-ene (XVIII) was, until recently, presumed to represent either a diagenetic product of hop-22(29)-ene (Ensminger, 1977; Brassell *et al.*, 1980c) or an input from ferns (Ageta *et al.*, 1968; Bottari *et al.*, 1972; Brassell *et al.*, 1980c). Similarly, $17\beta(H)$-hop-21-ene (XX) was seen as an intermediate in the diagenetic isomerization of hop-22(29)-ene (Brassell *et al.*, 1980c and references therein) and neohop-12-ene (XIX) appeared, like fernenes, to be derived from ferns (Ageta *et al.*, 1968; Bottari *et al.*, 1972; Brassell *et al.*, 1980c). This picture has now changed following the identification of neohop-13(18)-ene and $17\beta(H)$-hop-21-ene in a bacterium (Howard, 1980). The use of fernenes (XXI–XXIII) as biological markers of terrestrial higher plant inputs to sediments, notably from ferns (e.g. Berti and Bottari, 1968; Bottari *et al.*, 1972; Brassell *et al.*, 1980c), has also been reappraised following the recognition of these compounds in the same photosynthetic bacterium (Howard, 1980). Hence, sedimentary C_{30} hopenes and fernenes, with the exception of neohop-12-ene (XIX) whose status is uncertain, appear to reflect bacterial inputs (e.g. Brassell *et al.*, 1981a).

The importance of bacterial inputs of hopanoids and fernenes in sedimentary lipid distributions is illustrated in Fig. 3 (assignments are given in Table 5), where such compounds are major components of the branched/cyclic aliphatic hydrocarbon fraction (cf. Brassell *et al.*, 1981a). Indeed, since the C_{25} and C_{30} acyclic isoprenoid alkanes (peaks 4 and 5 in Fig. 3), and perhaps the phytenes, are derived from methanogenic bacteria (Brassell *et al.*, 1981a), this fraction provides good evidence for the imprint of bacterial lipids on sedimentary organic matter.

The triterpenoids referrred to as 'oleanoids' in Table 4 are derived from higher plants (e.g. Devon and Scott, 1972) and therefore represent terrigenous inputs to sediments (Table 2; e.g. Brassell *et al.*, 1980c). Examples of the distributions of triterpenones in Japan Trench sediments are given in Fig. 4; a similar range of compounds has been identified in sediments from the Middle ⁄ ˙erica Trench (Brassell *et al.*, 1981b). In both suites of sediments various triterpenols, notably olean-12-en-3β-ol (XXVIIIb), urs-12-en-3β-ol (XXIXb) and taraxer-14-en-3β-ol (XXVIIb) were also recognized (Brassell, 1980; Brassell *et al.*, 1980c, 1981b). These compounds were not detected as significant components of sediments from the Walvis Ridge where autochthonous inputs greatly outweigh those from allochthonous sources. Hence the apparent occurrence of 'oleanoids' in those sediments that contain a significant terrigenous component provides cir-cumstantial evidence in support of their assignments as terrestrial marker compounds.

In deep sea sediments 'oleanoids' tend to be accompanied by a variety of C_{24} cycloalkenes and cycloalkanes tentatively assigned as A-ring degraded triterpenoids (Corbet *et al.*, 1980). It is uncertain whether these compounds are formed by photochemical or bacterial degradation of 3-oxytriterpenoids (Corbet *et al.*, 1980), although the former possibility is perhaps the

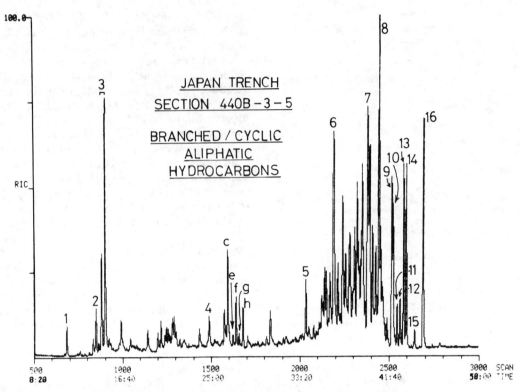

Fig. 3. Reconstructed ion chromatogram (RIC) of the branched cyclic aliphatic hydrocarbons of Section 440B-3-5 from the Japan Trench. The identities of the designated peaks are given in Table 5.

Table 5

Identities of components among the branched/cyclic aliphatic hydrocarbons of Japan Trench Section 440B-3-5 (Figure 4)

Peak (Fig. 3)	Assignment[a]	Structure
1	pristane	—
2	phytane	—
3	phytenes[b]	—
4	2,6,10,15,19-pentamethyleicosane[a]	XXIV
c		—
e	A-ring degraded	—
f	triterpenoids	—
g	(cf. Fig. 6)	—
h		—
5	squalane[d]	XXV
6	cholesta-3,5-diene	XXVI
7	hop-17(21)-ene[d]	XVII
8	neohop-13(18)-ene[d]	XVIII
9	neohop-12-ene[d]	XIX
10	fern-7-ene[d]	XXI
11	22(R)-17α(H),21β(H)-homohopane	XVId
12	17β(H),21β(H)-hopane	XVa
13	17β(H),21β(H)-hop-22(29)-ene[d]	XVb
14	17β(H)-hop-21-ene[d]	XX
15	17β(H),21β(H)-homohop-29(31)-ene	XVc
16	17β(H),21β(H)-homohopane	XVd

[α] assignments are based, unless stated otherwise, on comparison with reference or literature spectra.
[b] both phytenes possess spectra consistent with that of phyt-2-ene (Urbach and Stark, 1975).
[c] assignment recently confirmed by synthesis of an authentic standard (Rowland *et al.*, 1982).
[d] assignments confirmed by coinjection with authentic standards.

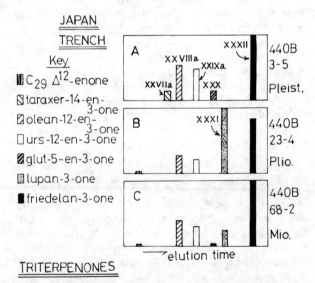

Fig. 4. Histograms of the relative abundances of triterpenones in three sediments from the Japan Trench. A, 440B-3-5; B, 440B-23-4; C, 440B-68-2. Compound assignments were made by reference to standard spectra.

more probable. In both instances the precursor 'oleanoids' are derived from terrigenous higher plants and therefore A-ring degraded triterpenoids can be regarded as biological markers, albeit altered ones, of sediment inputs from such sources (Table 2). Examples of the distributions of A-ring degraded triterpenoids in deep sea sediments are given in Fig. 5; that of Section 440B-3-5 is also apparent in the chromatogram of the

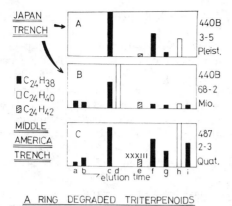

Fig. 5. Histograms of the relative abundances of compounds assigned as A-ring degraded triterpenoids in Japan and Middle America Trench sediments (A, 440B-3-5; B, 440B-68-2; C, 487-2-3). Only the structure of component e, an alkane, (XXXIII) is known.

branched/cyclic aliphatic hydrocarbons (Fig. 3). The structure of only one of these A-ring degraded triterpenoids is known, that of the alkane (XXXIII), which appears to be a degraded derivative of lupan-3-one (XXXI; Corbet *et al.*, 1980). Some of the other compounds do, however, possess mass spectral features which suggest that they may be related to olean-12-en-3-one (XXVIIIa) or urs-12-en-3-one (XXIXa).

The origin and significance of tetrahymanol (XXXIVa) and its reduced counterpart gammacerane (XXXIVb) are unclear (Table 2). Gammacerane, first identified in the Green River shale (Hills *et al.*, 1966), occurs in various ancient sediments and petroleums. However, its presumed biological precursor, tetrahymanol, which is a component of protozoa (Tsuda *et al.*, 1965), has yet to be confirmed as a constituent of sediments.

In summary, individual triterpenoids or classes of triterpenoids are valuable markers for organic matter from bacterial or terrestrial sources. Their value as indicators of inputs from marine algae is unproven and appears to be limited. The specificity of triterpenoids as biological markers of sources of sedimentary organic matter appears, however, to be less than that of the sterols (see above), an observation that is perhaps a function of various factors. First, it may reflect a bias in the literature, considering the greater research interest in sterols than in triterpenoids, notably hopanoids. Second, the potential structural variations of sterol side chains (Djerassi *et al.*, 1979; Djerassi, 1981 and references therein) are probably greater than those possible for other triterpenoids, including hopanoids, hence the range of sterol structures in both biota and sediments is wider. Third, the variability of sterol side chains is, at least partly, a response to their required role as rigidifiers of lipid membranes in eucaryotes. Since hopanoids appear to fulfil this same role in procaryotes, which are biochemically more primitive organisms (Ourisson *et al.*, 1979), evolutionary developments might be responsible for a greater variability and specificity in sterols. Overall, the potential of steroids and triterpenoids as biological markers of the sources of sedimentary organic matter is demonstrable, although there is considerable scope for further refinement of this approach.

Survival and lipid signatures

In trying to extend the recognition of molecular signatures characteristic of specific environmental features to sediments of greater age and maturity two major problems exist: evolutionary changes in the lipid compositions of organisms and diagenetic changes in the lipid compositions of sediments. The biological marker approach to the assessment of sediment inputs makes the major assumption that there have been no significant changes in the proclivity of different biosynthetic pathways within classes of organisms over geological time. Diagenetic effects tend to obscure or erase specific lipid features indicative of their origins, such as stereochemistry and functionality, although much information survives. These two facets of the survival of lipid signatures are examined and illustrated here.

The presence of sterols in Cretaceous sediments (Wardroper, 1979; Comet *et al.*, 1981) illustrates that such compounds can survive in ancient sediments. It is impossible to tell, however, the extent to which these sterol distributions have been affected in qualitative terms by diagenetic processes. Certainly the Cretaceous sterol distributions are markedly less complex than those of Pleistocene Japan Trench sediments (Fig. 2), although such differences are perhaps a reflection of their depositional environments. The presence of dinosterol (VIIq) in a Cretaceous 'black shale' (Comet *et al.*, 1981) may reflect sediment inputs from dinoflagellates (Boon *et al.*, 1979), although the sample does not contain their cysts (Comet *et al.*, 1981). Dinoflagellates can contain dinosterol when they do not bear cysts, for example when they are symbionts (e.g. Kokke *et al.*, 1981b), but the possibility also exists that a different, perhaps extinct, organism was the source of dinosterol in these sediments.

The distribution of fernenes in a variety of deep sea sediments of Cretaceous to Quaternary age are plotted in Fig. 6. In all the Pliocene and Pleistocene samples the predominant isomer is fern-7-ene (XXI), whereas in the Miocene and Cretaceous sediments is is fern-8-ene(XXII). It is uncertain whether this difference is effected by diagenesis or is a genuine environmental feature reflecting sediment inputs. In favour of the former explanation is the fact that fern-8-ene is the most

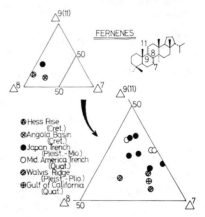

Fig. 6. Triangular plot of the relative abundance of fernene isomers in a variety of deep sea sediments.

stable of the three isomers (Berti and Bottari, 1968). However, the variability in the ratios of fernene isomers of the Pleistocene and Pliocene samples is unlikely to be a function of diagenesis, since all the sediments are highly immature. Rather, it may reflect minor differences in the bacteria contributing fernenes to the sediments, suggesting some measure of environmental control over the sedimentary fernene distributions. There might also be evolutionary changes in the fernene composition of bacteria that could explain the differences between the Miocene and Cretaceous sediments and those of Pliocene and Pleistocene age (Fig. 6). Hence, in this instance, it is unclear at present whether the differences observed are a function of diagenesis or of evolutionary changes in bacterial fernene compositions. Further studies of sedimentary fernene distributions may help to resolve this ambiguity.

Diagenetic considerations

In attempts to understand diagenetic processes in immature sediments the carbon number distributions of supposed precursors and products can be considered. In particular processes affecting steroidal nuclear functionalities should generally be independent of factors such as side chain alkylation patterns. Aspects of the early-stage diagenesis of sterols amenable to such treatment are considered herein, with reference to the information also obtained on steroidal inputs to sediments.

In Japan Trench sediments the distributions of 5α(H)-stanols (I), 5β(H)-stanols (III, IV), Δ^5-stenols (II), 5α(H)-stanones (XI), 5β(H)-stanones (XII) and Δ^4-stenones (X) differ markedly (Brassell, 1980), suggesting that there is no simple or direct diagenetic relationship between them. For example, although Δ^5-stenols tend to dominate their 5α(H)-stanol counterparts (Fig. 2) there is considerable variability in such Δ^5-stenol/5α(H)-stanol ratios (Brassell, 1980), suggesting that stenol hydrogenation (Gaskell and Eglinton, 1975) is not a significant diagenetic process in these sediments. A selective loss of Δ^5-stenols relative to stanols at very early stages of diagenesis in the sediments (Nishimura and Koyama, 1977) remains possible, although differences in stanol concentrations between the various growth stages of a given organism (Ballantine *et al.*, 1979) might also account for the apparent enhancement of stanols relative to stenols in sediments as compared with organisms. Although a wide range of 5α(H)-stanols is present in the Japan Trench sediments only two 5β(H)-stanols (5β(H)-cholestan-3β-ol(IIIg) and 5β(H)-cholestan-3α-ol(IVg); Fig. 2) were identified (Brassell and Eglinton, 1981). This discrepancy further argues against Δ^5-stenol hydrogenation in the sediments and suggests that both 5α(H)- and 5β(H)-stanols are principally derived directly from biological inputs (but see below). In that the sediments were saponified prior to fractionation and analysis, it is possible that differences between the stenol and stanol distributions may partly result from variations in the sterol content of free sterols and steryl esters. However, given this possibility of mixed sterol inputs, the recognition of only C_{27} 5β(H)-stanols still excludes Δ^5-stenol hydrogenation as a significant process for the full range (C_{27} to C_{29}) of sterols.

The range of steroidal ketones in the Japan Trench sediments is rather limited (Brassell, 1980) and markedly less complex than that reported for Namibian Shelf sediments (Gagosian and Smith, 1979; Gagosian *et al.*, 1980). In view of the presence of only C_{27} 5β(H)-stanols, the recognition of a single 5β(H)-stanone, 5β(H)-cholestan-3-one (XIIg), and a single Δ^4-stenone, cholest-4-en-3-one (Xg), in the Japan Trench samples suggest that there may be significant differences between the diagenesis of C_{27} versus other sterols. In particular the C_{27} 5β(H)-steroids may be microbial transformation products derived from cholest-4-en-3-one, since such pathways are known (e.g. Björkhem and Gustafsson, 1971; Edmunds *et al.*, 1980), although it is uncertain whether such transformations occur at a pre- or postdepositional stage. Studies of sediment trap particulates, however, show cholest-4-en-3-one as the major steroidal ketone (Wakeham *et al.*, 1980) decreasing in abundance with depth, which suggests that it may be undergoing microbial transformation in the water column. 5α(H)-Cholestan-3α-ol (XXXV) has been recognized in sediments from the Middle America Trench and Walvis Ridge (Brassell, unpublished data) together with two 5β(H)-stanols and may also be derived from cholest-4-en-3-one. Its recognition provides further evidence for specific sources of C_{27} steroids leading to discrepancies between the distributions of C_{27} versus other sterols.

The C_{27} v. C_{28} v. C_{29} carbon number distribution of 5α(H)-stan-3-ones in Japan Trench sediments is similar to that of the 5α(H)-stan-3β-ols, as can be seen in Fig. 7B when plotted in a triangular diagram (after Huang and Meinschein, 1979), selecting cholestane, 24-methylcholestane and 24-ethylcholestane as the specific side chains for the C_{27}, C_{28} and C_{29} apices, respectively.

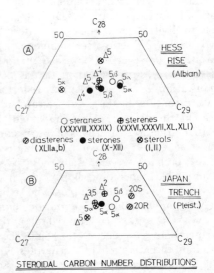

Fig. 7. Carbon number distribution of a number of steroidal compound classes in A, Section 465A-38-3 from the Hess Rise (Comet *et al.*, 1981) and B, Section 440B-3-5 from the Japan Trench (Brassell, 1980). The C_{27}, C_{28} and C_{29} apices represent compounds of cholestane, 24-methylcholestane and 24-ethylcholestane structural types.

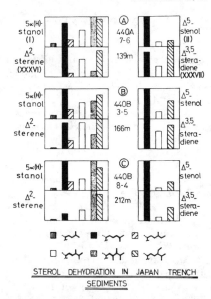

STEROL DEHYDRATION IN JAPAN TRENCH SEDIMENTS

Fig. 8. Histograms of the relative abundances of sterols with specific side chains and their postulated dehydration products in three Pleistocene sediments from the Japan Trench; A, Section 440A-7-6; B, Section 440B-3-5; C, Section 440B-8-4.

Index, despite the limitations of such plots in assessing sediment inputs (see above), they are useful for testing diagenetic relationships between different compound classes. Hence, $5\alpha(H)$-stanols and $5\alpha(H)$-stanones appear to be related either diagenetically or as inputs from a common source. In the same sample the distributions of 4α-methyl-$5\alpha(H)$-stanols (VII) and 4α-methyl-$5\alpha(H)$-stanones (IX) are also similar, and include Δ^{22} components (dinosterol, VIIq and dinosterone, IXq, respectively).

A major early-stage diagenetic process in marine sediments is the dehydration of sterols to sterenes (Dastillung and Albrecht, 1977; Gagosian and Farrington, 1978; Gagosian *et al.*, 1980), especially the conversion of $5\alpha(H)$-stanols (I) and Δ^5-stenols (II) to Δ^2-sterenes (XXXVI) and $\Delta^{3,5}$-steradienes (XXXVII), respectively. Figure 8 shows histograms of the side chain distributions of these proposed precursor/product pairings of sterol and sterene for three Japan Trench sediments. On visual inspection the pairings match quite well for Section 440B-3-5 (Fig. 8B), whereas for Sections 440A-7-6 and 440B-8-4 there are major discrepancies in the distributions (Fig. 8A and C). Such discrepancies can be explained as the result of one or a combination of at least two factors. First, it appears that certain sterol transformations mediated by microbes can show a preference for specific sterol carbon numbers (Boon *et al.*, this volume), although the proclivity of such processes in the open marine environment, as compared with Solar Lake, remains unknown. Second, sterenes have been recognised as major hydrocarbon constituents of sediment trap particulates (Wakeham *et al.*, 1980) and may therefore be formed by the selective dehydration of those sterols present in specific fractions of the sedimenting organic matter.

In summary, the steroid distributions of the Japan Trench sediments suggest (i) hydrogenation of Δ^5-stenols to $5\alpha(H)$-stanols is not significant, (ii) $5\beta(H)$-steroids may be derived from inputs of Δ^4-sterones, (iii)

$5\alpha(H)$-stanones are related in terms of diagenesis or of their source to $5\alpha(H)$-stanols, (iv) 4α-methyl-$5\alpha(H)$-stanones are similarly related to 4α-methyl-$5\alpha(H)$-stanols and (v) the dehydration of specific sterol fractions may initially occur.

The diagenetic processes discussed above are initial stages of the multistep transformation of biolipids into geolipids. Considering the steroidal carbon number distributions of a black shale from the Hess Rise (Fig. 7A; Comet *et al.*, 1981) the match between $5\alpha(H)$- and $5\beta(H)$-steranes (XXXVIII and XXXIX respectively) and their presumed precursor sterenes (Δ^4 and Δ^5, XL and XLI, respectively) is quite good, as is that between Δ^4-stenones (X) and $5\beta(H)$-stanones (XII). The distributions of the sterols ($5\alpha(H)$-stanols and Δ^5-stenols) do not, however, appear to resemble each other, or any of the other steroids. In the Japan Trench sample (Fig. 7B) the steranes plot fairly close to their presumed precursor sterols, whereas the 20(S)- and 20(R)-diasterenes (XLIIa and XLIIb, respectively) contain a higher proportion of C_{29} components. Such a difference may reflect allochthonous inputs of diasterenes, since the triangular diagram may distinguish steroids that do not share a common source. Alternatively, 24-ethylsteroids may be more susceptible to backbone rearrangement than C_{27} components or they may be more closely associated with the sedimentary clay matrix, being derived from terrestrial sources (see above), which acts as a promoter of the rearrangement process (Rubinstein *et al.*, 1975).

Similarity of lipid distributions

One feature of the molecular signature of deep sea sediments that has emerged from our analyses at Bristol is the remarkable similarity that exists between certain lipid distributions of geographically and temporally diverse sediments (e.g. Brassell *et al.*, 1980a and this volume). For example, the distributions of hopanoid alkanes, alkenes and alkanones of carbonaceous marly chalks from the Bay of Biscay and turbidites from the Moroccan Basin are remarkably similar (Brassell *et al.*, 1980a; Wardroper and Brassell, unpublished data), suggesting some common input of organic matter to the suites of samples. Figure 9 illustrates the similarity in diasterene distributions, including even the unknown minor components, between a diatomaceous vitric clay from the Japan Trench and a turbidite from the Moroccan Basin. It shows that the rearrangement of steroids is a consistent diagenetic process in deep sea sediments. The fundamental reason for similarities in the lipid distributions of deep sea sediments is probably related to common inputs or common depositional environments where microbial lipid signatures and overprints are uniform.

CONCLUSIONS

The major findings from this study of steroids and triterpenoids in deep sea sediments can be summarized as follows:

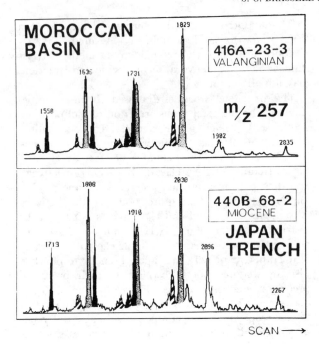

Fig. 9. m/z 257 Mass fragmentograms showing the diasterene distributions of Section 416A-23-3 from the Moroccan Basin and Section 440B-68-2 from the Japan Trench.

1. The steroidal and triterpenoidal lipids of the sediments include components that are specific markers for inputs from various marine, terrestrial and bacterial sources.
2. Labile marker compounds such as sterols can survive in deep sea sediments greater than 100 Ma old.
3. There is a need for further studies directed towards the distinction of evolutionary and diagenetic changes in sedimentary lipid compositions.
4. In sediments from the Japan Trench the $5\beta(H)$-steroids appear to derive from microbial transformation of Δ^4-stenones. Sterol hydrogenation does not appear to be a significant process in these sediments.
5. Remarkable similarities exist between certain lipid distributions of geographically and temporally diverse sediments suggesting that they contain common inputs or were laid down under similar depositional conditions.

Acknowledgements

We thank the Natural Environment Research Council for financial support (GR3/2951 and GR33758) and colleagues at Bristol, notably Drs James Maxwell and Tony Wardroper, Paul Comet, Vanessa Howell, Jim McEvoy and Iain Thomson, for helpful discussions, practical assistance and access to unpublished results. We are grateful to Mrs. Ann Gowar for help with C-GC–MS analyses. The samples were supplied with the aid of the National Science Foundation.

REFERENCES

Ageta, H., Shioima, K. and Arai, Y. (1968) Fern constituents: neohopene, hopene-II; neohopadiene and fernadiene isolated from *Adiantum* species. *Chem. Commun.*, 1005–1107.

Alam, M., Sansing, T. B., Busby, E. L., Martinez, D. R. and Ray, S. M. (1979a) Dinoflagellate sterols I: sterol composition of the dinfolagellates of *Gonyaulax* species. *Steroids* **33**, 197–203.

Alam, M., Martin, G. E. and Ray, S. M. (1979b) Dinoflagellate sterols II: Isolation and structure of 4-methylgorgostanol from the dinoflagellate *Glenodinium foliaceum*. *J. Org. Chem.* **44**, 4466–4467.

Alam, M., Sansing, T. B., Guerra, J. R. and Harmon, A. D. (1981) Dinoflagellate sterols IV: Isolation and structure of $4\alpha,23\xi,24\xi$-trimethylcholestanol from the dinoflagellate *Glenodinium hallii*. *Steroids* **38**, 375–382.

Ballantine, J. A., Williams, K. and Burke, B. A. (1977) Marine sterols. IV. C_{21} sterols from marine sources. Identification of pregnane derivatives in extracts of the sponge *Haliclona rubens*. *Tetrahedron Lett.*, 1547–1550.

Ballantine, J. A., Lavis, A. and Morris, R. J. (1979) Sterols of the phytoplankton — effects of illumination and growth stage. *Phytochem.* **18**, 1459–1466.

Barnes, P. J., Brassell, S. C., Comet, P. A., Eglinton, G., McEvoy, J., Maxwell, J. R., Wardroper, A. M. K. and Volkman, J. K. (1979) Preliminary lipid analyses of core sections 18, 24 and 30 from Hole 402A. In *Initial Reports of the Deep Sea Drilling Project, Vol. 48*. Ed. by Montadert, L., Roberts, D. G., *et al.* US Govt. Printing Office, Washington. pp. 965–976.

Berti, G. and Bottari, F. (1968) Constituents of ferns. In *Progress in Phytochemistry, Vol. 1*. Ed. by Reinhold, L. and Liwschitz, Y. Interscience. pp. 589–685.

Bird, C. W., Lynch, J. M., Port, S. J., Reed, W. W., Brooks, C. J. W. and Middleditch, B. S. (1971) Steroids and squalene in *Methylococcus capsulatus* grown on methane. *Nature* **230**, 473–475.

Björkhem, I. and Gustafsson, J. (1971) Mechanisms of microbial transformation of cholesterol into coprostanol. *Europ. J. Biochem.* **21**, 428–432.

Boon, J. J. and de Leeuw, J. W. (1979) The analysis of wax esters, very long mid-chain ketones and sterol ethers isolated from Walvis Bay diatomaceous ooze. *Mar. Chem.* **7**, 117–132.

Boon, J. J., De Leeuw, J. W. and Burlingame, A. L. (1978) Organic geochemistry of Walvis Bay diatomaceous ooze — III. Structural analysis of the monoenoic and polycyclic fatty acids. *Geochim. Cosmochim. Acta* **42**, 631–639.

Boon, J. J., Rijpstra, W. I. C., de Lange, F., De Leeuw, J. W., Yoshioka, M. and Shimizu, Y. (1979) The Black Sea sterol — a molecular fossil for dinoflagellate blooms. *Nature* **277**, 125–127.

Bottari, F., Marsili, A., Morelli, I. and Pacciani, M. (1972) Aliphatic and triterpenoid hydrocarbons from ferns. *Phytochemistry* **11**, 2519–2523.

Bouvier, P., Rohmer, M., Benveniste, P. and Ourisson, G. (1976) $\Delta^{8(14)}$-Steroids in the bacterium *Methylococcus capsulatus*. *Biochem. J.* **159**, 267–271.

Brassell, S. C. (1980) The lipids of deep sea sediments; their origin and fate in the Japan Trench. PhD Thesis, University of Bristol.

Brassell, S. C. and Eglinton, G. (1981) Biogeochemical significance of a novel sedimentary C_{27} stanol. *Nature* **290**, 579–582.

Brassell, S. C., Comet, P. A., Eglinton, G., McEvoy, J., Maxwell, J. R., Quirke, J. M. E. and Volkman, J. K. (1980a) Preliminary lipid analyses of cores 14, 18 and 28 from Deep Sea Drilling Project Hole 416A. In *Initial Reports* of the Deep Sea Drilling Project, Vol. 50. Ed. by Lancelot, Y., Winterer, E. L. *et al.* US Govt. Printing Office, Washington. pp. 647–664.

Brassell, S. C., Comet, P. A., Eglinton, G., Isaacson, P. J., McEvoy, J., Maxwell, J. R., Thomson, I. D., Tibbetts, P. J. C. and Volkman, J. K. (1980b) Preliminary analyses of sections 440A-7-6, 440B-3-5, 440B-8-4, 440B-68-2 and 436-11-4: Legs 56 and 57, Deep Sea Drilling Project. In *Initial Reports of the Deep Sea Drilling Project, Vols. 56/57, Part 2*. Ed. by Langseth, M., *et al.* US Govt. Printing Office, Washington. pp. 1367–1390.

Brassell, S. C., Comet, P. A., Eglinton, G., Isaacson, P. J., McEvoy, J., Maxwell, J. R., Thomson, I. D., Tibbetts, P. J. C. and Volkman, J. K. (1980c) The origin and fate of lipids in the Japan Trench. In *Advances in Organic Geochemistry 1979*. Ed. by Douglas, A. G. and Maxwell, J. R. Pergamon Press, Oxford. pp. 375–391.

Brassell, S. C., Gowar, A. P. and Eglinton, G. (1980d) Computerised gas chromatography–mass spectrometry in analyses of sediments from the Deep Sea Drilling Project. In *Advance in Organic Geochemistry 1979*. Ed. by Douglas, A. G. and Maxwell, J. R. Pergamon Press, Oxford. pp. 421–426.

Brassell, S. C., Wardroper, A. M. K., Thomson, I. D., Maxwell, J. R. and Eglinton, G. (1981a) Specific acyclic isoprenoids as biological markers of methanogenic bacteria in marine sediments. *Nature* **290**, 693–696.

Brassell, S. C., Eglinton, G. and Maxwell, J. R. (1981b) Preliminary lipid analyses of two Quaternary sediments from the Middle America Trench, Southern Mexico Transect, Deep Sea Drilling Project Leg 66. In *Initial Reports of the Deep Sea Drilling Project Vol. 66*. Ed. by Watkins, J. S., Moore, J. C., *et al.* US Govt. Printing Office, Washington. pp. 557–580.

Carlson, R. M. K., Popov, S., Massey, I., Delseth, C., Ayanoglu, E., Varkony, T. H. and Djerassi, C. (1978) Minor and trace sterols in marine invertebrates. VI. Occurrence and possible origins of sterols possessing unusually short hydrocarbon side chains. *Bioorg. Chem.* **7**, 453–479.

Charney, W. and Herzog, H. L. (1967) Microbial transformations of steroids. Academic Press, New York.

Comet, P. A., McEvoy, J., Brassell, S. C., Eglinton, G., Maxwell, J. R. and Thomson, I. D. (1981) Lipids of an Upper Albian limestone, Section 465A-38-3. In *Initial Reports of the Deep Sea Drilling Project, Vol. 62*. Ed. by Thiede, J., Vallier, T., *et al.* US Govt Printing Office, Washington. pp. 923–937.

Corbet, B., Albrecht, P. and Ourisson, G. (1980) Photochemical or photomimetic fossil triterpenoids in sediments and petroleum. *J. Amer. Chem. Soc.* **102**, 1171–1173.

Cranwell, P. A. and Volkman, J. K. (1981) Alkyl and steryl ethers in a Recent lacustrine sediment. *Chem. Geol.* **32**, 29–43.

Dastillung, M. and Albrecht, P. (1977) Δ^2-Sterenes as diagenetic intermediates in sediments. *Nature* **269**, 678–679.

Dastillung, M., Albrecht, P. and Ourisson, G. (1980a) Aliphatic and polycyclic ketones in sediments. C_{27}–C_{35} ketones and aldehydes of the hopane series. *J. Chem. Res.* (S), 166–167, (M) 2325–2352.

Dastillung, M., Albrecht, P. and Ourisson, G. (1980b) Aliphatic and polycyclic alcohols in sediments. Hydroxylated derivatives of hopane and 3-methylhopane. *J. Chem. Res.* (3), 168–169, (M) 2353–2374.

Delseth, C., Carlson, R. M. K., Djerassi, C., Erdman, T. R. and Scheuer, P. J. (1978) Identification de sterols à chaines laterales courtes dans l'éponge, *Damiriaria hawaiiana. Helv. Chim. Acta* **61**, 1470–1476.

Delseth, C., Tolela, L., Scheuer, P. J., Wells, R. J. and Djerassi, C. (1979) 5α-Norcholestan-3β-ol and (24Z)-

stigmasta-5,7,24(28)-trien-3β-ol, two new marine sterols from the Pacific sponges *Terpois zeteki* and *Dysidia herbacea. Helv. Chim. Acta* **62**, 101–109.

De Rosa, M., Gambacorta, A., Minale, L. and Bu'Lock, J. D. (1971) Bacterial triterpenes. *Chem. Commun.*, 619–620.

De Rosa, M., Gambacorta, A., Minale, L. and Bu'Lock, J. D. (1973) Isoprenoids of *Bacillus acidocaldarius. Phytochemistry* **12**, 1117–1123.

Devon, T. K. and Scott, A. I. (1972) Handbook of naturally-occurring compounds II. Terpenes, Academic Press, New York.

Djerassi, C. (1981) Recent studies in the marine sterol field. *Pure Appl. Chem.* **53**, 873–890.

Djerassi, C., Theobald, N., Kokke, W. C. M. C., Pak, C. S. and Carlson, R. M. K. (1979) Recent progress in the marine sterol field. *Pure Appl. Chem.* **51**, 1815–1828.

Edmunds, K. L. H., Brassell, S. C. and Eglinton, G. (1980) The short-term diagenetic fate of 5α-cholestan-3β-ol: *in situ* radiolabelled incubations in algal mats. In *Advances in Organic Geochemistry 1979*. Ed. by Douglas, A. G. and Maxwell, J. R. Pergamon Press, Oxford. pp. 427–434.

Ensminger, A. (1977) Evolution de composes polycycliques sédimentaires. Thèse de docteur es Sciences. Université Louis Pasteur, Strasbourg.

Gagosian, R. B. and Farrington, J. W. (1978) Sterenes in surface sediments from the southwest African shelf and slope. *Geochim. Cosmochim. Acta* **42**, 1091–1101.

Gagosian, R. B. and Smith, S. O. (1979) Steroid ketones in surface sediments from the Wouth–west African shelf. *Nature* **277**, 287–289.

Gagosian, R. B., Smith, S. O., Lee, C., Farrington, J. W. and Frew, N. M. (1980) Steroid transformations in Recent marine sediments. In *Advances in Organic Geochemistry 1979*. Ed. by Douglas, A. G. and Maxwell, J. R. Pergamon Press, Oxford. pp. 407–419.

Gaskell, S. J. and Eglinton, G. (1975) Rapid hydrogenation of sterols in a contemporary lacustrine sediment. *Nature* **254**, 209–211.

Hills, I. R., Whitehead, E. V., Anders, D. E., Cummins, J. J. and Robinson, W. E. (1966) An optically active triterpane, gammacerane, in Green River, Colorado, oil shale bitumen. *Chem. Commun.*, 752–754.

Howard, D. L. (1980) Polycyclic triterpenes of the anaerobic photosynthetic bacterium *Rhodomicrobium vannielli*. PhD Thesis, University of California, Los Angeles.

Huang, W.-Y. and Meinschein, W. G. (1976) Sterols as source indicators of organic material in sediments. *Geochim. Cosmochim. Acta* **40**, 323–330.

Huang, W.-Y. and Meinschein, W. G. (1979) Sterols as ecological indicators. *Geochim. Cosmochim. Acta* **43**, 739–745.

Idler, D. R., Khalil, M. W., Gilbert, J. D. and Brooks, C. J. W. (1976) Sterols of scallop Part II. Structure of unknown sterols by combination gas–liquid chromatography and mass spectrometry. *Steroids* **27**, 155–166.

Kemp, R. J. and Mercer, E. I. (1968) Studies on the sterols and sterol esters of the intracellular organelles of maize shoots. *Biochem. J.* **110**, 119–125.

Kokke, W. C. M. C., Fenical, W. and Djerassi, C. (1981a) Sterols with unusual nuclear unsaturation from three cultured marine dinoflagellates. *Phytochem.* **20**, 127–134.

Kokke, W. C. M. C., Fenical, W., Bohlin, L. and Djerassi, C. (1981b) Sterol synthesis by cultured zooanthellae; implications concerning sterol metabolism in the host–symbiont association in Caribbean gorgonians. *Comp. Biochem. Biophysiol.* **68B**, 281–287.

Langseth, M., *et al.* (eds.) (1980) *Initial Reports of the Deep Sea Drilling Project, Vol. 56/57, Part 1*. US Govt. Printing Office, Washington.

Lee, C., Farrington, J. W. and Gagosian, R. B. (1979) Sterol geochemistry of sediments from the Western North Atlantic

Ocean and adjacent coastal area. *Geochim. Cosmochim. Acta* **43**, 35–46.

Lee, C., Gagosian, R. B. and Farrington, J. W. (1980) Geochemistry of sterols in sediments from the Black Sea and the Southwest African shelf and slope. *Org. Geochem.* **2**, 103–113.

Mackenzie, A. S., Brassell, S. C., Eglinton, G. and Maxwell, J. R. (1982) Chemical fossils — the geological fate of steroids. *Science* **217**, 491–504.

Mandava, N., Anderson, J. D., Dutry, S. R. and Thompson, M. J. (1974) Novel occurrence of 5α-cholanic acid in plants: isolation from Jequirity bean seeds (*Arbrus precalorius L*). *Steroids* **23**, 257–261.

Maxwell, J. R., Mackenzie, A. S. and Volkman, J. K. (1980) Configuration at C-24 in steranes and sterols. *Nature* **286**, 694–697.

Mercer, E. I., London, R. A., Kent, I. S. A. and Taylor, A. J. (1974) Sterols, sterol esters and fatty acids of *Botrydicum granulatum, Tribonema aequale* and *Monodus subterraneus*. *Phytochem.* **13**, 845–852.

Nishimura, M. and Koyama, T. (1977) The occurrence of stanols in various organisms and the behaviour of sterols in contemporary sediments. *Geochim. Cosmochim. Acta* **41**, 379–385.

Orcutt, D. M. and Richardson, B. (1970) Sterols of *Oocystis polymorpha*, a green alga. *Steroids* **16**, 429–446.

Ourisson, G., Albrecht, P. and Rohmer, M. (1979) The hopanoids. Palaeochemistry and biochemistry of a group of natural products. *Pure Appl. Chem.* **51**, 709–729.

Rohmer, M. and Ourisson, G. (1976) Structure des bacteriohopanetetrols d'*Acetobacter xylinium*. *Tetrahedron letts.*, 3633–3636.

Rohmer, M., Kokke, W. C. M. C., Fenical, W. and Djerassi, C. (1980) Isolation of two new C_{30} sterols, (24E)-24-n-propylidenecholesterol and 24-n-propylidene-cholesterol from a cultured marine chrysophyte. *Steroids* **35**, 219–231.

Rowland, S. J., Lamb, N. A., Wilkinson, C. F. and Maxwell, J. R. (1982) Confirmation of 2,6,10,15,19-pentamethyleicosane in methanogenic bacteria and sediments. *Tetrahedron Letts.* **23**, 101–104.

Rubinstein, I. and Goad, L. J. (1974) Occurrence of (24S)-24-methylcholesta-5,22E-dien-3β-ol in the diatom *Phaeodactylum tricornutum*. *Phytochem.* **13**, 485–487.

Rubinstein, I., Sieskind, O. and Albrecht, P. (1975) Rearranged sterenes in a shale: occurrence and simulated formation. *J. Chem. Soc. Perkin I*, 1833–1835.

Schmitz, F. J. (1978) Uncommon marine steroids. In *Marine Natural Products, Chemical and Biological Perspectives, Vol. 1*. Ed. by Scheuer, P. J. Academic Press, Oxford. pp. 241–297.

Shimizu, Y., Alam, M. and Kobayashi, A. (1976) Dinosterol, the major sterol with a unique side chain in the toxic dinoflagellate, *Gonyaulax tamarensis*. *J. Amer. Chem. Soc.* **98**, 1059–1060.

Thomson, I. D., Brassell, S. C., Eglinton, G. and Maxwell, J. R. (in press) Preliminary lipid analysis of Section 481-2-2. In *Initial Reports of the Deep Sea Drilling Project, Vol. 64*. Ed. by Curray, J. R., Moore, D. G., *et al*. US Govt. Printing Office, Washington.

Tsuda, Y., Morimoto, A., Sano, T., Inubishi, Y., Mallory, F. B. and Gordon, J. T. (1965) The synthesis of tetrahymanol. *Tetra. Lett.*, 1427–1431.

Urbach, G. and Stark, W. (1975) The C-20 hydrocarbons of butterfat. *J. Agric. Food Chem.* **23**, 20–24.

Van Dorsselaer, A., Ensminger, A., Spyckerelle, C., Dastillung, M., Sieskind, O., Arpino, P., Albrecht, P., Ourisson, G., Brooks, P. W., Gaskell, S. J., Kimble, B. J., Philp, R. P., Maxwell, J. R. and Eglinton, G. (1974) Degraded and extended hopane derivatives (C_{27} to C_{35}) as ubiquitous geochemical markers. *Tetrahedron Lett.*, 1349–1352.

Volkman, J. K., Eglinton, G. and Corner, E. D. S. (1980) Sterols and fatty acids of the marine diatom *Biddulphia sinensis*. *Phytochem.* **19**, 1809–1813.

Volkman, J. K., Smith, D. J., Eglinton, G., Forsberg, T. E. V. and Corner, E. D. S. (1981) Sterol and fatty acid composition of four marine Haptophycean algae. *J. Mar. Biol. Ass. UK* **61**, 509–527.

Wakeham, S. G., Farrington, J. W., Gagosian, R. B., Lee, C., DeBarr, H., Nigrelli, G. E., Tripp, B. W., Smith, S. O. and Frew, N. H. (1980) Organic matter fluxes from sediment traps in the equatorial Atlantic Ocean. *Nature* **286**, 798–800.

Wardroper, A. M. K. (1979) Aspects of the geochemistry of polycyclic isoprenoids. PhD Thesis, University of Bristol.

Wardroper, A. M. K., Maxwell, J. R. and Morris, R. J. (1978) Sterols of a diatomaceous ooze from Walvis Bay. *Steroids* **32**, 203–221.

Withers, N. W., Tuttle, R. C., Holz, G. G., Beach, D. H., Goad, L. J. and Goodwin, T. W. (1978) Dehydrodinosterol, dinosterone and related sterols of a non-photosynthetic dinoflagellate, *Crypthecodinium cohnii*. *Phytochem.* **17**, 1987–1989.

Withers, N. W., Kokke, W. C. M. C., Rohmer, M., Fenical, W. H. and Djerassi, C. (1979) Isolation of sterols with cyclopropyl-containing side chains from the cultured marine alga *Peridinium foliaceum*. *Tetrahedron. Lett.*, 3605–3608.

STRUCTURES

N.B. Fernene structures (XXI, XXII and XXIII) should be 13α, 14β, 17α-trimethyl not 13β, 14α, 17β-trimethyl as shown.

Advances in Organic Geochemistry 1981, pp. 698–704
© *John Wiley & Sons Limited, 1983*

Diterpenoids in Crude Oils and Coals of South Eastern Australia

R. P. Philp*, B. R. T. Simoneit† and T. D. Gilbert*

*CSIRO Institute of Earth Resources, PO Box 136, North Ryde, NSW, 2113, Australia

†*School of Oceanography, Oregon State University, Corvallis, Oregon 97331, USA*

Diterpenoids are widely distributed in the resins of higher plants. The stability of diterpenoid hydrocarbons makes them extremely valuable as indicators of higher plant and resin contributions to sediments, coals, and crude oils. In a recent study of Australian crude oils, a series of nine diterpenoid hydrocarbons were found in oils from the Gippsland Basin, but were absent in oils examined from all the other basins. The presence of these compounds is indicative either of a contribution from higher plants or, more specifically, of resins to the source material for the oils, or passage of the oils through coal facies after their generation. In the latter case, it is proposed that diterpenoid hydrocarbons known to be present in the coal would have been dissolved by passage of the oil during migration or during accumulation in the reservoirs. In order to investigate these hypotheses further, two different approaches have been undertaken. First, the diterpenoid content of two resin samples from the onshore Yallourn brown coal deposits have been examined and compared with diterpenoids from the Gippsland crude oils. The diterpenoids in two brown coal samples have also been examined. Secondly, a series of maturation experiments have been undertaken using resins from the onshore portion of the basin. They have been heated for varying periods of time, extracted and the products analysed by computerized gas chromatography–mass spectrometry. The results of this study have supported the idea that the diterpenoids in the Gippsland oils are derived, at least partly, by dissolution from coals in the basin either in the reservoir, or during migration. The results do not eliminate the possibility of the diterpenoids also being derived from source rocks in deeper parts of the basin. Under the conditions used in this study none of the diterpenoids present in the crude oils were formed from maturation of the resin. However the absence of the crude oil-like diterpenoids may be explained by the relatively mild maturation conditions and the absence of any added water in the experiments.

INTRODUCTION

A previous study of oils from the Gippsland Basin, Australia, revealed the presence of a characteristic series of tricyclic diterpenoids (Philp *et al.*, 1981). Diterpenoids are generally associated with higher plant contributions, in particular resins, to sediments (Thomas, 1969) or crude oils (Snowdon, 1978). Thomas (1969) published a detailed survey of diterpenoids in resins from the genus *Agathis*. Snowdon (1978, 1980) reported a high concentration of tricyclic diterpanes, in particular of sandaracopimarane, thought to be derived from resins, in the extracts of drill cuttings from a well in the Mackenzie Basin of northern Canada. Simoneit (1975, 1977) discussed the presence of diterpenoids in DSDP sediments and their significance as markers of a terrigenous input to these sediments. Barrick and Hedges (1981) examined hydrocarbons from sediments in the Puget Sound region and found a variety of diterpenoids which were ascribed to a terrestrial source. Douglas and Grantham (1974) examined various fossil resins and analysed the distribution of the diterpenoids in these

resins. The major diterpenoid in the saturate fraction of retinite was identified as fichtelite and the minor component was an unidentified C_{19}-norditerpane. It was concluded that differences in the chromatograms of the hydrocarbons of retinite and other fossil resins examined may be of palaeochemotaxonomic importance reflecting essential differences between the resins produced from contributing plants.

In the present study an attempt has been made to obtain additional information on the precise origin of the diterpenoids in the Gippsland crude oils. Two questions in particular need to be answered. First, are these compounds source related and if so, can they be more specifically related to a resin contribution to the oils as previously proposed by Snowdon (1980) for oils in the Beaufort–Mackenzie Basin? Secondly, if the diterpenoids are not source related, are they present in the oil as a result of the migration of the oil through various overlying brown coal strata in the basin?

In an attempt to provide an answer to the first question, the hydrocarbons of two resins collected from the Yallourn brown coal deposits in the onshore part of the basin were analysed for the presence of diterpenoids by computerized gas chromatography–mass spectrometry (GC–MS). In addition, heating experiments were performed on one of the resins to determine whether or not the diterpanes could be formed by thermal maturation of possible precursors present in the resin. In an attempt to answer the second question, extracts from two samples of brown coals from the onshore part of the basin plus some coal pieces collected from a well in the offshore part of the basin were extracted and the hydrocarbons, in particular the diterpanes, analysed by GC–MS.

EXPERIMENTAL

Coals and resins   One sample of resin used in this study was collected as a large lump from the Yallourn brown coal deposits and after removal of the outer weathered layer, the remainder was ground and found to completely dissolve in CH_2Cl_2. The second resin sample was interspersed with a brown coal seam, but in sufficiently large pieces to be separated from the coal by hand-picking. This resin was also ground and found to dissolve in CH_2Cl_2. The brown coal samples from the Yallourn and Loy-Yang deposits were exhaustively extracted with $CH_2Cl_2/MeOH$ for a total period of 48 hours.

The coal and resin extracts were fractionated using the method described elsewhere (Philp *et al.*, 1981).

Maturation experiments   Samples of resin (500 mg) were sealed in pyrex tubes under nitrogen and heated for various periods of time (4, 12, 24, 48 and 96 hours) and at temperatures of 250 °C, 275 °C and 300 °C. After removal from the oven and cooling, the tubes were opened and CH_2Cl_2 added. The extracts were then immediately analysed by gas chromatography (GC) and/or computerized gas chromatography–mass spectrometry (GC–MS). No attempt was made to quantitate the results of these maturation experiments.

GC and GC–MS   For GC analyses a Hewlett–

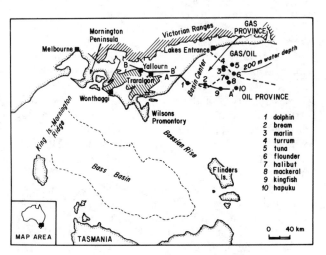

Fig. 1.   Location map showing the Gippsland and Bass Basins.

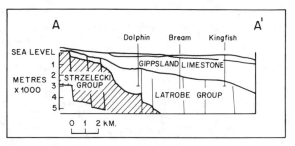

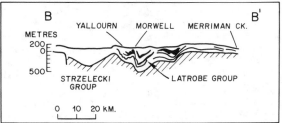

Fig. 2.   Simplified cross sections of the offshore (AA′) and onshore (BB′) Gippsland Basin (transects are indicated on Fig. 1).

Packard 5710A gas chromatograph was equipped with a SCOT OV-101 glass capillary column (50 m × 0.5 mm i.d.) and operated at 55 °C for 2 min and subsequently programmed at 4 °C min^{-1} to 260 °C. Injector and detector temperatures were 250 °C and the helium flow rate was 3 ml min^{-1}.

A Finnigan 4023 system was used for the GC–MS analyses. Conditions for the analyses were: fused silica WCOT capillary column (25 m × 0.2 mm i.d.) coated with OV-101; He flow rate 1 ml min^{-1}; oven temperature: 10 °C for 2 min, programmed at 20 °C min^{-1} and then at 4 °C min^{-1} to 270 °C; ion source temperature 260 °C; filament current 250 μA; electron energy 70 eV and scan speed 0.95 s scan^{-1}.

RESULTS AND DISCUSSION

The geographical location of the Gippsland Basin and the neighbouring Bass Basin are shown in Fig. 1. The Gippsland Basin is bounded to the north by the Victorian Ranges and to the south and south–west by the Bassian Rise. The basin is wedge-shaped, widening to approximately 120 km and deepening to the east. Four fifths of the basin lies offshore, where commercial quantities of oil and gas are found in Tertiary sediments under 30–120 m of water. Onshore commercial quantities of younger Tertiary brown coal occur in the non-marine sediments of the Latrobe group which rises steeply and outcrops. Simplified cross sections along AA′ and BB′ of Fig. 1 are shown in Fig. 2. Section AA′ illustrates the sharp dip of both the Latrobe group and the Cretaceous Strzelecki group in the offshore basin. Although the Strzelecki group has not been penetrated in the deeper parts of the basin by offshore drilling, it has been suggested as a source rock for the Gippsland crude oils (Shiboaka *et al.*, 1978).

In the previous study of crude oils from the Gippsland Basin, a series of diterpanes was identified in these oils

Table 1

Summary of mass spectrometric data for the major diterpenoidal hydrocarbons present in oils from Gippsland Basin brown coals and resins

Peak no.	M.W.	Base peak	Key ions (m/z)	Other references
1	—	?		
2	262	233	247, 191, 177, 123, 109, 95	Barrick and Hedges (1981)
3	276	247	261, 191, 177, 123, 109, 95	Snowdon (1978)
4	260	57	245, 231, 175, 163, 123, 83	
5	274	123	259, 245, 189, 161, 109, 95	
6	276	97	261, 247, 191, 163, 123	Barrick and Hedges (1981)
7	—	?	?	
8[a]	274	123	259, 231, 189, 109, 95	
9	274	82	259, 231, 189, 123	
10	262	109	247, 219, 191, 163, 123	
11	—	?	?	
12	270	255	185, 173, 159, 143, 129	
13	270	159	255, 185, 173, 143, 129	
14	274	109	245, 217, 189, 163, 123	

[a] In some of the oil samples peak 8 was a mixture of two components with the minor component having a molecular weight of 276.
? Indicates that very poor spectra were obtained for these components and their quality does not warrant their inclusion in this table.

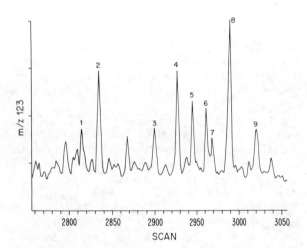

Fig. 3. Partial mass chromatogram for m/z 123 of a typical Gippsland Basin oil (numbers of peaks refer to Table 1).

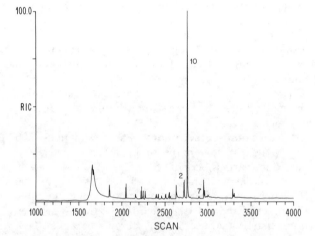

Fig. 4. Total ion current trace for the hydrocarbon fraction from resin of the Yallourn brown coal seam (numbers of peaks refer to Table 1, number 10 = fichtelite).

and was subsequently found to be absent in oils examined from all other Australian Basins. Figure 3 shows a partial single ion plot of m/z 123 in the diterpenoid region of the chromatogram from one oil of the Gippsland Basin. Mass spectrometric details of the major diterpenoid components in this region are listed in Table 1. The distribution of the diterpenoids in all the other oils from the Gippsland Basin analysed by GC–MS were virtually identical to that shown in Fig. 3. Although several authentic diterpenoid hydrocarbon standards were available, none of them corresponded to the diterpenoids detected in the oils.

Diterpenoid hydrocarbons in resins from the Yallourn brown coal deposits Snowdon (1978, 1980) has proposed that certain oils in the Beaufort–Mackenzie delta area of Canada are, at least partially, sourced from resins. In view of the widespread distribution of resins in the Yallourn brown coal deposits and their proximity to the oil-bearing formations of the

Gippsland Basin, it seemed logical to try and expand Snowdon's (1980) hypothesis to these Australian oils. Two samples of resin were collected from the deposits. One of these samples was distributed fairly homogeneously within the coal, whereas the second was collected as a large lump of resin (about 500 g in weight).

The total ion current chromatogram obtained by GC–MS analysis of the hydrocarbon extract from the first resin is shown in Fig. 4. The major component in this chromatogram has been identified by GC–MS and comparison with standard spectra as fichtelite (Barrick and Hedges, 1981). This is of some interest since the major component present in a resin collected from lignite deposits in nearby Tasmania was also dominated by fichtelite (Douglas and Grantham, 1974). In addition to fichtelite, the next most abundant component in this resin has a mass spectrum directly comparable to that of peak 2 in the oil (Fig. 3 and Table 1). However, it is noteworthy that fichtelite could not be detected in the oils from the Gippsland Basin.

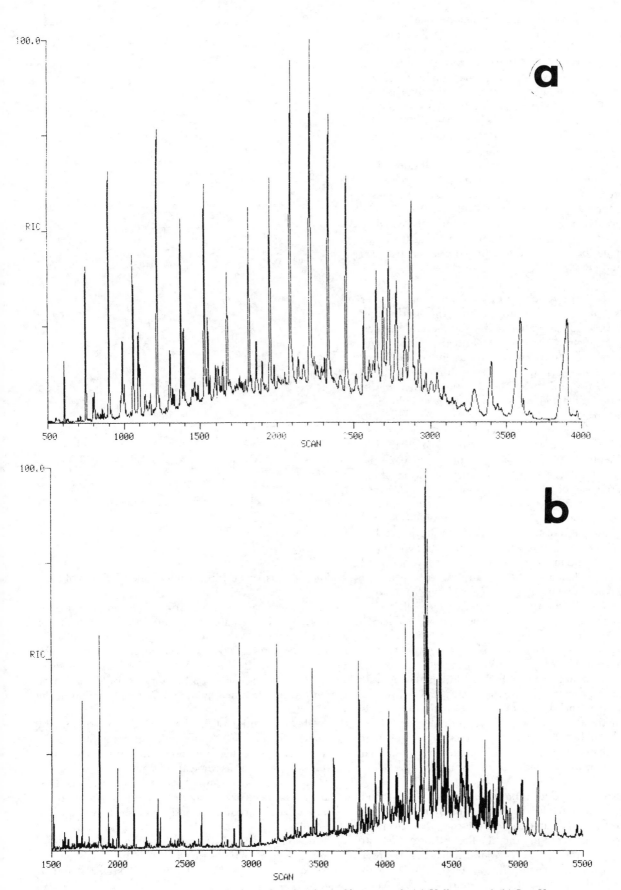

Fig. 5. Total ion current traces for hydrocarbon fractions of brown coals (a) Yallourn and (b) Loy-Yang.

The second sample of resin contained a far more complex mixture of hydrocarbons. The mixture comprises both di- and tricyclic components with varying degrees of unsaturation and aromatization. Single ion plots of m/z 123, 191, 260, 262, 274 and 276 failed to reveal the presence of any of the diterpenoids listed in Table 1. A detailed analysis of this fraction will be given elsewhere.

A comparison between the diterpenoid hydrocarbons of the two resins and the crude oils of the Gippsland Basin shows few, if any, similarities in distribution. This would suggest that there is little direct contribution of unaltered resin components to these crude oils. This is unlike the case reported by Snowdon (1980) for the Beaufort–Mackenzie Basin where a strong case could be made for the presence of resin components in the crude oils on the basis of the diterpane correlation between resin and oils.

Maturation experiments To investigate further the possibility of a resin contribution to the oils resulting from burial and maturation of the resin, several thermal alteration experiments were performed on the second sample of resin from above. It was found that over heating periods of from 4 to 96 hours at temperatures of 250 °C, 275 °C and 300 °C, maturation of the resin in glass tubes sealed under nitrogen produced distributions of hydrocarbons which were qualitatively very similar to each other. The major products formed were partially aromatized bicyclic and partially aromatized tricyclic components. In addition a phenanthrene carboxylic acid was also detected in the products of this reaction. The presence of the partially aromatized tricyclic components correlates well with the scheme previously proposed by Shaw *et al.* (1981) for the products formed by the diagenesis of the diterpenoid carboxylic acids.

Analysis of the extracts of the maturation experiment by GC–MS and in particular SIM of the key ions listed in Table 1 failed to detect any of the saturated diterpenoids previously detected in the crude oils. Despite the mild maturation temperatures of this study, the absence of saturated diterpenoids and predominance of aromatic products suggest it is unlikely that saturated diterpenoids would be formed if the experiments were performed at higher temperatures or for longer periods of times. It should be noted that no additional water was used in these maturation experiments and this could contribute to the absence of any saturated diterpenoids in the maturation products. However on the basis of the results from these experiments, it seems improbable that this particular type of resin has made any substantial contribution to the crude oils of this basin.

Diterpane hydrocarbons in coals The second proposal postulated for the presence of diterpanes in the oils was that they had dissolved these components from the coals present in the LaTrobe formation at depths where the reservoirs are known to occur. In order to investigate this theory, two samples of brown coals from the onshore deposits at Yallourn and Loy-Yang were extracted and the hydrocarbons analysed by GC–MS. The total ion current chromatogram for each of the hydrocarbon extracts is shown in Fig. 5. Single ion plots

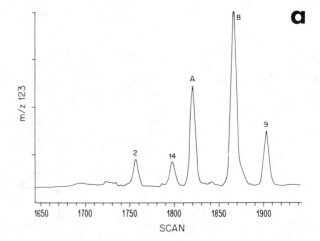

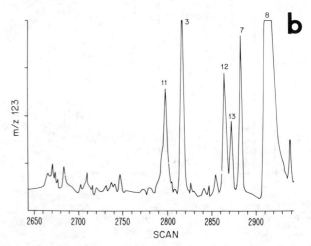

Fig. 6. Partial mass chromatograms for m/z 123 of the hydrocarbon fractions of brown coals (a) Yallourn and (b) Loy-Yang (numbered peaks refer to Table 1).

for m/z 123 over the diterpenoid region for each of these samples is shown in Fig. 6.

The first coal sample from Yallourn produced a relatively simple chromatogram containing four major diterpenoid peaks in this region (peak A is a *n*-alkane). The major peaks 8, 9 correspond to the peaks numbered 8 and 9 in the oil samples (Table 1). Peak 2 is identical to peak 2 in the oil samples and peak 14 has been tentatively identified as the unsaturated version of the peak labelled 6 in the oils.

The distribution of the diterpenoids from the nearby Loy-Yang sample is quite different from that of the previous sample (Fig. 6b). The dominant component in this sample has a mass spectrum similar to peak 8 in the crude oils and is a C_{20}-unsaturated diterpane. Peak 3 has a mass spectrum virtually identical to that of sandaracopimarane previously published by Snowdon (1978), whereas peak 7 has the same mass spectrum as 7 in the oils and peaks 12 and 13 appear to be structural isomers which have a dehydroabietane type structure based on a comparison with published data (Kitadani *et al.*, 1970).

In addition to examining diterpenoid distributions from the onshore brown coals several pieces of coal from various depths down a well in the offshore part of the

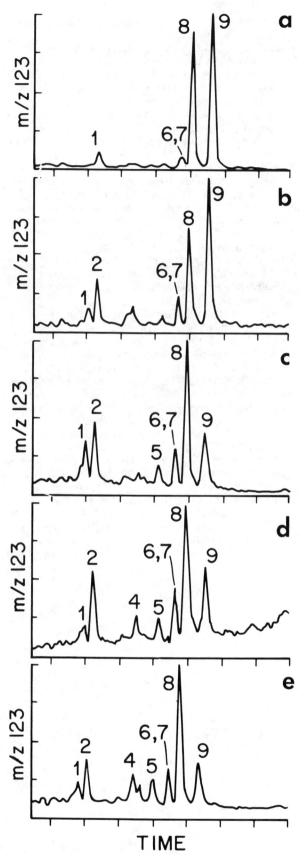

Fig. 7. Partial mass chromatograms for *m/z* 123 of the hydrocarbon fractions of well cuttings from increasing depths (see text; numbered peaks refer to Table 1).

basin were also available. Five such samples were extracted and the hydrocarbon fractions analysed by GC–MS. Figure 7 shows the plot of *m/z* 123 for these hydrocarbon fractions. Interpretation of these single ion plots would suggest that two different effects are being observed here. In the top two samples the major components are peaks 8 and 9 (same numbering system as in Table 1). With increasing depth the relative intensity of these peaks is observed to change which would suggest that these components are either stereochemically related or alternatively the compound producing peak 8 is more thermally stable than that which gives rise to peak 9. The lower three samples show a distribution of components which strongly resembles that of the crude oils in the Basin (Fig. 3). These samples were taken from depths where the vitrinite reflectance values were in the range 0.25 to 0.35 and had not reached the values commonly accepted for oil generation. The lower two samples were taken from zones previously designated as reservoir zones.

Examination of the diterpenoid distribution in the third sample (Fig. 7c), which is above the reservoir zone, and also has a vitrinite reflectance value below the oil generation window, shows an increasing complexity, which to some extent resembles that in the crude oil. The presence of the diterpenoids in this sample (Fig. 7c), which is of relatively low maturity, above the reservoir zone and not contaminated by migrating oil, demonstrates that they originate from the coal known to be present in this sample. The coals in the slightly deeper reservoir zones, if uncontaminated by migrating oil could also be expected to have similar distributions of diterpenoids to the uncontaminated sample shown in Fig. 7c. The very close similarity in diterpenoid distributions in the coals from this well and in oils from the basin has led to the proposal that the diterpenoids in oils are derived, at least partly, from coal by dissolution in the reservoir or during migration. Additional possibilities for the origin of the diterpenoids such as source rocks deeper in the basin cannot be eliminated on the basis of the results presented here. The significant concentration of diterpenoids in the coals of this basin from both onshore and offshore areas; similarities in distribution of diterpenoids between these sources and the oils; combined with presence of dispersed and immature coaly material in the reservoir zones, are the major factors which tend to support the proposal mentioned above.

CONCLUSION

This paper has attempted to determine the origin of the diterpenoid hydrocarbons previously encountered in oils from the Gippsland Basin. The first approach has been to examine the distribution of the diterpanes in resins from the nearby brown coal deposits and also to examine their maturation products. The diterpanes from the resin and the maturation products showed little resemblance to those previously observed in the crude oils although no maturation experiments were performed in the presence of additional water which could have had a marked effect on the distribution of maturation products. On the basis of this limited evidence it would appear that the resin contribution to the oils in the Gippsland Basin is negligible or non-existent. Correlation of diterpanes from the brown coals with diterpanes from the crude oils appears to be more promising. Several of the diterpenoids present in the brown coals were also present in the crude oils albeit in slightly different proportions. Similarities in diterpenoid distributions from the brown coals, from coals recovered from offshore parts of the basin and from the crude oils has led to the proposal that their presence in the oils is, at least partly, a result of dissolution of diterpenoids by the oil either in the reservoir or during migration. Source rocks from deeper parts of the basin could also be responsible for these compounds and this additional source cannot be eliminated on the basis of the evidence presented in this paper.

Acknowledgements

We wish to thank Esso Australia Ltd. and Haemetite Petroleum Ltd. for supplying the oils and cuttings used as part of this study. Support was provided under the National Energy Research, Development and Demonstration Program administered by the Commonwealth Department of National Development and Energy.

REFERENCES

Barrick, R. C. and Hedges, J. I. (1981) Hydrocarbon geochemistry of the Puget Sound region — II. Sedimentary diterpenoid, steroid and triterpenoid hydrocarbons. *Geochim. Cosmochim. Acta* **45**, 381–392.

Douglas, A. G. and Grantham, P. J. (1974) Fingerprint gas chromatography in the analysis of some native bitumens, asphalts and related substances. In *Advances in Organic Geochemistry 1973*. Ed. by Tissot, B. and Bienner, F. Editions Technip, Paris. pp. 261–276.

Kitadani, M., Yoshikoshi, A., Kitahara, Y., DePaiva Campello, J., McChesney, J. D., Watts, D. J. and Wenkert, E. (1970) Natural *ar*-abietatriene. *Chem. Pharm. Bull.* **18**, 402–405.

Philp, R. P., Gilbert, T. D. and Friedrich, J. (1981) Bicyclic sesquiterpenoids and diterpenoids in Australian crude oils. *Geochim. Cosmochim. Acta* **45**, 1173–1180.

Shaw, G. J., Franich, R. A. and Eglinton, G. (1981) Diterpenoid acids in Yallourn lignite. In *Advances in Organic Geochemistry 1979*. Ed. by Douglas, A. G. and Maxwell, J. R. Pergamon Press, Oxford. pp. 281–286.

Shibaoka, M., Saxby, J. D. and Taylor, G. H. (1978) Hydrocarbon generation in Gippsland Basin, Australia — Comparison with Cooper Basin, Australia. *Am. Ass. Petrol. Geol. Bull.* **62**, 1151–1158.

Simoneit, B. R. T. (1975) Sources of organic matter in oceanic sediments. PhD Thesis, University of Bristol, 300 pp.

Simoneit, B. R. T. (1977) Diterpenoid compounds and other lipids in deep sea sediments and their geochemical significance. *Geochim. Cosmochim. Acta* **41**, 463–476.

Snowdon, L. R. (1978) Organic geochemistry of the Upper Cretaceous/Tertiary delta complexes of the Beaufort–Mackenzie sedimentary basin, northern Canada. PhD Thesis, Rice University, Houston, Texas, 130 pp.

Snowdon, L. R. (1980) Resinite — a potential petroleum source in the Upper Cretaceous/Tertiary of the Beaufort–Mackenzie Basin. In *Facts and Principles of World Petroleum Occurrence*. Ed. by Miall, A. D. *Can. Soc. Petrol. Geol. Memoir* **6**, 509–521.

Thomas, B. R. (1969) Kauri resins — modern and fossil. In *Organic Geochemistry — Methods and Results*. Ed. by Eglinton, G. and Murphy, M. T. J. Springer–Verlag, Berlin. pp. 599–618.

Advances in Organic Geochemistry 1981, pp. 705–709
© *John Wiley & Sons Limited, 1983*

Determination of Isomers of Monomethyl Phenanthrene extracted from Petroleum by Capillary Gas Chromatography coupled to Mass Spectrometry and by High Resolution Spectrofluorimetry in Alkane Crystals at a Temperature of 15 K

M. Ewald*[1], M. Lamotte[1], P. Garrigues[1], J. Rima[1], A. Veyres[1] and R. Lapouyade[2]

Laboratoires de Chimie Physique A[1] et de Chimie Organique[2]. ERA du CNRS no 167 — Université de Bordeaux I, 351 Cours de la Libération, 33405 TALENCE CEDEX

G. Bourgeois

Centre d'Etude Structurale et d'Analyse des Molécules Organiques. Université de Bordeaux I, 351 Cours de la Libération, 33405, TALENCE CEDEX

Analysis of the petroleum fraction obtained by a two-step high-performance-liquid-chromatography (HPLC) procedure (normal and reverse phase) enabled the identification by capillary GC–MS and by high resolution spectrofluorimetry (HRS) at 15 K (Shpolskii effect) of the five isomers of monomethyl-phenanthrene. Preliminary results of absolute and relative quantitative analysis of the isomers indicates the occurrence of general trends in the distribution of the isomers in three different petroleums which are dependent upon their origin. A tentative geochemical interpretation of the isomer distribution is discussed.

INTRODUCTION

In a previous publication we presented the preliminary results of the analysis of aromatic geochemical markers in marine sediments and petroleum (Ewald *et al.*, 1980). The present contribution describes the analysis of a specific series of polycyclic aromatic hydrocarbons (PAH) — the five isomers of monomethyl-phenanthrene (MP) — in three petroleums. The aim of the study was to use a combination of techniques (capillary gas chromatography–mass spectrometry (GC–MS) and high resolution spectrofluorimetry (HRS) at low temperature in an *n*-alkane polycrystalline matrix (see Ewald *et al.*, 1980) to identify each isomer in a natural extract.

The analysis of petroleum PAH was restricted to the MP series in order to obtain the most reliable results for each technique and to illustrate the application of HRS analysis in addition of that of capillary GC–MS. Further analytical developments are currently under way with the aim of providing quantitative results of the MP-isomer distribution in several petroleums and recent sediments In this preliminary report we present the results of an investigation into the relative distribution of the five isomers of MP in HPLC fractions of three petroleums, together with a brief discussion.

EXPERIMENTAL

Authentic isomers of MP were synthesized in the laboratory (Lapouyade *et al.*, unpublished) with the exception of 2-methyl-phenanthrene (2MP) which was from ICN Pharmaceuticals (Plainview, New York); all compounds were purified by HPLC and verified as pure by capillary GC–MS analysis.

Solvents were purified by distillation and/or the use of molecular sieves. Residual background emission was determined by room temperature spectrofluorimetry (Perkin–Elmer MPF-44).

Three crude petroleum samples were studied, from Indonesia (continental origin), Tunisia and the North Sea (marine origin). The results presented in all accompanying figures were obtained with the North Sea petroleum sample.

Fractionation

The MP were extracted from crude petroleum by a three-step procedure (Fig. 1), summarized as follows.

1. Adsorption chromatography (open column) on Florisil (SiO$_2$ and MgO) with pentane elution, to remove aliphatics (which are first-eluted) and most

PETROLEUM FRACTIONATION

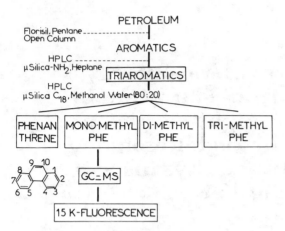

Fig. 1. Diagram of petroleum fractionation procedure and analysis.

of the resins and asphaltenes (retained on the column).

2. HPLC on μ-silica-NH_2, Spherisorb 5 μm, using an analytical column (L = 20 cm, i.e. = 4.7 mm) and elution with heptane.
3. HPLC on μ-silica-C 18, Spherisorb 5 μm, column dimensions as above, and elution with methanol–water (80:20).

Elution of the aromatic compounds was monitored at 254 nm using a UV-VIS monochromatic absorption detector (LDC Spectromonitor III). The MP fraction eluted in methanol–water solution (fractionation step 3) was extracted with *n*-hexane. The final concentration in this solvent was in order of 10^{-6}M.

High resolution spectrofluorimetry (HRS)

Fused silica tubes containing the solutions were attached to the cold head of a closed-cycle cryogenerator (CTI Cryodyne 21S) operated at 15 K. Preliminary fast-cooling to 77 K by immersion of the tubes in liquid nitrogen gave satisfactory conditions for observing sharp spectra (Garrigues *et al.*, 1981). Fluorescence spectra were obtained with a home-made spectrofluorimeter. Excitation was provided by a Xenon lamp (XBO Osram 450 W) and by a monochromator (Jobin Yvon HR 20) with a bandwidth of about 2.5 nm. Fluorescence emission was observed at 90° through a high resolution monochromator (Jobin Yvon HR 100) with bandwidth of 0.1 nm, detected with a photomultiplier (EMI 9789 QB) and measured using an *f(t)* recorder.

Capillary gas chromatography–mass spectrometry (GC–MS)

Gas chromatographic analysis involved the use of two fused silica WCOT capillary columns (50 m × 0.3 mm i.d.) coated with SE-52 and FFAP (phases are described further in Results). Gas chromatography (GC) was done on a Pye-Unicam 204 with moving needle-solid injector and split injector, with the oven operated isothermally at 190 °C for FFAP and 170 °C for SE-52. The gas chromatograph was directly coupled to a VG Micromass 16 F mass spectrometer with a resolving power of 1000. Carrier gas was helium, electron ionization energy = 70 eV, source temperature = 200 °C. The system was operated in the selected ion detection made using a VG Micromass–DIG MID interfaced to a VG 2040 computer.

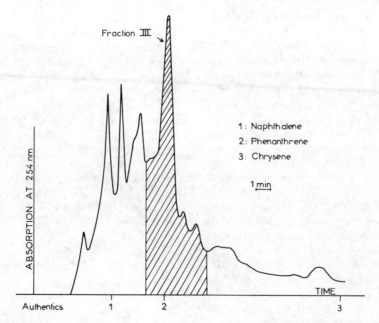

Fig. 2. HPLC on μ-silica-NH_2 of the petroleum fraction obtained after elution on Florisil (see text). Elution with *n*-heptane, 1 ml min^{-1}. UV detector at 254 nm on 2 FSAU. Elution of authentic naphthalene, phenanthrene and chrysene is referred by number 1,2,3 respectively.

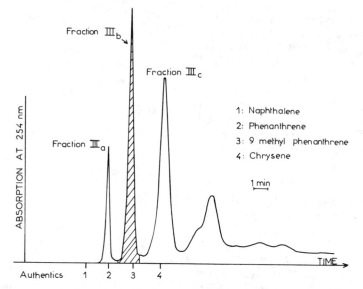

Fig. 3. HPLC on μ-silica-C_{18} of petroleum fraction III obtained as described in Fig. 2. Elution with methanol–water (80:20), 1 ml min^{-1} UV detector at 254 nm on 1 FSAU. Elution of authentic of naphthalene, phenanthrene, 9 methyl-phenanthrene and chrysene is referred by number 1,2,3,4 respectively.

RESULTS

HPLC

HPLC on μ-silica NH_2 is known to fractionate PAH according to the degree of aromaticity, with little effect on alkyl substituents (Wise *et al.*, 1977) The triaromatic fraction (fraction III, Fig. 2) obtained in the initial HPLC step is fractionated further by HPLC on μ-silica-C_{18}, which separates components according to the degree of alkylation (Fig. 3). In this step, peaks IIIa, IIIb and IIIc were shown, by UV-VIS absorption and room-temperature-fluorescence-spectra, to contain phenanthrene derivatives as dominant products (phenanthrene, in IIIa; monomethyl-phenanthrenes (MP), in IIIb; and dimethyl-phenanthrenes, in IIIc).

High resolution spectrofluorimetry (HRS)

In the previous Symposium proceedings (Ewald *et al.*, 1980), we reported the results of analyses of 1-methyl-phenanthrene (1 MP) and 9-methyl-phenanthrene (9 MP) using HRS at 4 K in a *n*-heptane polycrystalline matrix. In these experiments a cryostat operating with helium as cryogenic liquid was used but for routine analysis this can be inconvenient since measurements depends on the helium supply. This difficulty has now been overcome by the use of a closed-cycle cryogenerator which can operate continuously at 15 K.

With MP the best quasilinear spectra are obtained using a low solute concentration (to minimize solute aggregate formation (Rima *et al.*, in press)) in either *n*-heptane or *n*-hexane. However, spectrum structure appears to be more resolved and simpler in *n*-hexane, allowing improved isomer identification. Using an equimolar synthetic mixture of the five isomers of the monomethyl-phenanthrene (2×10^{-7} M each isomer) it

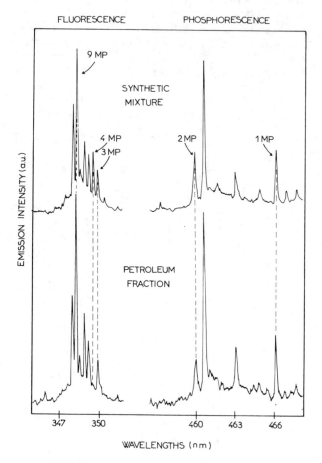

Fig. 4. Emission spectra of monomethyl-phenanthrenes (MP) in a synthetic mixture (each isomer at 2×10^{-7} M) and in a North Sea petroleum fraction (IIIb) (at similar concentrations of the isomers compared to the synthetic mixture), frozen in polycrystalline *n*-hexane at 15 K. Excitation at 298 nm for fluorescence spectra. Excitation at 296.5 nm for phosphorescence spectra. For simplicity, each isomer is identified by one of the most characteristic emission peaks.

is possible to associate a pure emission band with each of the five isomers. By judicious choice of the excitation wavelength, a characterization of each compound may be obtained either from fluorescence spectra (for 3 MP, 4 MP and 9 MP) or from phosphorenscence spectra (for 1 MP and 2 MP) (Fig. 4)..

Comparison of fraction IIIb from the North Sea petroleum with the synthetic mixture (Fig. 4) shows the very small amount of 4 MP compared with the four other isomers, each of which was unambiguously identified in the natural extract by its HRS spectrum.

Capillary gas chromatography–mass spectrometry

Under electron impact, the fragmentation of each MP-isomer gives an intense molecular ion ($M^{+\cdot} = 192$) which is useful in mass fragment detection. The mass fragments distribution for $m/z = 192$ is similar for all isomers of MP (Nounou, 1968) with the exception of that in 4 MP, where the molecular ion is less intense.

The separation of the five MP-isomers by capillary gas chromatography depends on the coating used; on SE-52 (methyl–phenyl–silicone), 9 MP and 4 MP cannot be separated (Fig. 5). The separation is comparable to that obtained by Lee *et al.* (1979) who used the same compounds and stationary phase, an a programmed oven temperature. On the more polar FFAP (Free Fatty Acid Phase, Carbowax 20 M (Polyol) reticulated with

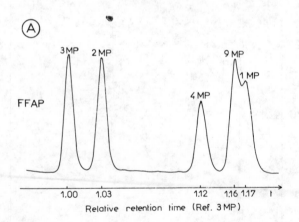

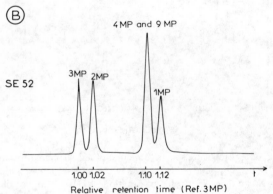

Fig. 5. GC–MS of the synthetic mixture of the five isomers of the MP (each at 10^{-6} M); fragmentogram at $m/z = 192$. Part A: elution on FFAP (see text). Part B: elution on SE-52 (see text).

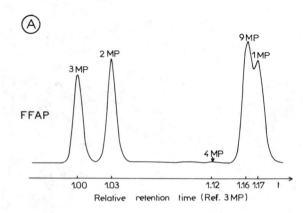

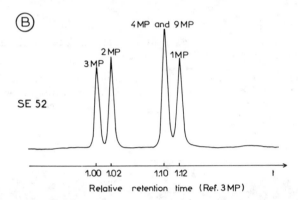

Fig. 6. GC–MS of the petroleum fraction IIIb from North Sea; fragmentation at $m/z = 192$. Part A: elution on FFAP (see text). Part B: elution on SE-52 (see text).

nitroterephtalic acid) 9 MP and 4 MP are well separated but 9 MP and 1 MP are only partially resolved (Fig. 5). Capillary gas chromatographic analysis using each of the two phases therefore allows complete identification and quantification of each MP-isomer.

Under the same conditions of analysis the North Sea petroleum fraction IIIb was found to contain only a very small amount of 4 MP compared with the fours others isomers (Fig. 6).

DISCUSSION

Numerous papers have appeared in the recent literature on the separation and identification of PAH by capillary GC–MS. Many reports have been concerned with the identification of PAH and alkyl homologs from the environmental viewpoint. Although some authors have given particular attention to MP-isomer identification (Lee *et al.*, 1979; Grimmer and Böhnke, 1978; Grimmer *et al.*, 1981) they have always involved in analysis of complex PAH mixtures and have used GC analysis with oven temperature programming.

To our knowledge, the present contribution represents the first report of the occurrence of all five MP isomers in natural samples (two petroleums of marine origin and one of continental origin). The complementary results obtained by HRS illustrate the interesting capability of this technique in MP isomer identification.

Quantitative analysis is underway using the two techniques, and generally trends in isomer distribution in the three examined petroleums can already be drawn. It has been found that 4 MP is a very minor component compared with 1 MP, 2 MP, 3 MP and 9 MP, the relative abundance of which is of the same order in each of the three petroleums. The observation that 4 MP is less abundant could indicate either a lack of precursors with the methylation site (Mair, 1964) or a thermodynamic instability related to the steric hindrance of the methyl group. 1 MP and 2 MP may be formed upon partial degradation of natural steroid or terpenoid precursors. The origin of 3 MP and 9 MP is not easily deduced from known natural precursors and the hypothesis of methyl mobility catalysed by minerals during the diagenesis (Ensminger et al., 1978) could be suggested. The formation of 4 MP by this last mechanism may be reduced to the steric hindrance at this substitution site.

In conclusion, these analytical experiments provide a good example of the application of a combination of capillary GC–MS and HRS for the specific identification of the five MP-isomers. These techniques have also been applied with success to more informative biogeochemical markers: phenanthrene and chrysene-derivatives of triterpenoid compounds (Ewald et al., 1980, 1981).

Acknowledgements

We are indebted to Professor J. Joussot-Dubien for his continuous interest and support, and to J. Bellocq and C. Jobet-Belin for technical assistance.

This work was supported by CNRS in the provision of funds, by Compagnie Française des Pétroles and by Société Nationale Elf Aquitaine (Production) in the provision of petroleum samples. Discussions with J. L. Oudin (CFP) and D. Jonathan (SNEA(P)) are gratefully acknowledged.

The results presented here are a specific contribution from University of Bordeaux researchers belonging in part to the French group, issued from ORGON programs dealing with the biogeochemical markers determination. Dr P. Albrecht and Dr A. Saliot are gratefully acknowledged for valuable contribution and discussions.

REFERENCES

Ensminger, A., Joly, G. and Albrecht, P. (1978) Rearranged steranes in sediments and crude oils. *Tetr. Lett.* **18**, 1575–1578.

Ewald, M., Lamotte, M., Redero, F., Tissier, M. J. and Albrecht, P. (1980) Identification of aromatic geochemical markers by quasilinear Shpolskii fluorescence spectra at 4 K in extracts from marine sediments and petroleum. *Phys. Chem. Earth* **12**, 275–279 (*Adv. Org. Geochem.* 1979).

Ewald, M., Moinet, A., Bellocq, J., Wehrung, P. and Albrecht, P. (1981) Identification de marqueurs géochimiques aromatiques de la série du hopane, extraits de sédiments marins d'origine autochtone, par leur spectre de fluorescence quasi-linéaire dans l'heptane à 4 K (effet Shpolskii). In *Géochimie Organique des Sédiments Marins Profonds, Orgon IV, Gulf of Aden–Oman sea.* Ed. of CNRS, Paris. pp. 405–414.

Garrigues, P., Lamotte, M., Ewald, M. and Joussot-Dubien, J. (1981) Utilisation d'un cryogénérateur à cycle fermé pour l'analyse fluorimétrique des hydrocarbures aromatiques polynucléaires (HAP) en matrice Shpolskii à 15 K. Application à l'analyse des méthyl-phénanthrènes dans un pétrole. *C.R. Acad. Sci. (Paris)* **293**, 567–571.

Grimmer, G. and Böhnke, H. (1978) Polycyclische aromatische kohlenwasserstoffe und heterocyclen. *Erdöl Kohle* **31**, 272–277.

Grimmer, G., Jacob, J. and Naujack, K.-W. (1981) Profile of the polycyclic aromatic hydrocarbons from lubricating oils. Inventory by GCGC/MS-PAH in environmental materials, part 1. *Fresenius Z. Anal. Chem.* **306**, 347–355.

Lapouyade, R., Veyres, A., Hanafi, N., Couture, A. and Lablanche-Combier, A. (unpublished) Photocyclisation of 1,2-diarylethylenes in primary amines: a convenient method for the synthesis of dihydroaromatic compounds and a means of reducing the loss of methyl groups during the cyclisation of orthomethylstilbenes. *J. Org. Chem.*

Lee, M. L., Vassilaros, D. L., White, C. M. and Novotny, M. (1979) Retention indices for programmed-temperature capillary-column gas chromatography of polycyclic aromatic hydrocarbons. *Anal. Chem.* **51**, 768–774.

Mair, B. J. (1964) Terpenoids, fatty acids and alcohols as source materials for petroleum hydrocarbons. *Geochim. Cosmochim. Acta* **28**, 1303–1321.

Nounou, P. (1968) Etudes fondamentales des processus d'ionisation et de dissociation des molécules aromatiques par impact électronique et application de la théorie du quasi-équilibre au phénanthrène et aux méthyl-phénanthrènes. PhD Thesis, Université de Grenoble.

Rima, J., Lamotte, M. and Merle, A. M. (in press) Low concentration phenanthrene associations in Shpolskii matrices. *Nouv. J. Chim.*

Wise, S. A., Chesler, S. N., Hertz, H. S., Hilpert, L. R. and May, W. E. (1977) Chemically-bonded aminosilane stationary phase for the high-performance liquid chromatographic separation of polynuclear aromatic compounds. *Anal. Chem.* **49**, 2306–2310.

Advances in Organic Geochemistry 1981, pp. 710–724
© *John Wiley & Sons Limited, 1983*

Geomimetic Synthesis, Structure Assignment, and Geochemical Correlation Application of Monoaromatized Petroleum Steroids

W. K. Seifert, R. M. K. Carlson, and J. M. Moldowan

Chevron Oil Field Research Company, Richmond, California 94802

Monoaromatized steroids are powerful source parameters. In this report, their formation via cholestane isomerization/catalytic dehydrogenation is described and their presence (i.e., the four predominant isomers of C_{27}, C_{28}, and C_{29} monoaromatic steroids) in petroleum is demonstrated. In addition, their structures are partially elucidated by 500 MHz ^{1}H-NMR, mass spectrometry, and UV spectroscopy. In contrast to previous reports, these studies show a methyl group at the quaternary carbon C-17. The previous assignment of Ring C to be aromatic is confirmed. Distribution by carbon numbers within these predominant monoaromatized steroids is shown to be useful as source parameters in Prudhoe Bay, and in the Overthrust Belt, Wyoming, supplementing previously reported findings based on fully saturated steranes and terpanes. Oils from the Tarragona Basin, Spain, were chosen to further exemplify the use of the new source parameters. In addition, isomerization catalytic dehydrogenation of isolated monoaromatic steroids are found to yield triaromatic steroids identical to those present in petroleum.

INTRODUCTION

The existence of aromatized biological markers related to steroids was first recognized by Tissot *et al.* (1972) who realized the potential of these stable relics for geochemical correlation. The first published application (Tissot *et al.*, 1974) using monoaromatized steroids (henceforth abbreviated MA-steroids) detected by a mass spectral group-type method, followed shortly. When isolation and characterization work was begun at Strasbourg (Spyckerelle, 1975), two general types of MA-steroids were recognized, one type having ring A aromatization and the other having ring C aromatization. The ring C aromatized type, characterized by a high ion current m/e 253 mass spectral base peak for loss of side chain (Spyckerelle, 1975), is addressed in this report because it has since been recognized as the predominant series in ancient bitumens and crude oils (Seifert and Moldowan, 1978; Schaefle, 1979; Seifert *et al.*, 1980).

Comparison of m/e 253 fingerprints was used empirically for oil–oil source and maturity correlation by Seifert and Moldowan (1978) and as a further extension, the series of MA-steroids having one less nuclear methyl group, characterized by a m/e 239 mass spectral base peak, was also used for source correlation. This empirical method was further extended to oil–source rock correlation, and using the m/e 239 fingerprints was presented as evidence for a co-sourcing concept for the origin of the oil at Prudhoe Bay (Seifert *et al.*, 1980). The carbon numbers of individual GC–MS

peaks were not known with certainty due to weak molecular ions and coeluting compounds.

Structural investigation continued at Strasbourg where the synthesis of two series of MA-steroids was performed in an attempt to prove the structure of those occurring in petroleum. However, with the possible exception of one epimer which appeared to coelute with a major MA compound, the compounds prepared were not products of the geosphere (Schaefle *et al.*, 1978). Careful re-examination of the data on the one compound (Schaefle, 1979), however, revealed peak broadening in the coelution experiment indicating that none of the major MA petroleum steroid series had been synthesized.

Aromatization of the steroid nucleus proceeds from ring C into ring B and finally into ring A to produce di- and triaromatized steroids (DA- and TA-steroids), respectively (Schaefle, 1979; Mackenzie *et al.*, in press b) and these higher series of aromatized steroids have outstanding mass spectral side chain loss base peaks for convenient mass fragmentographic detection. Numerous series have been reported depending upon retention or loss of nuclear methyl groups during the aromatization process (Schaefle, 1979; Mackenzie *et al.*, in press b). In general, concentrations of the DA-steroids have been below our methods of detection in crude oils and ancient shales; so for practical purposes, the MA- and TA-steroids have the greatest correlation potential.

Gradual cleavage and loss of side chain in the MA-steroids was recognized as a measure of relative thermal maturity among crude oil samples (Seifert and

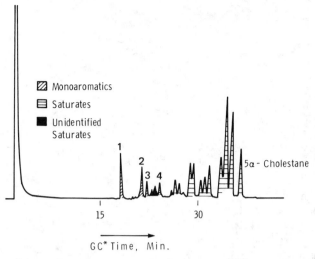

Fig. 1. Dehydrogenation/isomerization, (10% Pd on C, 300 °C, 407 h) 5α-cholestane. GC: Dexsil 300 Scot 100 ft × 0.02 in i.d.

Moldowan, 1978). This concept has been extended to include side chain loss in the TA-steroids as well as conversion of MA- to TA-steroids and both processes increase with increased thermal maturity in a series of Toarcian shales from the Paris Basin (Mackenzie *et al.*, in press b) and Cretaceous shales from the Wyoming Overthrust Belt (Mackenzie *et al.*, this volume).

Recent speculation on the origin of MA-steroids (Schaefle *et al.*, 1978, Schaefle, 1979) centres on generation from rearranged or partially rearranged sterenes (I. Rubinstein *et al.*, 1975). Rearrangement places a double bond in the vicinity of ring C (Kirk and Shaw, 1975) as a potential starting point for the aromatization process.

In this paper, we report the in-laboratory formation and partial structural elucidation of the entire major series of geological MA-steroids; selected DA- and TA-steroids are also formed, and some structural information is given. Greater understanding of the structure and genesis of the aromatics allows advancement in applications to correlations. Demonstration of the latter in different basins is presented.

RESULTS AND DISCUSSION

Preparation of aromatized steroids

Isomerization of 5α-cholestane with Pt on carbon at 50 atm H_2 pressure and 300 °C has been reported (Petrov *et al.*, 1976) to yield a mixture of fully saturated petroleum steranes whose structures were elucidated by spectroscopic methods (Seifert and Moldowan, 1979). We now wish to report that the use of 10% Pd on carbon catalyst at 300 °C *in vacuo* in a sealed quartz tube, conditions similar to classical catalytic dehydrogenation (Fu and Harvey, 1978), gives high yields of the saturated isomerized sterane mixture accompanied by a minor portion (20–30% by weight for a 1:1 cholestane to catalyst weight-to-weight ratio) of aromatic material.

Figure 1 depicts the relative composition. Peaks 1–4 (Fig. 1) possess mass spectra (Fig. 2) identical to petroleum MA-steroids (Fig. 3) and coelute with the latter on two different capillary GC columns (Fig. 4). These results were extended from cholestane to C_{28} and C_{29} steranes. In view of postulated rearrangement intermediates (Schaefle *et al.*, 1978) in the formation of MA-steroids, a search of the Pd on C-isomerizate/dehydrogenate for diasteranes was made by GC–MS; but none could be identified.

Isolation of the MA-steroids by thin layer chromatography (TLC) on alumina or reversed-phase high performance liquid Chromatography (HPLC) and subsequent subjection to the dehydrogenation/isomerization experiments described above resulted in formation (Fig. 5) of further dehydrogenated products, including TA-steroids as recognized in petroleum (Fig. 6).

Thus, the catalytic dehydrogenation/isomerization methods described here can be used to prepare the entire series of saturated isomeric, monoaromatic, and triaromatic steroids which are identical with the natural products present in petroleum and other geochemical sources.

Development of nonaqueous reversed-phase and adsorptive HPLC methods described below has allowed us to isolate the individual monoaromatic compounds prepared by our methods and high field NMR spectroanalysis of these isolated compounds has permitted us to make assignments which reveal the structure of the monoaromatic petroleum steroids to be

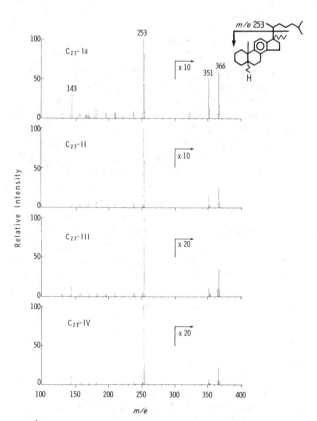

Fig. 2. Mass spectra of four major synthetic monoaromatized steroids. Nuclide GC–MS at 70 eV, Dexsil 400, 200 ft, stainless steel capillary column.

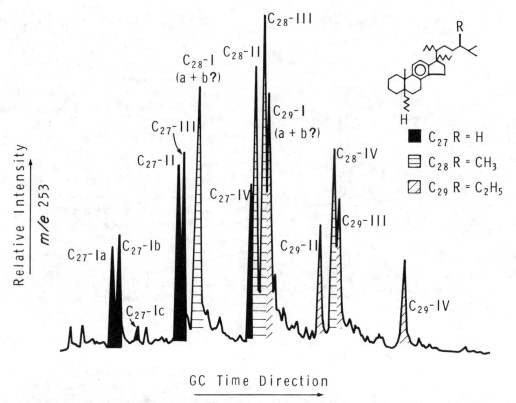

Fig. 3. Monoaromatized steroids of a California crude oil in the C_{27}–C_{29} range. (Finnigan 400 GC–MS, OV-101, 50 m Glass Capillary Column.)

different from previously suggested structures (Seifert *et al.*, 1981).

Structural elucidation

Mass spectrometry of monoaromatics The mass spectra for the main MA-steroid products of 5α-cholestane dehydrogenation are shown in Fig. 2. The most important feature, the base peak at m/e 253 in all four spectra, establishes the site of aromatization as ring C of the steroid nucleus. The intense m/e 253 ion results from homolytic cleavage of the side chain (see Fig. 2) which leads to a highly stabilized benzylic carbonium ion in the gas phase. Further decomposition of the m/e 253 ion by cleavage through ring B leads to the only other major ion at m/e 143 (Cheung *et al.*, 1979).

Other important ions, the molecular ion at m/e 366 and loss of methyl at m/e 351, confirm the molecular formula as $C_{27}H_{42}$. Differences shown in the intensities of these later ions between isomers Ia–IV (Fig. 2) are probably real but cannot be used effectively to distinguish the epimers as those ion intensities are too low. The general characteristics of these mass spectra are the same as those for previously synthesized nonpetroleum ring C monoaromatized C_{27}-steroids (Schaefle, 1979).

The identity of the synthetic C_{27} MA-steroids with the natural products as found in petroleum and rock extracts is demonstrated by GC–MS coinjection shown in Fig. 4 using a 50 m OV-101 phase capillary column. Coelution of all major isomers was also observed on the Dexsil 400 phase (60 m). In addition, the individually isolated

compounds (Fig. 7) were coinjected under the same conditions and found to coelute with the natural petroleum products. A minor fraction in the isolation scheme, not shown in Fig. 7, enriched in compounds C_{27}-Ib and C_{27}-Ic (compare Fig. 3) also showed these minor synthetic products to coelute with compounds in petroleum as indicated in Fig. 4. When the GC–MS coinjection experiments were repeated, using a monoaromatic dehydrogenate derived from sitostane (C_{29}) plus ergostane (C_{28}), all major synthetic compounds coeluted with petroleum natural products.

The GC–MS coinjection work is summarized as illustrated in Fig. 3. All labeled peaks have been identified by coinjection with materials produced by our catalytic sterane dehydrogenation method. These compounds are repeatedly encountered in different basins world-wide and identified by GC retention time to be the major MA-geosteroids.

NMR assignments The ^{1}H-NMR spectrum (Fig. 8) of the third C_{27} monoaromatic steroid (third with respect to elution order on Dexsil 300, Fig. 1) isolated by HPLC and shown to be pure by GC (Fig. 7), exhibits resonance signals in the aromatic region with the AB pattern characteristic of two strongly coupled aromatic protons. Also, integrated intensities correspond to two aromatic hydrogens for each of the four C_{27} monoaromatic steroids. These data, along with mass spectral data which demonstrate the presence of a ring-C aromatic structure, allow the firm assignment of the aromatic signals to hydrogens at C-11 and C-12 for each of the four major C_{27} monoaromatic petrosteroids. The

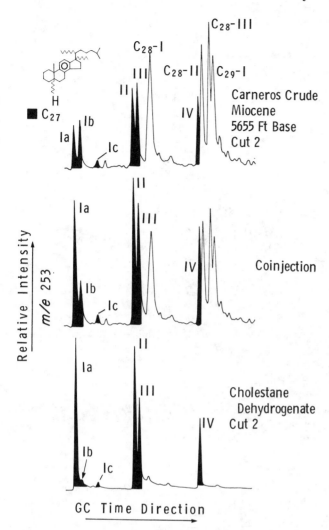

Fig. 4. Comparison by GC–MS coinjection of synthetic C_{27} monoaromatized steroids with natural monoaromatized steroids in a California crude oil. Finnigan 4000 GC–MS, OV-101, 50 m glass capillary column.

two aromatic hydrogens and the absence of a benzylic methyl resonance eliminate the possibility of a methyl at C-12 (resulting from a C-13 to C-12 migration of the C-18 methyl group) postulated previously (Schaefle *et al.*, 1978).

Five methyl resonance signals are present in the spectrum of each of the monoaromatic steroids. Each of the four isomers has two singlet resonances and two doublet methyl resonances. One of the doublets exhibits a two-methyl intensity (6H) and a slight nonequivalence of methyls, often observed for the C-26 and C-27 methyls of the terminal isopropyl group of the C_{27} sterol side chain. Therefore, the large doublet (6H) present in each spectrum can be assigned to the C-26 and C-27 methyls of the terminal side chain isopropyl group. The single methyl doublet (3H) is assigned to the C-21 methyl.

The two singlet methyl resonances, each with a three-proton intensity, demonstrate the presence of methyls at two quaternary carbons. The C-18 methyl has migrated from C-13, and the presence of hydrogens at C-11 and C-12 and lack of a benzylic methyl have shown that it has not migrated to C-12. Migration of the C-18 from C-13 to C-17 is the only reasonable alternative, and the data

support this occurrence. Migration of the C-18 methyl to C-17 makes C-17 a quaternary carbon (hence the presence of a singlet methyl). The C-21 methyl doublet discussed above indicates that the C-20 tertiary center is intact. Furthermore, migration of the C-18 methyl to C-17 is well known (Cheung *et al.*, 1979) and is a reasonable path of C-18 methyl migration associated with ring-C aromatization.

These data establish the skeletal structure of the C and D rings and side chain and further suggest that differences in configuration at the epimer centers (e.g., C-5, C-17, and C-20) are a source of differences in the structures of the four isomers. Mechanistically speaking, it seems unlikely that major amounts of 17α-methyl epimers are formed since this would require the 18-methyl to migrate to the opposite side of the ring system during the aromatization/methyl migration process. By this reasoning, we speculate that the four major dehydrogenate monoaromatized steranes (Fig. 4, peaks 1a, II, III, and IV) are 20R/20S pairs with 5α(H) and 5β(H) epimers (see below).

The remaining structural question concerns the location of the final methyl in the A/B ring system. The singlet methyl signal implies the presence of a methyl at quaternary carbons C-5 or C-10. Comparison of spectra of synthetic monoaromatic steroids now known not to be the major petroleum MA-steroids, prepared by Schaefle (1979), supports the presence of a methyl at C-10 because they differ from our compound in the following way. First, the singlet methyl resonances assigned to the C-5 methyl groups for four synthetic analogs are consistently lower than both singlet methyl resonances in the spectrum of our compound and, secondly, MA-steroids with a methyl at C-10 have a chemical shift assigned to that methyl in the range of the singlet methyl resonances observed for our compounds (Turner, 1972; Schaefle, 1979).

A methyl at C-5 requires five benzylic protons in the spectrum (two at C-7, one at C-10, and two at C-15); whereas a methyl at C-10 requires only four benzylic protons in the spectrum (two at C-7 and two at C-15).

The assignment is complicated by nonbenzylic protons which resonate above 2 ppm (e.g. the C-16 hydrogens which correspond to the C-2 hydrogens of indane). Integrated intensities tend to support the presence of only four purely benzylic hydrogens, thus implying a normal steroid A/B ring structure (with the C-19 methyl at C-10) for the monoaromatic steroids. Additional NMR experiments involving difference decoupling, NOE, and 2DJ techniques are in progress and should fully resolve the structure.

Proof of structure by synthesis and coinjection with the natural product of C_{27} ring-C monoaromatized steroids has presently been accomplished independently by Albrecht (1981). They synthesized the epimeric pair with 5α(20R) and 5β(20R) stereochemistry. Mackenzie *et al.* (in press a) have subsequently synthesized a pair of C_{27} ring-C monoaromatized steroids which have been assigned as 5α(20R) and 5α(20S) epimers on the basis of the synthetic route used and NMR interpretations. These results reinforce and confirm our NMR-based structure assignments for the positions of the methyl groups at C_{10} and C_{17}. They also reassert indirectly the

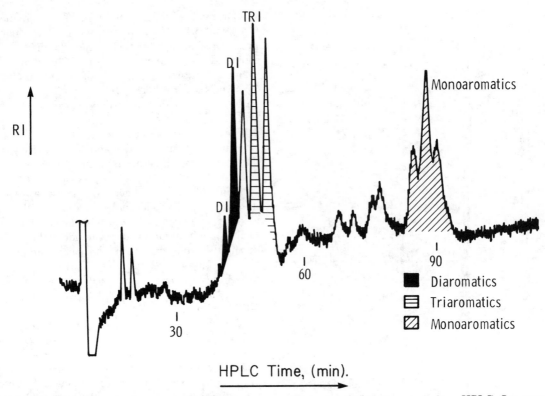

Fig. 5. Dehydrogenation–isomerization of synthetic C_{27} monoaromatized steroids. (Reversed-phase HPLC. See experimental section for details.)

probability of fixed $17\beta(CH_3)$ stereochemistry.

Two articles directly related to this work came to our attention in January 1982. These articles, in the Russian literature and from the laboratory of Al. A. Petrov demonstrate that V. G. Zubenko *et al.*, have recognized Pt/charcoal-induced dehydrogenation of cholestane (at 310 °C) as a means of preparing petroleum monoaromatic steroids (Zubenko *et al.*, 1980). Furthermore, although no chromatographic isolation of the individual isomers is reported, ^{13}C NMR analyses, presumably of the monoaromatic steroid mixture, allowed them to hypothesize the general structure for the

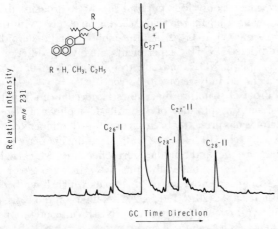

Fig. 6. Triaromatized steroids of a California crude oil in the C_{26}–C_{28} range, Finnigan 4000 GC–MS, OV-101, 50 m glass capillary column.

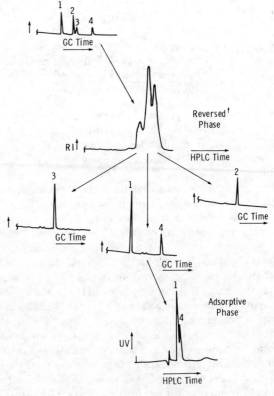

Fig. 7. HPLC isolation of major C_{27} monoaromatic petrosteroids.[†] Formed by catalytic dehydrogenation–isomerization of 5α-cholestane. † See experimental section for details.

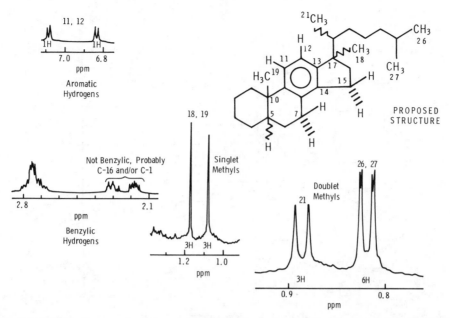

Fig. 8. 500 MHz ^{1}H NMR spectrum of a pure synthetic C_{27} monoaromatic petrosteroid. (Prepared by catalytic dehydrogenation–isomerization and isolated by preparative HPLC. The spectrum (in CDCl$_3$) is of the third (with respect to elution order on Dexil 300 SCOT column) (see Fig. 1) C_{27} monoaromatic steroid (98% purity by GC). The general skeleton of the four major C_{27} monoaromatics is drawn, carbons are numbered and the carbon numbers used to label spectral peaks. See the text for a discussion of the assignments.)

monoaromatic steroid which is presented in our paper Zubenko *et al.* (1981).

Products of MA-steroid dehydrogenation

The further catalytic dehydrogenation of the isolated MA-steroids derived from cholestane (see above) gave products of greater unsaturation (peaks eluting between 30 and 60 minutes, Fig. 5). Analysis by GC–MS, illustrated by the fragment ion map in Fig. 9, revealed eight compounds in the product mixture eluting in the form of four doublets, presumably epimers at C-20 or C-17. Both compounds of each doublet had one of the following base peak ions due to side chain loss: m/e 251, 249, 233, and 231 (two compounds for each ion). Molecular ions m/e 364, 362 (weak), 346, and 344, respectively, were observed. Other compounds with a m/e 251 base peak were also observed, presumably due to additional isomeric positions of the double bond and to stereoisomerization at sites other than C-17 or C-20. Only the doublets shown in Fig. 9 were observed for m/e 249, 233, and 231. Extended conjugation and aromatization reduce stereoisomerism possibilities in the steroid nucleus for those compounds.

We interpret these data as indicating increasing units of unsaturation from starting MA-steroids (m/e 253), beginning with one double bond (m/e 251), two double bonds (m/e 249), three double bonds plus methyl loss (m/e 233), and four double bonds plus methyl loss (m/e 231). Interestingly, the m/e 249 compounds, which could be DA-steroids have not undergone C-19 methyl loss, leading to speculation that these are actually diene-monoaromatics. If the methyl group were retained by shift to another position, a m/e 245 triaromatic analogue would be expected; not found. The m/e 233 pair is

apparently an ene-diaromatic, the precursors of the m/e 231 pair of TA-steroids.

The m/e 231 doublet of compounds was identified by GC–MS coinjections (conditions as for MA-steroids above) as C_{26}-I and C_{26}-II in Fig. 6. That is, the naturally occurring TA-geosteroids were formed as reaction products in our dehydrogenation experiment. The first TA-steroid eluting from reversed-phase HPLC (Fig. 5) coeluted with the peak labeled C_{26}-I (Fig. 6) on GC–MS and the second TA-steroid (Fig. 5) from HPLC coeluted with the peak labeled C_{26}-II (Fig. 6) on GC–MS.

Parallel to and independent of our work, the structure of the triaromatized steroids has been proven by synthesis and comparison with the natural product (Ludwig *et al.*, 1981; preprint received as personal communication from Dr P. Albrecht during the preparation of this paper). Their synthesis was carried out via phenanthrenequinone oxidation of cholesta-3,5-diene, followed by further oxidation of rings-A,B diaromatic intermediates with chloranil and subsequent hydrogenation of the C-15(16) double bond introduced by the oxidations. Comparison of ^{1}H-NMR data revealed that the 17S, 20R C_{26} compound of Ludwig *et al.* (1981) corresponds to our second C_{26} triaromatic steroid eluted by reversed-phase HPLC (Fig. 5). Each spectrum exhibits a three-proton methyl doublet (C-21) at 0.74 ppm (J = 6.7 Hz, Ludwig *et al.*: J = 6.5 Hz). The six-proton doublet at 0.88 ppm (J = 6.5 Hz) (C-26 and C-27) in the spectrum of the C_{27}-derived C_{26} triaromatic steroid of Ludwig *et al.* is split slightly at 500 MHz, revealing a three-proton methyl doublet at 0.880 ppm and one at 0.875 ppm, each exhibiting a 6.4 Hz coupling constant. Both spectra exhibit a methyl singlet (1.34 ppm, Ludwig *et al.*: 1.33 ppm) which can be assigned to the methyl attached at the C-17 position. A

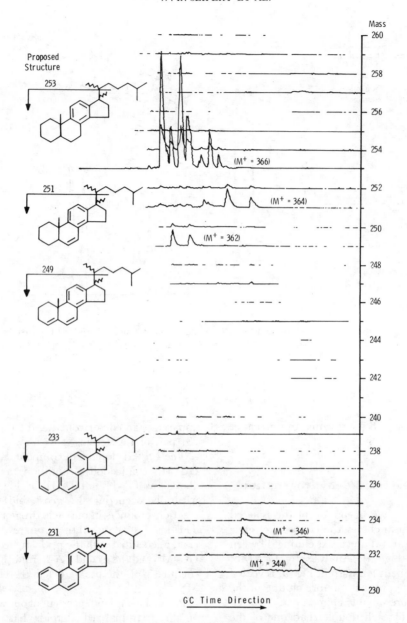

Fig. 9. Monoaromatized steroid dehydrogenate–isomerizate GC–MS fragment ion MAP. (Finnigan, INCOS computer software chromatogram display.)

two-proton multiplet (C-16) is observed at 2.33 ppm (Ludwig *et al.*: 2.29 ppm) and at 3.27 ppm (C-15) (Ludwig *et al.*: 3.23 ppm) in each spectrum. Finally, each compound exhibits signals in the aromatic region which total eight protons.

Diagenesis

Because the only biologically occurring ring-C aromatized steroid, Viridin (Neidle *et al.*, 1972) is a rare fungal natural product which has no side chain, it appears certain that the ring-C aromatized geosteroids arise from aromatization of sterol-derived steranes rather than ring-C aromatized biological precursors.

Saturated petrosteroids with a methyl group at C-17 have not been reported to date; and, therefore, this structural feature in the aromatized transformation products deserves some comment.

The early literature (Bergmann, 1935; Bergmann and Bergmann, 1939) suggested, based on steroid thermolysis studies, that the C-18 methyl migration to C-17 during the formation of Diel's hydrocarbon (3′-methylcyclopentenophenanthrene, a product of selenium-induced dehydrogenation of steroid natural products, Harper *et al.*, 1934) is initiated by thermolytic loss of the C-17 side chain and is independent of aromatization. These early experiments suggesting free radical-type pathways have recently been supplemented by similar observations in ionic media (Cheung *et al.*, 1979). Interestingly, the question of methyl migration in Diel's hydrocarbon is paralleled by the structural question of the petroleum MA-steroids. It is now clear that, in the MA-steroids, as well as in Diel's hydrocarbon, migration of the C-18 methyl is directed to the C-17 position. The parallel has come full circle with the structural elucidation of the probable precursors for the Diel's hydrocarbon found (Mair and Martinez-Pico, 1962) in petroleum, the TA-steroids, which also show a methyl shift to C-17.

In our high temperature dehydrogenations, as in petroleum and mature source rocks, a free radical hydrogen atom removal from the saturated sterane is needed to initiate the chain of events leading to MA-steroid production. The driving force for migration of the methyl group to C-17 appears to be either aromatization of ring-C or release of C/D ring strain or, most likely, both in combination, which would explain why aromatization is favored for ring-C over rings A or B.

In spite of the early work on Diel's hydrocarbon, there is evidence against a 1,2-methyl shift by a strictly free radical mechanism (de Mayo, 1963). A possible alternative explanation is the development of a partial or complete positive charge or formation of a carbon metal bond (McKervey et al., 1973) at the C-20 position in the sterane. This would occur by interaction with the catalyst metal after hydrogen abstraction from C-20. The positive charge or C–Pd bond could migrate to C-17 then to C-13 with a simultaneous methyl group shift from C-13 to C-17. The finding of monoaromatized steroids in sediments which have only been exposed to low temperatures (Mackenzie et al., in press b; Schaefle, 1979) supports the possibility of such an ionic mechanism. A starting point is envisioned through protonation of C-22,23 double bonds which occur commonly in sterols (e.g. Goodwin, 1973; Nes and Nes, 1980; Scheuer, 1973). The positive charge could shift from C-22 to C-20 and continue into the steroid C-ring.

These mechanistic considerations point to the possibility of different pathways for monoaromatized steroid formation depending on the temperature, catalysis, and starting material. This does not appear to be the case with steroid diagenesis to diasteranes (Seifert and Moldowan, 1978; Ensminger et al., 1978). The backbone rearrangement to diasterenes (Kirk and Shaw, 1975) can be considered separate and distinct, requiring acidic catalysis and specific sterenes as precursors (e.g. Dastillung and Albrecht, 1977). The lack of diasterane formation in the Pd/C catalytic treatments of steranes makes the geological conversion of steranes to diasteranes also seem unlikely. Since diasteranes are not formed and the NMR analyses indicate the likelihood of a retained methyl group at C-10 in the MA-steroids, the involvement of diasteranes or diasterenes in this aromatization process is considered remote. The scheme included below depicts steroid interconversions which have been simulated in the laboratory.

The above results lead to novel hypotheses, forming a platform for understanding sterane diagenesis. We have shown that starting with one sterane of natural biological skeleton (e.g. 5α-cholestane) the entire related series (of proper carbon number) of saturated steranes (Seifert and Moldowan, 1979; Moldowan et al., 1980) and aromatized geosteroids can be formed by the action of heat and catalyst. Excess hydrogen prevents the formation of aromatics (see Experimental section, this paper; cf. Petrov et al., 1976) while hydrogen deficiency promotes aromatics formation. Part of the diagenesis of steranes, particularly at elevated temperatures (i.e. petroleum generation), can therefore be thought of as a

Scheme. Simulated diagenesis of aromatics, proposed mechanisms — legend legend two pages on.

Table 1

Quantitative source-specific parameters, regular and monoaromatized steroids, Rocky Mountain Overthrust Belt

Type	Sample	No.	Field	Age	Depth (ft)	$\dfrac{C_{27}}{C_{29}}$	$\dfrac{C_{28}}{C_{29}}$	$\dfrac{C_{27}{}^b}{C_{27}-C_{29}}$	$\dfrac{C_{28}{}^b}{C_{27}-C_{29}}$	$\dfrac{C_{29}{}^b}{C_{27}-C_{29}}$
						\multicolumn{2}{}{5α-Steranes (20R)}		\multicolumn{3}{}{Monoaromatized steroids}	
I	Shale	182	Mowry	Cretaceous	9000	a	a	0.33	0.43	0.24
I	Oil	161	Spring Valley	Cretaceous	1000	2.1	1.5	0.27	0.50	0.24
I	Oil	179	Bridger Lake	Cretaceous	15 500	2.0	1.4	0.27	0.47	0.26
II	Oil	81–3	Hamilton Dome	Permian	3200	2.7	0.8	0.40	0.36	0.24
Parameter						1	2	3	4	5	6

[a] Sterane concentration too low to give reliable quantitative data.
[b] Compare Fig. 3.

long-term heating of steroids with many results similar to what we can do in a catalyzed short-term laboratory experiment.

1. Formation of identical saturated sterane epimers, similar in distribution to mature petroleum.
2. Formation of the identical suite of monoaromatized steroids, as found in petroleum.
3. Lack of formation of ring-B,C diaromatized steroids with nuclear methyl group loss, which have also not been detectable in the petroleums we have studied worldwide.
4. Formation of identical triaromatized steroids, as found in petroleum.

The striking similarity between the products of our catalytic dehydrogenation–isomerization procedure and biological marker compounds in petroleum clearly implies that mechanistic parallels exist between our chemical processes and organic geochemical diagenesis. In spite of these similarities, there appear to be differences between the two processes related to reaction mechanisms: pyrolysis (Seifert, 1978) and catalytic sterane isomerization (this paper) have in common the absence of diasterane formation. Also, both reactions have in common free radical-type reaction conditions. In contrast, natural petroleum diagenesis is complicated by carbonium ion-type reactions competing with the free radical pathways, thus allowing additional products such as diasteranes to be formed (Kirk and Shaw, 1975).

Applications of aromatics to correlation studies

The recognition of the structure of the monoaromatics and triaromatics on the molecular level, combined with a better understanding of their diagenesis, present the platform for progress in correlation studies, as described below. More specifically, the mono- and triaromatics — when used on the molecular level in a similar fashion as described previously for steranes and terpanes (Seifert and Moldowan, 1978, 1979, 1980, 1981; Seifert et al., 1980) — are now identified as powerful source parameters capable of converting *qualitative* conclusions into *quantitative* ones, in regard to cosourcing. In addition, the combination (the ratio) of MA- with TA-steroids turns out to be a welcome supplement to the repertoire of maturation parameters, as has been pointed

out previously (Mackenzie et al., in press b). Examples from three basins have been selected to illustrate the points made above.

Overthrust Belt, Wyoming In a previous paper (Seifert and Moldowan, 1981) source distinction between Cretaceous and Phosphoria oils via qualitative sterane and terpane fingerprinting has been described. Because of the varying sterol composition among all organisms, the ratio of C_{28}/C_{29} regular 5α-steranes (Table II of Seifert, 1980) has been found particularly useful as a source parameter which is insensitive to maturation and migration. An obvious extension is, of course, the use of the C_{27}/C_{29} ratio. Using the same rationale, the monoaromatized steroids of the three different carbon numbers should supplement the parameters derived from the saturated steranes. In Table 1, the distinction by quantitative sterane ratios of Cretaceous (Type I) from Phosphoria (Type II) sourced oils is illustrated. While the saturated sterane approach fails for the Mowry Shale, for reasons of low sterane concentration, it succeeds with the MA-steroids. This success is due, in particular, to extraordinarily high mass spectral sensitivity (ion current) of the m/e 253 ion (see Fig. 2) rather than high concentrations of MA-steroids. Thus, when comparing the concentrations in the entire monoaromatized ($C_{27}-C_{29}$) biomarker steranes (Table 1), the quantitative saturated sterane-based conclusions are strengthened.

On the other hand, while the C_{29}-based saturated sterane parameter responds well to this established source difference, between Cretaceous and Phosphoria, the C_{29}-based MA-steroid parameter fails to make the distinction (column 6, Table 1). In summary, all five parameters listed in Table 1, in combination, produce a clear, quantitative picture in this particular correlation example.

It is noteworthy that in spite of the greater depth and substantially higher degree of thermal maturation (Seifert and Moldowan, 1981) in the 15,500 ft Bridger Lake oil (179) versus the 1000 ft Spring Valley oil (161), the sterane and monoaromatized steroid ratios in Table 1 are insensitive to those differences. This maturation insensitivity strengthens their use as source-specific parameters.

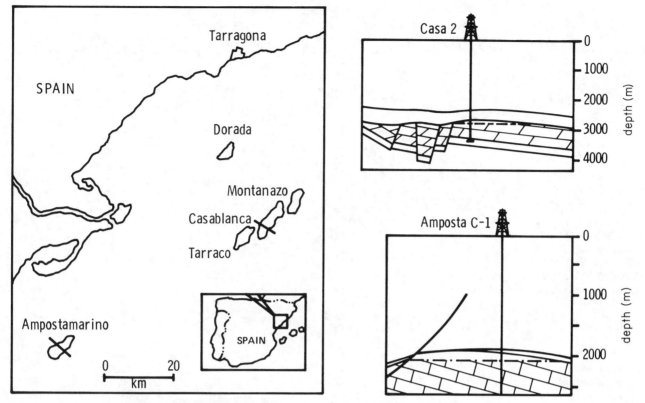

Fig. 10. Location of Tarragona Basin oil fields, off-shore Spain.

Western Mediterranean, off-shore Spain Since 1970, four commercial fields have been discovered within a relatively small area off the Ebro Delta in the Spanish Mediterranean in the Tarragona Basin. They contain the bulk of the oil reserves at present. A location map modified from that reported by Sineriz *et al.* (1980) is shown in Fig. 10.

The oils sampled in the Casablanca field (Casablanca C-4 and Montanazo D-1) are reservoired in Jurassic limestones unconformably overlain by thick Tertiary sediments, which provide both source and seal. The source beds for the Casablanca oil have been identified as parts, but not the whole, of a carbonate unit at the very base of the Tertiary transgression: the Alcanar Formation of Middle Miocene age (Demaison *et al.*, 1980).

The oil in the Amposta field, on the other hand, is emplaced mainly in Lower Cretaceous limestones that are also unconformably draped by Miocene sediments. However, the base of the Miocene in the Amposta field is under a chalk facies with marginal reservoir characteristics: The Amposta Chalk. The latter is oil saturated, but not believed to have any source character, like the Alcanar formation in Casablanca. The oil in the Amposta field was already recognized by Albaiges and Torradas (1977) to be dissimilar to the oil in the Tarraco field, an accumulation location immediately south of the Casablanca field. The actual source of the Amposta oil (if known, perhaps, to the operators of the field) is still unpublicized. On the basis of geologic considerations and other existing restraints, such as insufficient maturation of the mid-Miocene close to the Amposta structure, it is considered likely that the source for the Amposta oil is within the Mesozoic (Lower Cretaceous?) itself (Demaison, personal communication).

In the following, we wish to demonstrate a source identity between Casablanca and Montanzo oils, both sourced from the Alcanar (Miocene), and a source difference from Amposta Marino oil (Fig. 10) relying heavily on mono- and triaromatized steroids in combination with a variety of other parameters, which have been established previously by us.

Data are summarized in Table 2. Parameters 1–5 show that, in both the regular steranes and the MA-steroids, the source differentiation between Amposta oil and the other two oils as a group is straightforward using the C_{28}/C_{29} ratios, but not the C_{27}/C_{29} ratios. Two specific TA-steroid ratios (Parameters 6 and 7), as depicted in Fig. 6, strengthen the source identity between Montanazo and Casablanca and their source difference from Amposta. The diasterane/regular sterane ratio (Parameter 12) has previously been used as a means of differentiating source and maturity (Table X in Seifert and Moldowan, 1978) and is equally applicable to this correlation in the same manner. A further case in evidence of increasing diasterane content, relative to regular steranes with increasing maturity, as shown in Table 2, was found in a sequence of immature shales in the Overthrust Belt, Wyoming, which is described in this volume by Mackenzie *et al.* The lesser maturity of the shallower Amposta oil is further signaled (Parameter 9) by its lower TA-steroid content relative to MA-steroids (Mackenzie *et al.*, 1981). Parameter 8, the 5α-sterane to MA-steroid ratio, is interpreted as mainly source-controlled, in this case, because if it was controlled by maturation the reverse trend should be

Table 2
Source correlation in western Mediterranean, off-shore Spain

Oil	Amposta Marino C-1	Montanazo C-1	Casa Blanca C-4	Parameter
Age	Jurassic to L. Cretaceous	U. Jurassic	Jurassic	
Depth, (ft)	6150–6400	8505–8568	8533–8658	
Steranes 5α, 20R				
C_{27}/C_{29}	1.7	1.7	1.6	1
C_{28}/C_{29}	0.6	1.4	1.3	2
MA-Steroids[a]				
$C_{27}/C_{27}-C_{29}$	0.36	0.27	0.29	3
$C_{28}/C_{27}-C_{29}$	0.25	0.45	0.44	4
$C_{29}/C_{27}-C_{29}$	0.39	0.29	0.27	5
TA-Steroids[b]				
C_{26}-I/C_{28}-I	0.65	0.37	0.42	6
C_{27}-II/C_{28}-II	0.65	1.28	1.21	7
5α-Steranes/MA-Steroids	0.12	2.7	3.0	8
MA-Steroids/TA-Steroids	7.3	1.3	1.5	9
14β, (20R)/5α, (20R) Steranes	1.74	1.69	1.72	10
5α, (20S)/5α, (20R)	[c]	1.25	1.21	11
$\beta\alpha$, Diasteranes/5α, (20R)	0.75	3.9	3.3	12
nC$_{31}$/nC$_{19}$	0.51	0.30	0.27	13
iC$_{19}$/iC$_{20}$	0.68	1.62	1.68	14
CPI[d]	0.89	1.00	1.00	15
Bulk				
δC^{13}/C^{12}	3.17	8.5	8.5	16
Sat/DA + TA	0.6	4.4	5.2	17
% Sulfur	4.34	0.2	0.1	18
API Gravity	14.1	30.5	34.4	19

[a] Compare Figure 3.
[b] Compare Figure 6.
[c] Interference by coelution with another compound.

[d] $$\frac{2(nC_{23} + nC_{25} + nC_{27} + nC_{29})}{2(nC_{24} + nC_{26} + nC_{28}) + nC_{22} + nC_{30}}.$$

apparent. The often-used sterane maturation parameters, 10 and 11 (Seifert and Moldowan, 1981), do not distinguish the oils, presumably because these sterane isomers in all oils have reached thermodynamic equilibrium.

The elevated n-C$_{31}$/n-C$_{19}$ ratio (Parameter 13) in Amposta oil may reflect a maturity difference from the other oils or it could be interpreted as a terrestrial component. Increase in the n-C$_{31}$/n-C$_{19}$ parameters is thought to reflect a greater quantity of high molecular weight plant waxes from terrestrial source inputs (cf. Albrecht and Ourisson, 1971). The gammacerane present in Amposta oil lends support to the terrestrial interpretation. Supplementing the source parameters described so far is the occurrence of methylhopanes (Fig. 2 in Seifert and Moldowan, 1978) in Amposta oil and their absence in the other two.

A difference in the diagenetic history of Amposta oil is evidenced by its even-numbered paraffin predominance (Parameter 15) which might stem from a direct reduction mechanism of fatty acids to hydrocarbons of equal chain lengths (Seifert, 1975). Thus, parallel with fatty acid reduction, we speculate that the preferred reduction of phytanic acid to phytane rather than decarboxylation to pristane could explain the lower pristane/phytane ratio (Parameter 14) of Amposta oil. This interpretation requires the same parallelism of low pristane/phytane ratios with even-paraffin predominance in other basins.

The carbon isotope ratios (Parameter 16) confirm the biomarker source differentiation. In the shallower Amposta oil, the lower saturate to aromatic ratio (Parameter 17), the higher sulfur content (Parameter 18), and the lower API gravity (Parameter 19) all strengthen biomarker-based conclusions (Parameters 9 and 12) of lower maturity for this oil.

In summary, the MA- and TA-steroids are major contributing parameters in unraveling the source and maturation components of this basin.

Prudhoe Bay, Alaska For background information, the reader is referred to a previous paper (Seifert et al., 1981) in which cosourcing of the major commercial deposits from three different shales (Post Neocomian, Shublik and Kingak) was presented. The only exception was one oil (Kingak) which originated from a single shale (Kingak). The relative quantitative contribution of Shublik shale, Post Neocomian shale, and Kingak shale to the oils remained unknown. The application of MA- and TA-steroids to this correlation problem enables us now to extend the qualitative cosourcing concept to a quantitative assessment of relative contributions. The new data are summarized in Table 3. For convenience, carbon isotope data reported in our previous paper and pertinent to this discussion are repeated here.

First, both the MA-steroids and the TA-steroids indicate a predominant contribution of Post Neocomian

Table 3
Prodhoe Bay, Alaska. Quantitation of cosourcing via aromatized steroids

			MA-Steroids $\dfrac{C_{28}}{C_{27}-C_{29}}$		TA-Steroids $C_{27}II/C_{28}II$		C^{13}/C^{12}		
Sample No.	Formation	Depth	Bitumen	Oil	Bitumen	Oil	Bitumen	Oil	Column
Shale 209	Post Neocomian	11 500	0.44		2.1		+ 0.4		1
Oil 220	Kuparuk River	6800		0.45		1.8		+ 0.2	2
Shale 207	Shublik	8800	0.31		0.9		− 0.8		3
Shale 208	Shubik	8900	0.29		0.8		− 1.0		4
Oil 218	Sag River	8900		0.28		1.0		− 1.4	5
Shale 213	Kingak	9400	0.34		1.1		− 1.7		6
Shale 210	Kingak	8400	NA		1.1		− 1.8		7
Oil 219	Kingak	7700		0.32		0.9		− 2.0	8
Oil 202	Sadlerochit	9100		0.41	1.4			− 0.3	9
Oil 205	Lisburne	10000		0.34	1.0			− 0.4	10

source, to the Kuparuk River reservoir (columns 1 and 2, Table 3). This makes perfect geological sense, because of the stratigraphic proximity and potential migration pathway along the 'pipeline' (compare Fig. 2 in Seifert *et al.*, 1980). Carbon isotopes strengthen the aromatic biomarker-based conclusion.

Both MA- and TA-steroids document a predominant contribution of Shublik source to Sag River Oil (columns 3–5, Table 3), a conclusion indicated by previous pyrolysis work (compare Fig. 6 in Seifert *et al.*, 1980).

The previous conclusion of a one-to-one correlation between Kingak shale and Kingak oil (columns 6 and 8, Table 3) is reinforced by MA- and TA-steroids and a perfect isotope correlation.

Finally, the MA- and TA-steroid data (column 9, Table 3) of the Sadlerochit oil (0.41 and 1.4, respectively) are intermediate between those of the Post Neocomian (0.44 and 2.1, respectively) and the average of Kingak and Shublik (0.32 and 1.0 average) indicative of major contributions from all three sources to this reservoir.

The TA-steroids of Lisburne oil indicate heavy contributions from Shublik and Kingak sources, and the MA-steroids can be interpreted likewise.

Thus, the aromatized steranes allow an extension of previous conclusions to say that Kuparuk River oil mainly comes from Post Neocomian shale, that Sag River oil mainly comes from Shublik, and that Sadlerochit is truly cosourced from all three sources. The previous Kingak shale/Kingak oil one-to-one correlation is further reinforced.

In summary, the correlation results described for the three basins chosen as examples to illustrate the power of the novel aromatized steroid biomarker parameters on an individual compound level, rest on quantitative rather than qualitative aspects. In the case of Prudhoe Bay, this kind of quantitation adds a new dimension to the ability to more precisely pinpoint the relative contribution of individual cosources.

EXPERIMENTAL

Gas chromatography

Gas chromatographic analyses (Fig. 1) using a 100 ft × 0.02 in i.d. stainless steel Dexsil 300 SCOT column (Perkin–Elmer) were performed on a Hewlett–Packard Model 5710A chromatograph equipped with a Model 7671A autosampler and 3388A reporting integrator with splitless injection using cyclohexane as solvent. Helium was used as carrier gas at 2 ml min^{-1}. Normal oven temperature (Fig. 1) was 255 °C. Retention indices were calculated using *n*-pentacosane, *n*-hexacosane, and *n*-triacontane internal references.

Gas chromatography–mass spectrometry

Data were obtained using a Nuclide 12-90-G mass spectrometer coupled to a Hewlett–Packard 7620A gas chromatograph or a Finnigan 4000 quadruple system. All data were handled through the INCOS, Finnigan Corporation data system. Capillary chromatography columns employed were either Dexsil 400-coated stainless steel, 200 ft, 0.5 mm i.d. or OV-101 coated glass, 50 m, 0.25 mm i.d. from Chrompack, Inc., U.S.A. All full spectra were recorded from the Nuclide system, INCOS 'SCAN' made at a rate of 6 s per scan. Selective ion monitoring was performed on either instrument, INCOS 'MID' made at a rate of 1 s per scan for aromatics, 2 s per scan for saturates.

High performance liquid chromatography

High performance liquid chromatography (Figs. 5 and 7) was performed using a Model 7500 Micromeritics pump, 7000 psi Valco loop injector, and a Waters Model R401 refractive index detector or an Altex Model 153 UV (254 nm) detector. Columns were protected by Brownlee MPLC guard columns and Rheodyne 2-

micron filters. Nonaqueous reversed-phase HPLC employing an octadecylsilane bonded-phase column (Whatman M9 10 μ 50 cm^{-1} ODSII) and acetonitrile mobile phase (3.00 ml min^{-1}, 700 psi) was found to provide separations for both the C_{27} monoaromatic (Fig. 7) and di- and triaromatic (Fig. 5) steroids (saturated steranes do not elute under these conditions). Using the reversed-phase system (Fig. 7), two of the four major C_{27} monoaromatic steroids (No. 2 and 3, Fig. 1) could be isolated in high purity (thus providing samples for NMR spectroscopy and other physical measurements, Fig. 8). Sample loading was 5 mg in 0.5 ml of acetonitrile for the monoaromatics (Fig. 7) and 2.8 mg in 0.65 ml (Fig. 5) for the di- and triaromatics. The remaining two monoaromatics (1 and 4, Fig. 1) coelute in the reversed-phase system (Fig. 7) but can be separated by adsorptive chromatography (Fig. 7) over aluminum oxide (Lichrosorb Alox T) with a dry hexane mobile phase.

Reversed-phase HPLC of the product of the dehydrogenation–isomerization of isolated mono-aromatic steroids revealed four major peaks that begin eluting at half the retention time of the monoaromatics and several minor peaks eluting before and after the major products (Fig. 5). Analysis by GC–MS of these components is described above. The HPLC separation of the monoaromatic from saturated products of the catalytic sterane dehydrogenation–isomerization is performed on the Whatman M9 10/50 ODS II column using a dichloromethane-acetronitrile (50:50 v/v) mobile phase.

Thin layer chromatography

Thin layer chromatography (TLC) of 5α-cholestane catalytic dehydrogenation–isomerization reaction mixtures over activated alumina (E Merck 60, 20 cm × 20 cm plates with dry hexane as the developing solvent) reveals a UV active component which is less mobile ($R_f = 0.59$) than the saturated steranes ($R_f = 0.72$). In reversed-phase TLC analyses (Whatman KC18 20 cm × 20 cm plates with a methanol-dichloromethane (60:40 v/v) development solvent), the UV active component was more mobile ($R_f = 0.44$) than the saturated components ($R_f = 0.33$). Preparative TLC isolation of the UV active component, followed by GC analysis, revealed that the four short retention time side products correspond to this UV-active TLC band. Plates were visualized with a light application of a phosphomolybdic acid solution (5%) and gentle heating. All solvents were Burdick and Jackson distilled in glass UV grade.

Nuclear magnetic resonance

Nuclear magnetic resonance spectra were recorded at 500 MHz on the Bruker WM500 at the Southern California Regional NMR facility, using CDCl$_3$ as solvent with TMS internal reference.

Catalytic dehydrogenation–isomerization

The 5α-cholestane (gold label) was obtained from Aldrich Chemical Company, 5β-cholestane from Sigma Chemical Company. Catalysis, 10% palladium on carbon, 5% palladium on aluminum oxide, 5% platinum on calcium carbonate, nickel (64%) on silica-alumina, and platinum oxide (Adam's catalyst), were obtained from Aldrich Chemical Company; and catalysts, 5% rhodium on carbon, 5% platinum on carbon, 5% palladium on carbon, 5% palladium on calcium carbonate, 5% palladium on barium carbonate, 5% palladium on barium sulfate, and 0.5% palladium on kaolin, were obtained from Strem Chemical Company. Dolomitic limestone was obtained from the National Bureau of Standards, and sodium montmorillonite (Wyoming) was obtained from the Clay Mineral Repository at the University of Missouri.

In a typical dehydrogenation–isomerization experiment, catalyst was carefully weighed into a quartz tube 17.5 cm × 7 mm i.d. with a 1 mm wall thickness. Proper care must be exercised because some of the listed catalysts are pyrophoric. A measured volume of the steroid solution at a specific concentration in hexane was added to the tube; and the hexane was evaporated under a stream of dry, high purity nitrogen or argon. The tube containing the steroid-catalyst gel (Fig. 1 — at a 1:1, w/w ratio) was evacuated and sealed with a hydrogen-oxygen torch. The sealed tube was then placed in a Lindberg Solabsic Model 51422 furnace at a fixed temperature (300 °C for the comparative studies and preparative work, Fig. 1) for a specific period of time (Fig. 1, 407 h), followed by cooling, after which the tube was opened and the contents thoroughly extracted with hexane and evaporated to dryness under a stream of dry nitrogen. Catalytic dehydrogenation–isomerization of the 5α-C$_{28}$ and 5α-C$_{29}$ sterane mixture was carried out at a 1:1 w/w ratio of catalyst to sterane at 300 °C for 500 h.

The catalysts and minerals can be grouped into five categories with respect to their ability to generate MA-steroids.

1. Those materials that produced no detectable levels (by GC) of MA-steroids and produced no measurable isomerization of the 5α-cholestane, which included the Al$_2$O$_3$, Type X zeolite, dolomite, activated carbon, and Type Y zeolite.
2. Those materials that produced compounds with GC retention times identical to those of the MA-steroids but at levels less than 1% of the product mixture (as measured by GC–FID integrated peak intensities), which included 0.5% palladium on kaolin, 5% palladium on alumina (presence of MA-steroids confirmed by GC–MS), 5% palladium on barium carbonate and calcium oxide.
3. Those catalysts that produced compounds with GC retention times of the MA-steroids and at levels between 2% and 10% of the product mixture, which included 5% palladium on calcium carbonate and 5% platinum on calcium carbonate (presence of MA-steroids confirmed by GC–MS).
4. Those catalysts producing a good yield of MA-steroids (over 20% of the reaction mixture), which included 5% palladium on carbon, 10% palladium on carbon, and 5% platinum on carbon).
5. Those catalysts producing unusual results, that is, significant amounts of compounds with GC retention times different from the compounds produced by the other catalysts, which included 5%

rhodium on carbon, 64% nickel and silica-alumina, platinum oxide, sodium montmorillonite, and 5% palladium on barium sulfate.

The unusual products produced by catalysts in Group 5 are currently being studied. Anomalous variations in product composition with various supported noble metal heterogeneous catalyzed hydrogenations have been reported (Augustine and van Peppen, 1970). In view of the link between the mechanisms of heterogeneous catalyzed hydrogenation and dehydrogenation (Fu and Harvey, 1978), it is perhaps not surprising that unusual results would be observed with various catalysts in our dehydrogenation–isomerization experiments.

The best catalyst for MA-steroid production is palladium on carbon. In experiments in which the ratio of 5α-cholestane to 10% palladium on carbon was varied between 1 and 50, w/w (300 °C for 94 h), it was found that production of MA-steroids increased with increasing quantities of catalyst, whereas saturated sterane isomerization occurred readily for all 5α-cholestane/catalyst ratios studied. Time studies showed that MA-steroids are produced early during the dehydrogenation–isomerization experiments (the bulk of the MA-steroids forming before 26 h at 300 °C) and the ratios of the quantities of the four C_{27}-MA-steroids (Fig. 1) did not change significantly over the course of their production.

Analysis of the isomerization by platinum on carbon of 5α-cholestane (Petrov *et al.*, 1976), which was done under 50 atm H_2 pressure by GC–MS, revealed no MA-steroids present, while the similar catalyst under our evacuated system produced a good yield of MA-steroids. This confirmed the expected result of a quenching of the dehydrogenation reaction by excess hydrogen.

Preparation of 5α-C_{28} and 5α-C_{29} steranes

Stigmastanol (Aldrich Chemical Company) was analyzed as the trimethylsilyl ether via Dexsil 300 SCOT gas chromatography and was shown to be 40:60 w/w ratio of 24-methyl-5α-cholestan-3β-ol and 24-ethyl-5α-cholestan-3β-ol (essentially free of olefinic, Δ^5, analogs). The stigmastanol was then treated with fresh *p*-toluenesulfonyl chloride in dry pyridine at ice bath temperatures (Tökes *et al.*, 1967). After 24 h, the reaction mixture was poured into a mixture of ice and dilute hydrochloric acid (HCl) and extracted with diethyl ether. The ether phase was washed with dilute HCl, then water, and dried over anhydrous Na_2SO_4. Conversion to the stanyl tosylate was complete as judged by reversed-phase TLC.

The stigmastanyl tosylate was added to a boiling suspension of lithium aluminum hydride in fresh, dry diethyl ether. The mixture was allowed to reflux for eight hours. After cooling, excess lithium aluminum hydride was destroyed by the careful addition of water. The mixture was filtered, dried, evaporated, and chromatographed on a 50 g column of Al_2O_3 Act I N (Woelm) eluted with dry hexane. The sterane hydrocarbon fractions were analyzed by GC–MS and shown to be a mixture of 24-methyl-5α,14α,17α(H), 20R-cholestane and 24-ethyl-5α,14α,17α(H), 20R-cholestane.

CONCLUSIONS

1. Twelve monoaromatic steroids (C_{27}–C_{29}) prepared by catalytic isomerization–dehydrogenation from pure model 5α-steroids were proven to be identical with the predominant geoaromatic steroids abundant in geochemical samples worldwide.

2. Proposals for their structures are based on 500 MHz NMR and mass spectral interpretations of pure compounds isolated by preparative HPLC.

3. Triaromatic steroids generated from synthetic monoaromatic steroids were found to be identical to geological triaromatized steroids. 500 MHz NMR data on their structure are compatible with data on compounds synthesized unequivocally in a parallel and independent effort (Ludwig *et al.*, 1981).

4. Absence of diasteranes during isomerization–dehydrogenation, which proceeds by a free radical mechanism, requires dual mechanisms (ionic plus radical) for petroleum diagenesis.

5. Application of mono- and triaromatics to oil–oil source correlations on a molecular level adds a new dimension to sterane/terpane-based conclusions.

6. Aromatized steroids permit quantitative assessment of individual cosources on a relative scale in commerical oil deposits in Prudhoe Bay, Alaska.

Acknowledgement

The authors wish to thank Dr E. J. Gallegos for assistance with GC–MS-computer equipment and Mr G. J. Demaison for geological background information on the Spanish oils. We gratefully acknowledge Dr W. R. Croasmun of the Southern California Regional NMR facility (supported by National Science Foundation Grant No. CHE-7916324A1) for providing 500 MHz NMR data and for valuable discussions concerning those data. A contribution to the mechanism hypothesis was made by Dr P. Sundararaman. Technical assistance was by Messrs. D. E. Chamberlain, P. Novotny, R. G. Prince, and M. J. Painter. Appreciation to the management of Chevron Oil Field Research Company for permission to publish.

REFERENCES

Albaiges, J. and Torradas, J. (1977) Geochemical characterization of the Spanish crude oils. In *Advances in Organic Geochemistry 1975*. Ed. by Campos, R. and Goni, J. Enadimsa, Madrid. pp. 99–115.

Albrecht, P. (1981) Personal communication and oral presentation, Tenth International Meeting on Organic Geochemistry, Bergen, Norway, September 1981.

Albrecht, P. and Ourisson, G. (1971) Biogenic substances in sediments and fossils. *Angew. Chem. Int. Ed.* **10**, 209–225.

Augustine, R. L. and van Peppen, J. F. (1969) Mechanistic comparison of heterogeneous and homogeneous hydrogenation. *Ann. N.Y. Acad. Sci.* **158**, 482–491.

Bergmann, E. (1935) Migration of the quaternary methyl group during dehydrogenation of sterols and similar compounds. *Chem. Ind.* **55**, 175–176.

Bergmann, E. and Bergmann, F. (1939) Further experiments on thermolysis of cholesteryl chloride. *J. Chem. Soc.*, 1019–

1021.

Cheung, H. T. A., McQueen, R. G., Vadasz, A. and Watson, T. R. (1979) Ring-C aromatic steroids. 17β-methyl-18-norpregna-8,11,13-trienes. *J. Chem. Soc. Perkin I*, 1048–1055, and references cited therein.

Dastillung, M. and Albrecht, P. (1977) Δ²-Sterenes as diagenetic intermediates in sediments. *Nature (London)* **269**, 678–679.

Demaison, G. J., Bourgeois, F. and Melendez, F. (1980) Geochemistry and petrology of Miocene (Alcanar) carbonate source beds, Casablanca Field, Tarragona Basin, Spain. (Abstract) in *Symposium on the Petroleum Geochemistry and Source Rock Potential of Carbonate Rocks*. Annual Meeting of the Geological Society of America, 1980, (Atlanta, Georgia).

de Mayo, P. (1963) *Molecular Rearrangements*. Interscience Publishers. p. 416.

Ensminger, A., Joly, G. and Albrecht, P. (1978) Rearranged steranes in sediments and crude oils. *Tetr. Lett.*, 1575–1578.

Fu, P. P. and Harvey, R. G. (1978) Dehydrogenation of polycyclic hydroaromatic compounds. *Chem. Rev.* **78**, 317–361.

Harper, S. H., Kon, G. A. R. and Ruzicka, F. C. J. (1934) Synthesis of polycyclic compounds related to the sterols, Part II, Diels's hydrocarbon $C_{18}H_{16}$. *J. Chem. Soc.*, 124–128.

Goodwin, T. W. (1973) Comparative biochemistry of sterols in eukaryotic microorganisms. In *Lipids and Biomembranes of Eukaryotic Microorganisms*. Ed. by Erwin, J. A. Academic Press, New York, pp. 1–40.

Kirk, D. N. and Shaw, P. M. (1975) Backbone rearrangements of steroidal 5-enes. *J. Chem. Soc. Perkin I*, 2284–2294.

Ludwig, B., Hussler, G., Wehrung, P. and Albrecht, P. (1981) C_{26}–C_{29} Triaromatic steroid derivatives in sediments and petroleums. *Tetr. Lett.* **22**, 3313–3316.

Mackenzie, A. S., Lamb, N. A. and Maxwell, J. R. (in press a) Steroid hydrocarbons and the thermal history of sediments. *Nature*.

Mackenzie, A. S., Lewis, C. A. and Maxwell, J. R. (in press b) Molecular parameters of maturation in the Toarcian shales, Paris Basin, France — V. Laboratory thermal alteration studies.

Mackenzie, A. S., Ren-wei, Li, Maxwell, J. R., Moldowan, J. M. and Seifert, W. K. (this volume) Molecular measurement of thermal maturation in the Overthrust Belt, Wyoming, U.S.A.

Mair, B. J. and Martinez-Pico (1962) Composition of the trinuclear aromatic portion of heavy gas oil and light lubricating distillate. *Proc. Am. Petrol. Inst.* **42**, Section 3, 173.

McKervey, M. A., Rooney, J. J. and Samman, N. G. (1973) A novel mechanism for 1,2-bond shift isomerizations of alkanes on noble metals. *J. Catal.* **30**, 330–331.

Moldowan, J. M., Seifert, W. K., Haley, M. J. and Djerassi, C. (1980) Proof of structure by synthesis of 5α, 14β, 17β(H)-cholestane (20R), a major petroleum sterane. Correction of previous assignment. *Geochim. Cosmochim. Acta* **44**, 1613.

Neidle, S., Rogers, D. and Hurtsthouse, M. B. (1972) Crystal and molecular structure of viridin. *J. Chem. Soc. Perkin II*, 760–766.

Nes, W. R. and Nes, W. D. (1980) In *Lipids in Evolution*. Ed. by Kritchevsky, D. Plenum Press, New York.

Petrov, A. A., Pustil'nikova, S. D., Abriutina, N. N. and Kagramonova, G. R. (1976) Petroleum steranes and triterpanes. *Neftekhimiia* **16**, 411–427.

Rubinstein, I., Sieskind, O. and Albrecht, P. (1975) Rearranged sterenes in a shale: Occurrence and simulated formation. *J. Chem. Soc. Perkin I*, 1833–1836.

Schaefle, J. (1979) Marqueurs biologiques hydroaromatiques de sédiments et pétroles. PhD Thesis, L'Universite Louis Pasteur de Strasbourg.

Schaefle, J., Ludwig, B., Albrecht, P. and Ourisson, G. (1978) Aromatic hydrocarbons from geological sources, VI. New aromatic steroid derivatives in sediments and crude oils. *Tetr. Lett.*, 4163–4166.

Scheuer, P. J. (1973) 'Chemistry of Marine Natural Products', Academic Press, New York.

Seifert, W. K. (1975) Carboxylic acids in petroleum and sediments. *Progress in the Chemistry of Organic Natural Products*, Vol. 32, Springer-Verlag, Berlin. pp. 1–49.

Seifert, W. K. (1980) Impact of Treibs' discovery of porphyrins on present day biological marker organic geochemistry. *Proc. Treibs Internat. Symposium*, Munich, July 1979.

Seifert, W. K. and Moldowan, J. M. (1978) Applications of steranes, terpanes, and monoaromatics to the maturation, migration, and source of crude oils. *Geochim. Cosmochim. Acta* **42**, 77–95.

Seifert, W. K. and Moldowan, J. M. (1979) The effect of biodegradation on steranes and terpanes in crude oil. *Geochim. Cosmochim. Acta* **43**, 111–126.

Seifert, W. K. and Moldowan, J. M. (1980) The effect of thermal stress on source rock quality as measured by hopane stereochemistry. *Advances in Organic Geochemistry 1979*. Ed. by Douglas, A. G. and Maxwell, J. R. pp. 229–237.

Seifert, W. K. and Moldowan, J. M. (1981) Paleoreconstruction by biological markers. *Geochim. Cosmochim. Acta* **45**, 783–794.

Seifert, W. K., Moldowan, J. M. and Jones, R. W. (1980) Application of biological marker chemistry to petroleum exploration. *Proc. Tenth World Petroleum Congress*, Bucharest, Romania, September 1979. Paper SP8. Heyden & Sons, London, pp. 425–440.

Seifert, W. K., Carlson, R. M. K. and Moldowan, J. M. (1981) Geomimetic synthesis and structure assignment of monoaromatized petroleum steranes. 182nd ACS National Meeting. New York, NY, August 1981, Abstract No. 20.

Sineriz, B. G., Querol, R., Castillo, F. and Arribas, J. R. F. (1980) A New Hydrocarbon Province in the Western Mediterranean. *Proc. Tenth World Petroleum Congress*, Bucharest, Romania, September 1979. Paper PD4(4). Heyden & Sons, London.

Spyckerelle, Ch. (1975) Constituants aromatiques de sediments. PhD Thesis, L'Universite Louis Pasteur de Strasbourg.

Tissot, B., Oudin, J. L. and Pelet, R. (1972) Critères d'origine at d'évolution des pétroles. Application a l'étude geochimique des bassins sédimentaires. *Advances in Organic Geochemistry 1971*. Ed. by von Gaertner, H. R. and Wehner, H. Pergamon Press, Oxford. pp. 113–134.

Tissot, B., Espitalié, J., Deroo, G., Tempere, C. and Jonathan, D. (1974) Origine et migration des hydrocarbures dans le Sahara oriental (Algeria). *Advances in Organic Geochemistry 1973*. Ed. by Tissot, B. and Bienner, F. Editions Technip, Paris. pp. 315–334.

Tökés, L., LaLonda, R. T. and Djerassi, C. (1967) Mass spectrometry in structural and stereochemical problems CXXVI. Synthesis and fragmentation behavior of deuterium labeled 17-keto steroids. *J. Org. Chem.* **32**, 1012–1019.

Turner, A. G. (1972) Selective ring-C aromatization of steroids. *Chem. Ind.*, 932–933.

Zubenko, V. G., Pustil'nikova, S. D., Abryutina, N. N. and Petrov, Al. A. (1980) Petroleum monoaromatic hydrocarbons on the steroid type. *Neftekhimiia* **20**, 490–497; *C.A. Abstracts* **94**, 65932r (1981).

Zubenko, V. G., Vorob'eva, N. S., Zemskova, Z. K., Penk, T. and Petrov, Al. A. (1981) Equilibrium of cis- and trans-isomers of octahydrophenanthrenes as structural fragments of monoaromatic steroids. *Neftekhimiia* **21**, 323–328; *C.A. Abstracts* **95**, 149806m (1981).

Advances in Organic Geochemistry 1981, pp. 725–732
© *John Wiley & Sons Limited, 1983*

Low Temperature Degradation of Carotenoids as a Model for Early Diagenesis in Recent Sediments

J. D. Byers and J. G. Erdman

Phillips Petroleum Company, Bartlesville, Oklahoma 74004

The respective pathways of degradation of the carotenoid pigments lead to distinctive compounds which are stable over long intervals of geologic time. Since the kinetic rates of the competitive reactions vary, the type and relative amounts of the products provide a key to the ecological origin of the source material and the changes which it has undergone prior to and immediately following deposition. *Meso*-carotene; lexene; philene; 1,1,3-trimethylcyclohexane; *p*-xylene; 1-methyl-3-ethylbenzene; 1,6-dimethylnaphthalene; 2,3-dimethylnaphthalene and 2,7-dimethylnaphthalene, have been identified as thermal degradation products of β,β-carotene. At temperatures characteristic of aquatic environments, fucoxanthin degrades more rapidly than β,β-carotene. The activation energies for the thermal decomposition of fucoxanthin and β,β-carotene are 25.1 and 34.6 Kcal mol^{-1} respectively. At 5°C, typical of the ocean bottom temperature, those activation energies represent half lives of 5.2 $\times 10^3$ and 1.4×10^6 years respectively. Ligh hydrocarbons, such as toluene, *m*-xylene, β-ionene and 2,6-dimethylnaphthalene, therefore, should appear very early in the sedimentary column.

INTRODUCTION

The highly colored, brown, red, and yellow carotenoid pigments are isoprenoid natural products characterized by a chain of conjugated double bonds with methyl groups spaced along the chain. Many carotenoids have terminal cyclohexyl or cyclohexenyl groups with 1,1,5-trimethyl substitution.

Beta,beta-carotene (Fig. 1), a carotene or hydrocarbon product, is one of the four most abundant carotenoids in plants inhabiting the land and ocean margins. Fucoxanthin (Fig. 1), a xanthophyll or oxygen containing product, is one of the most abundant carotenoids in marine organisms.

The carotenoid pigments make up roughly one per cent of all the organic matter in marine biomass.

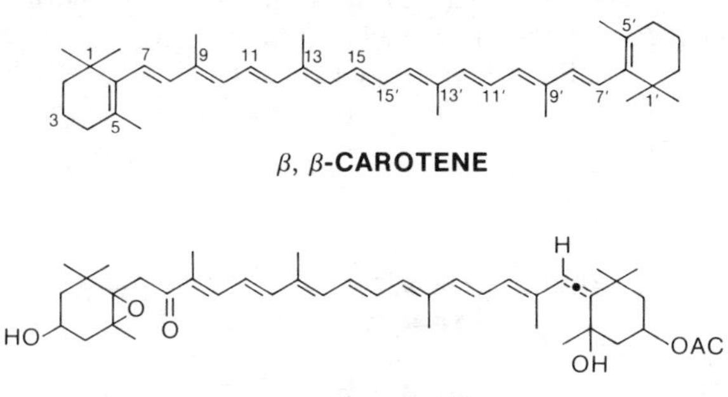

β, β-CAROTENE

FUCOXANTHIN

Fig. 1. Skeletal formulas of two typical carotenoid pigments.

Schwendinger (1969) has estimated that 1.2 million trillion tons of these pigments are generated each year in the marine environment.

The time involved in the transport of organic matter containing carotenoid pigments varies. Fine detritus may be transported down rivers and circulated in ocean currents for years before final deposition. Long residence times in the water column may result in oxidative and photochemical degradation of the carotenoid molecule. Conversely, carotenoids contained in organic matter may be ingested by zooplankton and only slightly metabolized. They may be protected from oxygen and light by rapid transport to the ocean floor in relatively large and dense fecal pellets. Once they become a part of the sedimentary organic matter, oxidative and photochemical processes normally decrease, resulting in the preservation of some of the polyene products.

Numerous reports of carotenoids in sediments have appeared in the literature. Reviews by Vallentyne (1960) and Schwendinger (1969) summarize data on carotenoids in sediments prior to 1969.

Carotenoids are present in many different types of sedimentary environments (Schwendinger and Erdman, 1963). The oldest known sediment reported to contain carotenoids is a lower Miocene sample from the Blake–Bahama basin in the western North Atlantic Ocean (Cardosa *et al.*, 1975). Beta,beta-carotene, canthaxanthin, zeaxanthin, and spheroidenone have been identified in 340 000 years b.p. sediments from the Cariaco Trench off Venezuela (Watts and Maxwell, 1977).

This investigation seeks to answer three basic questions:

1. Which petroleum-type hydrocarbons, or intermediates leading to them, are formed in the anaerobic degradation of the carotenoids?
2. Is it necessary to invoke biochemical pathways for generation of petroleum-like hydrocarbons from carotenoids or can these compounds be formed at significant rates without enzymatic catalysis?
3. Can the products formed in the thermal and oxidative degradation of carotenoids, specifically *beta,beta*-carotene, be indicators of the time of transport and the environmental conditions encountered during transport and subsequently in the sediments?

EXPERIMENTAL

Because of the sensitivity of the carotenoids to light and oxygen, procedures were carried out in a laboratory illuminated with yellow light and in an inert atmosphere (Model 1024, Forma Scientific Company). The light was of the type recommended for the processing of autopositive film. The atmosphere of the chamber consisted of 93 per cent nitrogen and 7 per cent hydrogen which was continuously circulated through a palladium catalyst to remove any atmospheric oxygen that might have diffused into the chamber. The quality of the atmosphere was monitored using Gas Pak disposal anaerobic indicators which are sensitive to 5 ppm of oxygen. Oxygen was removed from solvents by vigorously bubbling argon through the solvent for 60 minutes. This essentially removes all oxygen as indicated by the Gas Pak indicators. Solvent was then stored in the anaerobic chamber.

Mass spectra of the polyene products were obtained by solid probe injection (Finnigan Model 4000 mass spectrometer). Very rapid heating of the probe to 300 °C resulted in minor thermal degradation prior to introduction of the molecules into the 70 eV beam. The mass spectra showed intense molecular ions.

NMR data were obtained on a Varian EM-390 spectrometer operating at 90 MHz. $CDCl_3$ was used as a solvent with TMS (tetramethylsilane) as a standard.

Carotenoids

Fucoxanthin was extracted from a *Fucus* species common to Cape Cod. The freshly collected algae were kept frozen until extracted. The algae (371 g) were ground with acetone in a mechanical blender. After removal of the acetone by vacuum evaporation, the aqueous suspension was extracted with ethyl acetate. The combined extracts were dried over magnesium sulfate and concentrated under vacuum. The residue was fractionated on C18 bonded phase packing using methanol as eluant. The fucoxanthin fraction was concentrated and crystallization induced by the addition of low-boiling petroleum ether. Approximately 75 to 100 mg of pure fucoxanthin were obtained. IR,

optical, and mass spectra indicated that the product was isolated without significant decomposition.

Beta,beta-carotene (0.5 g) and *n*-dodecane (3 ml) were sealed under vacuum in thick-walled glass tubes. Thermolysis at 170 °C for 12–18 hours gave the intermediates *meso*-carotene, lexene, and philene.

Thermolysis of crystalline *beta,beta*-carotene in an evacuated sealed glass tube at 275 to 300 °C for 45 minutes produced a yellow oil that contained a number of cycloalkane and aromatic hydrocarbons. Heating a mixture of *beta,beta*-carotene and *n*-dodecane at 170 °C in the absence of oxygen for 7–14 days produced a similar product mixture.

The individual components of the product mixture were identified by GC–MS (Perkin–Elmer Sigma II chromatograph and a Kratos MS 24 mass spectrometer). Separations were made with an SE-54 glass capillary column (60 m × 0.24 mm). Flow rates were approximately one milliliter per minute. A temperature program rate of 4 °C per minute from 44 to 300 °C was used. Hexane was used as solvent. The mass spectrometer was operated in the EI mode at 70 eV. Standard compounds were used as references by co-injection.

Thermal degradation of beta,beta-carotene kinetic studies

Beta,beta-carotene was dissolved in mesitylene to a concentration giving an optical absorbance of 0.9 to 1.2 at 445 nm in 1 mm quartz spectrometer cells. The cells were sealed under vacuum after cooling to dry ice temperatures. The cells were placed in a thermostated oil bath with the temperature controlled to ±0.02 °C. Three runs at each temperature (150, 160, and 170 °C) were carried out. At designated intervals, the cell was removed from the oil bath and immediately cooled to room temperature. An absorbance scan from 320 to 600 nm was made using a Perkin–Elmer Model 320 spectrophotometer. The cell was then returned to the oil bath for further reaction. Warm-up and cool-down times were considered negligible. Since the reaction rate is essentially zero at room temperature, the time at room temperature is not included in calculation of rate constants. An independent plot of absorbance against concentration indicated that Beer's law is obeyed in the concentration ranges used in these experiments. Rate constants were obtained from plots of the natural logarithm of absorbance against time. Activation energies were obtained from plots of the logarithm of the rate constant against the reciprocal of the absolute

Thermal degradation of fucoxanthin — kinetic studies

Kinetic data were obtained in a manner similar to that for *beta,beta*-carotene. Because of a faster rate of degradation, lower temperatures (120, 140, and 160 °C) were used.

Synthesis of lexene — (Stern, 1970)

Hydrogen chloride (0.368 g, 0.01 mol) in methanol (2.7 ml) was added at 30–35 °C to a stirred mixture of triphenylphosphine (2.87 g, 0.011 mol) and *beta*-ionly acetate (2.53 g, 0.01 mol) in methanol (4 ml). After four hours, this solution and a solution of potassium hydroxide (0.778 g, 0.0139 mol) in methanol (3 ml) were added simultaneously to a stirred slurry of retinal (1 g, 0.0035 mol) in methanol (3 ml) at 0 °C. After addition, the reaction mixture was poured into water and extracted with diethyl ether. The combined ethereal extracts were washed with water and then dried over magnesium sulfate. Following filtration, the solvent was removed under reduced pressure. Chromatography on alumina (Brockman Activity I) using hexane as eluant gave the purified product in 55% yield.

^{1}H-NMR (CDCl$_3$, ppm) 1.05, S, 12 H, gem-dimethyl; 1.40–1.70, 8 H, –CH$_2$–; 1.70, 6 H, C=C–CH$_3$; 1.95, 13 H, in-chain methyls and –CH$_2$–C=C; 6.0–6.8, 9 H, olefinic protons.

IR (cm^{-1}, neat) 2840–3150, CH; 970, *trans*-alkene; 1363, 1387, gem-dimethyls, 1380, methyl.

MS (*m/e*) 444 (parent ion), 442, 429, 399, 359, 333, 307, 267, 239, 211, 159, 133, 119, and 105.

UV (hexane) = 386 nm.

Isolation and characterization of the polyene intermediates

Lexene, philene, and *meso*-carotene were separated from other reaction products by chromatography on magnesium hydroxide using hexane as eluant. The first yellow fractions contained mainly the three polyene intermediates. *Meso*-carotene was separated from lexene and philene by HPLC on 5 micron Spherisorb cyano packing (60 cm × 4.1 mm) using hexane as solvent. The flow rate was 0.6 ml min^{-1}. The absorbance at 436 nm was monitored. The first eluting peak contained lexene and philene.

Lexene was separated from philene by HPLC on 5 micron C18 packing (Waters Radial Compression Column, 8 mm × 10 cm) using methanol as eluant. The flow rate was 2 ml min^{-1}. The absorbance at 436 nm was monitored. Retention volumes of philene and lexene were 35.2 and 39.2 ml, respectively.

Lexene isolated by this procedure exhibited identical ^{1}H-NMR, MS, IR, and UV spectra to the synthesized product.

Philene exhibited the following spectral characteristics. ^{1}H-NMR (CDCl$_3$, ppm) 1.05, s, 12 H, gemdimethyls; 1.40–1.70, 8 H, –CH$_2$–, 1.70, 6 H, C=G–CH$_3$; 1.95, 10 H, in-chain methyls and CH$_2$–C=C; 6.0–6.8, 10 H, olefinic protons.

UV (hexane) = 389 nm.

MS (*m/e*) 430 (parent ion), 428, 415, 378, 361, 346, 320, 265, 240, 225, 201, 175, 157, 133, and 109.

IR (cm^{-1}, neat) 2840–3150, CH; 970, *trans*-alkene; 1363, 1387, gem-dimethyls; 1380, methyl.

Calculated for C$_{32}$H$_{46}$: 430.3600 *m/e* Found: 430.3584 *m/e*.

Meso-carotene exhibited the following spectral characteristics.

UV (hexane) = 405 nm; shoulders at 380 and 430 nm.

MS (*m/e*) parent ion at 536.

Hydrogenation of lexene and philene

Each polyene intermediate (1 mg) was dissolved in ethyl acetate (5 ml). Palladium on activated carbon (100 ml) was added and the suspension stirred under a hydrogen gas pressure of 50 psi for eight hours at room temperature. The catalyst was removed by filtration and the sample concentrated *in vacuo*. No UV maxima were noted after the hydrogenation.

IR (cm^{-1}, neat) 2830–2950 CH; 1458, –CH$_2$–; 1362, 1380 gem-dimethyls; 1370, methyl. All saturated derivatives had similar IR spectra.

MS of saturated philene (*m/e*) 446 (parent ion), 431, 390, 291, 249, 221, 179, 138, 125 (base peak), and 111.

MS of saturated lexene (*m/e*) 460 (parent ion), 445, 404, 305, 249, 235, 179, 138, 125 (base peak), and 111.

RESULTS AND DISCUSSION

There are presently three recognized zones of carotenoid degradation: 1. water column during transport to and into the sediment; 2. sediment water interface where anaerobic organisms are abundant; and 3. deep in the sediment where microbial activity is limited and thermal alteration predominates.

The carotenoids are degraded by interaction with light and dissolved oxygen in the water and sediment columns. Partial oxidation to products such as 5,6-epoxy-carotene and mutatochrome may decrease the yield of cycloalkane and aromatic hydrocarbons but not eliminate their formation (Fig. 2).

Extensive oxidation, to short chain ketones like *beta*-ionone, may decrease or eliminate the potential of these products to yield the petroleum-type hydrocarbons derived by thermolytic degradation in the absence of light or oxygen (Fig. 2). The generation of hydrocarbons from the carotenoids is directly linked to the concentration of oxygen present in the water and upper

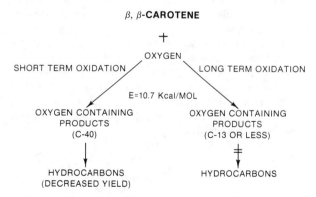

Fig. 2. Pathways and kinetics of the degradation of β,β-carotene in the presence of oxygen.

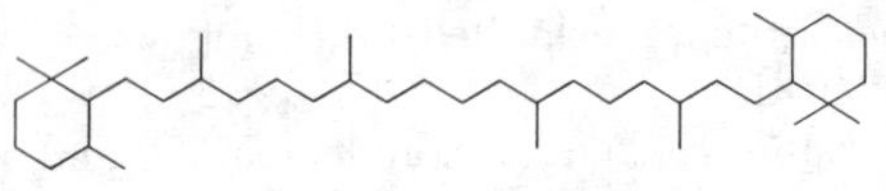

PERHYDRO-*β*, *β*-CAROTENE

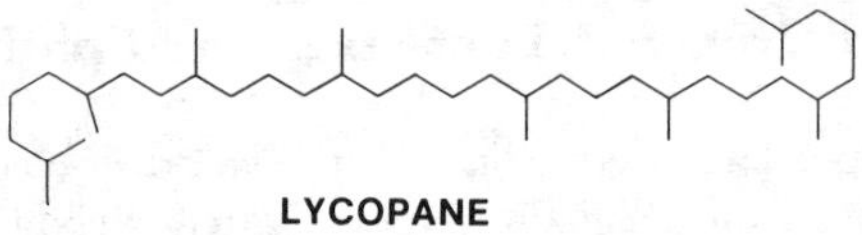

LYCOPANE

Fig. 3. Skeletal formulas of hydrogenated carotenoids identified in deep sea sediments.

sediments and the duration of contact. Therefore, higher yields of petroleum-type hydrocarbons might be expected in environments where the organic source material has undergone limited exposure to light and oxygen.

The polyene chains of *beta,beta*-carotene and other carotenoids are highly susceptible to chemical and biochemical reduction. In shallow sediments the hydrogen probably is the product of anaerobes such as *Clostridium butyricum*. Carotenoids in such sedimentary environments may undergo a reduction reaction with the time scale of the process depending upon the structure of the carotenoid molecule. Watts and coworkers (1977) found that zeaxanthin and canthaxanthin (xanthophylls) were partially reduced over the 340 000 year time period covered by their samples. *Beta,beta*-carotene showed no evidence of reduction in the same samples.

However, fully hydrogenated carotenoids have been observed (Fig. 3). Perhydro-*beta,beta*-carotene was identified in Green River shale by Murphy and co-workers (1967). In several other deep-sea sediments, Simoneit and co-workers (1971) identified perhydro-*beta,beta*-carotene as well as an alkene, $C_{40}H_{74}$, having the carbon skeleton of *beta,beta*-carotene. Lycopane, the fully hydrogenated analogue of lycopene, and several partially hydrogenated analogues were found in the Messel shale by Kimble and co-workers (1974).

Reduction of the double bonds in the carotenoid chain precludes a low energy pathway to the formation of lower molecular weight cycloalkane and aromatic hydrocarbons. Fossil rock lipids and petroleum derived from initially strongly reducing sediments may contain the hydrogenated carotenoids but be deficient in the lower molecular weight cycloalkane and aromatic hydrocarbons.

In environments where the oxidative and reducing conditions mentioned above are limited, the degradation of polyene pigments like *beta,beta*-carotene is primarily thermolytic. Cycloalkane, substituted benzoid, tetrahydronaphthalenic, and naphthalenic hydrocarbons can be generated in good yields at moderate temperatures.

Early investigators reported the thermal degradation of polyene pigments such as bixin, capxanthin, and *beta,beta*-carotene to yield aromatic hydrocarbons among which were identified toluene, *m*-xylene, and 2,6-dimethylnaphthalene (Van Hasselt, 1911; Zechmeister and Cholnoky, 1930; Kuhn and Winterstein, 1932,

1933). Day and Erdman (1965) identified *beta*-ionene (1,1,6-trimethyl-1,2,3,4-tetrahydronaphthalene) as a product of the thermal degradation of *beta,beta*-carotene. Edmunds and Johnston (1965) identified 1,2-dihydro-1,1,6-trimethylnaphthalene, 3-(2,2,6-trimethylcyclohexyl) toluene, and *beta*-ionene (49.5 per cent yield) as degradation products of *beta,beta*-carotene heated *in vacuo* at 300 °C.

Erdman (1961) proposed that the carotenoids in recent aquatic sediments are the precursors of part of the aromatic fraction of petroleum. Mulik and Erdman (1963) demonstrated that thermolysis of Santa Barbara, Calif., basin sediments, at temperatures used to thermally degrade *beta,beta*-carotene resulted in the formation of toluene, *meta*- and/or *para*-xylene, 2,6-dimethylnaphthalene, and *beta*-ionene. Ikan and co-workers (1975) found that heating Tanner basin sediments to 100 °C or higher caused degradation of *beta,beta*-carotene. Toluene and *m*-xylene were recognized among the products. Sediment heated to 15 °C yielded in addition, *beta*-ionene and 2,6-dimethylnaphthalene.

Thermolytic degradation products

Compounds identified as thermolytic degradation products of *beta,beta*-carotene under oxygen-free conditions are listed in Table 1. The numbers in parenthesis indicate relative product abundance with (1) indicating greatest abundance. The lower case (t) indicates formation in trace amounts. The lower case (i) indicates isolable intermediates, compounds which will with time degrade to the cycloalkane and aromatic products listed.

The compounds *meso*-carotene, lexene, philene, 1,1,3-trimethyl-cyclohexane, *p*-xylene, 1-methyl-3-ethylbenzene, 1,6-dimethyl-naphthalene, 1,5-dimethyl-naphthalene, 2,3-dimethylnaphthalene, and 2,7-dimethylnaphthalene have not been previously reported as thermal degradation products of *beta,beta*-carotene. *Meso*-carotene and philene have not been previously described.

Table 1.
Anoxic thermal derivatives of β,β-carotene.

Alkanes
1,1,3-trimethylcyclohexane (5)

Alkenes
Meso-carotene, MW 536 (i)
Lexene, MW 444 (i)
Philene, MW 430 (i)

Aromatics
Toluene (2)
m-xylene (3)
o-xylene (t)
p-xylene (t)
1-methyl-3-ethylbenzene (6)
β-ionene (1)
2,6-dimethylnaphthalene (4)
1,6-dimethylnaphthalene (7)
other dimethylnaphthalenes (t)

Identification of intermediate products

By interrupting the degradation of *beta,beta*-carotene at an early stage, lexene, philene, and *meso*-carotene can be isolated in good yields. The yields vary with the temperature and length of thermolysis but may be as high as 30, 20, and 5 per cent, respectively.

Meso-carotene has the same molecular weight as *beta,beta*-carotene. The shift in absorption maximum from 436 nm for *beta,beta*-carotene to 405 nm for *meso*-carotene indicates a decrease in the length of polyene conjugation. Therefore, the intermediate is formed by a rearrangement involving interruption of the conjugated polyene backbone of *beta,beta*-carotene.

Lexene has eight conjugated double bonds and a molecular weight of 444, corresponding to the loss of C_7H_8 from *beta, beta*-carotene. Lexene was independently synthesized according to the procedure of Stern (1970). The synthetic product proved identical to the product isolated from the thermal degradation mixture of *beta,beta*-carotene.

Philene has a molecular weight of 430, corresponding to a loss of C_8H_{10} from *beta,beta*-carotene. As in lexene, there are eight conjugated double bonds. NMR data indicate the presence of two in-chain methyl groups. The data are consistent with the structure shown in Fig. 4.

Reaction mechanisms

The polyene backbone of *beta,beta*-carotene with eleven conjugated double bonds renders the molecule very reactive. The extended *pi* electron cloud makes many types of pericyclic processes energetically possible. The predominance of a small number of thermal degradation products indicates that only a few of the many possible thermal reaction pathways are favorable.

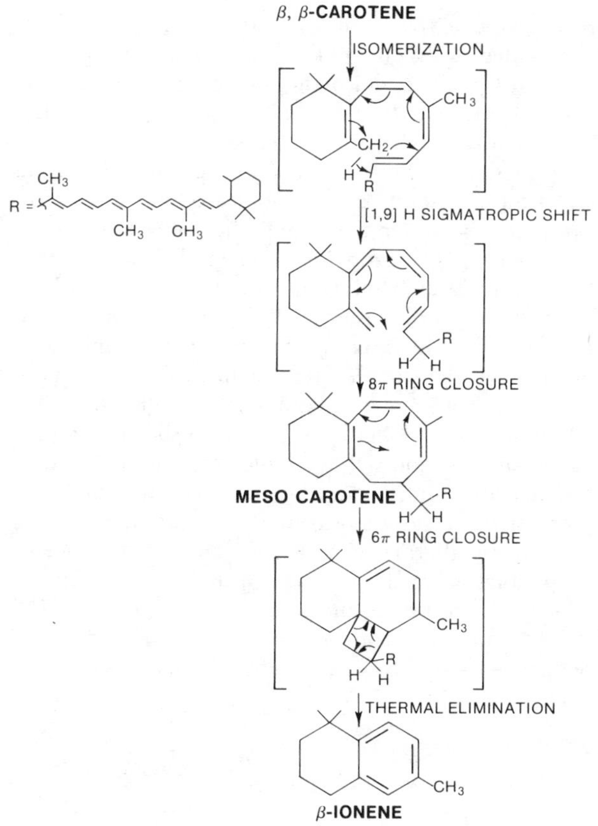

Fig. 5. Proposed mechanism for the thermolytic degradation of β,β-carotene to *meso*-carotene and β-ionene.

Studies of the thermal degradation of isotopically labeled *beta,beta*-carotene and related open chain conjugated olefins by Schwieter and co-workers (1969), Enzell and co-workers (1969), Kjøsen and co-workers (1971), and Liaaen-Jensen (1977) indicate that

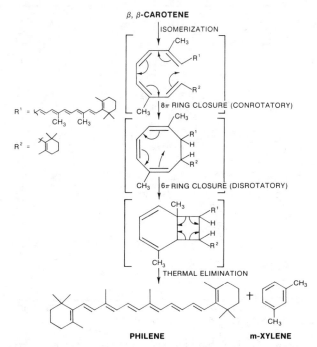

Fig. 4. Proposed mechanism for the thermolytic degradation of β,β-carotene to philene and *m*-xylene.

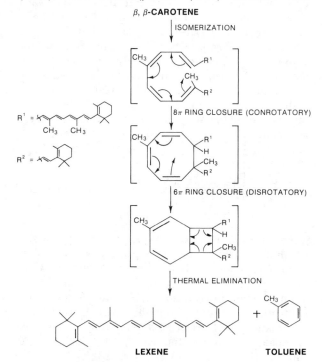

Fig. 6. Proposed mechanism for the thermolytic degradation of β,β-carotene to lexene and toluene.

reactions take place in well defined regions of the conjugated olefin chain. Toluene was shown to derive from the C_{10}–$C_{10'}$ region of the conjugated olefin chain of *beta,beta*-carotene whereas *m*-xylene derives from the C_8–$C_{8'}$ region.

In Figs. 4, 5, and 6 are shown proposed mechanisms for transformation of *beta,beta*-carotene into *meso*-carotene, lexene, and philene. These mechanisms are consistent with existing experimental data and the Woodward and Hoffmann (1970) rules of orbital symmetry. Zechmeister (1960) has shown that isomerization takes place in open chain conjugated olefins exposed to elevated temperatures. A quasi-equilibrium of geometrical isomers is established in 10 to 60 minutes in cyclohexane solution. As shown in Fig. 5, steric isomerization of the *beta,beta*-carotene, followed by a sigmatropic shift and a ring closure forms a molecule postulated to be *meso*-carotene. An additional ring closure and thermal elimination can give *beta*-ionene. A parallel mechanism (Fig. 6) has been proposed which leads to lexene and toluene (Vetter *et al.*, 1971). Philene and *m*-xylene are formed from a different segment of the polyene chain by a similar mechanism (Fig. 4).

Kinetics

Following the termination of biochemical reactions in the upper layer of aquatic sediments, further degradation of biomass to fossil organic matter is mostly thermolytic. It is usually assumed that most degradation reactions obey Arrhenius pseudo first-order kinetics.

Application of the Arrhenius equation is complicated by the fact that for each rock unit in a sedimentary section of a particular basin there is a complex relation between temperature and time extending back to when deposition took place. Furthermore, if the genesis of a particular fossil product is being considered, it is necessary to recognize that only a portion of either the entire organic biomass or even of a single compound entering a sediment can ultimately be converted to the fossil product. This subject has been treated in depth by Erdman (1972). In 1975, Erdman provided a modification of the Arrhenius equation which took these factors into account:

$$P = C_0 \left[1 - \exp\left\{ -A \sum_{i=1}^{i+n} (\exp[-E/RT_{i+1}]) \right\} \right]$$

where P = product; C_0 = proportion of precursors which ultimately will be converted to product, P; A = frequency factor (constant); E = activation energy; R = universal gas constant; and T_{i+1} is the temperature during the time interval (t_i, t_{i+1}). Methods for deducing the temperature–time relationship, particularly for passive margin basins are being developed by a number of investigators (Royden and Keen, 1980; Sclater and Christie, 1980; Watts and Steckler, 1981).

The implied use of a single activation energy is unacceptable except in rare instances involving the

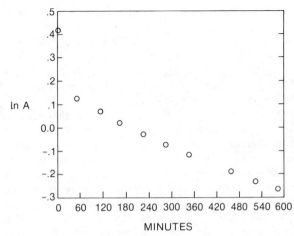

Fig. 7. Kinetic plot of the rate of decrease of optical absorbance of β,β-carotene with time at 170 °C. Light path is 1.0 mm.

degradation of a single precursor by a one step reaction. For the genesis of fossil organic matter, such as petroleum or coal, many parallel reactions are taking place. Even a single compound may be formed by two or more reactions with different activation energies. Accordingly, complex fossil materials develop both in composition and amount over a wide interval of geological time.

One objective of the present study was to determine and compare the rate constants and thence the activation energies for the thermolytic degradation of several typical carotenoids. These reactions probably are among the fastest, that is have the lowest activation energies, of those that produce constituents of the condensate and naphtha fractions of petroleum.

A typical plot of the natural logarithm of absorbance versus time for the degradation of *beta,beta*-carotene is

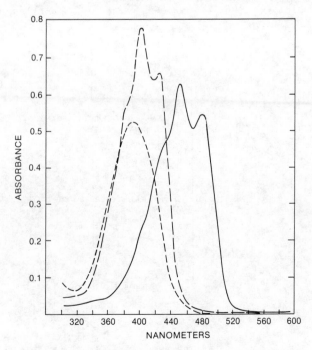

Fig. 8. Optical absorption spectra of β,β-carotene, ———; *meso*-carotene, – – –; and lexene and philene, - - - -. The spectra of lexene and philene are essentially superimpossible.

shown in Fig. 7. There is an initial rapid decrease in absorbance as a consequence of isomerization. The degradation of *beta,beta*-carotene then proceeds more slowly and degradation follows first order kinetics. The activation energy derived from a plot of ln k against 1/T K is 34.6 Kcal per mole. At 5 °C, which approximates the temperature of the uppermost layer of ocean bottom sediments, the half-life would be 1.4 million years. The activation energy for the equivalent phase of degradation of fucoxanthin is 25.1 Kcal per mole. For fucoxanthin, the half-life at 5 °C would be 5.2 thousand years.

The degradation of the colored intermediates, *meso*-carotene, lexene, and philene proceeds more slowly than *beta,beta*-carotene. This accounts for their increase in concentration with time relative to the concentration of *beta,beta*-carotene.

The degradation of *beta,beta*-carotene is much faster in the presence of oxygen. An activation energy for the oxidative degradation of *beta,beta*-carotene of 10.7 Kcal per mole was reported by El-Tinay and Chichester (1970). At 5 °C in the water column, the estimated half-life for this reaction is only 6.3 hours.

In Table 2, the activation energies and half-lives for the thermal degradation of *beta,beta*-carotene and fucoxanthin are compared with those for amino acids and hydrocarbons. The thermal degradation of amino acids and hydrocarbons is believed to contribute to intermediate and late stages of petroleum genesis. At ocean bottom or near surface sediment temperatures, the amino acid and hydrocarbon degradations would not be expected to proceed to a significant extent in all geological time. For them to occur, the elevated temperatures which develop with increasing depth are necessary. It is evident from these data that genesis of fossil organic matter such as petroleum must proceed over a tremendous interval of geological time and a wide range of temperature.

Table 2.

Activation energies and half lives of some reactions typical to the generation of fossil organic matter including petroleum.

FAST

β,β-carotene
  E = 32 Kcal mol^{-1} Toluene
  H.L. = 1.4 × 10^6 years at 5 °C   *m*-xylene
  Fucoxanthin   2,6-dimethyl
  E = 25 Kcal mol^{-1} naphthalene
  H.L. = 5.2 × 10^3 years at 5 °C   other HC's

INTERMEDIATE

Alanine (cH$_3$CHOOH) ————→ Ethylene
  | carbon dioxide
  NH$_2$ ammonia
  E = 45 Kcal mol^{-1}
  H.L. = 100 × 10^6 years at 55 °C

SLOW

n-alkane (CH$_3$CH$_2$CH$_2$ . . .) ————→ Methane
  E = 63 Kcal mol^{-1} higher HC's
  H.L. = 200 × 10^6 years at 182 °C

CONCLUSION

At tbe beginning of the paper, three questions were posed and answers provided thereafter.

What petroleum-type hydrocarbons or their intermediates are formed in the anaerobic degradation of the carotenoids? For *beta,beta*-carotene there are four major products: *beta*-ionene, toluene, *m*-xylene, and 2,6-dimethylnaphthalene. Minor components in decreasing amounts are 1,1,3-trimethylcyclohexane, 1-methyl-3-ethylbenzene, 1,6-dimethylnaphthalene, *p*-xylene, *o*-xylene, and trace amounts of the other dimethylnaphthalenes. Three polyene intermediates have been identified. The first, *meso*-carotene, has the same molecular weight as *beta,beta*-carotene but fewer than eleven conjugated double bonds. Lexene and philene, both with eight conjugated double bonds, appear to be formed by the expulsion of toluene and *m*-xylene, respectively, from *beta,beta*-carotene.

REFERENCES

Cardoso, J. N., Wardroper, A. M. K., Watts, C. D., Barnes, P. J., Maxwell, J. R., Eglinton, G., Mound, D. G. and Speecs, G. C. Preliminary Organic Geochemical Analyses. In *Initial Reports of the DSDP Project* Vol. XLIV. Ed. by Benson. pp. 617–623.

Day, W. C. and Erdman, J. G. (1963) *Science* **141**, 808.

Edmunds, F. S. and Johnstone, R. A. W. (1965) *J. Chem. Soc.*, 2892–2897.

El-Tinay, A. H. and Chichester, C. O. (1970) *J. Organic Chem.* **35**, 2290–2293.

Enzell, C. R., Francis, G. W. and Jensen, S. L. (1969) *Acta Chem. Scand.* **23**, 727.

Erdman, J. G. (1961) *Geochim. Cosmochim. Acta* **22**, 16.

Erdman, J. G. (1972) Princeton University Conference No. 109, March 10–11. In *Petroleum and Global Tectonics*. Ed. by Fischer, G. and Judsen, S. Princeton University Press (1975). pp. 225–248.

Erdman, J. G. (1975) Proc. 9th World Petroleum Congress **2**, Tokyo. pp. 139–148.

Ikan, R., Aizenshtat, A., Baedecker, M. J. and Kaplan, I. R. (1975) *Geochim. Cosmochim. Acta* **39**, 173–185.

Kimble, B. J., Maxwell, J. R., Philp, R. P., Eglinton, G., Albrecht, P., Ensminger, A., Arpino, P. and Ourisson, G. (1974) *Geochim. Cosmochim. Acta* **38**, 1165–1181.

Kjøsen, H., Liaaen-Jensen, S. and Enzell, C. R. (1971) *Acta. Chem. Scand.* **25**, 85–93.

Kuhn, R. and Winterstein, A. (1932) *Ber. Deut. Chem. Ges.* **65**, 1873.

Kuhn, R. and Winterstein, A. (1933) *Ber. Deut. Chem. Ges.* **66**, 1733.

Liaaen-Jensen, S. (1977) *Marine Natural Products Chemistry*. Ed. by Fenical, W. H. Plenum Press, New York and London. pp. 239–259.

Mulik, J. D. and Erdman, J. G., (1963) *Science* **141**, 806.

Murphy, M. J. T., McCormick, A. and Eglinton, G. (1967) *Science* **157**, 1040–1042.

Royden, L. and Keen, C. E. (1980) *Earth and Planetary Science Letters* **51**, 343–361.

Sclater, J. G. and Christie, P. A. F. (1980) *J. Geophys. Research* **85**, 3711–3739.

Schwendinger, R. B. and Erdman, J. G. (1963) *Science* **141**, 809–810.

Schwendinger, R. B. (1969) Carotenoids. In *Organic Geochemistry, Methods and Results*. Ed. by Eglinton, G. and Murphy, M. T. J. Springer–Verlag, New York, Heidelberg, Berlin. pp. 425–437.

Schwieter, U., Englert, G., Rigassi, N. and Vetter, W. (1969) *Pure and Applied Chem.* **20**, 365–420.

Simoneit, B. R. and Burlingame, A. L. (1971) Preliminary Organic Analyses of the DSDP (JOIDES). Cores, Legs V–IX. In *Advances in Organic Geochemistry*. Ed. by Gaerther, H. R. V. and Wehner, H. Pergamon Press, Oxford. pp. 189–229.

Stern, M. H. (1970) U.S. Patent no. 3,517,067 assigned to the Eastman Kodak Company.

Valentyne, J. R. (1960) *Fossil Pigments: The Fate of the Carotenoids*. Symposia on Comparative Biology **1**, 83–105.

Van-Hasselt, J. F. B. (1911) *Rec. Trav. Chim, Pays-Bas*. **30**, 1.

Vetter, W., Englert, G., Rigassi, N. and Schwieter, U. (1971) *Carotenoids*. Ed. by Isler, O. Birkhauser–Verlag, Basel and Stuttgart. pp. 249–250.

Watts, C. D. and Maxwell, J. R. (1977) *Geochim. Cosmochim. Acta* **41**, 493.

Watts, C. D., Maxwell, J. R. and Kjøsen, H. (1977) The Potential of Carotenoids as Environmental Indicators. In *Advances in Organic Geochemistry*. 1975.

Watts, A. B. and Steckler, M. S. (1981) Oceanol. Acta, Proceedings, 26th International Geological Congress, Geology of Continental Margins Symposium 1980. Paris. pp. 143–153.

Woodward, R. B. and Hoffmann, R. (1970) *The Conservation of Orbital Symmetry*. Verlag Chemie GmbH, Academic Press Inc.

Zechmeister, L. and Cholnoky, L. V. (1930) *Ann. Chem.* **95**, 478.

Zechmeister, L. (1960) *Fortschr. Chem. Org. Naturst.* **18**, 264.

Advances in Organic Geochemistry 1981, pp. 733–745
© John Wiley & Sons Limited, 1983

Friedel-Crafts Acetylation of Petroporphyrins: A Valuable Method for Structural Elucidation and Correlation Studies

J. M. E. Quirke

*Department of Chemistry, University of Durham, Science Laboratories, South Road, Durham DH1 3LE**

Acetylation of the unsubstituted β-positions of porphyrins by the Friedel-Crafts reaction, provides a facile method for the rapid separation of petroporphyrin mixtures into their fully alkylated, and mono- and di-β-unsubstituted components. The presence of isomeric mono-β-unsubstituted petroporphyrins from Gilstonite was revealed. The applications of the derivatization method both for structural elucidation investigations and for correlation studies are discussed.

INTRODUCTION

In 1934, alkyl metalloporphyrins were first isolated from petroleums, shales, coals and bitumens (Treibs, 1934a, b). They occur mainly as complex mixtures of nickel and vanadyl complexes of two major skeletal types, the DPEP (1) and aetio (2) species:

(1)   (2)

$R^1, R^2 \ldots R^8 = H$ or alkyl β-substituents

2a $R^1 = R^3 = R^5 = R^7 = CH_3$;

         $R^2 = R^4 = R^6 = R^8 = C_2H_5$

2b $R^1 = R^3 = R^5 = R^8 = CH_3$;

         $R^2 = R^4 = COCH_3$; $R^6 = R^7$
         $= (CH_2)_2CO_2H$

2c $R^1 = R^3 = R^5 = R^8 = CH_3$;

         $R^2 = R^4 = H$; $R^6 = R^7 = (CH_2)_2CO_2H$.

---

* Present address: Department of Physical Sciences, Florida International University, Tamiams Trail, Miami Florida 33199 USA.

Recent ^{1}H nuclear magnetic resonance (NMR) studies (Quirke *et al.*, 1979) and high performance liquid chromatography (HPLC) studies (HajIbrahim *et al.*, 1981) revealed that the aetioporphyrins and possibly the DPEP porphyrins may be sub-divided into three groups:

1. porphyrins with fully alkylated β-positions (the X series);
2. porphyrins with one unsubstituted β-position (the Y series);
3. porphyrins with two unsubstituted β-positions (the Z zeries).

The geologically occurring porphyrins (petroporphyrins) have potential as maturation parameters in oil–oil and oil–source rock correlation studies (e.g. Barwise and Park, this volume; Eglinton *et al.*, 1979; Eglinton *et al.*, 1980; Mackenzie *et al.*, 1980; Flom and Thompson, 1980). The complete resolution of these porphyrin mixtures remains, however, a difficult problem (e.g. Baker and Palmer, 1978; HajIbrahim *et al.*, 1978; Barwise and Whitehead, 1980; HajIbrahim *et al.*, 1981). The introduction of a functional group at a specific site, or sites, on the porphyrin macrocycle should improve the resolution of petroporphyrin mixtures by increasing the range of polarity of the components. Such derivatizations would provide a rapid method for the separation of the X, Y and Z series of DPEP and aetioporphyrins, and also might reveal additional components. Two approaches to the derivatization of petroporphyrin mixtures were considered initially.

(i) *Substitution of the meso (bridge) positions.* This approach was discounted because *meso* substitution reactions are difficult to control, and mixtures of products are often formed (e.g. Bonnett and Stephenson, 1965; Fuhrop, 1978). In addition, reactivity at the *meso* positions is dependent on the nature of the chelated metal (Kenner *et al.*, 1973).

(ii) *Electrophilic substitution at unsubstituted β-positions.* This appeared to be a more promising approach. Metalloporphyrins readily undergo Friedel-Crafts

Table 1

Spectrometric and chromatographic data for the demetallated Gilsonite Aetio and DPEP porphyrins selected for acetylation studies

Compound no.	TLC[a] Rf	Significant ions m/z (%)	No. and type of β-substituents[b]		Assignment	Comment
A1	0.31–0.33	450 (100), 435 (35), 225 (25)	6CH$_3$ 2C$_2$H$_5$		C$_{30}$ Aetio	
A2	0.47–0.50	450 (2), 436 (100), 421 (30), 218 (20)	5CH$_3$ 2C$_2$H$_5$ 1H		C$_{29}$ Aetio	Trace C$_{30}$ aetio impurity
A3	0.52–0.54	450 (100), 435 (30), 225 (22)	4CH$_3$ 3C$_2$H$_5$ 1H		C$_{30}$ Aetio	
D1	0.08–0.10	462 (100), 447 (28), 231 (18)	5CH$_3$ 2C$_2$H$_5$		C$_{31}$ DPEP	

[a] Kieselgel G plates using CH$_2$Cl$_2$: Toluene (1:1, v:v) as eluent (Quirke *et al.*, 1979)

[b] Based on previous ^{1}H NMR study by Quirke *et al.*, (1979)

acylation at their unsubstituted β-positions, but the *meso* positions are not acylated (e.g. Brockmann *et al.*, 1968). It was hoped that Friedel–Crafts acylation and subsequent chromatography would be a facile method for the separation of the X, Y and Z series of porphrins.

Porphyrins isolated from the bitumen Gilsonite (Eocene, Uinta Basin, Utah, USA) were selected to examine the potential of the derivatization method. The results of the investigation are presented, and the value of the method both for quantitative and for qualitative analysis of petroporphyrin mixtures is assessed. In addition the potential of the method in the structural elucidation of petroporphyrins is discussed.

EXPERIMENTAL

Electron impact mass spectra were obtained using a VG 16F spectrometer. UV-visible spectra were obtained on a Unicam SP800 spectrophotometer. Thin-layer chromatography (TLC) separations were carried out on Kieselgel G Type 60 (0.3 mm) pre-eluted with CH$_3$CO$_2$C$_2$H$_5$ and re-activated at 100 °C (4 h), or on SiO$_2$-60F$_{254}$ high-performance thin-layer chromatography (HPTLC) plates with a concentrating zone (Merck). All solvents were distilled before use.

The geological history of Gilsonite (Eocene, Uinta Basin, Utah, USA) and the Uinta Basin has been reported (Hunt *et al.*, 1954; Tissot *et al.*, 1978). The demetallated single carbon number porphyrins were isolated and purified by the method of Quirke and Maxwell (1980), and the TLC Rf values and mass spectrometric data are summarized in Table 1.

The weight of nickel porphyrin starting materials and products were estimated from visible spectrometry using the molar extinction coefficient 34 820 at 550 nm for the alkyl porphyrins (Baker *et al.*, 1978) and at 560 nm for acetylated species.

Estimation of the percentage recovery of fully β-alkylated porphyrins from Friedel–Crafts acylation reactions

To a solution of nickel aetioporphyrin-I (2a; 1.0 mg) in CH$_2$Cl$_2$ (1 ml) was added acetic anhydride (0.5 ml), and the solution was cooled to 0 °C. Anhydrous Sn(IV)Cl$_4$ was added under dry N$_2$ and the mixture was stirred for 20 min at 0 °C. It was then diluted with CH$_2$Cl$_2$ (5 ml), poured onto ice (c. 10 g) and stirred for 2 h. The organic

phase was separated, washed with water (2 × 5 ml) and evaporated. Analysis by mass spectrometry (MS), UV-visible spectrometry and TLC indicated that the starting material was unchanged. The yield was 0.90 mg (90%). The reaction was repeated five times and the average recovery yield was 86%.

The acetylation experiment was also carried out using a C$_{31}$ DPEP porphyrin from Gilsonite (D1, Table 1 0.50 mg) in place of aetioporphyrin-I. The starting material was recovered in 84% yield (0.42 mg).

Separation of porphyrin mixtures by Friedel–Crafts acylations

A mixture of the nickel (II) complexes of aetioporphyrin-I (0.22 mg), A1, a fully β-alkylated C$_{30}$ aetioporphrin (Table 1 0.15 mg) and A2, a C$_{29}$ aetioporphyrin with one unsubstituted β-position (Table 1, 0.12 mg) was dissolved in CH$_2$Cl$_2$ (0.5 ml) and acetic anhydride (0.25 ml). The solution was cooled to 0 °C and anhydrous Sn(IV)Cl$_4$ (2 drops) was added under dry N$_2$. The solution, which rapidly acquired a green tinge, was stirred for 20 min. It was then diluted with CH$_2$Cl$_2$ (5 ml), and poured onto ice. The organic layer turned red immediately. The mixture was stirred for 2 h, and worked up as described above. The product was separated into two fractions: the two fully β-alkylated components (0.31 mg, 84% recovery) Rf 0.93–0.96, and mono-acetylated A2 (0.11 mg, 76%) Rf 0.52–0.54 by TLC on Kieselgel G using CH$_2$Cl$_2$ as eluant. MS analysis of the less polar fraction showed A2 was absent.

The reaction was repeated using a mixture of nickel (II) complexes of D1, a fully alkylated C$_{31}$ DPEP (Table 1; 0.20 mg), and A3 a mono-β-unsubstituted C$_{30}$ aetioporphyrin (Table 1; 0.15 mg). The product was separated into two fractions D1 (0.18 mg; 90% recovery) Rf 0.90–0.92 and acetylated A3 (0.14 mg 78%). The assignment of the fractions was confirmed by MS.

Separation of acetylated petroporphyrin isomers

The nickel (II) complex of A2 (0.3 mg) was acetylated as described above, and demetallated using the method of Quirke *et al.* (1979). The demetallated porphyrin was separated into two fractions A2.1 (0.18 mg) Rf 0.25–0.27 and A2.2 (0.08 mg) Rf 0.30–0.32 on HPTLC using CHCl$_3$/CH$_3$CO$_2$C$_2$H$_5$ (10:1) as eluant. The fractions gave similar mass spectra. The significant ions were 478

(100%; molecular ion), 463 (c. 38% M-15) 239 (c. 20% M^{2+}).

RESULTS AND DISCUSSION

The acetylation of porphyrins with unsubstituted β-positions is a new approach to the separation of petroporphyrin mixtures. The derivatization must be carried out on the metalloporphyrins to prevent dication formation (Fuhrop, 1975).* Petroporphyrin mixtures should, therefore, be acetylated before they are demetallated. Fully β-alkylated porphyrins are recovered unchanged in high yield. Similarly, the mono-β-unsubstituted compounds are efficiently acetylated. The X series (fully β-alkylated) porphyrins are separated readily from the derivatized Y series (mono-β-unsubstituted), and the concentration of each species may be determined by UV-visible spectrometry. It is assumed that the Z series (di-β-unsubstituted

* Derivitization on vanadyl porphyrins were not attempted, however, both iron (III) and copper (II) deuteroporphyrin-IX were efficiently acetylated (Quirke, unpublished).

porphyrins) will behave in an analogous way. The formation of the bis-acetylated derivative (2b) from the Friedel-Crafts acetylation of nickel (II) deuteroporphyrin-IX (2c) supports this assumption: The separation of A2 into two isomers gives further evidence of the importance of the derivatization technique. HPTLC is a valuable method for analysis and micro scale preparative studies of petroporphyrins. The bands are narrower than those from conventional TLC. This is due to the presence of the concentration zone on the HPTLC plates which produces a very narrow baseline, and the uniformity of both the thickness and the particle size of the silica layer.

Assessment of the acetylation reaction for correlation studies

In the evaluation of petroporphyrins as geochemical parameters it is essential to be able to separate and analyse mixtures rapidly. HPLC provides a method of considerable potential, but neither totally demetallated petroporphyrin mixtures nor the metal complexes have been fully resolved on 5 μ Partisil (HajIbrahim et al.,

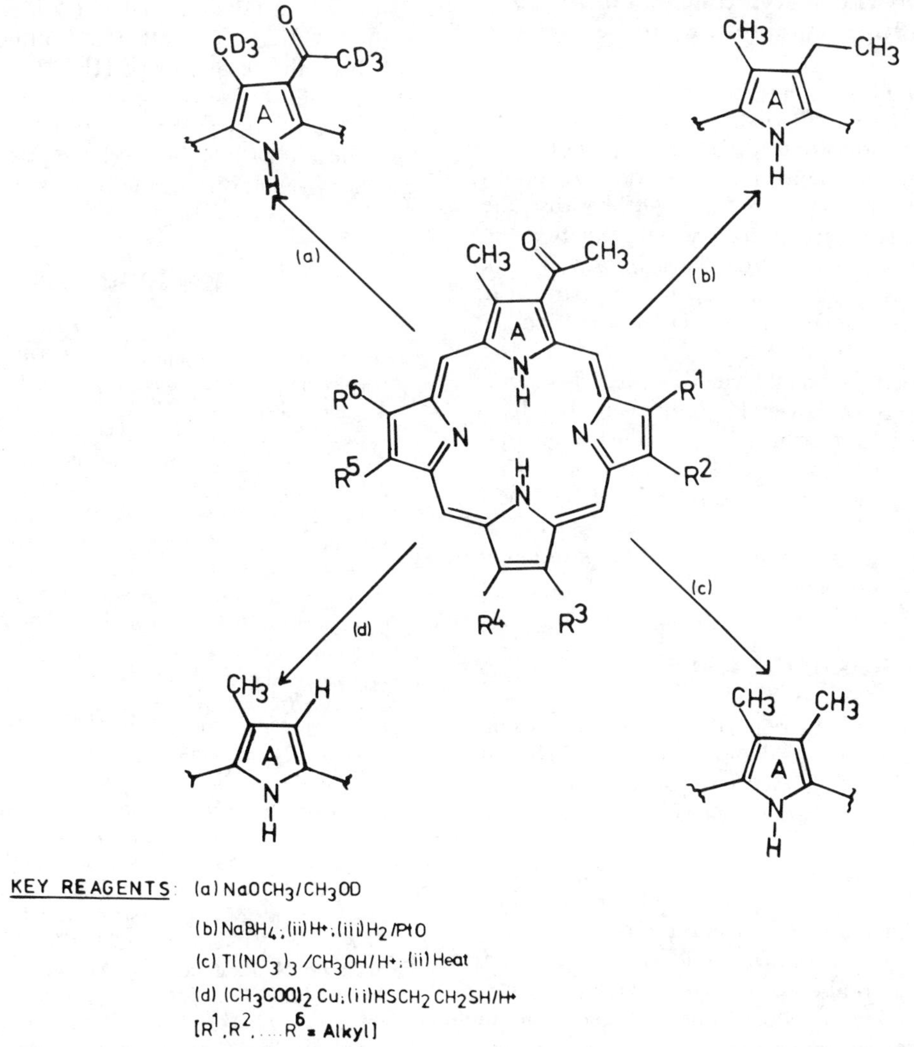

KEY REAGENTS: (a) NaOCH₃/CH₃OD
(b) NaBH₄; (ii) H⁺; (iii) H₂/PtO
(c) Tl(NO₃)₃/CH₃OH/H⁺; (ii) Heat
(d) (CH₃COO)₂Cu; (ii) HSCH₂CH₂SH/H⁺
[R¹, R²,...R⁶ = Alkyl]

Fig. 1. Important reactions of the acetyl group.

1981; Barwise and Whitehead, 1980). The polarity of the demetallated porphyrins is inversely proportional to both carbon number (C_{no}) and the number of unsubstituted β-positions. In addition, the decrease in polarity from the presence of an unsubstituted β-position is approximately equivalent to the removal of a 'saturated alkyl unit' of 2.5 carbons. Thus the fully alkylated C_{32} acetioporphyrin, and the di-β-unsubstituted C_{27} aetioporphyrin present in Bermuda Rise sediments coelute on HPLC using 5 μ Partisil (Quirke *et al.*, in press).

The derivatization of the petroporphyrins should enhance HPLC separations in the following ways:

1. The separated X, Y and Z series will be less complex than the total mixture.
2. High C_{no} ($\geqslant C_{32}$) fully β-alkylated components will be separated from low C_{no} ($\leqslant C_{28}$) porphyrins of similar polarity as the latter will be acetylated.
3. Isomeric mono-β-unsubstituted porphyrins may be separated more readily. Similarly, the derivatization may be useful for the isolation of very low C_{no} ($\leqslant C_{26}$) aetioporphyrins present in many deep sea sediments (e.g. Baker *et al.*, 1978; Quirke *et al.*, in press).

Potential of the acetylation technique in structural elucidation studies

The acetylation of the Y and Z series of porphyrins has potential applications in structural elucidation studies. The following factors are of particular importance.

1. The resolution of non-equivalent *meso* protons and β-alkyl groups should be improved because the presence of an acetyl moiety will enhance the differences in their environments. Improved peak resolution is of particular importance for nuclear Overhauser enhancement ^{1}H NMR studies (Quirke *et al.*, 1980).
2. The methyl or methylene on the β-position adjacent to the acetyl group can be fully deuteriated by treatment with deuteriomethanol (CH_3OD) and base (Fig. 1; La Mar *et al.*, 1978). This will allow partial confirmation of ^{1}H NMR assignments.
3. The acetylation technique allows the separation of previously unresolved isomers.

Reactions of the acetyl group

The acetyl group may be removed quantitatively using ethane dithiol and boron trifluoride-ether (Fig. 1; Smith and Landry, 1981). Thus it will be possible to remove the functionality, after separating the porphyrins into the X, Y and Z series.

Similarly, it is possible to convert the acetyl group into a methyl, by the formation of the methyl porphyrinyl acetate using thallium (III) trinitrate and methanol, and subsequent decarboxylation (Fig. 1; Quirke, unpublished). It is also possible to convert the acetyl group into an ethyl by reduction of the carbonyl to an alcohol, dehydration and reduction of the resultant vinyl group (Fig. 1; Quirke, unpublished). Thus, a mono-β-

unsubstituted porphyrin may be converted into a fully β-alkylated porphyrin with an additional methyl or ethyl group. These reactions provide a method for the preparation of fully β-alkylated porphyrin standards from characterized porphyrins with a single β-unsubstituted position.

CONCLUSIONS

The acetylation of unsubstituted β-positions is a novel technique for the analysis of petroporphyrins. Already it permits a rapid method for the quantitation of fully-β-alkylated and mono-β-unsubstituted porphyrin components in mixtures. The technique has potential for structural elucidation investigations and correlation studies, and has resulted in the isolation of previously unresolved isomers.

Acknowledgements

I thank Dr J. A. H. MacBride and Mr R. Hill and Sunderland Polytechnic for mass spectra. I also thank Professor K. M. Smith (University of California, Davis) for the gift of aetioporphyrin-I, and Merck (Darmstadt) for the gift of HPTLC plates. I am grateful to Dr A. Seubert (University Hautklinik, Göttingen) for advising me about the technique of HPTLC. I wish to thank Morris Ashby Ltd. (Kingston, Surrey) for the gift of Gilsonite. I am particularly grateful to Professor G. Eglinton and Dr J. R. Maxwell for introducing me to the fascinating chemistry of the petroporphyrins.

REFERENCES

Baker, E. W. and Palmer, S. E. (1978) Geochemistry of porphyrins. In *The Porphyrins Vol. I*. Ed. by Dolphin, D. Academic Press, New York. pp. 485–551.

Baker, E. W., Palmer, S. E. and Huang, W. Y. (1978) Chlorin and porphyrin geochemistry of DSDP Leg 40 sediments. In *Initial Reports of the Deep Sea Drilling Project*, Vol. 40. Ed. by Bolli, H. M., Ryan, W. B. F. *et al.* U.S. Government Printing Office, Washington. pp. 639–647.

Barwise, A. J. G. and Whitehead, E. V. (1980) Separation and structure of petroporphyrins. In *Advances in Organic Geochemistry 1979*. Ed. by Douglas, A. G. and Maxwell, J. R. Pergamon Press, Oxford. pp. 181–192.

Bonnett, R. and Stephenson, G. F. (1965) The *meso* reactivity of porphyrins and related compounds I. Nitration. *J. Org. Chem.* **30**, 2791–2798.

Brockmann, H. Jr., Bliesner, K.-M. and Inhoffen, H. H. (1968) Zur weiteren Kenntnis des Chlorophylls und des Hämins XX. Formyl- und Acetyl-Substituierte Deuteroporphyrine. *Ann. Chem.* **718**, 149–161.

Eglinton, G., HajIbrahim, S. K., Maxwell, J. R., Quirke, J. M. E., Shaw, G. J., Volkman, J. K. and Wardroper, A. M. K. (1979) Lipids of aquatic sediments, Recent and ancient. *Phil. Trans. R. Soc. Lond. A* **293**, 69–91.

Eglinton, G., HajIbrahim, S. K., Maxwell, J. R. and Quirke, J. M. E. (1980) Petroporphyrins: structural elucidation and the application of HPLC fingerprinting to geochemical problems. In *Advances in Organic Geochemistry 1979*. Ed. by Douglas, A. G. and Maxwell, J. R. Pergamon Press,

Oxford. pp. 193–203.

Flom, E. A. and Thompson, S. J. (1980) A geochemical method for determining heat history of retorted shale oils. *Report 1980 FJSRL-7R-80-0014*. Order no. AO88909, 30 pp.

Fuhrop, J. H. (1975) Irreversible reactions at the porphyrin periphery (excluding photochemistry). In *Porphyrins and Metalloporphyrins*. Ed. by Smith, K. M. Elsevier, Amsterdam. pp. 625–666.

Fuhrop, J. H. (1978) Irreversible reactions on the porphyrin periphery. In *The Porphyrins*, Vol. II. Ed. by Dolphin, D. Academic Press, New York. pp. 131–159.

HajIbrahim, S. K., Tibbetts, P. J. C., Watts, C. D., Maxwell, J. R., Eglinton, G., Colin, H. and Guiochon, G. (1978) Analysis of carotenoid and porphyrin pigments of geochemical interest by high-performance liquid chromatography. *Anal. Chem.* **50**, 549–553.

HajIbrahim, S. K., Quirke, J. M. E. and Eglinton, G. (1981) Petroporphyrins V. Structurally-related porphyrin series in bitumens, shales and petroleums. Evidence from HPLC and mass spectrometry. *Chem. Geol.* **32**, 173–188.

Hunt, J. M., Stewart, F. and Dickey, P. A. (1954) Origin of hydrocarbons of Uinta Basin, Utah. *Bull. Am. Ass. Petrol. Geol.* **38**, 1671–1698.

Kenner, G. W., Smith, K. M. and Sutton, M. J. (1973) *Meso*-deuteriation of magnesium porphyrins. *Tetr. Lett.* 1303–1306.

La Mar, G. N., Viscio, D. B., Smith, K. M., Caughey, W. S. and Smith, M. L. (1978) NMR studies of low spin ferric complexes of natural porphyrin derivatives I. Effect of peripheral substituents on the π Electronic Asymmetry in Biscyano complexes. *J. Am. Chem. Soc.* **100**, 8085–8092.

Mackenzie, A. S., Quirke, J. M. E. and Maxwell, J. R. (1980) Molecular parameters of maturation in the Toarcian shales, Paris Basin, France II. Evolution of metalloporphyrins. In *Advances in Organic Geochemistry 1979*. Ed. by Douglas, A. G. and Maxwell, J. R. Pergamon Press, Oxford. pp. 239–248.

Quirke, J. M. E., Eglinton, G. and Maxwell, J. R. (1979) Petroporphyrins I. Preliminary characterisation of the porphyrins of Gilsonite. *J. Am. Chem. Soc.* **101**, 7693–7697.

Quirke, J. M. E. and Maxwell, J. R. (1980) Petroporphyrins III. Characterisation of a C_{32} aetio porphyrin from Gilsonite as the bis(porphyrinato-Mercury (II) Acetato) Mercury (II) complex. Origin and significance. *Tetr.* **36**, 3453–3458.

Quirke, J. M. E., Eglinton, G., Maxwell, J. R. and Sanders, J. K. M. (1980). Petroporphyrins IV. Nuclear Overhauser enhancement ¹H NMR studies of deoxophylloerythroetio-porphyrins from Gilsonite. *Tetr. Lett.* **21**, 2987–2990.

Quirke, J. M. E., Eglinton, G., Palmer, S. E. and Baker, E. W. High performance liquid chromatographic (HPLC) and mass spectrometric analyses of porphyrins from deep sea sediments. *Chem. Geol.*, in press.

Smith, K. M. and Landry, K. C. (1981) Protodeacetylation of porphyrins and pyrroles: A new partial synthesis of dehydrocoproporphyrin (S411-Porphyrin). *J. Chem. Soc. Chem. Commun.* 283–284.

Tissot, B., Deroo, G. and Hood, A. (1978) Geochemical study of the Uinta Basin: formation of petroleum from the Green River formation. *Geochim. Cosmochim. Acta* **42**, 1469–1485.

Treibs, A. (1934a) Uber das Vorkommen von Chlorophyll derivaten in einen Olsehiefer aus der Oberen Trias. *Ann. Chem.* **509**, 103–114.

Treibs, A. (1934b) Chlorophyll- und Häminderivate in bituminösen, Gesteinen, Erdolen Erdwachsen und Asphalten. *Ann. Chem.* **510**, 42–62.

Advances in Organic Geochemistry 1981, pp. 738–745
© *John Wiley & Sons Limited, 1983*

Tricyclic Diterpane Distributions in the Correlation of Paleozoic Crude Oils from the Williston Basin

J. E. Zumberge

Cities Service Company, Energy Resources Group, Exploration and Production Research, Tulsa, Oklahoma

Crude oils from Paleozoic reservoirs in the Williston Basin, North Dakota and Montana, were analyzed by gas chromatography–mass spectrometry in order to determine terpenoid distributions. A homologous series of tricyclic diterpanes, ranging in molecular weight from 262 to 360 amu, appears to be especially useful in correlating crude oils; each genetically related family of crude oils has a unique normalized pattern of tricyclic diterpanes as determined by the $m/z = 191$ mass fragmentograms. Apparently, C_{19} and C_{20} diterpanes can be derived from marine as well as terrestrial organic sources because they are found in oils generated from Ordovician source rocks.

INTRODUCTION

A number of recent publications describe the use of terpenoid biomarkers for evaluating depositional environments, correlating crude oils and source rocks, and determining degrees of thermal maturation in oils and sediments (e.g., Reed, 1977; Simoneit, 1977; van Dorsselaer *et al.*, 1977; Ensminger *et al.*, 1978; Seifert and Moldowan, 1978, 1979, 1980, 1981; Mackenzie, 1980; Mackenzie *et al.*, 1980, 1981; Barrick and Hedges, 1981). Diterpenoid components have been reported in weathered petroleum from the Uinta Basin by Reed (1977) and appeared not to be seriously affected by bacterial degradation. Zumberge (1980) showed that biodegraded oils could be successfully correlated to nondegraded oils from Colombia using diterpanes. Philp *et al.* (1981) and Richardson and Miller (1981) reported diterpenoids in crude oils from Australia and Indonesia, respectively. It appears that diterpenoid hydrocarbons are relatively common in crude oils, and an attempt is made in the present study to show the usefulness of tricyclic diterpanes in correlating Paleozoic crude oils from the Williston Basin.

The Williston Basin is situated in North Dakota, South Dakota, Montana, and Saskatchewan and is the largest intracratonic Paleozic basin in the United States (Kohm and Louden, 1979). Most oil production from this basin is from carbonate reservoirs ranging in age from Pennsylvanian to Cambrian. A generalized stratigraphic column of the central Williston Basin (after Meissner, 1978) and a location map of the wells sampled are illustrated in Figs. 1 and 2, respectively. Oils analyzed in this study are from the Mississippian Mission Canyon Formation (5 samples), Devonian Duperow Formation (4 samples), Ordovician Red River Formation (3 samples), Mississippian Nesson Formation (1 sample), Devonian Nisku and Winnipegosis

Formations (1 sample each), and a single oil produced from the Cambrian Deadwood Formation.

Williams (1974) published an extensive study on the geochemical correlation of oils from the Williston Basin. Two major oil families were identified: in general, oils produced from the Ordovician Red River Formation (Type I oils) were compositionally different from oils extracted from the Mississippian Mission Canyon Formation (Type II oils) based on a number of geochemical parameters including data derived from infrared spectroscopy, optical rotation measurements, gas chromatography, and stable carbon isotope ratio determinations. These results imply that the two groups of oil were generated by disparate source rocks. Further, by analyzing and comparing the organic matter in rock samples from various wells, it was determined by Williams (1974) that the Lower Mississippian Bakken Shale was responsible for sourcing the Mission Canyon oil (Type II) and that the Ordovician Winnipeg Shale generated the Red River oils (Type I). However, Kohm and Louden (1979) and Kendall (1976) postulated that kerogen-rich beds within the Red River Formation ('C' burrowed member) internally generated the Red River oil. Williams (1974) also observed a number of volumetrically smaller oil families, some of which were simply the result of biodegradation or commingling of oils from the two major sources and others which had unique, and perhaps, local source rocks. A third type of oil identified, found exclusively in the Tyler Formation (Pennsylvanian), may have been sourced from shales within this formation.

EXPERIMENTAL

Oils were characterized using liquid chromatography (combined alumina/silica columns) in order to separate

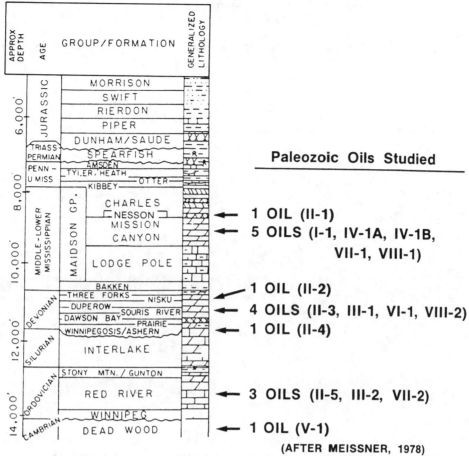

Fig. 1. Generalized section of the Williston Basin showing the stratigraphic relationship between the Paleozoic oils studied.

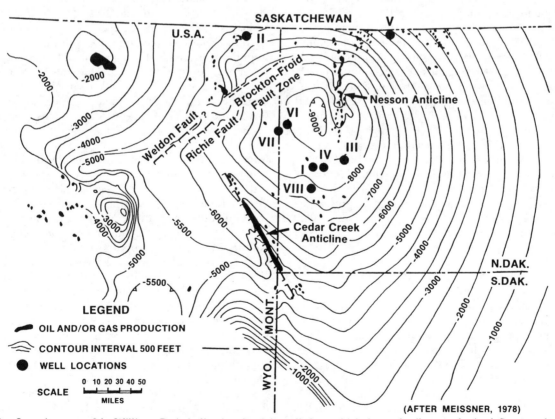

Fig. 2. Location map of the Williston Basin indicating the eight wells from which the crude oils were obtained. Structural contours are on the base of Mississippian strata.

Table 1

Gross oil composition

	I-1	II-1	II-2	II-3	II-4	II-5	III-1	III-2	IV-1A	IV-1B	V-1	VI-1	VII-1	VII-2	VIII-1	VIII-2
	Mission Canyon	Nesson	Nisku	Duperow	Winnipegosis	Red River	Duperow	Red River	Mission Canyon	Mission Canyon	Deadwood	Duperow	Mission Canyon	Red River	Mission Canyon	Duperow
Gross oil composition																
% Less than C$_{15}$+	45.9	33.3	38.4	41.0	42.5	40.9	47.9	53.7	48.1	48.9	10.6	36.8	38.9	45.0	46.1	37.4
% C$_{15}$+	54.1	66.7	61.6	59.0	57.5	59.1	52.1	46.3	51.9	51.1	89.4	63.2	61.1	55.0	53.9	62.6
C$_{15}$+ composition																
% aliphatic hydrocarbons	73.5	56.2	46.7	57.9	70.8	59.5	67.6	78.5	66.3	70.0	61.8	77.1	64.3	72.9	73.3	81.1
% aromatic hydrocarbons	20.0	34.3	33.0	31.6	24.4	25.1	20.0	14.2	23.0	23.3	17.7	19.1	32.1	19.4	25.3	14.4
% hydrocarbons	93.5	90.5	79.7	89.5	95.2	84.6	87.6	92.7	89.3	93.3	79.5	96.2	96.4	92.3	98.6	95.5
% NSO compounds	6.3	5.3	18.4	5.3	3.7	13.4	12.0	7.2	10.5	6.1	14.4	2.5	3.1	7.4	0	4.0
% asphaltenes	0.2	2.8	1.9	5.2	1.1	2.0	0.4	0.1	0.2	0.6	6.1	1.3	0.5	0.3	1.4	0.5
% nonhydrocarbons	6.5	8.1	20.3	10.5	4.8	15.4	12.4	7.3	10.7	6.7	20.5	3.8	3.6	7.7	1.4	4.5
C$_{15}$+ Hydrocarbon composition																
% *n*- and isoalkanes	27.2	19.4	23.4	25.8	25.6	22.9	33.2	35.4	16.2	15.9	29.8	31.8	19.7	29.7	25.2	36.5
% cycloalkanes	51.4	42.7	35.2	38.2	48.8	47.4	44.0	49.6	58.0	59.1	47.9	48.3	47.0	49.3	49.1	48.4
% aromatics	21.4	37.9	41.4	36.0	25.6	29.7	22.8	15.0	25.8	25.0	22.3	19.9	33.3	21.0	25.7	15.1
Carbon isotope ratios[a] of C$_{15}$+ fractions																
Aliphatic hydrocarbons	−29.9	−31.8	−25.7	−25.9	−29.4	−28.4	−30.9	−30.4	−30.0	−30.0	−26.2	−28.3	−30.2	−29.2	−30.3	−29.8
Aromatic hydrocarbons	−29.5	−31.0	−24.6	−24.6	−28.8	−28.3	−29.1	−29.0	−29.4	−29.3	−25.3	−25.9	−30.2	−28.6	−29.9	−27.1
Pristane/Phytane	0.74	0.71	0.67	0.69	1.37	1.44	1.27	1.75	1.00	0.96	0.35	1.17	0.80	1.64	0.78	1.13
Pristane/*n*-C$_{17}$	0.22	0.34	0.12	0.18	0.07	0.09	0.11	0.07	0.26	0.25	0.22	0.14	0.26	0.04	0.23	0.13
API Gravity (60 °F)	40.6	33.2	35.4	32.7	40.0	40.8	30.8	47.2	42.3	42.3	28.6	39.2	34.1	44.4	40.3	41.5

[a] $\delta^{13}C_{PDB}$

aliphatic (pentane eluates) and aromatic (toluene eluates) hydrocarbons from one another and from nonhydrocarbons, gas chromatography of the C$_{15+}$ aliphatic hydrocarbon fractions (Hewlett Packard 5880 gas chromatograph equipped with a 12.5 m × 0.2 mm, SP2100 fused silica column; temperature programmed from 100 to 280 °C at 8 °C min^{-1}), stable carbon isotope ratio mass spectrometry of both C$_{15+}$ aliphatic and aromatic hydrocarbon fractions (VG Micromass 602D mass spectrometer, using the method of Sofer, 1980), and by combined gas chromatography–mass spectrometry (GC–MS) of the C$_{15+}$ aliphatic hydrocarbon fractions (Finnigan 4000 GC–MS, equipped with an INCOS 2900 data processing system; analyses performed by Global Geochemistry Corp.). Normalized tricyclic diterpane distributions were determined by measuring peak heights from the m/z = 191 mass fragmentograms. Molecular weights were determined by monitoring the m/z = 262, 276, 290, 304, 318, 332, 346, and 360 fragmentograms.

RESULTS AND DISCUSSION

Gross oil compositional data, including carbon isotope ratios, are given in Table 1. Gas chromatograms of the C$_{15+}$ aliphatic hydrocarbon fractions are shown in Fig. 3. Based on gas chromatographic data (*n*-alkane distributions, isoprenoid ratios, odd–even preference (OEP) values) and stable carbon isotope ratios of C$_{15+}$ aliphatic and aromatic hydrocarbon fractions, six groups, or families, of geochemically distinct oils can be delineated. For example, Fig. 4 graphically portrays these groups by cross plotting pristane–phytane ratios

(Pr/Ph) against stable carbon isotope ratios of the aliphatic hydrocarbon fractions.

Generally, with two exceptions, oils produced from the same formation are similar to one another, regardless of the well location in the basin. In agreement with Williams (1974), Mississippian Mission Canyon oils (Group 2) were sourced from rocks distinctly different from the source rocks which generated Ordovician Red River oils (Group 1). Devonian Duperow oils (Group 3) had another source. (It is unknown why a relatively large, i.e. > 2‰, carbon isotopic variation exists among these Duperow oils.) The two exceptions mentioned above are the Devonian Winnipegosis oil, which is grouped with the Red River oils, and one Duperow oil from the Raymond Field, Montana (Well II, Fig. 2) which is similar to the Devonian Nisku oil (Group 4) rather than to the other Duperow oils from different fields. Although the Mississippian Nesson oil (Group 6) is slightly different than the Mission Canyon oils based on gas chromatographic data and carbon isotopes, the Nesson oil actually appears to be an immature counterpart of the Group 2, Mission Canyon oils. Finally, the single Cambrian Deadwood oil (Group 5) was generated from yet another source. The abundant C$_{20+}$ *n*-alkanes with a distinct odd–even carbon preference (characteristic of terrestrial organic matter) suggest that this oil, reservoired in Cambrian strata, was sourced from younger rocks simply because of the fact that vascular land plants did not evolve until Silurian or Devonian time.

A representative suite of 12 samples from the oil groups described above were analyzed by GC–MS for terpenoid components. The resulting normalized tricyclic diterpane distributions are shown in histogram

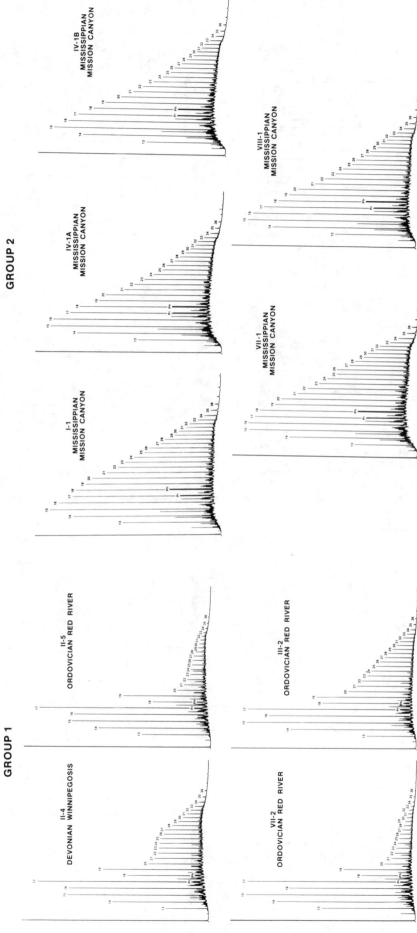

Fig. 3. Gas chromatograms of the aliphatic hydrocarbon fractions. Numbered peaks refer to corresponding *n*-alkanes; Pr and Ph stand for pristane and phytane, respectively. Gas chromatographic conditions are in the text.

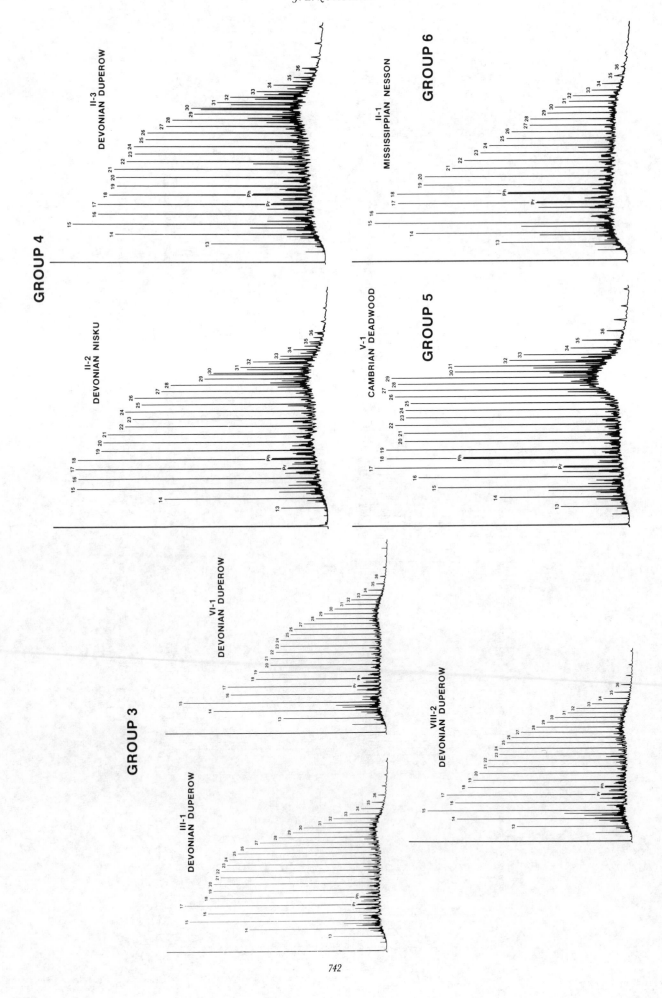

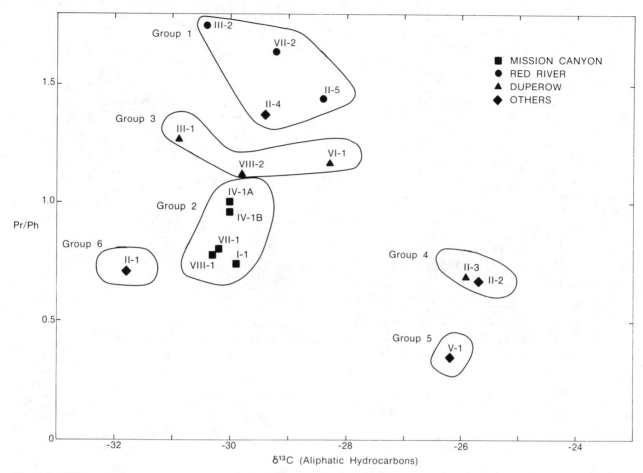

Fig. 4. Williston Basin oils divided into six groups based on pristane–phytane ratios (Pr/Ph) and stable carbon isotope ratios (relative to the PDB standard) of the aliphatic hydrocarbon fractions.

form for ease of comparison in Fig. 5, and each lettered component is identified in Table 2. The diterpane distribution patterns illustrated in Fig. 5 are distinctly different between the various oil families (representing different source rocks) but are remarkably similar within oils from the same family even though the samples represent a wide geographical range (Fig. 2). Thus, this technique appears promising as a correlation tool in crude oil and source rock geochemistry. However, more information regarding diterpenoid distributions in other crude oils and the origin of these compounds is needed.

Relatively little is known concerning the origin and fate of these diterpenoid hydrocarbons, although C_{19} and C_{20} components (peaks a and b, Fig. 5) are thought to be derived from vascular land plants (e.g. Reed, 1977; Simoneit, 1977; Richardson and Miller, 1981). Peaks a and b are most abundant relative to the other diterpanes in oil samples from the Duperow (Devonian), Nisku (Devonian), Deadwood (Cambrian), and Red River (Ordovician) Formations. Plant fossil evidence supports the existence of land plants during Devonian times (only seedless vascular plants), and the Cambrian Deadwood oil has been established to originate from younger source strata. The presence of C_{19} and C_{20} diterpanes in the Ordovician Red River oil, which is likely sourced from Red River or older sediments (i.e. Winnipeg Formation), presents a paradox because no vascular land plants existed in Ordovician time. One possible

explanation is that primitive marine plants may possibly have biosynthesized these diterpanes. Alternatively, they may have been derived from thermal degradation of the higher molecular weight diterpanes and/or triterpanes. Apparently, diterpanes can be derived from marine as well as terrestrial sources.

Table 2.
List of identified diterpanes.

Peak designation	Molecular formula	Molecular weight
a	$C_{19}H_{34}$	262
b	$C_{20}H_{36}$	276
c_1	$C_{21}H_{38}$	290
c_2	$C_{21}H_{38}$	290
c_3	$C_{21}H_{38}$	290
d_1	$C_{22}H_{40}$	304
d_2	$C_{22}H_{40}$	304
e	$C_{23}H_{42}$	318
f	$c_{24}H_{44}$	332
g	$C_{25}H_{46}$	346
h_1	$C_{26}H_{48}$	360
h_2	$C_{26}H_{48}$	360

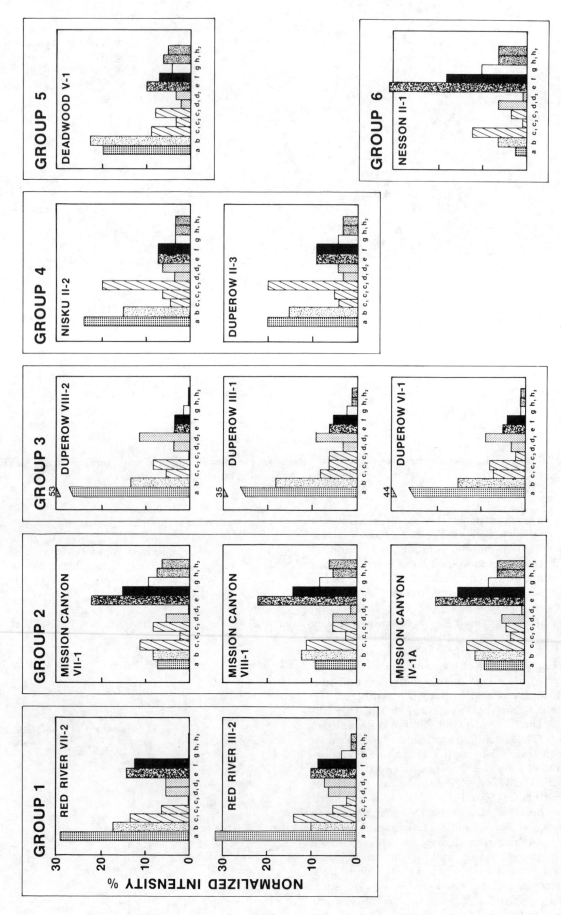

Fig. 5. Tricyclic diterpane normalized distributions as determined from the $m/z = 191$ mass fragmentograms. Molecular weights of each of the components are given in Table 2.

Acknowledgements

I would like to thank Cities Service US Interior Region, Denver, for providing samples and L. Baie, M. Leenheer, S. Palmer, Z. Sofer, and C. Sutton, Cities Service Research Laboratory, for helpful comments and suggestions. Special thanks to J. Heard, A. Jones, S. Sellers, and C. Schiefelbein for technical analyses; M. Draughon for typing the manuscript; and T. Edmondson and D. Wilkins for drafting the figures.

REFERENCES

Barrick, R. C. and Hedges, J. I. (1981) Hydrocarbon geochemistry of the Puget Sound region II. Sedimentary diterpenoid, steroid and triterpenoid hydrocarbons. *Geochem. Cosmochim. Acta* **45**, 381–392.

Ensminger, A., Joly, G. and Albrecht, P. (1978) Rearranged steranes in sediments and crude oils. *Tetr. Lett.* **18**, 1575–1578.

Kendall, A. C. (1976) The Ordovician carbonate succession (Bighorn Group) or southeastern Saskatchewan. *Sask. Dept. Miner. Resour. Rept.* 180.

Kohm, J. A. and Louden, R. O. (1979) Ordovician Red River 2. *Oil and Gas Jour.* **77**, 89–94.

Mackenzie, A. S. (1980) Application of biological marker compounds to subsurface geological processes. PhD Thesis, University of Bristol.

Mackenzie, A. S., Patience, R. L., Maxwell, J. R., Vandenbrouke, M. and Durand, B. (1980) Molecular parameters of maturation in the Toarcian shales, Paris Basin, France I. Changes in the configuration of acyclic isoprenoid alkanes, steranes, and triterpanes. *Geochim. Cosmochim. Acta* **44**, 1709–1721.

Mackenzie, A. S., Hoffman, C. F. and Maxwell, J. R. (1981) Molecular parameters of maturation in the Toarcian shales, Paris Basin, France III. Changes in aromatic steroid hydrocarbons. *Geochim. Cosmochim. Acta* **45**, 1345–1355.

Meissner, F. F. (1978) Petroleum geology of the Bakken Formation, Williston Basin, North Dakota and Montana. *Montana Geol. Soc.*, 24th Annual Conference, Billings, Montana.

Philp, P. R., Gilbert, T. D. and Friedrich, J. (1981) Bicyclic sesquiterpenoids and diterpenoids in Australian crude oils. *Geochim. Cosmochim. Acta* **45**, 1173–1180.

Reed, W. E. (1977) Molecular compositions of weathered petroleum and comparison with its possible source. *Geochim. Cosmochim. Acta* **41**, 237–247.

Richardson, J. S. and Miller, D. (1981) Di- and tricyclic hydrocarbons as indicators of higher terrestrial input in the Salavati (Indonesia) reservoir. *ASMS Annual Conf.*, Minneapolis, p. 62.

Seifert, W. K. and Moldowan, J. M. (1978) Applications of steranes, terpanes, and monoaromatics to the maturation, migration, and source of crude oils. *Geochim. Cosmochim. Acta* **42**, 77–95.

Seifert, W. K. and Moldowan, J. M. (1979) The effect of biodegradation on steranes and terpanes in crude oils. *Geochim. Cosmochim. Acta* **43**, 111–126.

Seifert, W. K. and Moldowan, J. M. (1980) The effect of thermal stress on source rock quality as measured by hopane stereochemistry. *Advances in Organic Geochemistry, 1979*. Ed. by Douglas, A. G. and Maxwell, J. R. pp. 229–237.

Seifert, W. K. and Moldowan, J. M. (1981) Paleoreconstruction by biological markers. *Geochim. Cosmochim. Acta* **45**, 783–794.

Simoneit, B. R. T. (1977) Diterpenoid compounds and other lipids in deep-sea sediments and their geochemical significance. *Geochim. Cosmochim. Acta* **41**, 463–476.

Sofer, Z. (1980) Preparation of carbon dioxide for stable carbon isotope analysis of petroleum fractions. *Anal. Chem.* **52**, 1389–1391.

van Dorsselaer, A., Albrecht, P. and Ourisson, G. (1977) Identification of novel (17αH)-hopanes in shales, coals, lignites, sediments, and petroleum. *Bull. Soc. Chim. Fr.* No. 1–2, 165–170.

Williams, J. A. (1974) Characterization of oil types in Williston Basin. *AAPG Bull.* **58**, 1243–1252.

Zumberge, J. E. (1980) Oil–oil and oil–source rock correlations of bacterially degraded oils and Cretaceous outcrops from Colombia, South America. *26th Int. Geological Congress*, Paris, France, Abstract p. 806.

Advances in Organic Geochemistry 1981, pp. 746–766
© John Wiley & Sons Limited, 1983

Tricyclic Terpanes in the Athabasca Oil Sands: Their Geochemistry

C. M. Ekweozor* and O. P. Strausz

Hydrocarbon Research Centre, Department of Chemistry, University of Alberta, Edmonton, Alberta, Canada T6G 2G2

The bitumen of the Athabasca oil sands contains a homologous series of tricyclic alkanes with 19–30 C atoms per molecule and with absolute concentrations of the individual members ranging from 20 to 300 ppm of the bitumen. The basic structure of the series consists of a pentamethyl perhydrophenanthrene system with a branched side-chain attached to the C-ring. Members with > 24 C atoms per molecule occur in diastereomeric (R and S) pairs. While these hydrocarbons are present in the saturate fraction of the oil, the aromatic, resin and asphaltene fractions also contain them but in chemically bound form, one of the major derivatives being the C_{24}-carboxylic acids and its esters. On mild thermolysis the fractions afford the entire suite of tricyclanes, the relative concentrations of which depend upon the conditions employed. The most abundant source of tricyclanes is the asphaltene. Kinetic studies of tricyclane formation in maturation simulation of the oils sand as a function of time indicate two yield maxima which correspond to the principal phases of their primary production by defunctionalization and degradation by C—C bond cleavages of the alkyl side chain. The variations in yield, with thermal stress, of total tricyclanes, total saturates, and the individual members of the series exhibit parallel trends. These results suggest that the ratio of the C_{23} to the C_{21} members may serve as a potential maturity indicator of petroleum: the higher the ratio, the younger the diagenetic age of the oil. Supporting this are the values of 3.3 obtained for the Athabasca oil and 0.9 obtained for a mature Nigerian oil.

INTRODUCTION

The Athabasca oil sand deposits as well as the heavy oils of northern Alberta have been the subject of intensive geochemical investigations within the last decade (see for example, Evans *et al.*, 1971; Deroo and Powell, 1978; Rubinstein and Strausz, 1979). These huge deposits of oil, estimated to be of the order of one trillion barrels, are thought to have resulted mainly from the biodegradation and waterwashing of conventional oils migrating undip from reservoirs in the Lower Cretaceous Mannville Group of the central Alberta syncline (Vigrass, 1968). However, there is a growing body of geochemical evidence in support of a relatively low thermal maturity status for the bitumen of the oil sand (Montgomery *et al.*, 1974; Samman *et al.*, 1981; Cyr *et al.*, in preparation).

During our ongoing exercise of screening the oil sand bitumens for potentially useful biomarkers, we noted the ubiquitous occurrence of tricyclic terpenoid derivatives in the asphaltene and maltene fractions. An investigation of the organic geochemistry of the cycloalkanes was therefore undertaken. Some of the results of that study are reported here.

The first reports of the occurrence of $\geqslant C_{20}$ tricyclic terpanes in geological samples were simultaneously made by Anders and Robinson (1971) and Gallegos

* Visiting Professor, Present Address: Department of Chemistry, University of Ibadan, Ibadan, Nigeria.

(1971), who discovered C_{20}–C_{26} tricyclanes in the shales of the Green River formation of the Uinta basin, Utah. Reed (1977) subsequently found the same series of compounds in the extracts from surface outcrops and cores of oil-impregnated sandstones of the P.R. Spring Seep of the same basin.

But it was probably not until Seifert and Moldowan (1978) successfully exploited the compositional and distributional variations of the tricyclic terpanes and other biomarkers in the oils and shales of the McKittrick Field, California, for source-input studies, that the great potential of these chemical fossils for geochemical correlations became evident. Since then, Seifert's group has provided additional examples to illustrate the utility of the tricyclanes for differentiating bitumens, kerogens and oils from adjacent stratigraphies within the same basins (e.g. Seifert, 1978; Seifert *et al.*, 1979). It has also been suggested, although not yet conclusively proved, that the relative extents of migration of oils from a common source could be reflected by their concentration of tricyclic terpanes relative to the hopanes (Seifert *et al.*, 1979).

Tricyclic terpanes survive even severe biodegradation of petroleum (Reed, 1977; Seifert and Moldowan, 1979; Connan *et al.*, 1979). The literature on the biodegradability of tetracyclic terpanes and pentacyclic triterpanes, however, is not so unambiguous. Reed (1977) concluded that tetracyclic terpanes are unaffected whereas pentacyclic triterpanes suffer partial degradation. Seifert and Moldowan (1979) found that both regular steranes and hopanes are partially transformed. On the other hand, Rubinstein *et al.* (1977) and Connan *et al.* (1979) found that these classes of biomarkers remain essentially unchanged during biodegradation in vitro or in nature.

Utilizing the extreme resistance of tricyclanes against biodegradation Seifert and Moldowan (1979) were able to correlate intensely biotransformed oils with non-degraded oils of the same origin within the Gulf Coast and California basins. These biomarkers afforded significant evidence, at the molecular level, of petroleum pollution in the Southern California Bight as well as in several other aquatic environments located in other parts of the world (Simoneit and Kaplan, 1980; Venkatesan *et al.*, 1980).

One major deficiency in the tricyclic terpane literature is the paucity of basic chemical structural information. There has been little advancement in our knowledge in this regard ever since Anders and Robinson (1971) and Gallegos (1971) inferred *1* as the basic carbocyclic system of the tricyclanes from their mass spectral data.

R = alkyl group

1

This lack of a precise structural basis has resulted in some confusion in nomenclature and in other cases has also caused difficulties in the interpretation of data from different laboratories.

However, quite recently and contemporaneously with the present study, Albrecht's group (1981) reported the distribution of tricyclanes in several crude oils and the structural elucidation of the C_{19} and C_{20} members of the series.

We have recently made a search for the presence of tricyclic terpanes in the Athabasca oil sand and its separated hydrocarbon, resin and asphaltene fractions. A detailed study was made of the distribution of the tricyclic alkanes in the native bitumen and in the pyrolysis products of the whole bitumen and its fractions. Details of these studies are reported here.

EXPERIMENTAL PROCEDURES

Materials

The Athabasca oil sand used in this study was collected from a depth of 18 m below the surface at Syncrude Mine Site located in Alberta at 1–2–93–11–W4 (government coordinates). The oil sand assay results were: 12.0 wt % bitumen, 2.96 wt % H_2O, 85 wt % solids (9.08 wt % <325 mesh solids), 7.15 pH of water phase.

Samples of the oil sand were soxhlet extracted with dichloromethane for 72 h to afford the bitumen which was deasphaltened by the addition of a large excess of *n*-pentane to a concentrated solution of bitumen in dichloromethane as previously described (Ignasiak *et al.*,

1977). The resultant asphaltene was then pre-extracted with *n*-pentane for 48 h by soxhlet to afford the purified asphaltene, c. 18.1% of the bitumen. The maltene was fractionated by silica gel (Merck Silica Gel 60; 1:30 w/w) column chromatography into the crude saturated hydrocarbons, aromatic and resin fractions by step-wise elution with hexane (Skelly Solve B), benzene and methanol, respectively. The purified saturate fraction was obtained by TLC (10% Ag⁺ on silica gel G w/w; 100% Skelly Solve B developer; R_f 0.9–1.0) of aliquots of the crude saturated hydrocarbon fraction. No further purification of the resin fraction was carried out.

METHODS

Isolation of tricyclic terpanes concentrate

A concentrate of the tricyclanes was isolated from the saturated hydrocarbon fraction (SHC) by a modification of the procedure used by Pym *et al.* (1975) for concentrating pentacyclic triterpanes in crude oils. 1.98 g of the SHC was chromatographed on a 3 m × 14 mm O.D. glass column packed with 260 g of neutral alumina (CAMAG) by elution with *n*-pentane at a flow rate of ~30 ml/h. The solute front emerged after 6.0 h and >95% of the tricyclanes were concentrated within a fraction that was collected for 30 min after 1 h 40 min from the emergence of the solute front. This fraction was then clathrated by urea and thiourea (Rubinstein and Strausz, 1979), finally yielding a thiourea non-adduct (TUNA) fraction, c. 7% of the SHC, which was the tricyclic terpane concentrate.

Thermal alteration experiments

2.0–2.5 g of asphaltene, resin, maltene and SHC fractions were each placed in a thick-walled glass tube (12 cm × 2.6 cm O.D.) which was then sealed after evacuation (~0.1 torr). Pyrolysis was accomplished by heating at 300 °C for 72 h (Rubinstein *et al.*, 1979). The glass tubes were broken after cooling with liuqid N_2 and the pyrolyzates retrieved by 48 h-soxhlet extraction with dichloromethane in the case of asphaltene or *n*-pentane for the others. The purified saturated hydrocarbon fraction was obtained in each case by TLC (10% Ag⁺) of the *n*-pentane or deasphaltened dichloromethane extracts. 10–20 mg of each SHC fraction was then dewaxed by refluxing for 48 h in isoctane with 5 Å molecular sieves (Rubinstein *et al.*, 1977) to afford the molecular sieve non-adduct fractions consisting of the branched and cyclic alkane components. Due to the relatively large quantities of acyclic alkanes in the SHC of the asphaltene pyrolyzates, clathration in that case was by urea and thiourea adduction. The thiourea non-adduct, which was analogous to the branched and cyclic alkane fractions of the maltene and resins, contained >95% of the tricyclanes (checked by gc/ms cross scans).

Pyrolyses of whole oil sand were accomplished by heating ~4.0 g portions of the oil sand in Carius tubes, as described above, for 6, 12, 24, and 72 h. Soxhlet extraction of the pyrolysis products with dichloromethane in each case afforded thermally altered bitumen which was then de-asphaltened as usual. The SHC fraction isolated from the resultant maltene by silver TLC was then adducted by molecular sieve to yield the branched and cyclic alkane fraction as described above.

Gas chromatography (gc)

Analytical gc runs were carried out on a 60 m × 0.25 mm WCOT glass-capillary column, stationary phase OV 101, fitted to a Hewlett Packard 5830A gas chromatography which was interfaced to a Hewlett Packard 18850A integrator. The carrier gas (He) flow rate was ~3.0 ml/min; the split ratio, 1:10, and the injector and flame ionization detector temperatures were 285° and 350 °C, respectively. The oven was heated from 140–280 °C at a rate of 2°/min. The maximum column efficiency obtainable was c. 104 088 theoretical plates for n-C_{28} alkane at 260 °C. Kovats indices of the tricyclanes were computed after isothermal analyses (215 °C and 230 °C) from adjusted retention time data (Ettre, 1967).

Quantitative measurements were made according to the method of Ettre (1967). The oven was programmed from 100–280 °C at a rate of 1.5 °C/min and the other conditions were as described above for the analytical runs. In order to ensure uniformity of conditions, 2 μl of an isooctane solution of the branched and cyclic alkane fraction was injected into the gas chromatograph with the same syringe in each case. The soluble concentration of each tricyclic terpane was computed from the corresponding integrator counts multiplied by the predetermined response factor for the C_{23} tricyclane, the C_{23} tricyclic terpane having previously been isolated from a concentrate of the cycloalkanes by preparative gc (Ekweozor and Strausz, 1981). Only a narrow margin of error should result from the assumption that each member of the entire series of tricyclanes had the same response factor (Ettre, 1967).

Gas chromatography–mass spectrometry (gc/ms)

Mass spectral data were acquired automatically from an AEI MS 12 mass spectrometer coupled via a Watson–Biemann separator to a Varian 1400 gc and interfaced to a Data General Corporation Nova 2 computer (Rubinstein *et al.*, 1977). Either a 3 m × 3 mm stainless steel column packed with 3% Dexsil 400 on Chromosorb W AW DMCS 100/120 mesh or a 3 m × 3 mm stainless steel column packed with 3% OV-17 on Gas-Chrom Q 80/100 mesh was fitted into the gc. In each case, the column was heated from 110 °C to 300 °C at a rate of 4 °C/min.

RESULTS

The composition and distribution of the tricyclic alkanes in the saturated hydrocarbon fraction of the oil sand bitumen

Figure 1 shows the gas chromatogram of the branched and cyclic alkane fraction of the saturates of the Athabasca oil sand. The gas chromatogram of a concentrate of the tricyclanes is shown in Fig. 2 (see the Experimental Section for the method of isolating the tricyclane concentrate). The peaks numbered 1–12 represent the C_{19}–C_{30} tricyclic alkanes. The late-eluting components, peaks 13–24 are mainly C_{27}–C_{35} pentacyclic triterpanes (hopanes; Fig. 1). Figure 3 shows the total ion chromatogram (TIC) and the m/e 191 mass chromatogram of the same tricyclane concentrate, while the mass spectra of the entire series, except for the C_{27} member, are presented in Figs. 4–15.

The molecular formulae of the C_{19}–C_{30} cycloalkanes are, respectively, $C_{19}H_{34}$ (peak 1), $C_{20}H_{36}$ (peak 2), $C_{21}H_{38}$ (peak 3), $C_{22}H_{40}$ (peak 4), $C_{23}H_{42}$ (peaks 5a and 5b), $C_{24}H_{44}$ (peak 6), $C_{25}H_{46}$ (peaks 7a and 7b), $C_{26}H_{48}$ (peaks 8a and 8b), $C_{27}H_{50}$ (peak 9), $C_{28}H_{52}$ (peaks 10a

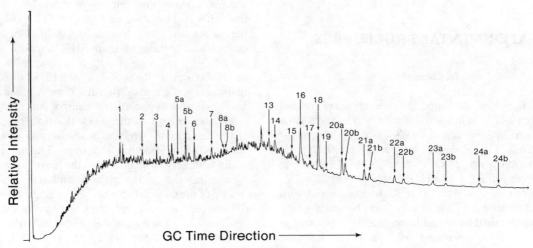

Fig. 1. Gc of branched and acyclic alkanes fraction of the saturates of the Athabasca bitumen.

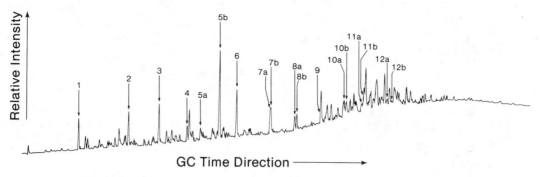

Fig. 2. Gc of a concentrate of the tricyclic alkanes of the Athabasca bitumen.

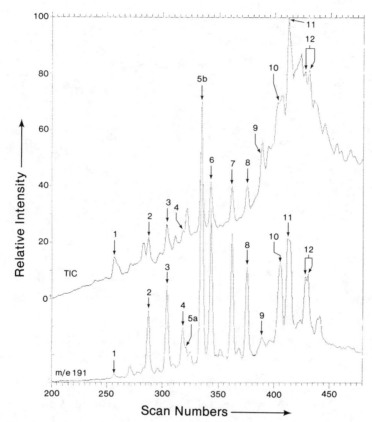

Fig. 3. TIC and *m/e* 191 chromatogram of the tricyclanes concentrate.

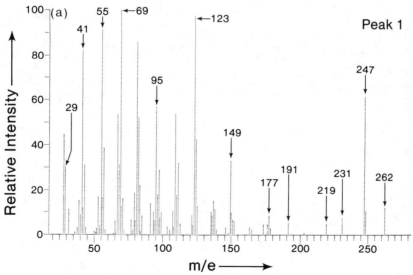

Fig. 4. Mass spectrum of the $C_{19}H_{34}$ tricyclane (peak 1).

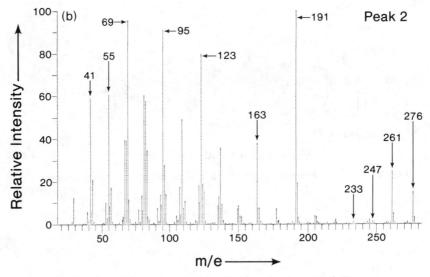

Fig. 5. Mass spectrum of the $C_{20}H_{36}$ tricyclane (peak 2).

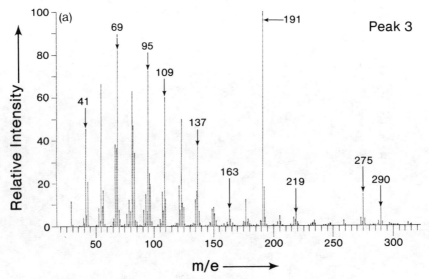

Fig. 6. Mass spectrum of the $C_{21}H_{38}$ tricyclane (peak 3).

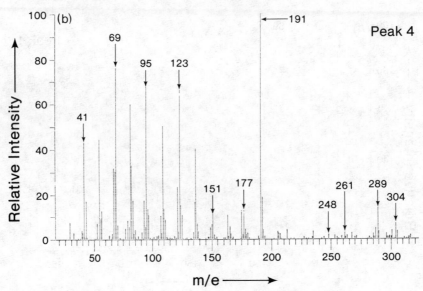

Fig. 7. Mass spectrum of the $C_{22}H_{40}$ tricyclane (peak 4).

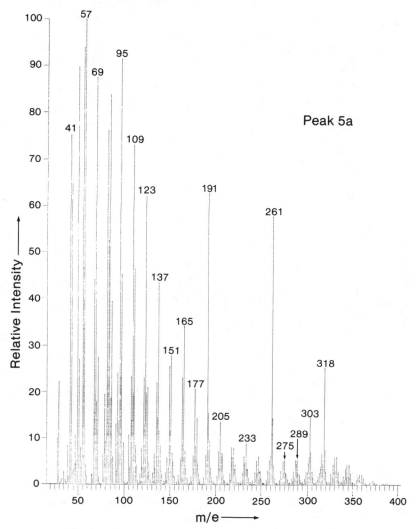

Fig. 8. Mass spectrum of a $C_{23}H_{42}$ tricyclane (peak 5a).

and 10b), $C_{29}H_{54}$ (peaks 11a and 11b), and $C_{30}H_{56}$ (peaks 12a and 12b). These molecular formulae correspond to a homologous series of tricyclic alkanes with the C_{23} as well as the $> C_{24}$ members occurring as isomeric pairs (see Fig. 2).

The mass spectra of the C_{20}–C_{30} tricyclanes show a base peak at m/e 191 (except peak 5a, Fig. 2) and intense M^+ and M^+-15 as well as diagnostic fragment ions at m/e 219, 261, 275, 289, 303, 317, 331, and 345 in most relevant cases. The spectral data are consistent with a basic carbocyclic skeleton such as 1 as had been noted before (e.g., Anders and Robinson, 1971). The determination of the exact chemical structure is in progress (Ekweozor and Strausz, 1982). Although it was not possible to obtain the spectrum of the C_{27} homologue (peak 9, Fig. 2), because it was highly contaminated by the ions from a relatively more preponderant co-eluting sterane (5β cholestane?), there is no doubt that the tricyclane is also present, as evidenced by the m/e 191 and M^+ mass chromatograms in Fig. 3 and Fig. 16, respectively.

The Kovats indices (I_x) of the entire series of tricyclic alkanes were determined as 215 °C and 230 °C, Table 1. The I_x values ranged from 1926 (peak 1)–2839 (peak 12b) and 1952 (peak 1)–2868 (peak 12b) at 215 °C and

230 °C, respectively. The plot of the logarithm of the adjusted retention times ($\log R_x$) *versus* the numbers of carbon atoms per molecule of the tricyclanes is essentially linear, Fig. 17. Deviations from the linear relationship are clearly evident for the C_{19} and C_{24} homologues and less so for the C_{29} tricyclane.

The absolute concentration of each tricyclane per gram of the oil sand was also determined, Table 1. The values ranged from 2.6–40.2 μg. These values correspond to 0.15–2.41 mg per gram of the saturated hydrocarbon fraction of the oil sand bitumen. The combined content of the C_{19}–C_{30} tricyclic alkanes is 143.40 μg g^{-1} of the oil sand or 9.29 mg g^{-1} of the saturated hydrocarbon fraction. The C_{19}–C_{26} members comprise $\sim$90% of the entire tricyclane content.

The composition and distribution of the tricyclic alkanes in the maltene pyrolyzates (300 °C, 72 h)

Figure 18 shows the m/e 191 mass chromatogram of the branched and cyclic fraction of the maltene pyrolyzates. All members of the tricyclic alkane series are present in various amounts, Table 2. The range of concentrations is

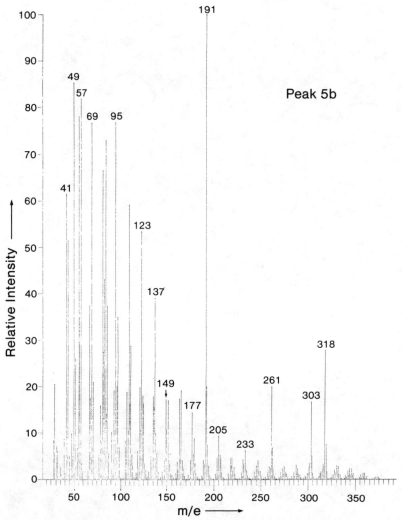

Fig. 9. Mass spectrum of a $C_{23}H_{42}$ tricyclane (peak 5b).

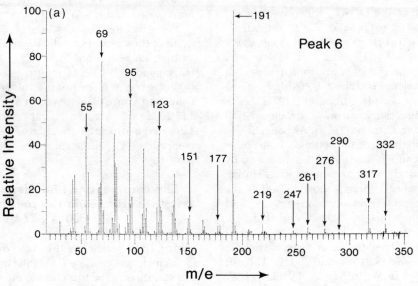

Fig. 10. Mass spectrum of the $C_{24}H_{44}$ tricyclane (peak 6).

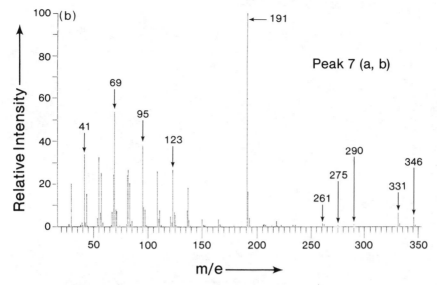

Fig. 11. Mass spectrum of the $C_{25}H_{46}$ tricyclane (peak 7a, b).

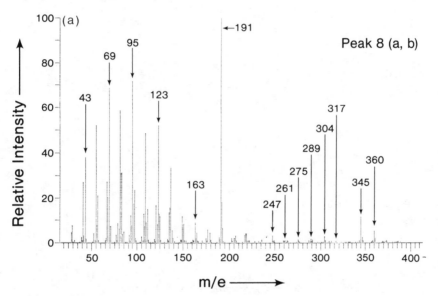

Fig. 12. Mass spectrum of the $C_{26}H_{48}$ tricyclane (peak 8a, b).

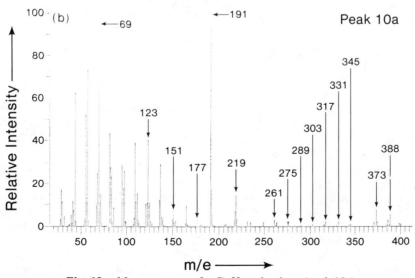

Fig. 13. Mass spectrum of a $C_{28}H_{52}$ tricyclane (peak 10a).

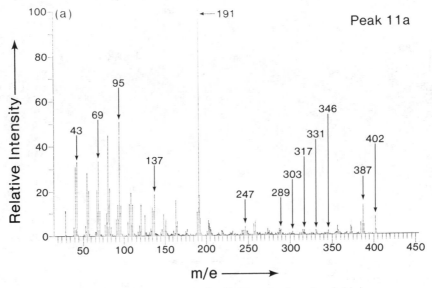

Fig. 14. Mass spectrum of a $C_{29}H_{54}$ tricyclane (peak 11a).

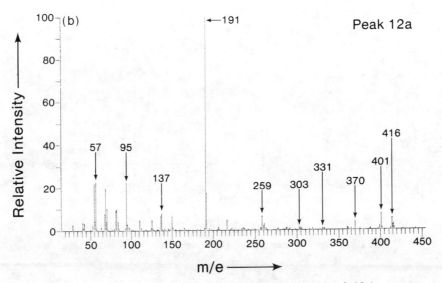

Fig. 15. Mass spectrum of a $C_{30}H_{56}$ tricyclane (peak 12a).

0.21–1.72 mg g⁻¹ of the saturated hydrocarbon fraction of the pyrolyzates or 3.2–26.5 µg g⁻¹ of the equivalent oil sand. The equivalent oil sand (EOS) is simply the hypothetical quantity of the unpyrolyzed oil sand that would contain the corresponding amount of the bitumen fraction, e.g. maltene, resin, etc. The equivalent oil sand concept facilitates easy comparison of the contents of the tricyclanes in the various bitumen fraction (natural and unpyrolyzed) as well as in the whole oil sand pyrolyzates (*vide infra*). The combined content of the C_{19}–C_{26} tricyclanes in the maltene pyrolyzates is 107.2 µg g⁻¹ EOS as compared to 128.5 µg g⁻¹ EOS for unpyrolyzed maltene.

The composition and distribution of the tricyclic alkanes in the resin pyrolyzates (300 °C, 72 h)

Figure 19 shows the m/e 191 mass chromatogram of the branched and cyclic alkane fraction of the resin pyrolyzates. The C_{22} member as well as the $> C_{25}$ homologues are present only in trace amounts. The contents of the rest of the tricyclanes were quantified, Table 2; of these, the C_{20} and C_{23} members constitute ~90%. The occurrence of the C_{23} tricyclane isomer with shorter retention time (i.e. peak 5a, Fig. 19) is documented here for the first time. This cycloalkane is

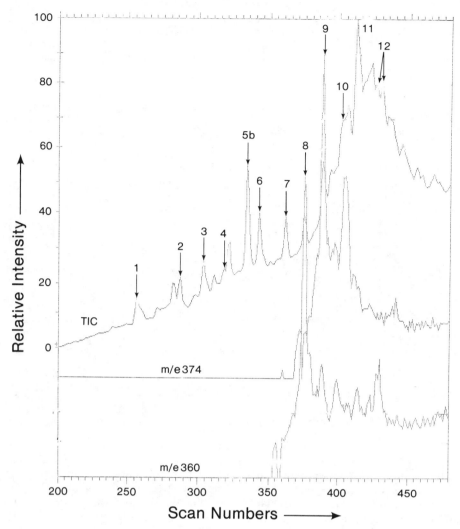

Fig. 16. TIC and molecular ion mass chromatograms of the tricyclane concentrate.

present in relatively high concentration in the saturates of the resin pyrolyzates (2.13 mg g^{-1} of saturates) and of the asphaltene pyrolyzates but occurred in much lower amounts in the corresponding fraction of the natural maltene (0.17 mg g^{-1}). It has a peculiar mass spectrum, indicating very facile loss of the alkyl side chain, Fig. 5a.

Although a few tricyclanes are highly concentrated in the saturates of the resin pyrolyzates, the total content of the C$_{19}$–C$_{26}$ compounds is only 12.5 µg g^{-1} EOS, one order of magnitude less than in unpyrolyzed oil sand, that is, the natural maltene, Table 1.

The composition and distribution of the tricyclic alkanes in the asphaltene pyrolyzates (300 °C, 72 h)

Figure 20 shows the *m/e* 191 mass chromatogram of the thiourea non-adduct fraction of the saturates isolated from the pyrolyzate of the asphaltene component of the Athabasca oil sand bitumen. The entire series of tricyclanes is present and the corresponding quantitative data are shown in Table 2. The C$_{20}$ and C$_{23}$ members are again present in relatively high amounts but constitute only ~65% of the combined content of the C$_{19}$–C$_{26}$ tricyclanes compared to ~90% in resin pyrolyzates;

~40% in maltene pyrolyzates; ~40% in natural maltene. The total concentration of the C$_{19}$–C$_{26}$ tricyclanes in the asphaltene pyrolyzates, 204.4 µg g^{-1} EOS, is significantly higher than in the resin pyrolyzates (12.5 µg g^{-1} EOS), maltene pyrolyzates (107.2 µg g^{-1} EOS) and natural maltene (128.5 µg g^{-1} oil sand).

The composition and distribution of the tricyclanes in the pyrolyzates of whole oil sand.

Figures 21 a, b, c, d show the gas chromatograms of the branched and cyclic alkane fraction obtained after pyrolysis of the Athabasca oil sand for 6, 12, 24 and 72 h. The absolute concentrations of the C$_{19}$–C$_{26}$ tricyclanes were determined in each case, Table 3. The combined concentrations of the C$_{19}$–C$_{26}$ tricyclanes in the 6, 12, 24 and 72 h pyrolyzates are 194.3, 56.7, 59.2 and 102.8 µg g^{-1} oil sand, respectively. The corresponding yields of the total saturated hydrocarbon fractions from the pyrolyses are, respectively, 23.9, 12.3, 10.1 and 23.0 mg g^{-1} oil sand. The high yield of tricyclanes from the 6 h pyrolyzates parallels only that of the asphaltene pyrolyzates, Table 2. The contents of individual tricyclanes also varied with pyrolysis time. Thus, 5.9 and

Table 1

Kovats indices and absolute concentrations of the tricyclic alkanes of the Athabasca oil sand

Peak number[a]	Tricyclane Molecular formula	Kovats Index (I_x)[b] I_x at 215°C	I_x at 230°C	Absolute concentration g^{-1} of saturated hydrocarbons fraction (mg)	g^{-1} of oil sand (μg)
1	$C_{19}H_{34}$	1926	1952	0.68	11.4
2	$C_{20}H_{36}$	2058	2068	0.35	5.8
3	$C_{21}H_{38}$	2137	2166	0.72	12.0
4	$C_{22}H_{40}$	2209	2242	0.29	4.9
5a	$C_{23}H_{42}$	2248	2257	0.17	2.8
5b	$C_{23}H_{42}$	2296	2319	2.41	40.2
6	$C_{24}H_{44}$	2345	2366	1.60	26.6
7a	$C_{25}H_{46}$	2447	2467	1.17	17.8
7b	$C_{25}H_{46}$	2450			
8a	$C_{26}H_{48}$	2527	2549	0.23	3.2
8b	$C_{26}H_{48}$	2536	2555	0.42	3.8
9	$C_{27}H_{50}$	2604	2632	n.d.[c]	n.d.
10a	$C_{28}H_{52}$	2692	2714	0.54	9.5
10b	$C_{28}H_{52}$	2699	2720		
11a	$C_{29}H_{54}$	2750	2766	0.20	3.5
11b	$C_{29}H_{54}$	2751	2774		
12a	$C_{30}H_{56}$	2826	2858	0.15	2.6
12b	$C_{30}H_{56}$	2839	2868		

[a] Peak numbers refer to Fig. 2.
[b] GC conditions: 60 m × 0.25 mm WCOT glass capillary column, stationary phase OV 101 (cf. Experimental section).
[c] Not determined.

22.3 μg g^{-1} (of oil sand) of the C_{19} member were afforded by the 12 h and 72 h pyrolyzates, respectively. This increasing generation of relatively lower molecular weight tricyclanes was accompanied by significant decreases in the amounts of C_{23} and higher homologues. Thus, the concentration of the C_{24} tricyclane dropped from 32.7 to 13.9 μg g^{-1} after 6 and 72 h pyrolysis, respectively.

DISCUSSION

The origin of the tricyclic alkanes of the Athabasca oil sand

Although a full report on the basic chemical structure of the tricyclanes is to be published elsewhere (Ekweozor and Strausz, 1982), a brief discussion of the mass spectral and retention data of the cycloalkanes as they relate to certain aspects of the proposed structure will be presented here for the sake of coherency.

The salient features of the mass spectra of the C_{20}–C_{30} cycloalkanes (Figs. 4–15), such as the very intense *m/e* 191 ion, are consistent with at least the A and B ring portions of structure *1* of Anders and Robinson, 1971 (see Introduction).

The mono-acid fraction of the saponifiable portion of the unpyrolyzed resin and asphaltene fractions from the same Athabasca oil sand sample was dominated by the C_{21} and C_{24} tricyclic acids, which afforded mass spectra (methyl esters) that correlated well with those of the C_{20} and C_{23} hydrocarbons (Cyr *et al.*, in prep.).

Therefore, a precursor–product relationship might exist between the tricyclic acids/acid derivatives of the unaltered resin (and asphaltene) and the tricyclanes of the corresponding pyrolyzates.

The mass spectra of the two isomeric C_{23} tricyclanes differ most significantly in the intensities of the *m/e* 261 (or 262) (M$^+$–C$_4$H$_9$, with or without hydride transfer; loss of the alkyl group R, *1*; c. Figs. 8 and 9). The apparently highly facile side-chain loss for the less abundant C_{23} tricyclane isomer (peak 5a, Fig. 19) is clearly indicative of the presence of a hindered alkyl group attached to the ring C (*1*). The relatively low abundance of the same compound in the natural maltene (c. Tables 1 and 2) supports the conclusion that it is thermodynamically less stable than the predominant isomer, peak 5b (Fig. 19). The simplest explanation of the relatively greater abundance of the apparently less stable C_{23} tricyclane in the resin pyrolyzate is that decarboxylation of the corresponding C_{24} tricyclic acid derivatives during pyrolysis generates a planar C$^+$ or C at the point of attachment of the alkyl side chain to the rinc C, thus favouring equally the formation of epimers *2* and *3*. The epimer with the 14α alkyl substituent should be less stable (Hirsch, 1974) and consequently the activation energy required for its formation should be higher than for epimer *3*.

756

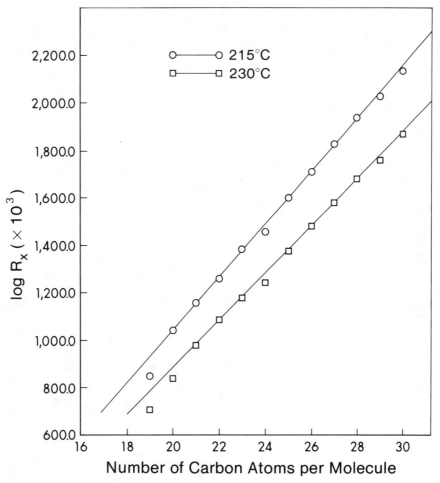

Fig. 17. Logarithms of the adjusted retention times of the tricyclanes versus the corresponding number of carbon atoms per molecule.

Therefore, thermolysis at 300 °C results in the generation of a relatively greater abundance of epimer *2* than would be the case during natural petroleum diagenesis and maturation. Hence, it follows that the alkyl side chains of the C_{21}–C_{30} tricyclanes of the natural maltene are most probably oriented as shown in *3*.

Mass spectral and retention time data of the C_{22}–C_{30} tricyclanes, some of which are being presented here for the first time, have also shed some light on the structure of the alkyl side chain, R (*2*). On going from the C_{23} tricyclanes to the C_{30} member, the mass spectra showed a series of low intensity fragment ions, at *m/e* 275(276), 289(290), 303(304), 317, 331(332) and 345(346), typical of fragmentation, with or without hydride transfer of long chain alkanes. On a high efficiency capillary column, the C_{25}–C_{30} tricyclanes were resolved into pairs of isomers (Fig. 2, Table 1). A plot of the logarithm of the adjusted retention times versus the number of carbon atoms per molecule of the cycloalkanes was linear, confirming partial acyclic alkane-type homology (Ettre, 1967), but showed diagnostic deviations for the C_{19}, C_{24} and C_{29} members (Fig. 17). These observations are consistent with a branched acyclic alkane structure, *4*, or portions thereof, for the tricyclane side chain.

A chiral centre is therefore present at the C-17 position, giving rise to the existence of pairs of diastereoisomers (R and S; ratio approximately 1:1) for the tricyclanes having more than 5 carbon atoms on the side-chain (i.e. the C_{25}–C_{30} members). Similarly, the chiral centre at C-21 should generate a second pair of C_{30} diastereoisomers. Mass spectral data confirm the occurrence of one pair; the other pair is probably also present but in relatively lower concentration as evidenced by the *m/e* 191

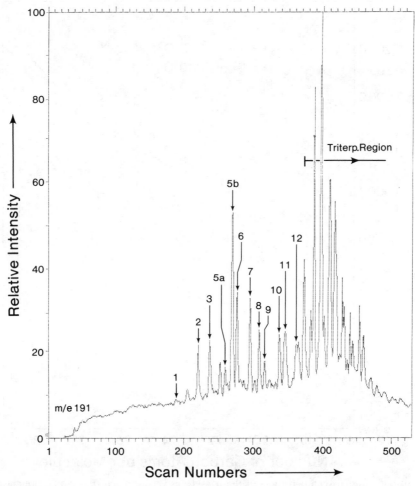

Fig. 18. The m/e 191 chromatogram of the branched and cyclic alkanes fraction of the maltene pyrolyzates.

Table 2

Absolute concentrations of the C_{19}–C_{26} tricyclanes in the saturates of the pyrolyzed fractions of the Athabasca oil sand bitumen[a] maltene (a); resin (b); asphaltene (c)

	(a) Concentration in maltene pyrolyzates		(b) Concentration in resin pyrolyzates		(c) Concentration in asphaltene pyrolyzates	
Tricyclane carbon no.	g^{-1} saturated hydrocarbon fraction (mg)	g^{-1} equivalent oil sand[b] (μg)	g^{-1} saturated hydrocarbon fraction (mg)	g^{-1} equivalent oil sand (μg)	g^{-1} saturated hydrocarbon (mg)	g^{-1} equivalent oil sand (μg)
C_{19}	1.07	16.4	0.90	0.7	4.45	18.2
C_{20}	0.82	12.6	5.02	4.0	11.85	48.6
C_{21}	0.66	10.2	0.65	0.5	7.06	28.9
C_{22}	0.31	4.8	trace	trace	1.35	5.5
[a]C_{23}(a)	0.21	3.2	2.13	1.7	2.45	10.0
C_{23}(b)	1.72	26.5	6.63	5.3	18.58	76.1
C_{24}	1.00	15.5	0.27	0.2	3.08	12.6
C_{25}(a, b)	0.78	12.1	0.12	0.1	0.47	1.9
[d]C_{26}(a)	0.19	2.9	trace	trace	0.63	2.6
C_{26}(b)	0.19	3.0				

[a] Pyrolysis temp.: 300°C; duration: 72 h.
[b] g^{-1} equivalent oil sand refers to the concentration of the tricyclane in a gram of the corresponding oil sand computed from the known proportion of the bitumen fraction in unpyrolyzed oil sand.
[c] C_{23}(a), C_{23}(b) are the two C_{23} tricyclane isomers (see peaks 5a and 5b, Fig. 2).
[d] C_{26}(a) and C_{26}(b) are the two C_{26} tricyclane isomers.

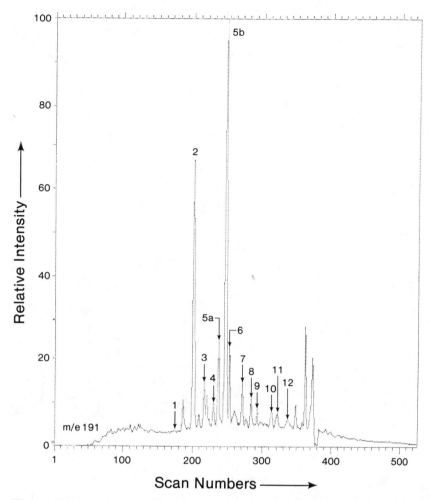

Fig. 19. The *m/e* 191 mass chromatogram of the branched and cyclic alkanes of the resin pyrolyzates.

chromatogram, Fig. 3. Further evidence in support of the assignment for the first branch-point on the side-chain comes from the relatively low abundances of the C_{22} tricyclane in the natural maltene as well as in the various pyrolyzates (Tables 1, 2 and 3). The formation of the C_{22} tricyclane by C–C cleavage from higher members (C_{24}–C_{30}) is not expected to be a favourable process since that would involve simultaneous cleavages of geminal C–C bonds; hence the observed low abundances on the C_{22} member.

Simoneit and Kaplan (1980) and Venkatesan *et al.* (1980) have recently reported the occurrence of diastereomeric pairs (R and S) of the C_{26}–C_{30} tricyclanes. It is most likely that the C_{25} epimers were also present in their sample but they eluded detection on account of inadequate gas chromatographic resolution.

The data now available to us seem to rule out the possibility that the tricyclic alkanes with >25 C atoms per molecule are diterpenoid or sesterterpenoid derivatives which are usually C_{20} and C_{25} compounds, respectively. Since the highest member of the series had 30 C atoms per molecule, pending the outcome of the structural determination (Ekweozor and Strausz, 1982), it is reasonable to regard the C_{26}–C_{30} cycloalkanes as triterpenoid derivatives.

Naturally-occurring tricyclic triterpenoids are unknown, although *in vitro* cyclization of squalene 2,3-

oxide results in a tricyclic alcohol with a five membered C ring (van Tamelen *et al.*, 1966). However, a tricyclic sesterterpenoid, cheilanthatriol, 5, a fern constituent (Khan *et al.*, 1971) with a basic carbocyclic system similar to that being proposed for the Athabasca petroleum tricyclanes (Ekweozor and Strausz, 1982) is known.

Therefore, it is possible that some of the tricyclanes with <26 C atoms per molecule originated from appropriate sesterterpenoid precursors. Similarly, the possibility that some diterpenoids may also be the precursors of the cycloalkanes with <21 C atoms per molecule cannot be ruled out at this stage.

Free tricyclic carboxylic acids with 21 and 24 C atoms per molecule have been found to be present in relatively large amounts in a Pliocene crude oil from California (Seifert, 1975). It is not yet clear whether these so-called naphthenic acids have identical structures and similar

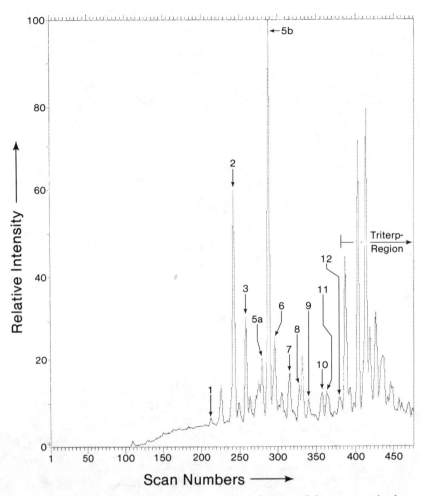

Fig. 20. The *m/e* 191 mass chromatogram of the thiourea non-adduct fraction of the saturates in the asphaltene pyrolyzate.

biotic source(s) as those of the corresponding C_{21} and C_{24} acids isolated from the saponifiable fraction of the resin and asphaltene of the Athabasca bitumen (Cyr *et al.*, in prep.). More work is now directed to isolating and identifying the tricyclic acid derivatives present in the Athabasca bitumen. The origin of the entire series of tricyclic terpanes cannot be completely explained until at least some of these possible precursors of the tricyclanes are identified.

The significance of the composition and distribution of the tricyclanes in the natural and thermally treated oil sand and pyrolyzed bitumen fractions

Unaltered maltene and pyrolyzed bitumen fractions The most dominant tricyclane in the natural maltene, peak 5b (Fig. 2; $C_{23}H_{42}$), has a concentration of 40.2 μg g^{-1} of the oil sand or 330 ppm of the corresponding bitumen fraction (% bitumen in the oil sand, c. 12.0). Another important geochemical marker, squalene, which was recently isolated from the same Athabasca oil sand, had a concentration of 200 ppm of the bitumen (Samman *et al.*, 1981). From the data of Anders and Robinson (1971) we have computed an abundance of 970 ppm for the C_{23} tricyclic terpane present in the bitumen of the Green River Shale.

Comparison of these abundance data with the reported highest concentrations, in oils, of some established geochemical markers such as pristane (5000 ppm; Bendoraitis *et al.*, 1962) and phytane (3000 ppm; Dean and Whitehead, 1961) clearly signifies that the tricyclanes were present in the shales and petroleums in quantitatively significant proportions.

A comparison of the aggregate amount of the C_{19}–C_{26} tricyclanes present in the unaltered maltene and in the products of 72 h pyrolysis (at 300 °C) of the maltene, resin, and asphaltene fractions implicates asphaltene as the most important source of the cycloalkanes within the oil sand bitumen (Fig. 22, Table 2). The resin fraction affords <10% of the yield of the asphaltene fraction.

It is significant that in the bitumen of the Athabasca oil sand, the tricyclic terpenoid derivatives appear to be mostly concentrated in the asphaltene fraction. Previous studies had established that several geochemical markers, such as sterol and triterpene derivatives, were also trapped within the polymeric matrix of the Athabasca asphaltene (Rubinstein *et al.*, 1979). Virtually all the squalene of the Athabasca bitumen was located in the asphaltene (Samman *et al.*, 1981). It is noteworthy also that some kerogens release significant amounts of tricyclic terpanes on pyrolysis (Gallegos, 1975; Seifert, 1978). Both kerogen and asphaltene are high molecular weight polymeric substances originating from sedimentary organic matter. Although it is

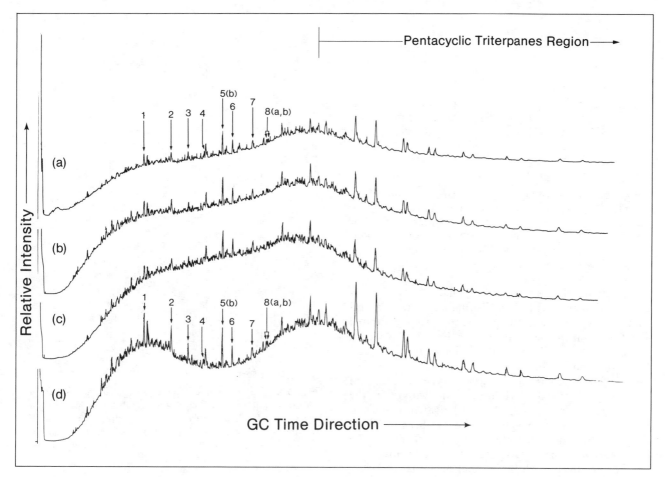

Fig. 21. Gc chromatograms of the branched and cyclic alkanes of the whole oil sand pyrolyzates: (a) 6 h; (b) 12 h; (c) 24 h; (d) 72 h.

Table 3

Absolute concentrations of the C_{19}–C_{26} tricyclanes in the saturates of whole pyrolyzed oil sand (300°C)

Tricyclane carbon number	Concentration in 6 h pyrolyzates		Concentration in 12 h pyrolyzates		Concentration in 24 h pyrolyzates		Concentration in 72 h pyrolyzates	
	g^{-1} SHC[a] (mg)	g^{-1} OS[b] (μg)	g^{-1} SHC (mg)	g^{-1} OS (μg)	g^{-1} SHC (mg)	g^{-1} OS (μg)	g^{-1} SHC (mg)	g^{-1} OS (μg)
C_{19}	0.99	23.6	0.48	5.9	0.70	7.0	0.97	22.3
C_{20}	0.77	18.4	0.31	3.8	0.53	5.3	0.60	13.7
C_{21}	0.80	19.1	0.43	5.2	0.57	5.7	0.64	14.7
C_{22}	0.30	7.1	0.09	1.2	0.31	3.1	0.06	1.5
C_{23}(b)	2.56	61.2	1.43	17.6	1.64	16.4	1.39	31.8
C_{24}	1.37	32.7	0.90	11.1	1.03	10.4	0.61	13.9
C_{25}(a, b)	1.03	24.8	0.60	7.4	0.68	6.9	0.15	3.4
C_{26}(a, b)	0.31	7.4	0.37	4.5	0.44	4.4	0.13	1.5

[a] Saturated hydrocarbon fraction.

[b] Oil sand.

believed that most of the geochemical markers released by pyrolysis of these substances were initially chemically bonded within the polymeric matrices (e.g. Gallegos, 1975; Samman *et al.*, 1981) no direct evidence for the presumed bond-breaking processes could so far be advanced. The precursor–product relationship which apparently exists between some tricyclic carboxylic acid derivatives of the asphaltene and resin fractions of the Athabasca petroleum and the tricyclanes of the corresponding pyrolyzates points to decarboxylation and related reactions as important processes governing the release of the biomarkers from the polymeric materials. In that case, at least some of the precursors of the tricyclic terpanes are most probably bound in the bitumen by carboalkoxyl bonds (ester linkages).

The C_{20} and C_{23} tricyclanes comprise relatively high

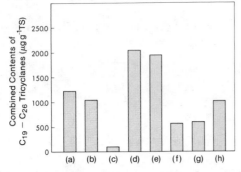

Fig. 22. Combined $(C_{19}-C_{26})$ tricyclanes contents of: (a) natural maltene; (b) maltene pyrolyzate; (c) resin pyrolyzate; (d) asphaltene pyrolyzate; (e) oil sand pyrolyzate, 6 h; (f) oil sand pyrolyzate, 12 h; (g) oil sand pyrolyzate, 24 h; (h) oil sand pyrolyzate, 72 h. (*OS — oil sand.)

proportions of the resin and asphaltene pyrolyzates when compared with their distribution in the natural maltene as well as in the pyrolyzates of the saturated hydrocarbon and maltene fractions (Fig. 22). Two main routes can be envisioned for the formation of the C_{20} and C_{23} tricyclanes. These are:

1. primary production, by decarboxylation of C_{21} and C_{24} tricyclic carboxylic acid derivatives in the bitumen fractions; $> C_{24}$ acid derivatives could also be involved although none has yet been found.
2. generation from higher tricyclic cycloalkanes by carbon–carbon cleavages of the side chains.

The relatively high proportions of the C_{20} and C_{23} cycloalkanes in the resin and asphaltene pyrolyzates when compared with the distribution of the same compounds in the pyrolyzates of the saturated hydrocarbon and maltene fractions strongly suggest that primary production of the hydrocarbon was still the dominant process throughout the 72 h pyrolysis of these bitumen fractions (Fig. 23). However, the proportions of these compounds in the products of the same 72 h pyrolysis of whole oil sand were significantly reduced (Fig. 23f). The most plausible explanation of this observation is that the more preponderant catalytic (mineral) surfaces of the oil sand substantially accelerated the rate of degradation of the cycloalkanes.

Pyrolyzates of whole oil sand The profound effect of mineral catalysis, occurring within the bulk oil sand, in substantially increasing the rates of both generation and degradation of the tricyclanes is even better demonstrated by the variations of the contents of the cycloalkanes in the 6, 12, 24 and 72 h pyrolyzates of the whole oil sand (Fig. 24, Table 3). Maximum production of the entire series appeared to have been achieved within the first 6 h of pyrolysis. After that, the yields of the cycloalkanes dropped significantly but commenced to increase again after about 12 h. The trends of the changing tricyclane contents become more evident when the absolute concentrations of individual cycloalkanes are plotted against pyrolysis time (Fig. 25).

The yields of the C_{23} tricyclane (peak 5b, Fig. 2) as well as those of the homologues with < 23 C atoms per molecule peaked within the first 6 h of pyrolysis and then sharply dropped to their lowest concentrations during

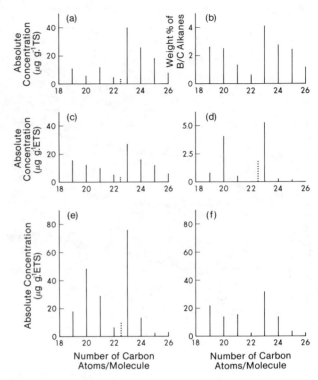

Fig. 23. Distribution of the $C_{19}-C_{26}$ tricyclanes in: (a) natural maltene; (b) saturates pyrolyzate; (c) maltene pyrolyzate; (d) resin pyrolyzate; (e) asphaltene pyrolyzate; (f) oil sand pyrolyzate, 72 h. (Stippled lines represent peak 5a, Fig. 2.) (*OS — oil sand; EOS — equivalent oil sand; B/C — branched/cyclic.)

the next 6 h. Thereafter (12–72 h), each of the tricyclanes with < 23 C atoms per molecule increased in absolute concentration while the content of the C_{23} member decreased. The concentrations of the tricyclanes with > 23 carbon atoms per molecule also decreased after 24 h of pyrolysis.

Therefore, at least 2 yield maxima of the tricyclic terpanes are distinguishable from Fig. 25 and Table 3.

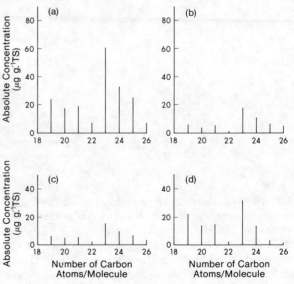

Fig. 24. Distribution of the $C_{19}-C_{26}$ tricyclanes in the: (a) 5 h; (b) 12 h; (c) 24 h; (d) 72 h oil sand pyrolyzates.

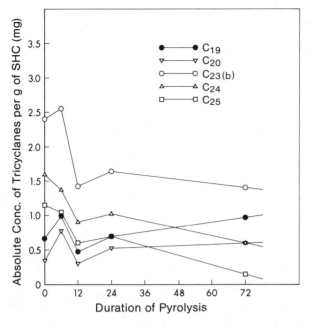

Fig. 25. Trends of the changing concentrations of the tricyclanes with increasing thermal stress (whole oil sand thermolyses).

thermal maturation of geological organic matter (e.g. Tissot and Welte, 1978). Therefore, the dominant processes in the second phase should correspond to the intensive transformations of the tricyclanes having relatively long alkyl substituents to shorter-chain homologues. Although there was an overall increase in the concentration of the combined C_{19}–C_{26} tricyclanes at this stage, the dominance of secondary degradation over primary generation under these extreme conditions resulted in significantly higher contents of the tricyclanes with < 23 C atoms per molecule relative to the $> C_{22}$ members.

Therefore, it appears as though the main stages of *in situ* geological maturation of petroleum, namely, primary generation of hydrocarbons from labile components followed by catagenesis, i.e. the degradation of the hydrocarbons by carbon–carbon cleavages and related reactions (Milner *et al.*, 1977), were effectively simulated in our thermal alteration experiments. This conclusion is confirmed by the parallel trends in the variations of the total saturates yields and the combined contents of the tricyclanes with increasing artificial maturation of the oil sand (Fig. 26).

Correlation of the distribution of tricyclic terpanes with maturity status of reservoired petroleum

It was demonstrated in the previous section that the variations in the distribution of petroleum tricyclanes arising from increasing thermal stress (*in vitro*) are both predictable and quantifiable. Thus, the tricyclic terpane content of an immature petroleum should be characterized by a relatively high abundance of primary tricyclanes such as the C_{23} homologue. On the other hand, in a mature crude oil, there should be a dilution of the concentration of the primary tricyclanes due to the additional generation of the cycloalkanes with shorter alkyl substituents. The relative concentrations of some key petroleum tricyclanes should, therefore, correlate with the different thermal histories of the oils, provided of course, that the biomass from which the oils evolved had similar abundances of the precursors of the cycloalkanes.

The concentration ratio that should be most sensitive to the two major competing processes during thermal alteration, i.e. primary production via de-functionalization and alkyl substituent degradation via carbon–carbon cleavage reactions, appears to be the one between the C_{23} and C_{21} tricyclic terpanes. While the C_{23} tricyclane was generated by decarboxylation and possibly other transformations of functionalized precursors, the C_{21} homologue was mainly produced by degradation of the side-chains of the tricyclanes with a longer alkyl substituent. Therefore, the C_{23}:C_{21} tricyclanes concentration ratio should be a sensitive and reliable indicator of the structural transformations taking place amongst the terpenoid derivatives as a result of the variations in thermal stress.

The increasing thermal stress on the Athabasca oil (*in vitro*) is reflected by different trends of the plots of the concentrations ratio C_{23}:C_x ($x = 19, 20, 21, 24$) versus the duration of thermal stress (Fig. 27). The C_{23}:C_{21} ratio

The first, which is also the highest, occurring within the first 6 h of pyrolysis for the C_{23} member and the tricyclanes with < 23 C atoms per molecule; the second, occurring after 72 h of pyrolysis for only the cycloalkanes with < 23 C atoms per molecule, notable the C_{19}, C_{20} and C_{21} members. These two different tricyclane yield maxima are most probably related to the major phases of production and degradation of the cycloalkanes.

The first phase, reflected by the first maximum, should correspond to the stage of intense primary production of the cycloalkanes by decarboxylation and other defunctionalization reactions of appropriate precursors as evidenced by the substantial relative proportions of the inferred primary tricyclanes such as the C_{20} and C_{23} members. On the other hand, since C_{20} and C_{22} tricyclic acids or their derivatives appear to be completely absent or present only in negligible amounts in the unaltered bitumen (Cyr *et al.*, in preparation), it was concluded that substantial generation of the C_{18} and C_{21} tricyclanes directly from functionalized precursors was likely to be of only limited significance. Therefore, the substantially high production of these cycloalkanes within the first 6 h of pyrolysis should more appropriately be attributed to mineral matter-catalyzed carbon–carbon cleavages of the corresponding cycloalkanes with relatively longer side-chains. This assertion is supported by the observed rapid decrease in concentration of the C_{24}, C_{25} and C_{26} members within the first 6 h of pyrolysis (Fig. 25).

The second maximum, which is observed only for the relatively low molecular weight tricyclanes (C_{19}–C_{21}) is accompanied by a corresponding minimum for the cycloalkanes with longer side-chains, i.e. the tricyclanes with > 22 C atoms per molecule. This is consistent with the well-known conversions of long-chain acyclic alkanes to shorter-chain members with increasing

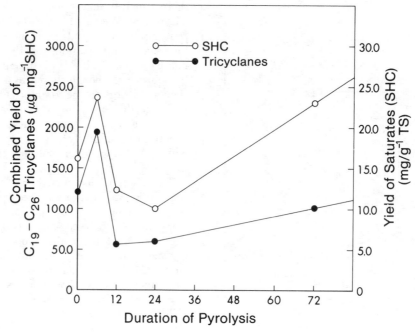

Fig. 26. Trends in the variations of the yields of the total saturates and the combined $(C_{19}-C_{26})$ tricyclanes contents of the natural and pyrolyzed whole oil sand.

was initially 3.4 in the unaltered oil sand ('zero thermal stress'), then dropped to 3.2 at the end of 6 h of pyrolysis, increasing once more to 3.3 within the next 6 h and subsequently decreasing steadily to 2.2 after 72 h of pyrolysis.

Since the tricyclic terpanes survive biodegradation of petroleum (e.g. Reed, 1977), it would appear that the ratio of the concentrations of the tricyclic terpane with 23 C atoms per molecule to that with 21 C atoms per molecule could be advantageously utilized as a measure of the thermal evolution of petroleum notwithstanding the secondary alterations history. This proposal is supported by our determination of the same ratio in a mature crude oil from the Bomu field, Nigeria. From gc peak area measurements of the tricyclane concentrate, the ratio of C_{23} tricyclane to C_{21} tricyclane was 0.9, a value significantly lower than the one obtained for the Athabasca oil.

SUMMARY AND CONCLUSIONS

1. An entire homologous series of tricyclic alkanes with 19–30 C atoms per molecule and distinguished by Kovats indices ranging from 1926–2839 and 1952–2868 at 215 °C and 230 °C, respectively, were identified in the saturated hydrocarbon fraction of the Athabasca bitumen. The absolute concentrations of the individual members of the series range from 2.6–40.2 $\mu g\ g^{-1}$ of the oil sand (20–330 ppm of the bitumen) with the $C_{19}-C_{26}$ homologues together constituting ~90% of the total tricyclanes content. Mass spectral fragmentation patterns of the cycloalkanes are consistent with a basic pentamethyl perhydrophenanthrene

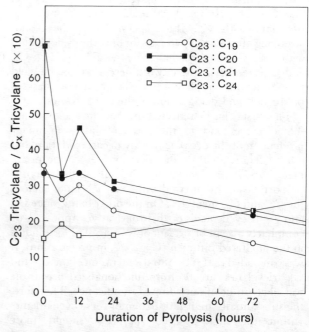

Fig. 27. Variations, with increasing thermal stress, of the concentrations of the C_{23} tricyclane relative to those of the C_{19}, C_{20}, C_{21} and C_{24} components.

structure possessing a branched acyclic substituent; the stereochemistry at the point of attachment to ring C appears to be beta to the plane of the rings. The tricyclanes with > 24 C atoms per molecule are present in pairs of diastereoisomers (R and S) in a ratio of approximately 1:1. A multiple origin of the cycloalkanes from various terpenoid classes is inferred from the spectral and other evidence. The series as a whole bears a parallel to the hopanoid pentacyclics.

2. Pyrolyses of the maltene, resin and the asphaltene fractions of the bitumen at 300 °C for 72 h yielded pyrolyzates which, respectively, afforded combined C_{19}–C_{26} tricyclanes contents of 107.2, 12.5 and 204.4 μg g^{-1} of the equivalent oil sand signifying that within the bitumen, the precursors of the cycloalkanes are mostly concentrated in the asphaltene fraction. An apparent precursor–product relationship between the C_{21} and C_{24} tricyclic acid derivatives of the unaltered resin and asphaltene with the C_{20} and C_{23} tricyclanes of the corresponding pyrolyzates led to the conclusion that, at least, some of the precursors of the tricyclic terpanes could be bound within the bitumen fractions by ester linkages.

3. Pyrolyses of the oil sand at 300 °C for 6, 12, 24 and 72 h yielded pyrolyzates which contained, respectively, 194.3, 56.7, 59.2 and 102.8 μg g^{-1} (of oil sand) of the combined C_{19}–C_{26} tricyclic terpanes. At least two tricyclic terpane yield maxima are distinguishable, the first maximum occurring within the first 6 h of pyrolysis and corresponding to the principal phase of primary production of the tricyclanes mainly by decarboxylation and other defunctionalization reactions and the second, probably occurring after 72 h and corresponding to mainly degradation of the cyclo-alkanes by carbon–carbon cleavage reactions. The variations in the combined contents of the C_{19}–C_{26} tricyclanes with increasing thermal stress are paralleled by the yields of the total saturates as well as by the changes in the concentrations of individual tricyclanes. The profound effect of mineral catalysis in accelerating both principal reactions was noted.

4. The concentration ratio of C_{23} to C_{21} tricyclic terpanes is proposed to be a useful measure of the thermal maturity of petroluem.

5. The detection of the tricyclic terpanes in the Athabasca oil sand bitumen constitutes additional evidence for the ubiquitous occurrence of this class of biomarkers in petroleums.

Acknowledgements

Financial support by the Natural Sciences and Engineering Research Council of Canada and Alberta Oil Sands Technology and Research Authority is gratefully acknowledged. The authors thank Dr M. L. Selucky for assistance in setting up the capillary gc, Mr J. Olekszyk for the gc/ms analyses and Dr D. S. Montgomery for his comments on the manuscript.

REFERENCES

Anders, D. E. and Robinson, W. E. (1971) Cycloalkane constituents of the bitumen from Green River Shale, *Geochim. Cosmochim. Acta* **35**, 661–678.

Aquino Neto, F. R., Trendel, J. M., Restle, A., Albrecht, P. and Connan, J. (1981) Tenth International Meeting on Organic Geochemistry, Program and Abstracts.

Bendoraitis, J. G., Brown, B. L. and Hepner, L. S. (1962) Isoprenoid hydrocarbons in petroleum. Isolation of 2,6,10,14-tetramethylpentadecane by high temperature gas–liquid chromatography. *Anal. Chem.* **34**, 49–53.

Connan, J., Restle, A. and Albrecht, P. (1979) Biodegradation of crude oil in the Aquitaine basin. *Prog. in Org. Geochem. (1979)*, p. 1.

Dean, R. A. and Whitehead, E. V. (1961) The occurrence of phytane in petroleum, *Tetrahedron Lett.* 768–770.

Deroo, G. and Powell, T. G. (1978) The oil sands deposits of Alberta: their origin and geochemical history. In *Oil Sand and Oil Shale Chemistry*. Ed. by Strausz, O. P. and Lown, E. M. Verlag Chimie. pp. 11–32.

Ekweozor, C. M. and Strausz, O. P. (1982). *Tet. Lett.* **23**, 2711–2714.

Ettre, L. S. (1967) The interpretation of analytical results; qualitative and quantitative analysis. In *The Practice of Gas Chromatography*. Ed. by Ettre, L. S. and Zlatkis, A. Interscience Publisher. pp. 373–406.

Evans, C. R., Rogers, M. A. and Bailey, N. J. L. (1971) Evolution of petroleum in Western Canada. *Chem. Geol.* **8**, 147–170.

Gallegos, E. J. (1971) Identification of new steranes, terpanes and branched paraffins in Green River Shale by combined capillary gas chromatography and mass spectrometry. *Anal. Chem.* **43**, 1151–1160.

Gallegos, E. J. (1975) Terpane–sterane release from kerogen by pyrolysis gas chromatography–mass spectrometry. *Anal. Chem.* **47**, 1524–1528.

Hirsch, J. A. (1974) *Concepts in Theoretical Organic Geochemistry*. Allyn and Bacon Inc., Boston. p. 255.

Ignasiak, T., Kemp-Jones, A. V. and Strausz, O. P. (1977) The molecular structure of Athabasca asphaltenes. Cleavage of the carbon–sulfur bonds by radical ion electron transfer reactions, *J. Org. Chem.* **42**, 312–320.

Khan, H., Zaman, A., Chetty, G. L., Gupta, A. S. and Dev, S. (1971) Cheilanthatriol — a new fundamental type in sesterterpenes. *Tet. Lett.* **46**, 4443–4446.

Milner, C. W. D., Rogers, M. A. and Evans, C. R. (1977) Petroleum transformations in reservoirs. *J. Geochem. Explor.* **7**, 101–153.

Montgomery, D. S., Clugston, D. M., George, A. E., Smiley, G. T. and Sawatzky, M. (1974) Investigation of oils in the Western Canada tar belt. *Can. Soc. Petrol. Geol. Mem.* **3**, 168–183, 184–185.

Pym, J. G., Ray, J. E., Smith, G. W. and Whitehead, E. V. (1975) Petroleum triterpane fingerprinting of crude oils. *Anal. Chem.* **47**, 1617–1622.

Reed, W. E. (1977) Molecular compositions of weathered petroleum and comparison with its possible source. *Geochim. Cosmochim. Acta* **41**, 237–247.

Rubinstein, I., Strausz, O. P., Spyckerelle, C., Crawford, R. J. and Westlake, D. W. S. (1977) The origin of the oil sand bitumens of Alberta: a chemical and a microbiological study. *Geochim. Cosmochim. Acta* **41**, 1347–1453.

Rubinstein, I. and Strausz, O. P. (1979) Geochemistry of the thiourea adduct fraction from an Alberta Petroleum. *Geochim. Cosmochim. Acta* **43**, 1387–1392.

Rubinstein, I., Spyckerelle, C. and Strausz, O. P. (1979) Pyrolysis of asphaltenes: a source of geochemical information, *Geochim. Cosmochim. Acta* **43**, 1–6.

Samman, N., Ignasiak, T., Chen, C. J., Strausz, O. P. and Montgomery, D. S. (1981) Squalene in petroleum asphaltenes. *Science* **213**, 1381–1383.

Seifert, W. K. (1975) Carboxylic acids in petroleum and sediments. *Fortschritte d. Chem. Org. Naturst.* **32**. Ed. by Herz, W., Grisebach, H. and Kirhy, G. W. Springer–Verlag. pp. 1–49.

Seifert, W. K. (1978) Steranes and terpanes in kerogen pyrolysis for correlation of oils and source rocks. *Geochim. Cosmochim. Acta* **42**, 473–484.

Seifert, W. K. and Moldowan, J. M. (1978) Applications of steranes, terpanes and monoaromatics to the maturation, migration and source of crude oils. *Geochim. Cosmochim. Acta* **42**, 77–95.

Seifert, W. K. and Moldowan, J. M. (1979) The effect of biodegradation on steranes and terpanes in crude oils. *Geochim. Cosmochim. Acta* **43**, 111–126.

Seifert, W. K., Moldowan, J. M. and Jones, R. W. (1980) Application of biological marker chemistry to petroleum exploration. 10th World Petroleum Congress, Bucharest, (1979). Special Paper SP8. Heyden & Son Ltd., London. pp. 425–440.

Simoneit, B. R. T. and Kaplan, I. R. (1980) Triterpenoids as molecular indicators of paleoseepage in recent sediments of the Southern California Bight. *Mar. Environ. Res.* **3**, 113–128.

Tamelen van, E. E., Willet, J., Schwartz, M. and Nadeau, R. (1966) Nonenzymic laboratory cyclization of squalene 2,3-oxide. *J. Am. Chem. Soc.* **88**, 5937–5938.

Tissot, B. P. and Welte, D. H. (1978) *Petroleum formation and occurrence.* Springer–Verlag.

Venkatesan, M. I., Brenner, S., Ruth, E., Bonilla, J. and Kaplan, I. R. (1980) Hydrocarbons in age-dated cores from two basins in the Southern California Bight. *Geochim. Cosmochim. Acts* **44**, 789–802.

Vigrass, L. W. (1968) Geology of Canadian heavy oil sands. *Bull. Am. Ass. Petr. Geol.* **52**, 1984–1999.

MISCELLANEOUS

Advances in Organic Geochemistry 1981, pp. 769–774.
© *John Wiley & Sons Limited, 1983*

Carbon Isotope Paleothermometry of Natural Gas

K. R. Sundberg and C. R. Bennett

Phillips Petroleum Company, Phillips Research Center, Bartlesville, Oklahoma 74004

The ^{13}C fractionation, or the relative values of the $^{13}C/^{12}C$ ratios, among the light hydrocarbon components of a wet petroleum gas define a paleothermometer. With appropriate isotopic and geologic data, the paleothermometer can be used to correlate gases with source rocks, estimate the age of a gas, and estimate paleotemperatures for use in other thermal studies. The $^{13}C/^{12}C$ ratios of the gas components depend on the isotopic composition of the gas precursor, the gas generation temperature, and the maturity of the source rock. For simple wet petroleum gases, the time, temperature and source effects are separable. In wet gas, the relative hydrocarbon carbon isotope compositions depend on the simple kinetic isotope effect. The Bigeleisen–Wolfsberg theory of the isotope effect is used to explain the relative wet gas isotope distributions in terms of a single variable corresponding to a gas generation temperature. The molecular force field calculations and isotopic bond number approximation by Galimov are used to evaluate the kinetic isotope effects as functions of temperature and produce a carbon isotope paleothermometer. When applied to a suite of gases from the Mississippi Interior Salt Dome Basin, the paleothermometer indicates a generation temperature of 105°C. Similar application to a suite of gases from Offshore Louisiana indicates a gas generation temperature of 120°C. Independent considerations of the geologic history, present day geothermal gradients, and organic geochemistry of the areas yield generation temperature estimates consistent with the predictions of carbon isotope paleothermometry.

CARBON ISOTOPE DISTRIBUTIONS IN NATURAL GAS

The ^{13}C fractionation, or the relative values of the $^{13}C/^{12}C$ ratios among the light hydrocarbon components of a gas, is expressed by ratios called fractionation factors. Between hydrocarbons C_mH_{2m+2} and C_nH_{2n+2}, this ratio

$$\alpha_{mn} = ([^{13}C]_m/[^{12}C]_m)/([^{13}C]_n/[^{12}C]_n),$$

implicitly depends on the gas precursor composition and maturity and the gas generation temperature (Amit and Bein, 1979; Fuex, 1977; Galimov, 1973; Galimov *et al.*, 1979; Garilov and Tiplinskiy, 1978; Prosolov and Logkev, 1977; Schoell, 1980; Silverman, 1964; Silverman and Epstein, 1958; Stahl, 1975, 1977; Stahl and Carey, 1975). Galimov (1980) has published an extended review of these issues. However, for a wet petroleum gas from a dominantly marine source, these effects can be separated, and the fractionation factors can be written in terms of temperature as the expansion

$$\log_e \alpha_{mn} = A_{mn} + B_{mn}(10^2)/T + C_{mm}(10^2/T)^2.$$

Here $[^{13}C]_m$ and $[^{12}C]_m$ are the amounts of ^{13}C and ^{12}C, respectively, associated with the hydrocarbon C_mH_{2m+2}. The expansion coefficients are shown in Table 1 for fractionations relative to methane. Fractionation factors for various temperatures are shown in Fig. 1.

Carbon isotope paleothermometry is basically the interpolation of an observed isotope distribution against the curves in Fig. 1, although the interpolation is formally accomplished by curve fitting using the coefficients in Table 1 and temperature as a variable. However, field data are frequently ambiguous because natural gases may be contaminated in different ways, and care must be taken to choose the right distribution for thermometry. The following examples illustrate some of these problems.

APPLICATIONS TO GASES FROM THE MISSISSIPPI INTERIOR SALT DOME BASIN

Paleothermometry and geochemistry of liquids and gases

Carbon isotope paleothermometry yields a generation temperature of 105 °C (Fig. 2) for gases from Pool Creek Field in the Mississippi Interior Salt Dome Basin, and this generation temperature is fairly typical for the area.

Based on geochemical data in Table 2 (Smith *et al.*, 1971), we conclude that the gases in this area of the basin are probably cogenetic; they are all associated with oils, and the isotopic data for the oils suggest they have a common source. Some oils, like those in Nancy Field (Fig. 3), are reservoired in the Smackover Formation, and for these oils, the Smackover Formation itself is a

Table 1

Expansion coefficients for $\log_e(\alpha_{m1})$ in terms of the reciprocal temperature. Determined by least squares fit to theoretical fractionation factors

Coefficients	$\log_e(\alpha_{21})$	$\log_e(\alpha_{31})$	$\log_e(\alpha_{41})$	$\log_e(\alpha_{51})$
A_{m1}	-4.896×10^{-3}	-6.930×10^{-3}	-8.327×10^{-3}	-9.220×10^{-3}
B_{m1}	6.062×10^{-2}	8.458×10^{-2}	9.987×10^{-2}	1.090×10^{-1}
C_{m1}	5.655×10^{-2}	6.484×10^{-2}	6.418×10^{-2}	6.382×10^{-2}

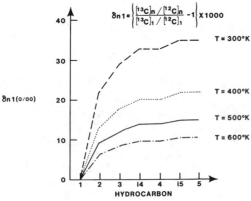

Fig. 1. Theoretical relative carbon isotope distributions for gases generated thermally from an isotopically uniform source material. Horizontal axis indicates hydrocarbons, C_1 (methane), C_2 (ethane), etc. Over the temperature ranges for petroleum genesis, there is no significant difference between the fractionation factors for the normal- and iso-hydrocarbons, and in this work, their isotopic compositions are set equal.

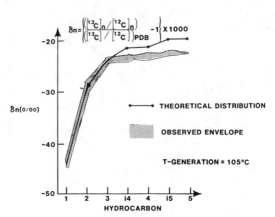

Fig. 2. Theoretical and observed carbon isotope distribution for gases from Pool Creek Field in the Mississippi Interior Salt Dome Basin. The generation temperature comes from fitting the isotopic composition of methane, ethane, and propane by the temperature and the coefficients in Table 1. Departures for the heavier hydrocarbon components are probably due to inhomogeneities in the source material.

Table 2

Carbon isotopic compositions of topped crude oils and natural gas components from Yellow Creek, Heidelberg, Pool Creek, and Nancy Fields in the Mississippi Interior Salt Dome Basin. (From Smith *et al.* 1971.)

Formation	Field	Depth[a]	Crude[b]	Methane	Ethane	Propane	i-Butane	Butane	i-Pentane	Pentane
Eutaw	Y-Creek, E.	4539	−24.8	−64.4		−32.0	−26.7	−24.1		
Eutaw	Y-Creek, E.	5121	−25.1	−62.3	−35.0	−28.3	−26.4	−24.0	−24.8	−21.8
Eutaw	Heidelberg, C	5060	−25.1	−40.4	−32.3	−28.5	−30.0	−26.3		
Eutaw	Heidelberg, E	4910	−25.4	−46.0	−32.8	−28.7	−29.2	−26.2	−26.7	−24.0
L. Tuscaloosa	Pool Creek	7246	−25.5	−40.7						
L. Tuscaloosa	Y-Creek, W	6736	−24.8	−39.6	−28.3	−28.9	−26.7	−25.7		
Paluxy	Pool Creek	9562	−25.0	−44.4	−28.7	−23.7				
Rodesa	Pool Creek	10765	−25.2	−44.0	−28.9	−23.5	−23.3	−23.5	−22.7	−22.6
Rodesa	Pool Creek	10710		−42.9	−27.5	−23.5	−22.8	−23.4	−22.3	−22.6
Pine Island	Pool Creek	10815	−25.0	−44.3	−29.4	−24.0	−23.7	−22.6	−22.8	−22.6
Sligo	Pool Creek	11142	−25.2	−43.7	−28.9	−23.6	−23.0	−22.5		−21.0
Smackover	Nancy	13413	−25.1	−50.1						

[a] Depth in feet
[b] δ-values in ‰ relative to PDB

likely source rock. Moreover, the oils and gases are reservoired all through the Cretaceous rocks (Fig. 3). Although the gases show a variety of carbon isotope distributions (Fig. 4), the Pool Creek gases show little isotopic variation and indicate that migration took place without much fractionation. Finally, the isotopic variability in the Yellow Creek and Heidelberg gases is probably due to modification in the reservoirs. These gases are associated with high sulphur crude oils, and they are reservoired in a sandstone–chalk system (Beebe,

1968) where modification is likely. In contrast, the Pool Creek gases are associated with lower sulphur oils and are reservoired in relatively inert sandstone.

Geological constraints on gas generation and the age of the gas

A gas generation temperature of 105 °C is physically reasonable for gases sourced in the Jurassic Smackover of

ERA	GROUP	FORMATION	FIELD	DEPTH	LITHOLOGY
C R E T A C E O U S	S E L M A	NAVARRO TAYLOR AUSTIN			
	T U S C A L O O S A	EUTAW	YELLOW CREEK HEIDELBERG HEIDELBERG YELLOW CREEK	4539' 4918' 5060' 5121'	SS, CHALK
	W A S H I T A	UPPER			
		LOWER	YELLOW CREEK	6736'	SS, SH
		PALUXY	POOL CREEK	9562'	
		RODESA	POOL CREEK POOL CREEK	10710 10710	SS, SILTSTONE, SH
		PINE ISLAND	POOL CREEK	10815'	LS, LIGNITE,
		SLIGO	POOL CREEK	11142'	PYRITE, MIC
		HOUSTON			
		COTTON VALLEY			
JURASSIC		SMACKOVER	NANCY		
		LOUANN			

Fig. 3. Generalized stratigraphic column for the Jurassic and Cretaceous in the Mississippi Interior Salt Dome Basin. Reservoirs in this study are distributed throughout the Cretaceous. Adapted from Beebe, 1968.

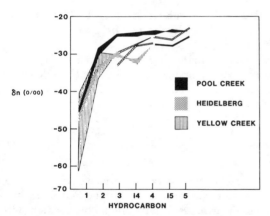

Fig. 4. Carbon isotope distributions observed throughout the area near Pool Creek Field. All the gases are associated with crude oils. The very tight distribution seen at Pool Creek probably corresponds to the true distributions for thermal gases generated in the Jurassic Smackover Formation. The Heidelberg and Yellow Creek oils are higher in sulphur (3–4%) than Pool Creek oils (1%), and their associated gases were probably modified in the reservoir.

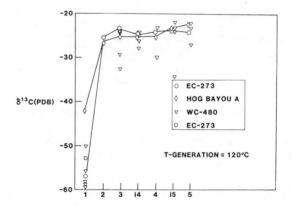

Fig. 5. Carbon isotope compositions of natural gases from East and West Cameron Parish, Offshore Louisiana. It appears that the gases are primarily thermal, but that contamination with early dry or biogenic gas is common. Furthermore, the close correspondences seen in the isotopic compositions of the heavier components of some of the gases indicate that there is a gas source common to both Parishes, however, there may be a second gas source in West Cameron. The Hog Bayou gas is the least contaminated gas and represents the basic isotope distribution for the thermal gases from the regional source. The gases are often wet, and they were probably generated from a marine source.

Mississippi. The modern Smackover is at about 130 °C in our study area (Smith, 1979), which sets an upper limit on the gas generation temperature. The Smackover has been in essentially continual subsidence in a thermally stable area since the late Cretaceous, and the formation has not been hotter than it is now. The minimum reasonable generation temperature is about 95 °C. This corresponds to a surface temperature of 25 °C, a geothermal gradient of 0.8 °C 100 ft and 8500 ft of sediment on top of the Smackover at the time of gas generation. The Austin Chalk, which locally caps the Jurassic hydrocarbons, is 8500 ft above the Smackover Formation (Smith, 1979). Hydrocarbon migration from the Smackover was probably rapid along faults caused by local salt movement so the cap rock was probably in place before the gas and oil genesis and migration.

Assuming our gas generation temperature is correct, the foregoing thermal data indicate that gas genesis in

the Smackover occurred under 10 000 ft of sediment in the late Cretaceous or early Tertiary.

APPLICATIONS IN EAST AND WEST CAMERON PARISH, OFFSHORE LOUISIANA

Paleothermometry and geochemistry of liquids and gases

Carbon isotope paleothermometry on gases from Hog Bayou (Fig. 5) in East Cameron Parish, Louisiana,

Table 3

Carbon isotopic compositions of the hydrocarbon components from gases from East and West Cameron Parish, Offshore Louisiana.

Location[a]	Methane	Ethane	Propane	i-Butane	Butane	i-Pentane	Pentane
EC-273	−57.3[b]	−25.8	−24.3	−25.2	−24.8	−24.2	−24.6
EC-273	−53.2						
Hog Bayou	−42.4	−26.7	−25.7	−25.7	−25.0	−23.7	−23.0
WC-480	−56.7		−24.5	−25.3	−23.6	−24.4	−23.8
WC-480	−50.7		−23.9	−24.8	−23.6	−22.1	−22.5
WC-480	−59.2		−32.6	−26.8		−34.8	
WC-480	−58.8		−29.5	−28.0	−30.0	−23.5	−27.2

[a] EC is East Cameron, WC is West Cameron. Hog Bayou is in East Cameron Parish.
[b] δ-values in ‰ relative to PDB.

indicates a gas generation temperature of 120 °C. Supporting data on other gases from East and West Cameron Parish (Table 3) suggest this value is characteristic for the area.

Many of the Offshore Louisiana gases contain a large fraction of early dry or biogenic methane, as indicated by the spread of $\delta^{13}C$ values for methane in Fig. 5. The thermal components of these gases appear to have only two sources, as we see in the close correspondence of the $\delta^{13}C$ values for the heavy gas components, and one of these is common to both East and West Cameron.

Although the methane fractions of these gases appear to have multiple sources, the Hog Bayou gas, which has the isotopically heaviest methane, is the most nearly pure thermal gas, and it is the best candidate for thermometry. This gas evolved from the common East and West Cameron source, and assuming a constant geothermal gradient for the area, we take its generation temperature as typical for all these gases.

Gas source rocks and gas generation depth

The source for the Hog Bayou type gas is probably in the Miocene below about 15 000 ft (Fig. 6). This depth corresponds to our isotopic generation temperature if we assume a warm water surface temperature of 15 °C and a geothermal gradient of 0.7 °C 100 ft (AAPG and

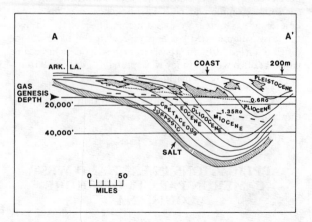

Fig. 6. Generalized cross section for Offshore Louisiana. The gas generation depth is determined by carbon isotope paleothermometry on the Hog Bayou gases. The oil generation window set by vitrinite reflectance was determined by Dow (1979). The probable oil and gas source in East Cameron is the large Miocene section below 15 000 ft.

USGS, 1976). This depth is also in the oil and gas generation window noted by Dow (1979) using vitrinite reflectance data (Fig. 6).

GAS GENESIS REACTIONS, KINETICS, AND ISOTOPE DISTRIBUTIONS

Reaction mechanisms and ^{13}C and ^{12}C balance in the gas

We assume that the genesis reactions for the hydrocarbon components are nominally independent, obey first-order kinetics, and that the mechanism can be written in the simple form:

$$T - C_n^j H_{2n+1} \rightarrow [T \ldots C_n^j H_{2n+1}] \neq \xrightarrow{[E]} C_n H_{2n+2} \cdot + \text{etc.}$$

[E] represents the general subsurface environment, and it is not specified except to say that it donates a hydrogen atom to the hydrocarbon functional being cracked from the precursor. The hydrogen atoms could come from the breakdown of the kerogen, petroleum-like hydrocarbons, or even from the mineral matrix of the source rock. Within the model used here, however, these sources are not isotopically different, because the major fractionation effects created by the carbon–carbon bond cleavage have already taken place. $[T \ldots C_n H_{2n+1}]^{\neq}$ is the activated complex (Eyring, 1935) the system passes through as it dissociates, and T is the body of the gas precursor. This model can reproduce the general features of the carbon isotope distribution in gases (Smith et al., 1971), and under the hypotheses used here, it is equivalent to some of the more advanced statistical models (Waples and Tornheim, 1978a, b). We assume only single isotope substitutions (that is that either all the carbon atoms in the functional $\cdot C_n H_{2n+1}$ are ^{12}C, or at most one carbon atom is a ^{13}C) so the rate equations for the gas genesis can be integrated to give both the gas yield and the ^{13}C and ^{12}C content of any gas component. Given the appropriate rate constants, we find

$$[^{12}C]_n = [T - C_n^0 H_{2n+1}]_0 [1 - \exp(-\tau_n^0)]$$

$$+ (n-1) \sum_j [T - C_n^j H_{2n+1}]_0 [1 - \exp(-\tau_n^j)].$$

Here $[T - C_n^j H_{2n+1}]_0$ is the initial quantity of the $C_n H_{2n+2}$ precursor substituted by ^{13}C of atom (j); a zero superscript indicates no isotopic substitution. τ_n^j is the time–temperature integral

$$\tau_n^j = \int dt k_n^j,$$

where k_n^j is a rate constant. The amount of ^{13}C in $C_n H_{2n+2}$ is

$$[^{13}C]_n = \sum_j [T - C_n^j H_{2n+1}]_0 [1 - \exp(-\tau_n^j)].$$

Wet petroleum gas, isotope ratios, and fractionation factors

In a wet petroleum gas, the effects of time–temperature integrals are small, and the gases are generated over a narrow temperature range. Moreover, for gas generated from a dominantly marine source, the ^{13}C fractionation factors among the gas components will not depend on the precursor's overall isotopic composition. In such material, the hydrocarbon functionals are lipid-like (Silverman, 1967; Silverman and Epstein, 1958), and will normally be attached to the precursor body by a carbon–carbon bond, rather than the carbon–oxygen bonds often found in humic or lignite sources (Cartz and Hirsch, 1960; Metzner, 1973), and we can assume the ^{13}C distribution in the precursor to be uniform. Consequently, the $^{13}C/^{12}C$ ratio in $C_n H_{2n+2}$ becomes, to first order in ^{13}C,

$$[^{13}C]_n / [^{12}C]_n = (1/n) R \sum_j k_n^j / k_n^0,$$

$$R = [T - C_n^j H_{2n+1}]_0 / [T - C_n^0 H_{2n+1}]_0.$$

R cancels out of α_{mn}, and we find the fractionation factor

$$\alpha_{mn} = (1/m) \sum_j k_m^j / k_m^0 / [(1/n) \sum_j k_n^j / k_n^0].$$

Kinetic isotope effect, isotopic bond numbers, and fractionation factors as functions of temperature

For hydrocarbon generation, the kinetic isotope effect, or the ratio k_n^j / k_n^0, can be written in terms of 'β-factors' as

$$k_n^j / k_n^0 = \beta[\cdot C_n^j H_{2n+1}] / \beta[T - C_n^j H_{2n+1}],$$

where $\beta[X]$ is the ratio of the molecular vibrational partition functions for the isotopically substituted and unsubstituted systems.

Bigeleisen and Wolfsberg's (Bigeleisen, 1949; Bigeleisen and Wolfsberg, 1959) application of transition state theory to the kinetic isotope effect would predict that

$$k_n^j / k_n^0 = (v_n^j / v_n^0) \beta[T \cdots C_n^j H_{2n+1}]^{\ddagger} / \beta[T - C_n^j H_{2n+1}],$$

where v_n^j and v_n^0 are the vibrational frequencies of the activated complex of the substituted and unsubstituted systems along the reaction path to dissociation. However, since the activated complex will be loosely bound, and the complex will tend to resemble the reaction products in a highly endothermic reaction, the hydrocarbon functional in the activated complex will be nearly independent of the precursor. Consequently, the partition function for the activated complex factors into partition functions for the hydrocarbon functional and the precursor body, and these latter factors cancel out of the expression above. In addition, v_n^j and v_n^0 will be nearly equal, since this vibrational mode in the activated complex will involve a bond that is already broken, and the frequencies disappear from the isotope effect. Other choices for this ratio give too great a kinetic isotope effect and produce larger fractionations than are observed in nature (Frank and Sackett, 1969).

The β-factors for a simple ^{13}C for ^{12}C substitution in a hydrocarbon can be further simplified and written as

$$\beta[\text{Hydrocarbon}]$$

$$= 1 + L_{CC} \times \text{number of C–C bonds to substituted atom}$$

$$+ L_{CH} \times \text{number of C–H bonds to substituted atom}$$

Here L_{CC} and L_{CH} are isotopic bond numbers (Galimov, 1973; Galimov et al., 1970). Isotope effects are located near the isotopically substituted atom. Furthermore, the close similarity of the formal theory of the isotope effect to equilibrium thermodynamics suggests that, like many thermodynamic properties, the kinetic isotope effect can be described by a linear free energy relation of the form above.

A least squares fit of the β-factors from normal mode theory give L_{CC} and L_{CH} as functions of temperature. The values of $\beta[\cdot C_n^j H_{2n+1}]$ and $\beta[T - C_n^j H_{2n+1}]$, and consequently the fractionation factors α_{mn} follow at once. The coefficients in Table 1 come from a least squares fit of these results.

RECOMMENDATIONS

Our work to date indicates that carbon isotope paleothermometry has useful exploration applications in correlation and basin modeling. However, more studies in areas with good geologic control and supplementary thermal studies are needed to more accurately calibrate the method. Also, the theory needs to be extended to allow for inhomogeneous isotope distributions in the gas precursor, and to treat more thermally mature gases.

REFERENCES

Am. Assoc. Pet. Geol. and U.S. Geol. Survey (1976) *Geothermal gradient map of North America*. Ed. by Kinney, D. M.

Amit, O. and Bein, A. (1979) The genesis of the Zohar gas as deduced from its chemical and isotopic composition. *J. Petrol. Geol.* **2**, 95–100.

Beebe, B. W. (1965) Natural gases in the Post-Paleozoic rocks of Mississippi; natural gases of North America. *Am. Ass. Petrol. Geol. Memoir 9*, Vol. 1, pp. 1176–1226.

Bigeleisen, J. (1949) The relative reaction velocities of isotopic molecules. *J. Chem. Phys.* **17**, 675–678.

Bigeleisen, J. and Wolfsberg, M. (1959) Theoretical and experimental aspects of isotope effects in chemical kinetics. *Adv. Chem. Phys.* **1**, 15–76.

Cartz, L. and Hirsch, P. B. (1960) A contribution to the structure of coal from X-ray diffraction studies. *Phil. Trans. Roy. Soc. (London) Ser A.* **252**, 557–559.

Dow, W. G. (1979) Petroleum source beds on continental slopes and rises. Geological and geographysical investigations of continental margins. *Am. Ass. Petrol. Geol. Memoir 29*, pp. 423–442.

Eyring, H. (1935) The activated complex in chemical reactions. *J. Chem. Phys.* **3**, 107–115.

Frank, D. J. and Sackett, W. M. (1969) Kinetic isotope effects in the thermal cracking of neopentane. *Geochim. Cosmochim. Acta.* **33**, 811–820.

Fuex, A. N. (1977) The use of stable carbon isotopes in hydrocarbon exploration. *J. Geochem. Expl.* **7**, 155–188.

Galimov, E. M. (1973) *Carbon Isotopes in Oil Gas Geology*. Nedra, Moscow.

Galimov, E. M. (1980) C^{13}/C^{12} in kerogen. In *Kerogen*. Ed. by Durand, B. pp. 270–299.

Galimov, E. M., Ivlev, A. A. and Kuznetsova, N. G. (1970) Carbon isotope composition of gaseous hydrocarbons in petroleum and the problem of their origin. *Geokimiya* 818–828.

Garilov, Y. Y. and Tiplinskiy (1978) Formation of oil and gas fields based on carbon-isotope data for methane (as in the Kuybyshev and Orenburg areas). *Geolojiya Nefti i Gaza* **6**, 14–19.

Metzner, H. (1973) *Biochemie der Pflanzen*. Emke, Stuttgart.

Prosolov, E. M. and Logkev, V. A. (1977) Carbon-isotope data on the formation and migration of methane. *Geokimiya*, 122–135.

Schoell, M. (1980) The hydrogen and carbon isotopic composition of methane from natural gases of various regions. *Geochim. Cosmochim. Acta* **44**, 649–661.

Silverman, S. (1964) Investigations of petroleum origin and evolution mechanism by carbon isotope studies. In *Isotope and Cosmic Chemistry*. Ed. by Craig, H., Miller, S. L. and Wasserburg, G. J. North Holland, Amsterdam, pp. 92–102.

Silverman, S. R. (1967) Carbon isotopic evidence for the role of lipids in petroleum formation. *J. Am. Oil Chem. Soc.* **44**, 691–695.

Silverman, S. R. and Epstein, S. (1958) Carbon isotopic compositions of petroleum and other sedimentary organic materials. *Am. Ass. Pet. Geol. Bull.* **42**, 998–1012.

Smith, J. E., Erdman, J. G. and Morris, D. A. (1971) Migration, accumulation, and retention of petroleum in the earth. *Proc. Eighth World Petrol. Cong.* pp. 13–26.

Smith, M. E. (1981) private communication.

Stahl, W. (1975) Kohlenstoff-Isotopenoverhattnisse von Erdgassen. *Erdol und Kohle-Erdgas-Petrochemie vereinigt mit Brennstoff-Chemie*, **28**, 188–191.

Stahl, W. (1977) Carbon and nitrogen isotopes in hydrocarbon research and exploration. *Chem. Geol.* **20**, 121–149.

Stahl, W. and Carey, B. D. (1975) Source-rock identification by isotope analysis of natural gases from fields in the Val Verde and Deleware basins, West Texas. *Chem. Geol.* **16**, 257–267.

Waples, D. W. and Tornheim, L. (1978a) Mathematical models for petroleum forming processes: *n*-paraffins and isoprenoid hydrocarbons. *Geochim. Cosmochim. Acta* **42**, 457–465.

Waples, D. W. and Tornheim, L. (1978b) Mathematical models for petroleum forming processes: carbon isotope fractionation. *Geochim. Cosmochim. Acta* **42**, 467–472.

Advances in Organic Geochemistry 1981, pp. 775–787
© *John Wiley & Sons Limited, 1983*

Comments on Pyrolytic Hydrocarbon Yields in Source-Rock Evaluation

W. L. Orr

Mobil Research and Development Corporation, Field Research Laboratory, Dallas, Texas, 75221, USA

Programmed-temperature pyrolysis of the 'Rock–Eval' type is discussed with respect to qualitative and quantitative significance. Pyrolytic results from both whole-rock and isolated kerogen are considered. Discussion is limited to the hydrocarbon-like products detected by a flame ionization detector (FID); the S_1 and S_2 peaks in Rock–Eval terminology. Carbon in the evolved products (FID-C) can be determined with an accuracy of ± 5 to 10%. Isolated kerogens usually give a single broad peak (S_2) at high temperature ($> 350\,^{\circ}$C). The equation for the relationship between FID-C yield and elemental composition is given. For the range of atomic ratios generally found in kerogens (H/C = 0.3 to 1.7, O/C = 0.02 to 0.3), the FID–C yield usually agrees with the measured value within the experimental error (i.e., ± 5 to 10%). The corresponding relationship in terms of the Rock–Eval *hydrogen index* (HI) is given. Consideration of these equations together with the evolution pathways of kerogen types (I, II, and III) on van Krevelen diagrams shows that the FID–C yield alone places narrow constraints on the H/C and O/C ratios, and therefore on kerogen type and maturity level. If vitrinite reflectance ($\%R_0$) is known in addition to FID-C, elemental composition (H/C and O/C) can be inferred within an even narrower range. These relationships between pyrolysis yields and elemental composition hold quite well for isolated kerogens and are also valid for whole-rock results in many cases. In cases where agreement is poor between whole-rock and kerogen results, two causes may be cited. One is the catalytic cracking effect of the mineral matrix reported by Espitallié *et al.* (1980). The other is the contribution of heavy bitumens to the S_2 peak reported by Clementz (1980). We conclude that the Rock–Eval type pyrolysis of whole-rock samples is a rapid and valuable analytical technique which can supply a great deal of information about kerogen type, maturity level and the hydrocarbon potential of sediments. There are some complicating factors, but with careful evaluation pyrolysis supplies semi-quantitative data not easily obtained by other methods.

INTRODUCTION

The abundance of petroleum (oil, gas and related bitumens) in sedimentary basins can be related in a systematic manner to three factors. These are:
1. the abundance of organic matter in the source sediments,
2. the nature of the sedimentary organic matter (kerogen type and composition), and
3. the maturity level or stage of evolution of the kerogen which is determined by its thermal exposure (time–temperature history).

These relationships have been established from the examination of sediments in depth sequences in various sedimentary basins, as well as by laboratory simulation experiments (Tissot *et al.*, 1974; Tissot and Welte, 1980; Monin *et al.*, 1980). Numerous techniques and methods from several disciplines have contributed to this understanding of the petroleum formation process.

Early geochemical techniques focused on the total amount of organic matter as measured by total organic carbon (TOC), and the amount and composition of the extractable organic matter (EOM). Although EOM (often called the bitumen or lipid fraction) makes up only a small portion of sedimentary organic matter in most cases, this fraction is most amicable to separation and characterization and has been analyzed in great detail (Eglinton and Murphy, 1969; Maxwell *et al.*, 1971). Advances in instrumentation and techniques, particularly modern GC–MS methods, continue to expand the resolution of components in this fraction (Seifert and Moldowan, 1980).

Parallel advances in methods for the isolation and characterization of kerogen (the non-extractable organic matter) have greatly extended our understanding of kerogen types and their evolution during thermal maturation. Major tools are visual kerogen description, elemental analysis, vitrinite reflectance ($\%R_0$), the thermal alteration index (TAI) based on spore and pollen colouration, IR and ESR spectroscopy, and the nature of kerogen degradation products resulting from either chemical or thermal treatment (Durand, 1980).

Notwithstanding recent advances and the existence of what now appears to be a coherent qualitative and semi-quantitative understanding of the petroleum generation process from the thermal maturation of kerogen, better quantitation of these concepts remains a challenging and frustrating problem. Improved quantitation is highly desirable for the evaluation of petroleum potential in sedimentary basins. A major goal in the application of organic geochemistry to exploration is to provide the best possible input data for mathematical models which integrate the geologic and geochemical information and predict the nature, amount and time of generation of oil and gas (Tissot and Espitalié, 1975; Tissot and Welte, 1978).

The scope of this paper is narrow relative to the goal stated above. Here we report and comment on observations regarding information which may be obtained from the simple analytical technique of high temperature pyrolysis and measurement of the quantity of evolved hydrocarbon-like products by a flame ionization detector (FID). This is essentially the well known Rock–Eval technique, neglecting the measurement of evolved carbon dioxide (the S_3 peak). Applications of this general method to the evaluation of petroleum potential of sedimentary rocks have been reported by Barker (1974), Claypool and Reed (1976), and others (with variations) prior to the development of

the Rock–Eval instrument by the Institut Francais du Pétrole (Espitalié et al., 1977).

Although various instruments and operating variables have been used by different investigators, the general approach is similar. The Rock–Eval instrument and protocol for data interpretation now are well known. Therefore, the terminology associated with this method offers an acceptable format for discussion (cf. Espitalié et al., 1977; Tissot and Welte, 1978).

The rapid and widespread acceptance of the Rock–Eval type pryolysis method by the petroleum industry for source-rock evaluation attests to its utility. However, a diversity of opinions prevails regarding interpretation and significance of the data. Some regard this technique as a rapid qualitative screening method useful mainly for selecting samples worthy of more thorough geochemical examination. Some question the reliability of the data and its real value to the geologist and geochemist. Others give great credence to the numeric values of S_1, S_2, S_3, T_{max}, production index $[S_1/(S_1 + S_2)]$, etc., as espoused by Espitalié et al. (1977) in the Rock–Eval protocol. We advocate a moderate position between these extremes. Rock–Eval data should be critically examined and evaluated with respect to other geological and geochemical information. It should not be forgotten that pyrolysis in the laboratory is an analytical method and does not simulate conditions of oil and gas formation under geologic conditions. It provides information about the quantity and nature of sedimentary organic matter, but the translation of this information into behaviour of sedimentary organic matter under natural conditions in the geologic environment must remain somewhat subjective for many reasons.

Our purpose here is not to examine or evaluate the Rock–Eval protocol *per se*, but is to offer some observations and comments regarding relationships between pyrolytic hydrocarbon yields and kerogen composition.

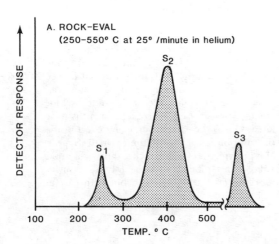

A. ROCK–EVAL
(250–550° C at 25° /minute in helium)

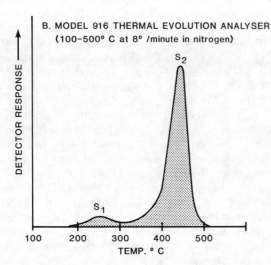

B. MODEL 916 THERMAL EVOLUTION ANALYSER
(100–500° C at 8° /minute in nitrogen)

Fig. 1. Schematic pyrolysis records from Rock–Eval A and Thermal Evolution Analyser B. S_1 and S_2 are monitored by a flame ionization detector in both cases. In A, carbon dioxide is trapped and measured separately (S_3) with a thermal conductivity detector. Peak temperatures and shapes are a function of temperature–program rate, gas flow, and other operating variables.

GENERAL METHOD AND TERMINOLOGY

The essence of the method is the thermal treatment of sedimentary organic matter (whole-rock or isolated kerogen) in a flow of inert gas, and measurement of the volatile reduced-carbon species carried in the gas flow to a flame ionization detector. Detector response is recorded as a function of temperature up to over 500 °C where pyrolytic decomposition is essentially complete.

Figure 1 shows schematically the type of pyrolysis record obtained for both the Rock–Eval instrument and the DuPont Thermal Evolution Analyzer (TEA). The Rock–Eval method and instrument are fully described by Espitalié et al. (1977). The standard program involves heating the sample from 250 °C to 550 °C at a rate of 25 °C min .[1]. The thermal evolution analyzer is an improved version of the instrument described by Eggerton et al. (1969). It is simpler than the Rock–Eval with the pyrolysis chamber closely coupled to the flame ionization detector. The temperature program rate is variable but our standard operation has been to program from 100 °C to 500 °C at 8 °C min .[1], and to hold at 500 °C until decomposition is complete. Generally the FID signal returns to base-line in a few minutes at 500 °C. The lower initial temperature and slower heating rate for the TEA program give slightly greater accuracy for the S_2 peak, but the S_1 peak is evolved more slowly, and for low S_1 values the accuracy may be less.

Ideally, from whole-rock samples, two well resolved peaks are obtained as illustrated in Fig. 1. The peak shapes and the temperatures at their maxima differ with instruments and with temperature program rate, but peak areas should be unaffected. For natural samples, peak shapes may not be as simple as illustrated, and the resolution between S_1 and S_2 may not be as definitive as shown.

The lower temperature peak (S_1) represents 'thermally extracted' hydrocarbons and related bitumens which already exist in the rock and which have sufficient volatility to be vapourized before pyrolytic reactions (thermal cleavage reactions) become significant. The S_1 peak, therefore, is taken as a measure of 'petroleum' or 'hydrocarbons' already present in the rock. Ideally, S_1 measures volatile hydrocarbon-like materials indigenous to a source rock. In practice, S_1 may include a significant contribution from contamination during drilling operations, and, of course, migrated hydrocarbons are measured also.

The second peak (S_2) occurring at higher temperature (generally > 350 °C) indicates hydrocarbons and related volatile bitumens formed by thermal cleavage from the kerogen. The S_2 peak, therefore, is taken to represent the remaining capacity of the kerogen to form hydrocarbons upon further and complete thermal degradation. This quantity has been called the *residual genetic potential*.

The peak areas (S_1 and S_2) are proportional to *carbon* in the volatile hydrocarbon-like products, although the Rock–Eval convention is to report these quantities in terms of 'hydrocarbons'(HC). Detector response is not NH_3 or H_2S. A precision (reproducibility) of about ± 5 to 10% can be obtained by careful operation on homogeneous samples.

The ideal FID gives the same response per unit weight of carbon regardless of molecular weight or the hydrogen content of the hydrocarbon species (Eggerton *et al.*, 1969). For example, equal weights of carbon in methane (CH_4) and benzene (C_6H_6) give about the same peak area, although the weight of methane would be about 20% greater than that of benzene. The difference in weight between carbon and hydrocarbons is significant; it is greater than the experimental error and varies with the nature of the HC species.

For this reason, it is more accurate to calibrate the detector in terms of carbon and to record primary data as 'flame-ionization-detectable carbon' (FID–C). Conversion of FID–C to HC units must employ an assumption as to the average hydrocarbon composition. Common practice is to calibrate the detector directly in hydrocarbon units using a high molecular weight *n*-alkane (e.g. $n\text{-}C_{20}H_{42}$) as the standard and to report results as hydrocarbon weight per unit weight of rock. This is equivalent to assuming that the hydrocarbon-like species measured in S_1 and S_2 have about 85%C by

weight. Therefore the conversion between FID–C and HC is:

$$FID\text{–}C \times 100/85 = HC$$

Data reported in terms of C or HC are equally satisfactory as long as the implicit assumptiona are recognized; relative trends are the same although absolute amounts differ.

Rock–Eval data on pyrolytic hydrocarbon yields are normally reported in parts per thousand based on either weight of rock (e.g. mg HC/g rock) or on weight of total organic carbon (e.g. mg HC/g TOC).

S_2 yields based on rock weight reflect both a quantity and a quality parameter relative to organic matter in the rock. The quantity parameter is measured by the % TOC.* The quality parameter refers to the convertibility of TOC to hydrocarbon-like products during the pyrolysis. HC yields normalized to a TOC basis (i.e. mg HC/g TOC) reflect only the quality parameter which has been designated the *hydrogen index* (HI) by Espitalié *et al.* (1977).

Likewise, FID–C yields commonly have been reported by us as part per million parts of rock (ppm) or as per cent of TOC [e.g. FID–C$_{\% \text{ of TOC}}$]. The latter is proportional to the hydrogen index, assuming 85%C in HC:

$$FID\text{–}C_{(\% \text{ of TOC})} \times 11.76 = HI$$

This quality or convertibility parameter [either HI or FID–C$_{(\% \text{ of TOC})}$] is a function of kerogen composition which in turn is a function of biogenic source materials and depositional environment (determining kerogen type), and the time–temperature history (determining stage of maturation).

RELATIONSHIP BETWEEN PYROLYSIS YIELDS AND ELEMENTAL COMPOSITION OF KEROGENS AND RELATED SUBSTANCES

The fact that the hydrocarbon yield measured by pyrolysis, or realized during natural maturation, is a function of elemental composition of the kerogen is well established (Tissot *et al.*, 1974; Tissot and Welte, 1978; McIver, 1967; Saxby, 1977). Yields increase with increasing atomic H/C ratios and decrease with increasing O/C ratios. Material balance considerations in C, H, and O in the conversion of kerogen to hydrocarbons, carbon dioxide, water, and a residual kerogen or carbon residue require such a relationship. Unfortunately, complete analysis of the amounts and compositions of all components necessary to define a complete material balance is not readily obtained and

---

* To be strict, the % TOC in this case should refer only to organic carbon in kerogen; i.e. organic carbon in bitumens (EOM) should be discounted. Thus, measurement of % TOC after solvent extraction would be more precise. This distinction, however, is generally ignored on the assumption that the contribution of EOM to % TOC is small relative to TOC in kerogen.

Table 1

Samples used to establish empirical relationship between atomic H/C and O/C ratios and hydrocarbon generative capacity as indicated by FID–carbon yields.

Sample No.	Lab. Identification number	Nature of sample	Atomic H/C	Atomic O/C	FID–C (% of TOC) observed	FID–C (% of TOC) Calc. by Eq. 1 (f)	Difference FID–calc. – FID–C Obs.
		NATURAL HUMIC ACIDS					
1	HA-565-5-1	From humate cemented sands[a]	0.78	0.55	0.60	−8.5	−9.1
2	HA-565-4-1	From humate cemented sands[a]	0.71	0.46	1.04	−6.5	−7.5
3	HA-565-4-2A	From humate cemented sands[a]	0.68	0.45	1.31	−7.6	−8.9
4	PQ-HAU-75	From brackish water estuarine sediment (reducing environment)[b]	1.19	0.55	15.2	15.7	+0.5
5	PQ-HAU-75	From shallow fresh water pond (oxidizing)[c]	1.01	0.47	4.3	15.8	+11.5
		SYNTHETIC HUMIC ACIDS (MELANOIDINS)[d]					
6	SHA-2B	From condensation of glucose and leucine	1.24	0.29	35.5	36.3	+0.8
7	SHA-3	From condensation of glucose and glutamic acid	1.07	0.34	15.8	22.9	+7.1
8	SHA-5	From condensation of glucose and phenylalanine	0.91	0.25	29.0	19.6	−10.0
		NATURAL KEROGENS[e]					
9	GRK-8-19-75	From Green River shale (Wyoming). Eocene age	1.55	0.081	69.3	68.8	−0.5
10	TDK-8-19-75	From Castile Fm. (West Texas) Permian age	1.46	0.092	66.6	62.8	−3.8
11	777–207		0.71	0.19	11.5	11.9	+0.4
12	777–208	From Mowry Shale	1.01	0.11	31.3	35.0	+3.7
13	777–209	(Wyoming)	1.08	0.13	32.7	37.8	+5.1
14	777–210	Cretaceous age	1.17	0.12	41.7	43.8	+2.1
15	777–218		0.74	0.12	6.7	18.4	+11.7
						Average	±5.5

[a] Samples supplied by V. E. Swanson (USGS) and were described by Swanson and Palacas (1965). Humic acids were separated and purified by K. E. Peters (FRL — Summer 1965).

[b] Sediment from upper basin of Pettaguamscutt River (RI) described by Orr and Galnes (1975).

[c] Sediment from Pausacaco Pond at head of Pettaguamscutt River (Orr and Galnes, 1974).

[d] Condensation products of glucost and amino acids from heating in water at pH 8 for several days. Products are soluble in base and precipitated by acid and were purified by the same methods as natural humic acids.

[e] Purified in usual way with HCl/HF and extracted with $CHCl_3$ to remove bitumens.

[f] A least squares fit of data gave the relationship: FID–C = 59 (H/C − 0.29) − 68 (O/C). (Eqn 1).

all attempts at material balance have required simplifying assumptions (Saxby, 1977; McIver, 1967; Laplant, 1974).

The extent to which any simple relationship between pyrolytic HC yields (S_2) and elemental composition of kerogen can be expected to hold for a broad range of kerogen types is not evident *a priori*. Nevertheless, we have examined pyrolytic hydrocarbon yields as a function of elemental composition in search of such a simple and useful semi-quantitative correlation. These results are reported here.

For this purpose fifteen substances were selected which have a broad range of atomic H/C and O/C ratios typical not only of kerogens but also of humic acids. Table 1 lists these substances with their atomic ratios and measured FID–C yields.

The H/C and O/C ratios of these substances are plotted on a van Krevelen diagram in Fig. 2. This

diagram, modified from Tissot and Welte (1978), illustrates how these substances relate to average kerogen types (I, II and III) and their evolution pathways. A few brief comments about the form of this diagram (Fig. 2) are in order before discussing the samples and results of this study. The parallel lines marked 10 to 80 refer to FID–C yields calculated from the derived correlation and will be discussed last.

The shaded area bounded by dotted lines delineates the field typical of kerogens from older sedimentary rocks. Materials which have O/C ratios > 0.3, although they are insoluble in organic solvents, are not included in the kerogen field because they are common only in young sediments and in the small amount of humic acids remaining in older sediments. The heavy lines marked I, II and III designate average evolution pathways for these kerogen types with arrows pointing in the direction of increasing maturity. Natural kerogens, of course, form

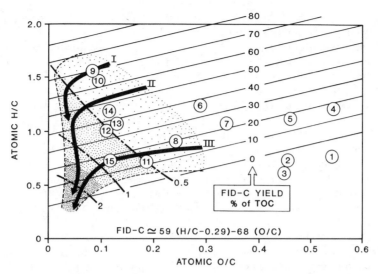

Fig. 2. Atomic H/C and O/C ratios of materials used to establish relationship between atomic composition and FID–C yields from pyrolysis (numbers refer to materials listed in Table 1). The general scheme of kerogen evolution paths of principal types of kerogens, I, II, and III, is adapted from Tissot and Welte (1980; Fig. 11.5.1, p. 149); approximate iso-values of vitrinite reflectance (0.5, 1 and 2) are shown by dot–dash lines.

a broad band around these average pathways (cf. Tissot and Welte, 1978). Approximate iso-values of vitrinite reflectance ($\%R_0$) are designated by dot–dash lines at % R_0 values of 0.5, 1 and 2, and serve to mark approximate maturity levels as recorded by vitrinite reflectance.

The kerogen field to the right of % $R_0 = 0.5$ (light dotted area) is the zone of *diagenesis* in which mostly CO_2 and H_2O are evolved from kerogens; hydrocarbon formation is minor. Kerogens in the diagenesis zone are considered to be immature with respect to significant hydrocarbon generation.

The kerogen zone between % $R_0 = 0.5$ and about 1.2 is the main zone of hydrocarbon formation (the higher density dotted pattern). At about 0.5% R_0 the evolution pathways turn downward, reflecting a more important loss of H than O in the evolved products (more hydrocarbons than carbon dioxide and water). This zone and its extension to % $R_0 = 2$ is called the zone of *catagenesis* by Tissot. In the higher maturity portion of the zone of catagenesis (% $R_0 = 1.2$ to 2) hydrocarbon generation continues but favours the formation of lower molecular weight products and the cracking of previously formed liquid hydrocarbons to gases.

The zone with % $R_0 > 2$ is called the zone of *metagenesis*. Hydrocarbon formation in this zone is slight, and methane (dry gas) is the dominant product. Previously formed liquid hydrocarbons exposed to this maturation interval also are cracked to dry gas concomitant with a significant portion of their carbon reverting to a carbon residue. Although a very large portion of original kerogen–carbon survives metagenesis as a carbon-rich residue, its capacity to generate hydrocarbons approaches zero when the H/C ratio has decreased to about 0.3 to 0.5.

It has been demonstrated that this general scenario for kerogen evolution is similar for both short-term laboratory pyrolysis and much slower maturation in geological settings (Tissot *et al.*, 1974; Robin *et al.*, 1977). However, the composition of accumulated hydrocarbon products is much more dependent than the residual

kerogen on the time–temperature conditions and on the product mobility in the system. Significant differences between laboratory pyrolysis experiments and natural maturation are recognized (Monin *et al.*, 1980). The rapid removal of initially formed volatile products from the high-temperature furnace in laboratory pyrolysis flow systems should greatly decrease secondary reactions, including cracking of initial products, compared to those which occur in a closed system or in geologic settings. Mechanisms of both primary and secondary reactions also are expected to differ under high- and low-temperature maturation conditions. These differences affect hydrocarbon product composition more than they do residual kerogen composition.

Let us now consider the materials in Table 1 in view of this background. Samples are plotted by H/C and O/C ratios in Fig. 2; numbers in the circles correspond to sample numbers in Table 1.

The natural kerogens (9–15) cover the range of types from I to III, and with the exception of 15 are relatively immature based on their positions with respect to the vitrinite reflectance line of 0.5%. These kerogens have a broad H/C range from 0.71 to 1.55 and a more restricted O/C ratio range of 0.08 to 0.19.

Compared to the kerogens, the natural humic acids (1–5) have very high O/C ratios, ranging from 0.45 to 0.55. The H/C ratios vary from 0.68 to 1.19. Samples 1–3 were separated from the 'humate cemented sand' from Florida described by Swanson and Palacas (1965). These are hydrogen-poor humic acids (H/C = 0.68 to 0.78) typical of soils, peats, and swamps. They are derived largely from higher plant materials rich in lignin. These 'humates' are believed to be precipitated in the sands from waters draining coastal swamps. Samples 4 and 5, considerably richer in hydrogen, are from organic rich sediments (8–16% TOC) deposited in subaqueous environments described by Gaines (1973) and Orr and Gaines (1974). These sediments have substantial contributions from both terrestrial (higher plant) and aquatic (algal) sources. The diatom contribution to 4 is particularly high, and this sediment was deposited in strongly anoxic bottom water.

The materials listed as synthetic humic acid or melanoidins (6–8) are condensation products formed by the reaction of glucose with three different amino acids as noted in Table 1. These amino acid–glucose condensation products have many properties resembling humic acids (Hoering and Hare, 1973). Melanoidins have been suggested as the kind of polycondensate materials contributing to the humic acids found in marine sediments which receive little terrestrial organic matter (Nissenbaum and Kaplan, 1972). Melanoidins can incorporate fatty alcohols and acids into their structures and have been considered possible precursors of amorphous kerogens (Larter and Douglas, 1980). These materials (6–8) have O/C ratios between 0.25 and 0.34, and were included to provide substances with

O/C ratios intermediate between those of humic acids and kerogens.

The relationship between elemental composition (H/C and O/C ratios) and FID–C yields for the materials in Table 1 can be approximated quite well by Eqn. 1.

$$\text{FID–C}_{(\% \text{ of TOC})} \simeq 59(\text{H/C} - 0.29) - 68(\text{O/C}) \quad (1)$$

The linear form of Eqn. 1 was assumed and a least square method was used to select the coefficients for H/C and O/C based on the data in Table 1. The equation is consistent with known FID–C yield limits of zero and 100%. For example, FID–C yields approach zero at H/C ratios of about 0.3 to 0.4 for over-mature kerogens with O/C in the range of 0.03 to 0.10. At the other limit, polyethylene with H/C = 1.98 to 2.00 and no oxygen gives an FID–C yield of 100 ± 5%.

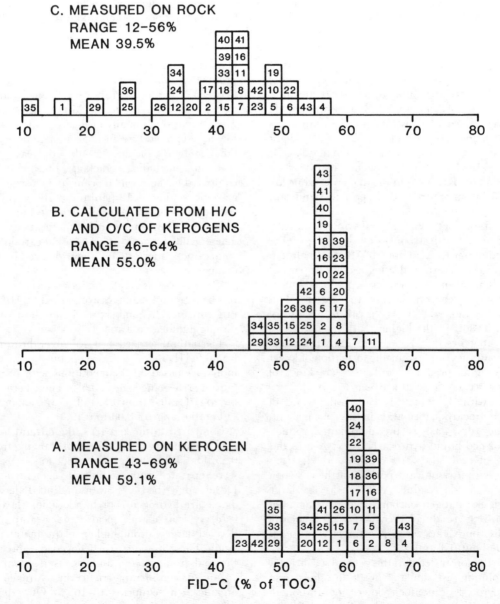

Fig. 3. Comparison of FID–C yields: A measured on isolated kerogens, B calculated from H/C and O/C ratios by Eqn 1, and C measured on whole-rocks. Samples are from Monterey Fm. (Miocene) outcrops along the California coast between Santa Barbara and Point Conception (Isaacs, 1980).

Table 1 lists the FID–C yields calculated by Eqn. 1 for each of the materials, and the difference between the measured and calculated yield is given in the last column. In view of the fact that the accuracy of FID–C measurements is only ±5 to 10% and elemental ratios also are not free of errors, the agreement between calculated and measured values is considered quite satisfactory. Agreement is better than 10% in 12 of the 15 samples and better than 6% in 8 of the 15. The average difference for all samples is about 6%.

Solutions to Eqn. 1 for 10% increments in FID–C are shown by the parallel lines as labelled in Fig. 2. A 10% range in FID–C corresponds to an H/C ratio range of 0.27. Because oxygen decreases the FID–C yield, the iso-yield lines have a positive slope; a higher H/C ratio is required for higher O/C ratios to maintain a given FID–C yield. The required increase in H/C is about 0.12 for each 0.10 increase in O/C. Thus, a given FID–C measurement (S_2) defines a restricted band of H/C and O/C values along a line parallel to those shown and with a bandwidth corresponding to the average experimental uncertainty (*ca.* ±6%).

Our experience with application of Eqn. 1 to a large number of kerogens generally shows measured and calculated FID–C yields to agree within ∼6% in about 80 to 90% of the cases.

Figure 3 illustrates results for 31 kerogen samples from the Monterey Formation in California. These samples are from outcrop sections along the coast between Santa Barbara and Point Conception. Samples were collected and described by C. Isaacs (1980). They include rocks of the various lithologies found in the Monterey at these locations.

The lower histogram (A) shows FID–C yields measured on separated kerogens and the middle histogram (B) shows yields calculated from H/C and O/C ratios (Eqn. 1). The range of values in A and B differs only slightly and the mean values differ by only 4.1% in FID–C yield. In these samples the difference between measured and calculated values exceed 10% in only 3 of the 31 samples.

The upper histogram (C) in Fig. 3 shows FID–C yields measured by pyrolysis of whole-rock samples for comparison. Whole-rock pyrolysis results show a much broader range of values and tend to be considerably lower than the values from kerogen pyrolysis. This difference must be attributed to the mineral matrix effect reported by Espitalié *et al.* (1980). Further comments on whole-rock pyrolysis are given in the next section.

Another test of this correlation between pyrolysis yield and elemental composition may be illustrated by the relationship between H/C and the *hydrogen index* reported in the literature. As pointed out earlier, the hydrogen index (HI) is $11.76 \times \text{FID–C}_{(\% \text{ of TOC})}$. Therefore, Eqn. 2 for HI is equivalent to Eqn. 1.

$$HI = 694 \ (H/C - 0.29) - 800(O/C) \qquad (2)$$

Figure 4 shows the correlation between HI and H/C reported by Espitalié *et al.* (1977) with data points from five different sedimentary basins. Superimposed on these data are correlation lines from Eqn. 2 for O/C ratios of 0.1 to 0.4. All data points fall within this range of O/C ratios, with most points being between the 0.1 and 0.3 lines as expected. Thus, Eqn. 2 represents the data presented for these basins quite well and much of the scatter in the H/C v. HI correlation may be attributed to variations in O/C ratios. It should be noted that the HI values reported by Espitalié *et al.* in Fig. 4 were from pyrolysis of isolated kerogens rather than whole rocks.

The iso-yield lines for FID–C superimposed on a van Krevelen diagram as in Fig. 2 allow an easy assessment of the relationship between elemental composition and FID–C yield measured on isolated kerogens. FID–C yields can be traced along the average kerogen evolution pathways; the difference in yield between two points gives an estimate of hydrocarbons generated in the selected maturation interval.

This correlation of FID–C yields with H/C and O/C ratios on the van Krevelen diagram together with iso-values of vitrinite reflectance makes possible the construction of a diagram (Fig. 5) showing FID–C yields as a function of maturity for the average kerogen evolution pathways. This construction (Fig. 5) required estimation of additional iso-value lines for vitrinite reflectance, selection of points for FID–C yields and % R_0 values along each average pathway, and then interpolation to give smooth curves through the points. The vitrinite reflectance scale (% R_0) on the abscissa is correlated also with the TAI scale for an additional maturity index. Two ordinate scales also are given for pyrolysis yields: the FID–C yield as % of TOC is on the left and the hydrogen index (HI) scale is on the right.

Although Fig. 5 contains a number of approximations, it is offered as a semi-quantitative illustration which may be useful in interpretation of

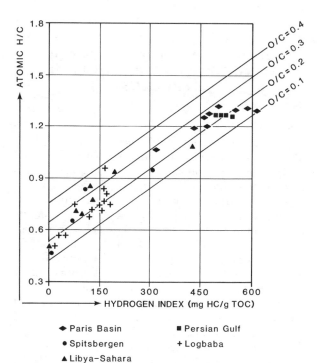

Fig. 4. Correlation of hydrogen index and H/C atomic ratios of kerogens as reported by Espitalié *et al.* (1977); superimposed lines show correlation according to Eqn. 2 for O/C ratios between 0.1 and 0.4.

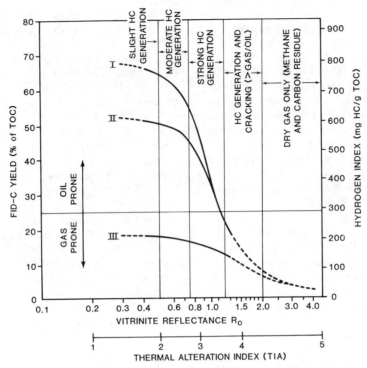

Fig. 5. Generalized relationship between pyrolytic hydrocarbon yield and state of evolution (maturation) for average kerogen types I, II, and III.

pyrolysis data. The figure indicates the magnitude of pyrolytic hydrocarbon yields (S_2) for immature kerogens of the three types in terms of both FID–C$_{(\% \text{ of TOC})}$ and HI; it shows how yields change with maturity as a function of vitrinite reflectance or TAI. Figure 5 also indicates the maturity levels at which pyrolysis yield curves converge for different kerogen types. For example, the type I and II curves converge in the % R_0 interval of about 0.8 to 1.0 and become indistinguishable at ~30% FID–C yield. Although a 30% FID–C yield at this maturity level cannot differentiate between types I and II, it is clearly higher than the 10–20% yield typical of type III kerogen. At % R_0 values > 1.2, all three curves converge and differences in pyrolysis yields are too small to give any hint of original kerogen type.

Of course, any evaluation of kerogen type and maturity level should draw on all available information. Pyrolysis data alone may be suggestive but are insufficient for a definitive decision. Interpretation of pyrolysis behaviour by any rigid rules can be quite misleading unless the conclusions are confirmed or corroborated by other criteria.

Many sediments contain a mixture of kerogen types which complicates classification schemes. Since pyrolysis yields and elemental composition both reflect a weighted average on mixed kerogens, the nature and amounts of actual components are not evident from these measurements. The presence of reworked or recycled organic matter together with kerogen from first cycle biogenic input to sediment is particularly troublesome and common. Recycled organic matter is usually overmature, highly oxidized, or both. This type of organic matter has been called 'dead carbon', 'inertinite', and 'type IV kerogen'. This material contributes to the TOC without making any significant

contribution to pyrolytic hydrocarbon yield. Therefore, the HI or FID–C based on TOC for a mixture containing reworked organic matter will be lower than the value for first generation material present. Microscopic visual kerogen examination and the nature of the vitrinite reflectance histogram can be very helpful in recognizing this situation.

COMPARISON OF PYROLYSIS OF WHOLE-ROCKS AND ISOLATED KEROGENS

Pyrolysis of isolated kerogens, as discussed in the previous section, is not routine because of the tedious nature of the kerogen separation process. Normally, Rock–Eval type pyrolysis is applied to untreated whole-rock samples from wells or outcrops. Direct analysis of whole-rock samples requires much less time, thus allowing rapid screening of large numbers of samples. This potential savings in time and cost has been a major stimulus in popularizing the Rock–Eval method. In principle, some of the same geochemical information can be inferred from whole-rock pyrolysis as is obtained by more intricate studies of kerogens. In practice, whole-rock pyrolysis introduces some different problems and uncertainties, but it also supplies some additional information not available from kerogens.

With respect to interpreting kerogen type and maturation level from the residual genetic potential (FID–C or HI as shown in Fig. 5), two complicating factors are recognized in whole-rock pyrolysis. The first and most significant is the so-called 'mineral matrix effect' first reported by Espitalié *et al.*, (1980). This effect in many cases causes the FID–C yield or HI to be markedly lower for whole-rocks than for isolated kerogen. The second is the contribution of heavy bitumens (EOM) to the S_2 peak in some cases. Both of these complications have been discussed in recent papers, so only brief comments and illustrations are given here (Katz, 1981; Patterson et al., 1981).

Mineral matrix effect on S_2 yields

In some cases, pyrolysis of whole-rock samples and of isolated kerogens from the rock have been shown to give conversions (FID–C or HI values) which are similar within experimental error. Good agreement indicates both that the organic matter is not fractionated during the kerogen separation, and that the pyrolytic behaviour (S_2) is similar in the rock-matrix and in the isolated state. In these ideal cases inferences from whole-rock and isolated kerogen are equivalent.

More commonly, however, pyrolysis yields or HI values based on S_2 are lower from whole-rocks than from kerogens. The results for Monterey samples, shown in Fig. 3, illustrate this point. The yields from whole-rocks (Fig. 3c) show a broader spread of values than yields from kerogens (Fig. 3a) and the mean value is significantly lower (39.5% v. 59.1% FID–C; a relative decrease of about 33% below the kerogen value). Although this is a significant decrease in S_2 or HI, all but 5 of the 31 values would still be interpreted correctly as Type II kerogen.

Espitalié established a number of facts about the mineral matrix effects on S_2 yields. In general, observations in our laboratory (unpublished) and by others have confirmed the behaviour reported by Espitalié et al. (1980). The mineral matrix effect is complex, variable, and difficult to predict or evaluate from whole-rock pyrolysis alone. Nevertheless, a few helpful generalizations can be made from available data.

1. **Mineral phases** The relative activity of different mineral phases is highly variable. Minerals with little or no activity include pure calcium carbonate, gypsum, pure quartz and probably many more. Smectite clays (montmorillonites and bentonites) are the

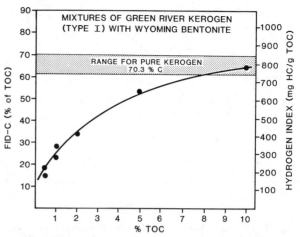

Fig. 6. Pyrolytic hydrocarbon yield as a function of % TOC for mixtures of Green River Kerogen (type I) with Wyoming bentonite. Shaded area shows the pyrolytic yield range for this pure kerogen which had 70.3% C (cf. Espitalié et al. (1980) for similar experiments).

only minerals which have been demonstrated to have a high activity in decreasing S_2 yields, and even smectites from different sources differ considerably in activity. Other clays have a variable but generally much lower activity. It is concluded that the level of activity is not related in a simple way to major clay types as determined, for example, by X-ray analysis.

2. **Organic matter type** Available data suggest that type III kerogens (low H/C and high O/C) are more prone to a large mineral matrix effect than kerogens of types I and II, but the effect can be substantial with type I and II kerogens in the presence of active smectites.

3. **Organic matter content** The ratio of organic matter to mineral matter exerts a major influence on the effect of active minerals in decreasing the S_2 yield. This has been demonstrated by pyrolysis of mixtures of isolated kerogens with active clays by Espitalié et al. (1980) and by us. Fig. 6 shows our results for mixtures of Green River Kerogen (type I) with Wyoming bentonite. Another apparent example of this effect is shown in

Table 2

Comparison of hydrogen index from whole-rock and isolated kerogen pyrolysis. Samples are from upper Miocene Puente Formation; well cuttings from a Wilmington offshore well, California.

| Sample depth feet | Whole-rock samples[a] | | | Isolated kerogen samples[a] | | Hydrogen index ratio |
	% TOC	Hydrogen index	% Ash	% TOC	Hydrogen index	Rock/ kerogen
5694	2.61	198	19.4	47.4	407	0.49
6228	1.68	236	24.2	43.4	543	0.44
6405	4.51	392	14.5	52.5	546	0.72
8125	11.0	583	15.1	57.1	609	0.96
8589	8.28	517	19.5	43.6	539	0.96
9094	6.89	501	14.8	58.8	530	0.95
9450	4.96	380	26.2	41.1	548	0.69

[a] Both whole-rock samples and isolated kerogens were extracted with chloroform to remove bitumens before pyrolysis.

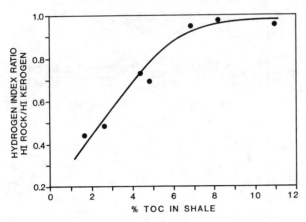

Fig. 7. Ratio of the pyrolysis yield for shale/kerogen as a function of % TOC in shale. Data for Puente Fm. samples from offshore California well (data from Table 2).

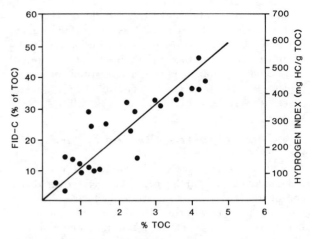

Fig. 8. Example of the often-observed trend of decreasing pyrolytic yield with decreasing % TOC. Samples are from the Shublik Fm. (Triassic), Alaska North Slope, depth interval 8980–9073 ft.

Table 2 and Fig. 7 for samples from the Puente Fm. (Miocene) of California.

Together, these observations indicate that the greatest mineral matrix effect will be found in clastic sediments which are rich in smectites and have low % TOC values.

The general nature of the mineral matrix effect may be understood somewhat as follows. A large part of the high molecular weight initial cleavage products from kerogen, which are evolved as FID detectable species during pyrolysis of isolated kerogens, are somehow 'retained' by certain minerals during whole-rock pyrolysis. Initially, this probably is due to strong surface adsorptive forces that decrease their vapour pressure and retard their escape into the gas phase. A significant retention of adsorbed bitumens is sustained long enough for them to encounter higher furnace temperatures, which cause secondary cracking and disproportionation to lower molecular weight products which vapourize and a nonvolatile carbon residue. Thus only a portion of the hydrocarbons and bitumens evolved from isolated kerogen are finally evolved as FID-detectable species during pyrolysis of some rocks. The total FID–C yield (or HI) is decreased and the products which are evolved contain more gaseous and low molecular weight components (Davis, 1981; Horsfield and Douglas, 1980).

Neither the nature of the adsorption or 'retention' process, nor the nature of the secondary disproportionation reactions is understood in detail. However, adsorptive properties of minerals can vary greatly, accounting for a wide range in mineral selectivity. A large part of the secondary reactions may be simply thermal cracking to gases and carbon residue. However, other reactions are possible which may be considered catalytic in nature and cause changes in product composition. For example, the more active minerals may increase evolution of hydrogen gas, thus greatly increasing carbon residue and decreasing FID-detectable species. It is possible that oxygen or hydroxyl groups from some minerals may contribute to the reactions by increasing species such as CO, CO_2, H_2O etc. which are not measured by the detector.

Figure 8 illustrates the often observed trend of decreasing pyrolytic yield with decreasing % TOC, and the dilemma presented in interpretation of such data. In this case the hydrogen index decreased from more than 500 to about 50 as % TOC decreased from about 4 to 0.5%. These samples are from a narrow depth interval of 93 feet, and therefore cannot have a large difference in depth–temperature history or maturity. Lithology in this interval is quite variable, reflecting rapid fluctuations in the depositional environment of these sediments. *Does this trend indicate inherent variations in kerogen genetic potential or the effect of mineral matter variations and organic matter/mineral ratio on pyrolytic behaviour?* One cannot answer this question from the pyrolytic data alone.

The importance of the answer to the above question depends on the answer to another difficult question. *Does the pyrolytic yield from whole-rock or isolated kerogen best represent the hydrocarbon potential which may be realized under natural geologic conditions of oil formation?* It is possible that the mineral matrix effect is largely an artifact of high-temperature laboratory pyrolysis conditions and may not operate at lower temperatures involved during natural oil generation. In this case, kerogen type (and kerogen pyrolysis) gives the desired information; the mineral matter effect distorts this information. On the other hand, under natural conditions initially evolved hydrocarbons and bitumens remain in contact with the mineral phases much longer, and the whole-rock pyrolytic results may give the desired information. The choice between these alternatives is not evident in my view.

Espitalié *et al.* (1980) appear to favour the view that the mineral matrix effect may operate under natural conditions and therefore that whole-rock pyrolytic results are more meaningful. On the other hand Monin *et al.* (1980) appear to favour the opposite view. They state:

'To eliminate the complex effects related to the organic carbon contents and to the activity of minerals, it appears preferable to perform pyrolysis on purified organic matter in order to compare hydrocarbons formed naturally and artificially.'

Bitumen effect on S₂ yields

The complication caused by heavy bitumens in whole-rock pyrolysis is simple compared to the mineral matrix effect. Bitumens [extractable organic matter, (EOM)] can contribute to the S_2 yield but in most source rocks they are present in such small quantities that their contribution to the kerogen peak (> 350 °C) is negligible. Nevertheless, there are exceptions which can lead to erroneous conclusions regarding kerogens if the effect is not recognized. This bitumen or heavy oil effect on S_2 was first reported by Clementz (1980) and more recently examples were given by Katz (1981) and Patterson *et al.* (1981).

Extractable bitumens generally contain components with a wide range in volatility. The most volatile components are 'thermally extracted' and appear in the S_1 peak at temperatures below 350 °C. Components with intermediate volatility evolve between the S_1 and S_2 peaks and decrease the resolution between these peaks. The least volatile components, generally rich in aromatic and NSO compounds (resins, asphaltenes etc.), are retained and pyrolyzed in the same temperature range as kerogens to produce FID-detectable fragments. Therefore, a rock with a large amount of heavy bitumen can produce a significant S_2 peak from the heavy ends of the bitumen. The bitumen contributions to S_2 could suggest kerogen which is not present at all or present in small amounts only.

A high bitumen contribution may be indicated by a high S_1 peak relative to S_2 as in examples shown by Clementz (1980). In other cases S_1 may not be large but bitumens may be indicated by a high background between S_1 and S_2. This background may be a rather uniform continuum between the peaks, broad shoulders on either S_1 or S_2, or may suggest intermediate peaks (Barker, 1974; Clementz, 1980). Fortunately, solvent extraction of the bitumens before pyrolysis can eliminate their contribution and therefore distinguish between the bitumen and kerogen contribution to the S_2 peak.

Examples of pyrolysis before and after extraction are given in Table 3 for rocks from the Monterey Fm. which contain both kerogen and bitumen. The Monterey Fm.

of California in many places contains a relatively immature hydrogen-rich kerogen (type II), as well as significant amounts of heavy oil or bitumen. This formation is considered to be both source- and reservoir-rock in many cases. Extraction decreased the S_2 yield (mgHC/g rock) by 15 and 32% (average 22%) of the value measured on the initial sample. This is a substantial contribution of bitumens to the S_2 peak. However, the % TOC decreased by almost the same proportion (17 to 25%, average 20%), resulting in very little difference in the hydrogen index for the extracted and unextracted samples. Therefore, inferences regarding kerogen type based on HI are unaffected by the bitumen contribution in these cases. These results suggest that the kerogen and bitumen have very similar gross elemental compositions if Eqn. 2 holds for both materials. The major difference between the kerogen and bitumen in these samples may be largely in molecular weight distribution which affects solubility.

SUMMARY AND CONCLUSIONS

The wide spread acceptance by the petroleum industry of the Rock–Eval type pyrolysis method for source-rock evaluation attests to its utility. Nevertheless, there are good reasons for the prevailing diversity of opinions regarding interpretation and significance of the data.

There is no question about the utility of whole-rock pyrolysis as a rapid screening technique to give a qualitative indication of the relative hydrocarbon potential of sediments. Barren sections in a well can be discounted and promising sections selected for further evaluation. However, questions and uncertainties increase in proportion to the specificity of attempted interpretation relative to 1. the quantitative significance of pyrolytic yields, 2. inferences regarding kerogen type and maturity level, and 3. the relationship between hydrocarbon potential measured by laboratory pyrolysis and that which may be realized naturally.

This study has shown that pyrolytic hydrocarbon yields (S_2) measured on isolated kerogens are related

Table 3

Examples of bitumen effect on S_1, S_2 and hydrogen index: well samples from Monterey Formation, South Elwood Field, California.

Sample depth in feet ([a])		% TOC	S_1 mgHC/g rock	S_2 mgHC/g rock	Hydrogen index mgHC/g TOC	% decrease due to extraction in % TOC	% decrease due to extraction in S_2	% decrease due to extraction in HI
4951	Unextracted	5.33	3.1	35.5	666			
4951	Extracted[a]	4.01	–	24.2	603	24.8	31.8	9.3
4956	Unextracted	6.94	3.6	36.6	616			
4956	Extracted	4.77	–	29.1	610	19.7	20.5	1.0
4961	Unextracted	5.36	2.8	29.8	556			
4961	Extracted	4.35	–	23.2	533	18.8	22.1	4.1
4966	Unextracted	2.33	2.3	13.2	566			
4966	Extracted	1.86	–	10.2	548	20.2	22.7	3.2
4971	Unextracted	8.33	6.9	47.9	575			
4971	Extracted	6.94	–	40.8	588	16.7	14.8	– 2.3

[a] Bitumens extracted with chloroform

systematically to gross elemental composition as given in Eqns. 1 and 2. These equations relate pyrolytic yields (S_2) to H/C and O/C ratios with an accuracy generally equivalent to the experimental error in measuring pyrolytic yields (± 5 to 10%). These correlations allow interpretation of pyrolytic yields in terms of kerogen type (I, II, and III) and maturity levels as established by average kerogen evolution pathways on a van Krevelen diagram. Applications and limitations of these relationships have been discussed.

These relationships established for pyrolysis of isolated kerogens must be applied with caution to whole-rock pyrolysis results. The mineral matrix effect can decrease S_2 yields significantly. This effect is particularly severe for clastic sediments containing smectite clays and a low % TOC. This effect always downgrades the kerogen in terms of inferred hydrocarbon potential; the true value for the kerogen will always be equal to or greater than the value indicated by whole-rock pyrolysis.

Heavy ends of bitumens can contribute to the S_2 peak in whole-rock pyrolysis and indicate an erroneously high 'kerogen genetic potential'. However, bitumens are seldom present in sufficient quantities for this effect to be significant. Pyrolysis before and after extraction of the bitumens can easily establish the contributions due to bitumens if this problem is encountered.

Sample quality and data reliability are sacrificed to some degree in whole-rock pyrolysis compared to kerogen pyrolysis. Nevertheless, the speed and simplicity of whole-rock pyrolysis dictates its common use and allows economical analysis of a large number of samples. In the evaluation of a well or basin, a large data base of less precise information may give a better assessment of petroleum potential than very precise information on a few samples. Furthermore, whole-rock pyrolysis gives information on S_1 and the production index $[S_1/(S_1 + S_2)]$ which is lost in kerogen separation. These parameters not only give an additional indication of maturity level, but also can indicate migrated (reservoired) hydrocarbons. Thus, whole-rock pyrolysis has both advantages and disadvantages.

In conclusion, we reiterate that any evaluation of hydrocarbon potential should draw on all available information. Pyrolysis is one analytical technique which may suggest kerogen type, maturity level and remaining genetic potential, but conclusions based on pyrolysis alone should be suspect unless corroborated by other criteria.

REFERENCES

Barker, C. (1974) Pyrolysis techniques for source-rock evaluation. *Am. Assoc. Petr. Geol. Bull.* **58**, 2349–2361.

Claypool, G. E. and Reed, P. R. (1976) Thermal analysis technique for source-rock evaluation: quantitative estimate of organic richness and effects of lithologic variation. *Am. Ass. Petr. Geol. Bull.* **60**, 608–612.

Clementz, D. M. (1980) Effect of oil and bitumen saturation on source-rock pyrolysis. *Am. Ass. Petr. Geol. Bull.* **64**, 2227–2232.

Davis, J. B. and Stanley, J. P. (1981) Thermal chromatography in source rock analysis. *Am. Ass. Petr. Geol. Bull.* (unpublished)

Durand, B., Ed. (1980) *Kerogen, Insoluble Organic Matter from Sedimentary Rocks.* Editions Technip, Paris. 519 pp.

Eggertsen, F. T., Joke, H. M. and Stross, F. H. (1969) A pyrolysis-flame detection technique for thermal analysis. In *Thermal Analysis* **1**, *Instruments, Organic Materials and Polymers.* Ed. by Schwenker, R. F. Jr. and Garn, P. D. Academic Press. pp. 341–351.

Eglinton, G. and Murphy, M. T. J. (1969) *Organic Geochemistry, Methods and Results.* Springer–Verlag, Berlin. 828 pp.

Espitalié, J., Laporte, J. L., Madec, M., Marquis, F., Leplat, P., Paulet, J. and Boutefeu, A. (1977) Méthode rapide de caractérisation des roches mères, de leur potentiel pétrolier et de leur degré d'évolution. *Rev. Inst. Fr. Pét.* **32**, 23–42. English edition available, Ref. 26 447, Inst. Francais du Pétrole (1978).

Espitalié, J., Madec, M. and Tissot, B. (1980) Role of mineral matter in kerogen pyrolysis: Influence on petroleum generation and migration. *Am. Ass. Petr. Geol. Bull.* **64**, 59–66.

Gaines, A. G., Jr. (1973) Papers on the geomorphology, hydrography and geochemistry of the Pettaquamscutt River. Ph.D. Thesis, University of Rhode Island.

Hoering, T. C. and Hare, P. E. (1973) Comparison of natural humic acids with amino acid–glucose reaction products. *Am. Ass. Pétr. Geol. Bull.* **57**, 784.

Horsfield, B. and Douglas, A. G. (1980) The influence of minerals on the pyrolysis of kerogens. *Geochim. et Cosmochim. Acta* **44**, 1119–1131.

Isaacs, C. M. (1980) Diagenesis in the Monterey Formation examined laterally along the coast near Santa Barbara, California. Ph.D. Thesis, Stanford University.

Katz, B. J. (1981) Limitations of Rock–Eval pyrolysis for typing organic matter. *AAPG Book of Abstracts*, San Francisco, May 31–June 3.

LaPlante, R. E. (1974) Hydrocarbon generation in Gulf Coast Tertiary sediments. *Am. Ass. Pétr. Geol. Bull.* **58**, 1281–1289.

Larter, S. R. and Douglas, A. G. (1980) Melanodins–kerogen precursors and geochemical lipid sinks: a study using pyrolysis gas chromatography (GPC). *Geochim. et Cosmochim. Acta* **44**, 2087–2095.

Maxwell, J. R., Pillinger, C. T. and Eglinton, G. (1971) Organic Geochemistry, *Quart. Rev.* **25**, 571–628.

McIver, R. D. (1967) Composition of kerogen — clue to its role in the origin of petroleum. *Proc. 7th World Pet. Conge.* **2**, 25–36.

Monin, J. C., Duran, B., VandenBrouche, M. and Huc, A. Y. (1980) Experimental simulation of the natural transformation of kerogen. In *Advances in Organic Geochemistry* 1979. Ed. by Douglas, A. G. and Maxwell, J. R. Pergamon Press. pp. 517–530.

Nissenbaum, A. and Kaplan, I. R. (1972) Chemical and isotopic evidence for the in situ origin of marine humic substances. *Limnol. Oceanogr.* **17**, 570–582.

Orr, W. L. and Gaines, A. G. (1974) Observations on rate of sulfate reduction and organic matter oxidation in bottom waters of an estuarine basin: The upper basin of the Pettaquamscutt River (Rhode Island). In *Advances in Organic Geochemistry* 1973. Ed. by Tissot, B. and Bienner, F. pp. 791–812.

Patterson, J. M., Kardash, W. F. and Jeffrey, D. A. (1981) Pyrolysis as a geochemical screening technique in oil exploration. *Abstracts 181st American Chem. Soc. Meeting*, Mar. 29–Apr. 3, Paper 26.

Robin, P. L., Rouxhet, P. G. and Durand, B. (1977) Caractérisation des kerogenes et de leur évolution par spectroscopie infrarouge: fonctions hydrocarbonées. In *Advances in Organic Geochemistry*, 1975. Ed. by Campos, R. and Goni, J. Enadisma, Madrid. pp. 693–716.

Saxby, J. D. (1977) Oil-generating potential of organic matter in sediments under natural conditions. *J. Geochemical Exploration* **7**, 373–382.

Seifert, W. K. and Moldowan, J. M. (1980) The effect of thermal stress on source-rock quality as measured by hopane stereochemistry. In *Advances in Organic Geochemistry*, 1979. Ed. by Douglas, A. G. and Maxwell, J. P. Pergamon Press. pp. 229–237.

Swanson, V. E. and Palacas, J. G. (1965) Humate in Coastal Samds of Northwest Florida. *US Geol. Sur. Bull.* 1214-B, B1-29.

Tissot, B., Durant, B., Espitalié, J. and Combaz, A. (1974) Influence of nature and diagenesis of organic matter in formations of petroleum. *Am. Ass. Petr. Geol. Bull.* **58**, 499–506.

Tissot, B. and Espitalié, J. (1975) L'évolution thermique de la matière organique des sédiments: Applications d'une simulation mathématique. *Rev. Inst. Fran. Pétr.* **30**, 743–777.

Tissot, B. P. and Welte, D. H. (1978) *Petroleum Formation and Occurrence.* Springer–Verlag, Berlin. 527 pp.

Advances in Organic Geochemistry 1981, pp. 788–798
© *John Wiley & Sons Limited, 1983*

Geochemical Characterisation of Crude Oils and Source Rocks using Field Ionisation Mass Spectrometry

G. W. M. Lijmbach, F. M. van der Veen and E. D. Engelhardt

Koninklijke/Shell Exploratie en Produktie Laboratorium Rijswijk, The Netherlands

Field ionisation mass spectrometry (FIMS) is an excellent method for analysing complex mixtures, since FIMS yields practically fragment-free molecular peak spectra. We have used FIMS of the saturated hydrocarbons for the characterisation of crude oils and rock extracts. Although crude oils and/or rock extracts can be differentiated on the basis of the shape of the FIMS spectra, it was found to be more accurate to compare ratios of peak intensities. The distributions of the mono-, di- and tricyclanes in the C_{15} region ($m/e = 206$, 208 and 210) and of the tri-, tetra- and pentacyclanes in the C_{30} region ($m/e = 410$, 412 and 414) in particular show very distinct differences. Using these distributions it is possible to type crude oils in terms of their original source material. The C_{30} typing is not affected by bacterial degradation, although the C_{15} ring distribution is. Apart from crude oils, rock extracts can also be characterised by the distribution of C_{15} and C_{30} cyclanes. Thus the method is useful for oil–oil and oil–source rock correlations. Finally, maturity information has been obtained from Fl-mass spectra. The degree of organic metamorphism (vr/e = vitrinite reflectance equivalent) of source rocks and crude oils can be measured from the C_{29} cyclane distribution in these oils or rock extracts. In this way the highest maturity which the oil or source rock has ever reached is determined. This maturity method cannot be used for biodegraded crude oils. Various examples of crude oil and source rock typing are given in this paper as well as examples of oil–oil and oil–source rock correlations using FIMS.

INTRODUCTION

Field ionisation mass spectrometry (FIMS) is a very suitable method for analysis of complex mixtures like crude oils and source rock extracts (Payzant *et al.*, 1979).

In FIMS, ions are generated by subjecting the sample to an extremely strong electric field (10^7–10^8 V cm^{-1}), which causes a quantum mechanical tunnelling of one electron of the molecule to the electric field producing surface (razor blade) (Payzant *et al.*, 1979). This type of ionisation produces an ion which has relatively little excess energy, so that fragmentation of the molecule is minimised. By choosing the right electric field, fragmentation is largely avoided and FIMS produces practically fragment-free molecular peak spectra (Beckey, 1977; Mead, 1968; Scolnick *et al.*, 1975; Scheppele *et al.*, 1976; Severin, 1976). Thus FIMS analysis of a mixture results in the molecular weight distribution of all components present. The concentration of each component is proportional to the intensity of the molecular ion with the appropriate mass.

We have been using FIMS of the saturated fractions of crude oils and source rock extracts extensively for geochemical characterisation since 1971. Ionisation efficiency of hydrocarbons in FIMS depends on hydrocarbon type and carbon number, but is approximately constant within a given class of hydrocarbons (Mead, 1968; Ryska *et al.*, 1975; Kuras *et*

al., 1976). We can therefore compare the spectra of various crude oils and source rock extracts. We use the distribution of cyclic alkanes in the C_{15} and C_{30} region of the FI-mass spectra of the saturated fraction for typing of crude oils and source rocks extracts in terms of their original source material, while the C_{29} distribution yields information on the maturity level of the sample.

Analytical techniques

The saturated fractions are subjected to gas chromatography and field ionisation mass spectrometry. rock samples are obtained as pentane eluates from alumina/silica columns.

The saturated fractions are subjected to gas chromatography and field ionisation mass spectrometry.

The gas chromatograph is an Intersmat, type ICG 120 DLF containing a 25 m WCOT glass capillary, ID 0.25 mm, stationary phase SE 30. Nitrogen is used as carrier gas, the temperature is programmed from 90 °C to 300 °C at a rate of 4 °C min^{-1}.

The mass spectrometer is a JEOL (Mattauch Herzog optics) instrument, type JMS-01 SG, interfaced with a JEOL computer, type JEC-6.

Field emission is achieved using part of a platinum-coated razor blade, which is activated by introducing the fraction of a crude oil (boiling up to 300 °C) in the ion source. Saturated concentrates to be analysed are

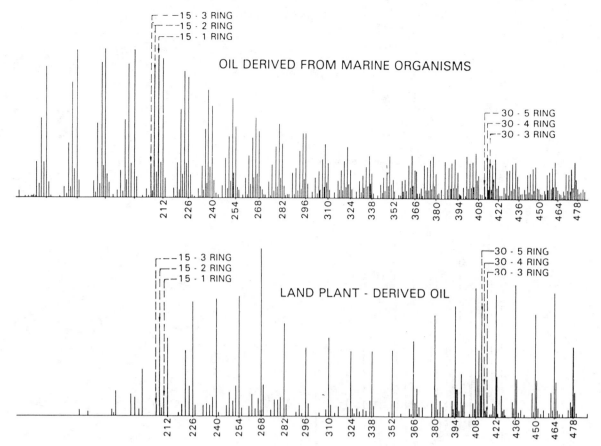

Fig. 1. Field-ionisation mass spectra of the saturated fraction of crude oils from well Yibal-7, Oman (Marine) and well A, S. China (Landplant).

introduced by a direct probe system and evaporated by slowly heating the probe.

A representative spectrum of the sample is obtained by accumulating 15 digitized spectra using the computer system.

Characterisation of crude oils

Geochemical typing of crude oils is largely based on the composition of the saturated hydrocarbons. The alkane distribution provides information about the original source material of the oil (Hedberg, 1968; Lijmbach, 1975), while the relative amounts of isoprenoids reflect the environment of deposition of that source material (Ljimbach, 1975; Brooks *et al.*, 1969). In addition, the composition of the cyclic alkanes is diagnostic of the oil type. Oils and source-rock extracts contain relatively large amounts of naphthenic ring components. It is generally assumed that part of these ring compounds (particularly those in higher boiling fractions) are related to specific precursors in animal and plant life e.g. steroids, carotenoids and terpenoids. As these precursors contribute in different amounts to the various oil-source materials, it is clear that the naphthenic composition of oils and source-rock extracts can be used for oil and source-rock characterisation. In FI-mass spectra (see Fig. 1) of the saturated fractions of crude oils the *n*-alkanes (and iso-alkanes having the same formula C_nH_{2n+2}) are found in one homologous series of masses: 198,

212, 226, 240 etc. Cyclic alkanes with one ring in their molecules are found under the masses corresponding with C_nH_{2n}; cyclic alkanes with 2 rings in their molecules under masses corresponding with C_nH_{2n-2} etc.

In Fig. 1, FI mass spectra are shown for a crude oil originating from landplant matter and one derived from structureless organic matter (SOM)*. There are clear differences in the overall shape of the spectra. However, it was found to be more useful to compare ratios of peak intensities, particularly in the intensities of the C_{30} 4- and 5-ring naphthenes. See also Table 1, in which some important properties of the two oils are summarised. The gas chromatograms of the two oils are shown in Fig. 2.

It is known from EB mass spectrometry that the C_{30} 4-ring ($m/e = 414$) is mainly due to the presence of steranes and tetracyclic triterpanes in crude oils, whereas the C_{30} 5-ring ($m/e = 412$) is mainly caused by pentacyclic triterpanes. The relative abundance of C_{30} 5-rings ($m/e = 412$) in landplant-derived crudes is probably caused by the fact that plant resins are the precursors of many pentacyclic triterpanes in oils (Hills *et al.*, 1970). In addition, the C_{15} 2-ring compound ($m/e = 208$) (abundant in landplant-derived crudes and low in crudes of planktonic origin) is a breakdown product of the C_{30} pentacyclic triterpane (Bendoraitis, 1974).

The different origin can be usefully presented by plotting the relative intensities (sum = 100%) of the

---

* SOM is thought to be the fossil form of bacterial biomass (Lijmbach, 1975).

Table 1

Well	Country	API	%S	pr/C_{17}	ph/C_{18}	pr/ph	Gross composition %Sat	%Ar.	%Het	Naphthene ring Distribution[a] 1	2	3	C_{15} 3	4	5	DOM[a] $_{30}$ of oil
Yibal-7	Oman	37	0.6	0.6	0.6	1.3	70	20	10	47	42	11	39	46	15	0.96
Well A	South China Sea	39	0.3	1.5	0.3	6.2	60	34	6	15	76	9	3	22	75	0.65

[a] Normalised to sum = 100%.
[b] DOM = degree of organic metamorphism, in vitrinite reflectance units.

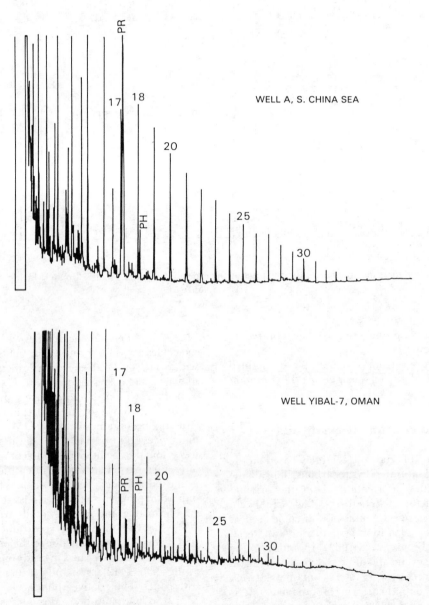

Fig. 2. Gas chromatograms of saturated hydrocarbons of two crude oils.

saturated (a) C_{15} 1-, 2- and 3-ring naphthenes and (b) C_{30} 3-, 4- and 5-ring naphthenes. Figure 3 shows that in this way a clear distinction can be made between crudes of different types.

In Table 2 crude oils from various parts of the world and different origins are collected. Plotting of the ring-number distribution shows how well oils from different origins can be differentiated (see Fig. 4). The type of source material for the oils in Table 2 is known from other geochemical and geological evidence. The naphthene ring distribution is similar within the various types, and different between groups. This allows characterisation of crude oils.

Biograded oils can also be typed by this method.

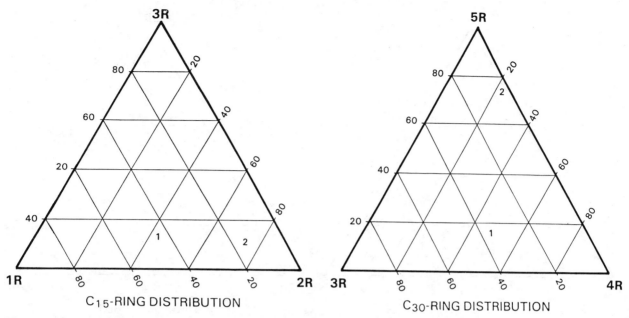

Fig. 3. Naphthene ring distribution of two crude oils. 1. Yibal-7, Oman (derived from marine organisms). 2. Well A, S. China Sea (derived from plant resins + waxes).

Table 2

No. Well	Country	API gravity	%S	pr/C_{17}	ph/C_{18}	pr/ph	Gross composition %Sat	%Ar.	%Het	1	C_{15} 2	3	3	C_{30} 4	5	Dom[b] of oil
I Landplant derived oils																
1 D	S. China Sea	40.8	0.1	1.8	0.2	9.1	75	19	16	21	60	19	7	28	65	1.04
2 E	S. China Sea	29.2	0.07	1.9	0.3	6.4	67	27	3	19	62	19	11	26	63	0.80
3 B	S. China Sea	19.9	0.2	n-d	n-d	n-d	40	49	11	7	72	21	7	26	67	—
4 C	S. China Sea	34.8	0.2	1.3	0.3	4.8	56	39	5	21	59	20	7	25	68	0.55
5 Umuechem-5	Nigeria	38.8	0.1	0.8	0.6	2.0	58	26	16	35	47	18	14	37	49	0.73
6 Egbema-1	Nigeria	37.3	0.1	1.0	0.4	2.6	77	24	9	29	56	15	11	41	48	0.55
III SOM-derived oils																
7 211/23-1	UK	35.7	0.5	1.0	0.8	1.6	52	32	16	47	37	16	19	52	29	0.73
8 211/29-2	UK	37.4		0.8	0.6	1.4	43	40	17	38	43	19	21	54	25	0.73
9 Fahud-N	Oman	32.1	1.3	0.4	0.5	0.9	53	32	15	54	36	10	37	39	24	0.88
10 Qaharir-3	Oman	19.3	2.6	0.4	0.9	0.6	31	44	25	60	35	15	26	46	28	0.80
11 Qarn Alam	Oman	15.0	2.0	n-d	n-d	n-d	44	37	19	17	56	27	29	44	27	—
12 Soudron-1	France	33.9	0.4	0.8	0.6	1.5	61	35	4	50	36	14	33	52	15	1.00
13 Soudron-1	France	33.8	0.5	0.8	0.6	1.4	61	35	4	55	35	10	26	54	20	0.96
14 Mara DM-3	W. Venezuela	28.7	2.1	0.3	0.5	0.7	43	37	20	41	47	12	22	54	25	—
15 Taylor DT653	California USA	34.8	0.6	0.9	0.8	1.2	56	26	18	49	37	14	27	48	25	0.85
II Oils of mixed origin																
16 W. Guara GG82	E. Venezuela	31.6	0.5	1.2	0.3	4.3	69	17	14	33	49	19	22	39	39	0.80
17 Officina	E. Venezuela	35.1	1.0	1.0	0.6	1.9	56	34	10	40	47	13	25	39	36	0.80
18 Alamein-1	Egypt	33.9	1.3	0.4	0.3	1.5	54	34	12	33	46	21	22	45	34	0.65
19 Meleiha-1	Egypt	39.1	0.3	0.5	0.2	2.7	62	35	3	23	53	24	17	39	44	1.04

[a] n-d = non detectable, because of biodegradation of the crude (see Fig. 6).
[b] DOM of oil = degree of organic metamorphism of oil; as determined from Fig. 16, in vitrinite reflectance unit.
Note The reproducibility of the C_{15} and C_{30} ring number distribution is about 10%.

Biological degradation (Bendoraitis, 1974) of crude oils generally hampers their typing as microbes preferentially remove certain compounds. In severely bacterially degraded crudes the amount of C_{15} 1- and 2-ring components is decreased. However the C_{30} 3-, 4-,

5-ring distribution is not affected by biological degradation.

In Fig. 5 examples are given of the typing of two severely biograded crudes (see also Table 2 and Fig. 6). For both crudes the C_{30} ring distribution can be used for

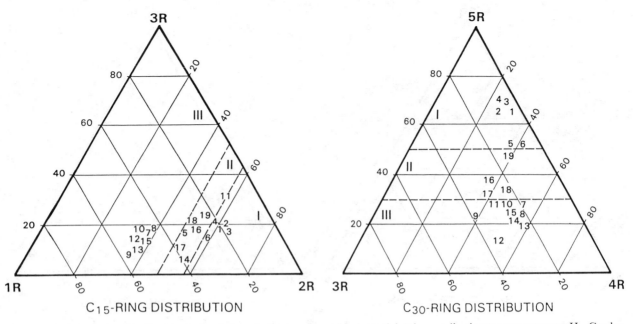

Fig. 4. Naphthene ring distribution. I – Landplant-derived crudes with substantial resin contribution to source matter; II – Crudes of mixed origin; III – Crudes derived from SOM and/or algal matter.

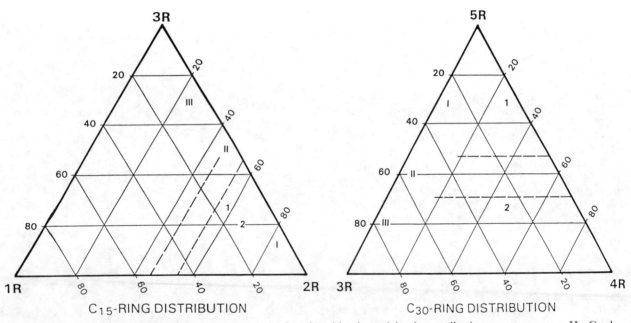

Fig. 5. Naphthene ring distribution. I – Landplant-derived crudes with substantial resin contribution to source matter; II – Crudes of mixed origin; III – Crudes derived from SOM and/or algal matter.

typing. In the case of the Qarn Alam crude it appears that the C_{15} 1-ring components have been affected by microbial degradation as well.

Source rock characterisation and oil-source rock correlation

The C_{15} and C_{30} ring number distribution can also be used for the typing of source rock extracts. Extracts of mature source rocks have a similar naphthene ring distribution as the crude oil that has been expelled from this source rock and has migrated as a bulk phase into a reservoir.

Immature source-rock extracts and low maturity oils show relatively high concentrations of C_{30} 4- and 5-ring compounds. Upon maturation (natural or artificial by heating (Gransch et al., 1974)) the C_{15} and C_{30} ring distribution becomes more or less identical with that of the related oil. This makes the naphthene ring distribution into a very useful oil–source rock correlation tool.

The South Sumatra (Indonesia) West Prabumulih oil can be correlated with the Tertiary Talang Akar source rock, containing plant resins and waxes. In Fig. 7 the chromatograms of the saturated fractions of the original and heated samples are compared with that of the crude

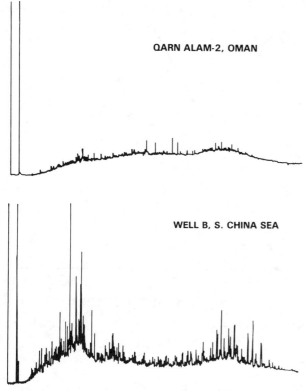

Fig. 6. Gas chromatograms of the saturates of two bacterially degraded crude oils.

oil. The chromatogram of the original sample does not resemble that of the oil. However after artificial maturation by heating in a bomb at 330 °C in the presence of water for 64 h the alkane distribution is very similar to that of the crude oil (Gransch *et al.*, 1974). The naphthene ring distribution is plotted in Fig. 8 showing the agreement between crude oil and extracts of the

heated sample. From these data it can be concluded that the tertiary Talang Akar source rock can generate a crude oil similar to the West Prabumulih oil if the source rock is buried deep enough.

Another example of an oil–source rock correlation is given in Figs. 9 and 10. The Soudron crude oil from the Paris basin, France, is correlated with the lower Jurassic Toarcian source rock. A good correlation is observed after artificial maturation both in alkane distributions and naphthene ring distributions. Thus the Soudron crude oil can originate from a mature Toarcian source rock, consisting of SOM (type II organic atter).

It appears that immature algal source rocks show a C_{30} ring number distribution similar to that of landplant derived source rocks (see Figs. 11 and 12). The C_{15} ring number distribution, however, does not show a two ring predominance as in plant resin related source rocks. This knowledge enables us to differentiate between landplant-derived source rocks (rich in plant resins), SOM (residual bacterial mass) source rocks and immature source rocks with a considerable algal contribution. In addition, heating experiments (Gransch *et al.*, 1974) with algal source rocks indicate a dramatic change in C_{30} ring distribution during maturation (see Figs. 13 and 14). Therefore no distinction can be made by this method between mature algal and SOM source rocks or their related oils.

The use of the naphthene ring distribution as a method for the characterisation of crude oils and source rocks is summarised in Table 3 and Fig. 15.

Determination of maturity level

Field ionisation mass spectra revealed that extracts of immature source rocks and low maturity oils show irregular C_{30} ring distributions. They are relatively rich

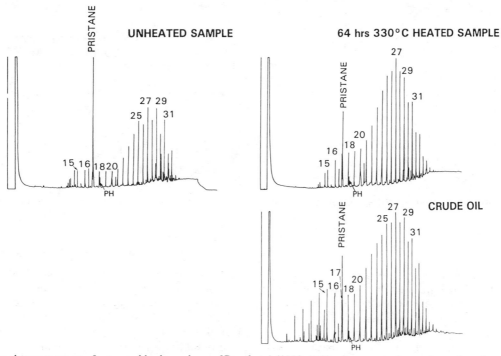

Fig. 7. Gas chromatograms of saturated hydrocarbons of Benakat-1 (1550–1560 m) source rock samples and a related crude oil of West Prabumulih (Indonesia).

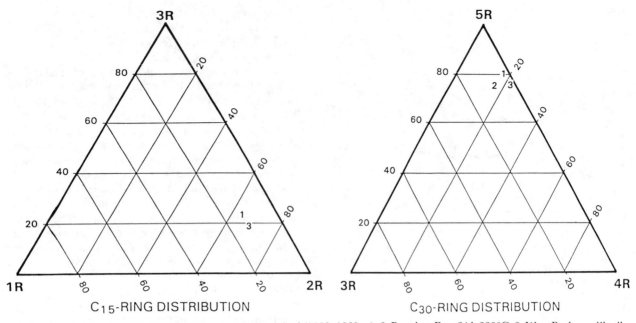

Fig. 8. Naphthene ring distribution. 1. Benakat-East original (1550–1560 m). 2. Benakat-East 64 h 330°C. 3. West Prabumulih oil.

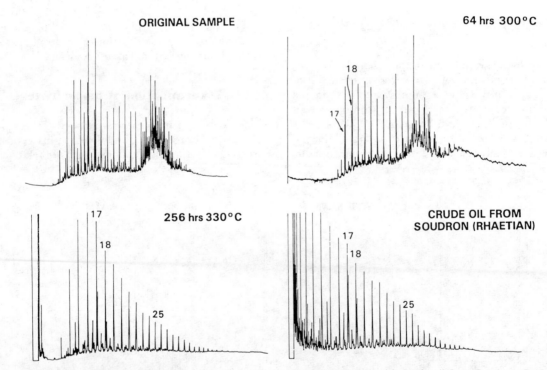

Fig. 9. Correlation of Toarcian SR sample from Dontrien-1, 1314.95–1315.8 m with crude oil from Soudron, Paris Basin.

in 4- and 5-ring compounds and poor in 1-, 2- and 3-ring compounds. Detailed inspection of the field-ionisation mass spectra of the early expelled oils and immature source-rock extracts showed a pronounced dominance of the 4- and 5-ring compounds in the range: C_{27}–C_{32}. This dominance decreases with increasing maturity or heating time of the samples. While the C_{30} 5-ring compounds are abundant in landplant-derived material, C_{29} ring compounds apparently show smaller dependence on type of organic matter. We have therefore studied the influence of maturity on the C_{29} ring distribution. For a series of source rocks with well established maturity (by vitrinite reflectance) the C_{29} ring number distribution was determined. It appeared that for SOM source rocks (the maturity being determined using coal-shale pairs) a linear relationship

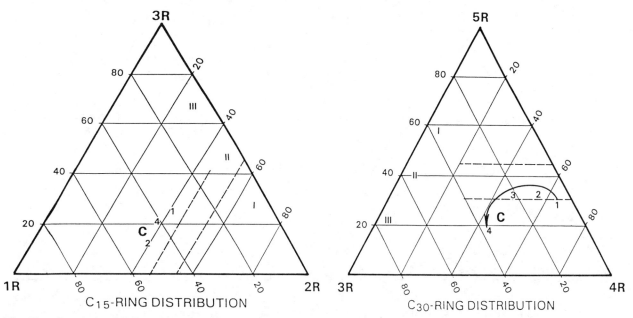

Fig. 10. Correlation Soudron oil with Toarcian SR. C – Soudron crude oil. 1. 64 hrs 300°C. 2. 64 hrs 330°C. 3. 256 hrs 330°C.

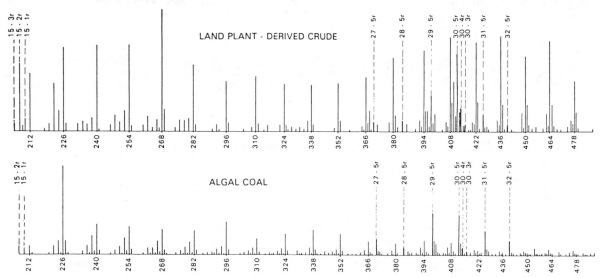

Fig. 11. Field-ionisation mass spectrum of the saturated fraction of crude oil from well A, S. China Sea and Torbanite, Australia.

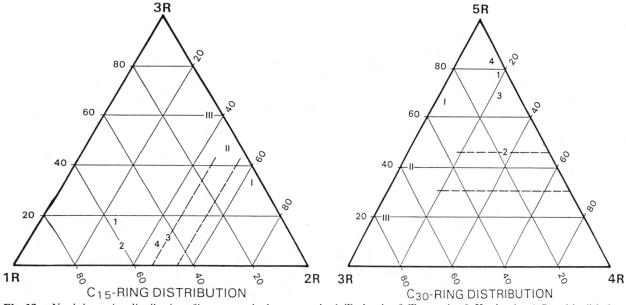

Fig. 12. Naphthene ring distribution of immature algal source rocks. 1. Torbanite. 2. Tasmanite. 3. Kuckersite. 4. Scottish oilshale.

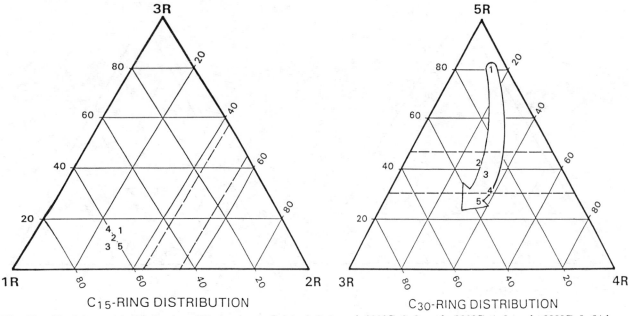

Fig. 13. Naphthene ring distribution of Torbanite. 1. Original. 2. 1 week 300°C. 3. 2 weeks 300°C. 4. 3 weeks 300°C. 5. 64 hrs 330°C.

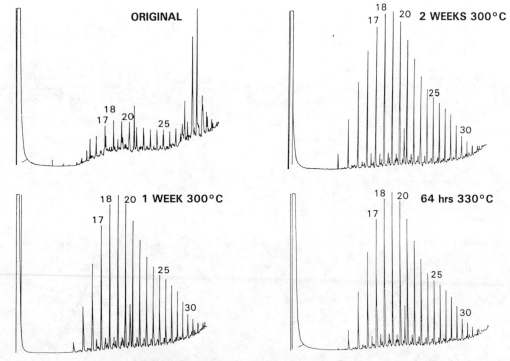

Fig. 14. GLC of saturates of Torbanite.

was found between

$$\log \frac{C_{29}\ 4\text{-rings} + C_{29}\ 5\text{-rings}}{C_{29}\ 1\text{-rings}} \text{ and DOM* (VR)}$$

(see Fig. 16 and Table 4). Using the relationship in Fig. 16 as a calibration line, the maturity of SOM source rocks can be established from the naphthene ring

* DOM = degree of organic metamorphism.

Table 3

Use of naphthene ring distribution.

Main contributor to source matter	Intensity	
	C_{15} 2-ring compounds	C_{30} 5 ring compounds
Plant resins	high	high
SOM and algal matter	low	low
Algal matter (immature)	low	high

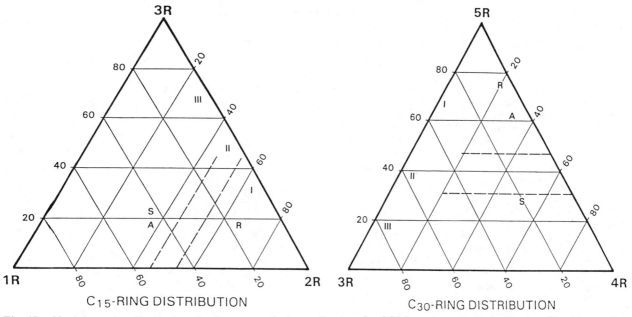

Fig. 15. Naphthene ring distribution. A – Immature algal contribution; S – SOM + mature algal contribution; R – Plant resin contribution.

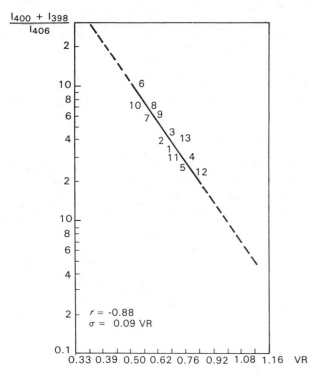

Fig. 16. Relationship between ratio of mass spectral intensities of $(C_{29}$ 4 + 5-rings$/C_{29}$ 1-ring$)[=(I_{400} + I_{398}/I_{406})]$ and VR.

The results of this method are very promising. For SOM source rocks and SOM related crude oils good data can be obtained. For landplant derived source rocks and crude oils the DOM values obtained are in general somewhat too high. A separate calibration set for landplant derived crude oils and source rocks is under development. For biodegraded crudes this method can not be used as the C_{29} 1-ring components are affected by microbial degradation.

CONCLUSIONS

The naphthene ring number distribution, determined by field ionisation mass spectrometry appears to be a good tool for the geochemical characterisation of crude oils and source rocks. It can be used for all crude oils, including biodegraded ones. The method offers a very useful additional tool for oil–oil and oil–source rock correlation. The naphthene ring number distribution can also be used to determine the DOM of SOM source rocks and their related oils.

number distribution of their extracts. For crude oils a DOM can also be determined. Generally, this is the DOM which the oil has acquired at the time of its expulsion from the source rock. However, in case of significant further maturation of the oil in the reservoir, the C_{29} DOM gives the final DOM value of the oil reached.

ACKNOWLEDGEMENT

We are indebted to Shell Internationale Research Maatschappij (SIRM) for permission to publish this paper.

Table 4
Calibration-set for 'DOM[a] of oil'

No.	Country	Sample	Depth	VR	$\dfrac{I_{400} + I_{398}}{I_{406}}$
1	The Netherlands	L2-2	2399 m	0.67	3.57
2	The Netherlands	F11-1	2660 m	0.65	3.88
3	The Netherlands	F3-3	3008–3094 m	0.68	4.47
4	The Netherlands	F3-3	3702–3792 m	0.80	3.00
5	Oman	Saih Nihayda-3	8470 ft	0.76	2.59
6	United Kingdom	211/29-1	8650–8694 ft	0.55	10.51
7	United Kingdom	211/29-3	8611.8 ft	0.58	6.13
8	United Kingdom	211/29-3	8767.4 ft	0.60	6.90
9	United Kingdom	211/29-3	9087.2 ft	0.62	6.46
10	United Kingdom	12/26-1	2460–3180 ft	0.53	7.18
11	United Kingdom	16/8-1	12703–12704 ft	0.68	3.32
12	United Kingdom	21/11-1	10908.3 ft	0.85	2.32
13	Australia	Cannel Coal		0.76	4.38

[a] DOM = degree of organic metamorphism

REFERENCES

Beckey, H. D. (1977) Principles of Field Ionisation and Field Desorption Mass Spectrometry. Pergamon Press.

Bendoraitis, J. G. (1974) Hydrocarbons of biogenic origin in petroleum: aromatic triterpenes and biocyclic sesquiterpenes. In *Advances in Organic Geochemistry* 1973. Ed. by Tissot, B. and Bienner, F. Editions Technip, Paris. pp. 209–224.

Brooks, J. D., Gould, K. and Smith, J. W. (1969) Isoprenoid hydrocarbons in coal and petroleum. *Nature* **222**, 257–259.

Gransch, J. A. and Posthuma, J. (1974) On the origin of sulphur in crudes. In *Advances in Organic Geochemistry* 1973. Ed. by Tissot, B. and Bienner, F. Editions Technip, Paris. pp. 727–739.

Hedberg, H. D. (1968) Significance of high-wax oils with respect to genesis of petroleum. *Bull. Am. Ass. Petr. Geol.* **52**, 736–750.

Hills, I. R. and Whitehead, E. V. (1970) Pentacyclic triterpanes from petroleum and their significance. In *Advances in Organic Geochemistry* 1966. Ed. by Hobson, G. D. and Speers, G. C. Pergamon Press, Oxford. pp. 89–110.

Kuras, M. and Ryska M. and Mostecky, J. (1976) Analysis of saturated hydrocarbons by field ionisation mass spectrometry. *Anal. Chem.* **48**, 196–198.

Lijmbach, G. W. M. (1975) On the origin of petroleum. *Proc. 9th World Petrol. Congress*, **Sect. 2**, 357–369.

Mead, W. L. (1968) Field ionisation mass spectrometry of heavy petroleum fraction waxes. *Anal. Chem.* **40**, 743–747.

Payzant, J. D., Rubinstein, I., Hagg, A. M. and Strausz, O. P. (1979) Field-ionisation mass spectrometry: application to geochemical analysis. *Geochem. Cosmochim. Acta* **43**, 1187–1193.

Kuras, M., Mosticky, J. and Ryska, M. (1975) Phenomenology of absorption processes on emitters in the field ionisation of hydrocarbon mixtures. *Int. J. Mass. Spec. Ion. Phys.* **16**, 257–269.

Scheppele, S. E., Greenwood, G. J., Grizzle, P. L., Marriot, T. D. and Perriira, N. B. (1976) Determination of field-ionisation relative sensitivities for the analysis of coal derived liquids and their correlation with low-voltage electron-impact relative sensitivities. *Anal. Chem.* **48**, 2105–2113.

Scolnick, M. E., Alberth, W. H. and Anbar, M. (1975) An integrating multiscanning field ionisation mass spectrometer. *Int. J. Mass. Spec. Ion. Phys.* **17**, 139–176.

Severin, D. (1976) Molekülionenmassen-spectrometrie für Analyse hoch- und niedersiedender Kohlen-wasserstoffgemische. *Erdöl und Kohle.* **29**, 13–17.

Advances in Organic Geochemistry 1981, pp. 799–807
© *John Wiley & Sons Limited, 1983*

Natural Combustion and Pyrolysis of Bituminous Rocks at the Margin of Hatrurim, Israel

B. Spiro*

Department of Geology, The Hebrew University, Jerusalem, Israel

Z. Aizenshtat

Department of Organic Chemistry and ERC, The Hebrew University, Jerusalem, Israel

The Hatrurim or 'Mottled Zone' is a metamorphic complex reaching, locally, pyroxene–sanidine–hornfels facies. These metamorphic rocks occur in separate sedimentary basins, in stratigraphic levels equivalent to those of formations composed of chalk and marly chalk, locally bituminous, of Campanian–Maestrictian and Eocene age. Combustion metamorphism affected exposed and probably highly bituminous rocks during the Miocene, about 50 My after deposition. Combustion and pyrolysis progressed along fissures and joints and was terminated either by decrease in concentration of organic matter or by insufficient availability of air. Pyrolytic and combustion effects were studied in the area of NebiMusa, near Jericho, in transition zones between bituminous and metamorphic facies. The bituminous rocks consist of chalk with about 5% non-carbonate minerals and up to 20% organic matter. The organic matter is primarily of algal, marine origin with local contribution of sulfate-reducing bacteria. Grades of increasing pyrolytic effects were defined by several geochemical markers, each sensitive in a specific range.

1. Tetrapyrrole pigments: chlorins of type e occur, which differ from the common pheophytin and pheophorbide.
2. *n*-alkanes have an increasing contribution of medium range homologues (around C_{20}).
3. Kerogen, a: Composition: decrease in hydrogen to carbon ratio. b: Infrared spectra indicate a decrease in aliphatic and increase in aromatic components. Occurrence of anhydrides and peroxides. Disappearance of discrete absorption bands.

   c: X-ray diffraction indicates a transition from saturated compounds to graphite with a progressive decrease in d_{002} spacing.

   d: Electron spin resonance spectra indicate an increase in spin density (N_g) by up to two orders of magnitude, followed by a drastic decrease until no resonance is recorded.

   e: Rock-Eval pyrograms indicate an increase of S_1 response, decrease of S_2, formation of two S_2 peaks (T_{max} around 440 and 550°C), while the amount of residual carbon increases.

Two types of thermal effects could be graded using this scale: combustion, affecting a margin of a few meters; and steam distillation, locally leaving blocks of bituminous rocks which show relatively low grade thermal effects. These rocks are surrounded by envelopes poor in organic matter showing strong thermal effects. The transition zone has a width of only a few millimeters. These natural features may be regarded as similar to the various processes of *in situ* retorting.

INTRODUCTION

The nature of organic matter in sedimentary rocks is determined by its biological precursors, the environment of deposition, and the early diagenetic and the thermal history. The nature and degree of a thermal effect can be determined from physical and chemical parameters of the rock constituents. The onset of metamorphic alteration in sedimentary organic matter takes place at temperatures lower than that of minerals. A variety of markers are used for the determination of the level of metamorphism based on characteristic physical and chemical properties of selected fractions of the organic matter. Simulation of natural thermal effects by experimental pyrolysis under controlled regimes clarifies some of the phenomena of thermal alteration which are observed in sedimentary organic matter.

The two main modes of metamorphism (i.e. regional and contact) can be effective on organic constituents also. A particular type of contact metamorphism is auto- or combustion-metamorphism. In this process the combustion of the organic matter contained in the rock

* Present address: Institute for Petroleum and Organic Geochemistry, KFA-Jülich, PO Box 1913, D-5170 Jülich, F.R.Germany

provides the source of heat for the metamorphic process. Studies on combustion metamorphism are numerous. Petrographic phenomena caused by combustion of the Monterey shales were described by Bentor and Kastner (1976). Combustion of rocks rich in organic matter have been observed for decades in outcrops of the 'Smoking Hills' of northern Canada and in western Greenland. The mineralogical and chemical composition of the 'Mottled Zone' (or Hatrurim Formation) metamorphic complexes in Israel suggest that these were formed by local combustion metamorphism of the Ghareb and Taqyia Formations (Gross, 1977).

The Ghareb and the overlying Taqyia Formations of Campanian–Maestrichtian and Paleocene age, respectively, were deposited in many parts of Israel in synclinal areas. The Ghareb Formation consists mainly of white argillaceous chalk, locally in depressions the sequence is shaley, pyritic and bituminous especially in its lower part (Bentor, 1960; Reiss, 1962). The Hatrurim or 'Mottled Zone' is a metamorphic complex which is situated in a level equivalent to the Ghareb and Taqyia Formations. Outcrops of this complex occur in separate basins over areas up to several tens of square kilometers. It consists of a low pressure, high temperature, predominantly calcium-rich mineral assemblage and reaches pyroxene–sanidinite facies (Gross, 1977). Temperatures up to 1300 °C were calculated from oxygen isotope composition (Matthews and Kolodny, 1978). The carbon isotope composition of the metamorphic rocks suggests that organic matter played a role in the metamorphic process (Kolodny and Gross, 1974). Dating by fission track analysis indicates that the metamorphic event occurred during the Miocene (Kolodny et al., 1971), about 50 million years after deposition. This means that the process of combustion metamorphism affected lithified sedimentary rocks which were exposed during that period. The formations are well-developed in the Maaleh Adumim–Nebi Musa basin, a synclinal area on the eastern slopes of the Judea Mountains, near Jericho. The spatial relations between metamorphic and non-metamorphic rocks are well-exposed in this area.

The Ghareb Formation in the Nebi Musa basin consists of chalk, containing minor amounts of silicate minerals and up to 20% organic matter. The organic matter is derived from algae with contributions from sulfate-reducing bacteria in the lower beds. The sedimentology, petrography, sulfur content, isotopic composition and organic geochemistry of sediments from several basins including Nebi Musa are reported in Spiro and Aizenshtat (1977), Spiro et al. (1978), Spiro (1980) and Dinur et al. (1980).

The organogeochemical study of bituminous rocks of the Ghareb Formation at the margin of the Hatrurim complex has the following objectives:

1. To identify and follow changes in the composition and distribution of selected organic components.
2. To compile these changes into a comprehensive scale of thermal alteration.
3. To identify factors which affected the initiation of the metamorphic process and restricted its propagation.
4. To apply this information, derived from natural phenomena, to processes of in situ retorting.

GEOLOGICAL DESCRIPTION AND SAMPLING

The metamorphic Hatrurim on 'Mottled Zone' complex is developed in several separate basins. The most spectacular are the Hatrurim Basin (south of Arad) and Maaleh Adumim (on the eastern slopes of the Judea Mountains). The metamorphic rocks have typical bright red, yellow and green colors. Their boundaries with non-metamorphic rocks are of two types: a concordant contact between metamorphic rocks and the underlying phosphate and chert beds of the Mishash Formation, and a discordant contact between metamorphic rocks and their stratigraphic equivalents (chalks and marls of the Ghareb and Taqyia Formations). Generally these chalks and marls have a very low organic matter content. Columnar jointing on a scale of several centimeters is a common feature of the boundary zones. Transition zones between bituminous to metamorphic rocks are uncommon. They occur mainly in sections where the Neogene Hazeva conglomerate covers the bituminous rocks. In several localities in the Nebi Musa basin these transitions are exposed. Another interesting morphological feature is found in various localities in the Nebi Musa basin. The bituminous rocks occur as dark hard blocks, locally angular, up to several meters in size. These are surrounded by light-colored, soft, fissile, chalk which is poor in organic matter. Individual laminae can be followed from the fissile to the hard chalk. The transition zone between fissile and hard chalk is very narrow, about one millimeter. Gypsum veins cut across the fissile chalk in various orientations but not across the hard bituminous chalk. These dark blocks generally contain abundant organic matter of which the bitumen fraction constitutes more than 30% as compared with less than 10% in the common bituminous rocks of the basin.

Samples were collected from the hard chalk (BI9) (Tables 1 and 2), fissile chalk (BI8) and along traverses from the bituminous to metamorphic rocks (BS56–59, BS65–67 and BS77–81). Samples of bituminous rocks from the Nebi Musa basin were studied for comparison (NM4A, NM4B). Reference is made also to bituminous rocks from other basins in Israel (Horon and Ef'e) which are not described in detail in this presentation.

EXPERIMENTAL

Rock samples were treated and extracted following the standard procedures as described by Aizenshtat et al. (1973). Kerogen was separated by the HCl, HF and LiAlH$_4$ method described by Saxby (1970) and subsequently extracted with benzene:methanol (7:3).

Pyrolysis was performed in a Rock-Eval[R] instrument using a 25 °C min^{-1} heating rate from 250 to 550 or to 600 °C. The Rock-Eval pyrolysis method is described in detail by Espitalié et al. (1977). Up to 200 mg rock samples and up to 5 mg of separated kerogen were used for analysis.

UV-visible spectra were recorded on an SP-800 Ultraviolet spectrometer Pye Unicam 190–700 nm. IR

Table 1
Pyrolytic characteristics of whole rock and kerogen samples

	C_{org}	S_1^a	S_2^a	S_3^b	T_{max1}	T_{max2}	HI^c	OI^d
			Whole rock					
Horon[e]	6.82	b.d.l.	38.33	3.32	425	—	562.1	49
Bit4C[e]	10.80	b.d.l.	66.11	3.86	418	—	612.2	36
NM4A[e]	15.35	2.89	108.52	2.28	428	—	707.0	15
BS65[f]	1.0	0.013	0.08	1.63	446	534	2.6	54
BI8[g]	1.0	0.015	0.11	2.35	440	520	11.0	(235)
BI9[g]	12.54	5.36	99.17	1.11	427	—	790.9	9
			Kerogen					
BI7[e]	71.45	4.41	376.0	6.43	417	—	527	9
BS58[f]	65.65	0.42	79.02	5.25	442	525	120	8
BS59[f]	71.60	0.93	21.47	9.30	436	—	30	13
BS56[f]	21.45	0.18	18.45	3.86	446	531	86	18
BS60[f]	4.60	0.04	0.30	0.64	436	516	77	14
BI8[g]	50.36	0.77	10.53	30.2	430	526	21	60

[a] mg HC g^{-1} rock
[b] mg CO_2 g^{-1} rock
[c] Hydrogen index = mg HC g^{-1} C_{org}
[d] Oxygen index = mg CO_2 g^{-1} C_{org}
[e] Bituminous rocks of the Campanian Maastrichtian Ghareb Formation from various basins
[f] Bituminous rocks from the Hatrurim margin
[g] Thermally affected rock in a narrow zone within the Nebi Musa basin
  b.d.l. = below detection limit

Table 2
Kerogen from Nebi Musa basin and Hatrurim margin

Sample	C (%)	Elemental composition			H/C (atomic)	ESR spectrum		X-ray diffraction	
		H (%)	N (%)	S (%)		N_g^a	g value	d_{002}A	w^b
NM4A	68.74	7.58	2.32	8.40	1.32	0.42	2.0039	4.8	10
NM4B	71.48	7.95	2.13	9.05	1.33	0.52	2.0040	4.8	10
BS56	21.45	1.61	0.58	1.29	0.90	0.142			
BS58	65.65	2.60	0.31	2.80	0.48	0.011	—	3.49	5
BS59	71.60	2.11	n.a.	0.67	0.35	—[c]	—	3.49	5
BS65	41.12	2.13	0.99	3.27	0.62	1.42	—		
BS66	43.13	2.72	1.64	2.97	0.76	11.6	2.0038	3.40	2.5
BS67	5.58	0.75	b.d.l.	0.66	0.014				
BS77	72.38	1.93	0.8	0.61	0.32	2.65	—	—	—
BS79	62.65	2.44	n.a.	4.58	0.47	8.5	—	—	—
BS81	16.10	0.95	1.51	tr.	1		—	—	—
BI8[d]	50.36	3.68	1.58	5.49	0.88	0.93	2.0037	3.37	2
BI9[e]	72.98	7.92	1.98	12.09	1.30	3.44	2.0045	4.8	10

[a] spins g^{-1} × 10^{18}
[b] Width at $\frac{1}{2}$ height in deg. (2θ)
[c] No spectrum obtainable
[d] Thermally affected rock in a narrow zone within the Nebi Musa basin
[e] Bituminous rock adjacent to BI8
  (NM4A, NM4B = non metamorphosed (Nebi Musa basin); n.a. = not analysed; b.d.l. = below detection limit; tr. = trace.)

spectra were recorded on a Perkin Elmer[(R)] 237 spectrophotometer from KBr disks dried at 110 °C for 24 h. ESR spectra were recorded from kerogen samples in quartz tubes in a Varian V-4502 spectrometer. A standard of DPPH in KBr was used.

X-ray diffraction patterns were recorded on a Phillips PW 1730 X-ray generator equipped with a copper tube.

RESULTS AND DISCUSSION

Pyrolysis

The pyrograms of whole rock of the bituminous rocks (Table 1, Fig. 1) have very low S_1 values, i.e. a low content of hydrocarbons volatilized at temperatures

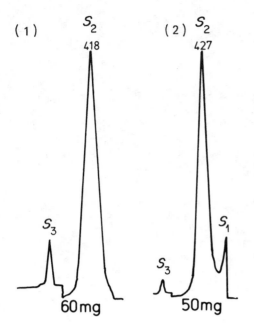

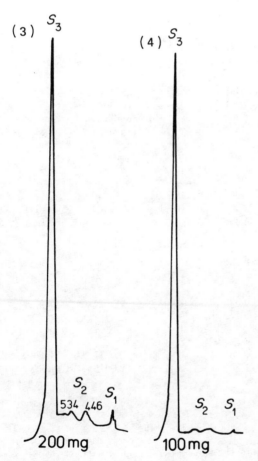

Fig. 1. Pyrograms of whole rock samples (Rock-Eval[(R)] 250–550 °C min[−1]). 1. Bituminous rocks from Efe basin not thermally affected. Note the low response S_1 and the broad response S_2. 2. Bituminous rocks from Nebi Musa basin. Note the response S_1 and the narrower response S_2 with higher T_{max}. 3. Bituminous rocks from the margin of the 'Mottled Zone'. Note the intense response S_1 and the bimodal S_2 response with T_{max} at 446 and 534 °C. 4. Thermally affected rock in a narrow zone within the Nebi Musa basin. Similar pyrolytic features as (3). This sample is adjacent to that shown in (2).

lower than 250 °C. The S_2 value represents the volatile hydrocarbons which are produced by pyrolysis between 250 and 550 °C. This value is large. The response is broad and starts at low temperatures. T_{max} of S_2 (temperature of maximum generation of hydrocarbons) ranges between 415–428 °C. The S_3 values, which represent the amount of CO_2 of organic origin releeased during pyrolysis, are low. The pyrograms of the thermally affected rocks have a high S_1 response. The S_2 response develops two maxima; the first is in the range 415–440 °C, the second in the range 515–535 °C.

The pyrograms of the kerogen from the bituminous rocks (Table 1, Fig. 2) differ from those of the whole rock in the S_2 response which starts at higher temperature and extends over a narrower temperature range. The kerogens of the thermally affected rocks give rise to a small S_1 response. The maxima of the S_2 peaks are again in the range 415–440 °C and 515–535 °C. A gradual change in these features is apparent. The temperature of maximum generation (T_{max}) shifts to higher temperatures and the ingensity of the second S_2 response increases relative to the first. Shifts of T_{max} to higher temperatures and the formation of two S_2 maxima have been described for artificially heated protokerogens isolated from Recent humic and sapropelic sediments (Peters *et al.*, 1981). These protokerogens differ, however, in composition from the presently described kerogen of bituminous rocks. Thus, the pyrolytic evolution of Recent sapropelic protokerogen differs from that of the post-early diagenetic kerogen of bituminous rocks.

Differences in the nature of the organic matter in the bituminous and thermally affected rocks are evident in their pyrograms. Differences can be observed both for the bitumen and kerogen components. The absence of a significant S_1 response in the pyrograms of the total bituminous rocks indicates that no appreciable amount of material undergoes pyrolysis up to 250 °C. By contrast, the presence of S_1 response in the thermally affected rocks indicates the presence of a higher proportion of components of this type. These components are concentrated in the bitumen fraction only, as indicated by the absence of a distinct S_1 response from the pyrograms of the isolated kerogen. The original kerogen is compositionally homogenous and is pyrolyzed at a low and narrow temperature range. The kerogen of the thermally affected rocks has two components, one having pyrolytic characteristics similar to the original (although with slightly higher T_{max}) and a second with a much higher T_{max}. This kerogen is a product of natural pyrolysis of the original kerogen. The process may involve cross linking of aromatic moieties following the cleavage of saturated structures.

X-ray diffraction

The X-ray diffraction pattern of the kerogen from the bituminous rocks shows a broad peak around $2\theta = 18°$ (d_{002} 4.8 Å) (Fig. 3). This pattern is assigned to straight chain and cyclic saturated structures (Yen *et al.*, 1961). The rraces recorded from kerogen of the thermally affected rocks do not show this pattern, instead, narrower peaks at lower d_{002} spacings down to 3.37 Å occur

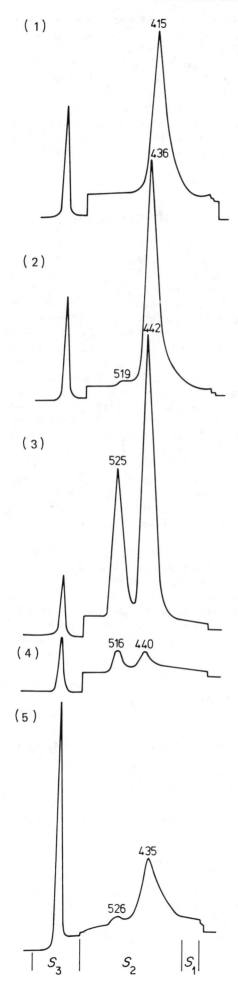

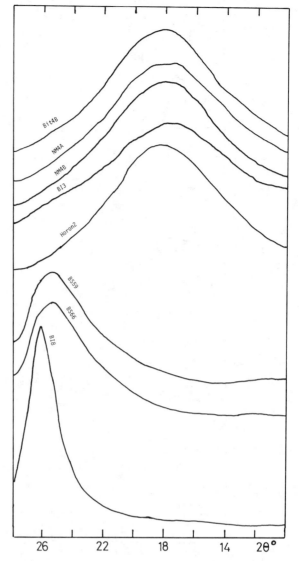

Fig. 3. X-ray diffractograms of kerogens showing the difference between bituminous rocks and the thermally affected rocks which develop a graphite-like structure.

(Fig. 3, Table 2). This pattern is assigned to aromatic layers. The peak width depends on the size of the crystallites and the ordering of the polyaromatic layers. Increase in crystallite size and perfection of the ordering give rise to narrower diffraction patterns. This trend is probably related to a decrease in concentration of hydrogen and heteroatoms. No pattern indicative of two-dimensional ordering could be detected. In this respect, the kerogens can be compared to coal of anthracite rank (Hirsch, 1954). The actual transition from aliphatic- to aromatic-dominated structures could

Fig. 2. Pyrograms of isolated kerogen (Rock-Eval[R] 250–550 °C, 25 °C min⁻¹. 1. Bituminous rock from Ef'e basin not thermally affected. 2–4. Sequence of thermally affected bituminous rocks at the margin of the 'Mottled Zone'. Note the shift in S_2 response to higher temperatures of maximum generation T_{max1} and the development of a second maximum generation temperature range T_{max2}. 5. Thermally affected rock in a narrow zone within the Nebi Musa basin shows pyrolytic features similar to that found in the margin of the 'Mottled Zone' same sample as shown for total rock in Fig. 1-4.

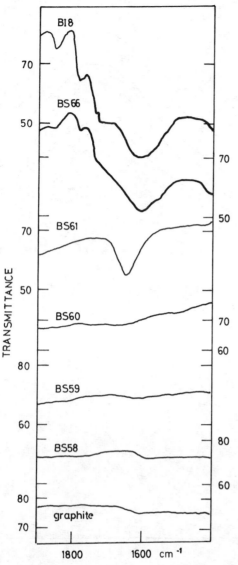

Fig. 4. Infrared spectra in the range 1900–1400 cm^{-1} of thermally affected kerogen from the margin of the 'Mottled Zone'.

H/C also decreases to 0.32 as compared to 1.3 in kerogen of the unaffected rocks. During stepwise pyrolysis experiments of bituminous rocks of the same formation and their separated kerogens (Aizenshtat *et al.*, unpublished), a similar gradual decrease in H/C ratios was measured. A drastic decrease in this ratio was observed in this type of kerogen in the range 450–550 °C, which corresponds to the main phase of hydrocarbon generation. A value of 0.32 was reached in kerogen of the same type during pyrolysis experiments at temperatures exceeding 600 °C (Aizenshtat *et al.*, unpublished).

Infrared spectra

In spectra of kerogen from the bituminous rocks, the dominating absorption bands are at 2980 and 2855 cm^{-1} and are assigned to C–H (aliphatic). Major bands at 1710 and 1630 cm^{-1} are assigned to C=O and C=C, respectively. The kerogens of the thermally affected rocks give rise to a variety of infrared spectra (Fig. 4). No bands are detectable at 2980 and 2855 cm^{-1}. Additional bands occur in several samples (e.g. BI8) at 1780 and 1850 cm^{-1} which are assigned to anhydrites or peroxides. This assignment is supported by the high oxygen index measured for the same samples by Rock-Eval pyrolysis (Table 1). In the gradual sequence of increasing thermal maturity the band at 1710 cm^{-1} also disappears. The last band which persists is at 1630 cm^{-1}. In several samples from the Hatrurim margin no discrete bands can be identified. The absence of discrete absorption bands is typical of graphite (Fig. 4).

Spectra recorded from laboratory-pyrolyzed kerogen of the same type show a gradual decrease in the abundance of C=O functional groups concomitant with increase in abundance of aromatic functions. The natural and experimental results further indicate that progressive aromatization is a major process in the thermal evolution of this type of kerogen, originally of predominantly aliphatic nature. No bands were recorded at 1780 and 1850 cm^{-1} (assigned to anhydrides and peroxides). The difference between the experimental anoxic conditions and the natural process which took place in the presence of oxygen, supports the assignment of these bands. Anhydrides and peroxides may have formed during the cooling of the thermally affected rocks.

not be followed gradually. In the original unaltered kerogen, the saturated structures are sufficiently large and ordered to give rise to their characteristic diffraction patterns, while the aromatic moieties are too small. With progression of the thermal effect the graphite-like structures increase in size and ordering as indicated by their typical diffraction patterns. This transition in kerogen of originally aliphatic-dominated composition is a significant marker of its thermal evolution. The subsequent development of the graphite-like structure probably occurs at levels of thermal effect different from those of coals which were initially rich in aromatic structures.

Elemental composition

The elemental composition of the kerogen C, H, N, S and O (calculated by difference) shows the following features (Table 2). The content of heteroatoms (N and S) decreases in the thermally affected rocks. The ratio of

Electron spin resonance (ESR) spectra

Electron spin resonance has been suggested and used as a measure of thermal effect. The most significant changes occur in the spin density (N_g value) which increases with increase of thermal effect and drops sharply at high levels of maturity (Pusey, 1973; Marchand and Conard, 1980; Aizenshtat *et al.*, unpublished). However, organic material of different biogenic sources (hence composition) give rise to different ESR parameters. These effects cannot be distinguished from those due to thermal evolution. This method is applicable and can be evaluated in sequences containing organic matter of homogeneous biogenic origin. This is exactly the case in

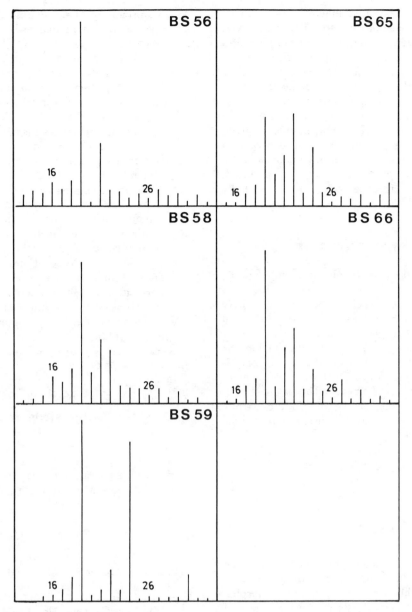

Fig. 5. Distribution of *n*-alkanes in the margin of the 'Mottled Zone'. The respective H/C ratios (atomic) and BS56 —0.90, BS58 — 0.48, BS59 — 0.35, BS60 — 0.74, BS61 — 0.55.

the Nebi Musa basin at the margin of the Hatrurim complex. There the ESR parameter N_g value (spins g^{-1}) shows significant variations. The bituminous rocks have values of around 0.5×10^{18} typical of early diagenetic algal derived material (Table 2). A gradual increase, up to 11×10^{18} was recorded from the thermally affected rock. Near the metamorphic rocks, the spin density decreases to below the detection limit (10^{17} spins g^{-1}). In the thermally affected narrow zones, intermediate values were recorded. A similar trend was observed in pyrolysis experiments. The highest spin density was recorded from kerogens of the same type pyrolyzed at 500–650 °C (Aizenshtat *et al.*, unpublished). A significant increase in spin density towards a sill in Cretaceous black shales and a sharp decrease in its vicinity was reported by Baker *et al.* (1977) and by Simoneit *et al.* (1981).

Distribution of *n*-alkanes

The bituminous rocks of the Nebi Musa basin have two types of *n*-alkane distribution patterns.

1. The prominent envelope is around n-C_{17} with minor contribution of longer chain alkanes in the range above C_{22} and weak odd over even preference. This pattern is typical of *n*-alkanes derived from algae.

2. In addition to the envelope around n-C_{17} there is a prominent envelope around n-C_{28} with strong even over odd preference. This pattern indicates that, in addition to the *n*-alkanes derived from algae, there is a contribution from sulfur-reducing bacteria.

The *n*-alkanes from the thermally affected rocks have different types of distribution patterns. The dominant *n*-alkanes are C_{19}, C_{21} and C_{22} (Fig. 5). Normal alkanes in this range are also predominant in artificial pyroproducts of kerogen of this type. There, however, the distribution pattern is smoother. The dominance of alkanes in the range $C_{20}-C_{24}$ was recorded also in thermally affected black shales (Claypool et al., 1978; Harrison, 1978; Perregaard and Schiener, 1979; Simoneit et al., 1981). It is interesting to note that alkanes in this range also predominate among those produced by the Fischer Tropsch reaction (Calvin, 1969) and probably represent a stable assemblage at elevated temperatures. These also contain alkenes, which are common products of kerogen pyrolysis. Alkenes were, however, not detected in the thermally affected rocks.

Tetrapyrrole pigments

The distribution of tetrapyrrole pigments in the bituminous rocks of the Ghareb Formation distinguishes the Nebi Musa basin. There, chlorins of type e only were identified, in contrast to the other basins in which phaeophytin and phaeophorbide are present (Spiro et al., 1978). This feature has a direct bearing on the elucidation of the thermal history of this basin. Chlorins of type e were formed during thermal treatment of phaeophytin and phaeophorbide (Ikan et al., 1975). Near the metamorphosed rocks and in the narrow thermally affected zones in the basin, tetrapyrrole pigments were not detected. From the regional distribution of e-type chlorins, it can be concluded that large areas of this basin were thermally affected to a low degree.

SUMMARY AND CONCLUSIONS

The bituminous rocks at the margin of the metamorphic Hatrurim or 'Mottled Zone' complex were thermally affected by the neighbouring combustion metamorphic process. Grades of thermal effects over traverses of several meters were defined by physical and chemical properties of the kerogen, the distribution of n-alkanes and the nature of tetrapyrrole pigments. These compose the following scale.
1. Chlorins of type e occur instead of phaeophytin and phaeophorbide.
2. Decrease in H/C ratio of the kerogen to around 0.8. Decrease in abundance of aliphatic structures, while aromatic structures become dominant, in the kerogen as indicated by i.r. spectroscopy. A graphite-like structure is ordered parallel to the c axis with $d_{002} = 3.5$ while no indication of saturated structures are detected in the X-ray diffractograms. A kerogen fraction develops, which has maximum hydrocarbon generation, by analytical pyrolysis at temperatures (T_{max}) higher than 500 °C. This grade is equivalent to anthracite rank in the coal classification.
3. Further decrease in H/C ratio to 0.4. Compaction and ordering of the graphite structure $d_{002} = 3.4$ Å. Increase in free radical density by up to two orders of magnitude up to 10×10^{18} spin g^{-1}.

4. Vanishing of discrete absorption bands in i.r. spectra and of resonance bands in ESR spectra (these occur at 650–700 °C in pyrolysis experiments).

This scale does not comprise low grades of thermal effect which were not observed in the samples investigated.

Two types of thermal processes were defined in the Nebi Musa area.
1. Combustion metamorphism, which produced the high temperature mineral assemblage and affected bituminous rocks gradually over a margin of several meters.
2. A thermal process effective along joints. The margin between the highly affected zone to bituminous rock enriched in natural pyroproducts is about one millimeter wide. This process is probably also related to the deposition of gypsum and may be a type of steam distillation under anoxic conditions. The process results in the enrichment of relatively cold areas in products of pyrolysis effective in zones of higher temperatures.

The development of either type is probably governed by the geometry of the bituminous rock beds with respect to exposed surface and overburden and the amount, size and orientation of joints which provide essential conduits for oxygen.

Acknowledgements

Thanks are due to Prof. L. Heller-Kallai for help and advice and to Dr K. E. Peters for improving the manuscript. This research was supported by the KFA-Jülich (F.R. Germany) through the NCRD, Israel.

REFERENCES

Aizenshtat, Z., Baedecker, M. J. and Kaplan, I. R. (1973) Distribution and diagenesis of organic compounds in JOIDES sediments from Gulf of Mexico and western Atlantic. Geochim. Cosmochim. Acta **37**, 1881–1898.

Aizenshtat, Z., Pinski, I. and Spiro, B. Stable free radicals in geo-organic matter and their significance. (Unpublished).

Baker, E. W., Huang, W.-Y., Rankin, J. C., Castaño, J. R. and Feux, A. N. (1977) Electron paramagnetic resonance study of thermal alteration of kerogen in deep sea sediments by basaltic sill intrusion. In Initial Reports of the Deep Sea Drilling Project **41**. US Govt. Printing Office, Washington. pp. 839–847.

bentor, Y. K. (1960) Israel. In Lexique stratigraphique international. Ed. by Dubertret, L. Vol. 3. Asie 10C2. CNRS, Paris.

Bentor, Y. K. and Kastner, M. (1976) Combustion metamorphism in Southern California. Science **193**, 486–488.

Calvin, M. (1969) Chemical Evolution. Oxford University Press, London.

Claypool, G. E., Love, A. H. and Maughan, E. K. (1978) Organic geochemistry, incipient metamorphism and oil generation in black shale members of Phosphoria Formation western interior United States. AAPG Bull. **62**, 98–120.

Dinur, D., Spiro, B. and Aizenshtat, Z. (1980) The distribution and isotope composition of sulfur in organic-rich sedimentary rock. Chem. Geol. **31**, 37–51.

Espitalié, J., Laporte, J. L., Madec, M., Marquis, F., Leplat, P., Paulet, J. and Boutefeu (1977) Méthode rapide de caractérisation des roches mères de leur potentiel pétrolier et de leur degré d'évolution. *Inst. Fr. Pétr. Rev.* **32**, 23–42.

Gross, S. (1977) The mineralogy of the Hatrurim Formation. *Isr. Geol. Surv. Bull.* **70**, 80 pp.

Harrison, W. E. (1978) Experimental diagenetic study of modern lipid-rich sediments. *Chem. Geol.* **21**, 315–336.

Hirsch, P. B. (1954) X-ray scattering from coals. *Proc. Roy. Soc. (London)* **226A**, 143–169.

Kolodny, Y., Bar, M. and Sass, E. (1971) Fission track age of 'Mottled Zone' event in Israel. *Earth Planet. Sci. Lett.* **11**, 269–272.

Kolodny, Y. and Gross, S. (1974) Thermal metamorphism by combustion of organic matter: isotopic and petrological evidence. *J. Geol.* **82**, 489–506.

Marchand, A. and Conard, J. (1980) Electron paramagnetic resonance in kerogen studies. In *Kerogen insoluble organic matter from sedimentary rocks*. Ed. by Durand, B. Technip, Paris. pp. 245–270.

Matthews, A. and Kolodny, A. (1978) Oxygen isotope fractionation in decarbonation metamorphism: The Mottled Zone event. *Earth Planet. Sci., Lett.* **39**, 179–192.

Perregaard, J. and Schiener, E. J. (1979) Thermal alteration of sedimentary organic matter by a basaltic intrusion (Kimmeridgian shales, Milne Land East Greenland). *Chem. Geol.* **26**, 331–344.

Peters, K. E., Rohrback, B. G. and Kaplan, I. R. (1981) Geochemistry of artificially heated humic and sapropelic sediments I. Protokerogen. *Am. Ass. Pet. Geo. Bull.* **65**, 688–705.

Pusey, W. C. (1973) Paleotemperatures in the Gulf Coast using the ESR-kerogen method. *Trans. Gulf Coast Ass., Geol. Soc.* **23**, 195–202.

Reiss, Z. (1962) Stratigraphy of phosphate deposits in Israel. *Isr. Geol. Surv. Bull.* **34**, 1–34.

Saxby, J. D. (1970) Technique for isolation of kerogen from sulfide ores. *Geochim. Cosmochim. Acta* **34**, 1317–1326.

Simoneit, B. R. T., Brener, S., Peters, K. E. and Kaplan, I. R. (1981) Thermal alteration of Cretaceous black shale by diabase intrusions in the Eastern Atlantic II. Effects on bitumen and kerogen. *Geochim. Cosmochim. Acta* **45**, 1581–1602.

Spiro, B. (1979) Thermal effects in oil shales — naturally occurring kaolinite and metakaolinite organic associations. *Chem. Geol.* **25**, 67–78.

Spiro, B. (1980) Geochemistry and mineralogy of bitumenous rocks in Israel. Thesis. Hebrew University of Jerusalem.

Spiro, B. and Aizenshtat, Z. (1977) Bacterial sulfate reduction and calcite precipitation in hypersaline deposition of bituminous shales. *Nature (London)* **269**, 235–237.

Spiro, B., Heller-Kallai, L. and Aizenshtat, Z. (1978) Environment of deposition and diagenesis of some oil shales in Israel. *10th Int. Assoc. Sedimentol. Cong. Jerusalem*, Abstract, 632–633.

Yen, T. F., Erdman, G. J. and Pollack, S. S. (1961) Investigation of the structure of petroleum asphalthenes by X-ray diffraction. *Anal. Chem.* **33**, 1587–1594.

Advances in Organic Geochemistry 1981, pp. 808–812
© *John Wiley & Sons Limited, 1983*

Possible Origin and Fate of α-Methylquinolines and α-Methylbenzo[h]quinolines from Crude Oils

J. M. Schmitter and P. J. Arpino

Ecole Polytechnique, Laboratoire de Chimie Analytique Physique, Route de Saclay – 91128 Palaiseau Cedex, France

The distributions of quinolines and benzoquinolines, two major classes of petroleum azaarenes, have been examined. A limited number of benzo[h]quinolines, all bearing a methyl group in the position α to the nitrogen atom, occur in crude oils. A comparison between the structures of identified quinolines and benzo[h]quinolines suggests a common origin. Possible sources of azaarenes are discussed with this in view.

INTRODUCTION

Alkylated benzoquinolines have been recognized as a major class of nitrogen bases from crude oils (Jewell and Hartung, 1964; Snyder, 1969; McKay *et al.*, 1976), but the complete identification of individual compounds was only achieved in an early work by Schenck and Bailey (1941a). Simple and very similar distributions of these tricyclic azaarenes have been found in crude oils varying greatly in their origin, indicating that neither the locations of the nitrogen atom, nor the sites of alkyl substitution are randomly distributed in the molecules (Schmitter *et al.*, 1980).

An analytical strategy has been developed in order to identify the major individual benzoquinolines. The method included chromatographic techniques (gas (GC) and liquid (LC)), combined with mass spectrometry and UV spectroscopy and synthesis of reference compounds. The identification of alkylbenzo-[h]quinolines, all bearing a methyl group in the position α to the nitrogen atom was achieved in this way (Schmitter *et al.*, 1982).

Alkylquinolines have also been investigated in the same samples in order to examine the structural relationship with their benzologs in terms of distributions and locations of the alkyl substituents. Considering the observed distributions of the major classes of petroleum azaarenes, their origin still remains an open question, but some potential sources can be discussed.

RESULTS AND DISCUSSION

The analytical methodology which has been used in our investigation of nitrogen bases from several crude oils has been described in other reports (Schmitter *et al.*, 1980 and 1982; Colin *et al.*, 1981). Reference compounds were prepared according to standard described procedures for the synthesis of di- and triaromatic azaarenes (Elderfield, 1952; Walls, 1952).

Distributions of quinolines (I) and isoquinolines (II)

The structures of the quinolines that we have identified in various crude oils (Nigerian, Middle East and Emeraude basin, Congo) by means of comparison with authentic compounds are listed in Table 1. These compounds were also identified in a California crude oil by Schenck and Bailey, who made numerous contributions to this field (for example, Schenck and Bailey, 1941b).

The number of isomers observed on computer-generated mass fragmentograms from a gas chromatography mass spectrometry (GCMS) run was found to increase with the increasing number of carbon atoms of substituents in the series C_1- to C_5-alkyquinolines, as expected and usually observed for aromatic compounds in petroleum. However, C_6-alkylquinolines (m/z 213) (or C_7-alkylquinolines, m/z 227 in some samples) show unusual mass fragmentograms, as they are dominated by one single peak, presumably due to a polymethylated species (Fig. 1). These particular structures were not synthesized, but the ratio of the $(M-H)^+/M^{+\cdot}$ ions in their mass spectra strongly suggests that only methyl groups are present as substituents (Draper and McLean, 1968; Novotny *et al.*, 1980).

Quinolines have been shown to range commonly, in crude oil and shale oil, from the unsubstituted

Table 1

Structures of quinolines and benzo[h]quinolines identified by means of comparison with authentic compounds

Structure	Molecular weight	Identification method
2,3-dimethylquinoline	157	GC,GCMS
2,4-dimethylquinoline	157	GC,GCMS
2,4-dimethyl-8-isopropylquinoline	199	GC,GCMS
2,3,4-trimethyl-8-isopropylquinoline	213	GC,GCMS
2-methylbenzo[h]quinoline	193	GC,GCMS
2,3-dimethylbenzo[h]quinoline	207	GC,GCMS,LCUV
2,4-dimethylbenzo[h]quinoline	207	GC,GCMS,LCUV
2,3,4-trimethylbenzo[h]quinoline	221	GC,GCMS,LCUV
2,4,6-trimethylbenzo[h]quinoline	221	GC,GCMS,LCUV

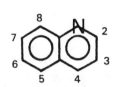
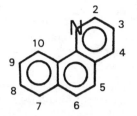

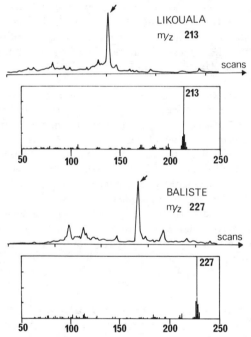

Fig. 1. Mass fragmentograms of C₆-alkylquinolines (*m/z* 213, Likouala crude oil) and C₇-alkylquinolines (*m/z* 227, Baliste crude oil). Mass spectra were recorded at the maximum of the peaks marked by an arrow.

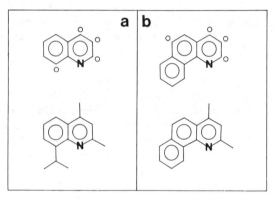

Fig. 2. Locations of side chains (symbolized by dots) and examples of structures of quinolines (a) and benzo[h]quinolines (b) identified up to now in petroleum.

Distributions of benzoquinolines (III)

The major analytical problem posed by this class of compounds is the determination of the location of the nitrogen atom (eight different structural arrangements). We have recently demonstrated that benzo[h]-quinolines represent the major structures of this type of azaarenes (Schmitter *et al.*, 1982). The identified compounds all bear methyl groups in the position α to the nitrogen atom (Table 1). The locations of substituents found are represented in Fig. 2b.

Detectable amounts of unsubstituted species are not found, and the higher homologs are C₉-alkylbenzoquinolines with a maximum for the distribution at $C_{15}H_{13}N$ or $C_{16}H_{15}N$. No detailed information could be gained about the structure of the

compound up to C₁₃-alkylated species, with a distribution centered around $C_{15}H_{19}N$ (Lochte and Littmann, 1955; Simoneit *et al.*, 1971; Uden *et al.*, 1979). A few alkylisoquinolines have also been identified (Lochte and Littmann, 1955), but quinolines represent the major structural type in this series.

A compilation of data from the authors cited above and our own results indicate that favoured positions of substituents are α > γ > β, with chain lengths usually shorter than five carbon atoms. A schematic representation of the sites of alkyl substitution found is given in Fig. 2a, with an example of identified structure.

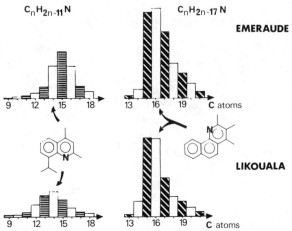

Fig. 3. Histograms of the distributions of alkylquinolines and benzoquinolines in two different crude oil samples (Emeraude and Likouala).

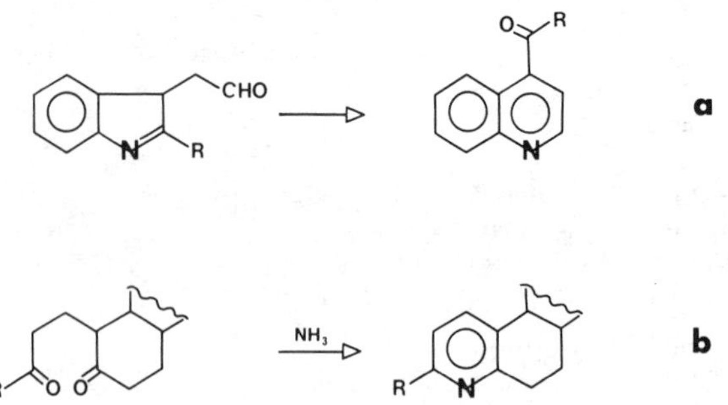

Fig. 4. (a) Partial reaction pathway leading to a quinoline ring system during the biosynthesis of Cinchona alkaloids (Uskorovic and Grethe, 1973). (b) Example of cyclization of 1,5-dioxo derivative leading to a pyridine ring closure (Sih *et al.*, 1965).

side chains, but polymethylated compounds seem to represent the majority of alkylbenzo[h]quinolines.

We have pointed out that the number of isomers of benzoquinolines found in crude oils is very low, being always much lower than the number of isomers which could be theoretically expected for a given number of carbon atoms with one single location of the nitrogen atom. For instance, one single major monomethyl-benzoquinoline, identified as 2-methylbenzo[h]-quinoline, appears in the mass fragmentograms (GCMS, *m/z* 193, $C_{14}H_{11}N$), among nine theoretically possible isomers. In comparison, neutral polynuclear aromatic hydrocarbons (PAH) show more complex distributions, since for example four methylphenanthrenes were identified in petroleum (Ewald *et al.*, 1981).

Comparisons of the distribution of quinolines and benzoquinolines

The relative abundance of quinolines versus benzoquinolines was found to differ significantly from one crude oil sample to another but in all cases studied up to now, the overall distributions of homologous compounds were very similar, as shown, for example, in Fig. 3.

The location of the nitrogen atom in the benzoquinolines and the alkylation sites observed in both series suggest that a relationship exists between these compounds, possibly through common precursors of higher molecular weight (Fig. 2).

Sources of the pyridine ring

Synthetic and natural ways of building azaarene ring structures will be briefly considered in order to explain tentatively the distributions of petroleum nitrogen bases. A review by Brody and Ruby (1960) covers the different sources of the pyridine ring. We shall discuss here three major pathways, which could possibly take place in geochemical conditions.

From degradation of natural products. Many compounds among the alkaloids are structurally related

to pyridine and the degradation of alkaloids has been often cited as a source of petroleum nitrogen bases (Whitehead, 1973).

From other ring systems. Modification of several ring systems can lead to the formation of a pyridine ring (Brody and Ruby, 1960). The ring expansion of a pyrrole nucleus to a more highly aromatic and stable pyridine is a well known reaction (Sundberg, 1970), which takes place in the biosynthesis of Chincona alkaloids (Uskorovic and Grethe, 1973) (Fig. 4(a)).

From acyclic compounds. The cyclization of a five-carbon chain, and particularly 1,5-dioxo compounds, is a very useful synthetic method (Brody and Ruby, 1960), which has been used for the isolation of an intermediate structure in the microbial oxidation of steroids (Sih *et al.*, 1965) (Fig. 4(b)). The same type of reaction is thought to be responsible for the isolation of artefacts (pseudo alkaloids) due to an ammonia treatment during the extraction of plant alkaloids (Hegnauer, 1966; Gross, 1970). 1,5-dioxo compounds, derived from the degradation of xanthophylls, were postulated as intermediates in the formation of two bicyclic tobacco alkaloids (Demole and Demole, 1975).

Discussion of the origin of petroleum azaarenes

The wide range of molecular weights of petroleum azaarenes and the occurrence of characteristic distributions of some specific and restricted classes of compounds, benzo[h]quinolines for instance, still leave the genesis of nitrogen bases as a difficult question to answer. Even processes which are generally considered as secondary could be involved in the formation of petroleum azaarenes, since these compounds occur in low concentration in most crude oils (0.01 to 0.5% w/w). The chemical stability of azaarenes is another factor which makes difficult the elucidation of product–precursor relationships, these compounds having probably undergone several transformations during their geochemical fate.

The major degradation products obtained by pyrolysis of alkaloids are alkylpyridines (Tenenbaum, 1961). Therefore, this source is probably a minor contribution to petroleum azaarenes which are rich in high-molecular-weight species. The great variation in concentration and occurrence of alkaloids are further limitations, which are hardly compatible with the similarity of distribution of azaarenes in crude oils of very different origins.

The ring expansion of pyrrolic precursors is a more likely source, since this type of reaction has been documented in thermal reactions of alkylpyrroles, which are common shale oil components (Jacobson and Jensen, 1966). Furthermore, Jackson and Decora (1975) identified alkylpyridines and quinolines in the pyrolysate of plant pigments. The transformation of some alkaloids to indoles, or benzcarbazoles as postulated by Snyder (1965), followed or accompanied by the described ring expansion, has to be considered as a possible source of petroleum azaarenes. However, detailed investigations of the structures of individual compounds like indoles, carbazoles and their benzologs would be required in order to lend support to this hypothesis. On the other hand, the occurrence of high molecular weight azaarenes incorporating only one nitrogen atom in their structures is difficult to explain from this single source.

The trapping of ammonia or amines in molecules possessing sites analogous to 1,5-dioxo derivatives is another possible source of azaarenes. A mechanism similar to the pathway proposed by Demole and Demole (1975), involving ubiquitous precursors such as xanthophylls, could explain the distribution of some isoprenoid related structures (Brandenburg and Latham, 1968). This type of condensation could occur in the polymeric material which is the precursor of kerogen; azaarenes, including high-molecular-weight compounds, would then be released during catagenesis, the oil formation stage in the evolution of organic matter (Arpino *et al.*, 1971; Tissot and Welte, 1978; Hunt, 1979). Such an hypothesis is consistent with the fact that the amount of soluble nitrogen compounds from Recent Sediments tends to decrease with depth, as is the case for oxygen and sulphur compounds. These compounds are reduced to yield ammonia or are complexed into kerogen (Bordovskiy, 1965; Tissot and Welte, 1978; Hunt, 1979). Furthermore, only azaarenes of anthropogenic origin were found in detectable amounts in recent lake sediments (Wakeham, 1979). However, specific sites or molecules should be involved in the condensation reactions in order to explain the occurrence of a limited number of azaarene structures.

CONCLUSION

The identification of benzo[h]quinolines as major tricyclic azaarenes in crude oils and the possible structural relationship existing with quinolines is a step which could be helpful in the elucidation of major structures among petroleum nitrogen bases. The identification of cycloalkanobenzoquinolines and tetra-aromatic structures is now under investigation in order to substantiate these results. A detailed study of sediments with different origins and also of cores from homogeneous sedimentary series could considerably

improve our knowledge of the genesis of petroleum azaarenes.

Acknowledgement

Financial support of Délégation Générale à la Recherche Scientifique et Technique (DGRST, Paris, France) is gratefully acknowledged (grant RAP-79-7-1306).

We thank Professor G. Guiochon for his interest and encouragement during the work.

REFERENCES

Arpino, P., Albrecht, P. and Ourisson, G. (1971) Studies on the organic constituents of lacustrine Eocene sediments. Possible mechanisms for the formation of some geolipids related to biologically occurring terpenoids. In *Advances in Organic Geochemistry* 1971, ed. by Gaertner, H. R. v. and Wehner, H. Pergamon Press, Oxford, pp. 173–187.

Bordovskiy, O. K. (1965) Accumulation and transformation of organic substance in marine sediments. *Mar. Geol.* **3**, 1–114.

Brandenburg, C. F. and Latham, D. R. (1968) Spectroscopic identification of basic nitrogen compounds in Wilmington petroleum. *J. Chem. Eng. Data* **13**, 391–394.

Brody, F. and Ruby, P. R. (1960) Synthetic and natural sources of the pyridine ring. In *Pyridine and derivatives*, ed. by Klingsberg, I. E. Interscience, New York, pp. 99–544.

Colin, H., Schmitter, J. M. and Guiochon, G. (1981) Liquid chromatography of azaarenes. *Anal. Chem.* **53**, 625–631.

Demole, E. and Demole, C. (1975) A chemical study of Burley tobacco flavour (Nicotiana tabacum L.) V — Identification and synthesis of the novel terpenoid alkaloids 1,3,6,6-tetramethyl-5,6,7,7-tetrahydroisoquinolin-8-one and 3,6,6-trimethyl-5,6-dihydro-7H-2-pyridin-7-one. *Helv. Chim. Acta.* **58**, 523–531.

Draper, P. M. and McLean, D. B. (1968) Mass spectra of alkyl quinolines. *Can. J. Chem.* **46**, 1487–1497.

Elderfield, R. C. (1952) The chemistry of quinolines. In *Heterocyclic compounds* Vol. 4, ed. by Elderfield, R. C. Wiley–Interscience, New York, pp. 1–81.

Ewald, M., Bellocq, J., Lapouyade, R., Veyres, A., Joussot-Dubien, J., Bourgeois, G., Moinet, A., Tissier, M. J. Saliot, A., Wehrung, P. and Albrecht, P. (1981) Identification of isomeric polycyclic aromatic hydrocarbons from petroleum and marine sediments after fractionation by two-step HPLC (normal and reversal phase), by quasi-linear fluorescence spectroscopy (Shpolskii) at 4 K and GC/MS analysis. Paper presented at the Vth International Symposium on Column Liquid Chromatography. May 11–15, Avignon, France.

Gross, D. (1970) Naturstoffe mit Pyridinstruktur und ihre Biosynthese. In *Progress in the chemistry of organic natural products*, Vol. 28, ed. by Grisebach, H., Herz, W. and Scott, A. I. Springer-Verlag, Vienna, pp. 109–161.

Hegnauer, R. (1966) Von Gentiopikrin abgeleite Pseudoalkaloide. In *Chemotoxonomie der Pflanzen* Vol. 4, Birkhäuser-Verlag, Basel, pp. 181–187.

Hunt, J. M. (1979) *Petroleum geochemistry and geology*. W. H. Freeman, San Francisco.

Jackson, L. P. and Decora, A. W. (1975) Thermal reactions of shale-oil components: plant pigments as probable precursors of nitrogenous compounds in shale oil. *Bur. Mines* RI 8018.

Jacobson, I. A. and Jensen, H. B. (1966) Thermal reactions of shale-oil components: methylpyrroles, butylpyrroles and isopropylpyrroles. *Bur. Mines* RI 6720.

Jewell, D. M. and Hartung, G. K. (1964) Identification of nitrogen bases in heavy gas oil; chromatographic methods of separation. *J. Chem. Eng. Data* **9**, 297–304.

Lochte, H. L. and Littmann, E. R. (1955) *The petroleum acids and bases*. Chemical Publishing Co., New York.

McKay, J. F., Weber, J. M. and Latham, D. R. (1976) Characterization of nitrogen bases in high-boiling petroleum distillates. *Anal. Chem.* **48**, 891–898.

Novotny, M., Kump, R., Merli, F. and Todd, L. J. (1980) Capillary gas chromatography/mass spectrometric determination of nitrogen aromatic compounds in complex mixtures. *Anal. Chem.* **52**, 401–406.

Schenck, L. M. and Bailey, J. R. (1941a) The nitrogen compounds in petroleum distillates. XXIII. Isolation of 2,3-dimethylbenzo[h]quinoline and 2,4-dimethylbenzo-[h]quinoline from California petroleum. *J. Am. Chem. Soc.* **63**, 2331–2333.

Schenck, L. M. and Bailey, J. R. (1941b) The nitrogen compounds in petroleum distillates. XXI. Isolation and synthesis of 2,3,4-trimethyl-8-i-propylquinoline. *J. Am. Chem. Soc.* **63**, 1364–1365.

Schmitter, J. M., Vajta, Z. and Arpino, P. J. (1980) Investigation of nitrogen bases from petroleum. In *Advances in Organic Geochemistry* 1979, ed. by Douglas, A. G. and Maxwell, J. R. Pergamon Press, Oxford, pp. 67–76.

Schmitter, J. M., Colin, H., Excoffier, J. L., Arpino, P. and Guiochon, G. (1982) Identification of triaromatic nitrogen bases in crude oils. *Anal. Chem.* **54**, 769–772.

Sih, C. J., Wang, K. C., Gibson, D. T. and Whitlock, H. W. (1965) On the mechanism of ring A cleavage in the degradation of 9,10-seco-steroids by microorganisms. *J. Am. Chem. Soc.* **87**, 1386–1387.

Simoneit, B. R., Schnoes, H. K., Haug, P. and Burlingame, A. L. (1971) High-resolution mass spectrometry of nitrogenous compounds of the Colorado Green River formation oil shale. *Chem. Geol.* **7**, 123–141.

Snyder, L. R. (1965) Distribution of benzcarbazole isomers in petroleum as evidence for their biogenic origin. *Nature (London)*, **16**, 277.

Snyder, L. R. (1969) Nitrogen and oxygen compound types in petroleum. Total analysis of a 400–700 °F distillate from a California crude oil. *Anal. Chem.* **41**, 314–323.

Sundberg, R. J. (1970) The chemistry of indoles. In *Organic chemistry* Vol. 18, ed. by Blomquist, A. J. Academic Press, New York, pp. 331–340.

Tenenbaum, L. E. (1961) Alkylpyridines and arylpyridines. In *Pyridine and derivatives* Vol. 2, ed. by Klingsberg, E. Interscience, New York, p. 158.

Tissot, B. P. and Welte, D. H. (1978) *Petroleum formation and occurrence*. Springer-Verlag, Berlin.

Uden, P. C., Carpenter, A. P., Hackett, H. M., Henderson, D. E. and Siggia, S. (1979) Qualitative analysis of shale oil acids and bases by porous layer open tubular gas chromatography and interfaced vapor phase infrared spectrophotometry. *Anal. Chem.* **51**, 38–43.

Uskorovic, M. R. and Grethe, G. (1973) The Chincona alkaloids. In *The Alkaloids* Vol. 14, ed. by Manske, R. H. F. Academic Press, New York, pp. 209–217.

Wakeham, S. G. (1979) Azaarenes in recent lake sediments. *Environ. Sci. Technol.* **13**, 1118–1123.

Walls, L. P. (1952) The benzoquinolines. In *Heterocyclic compounds* Vol. 4, ed. by Elderfield R. C. Wiley–Interscience, New York, pp. 627–661.

Whitehead, E. V. (1973) Molecular evidence for the biogenesis of petroleum and natural gas. *Proc. Symp. Hydrogeochem. Biogeochem.* **2**, 158–211.

Advances in Organic Geochemistry 1981, pp. 813–818
© *John Wiley & Sons Limited, 1983*

Qualitative and Quantitative Characterization of the Total Organic Matter in a Recent Marine Sediment

J. Klok, J. M. M. van der Knaap, J. W. de Leeuw, H. C. Cox and P. A. Schenck

Delft University of Technology, Department of Chemistry and Chemical Engineering, Organic Geochemistry Unit, Delft, The Netherlands

The total organic matter of a recent marine sediment is studied by extraction of the sediment with water, EDTA and acid. The extraction data reveal major contributions of carbohydrates (39%), peptides (10%) and carbonates (9%). Qualitative analysis of the neutral monosaccharides in the hydrolysate of the extracted carbohydrates is in accordance with an algal input into the sediment.

INTRODUCTION

The elucidation of the structure of insoluble organic matter in both recent and ancient sediments has been the subject of many investigations because of the quantitative importance of this insoluble part of the total sedimentary organic matter.

The study of the total organic matter in recent sediments may offer a good possibility to obtain information about the structure of the organic matter that might contribute to insoluble organic matter in ancient sediments, called kerogen. Several investigations have shown that in recent sediments a considerable part of the organic matter consists of carbohydrates and peptides (Modzeleski *et al.*, 1971; Handa and Mizuno, 1973; Degens and Mopper, 1975; Boon, 1978; Henrichs and Farrington, 1979; Mopper *et al.*, 1980).

In this study an attempt is made to characterize the total organic matter of a Namibian Shelf sample by a qualitative and quantitative survey of the individual fractions obtained after a sequence of extractions and acid treatments. For this investigation the diatomaceous ooze of the Namibian Shelf sediment was chosen because of its unique input parameters (Boon, 1978).

EXPERIMENTAL

An outline of the extraction procedure is given in Fig. 1. The lyophilized Namibian Shelf sediment sample (off S.W. Africa, 22°51.5′ S, 14°14.5′ E) was suspended in water and kept at 0 °C. On ultrasonic vibration during 3 × 5 min the diatomaceous frustules were disintegrated. The extract obtained after centrifugation of the mixture was filtered over a G4 filter. The procedure was repeated twice. Hot water and EDTA extractions were performed by refluxing for 24 h. The procedure was repeated three times with water in both cases. The acid treatments were performed in sealed ampoules. The residues were rinsed three times with water before lyophilization. The extracts were concentrated under reduced pressure (if necessary after neutralization).

In some cases brown precipitates developed in the extracts. Before GPC was performed these were removed by centrifugation. In case of extract-hydrolysis the integral extract was taken. GPC was carried out using Biogel P2–P100 with water as eluent. Dry weights of residues were determined by lyophilization. Dry weights of extracts were determined by evaporation of the solvent upon heating at 100 °C.

Carbon, nitrogen and hydrogen in the residues were determined using an automatic Perkin–Elmer 240 CHN-analyzer. Inorganic carbon in the residues and CO_2 which escaped upon water and EDTA treatment were determined according to the method described by Pieters (1948). Carbon in the extracts was analysed by wet combustion at 150 °C for inorganic carbon and at 900 °C for total carbon.

Silicon was determined as described by Fresenius *et al.* (1967). Silicon and other elements were quantitated using neutron activation analysis (NAA). Amino acids were analysed using a Kontron, Liquimat III equipped with a Durrum Resin DC-4A; Pico–buffer system 2 was used as an eluant. Quantitation was performed after ninhydrin derivatization and detection at 570 nm.

Neutral sugars were analysed as alditol acetates by capillary GC (Klok *et al.*, 1981). Identification was based on GC retention data and on comparison of the mass spectra obtained by capillary GC–MS with those published by Jansson *et al.* (1976) and with mass spectra of synthesized standard compounds.

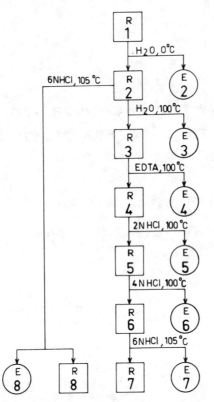

Fig. 1. Extraction scheme. R1 is the dry starting material. Before each extraction step the residues were lyophilized. (R: residue, E: extract).

RESULTS

The results of the dry weight determinations of residues and extracts (Fig. 1) are summarized in Table 1. Fig. 2

shows a graphical representation of these dry weights as percentages of the dry starting material (59.1 gram $= 100\%$).

Carbon present in residues and extracts as well as volatilized during the procedure, is also given in Table 1. The carbon balance as a percentage of the total amount of carbon present in R1 (5.66% of 59.1 gram $= 100\%$C) is visualized in Fig. 3 based upon these data.

Finally Table 1 shows the data of the elemental analyses of the residues. Amino acids quantitated in the extracts are summarized in Table 2. The individual contribution of the amino acids to the total carbon present in R1 is calculated from the individual concentrations and given at the bottom of Table 2.

Neutral sugars obtained after hydrolysis of E3 are analysed as their alditol acetates as shown in the gas chromatogram of Fig. 4. Table 3 summarizes the compounds identified.

DISCUSSION

The results from each extraction and hydrolysis step are discussed hereafter. The weight percentages given all refer to the original material.

Cold water extraction (step 1→2)

The cold water extraction is meant to remove the salts from the residue. By this extraction about 20% of dry starting material is solubilized (Fig. 2). The solubilized material mainly consists of salts (NaCl and KCl) as can be deduced from Table 1. About 13% of the carbon originally present is extracted by this procedure (Fig. 3).

Table 1

	Number of residue/extract							
	1	2	3	4	5	6	7	8
Dry weight residue (g)[a]	59.1	46.5	42.3	40.2	38.8	38.1	37.3	34.8
Dry weight extract (g)[a]	–	11.2	2.5	0.7	2.0	0.7	0.3	10.8
C_{org} in extract (mg)[a]	–	328	567	n.d.	327	209	182	849
C_{inorg} in extract (mg)[a]	–	20	7	n.d.	–	–	–	–
C_{tot} in residue (%)	5.66	6.20	5.47	4.64	4.37	4.19	3.60	4.12
C_{inorg} in residue (%)	0.40	0.62	0.39	0.01	–	–	–	–
$C_{org} = C_{tot} - C_{inorg}$ in residue (%)	5.26	5.58	5.08	4.63	4.37	4.19	3.60	4.12
C_{inorg} volatile (%)	–	n.d.	0.28	0.20	n.d.	n.d.	n.d.	n.d.
N (%) in residue	0.70	0.65	0.57	<0.56	0.25	0.33	0.11	0.39
H (%) in residue	1.16	1.09	1.08	<1.42	1.15	1.30	1.00	0.87
Si (%) in residue	34.4	34.7	33.3	35.2	33.9	36.5	38.1	39.9
Si (%)[b] in residue	<42	34.4	<42	<42	n.d.	n.d.	<42	n.d.
Na (%)[b] in residue	5.40	1.04	0.25	0.43	n.d.	n.d.	0.16	n.d.
Mg (%)[b] in residue	0.8	0.4	0.5	0.1	n.d.	n.d.	0.2	n.d.
Al (%)[b] in residue	0.8	1.0	1.2	1.1	n.d.	n.d.	0.3	n.d.
K (%)[b] in residue	<2.0	<0.7	0.5	<2.0	n.d.	n.d.	<1.8	n.d.
Ca (%)[b] in residue	1.9	<1.5	2.1	<0.3	n.d.	n.d.	<0.1	n.d.
Fe (%)[b] in residue	0.54	0.61	0.74	0.49	n.d.	n.d.	0.23	n.d.
Cl (%)[b] in residue	9.6	1.1	<0.1	<0.1	n.d.	n.d.	0.4	n.d.

[a] The dry weights all refer to the amount of dry starting material (R1).
[b] Elements analysed using neutron activation analysis. In some cases absolute concentrations can not be given because of: 1. low intensity of the contributing γ-rays and 2. γ-ray interference of abundant elements.
All percentages refer to the dry material of the corresponding residue. The amount of carbon in the extracts is given in milligrams.

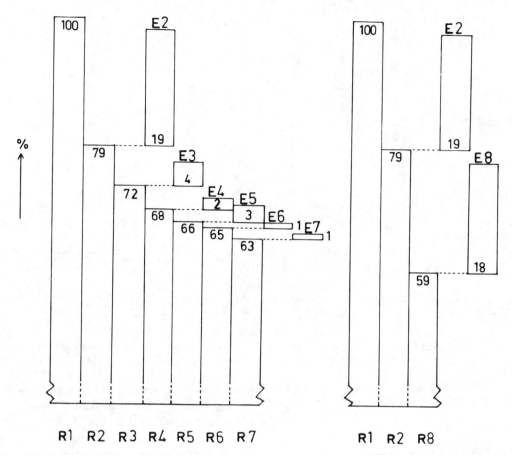

Fig. 2. Dry weight balance. The weight percentages all refer to the amount of dry starting material (59.1 g, Table 1). The representations of the data of corresponding extracts and residues are connected by dashed lines.

Table 2

Amino acid	E3	E4	E5	E6	E7	E8
Gly	11.6	13.6	10.5	7.7	6.7	9.4
Asp	16.9	27.1	8.4	7.7	5.3	12.1
Ala	8.9	6.8	9.5	7.7	6.7	7.8
Leu	8.0	6.8	7.9	11.1	14.7	7.5
Glu	10.7	10.2	10.0	9.4	6.7	8.3
Ser	5.4	3.4	4.2	4.3	2.7	5.6
Val	6.3	5.1	5.3	6.8	9.3	6.0
Lys	3.6	6.8	5.3	6.0	6.7	7.2
Thr	6.3	3.4	5.3	4.3	4.0	5.6
Orn[a]	–	–	3.2	1.7	1.3	5.3
His	1.8	–	1.6	1.7	1.3	6.3
i-Leu	6.3	5.1	6.8	6.8	9.3	5.3
Phe	5.4	5.1	6.8	8.5	12.0	5.0
Arg	2.7	1.7	6.3	5.1	2.7	4.0
Tyr	–	–	3.7	3.4	4.0	3.8
Cys	2.7	–	0.5	1.7	4.0	0.7
Pro	3.6	5.1	4.7	6.0	2.7	–
Σ amino acid carbon as % of total carbon	1	1	3	2	1	10

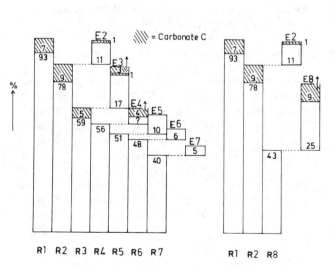

Fig. 3. Carbon balance. The carbon percentages all refer to the amounts of total carbon present in R1 (see Table 1). The shaded parts in the histogram depict the percentages of carbonate carbon. The carbonate which is volatilized is indicated with a vertical arrow. Representations of corresponding extracts and residues are connected by dashed lines.

Weight percentages of amino acids found in the hydrolysates of the various extracts. Summation of the organic carbon contribution of the individual amino acids results in a percentage of amino acid carbon of the total carbon original present in R1.

[a] tentative identification.

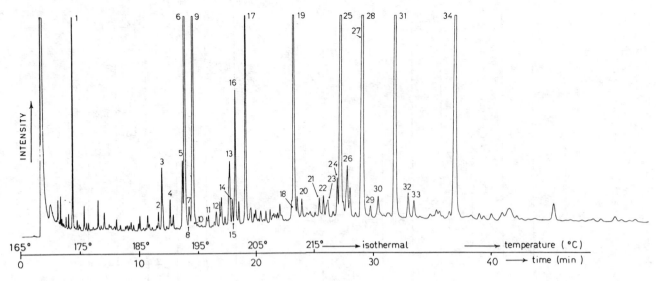

Fig. 4. Gas chromatogram of the alditol acetates obtained from the hydrolysate of extract E3. The numbers correspond with those of Table 3.

Table 3

Identification of the compounds indicated in Fig. 4.

peak number	Identification
1	glycerol-triacetate
2	tetritol-tetraacetate
3	1,3,4,5-O-acetyl-2-O-methyl-rhamnitol
4	1,3,4,5-O-acetyl-2-O-methyl-fucitol
5	1,2,4,5-O-acetyl-3-O-methyl-rhamnitol
6	rhamnitol-pentaacetate
7	1,2,4,5-O-acetyl-3-O-methyl-fucitol
8	1,2,4,5-O-acetyl-3-O-methyl-ribitol
9	fucitol-pentaacetate
10	1,3,4,5-O-acetyl-2-O-methyl-ribitol
11	1,3,4,5-O-acetyl-2-O-methyl-arabitol
12	1,2,4,5-O-acetyl-3-O-methyl-arabitol
13	6-deoxy-glucitol-pentaacetate
14	1,2,4,5-O-acetyl-3-O-methyl-xylitol
15	1,3,4,5-O-acetyl-2-O-methyl-xylitol
16	ribitol-pentaacetate
17	arabitol-pentaacetate
18	1,2,3,4,5-O-acetyl-6-O-methyl-glucitol
19	xylitol-pentaacetate
20	1,3,4,5,6-O-acetyl-2-O-methyl-mannitol
21	1,3,4,5,6-O-acetyl-2-O-methyl-galactitol
22	allitol-hexaacetate
23	1,3,4,5,6-O-acetyl-2-O-methyl-glucitol
24	1,2,4,5,6-O-acetyl-3-O-methyl-mannitol
25	mannitol-hexaacetate
26	1,2,4,5,6-O-acetyl-3-O-methyl-glucitol
27	1,2,4,5,6-O-acetyl-3-O-methyl-galactitol
28	galactitol-hexaacetate
29	1,2,3,5,6-O-acetyl-4-O-methyl-glucitol
30	unknown alditol acetate
31	glucitol hexaacetate
32	unknown alditol acetate
33	unknown alditol acetate
34	m-inositol-hexaacetate (internal standard)

11% is detected as organic carbon and 1% as carbonate. The extract (E2) was separated into two fractions by GPC. The low molecular weight fraction (<500 u) contains organic carbon. No carbohydrates or amino acids could be detected. Hydrolysis of the high molecular weight fraction (>100.000 u) and subsequent analysis of the hydrolysate indicates that this fraction consists mainly of carbohydrate material. No indication for the presence of peptides is found.

Hot water extraction (step 2→3)

The hot water extraction is expected to solubilize polysaccharides. This procedure results in a weight loss of 7% of the original sample. Only 4% of the material could be recovered (Fig. 2). The carbon content decreases by 23% relative to the value in the original sample, 18% is found in the extract and 3% is detected as CO_2 (Fig. 3). GPC of the extract also results in two fractions with molecular weight <500 u and molecular weight >100.000 u respectively.

Extract E3 contains carbohydrates (Table 3, Fig. 4), although amino acids have also been detected in a 6N HCl hydrolysate of this extract (Table 2).

Fig. 4 shows the complexity of the monosaccharide spectrum of a hydrolysate of E3. Besides all well known neutral monosaccharides a great number of partly methylated derivatives are present. Their presence could be of diagnostic value in tracing the organisms from which they have been derived.

The abundance of rhamnose and fucose is indicative for the presence of algal (diatomaceous) input (Parsons et al., 1961; Modzeleski et al., 1971; Handa and Mizuno, 1973; Myklestad, 1974; Smestad et al., 1974; Smestad et al., 1975).

EDTA treatment (step 3→4)

The intention of the EDTA treatment is to make the metal bound organic compounds accessible to extraction. Due to the EDTA procedure exact quantitation is impeded by the relatively large amount of this chelator present in the extract. Also some EDTA is shown to be retained by the residue. Taking into account the amount of EDTA used, the fraction released in this procedure has been estimated. About 4% of the original material is released, half of which is recovered (Table 1). Carbon escaping as CO_2 during this procedure accounts for 4% of the total carbon in the starting material. GPC of extract E4 yields a low molecular weight fraction consisting of EDTA and a high molecular weight fraction mainly consisting of carbohydrates. Amino acids have been found after hydrolysis of E4 (Table 2). Calcium and magnesium are the predominant metals in this extract.

2N HCl treatment (step 4→5)

The treatment with 2N HCl is meant to release the residual carbohydrates. About 2% of the original material present is released. 1% is recovered from the extract (Table 1). GPC of the extract gives only a fraction of low molecular weight. The amount of organic carbon in the residue decreased with 2% while 3% is recovered from the extract (Table 1). Qualitative analysis of this extract reveals the presence of monosaccharides, amino acids and EDTA. Table 2 summarizes the results of the amino acid analysis.

4N HCl treatment (step 5→6)

During 4N HCl hydrolysis the amino sugar fraction is supposed to be released from the residue. Upon this acid treatment 1% of the original material is removed and 1% is recovered from the extract. The amount of carbon in the residue R5 decreased with 3% while 6% is recovered from the extract (Table 1). This discrepancy is not well understood. GPC of the extract reveals one low molecular weight fraction consisting of neutral sugars, amino acids and probably amino sugars and uronic acids. The definite presence of the latter two has not yet been investigated. The results of the amino acid analysis are presented in Table 2.

6N HCl treatment (step 6→7)

This procedure is expected to release the residual proteinaceous material. The 6N HCl treatment causes the release of another 2% of the original material present; 1% is recovered from the extract. The amount of carbon in the residue decreases with 8% and 5% is recovered from the extract. It should be noted that by the combined steps (5→6 and 6→7), 11% of the carbon is released from the residue and is recovered from the extracts.

GPC reveals the presence of a low molecular weight fraction, partly consisting of amino acids (Table 2). The C_{org}/N ratio in residue R7 is 33. Comparison with the ratio of 7.5 in the original sample indicates that the greater part of the nitrogen has been removed from the sample.

Direct 6N HCl treatment of the residue after cold water extraction (step 2→8)

It was worthwhile to compare the results of the stepwise procedure with the results of a direct 6N HCl treatment. Application of the direct 6N HCl treatment may result in a partial loss of carbohydrate material. The amount of residual matter left after direct hydrolysis is somewhat lower than the amount of material left after the stepwise procedure (59% v. 63%). However, the amount of residual carbon after direct hydrolysis is somewhat higher than the one observed in residue R7 (Fig. 3). Obviously the milder stepwise procedure gives a slightly more efficient extraction of organic material.

Amino acids released by the 6N HCl procedure are summarized in Table 2. Differences in chemical reactions playing a role in both procedures are reflected by considerable difference of C/N ratios of the residues (R7:33 and R8:10.5). One might speculate that Maillard-type condensation reactions play a more important role in the direct 6N HCl treatment. As this procedure is the accepted one for overall amino acid analyses, the data given in Table 2 are nevertheless considered to be representative for the amino acid content of the sample.

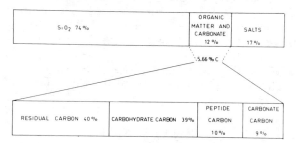

Fig. 5. Chemical composition of the sample. The silica content is calculated from the amount of silicon in R1. The percentage of salts has been estimated from the amount of salt found in E2. The subdivision of the carbon content has been calculated from the extraction data (Table 1).

Based on the qualitative and quantitative results we are able to give a preliminary reconstruction of the chemical composition of the sediment investigated (Fig. 5).

The remarkably high amount of silica in this sample almost certainly originates from diatoms.

In diatoms the silica content can be up to 50% of the dry weight of the cell i.e. 25% silicon of the total cell material. The silicon content of this sediment sample is still higher (Table 1). This can be explained by the loss of cell content other than silica during migration through the water column and early diagenesis. The silica concentration in sea water ranges from 2–14 ppm. This is far below saturation with respect to amorphous silica of which the diatom builds its wall (Iler, 1978). Considering the high silica content of the ooze, this silica must be bound in some form that is less soluble than amorphous silica. This would be in accordance with the suggestion by Iler (1978) that the diatomaceous silica is tightly encircled by organic material and is not exposed directly to the surrounding water.

Volcani (1978) also suggests that the siliceous 'shell' is

enclosed by an organic 'casing'. Its very complex composition includes a number of hitherto unknown amino acids and sugars, some of which have been characterized. Volcani also supplies evidence for a carbohydrate coating of the wall which is taking place during starvation. The material deposited on the wall is probably a secondary addition to the original wall. The assumption of such an addition might explain the high carbohydrate content of this sediment.

The mode of occurrence of carbon in this sediment sample is shown in Fig. 5. The amount of carbon originating from proteinaceous matter is at least 10% (Table 2). Since in the various hydrolysates only monosaccharides and amino acids are encountered, the amount of carbohydrate has been estimated to be 39% by subtracting the amount of amino acid carbon from the amount of organic carbon present in the various extracts. The way in which the carbon balance was made up, did not allow the quantitation of the lipid carbon content since organic solvents could not be used.

Because lipids generally are insoluble in aqueous media it is believed that the lipid material is present in the residual carbon.

Whether the residual organic carbon reflects organic matter originally present in the sediment which cannot be released by the applied procedure, or whether this organic matter has become insoluble as a consequence of the chemical treatment is hard to conclude at this stage of the investigation. At least 50% of the organic matter in this recent sediment consists of carbohydrates and peptides. To what extent this type of organic material might contribute to the future kerogen will be subject of further investigation.

REFERENCES

Boon, J. J. (1978) Molecular biogeochemistry of lipids in four natural environments. Thesis, Delft University of Technology.

Degens, E. and Mopper, K. (1976) Factors controlling the distribution and early diagenesis of organic material in marine sediments. *Chem. Oceanogr.* **3**, 59–111.

Eisma, D. (1969) Sediment sampling and hydrographic observations off Walvis Bay, S.W. Africa, Dec. 1968–Jan. 1969. NIOZ International Publication 1969–1, Texel, The Netherlands.

Fresenius, W. and Jander, G. (1967) *Handbuch der Analytischen Chemie III*, Band 4aα. Springer, Berlin, p. 484.

Handa, N. and Mizuno, K. (1973) Carbohydrates from lake sediments. *Geochem. J.* **7**, 215–230.

Henrichs, S. M. and Farrington, J. W. (1979) Amino acids in interstitial waters of marine sediments. *Nature* **279**, 319–322.

Iler, R. K. (1979) Silica in Biology. In *The Chemistry of Silica*. Wiley, New York, Chapt. 7, pp. 730–789.

Jansson, P.-E., Kenne, L., Liedgren, H., Lindberg, B. and Lönngren, J. (1976) A practical guide to the methylation analysis of carbohydrates. *Chem. Commun. Univ. Stockholm* No. 8.

Klok, J., Nieberg-van Velzen, E. H., de Leeuw, J. W. and Schenck, P. A. (1981) Capillary gas chromatographic separation of monosaccharides as their alditol acetates. *J. Chromatogr.* **207**, 273–275.

Mopper, K. (1977) Sugars and uronic acids in sediment and water from the Black Sea and North Sea with emphasis on analytical techniques. *Mar. Chem.* **5**, 585–603.

Modzeleski, J. E., Laurie, W. A. and Nagy, B. (1971) Carbohydrates from Santa Barbara Basin Sediments: Gas chromatographic–mass spectrometric analysis of trimethylsilyl derivatives. *Geochim. Cosmochim. Acta*, **35**, 825–838.

Myklestad, S. (1974) Production of carbohydrates by marine planktonic diatoms. I. Comparison of nine different species in culture. *J. Exp. Mar. Biol. Ecol.* **15**, 261–274.

Parsons, T. R., Stephens, K. and Strickland, J. D. H. (1961) On the chemical composition of eleven species of marine phytoplankters. *J. Fish. Res. Board Can.* **18**, 1001–1016.

Pieters, H. A. J. (1948) Notes on analytical procedures. I. Determination of carbon dioxide. *Anal. Chim. Acta* **2**, 263–269.

Pieterse, F. and van der Post, D. C. (1967) The Pilchard of South West Africa. Adm. S.W. Africa Mar. Res. Lab., *Investigational Report* No. 14.

Smestad, B., Haug, A. and Mykelstad, S. (1974) Production of carbohydrate by the marine diatom *Chaetoceros affinis* var. *Willei* (Gran) Hustedt. III. Structural studies of the extracellular polysaccharide. *Acta Chem. Scand.* **B28**, 662–666.

Smested, B., Haug, A. and Myklestad, S. (1975) Structural studies of the extracellular polysaccharide produced by the diatom *Chaetoceros curvisetus* Cleve. *Acta Chem. Scand.* **B29**, pp. 337–340.

Volcani, B. E. (1978) Role of silicon in diatom metabolism and silicification. In *Biochemistry of Silicon and related problems*, ed. by Bendz, G. and Lindqvist, I. Plenum Publishing Corporation, New York, pp. 177–204.

Advances in Organic Geochemistry 1981, pp. 819–823
© *John Wiley & Sons Limited, 1983*

Ammonia Formation in Laboratory Simulated Thermal Maturation: Implications Related to the Origin of Nitrogen in Natural Gas*

B. G. Rohrback,† K. E. Peters,‡ R. E. Sweeney§ and I. R. Kaplan

Institute of Geophysics and Planetary Physics and Department of Earth and Space Sciences, University of California, Los Angeles, USA

Ammonia content (exchangeable plus free) of heated sediment samples was monitored to trace the thermal evolution of nitrogen from organic matter. Ammonia quantities and stable nitrogen isotope ratios were measured for starting material and heated samples from four distinct Holocene sedimentary environments. In general, the quantity of free plus exchangeable ammonia increases to a maximum with increasing time and temperature of heating, and finally decomposes to nitrogen gas during prolonged heating and/or exposure to high temperatures. The amount of ammonia released depends on the depositional environment of the original organic matter. In the initial stages of heating, the ammonia released has an isotopic composition very similar to that of the bulk organic matter. At moderate to high maturity levels (starting at a vitrinite reflectance value of 0.8%) the ammonia becomes enriched in ^{15}N. For peat-derived organic matter exposed to high levels of thermal stress (experimental temperatures between 400 and 550°C) this $\delta^{15}N$ increase is dramatic; the residual ammonia can be enriched in ^{15}N by more than 40‰ relative to the starting material. Thus the thermal evolution and destruction of ammonia during maturation of terrigenous organic matter in sediments can account for $\delta^{15}N$ variations of ± 20‰ (relative to the atmospheric standard) for molecular nitrogen in natural gas. The ultimate nitrogen isotope ratio for N_2 in a natural gas reservoir would depend on the timing of separation of the thermally produced molecular nitrogen from the source ammonia.

INTRODUCTION

Diatomic nitrogen gas is frequently encountered in natural gas discoveries and can range from <1% to 85% by volume. There has been much discussion on the occurrence, origin and significance of this nitrogen (Headlee, 1962; Tiratsoo, 1967; Stahl *et al.*, 1977). Explanations of the presence of nitrogen in hydrocarbon reservoirs range from a magmatic origin, to remnants of ancient atmosphere, to products of radioactive decay reactions. These processes may contribute to the N_2 content of a natural gas in isolated instances, but the major source of nitrogen in a typical natural gas reservoir is the nitrogen evolved from the organic matter itself. Molecular nitrogen formation as a result of pyrolysis of organic-rich sediments has been suggested by Maksimov *et al.* (1976), among others, and was confirmed by Harrison (1978). In addition, Colombo *et al.* (1966) observed that high levels of N_2 in natural gas

correspond to high levels of C_2+ hydrocarbons, suggesting maturation-controlled generation.

Nitrogen isotope fractionation and distribution in nature, with regard to petroleum geochemistry, has been discussed by Letolle (1974) and Pankina *et al.* (1974). In addition, $\delta^{15}N$ values for diatomic nitrogen have been reported for a number of natural gas samples (Hoering and Moore, 1958; Bokhoven and Theeuwen, 1966; Stroud *et al.*, 1967; Eichmann *et al.*, 1971; Wollanke *et al.*, 1974; Stahl *et al.*, 1977). The range for these $\delta^{15}N$ values is typically ± 15‰. May *et al.* (1968) noted that ^{15}N is absorbed preferentially over ^{14}N during migration; therefore natural gas reservoirs should be enriched in the light isotope of nitrogen. Stahl *et al.* (1977) carried this concept one step further, using $\delta^{15}N$ of diatomic nitrogen as a migration index for a series of natural gas samples from northern Germany (the total variation exhibited was -15‰ to $+18$‰).

Because deamination is the first step in the release of nitrogen from sedimentary organic matter, this study was designed to trace the thermal evolution of ammonia from four different source environments under controlled conditions. The quantity and stable nitrogen isotopic composition of ammonia were monitored as a function of the degree of thermal alteration. Experimental design did not permit a quantitative or isotopic determination of N_2.

* Publication No. 2223, Institute of Geophysics and Planetary Physics.
† Present address: Cities Service Company, P.O. Box 642, Houston, Texas 77001, USA.
‡ Present Address: Chevron Oil Field Research Company, PO Box 446, La Habra, California 90631, USA.
§ Present Address: Union Oil Company of California, Brea, California 92621, USA.

METHODS

Holocene samples of Staten Island peaty soil ('peat'), Laguna Mormona algal mat, Tanner Basin sediment (offshore, marine), and Duck Lake sediment were freeze dried, powdered and homogenized. Each sample (typically 5 g Staten, 10 g Laguna Mormona, 5 g Tanner, 20 g Duck) was sealed in a separate glass tube under 0.2 to 0.7 atm of purified helium, after thorough evacuation to remove all traces of air contamination. The sealed tubes were then heated at constant temperatures within the range of 35 °C to 550 °C for specified periods of 1 hour to 15 000 hours (625 days).

After heating, the sediments were washed with acid and distilled water to extract the free and exchangeable ammonia. The ammonia was converted to ammonium sulphate and reacted in a vacuum line (Liu, 1979) with saturated sodium hypobromite solution, thereby oxidizing the ammonium ion to nitrogen gas (97% yield). This gas was then purified, quantified by manometer, and collected for stable isotope analysis. Nitrogen isotope ratios were measured using a Nuclide 6″60° dual collecting mass spectrometer.

A general location map is presented in Fig. 1, and details of both sample locations and methodology can be found in Rohrback (1979).

RESULTS AND DISCUSSION

The quantity and stable nitrogen isotope ratios of ammonia were measured for each of the four unheated

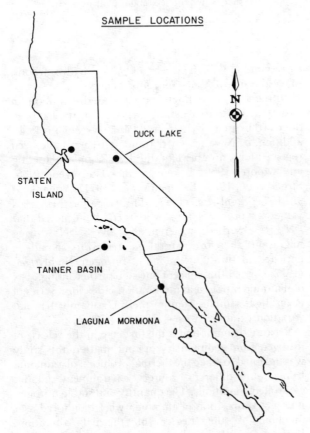

SAMPLE LOCATIONS

Fig. 1. General location map of the four sedimentary environments studied.

sedimentary environments plus 57 heated samples (Table 1). The heated samples are identified by a three-part code designating Environment–Heating Temperature–Heating Time. Temperature codes are 10% of the heating temperature, except that 03 was used for 35 °C. For example, the label S-10-15K defines: Staten Island peaty soil (S) — 100 °C heating temperature (10) — 15 000 hours of heating time (15 K). The quantities listed are given in micromoles of ammonia extracted per gram of dry sediment weight. Isotope ratios are given in the standard 'δ' notation with values in permil (‰) relative to the nitrogen standard (atmospheric nitrogen is defined as 0‰).

In general, the quantity of free plus exchangeable ammonia starts to be produced in small amounts, increases with time and temperature to a maximum, and finally decreases. Increases in ammonia concentration at the expense of other organic nitrogen forms have been noted for Holocene sedimentary environments by Bordovskiy (1965) and Kemp and Mudrochova (1972). The stable nitrogen isotope data for ammonia show small positive $\delta^{15}N$ values, and a slight depletion of ^{15}N relative to the starting material during heating at low temperatures and short times. At higher temperatures and longer times, the residual ammonia displays increasingly positive $\delta^{15}N$ values (up to +49‰) corresponding to the stage of ammonia depletion through thermal decomposition.

The variation in $\delta^{15}N$ for the ammonia produced from all four sample locations is illustrated in Fig. 2. The stable nitrogen isotope ratio is plotted against temperature of heating for each of the sample environments. Plotted points represent the numerical average of all measurements taken at a specific temperature.

Figure 2 shows a temperature-dependent trend in nitrogen isotope ratios. The ammonia released initially has an isotopic composition similar to that of the bulk organic matter. At moderate to high maturity levels (roughly 350 to 450 °C in these experiments), the ammonia becomes enriched in ^{15}N. For terrestrially sourced organic material, this $\delta^{15}N$ change for ammonia can be dramatic. Heated samples of Staten Island peat liberated ammonia which changed from an initial isotope value of about +5‰ to nearly +50‰. The Duck Lake samples displayed a $\delta^{15}N$ increase of 20‰. The difference in magnitude between the Staten Island and Duck Lane isotope effects is attributed to either their difference in terrestrial organic facies or to the variance in per cent organic matter per dry sediment weight (39% for Staten Island, 2% for Duck Lake).

The largely algal or planktonic organic matter from Laguna Mormona algal mat and Tanner Basin marine sediment exhibited less pronounced increases in ^{15}N concentration, approximation 10‰ and 3‰ respectively. The amount of ammonia relative to the organic matter content of the latter two environments is also greater than in Staten Island and Duck Lake samples (values in Table 1 must be compared with the organic matter content in each dry sediment: 2% for Duck Lake, 10% for Laguna Mormona, 11% for Tanner Basin, 39% for Staten Island). Therefore, it is evident that degree of organic maturity, type of organic matter

Table 1

Quantities of ammonia (exchangeable plus free) and stable nitrogen isotope ratios (‰)

Sample	μmol NH₃[a]	δ¹⁵N[b]
Staten Standard	64	+8.22
S-03-15K	54	+2.19
S-10-15K	157	+0.18
S-15-1	37	+6.42
S-15-25	87	—
S-15-100	135	+2.04
S-20-1	28	+5.16
S-20-25	67	+6.70
S-20-100	129	+2.35
S-20-250	183	+3.01
S-25-1	58	+2.55
S-25-500	120	+7.57
S-35-5	158	+10.95
S-35-50	168	+10.23
S-40-1	209	+14.81
S-40-10	188	+33.22
S-40-25	97	+41.59
S-40-25[f]	103	+29.85
S-40-100	143	+37.00
S-45-25	142	+37.07
S-50-25	131	+46.94
S-55-25	145	+48.88

Sample	μmol NH₃[a]	δ¹⁵N[b]
Algal Standard	28	+2.50
A-10-1	51	+0.93
A-10-25	13	+5.85
A-10-100	73	+0.18
A-10-1K	80	+2.50
A-10-10K	72	−0.10
A-15-100	32	+3.15
A-15-1K	142	+8.43
A-20-1	39	+1.47
A-20-10	57	+1.35
A-20-100	99	+2.03
A-25-10	125	—
A-25-500	190	+0.05
A-30-1	225	−2.23
A-30-5	310	+4.60
A-30-50	428	+10.13
A-35-50	125	+10.24
A-45-25	266	+10.77
A-50-25	202	+17.28
A-55-25	232	+12.18

Sample	μmol NH₃[a]	δ¹³N[b]
Duck Standard	7.7	+3.84
D-03-10K	3.0	+4.20
D-10-25	3.3	+4.85
D-10-5K	5.9	+4.07
D-15-25	6.1	+3.93
D-20-25	7.3	+7.58
D-30-25	6.0	+4.39
D-35-25	7.7	+4.85
D-40-25	7.4	+4.90
D-45-25	12.7	+19.77
D-50-25	9.5	+22.00
Tanner Standard	30	+10.28
T-10-25	14	+9.33
T-15-25	27	+8.67
T-20-250	96	+9.08
T-30-25	132	+6.63
T-35-25	172	+8.56
T-40-25	66	+14.22
T-50-25	245	+11.05

[a] μ moles NH₃ per gram dry sediment weight
[b] isotope values relative to atmospheric standard
[f] duplicate sample

present, and proportion of organic matter relative to inorganic constituents all play roles in determining the nitrogen isotopic composition of ammonia generated. Their importance decreases in the order listed.

The stages of ammonia formation and decomposition, along with the resulting stable isotope fractionation, are displayed on semi-logarithmic graphs in Fig. 3 and contain data from the 200 and 400 °C experiments for Staten Island peat samples. This environment serves as the best example, in that more data have been generated from the Staten Island heating experiments and the isotope variation is the most extreme. The early alteration regime is illustrated in the 200 °C data. The quantity of ammonia increases more than six-fold, from

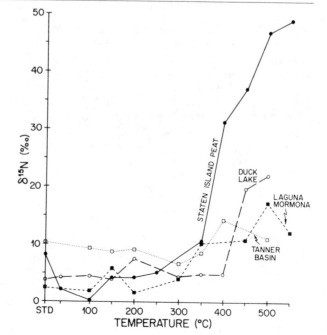

Fig. 2. Variation in δ¹⁵N of ammonia for all four environments as a function of experimental temperature. STD refers to the unheated starting material.

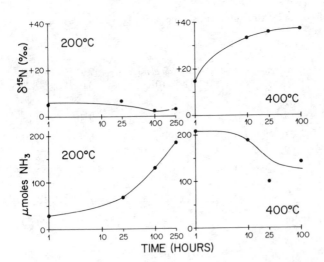

Fig. 3. Stages of ammonia formation and decomposition illustrated by the Staten Island peat 200 and 400 °C experiments.

28 micromoles (1 hour) to 183 micromoles per gram of sediment (250 hours). Over the same heating period, the nitrogen isotope ratio of the ammonia shows a negligible change. The more thermally mature samples heated to 400 °C exhibit over a 30% decrease in quantity of ammonia and a simultaneous 22‰ increase in $\delta^{15}N$.

Because the ammonia reservoir is being depleted during maturation and the remaining ammonia is becoming enriched in ^{15}N, a sink must exist for isotopically light nitrogen. The bitumen fraction extracted from these samples has a very low nitrogen content, and the once-abundant humic substances have been thermally altered to low molecular weight species and kerogen-like structures (which show very little change in $\delta^{15}N$; Peters et al., 1981). The kerogen isotope data of Peters and co-workers are consistent with other observations (Stiehl and Lehmann, 1980). One logical fate of this isotopically light nitrogen is participation of the ammonia in a redox reaction to generate molecular nitrogen. Unfortunately, the experimental design did not permit a quantitative molecular nitrogen determination.

Table 2 lists standard free-energy calculations for three possible nitrogen formation reactions. Ammonia is suggested as a source of hydrogen for saturation of double bonds and reduction of oxidized carbon species, because saturation reactions and reduction of CO and CO_2 have been observed in these samples (Rohrback, 1979). The calculated ΔG_{rxn}° values are for standard conditions and do not necessarily reflect actual values under the experimental or natural conditions. These free energies do point out, however, that the reactions as

Table 2

Standard free energies of three nitrogen generation reactions

Reactants	Products	ΔG_{rxn}° [a]
NH_3, $CH_2=CH_2$	N_2, CH_3-CH_3	−64.46
NH_3, CO	N_2, CH_4, H_2O	−26.01
NH_3, CO_2	N_2, CH_4, H_2O	−12.41

[a] Free energies listed in kacl g^{-1} mol^{-1} N_2.

written are favourable. Therefore, it is unnecessary to evoke the thermodynamically unfavourable reaction of Fe_2O_3 with ammonia (as proposed by Getz, 1977) to provide a generation medium for N_2. None of these four sample environments contained measurable Fe_2O_3.

Assuming that the ammonia lost from the closed Staten Island peat system between 1 hour and 100 hours at 400 °C was oxidized entirely to molecular nitrogen, the resulting nitrogen isotope ratio of the product N_2 would be fractionated 70‰ relative to the 400 °C, 100 hour ammonia (to $-33\odot$):

$$(209\ \mu mol\ NH_3)(+14.8‰) \rightarrow (143\ \mu mol\ NH_3)(+37.0‰)$$
$$+(66\ \mu mol\ N^\circ)(-33.3‰)$$

Therefore, maturation processes of a possible coal-precursor like Staten Island peat can account for very negative to very positive $\delta^{15}N_2$ values, depending upon the timing of the separation of the thermally produced molecular nitrogen from the source organic ammonia. The mechanism for separation of diatomic nitrogen and ammonia may be either nitrogen gas migration or removal of ammonia through water washing of a source rock. Three basic scenarios can be constructed:

(1) If early formed isotopically light nitrogen is isolated from its ammonia source either by migration of N_2 or dissolution removal of NH_3, then trapped in a natural gas reservoir, the resulting nitrogen will be enriched in ^{14}N relative to its organic nitrogen source.

(2) If this initial isotopically light nitrogen is lost and the remaining organic matter generates a gas reservoir, the isotopically heavy ammonia in this source rock will yield ^{15}N-enriched N_2.

(3) If little or no early-generated nitrogen escapes and if 100% of the ammonia oxidizes to N_2, the reservoired gas will reflect the stable nitrogen isotope of the original organic matter (typically +2‰ to +10‰).

Tracing quantities and stable nitrogen isotope ratios of exchangeable and free ammonia provides insight into the origin and isotopic distribution of diatomic nitrogen in natural gas. Migration effects suggested in the literature may be less significant than simple maturation effects. Isotopic distributions and abundances of nitrogen in petroleum gas can be accounted for by the release and subsequent oxidation of organic ammonia.

Acknowledgements

We acknowledge the National Aeronautics and Space Administration Grant No. NGR 05-007-221 for supporting this research. We thank Dr K. K. Liu for assistance in the vacuum line preparation of nitrogen from ammonia, D. Winter for isotope measurements, and Drs S. E. Palmer, S. R. Silverman and Z. Sofer for critical evaluation of the manuscript.

REFERENCES

Bokhoven, C. and Theeuwen, H. J. (1966) Determination of the abundance of carbon and nitrogen isotopes in Dutch coals and natural gas. *Nature (London)* **211**, 927–929.

Bordovskiy, O. K. (1965) Accumulation and transformation of organic substances in marine sediments. *Mar. Geol.* **3**, 3–114.

Colombo, U., Gazzarrini, F., Gonfiantini, R., Sironi, G. and Tongiorgi, E. (1966) Measurement of $^{13}C/^{12}C$ isotope ratios on Italian natural gases and their geochemical interpretation. In *Advances in Organic Geochemistry* 1964, ed. by Hobson, G. D. and Louis, M. C. Pergamon, Oxford, pp. 279–292.

Eichmann, R., Plate, A., Behrens, W. and Kroepelin, H. (1971) Das Isotopenverhältnis des Stickstoffs in einigen Erdgasen, Erdölgasen und Erdölen Nordwestdeutschlands. *Erdöl Kohle* **24**, 2–7.

Getz, F. A. (1977) Molecular nitrogen: clue in coal-derived-methane hunt. *Oil Gas J.* **75**, 220–221.

Harrison, W. E. (1978) Experimental diagenetic study of a modern lipid-rich sediment. *Chem. Geol.* **21**, 315–334.

Headlee, A. J. W. (1962) Carbon dioxide, nitrogen crucial to oil migration? *World Oil* **155**, 126–131.

Hoering, T. C. and Moore, H. E. (1958) The isotopic composition of the nitrogen in natural gases and associated crude oils. *Geochim. Cosmochim. Acta* **13**, 225–232.

Kemp, A. L. W. and Mudrochova, A. (1972) Distribution and forms of nitrogen in a Lake Ontario sediment core. *Limnol. Oceanogr.* **17**, 855–867.

Letolle, R. (1974) Present state of knowledge on the isotopic geochemistry of nitrogen. *Rev. Geogr. Phys. Geol. Dyn.* **16**, 131–138.

Liu, K. K. (1979) Geochemistry of inorganic nitrogen compounds in two marine environments: the Santa Barbara Basin and the ocean off Peru. Ph.D. Thesis, University of California, Los Angeles.

Maksimov, S. N., Mueller, E., Botneva, T. A., Goldbecher, K.,

Zor'kin, L. M. and Pankina, R. G. (1979) Origin of high nitrogen gas pools. *Int. Geol. Rev.* **18**, 551–556.

May, F., Freund, W., Muller, E. P. and Dostal, K. P. (1968) Modellversuche über Isotopenfraktionierung von Erdgaskomponenten während der Migration. *Z. Angew. Geol.* **14**, 376–380.

Pankina, R. G., Botneva, T. A., Mekhtiyeva, V. L., Ivlev, A. A., Yeremenko, N. A. and Maksimov, S. P. (1974) *Stable Isotopes and Petroleum Geochemistry*, Nedra, Moscow.

Peters, K. E., Rohrback, B. G. and Kaplan, I. R. (1981) Geochemistry of artificially heated humic and sapropelic sediments I: Petrokerogen. *Bull. Am. Assoc. Petrol. Geol.* **65**, 688–705.

Rohrback, B. G. (1979) Analysis of low molecular weight products generated by thermal decomposition of organic matter in Recent sedimentary environments. Ph.D. Thesis, University of California, Los Angeles.

Stahl, W., Boigk, H. and Wollanke, G. (1977) Carbon and nitrogen isotope data of Upper Carboniferous and Rotliegend natural gases from north Germany and their relationship to the maturity of the organic source material. In *Advances in Organic Geochemistry* 1975, ed. by Campos, R. and Goni, J. Enadimsa, pp. 539–559.

Stiehl, G. and Lehmann, M. (1980) Isotopenvariationen des Stickstoffs humoser und bituminöser natürlicher organischer Substanzen. *Geochim. Cosmochim. Acta* **44**, 1737–1746.

Stroud, L., Meyer, T. O. and Emerson, D. E. (1967) Isotopic abundance of neon, argon and nitrogen in natural gases. *U.S. Bur. Mines Rep. Invest.* **6936**, 1–27.

Tiratsoo, E. N. (1967) *Natural Gas: A Study*, Plenum Press, New York.

Wollanke, G., Behrens, W. and Hörgan, T. (1974) Stickstoffisotopenverhältnis von Erdgasen des Emslandes. *Erdöl Kohle* **27**, 523.

Advances in Organic Geochemistry 1981, pp. 824–827
© John Wiley & Sons Limited, 1983

Pyrolysis of Natural and Synthetic Humic Substances

P. Ioselis, Y. Rubinsztain and R. Ikan

Department of Organic Chemistry, Laboratory of Natural Products and Energy, Hebrew University, Jerusalem, Israel

K. E. Peters

Chevron Oil Field Research Company, La Habra, California, USA

Natural humic substances and synthetic melanoidins were complexed with clays, e.g. kaolinite and montmorillonite. Complexed and non-complexed humic substances were analysed by the Rock–Eval technique, as well as by pyrolysis at 600 °C under nitrogen atmosphere (laboratory pyrolysis). It was found that most synthetic melanoidins generated more hydrocarbons and related compounds than terrestrial humic substances.

INTRODUCTION

It is well known that humic substances account for much of the organic matter that occurs in soils, recent sediments and natural waters. Humic substances may be formed by reaction of degradation products of lignin with proteins and amino acids (Flaig, 1964). The 'water humus' (melanoidins) is probably formed by condensation of amino acids and carbohydrates (Abelson and Hare, 1971; Hoering, 1973; Nissenbaum, 1974). Hoering (1973) has suggested that synthetic melanoidins and natural humic acids have chemical similarity. It has been demonstrated recently by Larter and Douglas (1980) that synthetic melanoidins can react in aqueous solution with lipids producing products resembling sedimentary humic acids. The apparent chemical similarity of natural humic acids and synthetic melanoidins, and the important role of humic substances in kerogen formation (Huc and Durand, 1977) suggest that such polymers may provide model substances for studying the genesis of kerogen.

The purpose of this investigation was to compare the potential of hydrocarbon generation of humic substances (isolated from peat) and of synthetic melanoidins. This was accomplished by pyrolysing humic acids and synthetic melanoidins in an inert atmosphere. A similar series of experiments was performed with physical mixtures and wet complexes of humic acids and melanoidins with several minerals.

It is difficult to evaluate the catalytic and adsorptive effects of clays on organic matter trapped within the clays. Furthermore, no detailed information is available with respect to the contribution of each of the above-mentioned effects on the generation of hydrocarbon equivalents (HE). The term HE describes the hy-drocarbon part of the pyrolysed products detectable by flame ionization detector (FID) and defined as

$$\frac{S_1 + S_2}{1 \text{ g organic carbon}}$$

(Rock-Eval method, Espitalié *et al.*, 1977).

The factors which may affect a pyrolysis process are the mineral type, the organic matter/mineral ratio, the particle size of the clay and the organic matter; and at high temperatures the sample geometry, water content of the sample, presence of organic matter in interlamellar spaces of clays and lyophilization (Ikan, Baedecker and Kaplan, 1974). Almon and Johns (1975) have reported the formation of alkanes by decarboxylation of fatty acids in a clay-catalysed reaction.

The influence of minerals on the pyrolysis of kerogens was studied by Espitalié, Madec and Tissot (1980) and by Horsfield and Douglas (1980). Espitalié and co-workers have found that the adsorption of heavy hydrocarbons on mineral surfaces is one of the most important processes occurring during the pyrolysis of clay–organic matter mixtures. No logical relationship was found between the major mineral type of clay and the total hydrocarbon yield of pyrolysis of clay–kerogen mixture. Horsfield and Douglas (1980) have found that the content of low molecular weight pyrolysis products is higher for kerogens pyrolysed in a mineral matrix than for isolated kerogens. These results are in accordance with those reported by Espitalié *et al.* (1980).

EXPERIMENTAL

The melanoidins (Table 1) were prepared by condensation of amino acids and carbohydrates in hot alkaline

Table 1

Natural and synthetic substances used in this work

Sample No.	Substance	Molar ratio
1	Mel: Galactose–Lysine	1:9
2	Mel: Galactose–Lysine	1:1
3	Bovine Albumine	
4	Mel: Glucose–Methionine	1:9
5	Mel: Galactose–Lysine	9:1
6	Mel$_F$. Glucose–Valine	9:1
7	Mel: Glucose–Tyrosine	9:1
8	Mel: Glucose–Cystine	9:1
9	Mel$_F$: Glucose-β-Alanine	9:1
10	Fulvic acid	
11	Mel$_H$: Glucose–Valine	9:1
12	Mel: Galactose–Glycine	9:1
13	Mel: Galactose–Glycine	1:1
14	Mel$_H$: Glucose-β-Alanine	9:1
15	Humic acid (debitumenized)	
16	Humic acid	

Mel = Melanoid; Mel$_H$ = Melanoid fraction precipitated at pH 2; Mel$_F$ = Melanoid fraction soluble at pH 2.

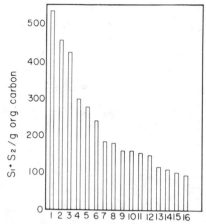

Fig. 1. Comparison of hydrocarbon equivalents obtained by Rock–Eval pyrolysis of humic substances and melanoidins.

solution (Hedges, 1978). The crude products were filtered through a Whatman No. 42 filter paper and purified by continuous dialysis followed by lyophilization. Some of the lyophilized samples were dissolved in water and acidified with hydrochloric acid to pH 2 yielding a precipitate Mel$_H$ (humic acid fraction). The supernatant was percolated through an Amberlite 120[H] column and lyophilized, yielding the Mel$_F$ ('fulvic' acid fraction).

The isolation and purification of humic acids were performed as described by Ioselis, Ikan and Frenkel (1980). Physical mixtures were prepared by thorough grinding of organic matter with clays (kaolinite and montmorillonite). Wet complexes were prepared by lyophilizing aqueous solutions of clay–organic matter complexes.

Most samples (described in Table 1) of about 50 mg each, were placed in a small porcelain boat and pyrolysed at 600 °C (laboratory pyrolysis) for 15 min in an inert atmosphere. The elementary analyses (carbon and hydrogen) of the neat samples were performed before and after the pyrolysis. The Rock–Eval analyses were performed at the Chevron Oil Field Research Company, La Habra, California.

RESULTS AND DISCUSSION

It was found that most of the synthetic melanoidins generate more hydrocarbon equivalents (HE) than terrestrial humic substances on pyrolysis (Fig. 1). The HE yield of melanoidins depends on the type of the amino acid and amino acid–carbohydrate ratio. It appears to us that natural humic substances and melanoidins synthesized from an excess of carbohydrates may be related to kerogen obtained from peat (Peters, Rohrback and Kaplan, 1981). Melanoidins synthesized from excess amino acids have HE values close to immature type-II kerogen.

There is a possibility that the increase in the HE values of melanoidins is due to the presence of lone pairs of electrons on heteroatoms (e.g. lysine, cystine) which probably generate free radicals during pyrolysis, and also the length of the carbon chain, or a combination of these factors. In relating HE values of immature organic matter to kerogens one should take into consideration the molecular weight, the presence of sulphur and nitrogen and many functional groups in the organic matter.

Examination of products obtained from pyrolysis by GC–MS techniques revealed the presence of hydrocarbon mixtures. This is in accordance with the results reported by Wershaw and Bohner (1969). This observation, coupled with the fact that the FID response depends strongly on the type and distribution of various constituents of the pyrolysate (Littlewood, 1970), indicates that the Rock–Eval technique provides only approximate values of the real hydrocarbon content of the immature organic matter. Good correlations between the HE obtained by Rock–Eval and laboratory pyrolysis were obtained (Fig. 2). A linear model for bivariate data gave a satisfactory fit as confirmed by the statistical regression coefficient of 0.84.

$$Y = 0.9X + 207$$

Y(mg) ΔHC increment for laboratory pyrolysis; X(mg) HE obtained by Rock–Eval.

Figure 2 shows that the value of ΔHC increment

$$\frac{[\Delta HC]}{1 \text{ g of organic matter}} =$$

$$\frac{100}{\text{weight of sample before pyrolysis (mg)}}$$

$$\left[\begin{array}{l} (\%C + \%H) \times \text{weight of sample before pyrolysis (mg)} - \\ (\%C + \%H) \times \text{weight of sample after pyrolysis (mg)} \end{array} \right]$$

at 600 °C, pyrolysis is higher by about 200 mg per 1 g of organic matter than the corresponding Rock–Eval value, which was calculated per 1 g of organic matter.

Since the correlation coefficient is close to 1, the constant difference of 200 mg is probably due to the loss of volatile compounds such as H_2O, NH_3, CO_2, which are not detectable by FID. We have observed that

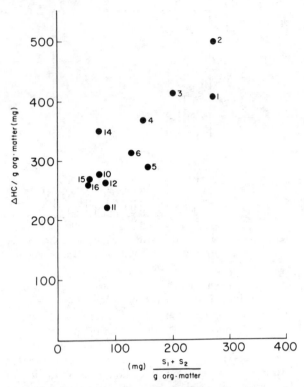

Fig. 2. Total hydrocarbon and hydrogen increment after laboratory pyrolysis versus Rock–Eval FID response.

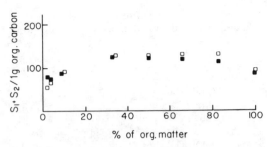

Fig. 4. Hydrocarbon equivalents (mg) obtained from Rock–Eval pyrolysis of humic acid-kaoline mixture. The black and the white squares denote two parallel series of experiments under identical conditions.

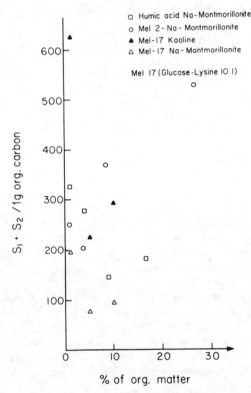

Fig. 5. Hydrocarbon equivalents (mg) obtained from Rock–Eval pyrolysis of humic acid and melanoidins with clays (wet complexes).

natural and 'synthetic' fulvic acids (isolated from the acidic supernatant of melanoidins) generate more HE than the corresponding humic acids and melanoidins. The relatively high HE values of the fulvic fractions of natural and synthetic humic substances support the idea that fulvic acids are composed of low molecular weight compounds joined together by hydrogen bonds (Schnitzer and Khan, 1972).

Another interesting observation of this study is that the physical mixture of kaolinite and organic matter generated on average about 35% more HE than the corresponding mixtures with alumina and montmorillonite (Fig. 3). The HE yield of wet kaolinite complexes was about three times greater than the corresponding montmorillonite complexes (Fig. 5).

At concentrations of 5–30% organic matter, especially in wet complexes, a strong adsorptive effect of organic matter on clays was observed (Figs 4 and 5). At very low concentrations ($\sim 1\%$) of organic matter in wet complexes (Fig. 5), however, a surprisingly high HE value (calculated per gram of organic carbon) was obtained. We propose that the high HE values might be due to the following effects: facile release of the pyrolysate constituents by water evolved during dehydration, a strong catalytic effect induced by a larger available surface area of the clay. Some of these effects are in accordance with those reported by Espitalié et al. (1980) and Horsfield and Douglas (1980).

CONCLUSIONS

1. Synthetic melanoidins usually generated more hydrocarbon equivalents (HE) than terrestrial humic

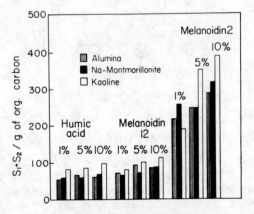

Fig. 3. Hydrocarbon equivalents (mg) obtained by Rock–Eval pyrolysis of humic acid and melanoidins in presence of minerals.

substances. Natural and synthetic fulvic acids generated more HE than humic acids and melanoidins.

2. The HE yield of melanoidins depends on the nature of the amino acid and the amino acid–carbohydrate ratio.

3. No significant catalytic effect of clays was observed in clay–organic matter complexes. At low concentration of organic matter especially in wet complexes, a strong absorptive effect was observed.

4. Although satisfactory correlation between the HE of Rock–Eval and laboratory pyrolysis (600 °C) methods was obtained, the absolute HE values were rather different.

5. Kaoline-organic complexes yielded more HE than the corresponding montmorillonite complexes.

Acknowledgement

The authors wish to thank Mr Bernard Crammer for critical reading of the manuscript.

REFERENCES

Abelson, P. H. and Hare, P. E. (1971) Reactions of amino acids with natural and artificial humus and kerogens. *Carnegie Inst. Washington Year Bk.* **69**, 327–334.

Almon, W. R. and Johns, W. D. (1975) Petroleum forming reactions: clay catalyzed fatty acid decarboxylation. *Proc. Int. Clay Conf.*, Mexico City, pp. 399–409.

Espitalié, J., Laporte, J. L., Madec, M., Marquis, F., Lepat, R., Paulet, J. and Bautefeu, A. (1977) Méthode rapide de caractérisation des roches mères, de leur potentiel petrolier et de leur degré d'évolution. *Rev. Inst. Fr. Pét.* **32**, 23–42.

Espitalié, J., Madec, M. and Tissot, B. (1980) Role of mineral matrix in kerogen pyrolysis: influence on petroleum generation and migration. *Am. Assoc. Pet. Geol. Bull.* **64**, 59–66.

Flaig, W. (1964) Effects of micro-organisms in the transformation of lignin to humic substances. *Geochim. Cosmochim. Acta* **28**, 1523–1535.

Hedges, J. J. (1978) The formation and clay mineral reactions of melanoidins. *Geochim. Cosmochim. Acta* **42**, 69–76.

Hoering, T. C. (1973) A comparison of melanoidin and humic acid. *Carnegie Inst. Washington Year B.* **72**, 682–690.

Horsfield, B. and Douglas, A. G. (1980) The influence of minerals on the pyrolysis of kerogens. *Geochim. Cosmochim. Acta* **44**, 1119–1131.

Huc, A. Y. and Durand, B. M. (1977) Occurrence and significance of humic acids in ancient sediments. *Fuel* **56**, 73–80.

Ikan, R., Baedecker, M. J. and Kaplan, I. R. (1974) Thermal alteration experiments on organic matter in recent sediments as a model for petroleum genesis. In *American Chemical Society Meeting, Atlantic City*, pp. 741–3.

Ioselis, P., Ikan, R. and Frenkel, M. (1980) Thermal degradation of metal-complexed humic substances. In *Advances in Organic Geochemistry*, ed. by Douglas A. G. and Maxwell, J. R. Pergamon Press, Oxford, pp. 567–577.

Larter, S. R. and Douglas, A. G. (1980) Melanoidins-kerogen precursors and geochemical lipid-sinks: a study using pyrolysis gas chromatography (PGC) *Geochim. Cosmochim. Acta* **44**, 2087–2095.

Littlewood, A. B. (1970) *Gas Chromatography: principles, techniques and applications*, Academic Press, London, pp. 301–308.

Nissenbaum, A. (1974) The organic geochemistry of marine and terrestrial humic substances: Implications of carbon and hydrogen isotope studies. In *Advances in Organic Geochemistry 1973*, ed. by Tissot, B. and Bienner, F. Editions Technip, France, pp. 39–52.

Peters, K. E., Rohrback, B. G. and Kaplan, I. R. (1981) Geochemistry of artificially heated humic and sapropellic sediments. I. Protokerogens. *Am. Assoc. Pet. Geol. Bull.* **65**, 688–705.

Schnitzer, M. and Khan, S. U. (1972) *Humic Substances in the Environment.* Marcel Dekker, New York.

Wershaw, R. L. and Bohner, G. E. (1969) Pyrolysis of humic and fulvic acids. *Geochim. Cosmochim. Acta* **33**, 757–762.

Advances in Organic Geochemistry 1981, pp. 828–833
© *John Wiley & Sons Limited, 1983*

The Organic Geochemistry of the Paraíba Valley and Maraú Oil-shales

J. N. Cardoso and M. I. Chicarelli

Institute of Chemistry, Federal University of Rio de Janeiro, Brazil

Hydrocarbon, carboxylic acid, aldehyde and ketone distributions in the Brazilian oil-shales from the Paraíba Valley (São Paulo) and Maraú (Bahia) formations were investigated. The higher plant input to the sediments denoted by characteristic *n*-alkane and *n*-carboxylic acid distributions is in accord with microscopical evidence for the presence of plant detritus. Original lipid distributions were, however, substantially modified by microbial activity in the sediments. Straight-chain ketone assemblages, for example, are closely similar to the *n*-alkane distribution patterns and probably derive from microbial oxidation of the corresponding hydrocarbons. The abundance of hopanoid skeletons in all lipid fractions examined confirms the major microbial contribution to the sedimentary biomass. Although similar in age and, apparently, maturity stage, major differences in the distributions of the hopane hydrocarbons were observed. $17\beta(H), 21\beta(H)$ configurations predominating for the Paraíba Valley (Oligocene) oil-shale, whereas $17\alpha(H), 21\beta(H)$ stereochemistries are preponderant in the Maraú (Miocene) sediment. This fact was rationalized in terms of impregnation of the Maraú oil-shale with hydrocarbons from underlying thermally altered Cretaceous sediments.

INTRODUCTION

In view of their abundance (second largest world reserve), the Irati oil-shales (Permian, c. 270×10^6) have attracted most of the work done on Brazilian oil-bearing shales (e.g. Padula, 1969; Gibert *et al.*, 1975; Costa Neto *et al.*, 1978). Yet, several smaller occurrences of oil-shales are present in various parts of the country. Some of these display very high organic carbon content, with the added benefit (at least for organic geochemical studies) of a less advanced stage of transformation. The present study constitutes the first lipid geochemistry evaluation of the oil-shales from the Paraiba Valley (Lower Oligocene; São Paulo; Fig. 1) and Maraú (Miocene, Bahia, Fig. 1) formations. Both shales have experienced mild thermal histories and not been buried to much greater depth than their current subsurface levels (*ca.* 200 m maximum burial depth).

The bituminous rocks of the Maraú formation (Marauito) are mainly of sapropelic origin (*Botryococcus braunii*) with subordinate amounts of higher-plant remains, cuticles, spores (Pteridophytae) and pollen grains (Moraes Rego, 1934). Sedimentation is believed to have been continental (lacustrine), under freshwater conditions, eolian transport of sand from the adjacent sea coast accounting for intercalations of sandstone layers amidst the organic rich clay strata (Tesch *et al.*, 1976).

The Paraíba Valley oil-shales feature a banded structure of clay (bentonite) and bituminous layers deriving from alternating cycles of deposition of eroded detritic matter from the catchment basin into a series of inter-linked fresh-water lakes (Paula Couto and Mezzalira, 1971). The aquatic environment, as judged from paleontological and palynological data, was encircled by a wooden belt of sub-tropical vegetation, warm temperatures and nutrient concentrations favouring development of an abundant aquatic fauna.

Outcrop samples of the two oil-shales were used in this work. Hydrocarbon, carboxylic acid, aldehyde and ketone distributions were examined with a view to determining the types of organic matter present in the samples and the extent of alteration of the sedimentary lipids.

EXPERIMENTAL

Sample collection

Outcrop samples of the Paraiba Valley oil-shale were collected from the mines of the Santa Fé farm in Tremembé (state of São Paulo). The sample used in this work comes from a semi-papiraceous layer (Padula, 1979) of the lithological strata.

The Maraú formation was sampled at João Branco, an outcrop sample of the bituminous shale (Marauito) being selected for this study.

Extraction and isolation of lipid fractions

Oil-shale samples (14–28 mesh) were Soxhlet extracted with chloroform (overnight, under nitrogen) and

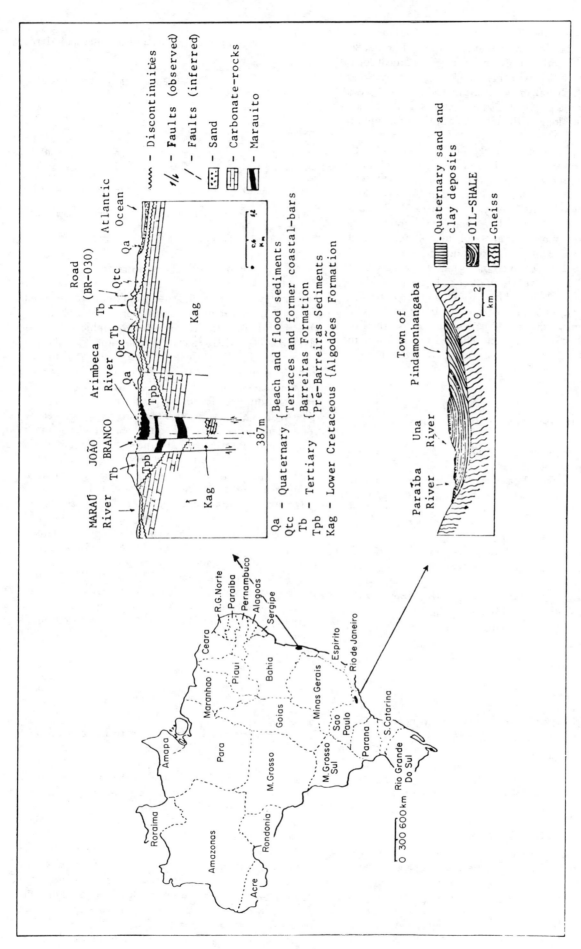

Fig. 1. Locations and lithologies at sampling sites for the Maraú[†] and Paraiba Valley[‡] oil-shales.

† Tesch *et al.* (1976)
‡ Moraes (1945).

extracts concentrated to dryness *in vacuo*. Aliquots were submitted to liquid chromatography (SiO_2, hexane, 80 ml) to afford isolation of the saturated hydrocarbons. Subsequent elution with benzene (*ca.* 200 ml) yielded fractions which, on mass spectrometric analysis, were shown to contain aldehydes and ketones as the major components, along with minor quantities of aromatic hydrocarbons.

Isolation of carboxylic acids was by extraction with methanolic KOH (0.5 N, 10 × 15 ml) of hexane solutions (50 ml) of aliquots (*ca* 3 g) of the total organic extracts. Alkaline extracts were combined, acidified (pH = 1) and finally extracted with diethyl ether (10 × 30 ml) and chloroform (5 × 10 ml). The combined extracts were concentrated in a rotary evaporator (to *ca.* 40 ml), treated with anhydrous $MgSO_4$, filtered and finally evaporated to dryness *in vacuo*. Conversion to methyl esters was by BF_3/MeOH and purification of ester fractions by thin-layer-chromatography (TLC) (SiO_2, hexane/ether 7:3 as developer). TLC plates were visualized under UV light (254 nm) using methyl palmitate as a standard, recovery of ester bands being effected by elution with ethyl acetate. Yields for the various fractions discussed in this work are given in Table 1.

Analysis of lipid fractions

Gas chromatographic (GC) analyses were performed on glass or fused silica capillary columns (25 m × 0.25 mm) coated with CP Sil 5 (PhaseSep, U.K.) or OV-101 liquid phases, respectively. GC conditions were: splitless injection at 50 °C, followed by a temperature programme of 5 °C min^{-1} up to 280 °C. Hydrogen (carrier) flow rate was *ca.* 1.5 ml min^{-1}.

Computerized gas chromatography–mass spectrometry (C-GC–MS) was on a Finnigan 4000 system with INCOS software, as previously described (Brassel *et al.*, 1980). SE-30 glass capillary columns (25 m × 0.25 mm) were used with helium (*ca.* 1 ml min^{-1}) as carrier gas. Operating temperatures were as for GC analyses (see above).

RESULTS

Straight-chain and acyclic isoprenoid components

Relative distributions of straight-chain and acyclic isoprenoidal (where present) alkanes, aldehydes, ketones and carboxylic acids are given in Fig. 2. Quantitations were by peak height measurement on gas chromatograms or, in the case of aldehydes and ketones, mass fragmentograms for m/z 82 and 58, respectively. Structural assignments were based on mass spectral interpretation and checked by comparison with literature mass spectra for the isoprenoids and at least one component in each straight-chain homologous series. Standards were co-injected (capillary GC; OV-101) for the *n*-alkane (C_{16}, C_{18}, C_{20}) and carboxylic acid (C_{12}, C_{16}; as the methyl esters) fractions.

Table 1

Amounts of lipid fractions in the Paraiba Valley and Maraú oil-shales.

Sediments	Concentration of lipid fraction (ppm)[a]		
	Hydrocarbons	Aldehydes and ketones[b]	Carboxylic acids[c]
Paraiba Valley	254	3.556	6.40
Maraú	125	1.538	1.2

[a] As quantitated by weighing. Values expressed relative to sediment weight.
[b] Benzene eluate (SiO_2) of total extract. Minor amounts of aromatic hydrocarbons also present.
[c] Quantitated as the methyl esters.

Polycyclic components

Distributions of polycyclic triterpanoids are represented in Fig. 3. Steroidal skeletons were present in low concentrations, as expected for oligotrophic sediments (Didyk *et al.*, 1978). Sterane distributions (not shown) for the Paraiba Valley sediment are dominated by C_{28} and C_{29} structures (2 stereoisomers each) accompanied by smaller amounts of methyl-steranes (C_{28}, C_{29}) as inferred from mass fragmentograms (m/z 217, 231, 372, 386, 400). The Maraú oil-shale features a C_{27} sterane (one stereoisomer) as the only relatively abundant component. Rearranged steranes (Ensminger *et al.*, 1978) occurred in much lower concentrations than their non-rearranged counterparts. Stereochemical assignments for the steranes were not made.

Hopanoid alkane, aldehyde and ketone structures were proposed on the basis of mass spectral interpretation (e.g. van Dorsselaer *et al.*, 1976; Simoneit and Didyk, 1978; Dastillung *et al.*, 1980) and GC retention characteristics.

Hopane-type skeletons ($17\beta(H)$, $21\beta(H)$ largely predominant) were also present in the carboxylic acid, alkene and alcohol fractions of the two oil-shales, as prominent ocmponents and will be discussed in a separate communication (Cardoso and Chicarelli, unpublished).

DISCUSSION

Straight-chain and acyclic branched components

n-Alkane and *n*-alkanoic acid distributions for both sediments feature one maximum in the C_{24}–C_{29} range (Fig. 2), in accord (Eglinton and Hamilton, 1967; see also review by Simoneit, 1978) with microscopical evidence (Paula Couto and Mezzalira, 1971; Tesch *et al.*, 1976) for a major higher-plant contribution. The low relative abundances of the lower homologues ($<C_{20}$) in the alkane and carboxylic acid distributions argue against eutrophic conditions of sedimentation and suggest a predominantly detrital origin for the sedimentary organic matter (Cranwell, 1973, 1974). Transport of allochthonous organic debris into an

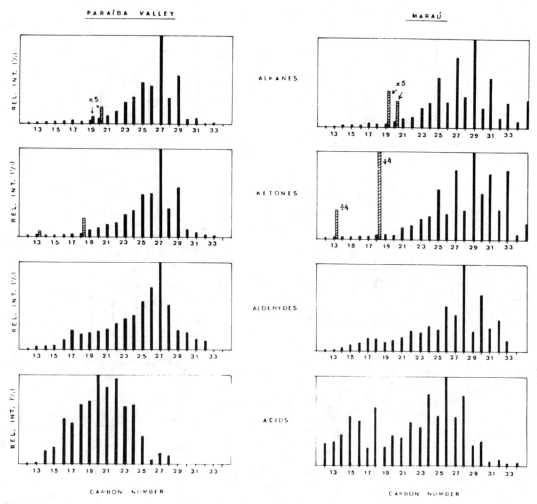

Fig. 2. Distributions of straight-chain and acyclic isoprenoid structures in the alkane, alkanoic, aldehyde and ketone fractions of the Maraú and Paraiba Valley oil-shales.

aquatic environment would be expected to favour oxidation of labile components (Didkyk *et al.*, 1978). In fact, the high relative abundances of the acyclic isoprenoid ketones (Fig. 2) and low concentrations of pristane and phytane are in keeping with deposition under oxic conditions. The presence of an homologous series of 2-alkanones bearing a close parallelism to the corresponding *n*-alkane patterns in both oil-shales is further evidence for oxic paleosedimentation conditions, microbial β-oxidation of the alkanes probably accounting for the ketone distributions (Arpino, 1973). The origin of the *n*-aldehydes in the sediments is still uncertain. No parallel between aldehyde distributions and *n*-alkane/*n*-alkanoic acid patterns (Fig. 2) was observed for Maraú. In the case of the Paraiba Valley oil-shale, aldehyde and alkane distributions (Fig. 2) bear enough similarity to suggest that there may be a product–precursor relationship. The α-oxidation of the alkanes, probably microbially-mediated, could provide a pathway to the aldehydes; structural selectivities of the enzymic complexes possibly involved determining the discrepancies between aldehyde/alkane distribution profiles.

Triterpanoid components

Contrary to the straight-chain ketones, the distribution

of hopanones, although certainly of microbial origin, bears no resemblance to the corresponding hydrocarbon assemblages (Fig. 3). Similarly, no obvious product–precursor relationship exists for the hopanoic aldehydes among the compound classes examined. A derivation of the aldehydes from the triterpanoid alcohols present in the sediments (Cardoso and Chicarelli, unpublished) through partial oxidation is possible. It is noteworthy that C_{30}–C_{32} aldehydes were detected in our samples, in contrast with a previous report for the presence of only extended skeletons (C_{31}, C_{32}) in a suite of sediments (Dastillung *et al.*, 1980).

Triterpanoid hydrocarbon distributions in the Paraiba Valley (Oligocene) shale essentially comprise homologues with the 17β(H), 21β(H) stereochemistry, attesting to the immaturity of the sediment (Ensminger *et al.*, 1977; van Dorsselaer *et al.*, 1977) as demonstrated by the excellent state of preservation of paleontological/palynological specimens (Paula Couto and Mezzalira, 1971). The predominance of hopanes with the mature, more stable 17α(H), 21β(H) configuration in the Maraú (Miocene) oil-shale was, however, unexpected for a sediment of similar age and burial history as the Paraiba Valley. Also, the high relative concentrations (and stereochemistries) of carboxylic acids, aldehydes and ketones in the Maraú

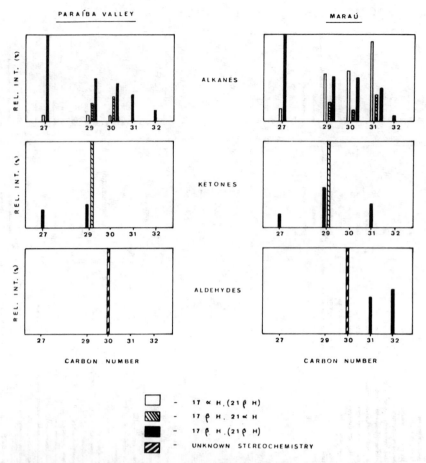

Fig. 3. Distributions of triterpanoid components in the alkane, aldehyde and ketone fractions of the Maraú and Paraiba Valley oil-shales.

organic extract (Table 1, Fig. 2) suggest an incipient evolution stage for the sediment. Such facts led us to examine the possibility of a contribution from an external, mature source to part of the Maraú hopane hydrocarbons. Examination of subsurface map of the Maraú formation (Fig. 1) reveal fractures and stratigraphic discontinuities characteristic of tectonic activity. Asphalt occurrences on the surface (and subsurface), notably in the Taipu-Mirim area (Tesch *et al.*, 1976), have been rationalized in terms of contact metamorphism by igneous intrusions on Cretaceous organic rich strata (Algodões formation) underlying the Marautio accumulations. The hydrocarbon composition of the thermally altered Mesozoic oil-shales (or of the asphalt samples) have not been examined. Nevertheless, it seems reasonable to assume (in the absence of other obvious sources of geologically mature organic matter) that upward migration of the oil formed in the deeper levels is the most likely source of the 17α(H), 21β(H), hopanes in the Maraú oil-shales.

CONCLUSIONS

Lipid distributions in the Brazilian oil-shales from Maraú (Bahia) and Paraiba Valley (São Paulo) confirmed palynological evidence for fresh-water, lacustrine environments of sedimentation. The major higher-plant input to both sediments as inferred from *n*-alkane/*n*-alkanoic acid distributions was in accord with reports on the common occurrence of plant detritus in the shales. Low amounts of typical molecular markers for an algal contribution and the occurrence of major concentrations of the C_{18} isoprenoid ketone (oxidation product of the labile alcohol, phytol), among others, could be interpreted in terms of oligotrophic conditions of deposition. Hopane distributions indicated a low maturity level for the two oil-shales, the predominance of structures with a 17αH stereochemistry fot the Maraú sediment being attributed to natural contamination of the shale deposit with migrated oil from thermally altered Cretaceous sediments, as supported by the occurrence of asphalt and (inactive) petroleum seeps in the area.

Acknowledgements

We are grateful to Professor G. Eglinton and Dr J. R. Maxwell, Organic Geochemistry Unit, Bristol University (U.K.) for use of the computerized GC–MS instrument and Mrs A. P. Gowar for assistance in data processing. The provision of a sample of the Maraú oil-shale by Dr C. Costa Neto is also gratefully acknowledged. Finally, we wish to thank the Ministry of Education (CAPES) for a scholarship (M.I.C.) and the Brazilian National Research Council (CNPq) for financial support.

REFERENCES

Arpino, P. (1973) Les Lipides des sédiments lacustres éocènes. PhD Thesis, Université Louis Pasteur de Strasbourg.

Brassell, S. C., Gowar, A. P. and Eglinton, G. (1980) Computerised gas chromatography–mass spectrometry in analyses of sediments from the Deep Sea Drilling Project. In *Advances in Organic Geochemistry 1979*. Ed. by Douglas, A. G. and Maxwell, J. R. Pergamon, Oxford. pp. 421–426.

Costa Neto, C., Furtado, E. G., Concha, F. J. M., Cardoso, J. N. and Quadros, L. P. (1978) Anomalies in the stratigraphic distribution of hydrocarbons in the Irati oil-shale. *Chem. Geol.* **23**, 181–192.

Cranwell, P. A. (1973) Chain-length distribution of *n*-alkane from lake sediments in relation to post-glacial environmental change. *Freshwat. Biol.* **3**, 259–265.

Cranwell, P. A. (1974) Monocarboxylic acids in lake sediments: Indicators, derived from terrestrial and aquatic biota, of paleoenvironmental trophic levels. *Chem. Geol.* **14**, 1–14.

Dastillung, M., Albrecht, P. and Ourisson, G. (1980) Cetones aliphatiques et polycycliques dans les sédiments: aldehydes et cetones en C_{27}–C_{33} de la serie hopanique. *J. Chem. Res. (M)*, 2325–2352.

Didyk, B. M., Simoneit, B. R. T., Brassel, S. C. and Eglinton, G. (1978) Organic geochemical indicators of paleoenvironmental conditions of sedimentation. *Nature (London)* **272**, 216–222.

Eglinton, G. and Hamilton, R. J. (1967) Leaf epicuticular waxes. *Science* **156**, 1322–1335.

Ensminger, A., Albrecht, P., Ourisson, G. and Tissot, B. (1977) Evolution of polycyclic alkanes under the effect of burial (Early Toarcian shales, Paris Basin). In *Advances in Organic Geochemistry 1975*. Ed. by Campos, R. and Goni, J. Enadimsa, Madrid. pp. 45–52.

Ensminger, A., Joly, G. and Albrecht, P. (1978) Rearranged steranes in sediments and crude oils. *Tetr. Lett*, 1575–1578.

Gibert, J. M., Bruning, I. M. R. A., Nooner, D. W. and Oro, J. (1975) Predominance of isoprenoids among the alkanes in the Irati oil shale, Permian of Brazil. *Chem. Geol.* **15**, 209–215.

Moraes Rego, L. F. (1934) O aproveitamento das rochas pyro-oleiferas do Brasil. *Bol. Inst. Eng. (São Paulo)* **98**, 12–18.

Moraes, L. J. (1945) Bacia Terciária do Vale do rio Paraiba, Estado de São Paulo. *Geologia* **2**, 4–25.

Padula, G. T. (1969) Oil-shale of Permian Irati Formation, Brazil. *Am. Ass. Petrol. Geol. Bull.* **53**, 591–602.

Padula, G. T. (1979) Folhelhos pirobetuminosos, reservas conhecidas e potenciais. In *Seminar on Energy Models*, State Secretary of Administration, Curitiba, Paraná.

Paula Couto, C. and Mezzalira, S. (1971) Nova conceituacão geocronológica de Tremembé, Estado de São Paulo, Brasil. *An. Acad. Brasil. Ci.* **43** (Suppl.), 473–488.

Simoneit, B. R. T. (1978) The organic chemistry of marine sediments. In *Chemical Oceanography*, Vol. 7. Ed. by Riley, J. P. and Chester, R. Academic Press, New York. pp. 233–311.

Simoneit, B. R. T. and Didyk, B. M. (1978) Organic geochemistry of a chilean paraffin dirt. *Chem. Geol.* **23**, 21–40.

Tesch, N. A., Moraes, Filho O., Barreto, L. A., Silva, P. E. L. and Brito, L. C. (1976) *Projeto Marauitó: Prospeccão de rochas oleigenas e barita*, Vol. 1, Companhia de Pesquisa de Recursos Minerais, Salvador. pp. 65, 76 and 172.

van Dorsselaer, A., Albrecht, P. and Ourisson, G. (1976) Identification of novel (17αH) hopanes in sediments and crude oils. *Bull. Soc. Chim. France.* 165–170.

van Dorsselaer, A., Albrecht, P. and Connan, J. (1977) Changes in composition of polycyclic alkanes by thermal maturation. In *Advances in Organic Geochemistry 1975*. Ed. by Campos, R. and Goni, J. Enadimsa, Madrid. pp. 53–59.

Advances in Organic Geochemistry 1981, pp. 834–838
© *John Wiley & Sons Limited, 1983*

Theoretical Organic Geochemistry. I — An Alternative Model for the Epimerization of Hydrocarbon Chiral Centers in Sediments

C. Costa Neto

Instituto de Química, Universidade Federal do Rio de Janeiro, Brasil

A model for the racemization of hydrocarbon chiral centers in a constrained environment is described in terms of an interaction between the chiral carbon and a proton supplied by the chemical network. A geometrical arrangement is needed to allow for a complex to be formed having the proton coordinated to the face of the tetrahedron opposing a bounded hydrogen. Allowing the 'asymetric' carbon to crossing through this face the other enantiomer will be formed. A potential energy surface was calculated for a model system using the CNDO II method.

INTRODUCTION

Maturation of the organic matter of sedimentary rocks occurs mainly under the following prevailing conditions:

1. Low temperatures (< 150–$200\ °C$).
2. Pressure can be high.
3. The organic matter is, in most cases (oil shales for instance), intimately dispersed into the inorganic matrix, forming a complex tridimensional network that can be characterized as a solid phase.
4. The time involved in these transformations is generally very long (millions of years).

These four characteristics together confer to georganic systems conditions for transformations that differ quite significantly from those found in conventional chemistry: here the reactions take place in solution (reagents are free to move) and are complete in a time interval of hours. Pressure is meant to be important only in gas reactions.

Very little is found in the chemical literature concerning mechanisms of transformations of the *materia prima* into the actual matter of sediments. A topic of greatest importance, the formation of saturated hydrocarbons in petroleums, is postulated as resulting from the transformation of carboxylic acids through decarboxylation reactions, reduction of the carboxyl group or even β-oxidation followed by decarboxylation*. For the formation of steranes and triterpanes, reductions or disproportionations have been the preferred pathways. In all cases, the proposed intermediates are the conventional ones, mainly free radicals, although some authors tend to suggest the presence of ions. In this way, the proposed mechanisms try only to map what is known for conventional chemical reactions to the possible reactions that are taking place in

the bulk of the sediment, without taking into account the great differences that exist between the two systems.

Contrasting with the conventional reactions where the reacting system is well known (reagents, products, conditions), very little or nothing is known about the original geometrical position in the solid network of a sediment, mainly the relationship between the organic and inorganic phases. Moreover, there are no more than speculations on the nature of the organic matter that could have been the origin of the organites[†]; on the other hand only a small fraction of the actual organic matter of sediments is known.

A way that has been used to justify hypotheses on mechanisms of geochemical reactions has been that of *experimental simulations*. In these experiments possible precursors are incubated reproducing natural conditions for maturation. The 'evidence' for the proposed mechanisms is reached if the products obtained in the artificial maturation are similar to those from the sediment.

This technique makes use of an artifice — that of compressing the time interval of the natural maturation (millions of years) to the time of the experiment (days) at the expense of heating the sample to temperatures higher than those to which it was subjected in nature. It is very difficult to defend the validity of such a procedure, since, although the rise in temperature may be favoring the process we are looking at, it will certainly hasten also dozens of other parallel processes that may be even more hastened with the rise in temperature, falsifying interpretations given to results. Although this is a strong objection, a great number of papers has been published in the field and this seems to be an active research area in organic geochemistry*.

[†] We shall use the term *organite* to designate all geological systems containing organic matter within an inorganic matrix.

* A comprehensive critical review on the literature on geochemical simulations can be found in Aquino Neto (1979). See also Eglinton (1972).

* For a general account of these reactions see Tissot and Welte (1978) and references contained therein.

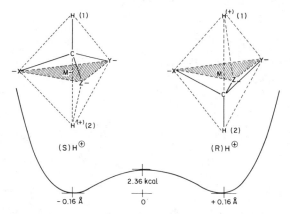

Fig. 1. Schematic diagram for the epimerization model. A potential energy function is also shown for this transformation.

A natural evolution in the method of simulation would be to go from the experimental to the *theoretical simulation*. In this approach the natural parameters (time, temperature etc.) can have their genuine values respected. Models for theoretical simulations are based, nowadays, on quantum mechanics; a Quantum Organic Geochemistry would be, at the present time, the working tool for a Theoretical Organic Geochemistry.

The task of proposing a pathway for a given reaction can be made very much easier when the reagents and products are known. As it was said before, this is not the picture that prevails in the transformations of organites. Nevertheless, one case exists in which the initial and final products are known: this is the racemization of optically active centers (chiral centers) of organic geolipids.

The degree of racemization of chiral centers has already been used to correlate with characteristics of the sediment: amino acids have been used for dating young organites (Schroeder and Bada, 1976) while isoprenoids (Patience *et al.*, 1978) and polycyclic terpenoids (Ensminger *et al.*, 1975) are used to define the degree of maturation of a sediment.

It has been proposed that the epimerization of amino acids may occur *via* carbanions (Bada and Schroeder, 1975) while in the epimerization of hydrocarbon centers, free radicals and carbonium ions have been the preferred intermediates.

For all that the racemization reaction offers to the study of geological processes — a reasonable simple system where reagents and products are known, ample documentation of facts determined in geological systems etc. — it was chosen as the starting point to our studies on Theoretical Organic Geochemistry. This paper reports the preliminary ideas on using an alternative route to describe the epimerization of a hydrocarbon chiral center, different from those that call for ions and free radicals.

THE MODEL

The proposed model deals with chiral centers that contain one hydrogen atom in a rigid network (solid phase). The solid matrix should be able to offer

hydrogen cations (Brønsted acid centers) to the system. These requirements are easily fulfilled by organites; all natural systems contain a hydrogen atom at the chiral center: amino acids, isoprenoid hydrocarbons, steroids, triterpenoids etc. A solid phase is what one has in a consolidated sediment, and acidic centers in clays are well known (Grim, 1968).

A simplified representation of the network of atoms required for the reaction is shown in Fig. 1. The pictures are placed in a way to make clear the suggested pathway for the epimerization in rigid phase. Each isomer, placed in the bulk of the rigid phase, coordinates a proton in the face opposite to the bound hydrogen atom resulting in a complex with a bipyramidal configuration.

The only difference between the two structures of Fig. 1 is the position of the carbon atom and, consequently, the position of the charge of the proton. Nevertheless, these two structures represent the two enantiomers bound to a proton. This shows that the conversion of the enantiomers may be obtained by the displacement of the carbon atom, from the center of one tetrahedron to the center of the other, all other atoms remaining in its original position.

The formation of planar intermediates as stable species in the epimerization reaction, would involve, necessarily, an increase in the distances XY, YZ and ZX, that is, a 'swelling' on the arrangement of XYZ in the plane, in order to accommodate the carbon atom in the center. Within fluids, this situation could be considered as trivial but it would not be so within a solid matrix, where one would expect a behavior more like that of a rigid network. Although some displacement could be allowed for the group XYZ, in this connection the limiting situation of fixed XYZ was chosen to stress the difference between the behavior of molecules in the bulk of a solid (constrained) from that of a free one. Moreover it would be necessary to characterize the stimulus responsible for the formation of the intermediate.

The crossing of the carbon atom from one position to the other as described in Fig. 1, involves, necessarily, crossing the center of the plane XYZ; this is, in the conditions of a rigid network, a high energy configuration; consequently a potential energy barrier (activation energy) would have to be transposed to allow going from one configuration to the other. The situation can be described by a symmetric double minimum potential energy function. The height of the barrier is an important factor to be determined in order to forsee the feasibility of the model. In any case we could expect that both, the Arrhenius type and tunnelling* effects could be expected to contribute to the epimerization reaction.

POTENTIAL ENERGY SURFACE

In order to estimate the order of magnitude of the barrier for the proposed system a potential energy function was calculated using the CNDO II approximation (Pople and Beveridge, 1970). No absolute values of energy are expected to be obtained from these calculations — since an approximate method is used — but only a relative,

* For a very complete account of the Tunnel Effect in Chemistry see Bell (1980).

Table 1

Ground state	Energy for the constrained protonated methane				
	Distances H(5)M (A) {H(1)M = 1.46 A}				
	1.26	1.36	1.46	1.56	1.66
Distances CMÅ	Energies (Hartrees)				
1.360	—	—	+ 8.6272	+ 8.6455	8.6618
1.260	—	− 2.0650	− 2.0454	− 2.0280	− 2.0127
1.160	− 5.6846	− 5.6633	− 5.6443	− 5.6275	− 5.6129
1.060	− 7.4932	− 7.4718	− 7.4529	− 7.4364	− 7.4222
0.960	− 8.5650	− 8.5432	− 8.5240	− 8.5073	− 8.4930
0.860	− 9.2507	− 9.2279	− 9.2079	− 9.1905	− 9.1758
0.760	− 9.7018	− 9.6777	− 9.6564	− 9.6379	− 9.6222
0.660	− 9.9971	− 9.9711	− 9.9481	− 9.9280	− 9.9109
0.560	− 10.1832	− 10.1552	− 10.1300	− 10.1078	− 10.0886
0.460	− 10.2920	− 10.2618	− 10.2341	− 10.2092	− 10.1875
0.360	− 10.3475	− 10.3154	− 10.2849	− 10.2570	− 10.2322
0.260	− 10.3688	− 10.3355	− 10.3026	− 10.2716	− 10.2434
0.160	− 10.3711	− 10.3383	− 10.3039	− 10.2700	− 10.2381
0.060	− 10.3646	− 10.3351	− 10.3008	− 10.2650	− 10.2299
0.000	− 10.3583	− 10.3330	− 10.3001	− 10.2638	− 10.2272
− 0.060	− 10.3501	− 10.3310	− 10.3008	− 10.2651	− 10.2275
− 0.160	− 10.3279	− 10.3251	− 10.3039	− 10.2718	− 10.2343
− 0.260	− 10.2833	− 10.3075	− 10.3026	− 10.2794	− 10.2455
− 0.360	− 10.1966	− 10.2627	− 10.2849	− 10.2780	− 10.2530
− 0.460	− 10.0404	− 10.1698	− 10.2341	− 10.2544	− 10.2458
− 0.560	− 9.7784	− 10.0024	− 10.1300	− 10.1925	− 10.2113
− 0.660	− 9.3591	− 9.7260	− 9.9481	− 10.0740	− 10.1351
− 0.760	− 8.7003	− 9.2915	− 9.6564	− 9.8768	− 10.0013
− 0.860	− 7.6473	− 8.6188	− 9.2079	− 9.5709	− 9.7898
− 0.960	− 5.8479	− 7.5550	− 8.5240	− 9.1109	− 9.4723
− 1.060	− 2.2488	− 5.7490	− 7.4529	− 8.4194	− 9.0044
− 1.160	+ 8.4334	− 2.1478	− 5.6443	− 7.3452	− 8.3092
− 1.260	—	+ 8.5314	− 2.0454	− 5.5381	− 7.2358
− 1.360	—	—	+ 8.6272	− 1.9453	− 5.4341

CM = distance between the 'asymetric' carbon and the centre of the plane XYZ.
H(5)M = distance between the aggregated proton and the centre of the plane XYZ.
Hartree = 27.21 eV = 627.54 kcal mol^{-1}.

consistent, description of the ideas of a proposed mechanism for epimerization, under a theoretical framework.

The simplest system $(X = Y = Z = H)$ was chosen for the first set of calculations in order to give the general pattern of the model. Further work will be necessary to show the disturbances that alkyl substitutions would introduce in the overall energy pattern.

Although a symmetrical model was depicted in Fig. 1 it would be interesting to know the behavior of the system when the position of the proton departs from the symmetrical configuration. The results are shown in Table 1. These points were used to build the potential energy surface shown in Fig. 2 for the constrained protonated methane (CPM).

It is important to know how the double well potential function varies as the reactions proton approaches the chiral center, coming from infinity, since these various configurations are likely to be present in a real case. A potential energy surface was calculated then to show how the energy of the system varies as the carbon moves along the axis HMH' for different values of the distance

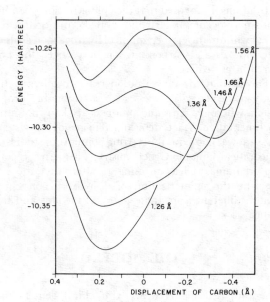

Fig. 2. Potential energy functions for the epimerization model at different distances of the aggregate proton.

MH′ (the distance HM = 1.46 Å was made constant).

The experimental distance of the C–H bond in methane (1.0936 Å) was used throughout. For comparison, the values of the total energy of the ground state of methane, calculated by the same method and with the same parameters was − 10.1149 Hartree.

The free CH_5^+ molecule has been subjected to many theoretical calculations. The most stable structure calculated using both semi-empirical (CNDO/II, Gamba *et al.*, 1969) and *ab initio* methods (Lathan *et al.*, 1970; for a comprehensive review on *ab initio* calculations see *Hehre*, 1977) was shown to have a C_s symmetry.

DISCUSSION AND CONCLUSIONS

1. In the proposed model the optical inversion of hydrocarbon centers (in a rigid system) was achieved by the displacement of the carbon atom through a barrier of a maximum value of 2.36 kcal mol^{-1} at the plane XYZ (symmetrical configuration).

2. This value of barrier is very low, which makes the process highly probable. Nevertheless, we feel it is a bit early to try to extrapolate this number to the real world, firstly because we are dealing with a semi-empirical method for calculating energies and secondly because this first model compound, as such, bears no relationship to the real situation. What one really has to take into account is a micro-region of the sediment where the charges are to be distributed among the various atoms of the unit. As can be seen, no account was made for the geometrical position of the anions in the model. This is certainly of great importance in deciding the shape of the potential energy functions. The results obtained in the present paper should be seen as bits of information toward a theory that is still far from being complete.

3. The presence of the proton in the system $CH_4.H^+$ seems to stabilize it relative to CH_4; the stabilization increases as the proton approaches the face of the tetrahedron.

4. When the proton is found at distances greater than the one in the symmetrical configuration, the potential energy surface shows the two minima very neatly. Both the height of the barrier and the distance between the two minima decrease as the proton approaches the symmetrical position. Also, the potential energy of the system decreases as the proton approaches the symmetrical position. In this way, these three factors act simultaneously to increase the probability of the carbon moving to the 'other' well with consequent inversion of the optical configuration.

This result transposed to geochemistry suggests that, the more *compact* is the sediment, that is, the greater the *pressure* the sediment has been subjected to, the greater will be the changes for the referred process to occur. Pressure has been neglected by organic geochemists as an important factor for the chemical reactions in the sediments. Perhaps this would not be so if reactions were to follow the model discussed in this paper.

It should be emphasized here that any asymmetry in the position of the 'opposing' hydrogen, that is, any departure of the symmetrical double well potential, always produces a large decrease in tunnelling frequency (Bell, 1980). This means that there is an optimal distance for the process to occur at if tunnelling would be an important factor in the process (in our symmetrical system this corresponds to the symmetrical distances between the protons and the center of the plane XYZ. This does not have to be so if different anion acceptors are considered).

5. This model needs a proton as the promotor of the process. One would expect then that the nature of the proton source would be an important factor in the epimerization. Transposing these results to the geological reality one would expect that the nature of the proton donor — clays — would play an important role in this epimerization reaction, not only as a source of protons but also on the geometry of the system that will allow for the correct geometrical relationship between the proton and the chiral carbon center. Frenkel and Heller-Kallai, 1977) have indeed shown that there exists a linear relationship between the acidity of the clay and the degree of racemization of hydrocarbon centers in a group of simulated experiments.

6. When the proton is at a distance smaller than the 'symmetrical' position, the second minimum tends to disappear leaving only one, of lower potential energy than any other in the larger-than-the-symmetrical configuration. This can be interpreted as the formation of a constrained CH_5^+ species. This configuration does not lead to epimerization.

7. In the model described, the pertinent structure was made rigid and only the carbon atom was allowed to move. Now it is important to say that, in principle, all the atoms are allowed to vibrate equally along the various axes of the molecule and consequently to move through the network. What we can say at this point is that the 'winning' processes will be those that will lead to products compatible with the network, that is, *stable in the global structure of the network*. This reasoning leads us to admit that other similar processes can occur in geological systems and perhaps this could be the fundamental mechanism for the long term, low temperature, high pressure processes in a rigid matrix, as is the case of consolidated sediments.

ACKNOWLEDGEMENTS

The author thanks Dr Marco Antonio C. Nascimento for helpful discussions and computer work. This work was supported by the Conselho Nacional de Desenvolvimento Científico e Tecnológico.

REFERENCES

Aquino Neto, F. R. (1978) *Transformation of cellulose and synthesis of clay minerals under simulated geological conditions and environments*. PhD Thesis, Univ. Fed. Rio de Janeiro, Inst. Quim. 555p.

Bada, J. L. and Schroeder, R. A. (1975) Amino acid racemization reactions and their geochemical implications. *Naturwiss enschaften* **62**, 71–79.

Bell, R. P. (1980) *The tunnel effect in chemistry*. Chapman and Hall, London.

Eglinton, G. (1972) Laboratory simulation of organic geochemical processes. *Advances in Organic Geochemistry, Proc. Int. Meet., 5th, 1971.* pp. 29–48.

Ensminger, A., Albrecht, P., Ourisson, G. and Tissot, B. (1977) Evolution of polycyclic alkanes under the effect of burial (Early Toarcian Shales, Paris Basin). *Advances in Organic Geochemistry, Proc. Int. Meet., 7th, 1975.* pp. 45–52.

Frenkel, M. and Heller-Kallai, L. (1977) Racemization of organic compounds by montmorillonite; implications for age determinations and stereocatalysis. *Chem. Geol.* **19**, 161–166.

Gamba, A., Morosi, G. and Simonetta (1969) An investigation of the geometry of the CH_5^+ ion by the CNDO method. *Chem. Phys. Lett.* **3**, 20–21.

Grim, R. E. (1968) *Clay mineralogy*. International Series in the Earth and Planetary Sciences, 2nd edn. McGraw Hill, New York, 596 p.

Hehre, W. J. (1977) Carbonium ions: structural and energetic investigations. In *Modern Theoretical Chemistry*. Ed. by Schaefer, H. F. Vol. 4. Plenum Press, New York.

Lathan, W. A., Hehre, W. J. and Pople, J. A. (1970) Theoretical structures for protonated methane and protonated ethane. *Tetrahedron Lett.* **31**, 2699–2701.

Patience, R. L., Rowland, S. J. and Maxwell, J. R. (1978) The effect of maturation on the configuration of pristane in sediments and petroleum. *Geochim. Cosmochim. Acta* **42**, 1871–1875.

Pople, J. A. and Beveridge, D. L. (1970) *Approximate molecular orbital theory*. McGraw Hill, New York. 214 pp.

Schroeder, R. A. and Bada, J. L. (1976) A review on the geochemical applications of the amino acid racemization reaction. *Earth-Sci. Rev.* **12**, 347–391.

Tissot, B. P. and Welte, D. H. (1978) *Petroleum formation and occurrence*. Springer-Verlag, Berlin. 538 pp.

Advances in Organic Geochemistry 1981, pp. 839–846
© *John Wiley & Sons Limited, 1983*

Asphaltenes Fractionation and Characterization by Liquid Chromatography

J. C. Monin and R. Pelet

Institut Francais du Pétrole, Direction de Recherche Synthèses Géologiques et Géochimie

Asphaltenes are the crude-oil fractions that are insoluble in light saturated hydrocarbons. They are a mix of complex molecules. Naturally, the properties of this mixture vary according to the procedure used to isolate them. We have based our work on the French standard NF-T-60-115 of May 1970. Asphaltenes are usually characterized by the entire arsenal of overall physicochemical methods (elemental analysis, different spectrometries, etc.) which given an accurate idea of the 'average' molecule. This characterization is valid only if all the constituents of the asphaltenes are roughly of the same nature. If several groups of quite different constituents exist, the concept of an average molecule loses any physical meaning. In the present paper we have tried to develop a series of fractionating methods to isolated these groups of different constituents when they exist. The techniques used are selective dissolution, steric-exclusion liquid chromatography and bonded phase liquid chromatography. The fractions thus isolated can then be characterized by overall methods under much more representative conditions than the initial asphaltenes.

INTRODUCTION

The word 'asphaltene' was used for the first time by Boussingault (1837). He used the word to represent the solid fraction of a bitumen (asphalt) that was insoluble in alcohol and soluble in turpentine, while petrolene was the volatile oily remainder, soluble in ethyl ether. From its results, Boussingault concluded that the composition of bitumen varied continuously between the two poles of asphaltene and petrolene.

At present, asphaltenes are defined purely operationally as the fraction of an oil that is insoluble in a solvent made up of one or several saturated hydrocarbons (and soluble in a more polar solvent). The operating conditions vary considerably depending on the author. For example, the precipitation solvent may be an *n*-alkane, with *n* varying from 3 to 10 (Corbett and Petrossi, 1978; Boduszynski, 1979; Wen *et al.*, 1978); a mixture such as petroleum ether (Bikbayeva *et al.*, 1973); or a ring hydrocarbon such as cyclohexane (Ling *et al.*, 1976). The other operating conditions also vary considerably and have an influence on the amounts precipitated (Schultz and Mima, 1980); these conditions include the ratios between the solvent/sample amounts, prior dilution of the sample by a good solvent (often benzene), temperature, agitation and contact time. Long (1979) has shown that these conditions, and especially the solvent used for precipitation, also generate considerable variations in the composition of the asphaltenes obtained. He has likewise shown that, for a given solvent, the precipitation limit of an asphaltene depended on its molecular weight and mean polarity.

Therefore, it is extremely important to use a well-defined asphaltene precipitation procedure so as to ascertain a suitable reproducibility. The procedure used here will be the one defined in the French standard NF-T-60-115 of May 1970.

Asphaltenes defined in this way occur as a mixture of different molecular species. They are normally characterized by overall physicochemical methods (elemental analysis, spectrometries of all sorts, viscosimetry, osmometry, etc.) which give a picture, that may be quite detailed, of the 'average' molecule. The main problem lies in knowing how representative this average molecule is, in relation to the mixture which is the asphaltene being analysed. If all the molecules present have about the same size, composition and structure, their representation by the average molecule will be entirely satisfactory. On the other hand if, for example, polycondensed aromatic structures and oxygenated functions are mutually exclusive and born by two distinct groups of molecules, then the representation by the average molecule loses any meaning since mixtures having entirely different properties correspond to the same average molecule. Because there are geochemical reasons for suspecting that this may be the case, it is obvious why prior fractionation must be performed before any overall characterization. But this fractionation must have a meaning. For instance, in the preceding example, it must separate the aromatic group from the oxygenated group — and not only two fractions having different sizes — since these two fractions would, at their scale, reproduce the same structural complexity as the initial

Table 1

Elemental analysis of asphaltenes

Sample	Measured % C	Corrected % C[a]	Atomic H/C	Atomic O/C × 100	Atomic S/C × 100	Atomic N/C × 100
Bati Raman (BR)	81.8	82.1	1.07	0.65	4.1	0.93
Hassi Messaoud (HM)	91.8	91.9	0.75	1.21	0.25	0.28

[a] Corrected % C = measured % C $\times \dfrac{100}{\Sigma \text{ measured } \% \text{ C, H, O, N, S}}$

mixture. This is the problem of 'rational' fractionating, which is discussed in the present paper.

EXPERIMENTAL

Samples

The asphaltenes used come from two oils: Bati Raman (BR) and Hassi Messaoud (HM). These two oils originate from the same type of oceanic organic matter but differ in age, i.e. Silurian for HM (Poulet and Roucaché, 1969) and Cretaceous for BR (Genla *et al.*, 1979). They have not been altered by biodegradation and/or oxidation. BR is a heavy oil of the aromatic–asphaltic type, whereas HM falls in the category of paraffinic oils according to the classification by Tissot and Welte (1978). This difference in overall composition between these two oils is the result of a different geological history.

The BR sample was distilled to remove the fraction having a boiling point lower than 210 °C. The residue was used to precipitate asphaltenes according to the French standard NF-T-60-115.

The HM asphaltene sample was obtained by using toluene to dissolve the insoluble residue obtained in an industrial propane deasphalting operation. The asphaltenes were precipitated from this solution in toluene according to the standard NF-T-60-115.

The elemental analysis of these asphaltenes is given in Table 1.

Chromatography

High-performance liquid-chromatography (HPLC) analyses were performed with a Varian 5060 chromatograph, which made possible the use of ternary solvent gradients. Detection was performed by a Varian UV 50 spectrophotometer with wavelengths ranging from 350 to 550 nm.

Size-exclusion chromatography (SEC) was performed in the analytical stage with a Shodex A 803 column, 50 cm long and 8 mm in diametre, with tetrahydrofuran as an eluant, at a flowrate of 1 cm³ min⁻¹. At the semi-preparative stage, a Shodex H 2003 column, 50 cm long and 20 mm in diametre was used. In this case the eluant was chloroform and the flowrate was 3.5 cm³ min⁻¹.

The molecular weights of asphaltenes given in this paper are merely references to the molecular weights of standard polystyrenes, having the same elution volume.

Bonded-phase chromatography (BPC) tests were performed with different phases: Varian C18, Micropak MCH 10, 30 cm long, 4 mm inside diametre Chrompack CN, Sil-60-D-10 CN, 25 cm long, 4.6 mm inside diametre; Chrompack Diol, LiChrosorb 10 Diol, 25 cm long, 4.6 mm inside diametre; Chrompack NO₂ Sil-60-D-10 NO₂, 25 cm long, 4.6 mm diametre.

Measuring solubilities

Solubilities were measured by agitating 10 mg of asphaltenes in 10 cm³ of solvent at room temperature. Agitation was performed by an Ila ultradispersing device of type CX with a generator 10 mm in diametre for 30 s. After resting for several hours at room temperature, the suspensions were filtered. The amounts of soluble and insoluble fractions were determined by weighing.

RESULTS

Solubility measurements

According to the theory developed by Hildebrand *et al.* (1970), there is a relationship between the cohesive energy density (*C*) and the miscibility or solubility. *C* is defined by:

$$C = \frac{\Delta E_v}{V}$$

where $\Delta E_v =$ energy variation for isothermal vaporization of saturated liquid in an ideal-gas stage (expressed in J mol⁻¹); $V =$ molar volume (expressed in m³ mol⁻¹); and *C* is expressed in J m⁻³.

The solubility parameter (δ) is the positive square root[†] of the cohesive energy density:

$$\delta = \sqrt{C} = \left[\frac{\Delta E_v}{V}\right]^{1/2}$$

or by using heat of vaporization (ΔHv) (expressed in J mol⁻¹)

$$\delta = \left[\frac{\Delta H_v - RT}{V}\right]^{1/2}$$

† The square root is taken because it appears empirically as an additive parameter for solvents mixtures.

Table 2
Solubility of asphaltenes in pure solvents

Name	Solubility parameter (MPa$^{1/2}$)	(mg asphaltene/cm³ solvent) BR	HM
n-heptane	15.1	0	0
cyclohexane	16.8	0.9	0.6
benzene	18.8	>1	>1
toluene	18.2	>1	>1
tetralin	19.4	0.80	0.88
cumene	17.1	0.40	0.41
methanol	29.6	0	0
isopropanol	20.4	0	0
ether diethyl	15.1	0.05	0.10
ether diisopropyl	14.6	0.03	0.12
ether dibenzyl	18.6	0.05	—
1,4 dioxane	20.5	0.08	0.15
1,2 epoxy propane	18.8	0.13	0.06
1,2 epoxy 3 phenoxy propane	17.4	0	—
2 methoxyethanol	23.3	0	—
acetone	20.0	0.03	0.06
ethyl acetate	18.6	0.06	0.06
tetrahydrofuran	18.6	>1	>1
dichloro methane	19.8	>1	>1
chloroform	19.0	>1	>1
carbon tetrachloride	17.6	0.90	0.65
ethylene tetrachloro	19.0	>1	>1
2 chloropropane	18.9	0	—
bis (βchloroethyl) ether	19.9	0	—
2 methoxyethylchloride	18.4	0	—
acetonitril	24.3	0.09	0.09
benzonitril	17.2	0.41	0.93
3 ethoxypropionitril	20.9	0	—
nitro methane	26.0	0	—
nitro benzene	20.4	>1	>1
formamide	39.7	0	0
dimethylformamide	24.8	0	0
ethylene diamine	24.9	0	0
tetramethylurea	33.3	0.05	—
N-methyl-2-pyrrolidone	22.0	0.18	0.12
pyridine	29.9	>1	>1
quinoline	28.4	>1	>1
carbon disulfide	20.4	>1	>1
dimethyl sulfoxide	24.5	0	0

R being the constant of ideal gases (expressed in J mol^{-1} K^{-1}); T the temperature in degrees Kelvin (expressed in K); or again:

$$\delta = \left[\frac{D(\Delta H_v - RT)}{M} \right]^{1/2}$$

D being the density (expressed in kg m^{-3}); M the molecular weight of the body being considered (expressed in kg). δ is expressed in $(J\ m^{-3})^{1/2}$ which corresponds to values of $(N\ m^{-2})^{1/2}$ and can thus be expressed in Pa$^{1/2}$ (in practice in MPa$^{1/2}$).

The correspondence between the solubility parameter (δ) expressed in MPa$^{1/2}$, or in (cal cm^{-3})$^{1/2}$-Hildebrand unit is:

$$1\ \text{Pa} = 1\ \text{N m}^{-2} = 1\ \text{J m}^{-3} = \frac{10^{-6}}{4.18}\ \text{cal cm}^{-3}$$

$$1\ \text{MPa} = 10^6\ \text{Pa} = \frac{1}{4.18}\ \text{cal cm}^{-3}$$

When the symbol of a prefix is placed before the symbol of a unit, the combination of the two symbols

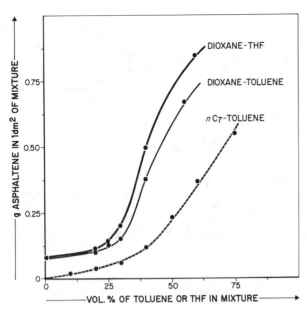

Fig. 1. Solubilities of Bati Raman (BR) asphaltene in mixtures of solvents at room temperature.

should be considered as one new symbol which can be raised to a positive or negative power without using brackets (UIP, 1978):

$$1 \text{ MPa}^{1/2} = \frac{1}{4.18} (\text{cal cm}^{-3})^{1/2}$$

$$1 \text{ MPa}^{1/2} = 0.489 (\text{cal cm}^{-3})^{1/2}$$

In order to be miscible, solvent and solute must have similar δ values. This rule worked out for nonpolar

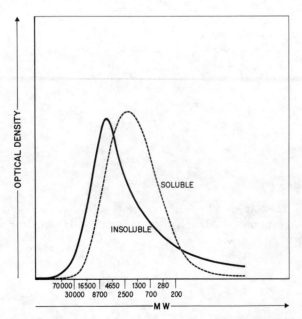

Fig. 2. Size-exclusion chromatography of fractions soluble (a) and insoluble (b) in dioxane–toluene (70:30 vol) of Bati Raman (BR) asphaltene. Column Shodex A 803 500 × 8 mm. Detector UV 350 mm. Mobile phase:tetrahydrofuran — Flowrate 1 cm³ min⁻¹.

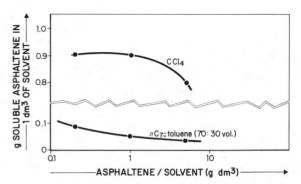

Fig. 3. Solubility of Bati Raman asphaltene against asphaltene/solvent ratio for carbone tetrachloride and a mixture *n*-heptane–toluene (70:30 vol).

compounds remains valid for polar compounds in a first approximation.

An examination of the results (cf. Table 2) shows that with solvents of $\delta < 17$ MPa$^{1/2}$ or > 30 MPa$^{1/2}$, the solubility of asphaltenes is practically nil. For δ values between these values, some solvents dissolve asphaltenes easily, while others dissolve them only slightly or not at all. The overall results are:
1. Non-cyclic compounds, containing oxygen and in some cases another heteroatom (N or S), are poor solvents.
2. Chlorinated solvents are good solvents.
3. Aromatic-hydrocarbon compounds and their derivatives are good solvents.
4. Nitrogen-containing heterocycles (pyridine, quinoline) and oxygen-containing heterocycles (tetrahydrofuran) are also good solvents.

Among the solvents investigated, very few partially dissolve asphaltenes and hence are suitable for asphaltenes fractionation. Furthermore, a practical limitation is the ease of elimination of a solvent with a too-high boiling point. For example, benzonitrile cannot be used because it is almost impossible to eliminate at acceptable temperatures. With carbon tetrachloride, the results are not always readily reproducible. Another possible method of separating asphaltenes on the basis of their solubilities, is to use a mixture of solvents. By using a good solvent (toluene or tetrahydrofuran) blended with a poor solvent (*n*-hexane or dioxane), the solubility of asphaltenes first increases slowly with the increasing proportion of good solvent in the mixture, and then increases rapidly when a particular proportion is reached (cf. Fig. 1). This threshold corresponds roughly to the same solubility, i.e. 0.10 to 0.12 mg of asphaltenes for 1 cm³ of solvent mixture for the three mixtures investigated. It is thus probable that this soluble portion represents a specific fraction of asphaltenes. For example, the steric-exclusion chromatograms for the soluble and non-soluble fractions are different (Fig. 2).

It was confirmed that the influence of the asphaltene/solvent ratio on asphaltene solubility is not very great, and this is true whatever the solubility of the asphaltenes may be (cf. Fig. 3). This again shows that soluble and non-soluble fractions of an asphaltene in a given solvent have different properties.

Mitchell and Speight (1973), analysing the partition of an Athabasca tar into soluble and insoluble fractions

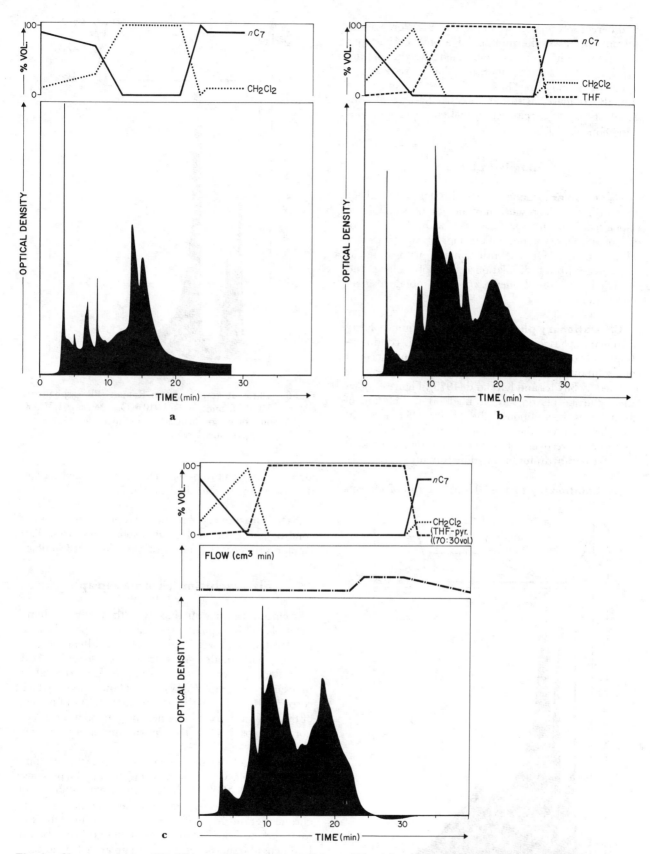

Fig. 4. Chromatography of Bati Raman (BR) asphaltene. Column 250 × 4.6 mm. Sil 60-D-10-CN. Detector UV 350 mm. a – mobile phase:gradient:n-heptane/methylene chloride. Flowrate 1 cm³ min⁻¹. b – mobile phase:gradient:n-heptane/methylene chloride/tetrahydrofuran. Flowrate 1 cm³ min⁻¹. c — mobile phase:gradient:n-heptane/methylene chloride/tetrahydrofuran-pyridine (50:50). Flowrate: gradient 1–2.5 cm³ min⁻¹.

in different solvents, showed that, when the force of the solvent increases, the number of aromatic rings per structural unit and the molecular weight of the precipitated asphaltenes increase. This corresponds to what we found. Speight's (1979) results cannot be directly compared with ours because he used nC_5 instead of nC_7 to precipitate asphaltenes (Speight and Moschopedis, 1979).

Bonded phase

C_{18} stationary phase Tests with this phase did not give any interestinf results. In particular, the solubility of asphaltenes in the solvents used with this type of stationary phase was not sufficient for a proper injection of asphaltenes. On the other hand, with different asphaltenes from a distillation residue of a blown and acidified crude oil, Zumer *et al.* (1981) obtained good chromatograms.

CN stationary phase With this medium-polarity stationary phase, the choice of elution conditions (especially of the solvent) was made taking into account our solubility results and the selectivity of solvents as defined by Snyder and Kirkland (1979). Figure 4 shows the influence of the solvent used on the elution of asphaltenes. In addition to the quality differences that can be seen on these chromatograms, a tentative quantitative recovery of asphaltenes required the final use of a tetrahydrofuran–pyridine mixture.

Diol stationary phase Using a series of solvents

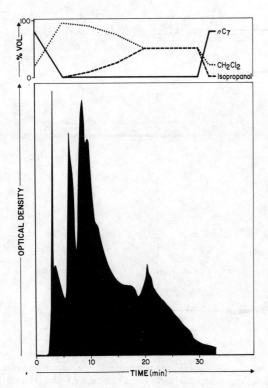

Fig. 5. Chromatography of Bati Raman (BR) asphaltene. Column 250 × 4.6 mm Sil-60-D-10 NO_2. Detector UV 350 nm. Mobile phase:gradient:*n*-heptane/methylene chloride/isopropanol. Flowrate 1 cm^3 min^{-1}.

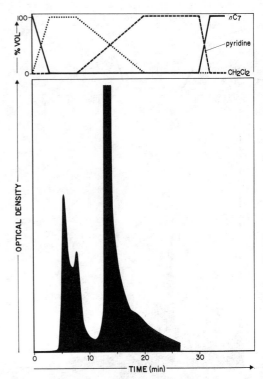

Fig. 6. Chromatography of Bati Raman (BR) asphaltene. Column 250 × 4.6 mm. Sil-60-D-10 NO_2. Detector UV 350 nm. Mobile phase:gradient:*n*-heptane/methylene chloride/pyridine. Flowrate 1 cm^3 min^{-1}.

for the elution, chromatograms were obtained having the appearance of the ones in Fig. 5.

NO_2 stationary phase Under the elution conditions shown in Fig. 6, asphaltenes from Bati Raman are separated into two quite distinct fractions.

Size-exclusion chromatography

The chromatograms obtained with the analysis column show that BR asphaltenes contain compounds with greater molecular weights than HM asphaltenes (Figs. 7 and 8), with modes going from 6700 to 3600. HM asphaltenes have a small fraction centered at a molecular weight (MW) of about 500, which corresponds to the MW of a resin fraction. As a function of the amount injected, neither the general appearance nor the position of the maximum is appreciably changed.

With one of the BR asphaltene preparations, quite different results were obtained (Fig. 9), i.e. the presence of a fraction MW> 100 000, very great influence of the amount injected on the appearance of the chromatograms, better return to the baseline after the total permeation volume. Asphaltenes from blown bitumens also show a fraction with great molecular sizes (Brulé, 1979), but the influence of the amount injected on the distribution of the molecular weights is the opposite of what was obtained with BR.

The cause of this difference between preparations of asphaltenes which are, in principle, identical has not been determined. Whatever the cause may be, this result

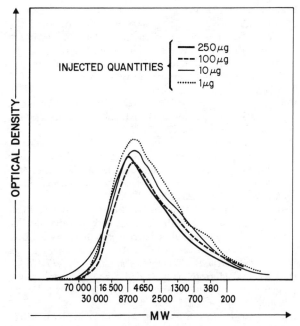

Fig. 7. Size-exclusion chromatography of Bati Raman (BR) asphaltene. Column Shodex A 803. 500 × 8 mm. Detector UV 350 nm. Mobile phase: tetrahydrofuran. Flowrate 1 cm^3 min^{-1}. Loop volume 50 mm^3.

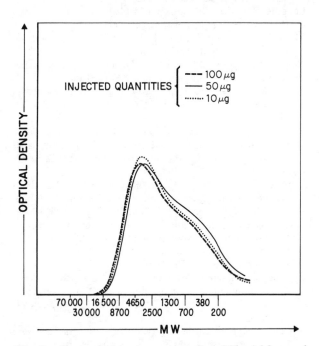

Fig. 8. Size-exclusion chromatography of Hassi Messaoud (HM) asphaltene. Conditions: see Fig. 7.

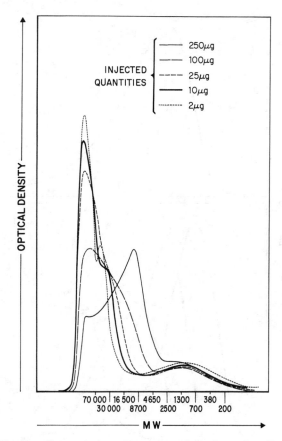

Fig. 9. Size-exclusion chromatography of another Bati Raman BR asphaltene. Conditions: see Fig. 7.

Figure 10 shows the fractionation of the soluble portions in a 70:30 (volume) dioxane/toluene mixture of BR. It should be noted that the chromatogram of each fraction shows some shift towards molecular weights higher than expected from the whole asphaltene chromatogram. This shift is more important for the low molecular weight fractions.

Small variations have been found quite often in the shape and intensity in chromatograms of a given sample without obvious causes. Asphaltenes can probably quite easily be dissociated or associated as a result of small variations in their environment, i.e. aging of solutions, oxidation, effect of light, etc.

CONCLUSION

The fractionation methods investigated can be used to separate an asphaltene sample into several fractions, each having different properties. Since each method has its own selectivity, the use of these methods in 'cascade' on the same sample should result in its 'rational' fractionation, in the sense given to this term in the introduction.

From a practical standpoint, the preferred scheme of fractionation would involve: first a selective dissolution step (this method is rapid, straightforward and enables one to process relatively important quantities of asphaltenes). Next, more detailed fractionation would be dealt with by liquid chromatography methods (less

confirms that asphaltenes are not stable products and that the same protocols must always be followed in preparation and preservation.

With the preparative column (and hence with chloroform as the solvent) the molecular weights for asphaltenes were generally greater than those obtained in THF with the analysis column, as observed by Hall and Herron (1979) who recommended THF, but is in contrast with what was observed by Brulé (1978) who also was using asphaltenes from blown bitumens.

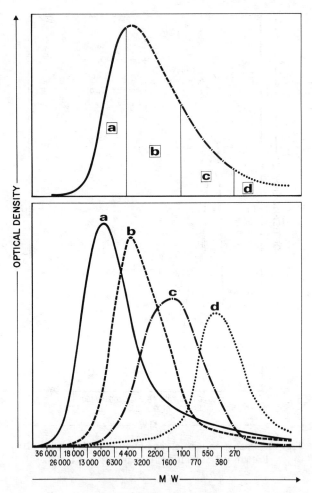

Fig. 10. Size-exclusion chromatography of the soluble fraction in dioxane/toluene (30:70) of Bati Raman (BR) asphaltene. Column Shodex H 2003. 500 × 20 mm. Detector UV 550 nm. Mobile phase chloroform. Flow rate 3.5 cm³ min ⁻¹. Loop volume: 2 cm³, quantity injected: 8 mg. Weight % of fractions — a: 26, b: 48, c: 19, d: 7.

easy to use, and not suitable for the processing of important quantities). The fractions thus isolated could then be characterized by the usual global methods, or by even more sophisticated ones (such as pyrochromatography). The specificity of these latter fractions would result in a characterization much more reliable than one based on the initial mixture.

REFERENCES

Bikbayeva, M. Z., Vyalkova, L. F., Ionon, V. I., Markhasin, I. L. and Umitbayev, R. B. (1973) On the composition of the fractions of crude oil asphaltenes. *Neftepererab Neftekiom (Kiev)* **5**, 14–16.

Boduszynkski, M. (1979) Asphaltenes in petroleum asphalts. Composition and formation. *Am. Chem. Soc. Petrol. Chem. Div. Preprints* **24**, 935–948.

Boussingault, J. B. (1837) Mémoire sur la composition des bitumes. *Ann. Chim. Phys.* **64**, 141.

Brulé, B. (1978) Contribution de la chromatographie sur gel perméable (G.P.C.) à la caractérisation qualitative et quantitative des bitumes. Structure colloidale. *Rapport LPC no 76* Lab. Central Ponts et Chaussées, Paris.

Brulé, B. (1979) Characterization of bituminous compounds by gel permeation chromatography. *Journ. Liq. Chrom.* **2**, 165–192.

Corbett, L. W. and Petrossi, U. (1978) Differences in distillation and solvent separated asphalt residues. *Ind. Eng. Chem. Prod. Res. Dev.* **17**, 342–348.

Durand, B., Espitalié, J. and Oudin, J. L. (1970) Analyse géochimique de la matière organique extraite des roches sédimentaires III — Accroissement de la rapidité du protocole opératoire par l'amélioration de l'appareillage. *Rev. Inst. Fr. Pétr.* **25**, 1268–1279.

Genca, M., Gurses, B., Kantar, K., Sener, I. and Tek, M. R. (1979) Prospects for enhanced recovery from Bati Raman field. Turkey, a two billion barrel heavy oil reservoir. *Report number 29. 1st Internat. Conf. on the future of heavy crude and tarsands, Alta, June 1979, Edmonton, Canada, UNITAR.*

Hall, G. and Herron, S. P. (1979) Size characterization of petroleum asphaltenes and maltenes. *Am. Chem. Soc. Petrol. chem. Div. Preprints* **24**, 924–934.

Hildebrand, J. H., Prausnitz, J. M. and Scott, R. L. (1970) *Regular solutions*. Van Nostrand–Reinhold Co., New York.

Ling, C. S., Cummins, J. J. and Robinson, W. E. (1976) Fractionation of soluble extracts obtained from kerogen thermal degradation with CO and H_2O. *Am. Chem. Soc. Fuel Chem. Div. Preprints* **21**, 265–271.

Long, R. B. (1979) The concept of asphaltenes. *Am. Chem. Soc. Petrol. Chem. Div. Preprints* **24**, 891–900.

Mitchell, D. L. and Speight, J. G. (1973) The solubility of asphaltenes in hydrocarbon solvents. *Fuel* **52**, 149–152.

Norme Française (May 1970) Dosage des asphaltènes précipités par l'heptane normal. NF-T-60-115.

Poulet, M. and Roucaché, J. (1969) Etude géochimique des gisements du Nord Sahara (Algérie). *Rev. Inst. Fr. Pétr.* **24**, 615–644.

Radke, M., Willsch, H. and Welte, H. (1980) Preparative hydrocarbon group type determination by automated medium pressure liquid chromatography. *Anal. Chem.* **52**, 406–411.

Schultz, H. and Mima, M. J. (1980) Comparison of methods for the determination of asphaltenes, oils and insolubles. Part II. *Am. Chem. Soc. Fuel Chem. Div. Preprints* **25**, 18–24.

Speight, J. G. (1979) Studies on bitumen fractionation. A — Fractionation by a cryoscopic method. B — Effect of solvent type on asphaltene solubility. *Information Series 84.* Alberta Research Council, 1979.

Speight, J. G. and Moschopedis, S. E. (1979) Some observations on the molecular 'nature' of petroleum asphaltenes. *Am. Chem. Soc. Petrol. Chem. Div. Preprints* **24**, 910–923.

Snyder, L. R. and Kirkland, J. J. (1979) *Introduction to modern liquid chromatography*. 2nd edition. John Wiley, Interscience, New York.

Tissot, B. and Welte, D. (1978) *Petroleum formation and occurrence*. Springer Verlag, Berlin, Heidelberg, New York.

U.I.P. (1978) International Union of Pure and Applied Physics. Document U.I.P. no. 20.

Wen, C. S., Chilingarian, G. V. and Yen, T. F. (1978) Properties and structure of bitumens. In *Dev. Petrol. Science* **7**, Elsevier. pp. 155–190.

Zumer, M., Such, C. and Brulé, B. (1981) Caractérisation d'un bitume (et de ses fractions) par chromatographie en phase liquide à polarité de phases inversées. *Analusis* **9**, 145–148.

List of Contributors

Aizenshtat, Z. 279, 799
Albrecht, P. A. 659
Aldridge, A. K. 99
Alexander, R. 69, 76
Allan, J. 534
Altebäumer, A. M. 80, 561
Altebäumer, F. J. 136
Amblès, A. 554
Andreux, F. 323
André, C. 251
Aquino Neto, F. R. 659
Arpino, P. J. 808

Baak, A. 675
Baker, E. W. 401
Barnard, L. A. 422
Barnes, M. A. 289
Barnes, W. C. 289
Barwise, A. J. G. 668
Bavor, H. J. 198
Behar, E. 129
Belayouni, H. 328
Benijoly, M. 323
Bennett, C. R. 769
Benshan, Wang 108
Bissada, K. K. 7
Bjorøy, M. 16, 49, 60, 87, 136
Boon, J. J. 207
Bouchard, G. 350
Bourgeois, G. 705
Brassell, S. C. 391, 465, 477, 684
Brooks, J. M. 422
Brooks, P. W. 87
Brukner, A. 175
Bue, B. 16
Burlingame, A. L. 207
Byers, J. D. 725

Cardoso, J. N. 828
Carlson, R. M. K. 710
Casagrande, D. J. 628
Chicarelli, M. I. 828
Claypool, G. E. 28
Cohen, Y. 279
Connan, J. 659
Costa Neto, C. 834
Cox, H. C. 813
Cranwell, P. A. 299

Daumas, R. 259
Debyser, Y. 259
De Leeuw, J. W. 207, 336, 471, 813
Discamps, D. 129
Djordjević, Lj. 554
Djuričić, M. V. 554
Douglas, A. G. 513, 568, 576
Durand, B. 117, 147, 156

Edmunds, K. E. 207
Eglinton, G. 207, 391, 477, 684
Ekweozor, C. M. 746
Elvsborg, A. 16
Engelhard, E. D. 788
Erdman, J. G. 725
Esdaile, R. G. 198
Ewald, M. 705

Farrington, J. W. 185, 228
Fenfang, Xu. 108
Ferguson, A. 628
Février, A. 251, 317
Forsberg, A. 60

Gadel, F. 317
Gagosian, R. B. 228, 369, 380
Galimov, E. M. 431
Garrigues, P. 705
Gilbert, T. D. 698
Gillan, F. T. 198
Goodwin, N. S. 650
Gormly, J. R. 597
Goutx, M. 251
Gowar, A. P. 477
Grantham, P. J. 675

Hagemann, H. W. 72
Hall, K. 87
Hall, P. B. 576
Haverkamp, J. 336
Hayes, J. M. 546
Hines, H. 207
Hollerbach, A. 72
Howell, V. 391
Howell, V. J. 477
Huc, A. Y. 465

Ikan, R. 824
Ioselis, P. 824

Jiamo, Fu. 108
Johns, R. B. 198

Kagi, R. I. 69, 76
Kaplan, I. R. 819
Kendall, C. G. St. C. 588
Klok, J. 207, 813
Kodina, L. A. 431
Krsmanović, V. D. 620
Kvenvolden, K. A. 422

Lamotte, M. 705
Lapouyade, R. 705
Larcher, A. V. 69
Larter, S. R. 513, 534
Leble, J. 350
Leenheer, M. J. 309
Leplat, P. 613
Lerche, I. 588
Lewan, M. D. 524
Leythaeuser, D. 80, 136, 164, 561
Lijmbach, G. W. M. 788
Los, A. 336
Louda, J. W. 401

McEnvoy, J. 449
McKirdy, D. M. 99
Mackenzie, A. S. 136, 496, 637
Magoon, L. B. 28
Maxwell, J. R. 391, 449, 496
Maxwell, R. J. 637
Mazurek, M. A. 355
Melotte, M. 613
Meyer, R. J. 588

Meyers, P. A. 309, 465
Moldowan, J. M. 710
Monin, J. C. 839
Monnier, F. 487
Monrozier, L. J. 259, 323
Mørk, A. 49
Mukhopadhyay, P. K. 597

Nichols, P. D. 198
Nielsen, H. 279
Nigrelli, G. E. 369

Orr, W. L. 775
Oudin, J. L. 147, 156

Park, P. J. D. 650, 668
Paulet, J. 613
Pelet, R. 241, 323, 839
Peters, K. E. 819, 824
Petroy, D. E. 588
Pfendt, P. A. 620
Philp, R. P. 698
Pillon, P. 323
Posthuma, J. 675
Powell, T. G. 487

Quirke, J. M. E. 733

Radke, M. 504
Rawlinson, A. P. 650
Reed, W. E. 355
Reinhardt, S. B. 362
Ren-Wei, Li. 496
Repeta, D. J. 380
Restle, A. 659
Rijpstra, W. I. 207
Rima, 705
Rohrback, B. G. 39, 819
Rubinsztain, Y. 824
Rullkötter, J. 438

Sackett, W. M. 362
Saliot, A. 251, 268, 317
Sassen, R. 94
Sautriot, D. 259
Schaefer, R. G. 80, 136, 164, 561
Schenck, P. A. 336, 371, 813
Schmitter, J. M. 808
Schoell, M. 156
Seifert, W. K. 710
Schanchum, Jiang. 108
Shanfa, Fan. 108
Silverberg, N. 350
Simoneit, B. R. T. 355, 698
Snowdon, L. R. 487
Solli, H. 513
Souchier, B. 323
Spiro, B. 799
Stoler, A. 279
Strausz, O. P. 746
Sundberg, K. R. 769
Sundby, B. 350
Suzuki, N. 607
Sweeney, R. E. 819

Taguchi, K. 607
Teschner, M. 156
Tissier, M. J. 251, 268
Toth, D. J. 588
Trendel, J. M. 659
Trichet, J. 328
Tusseau, D. 317

Ungerer, P. 129

van de Meent, D. 336
Vandenbroucke, M. 147
van der Knapp, J. M. M. 813

van der Veen, F. M. 788
van Graas, G. 471
Van Vleet, E. S. 362
Verheyen, T. V. 198
Vetö, I. 175
Veyres, A. 705
Viets, T. C. 471
Vigran, J. 49
Vitorović, D. 554, 620
Volkman, J. K. 185, 228, 369
von der Dick, H. 164

Wakeham, S. G. 185, 228

Weber, F. F. Jr. 362
Wedeking, K. W. 546
Wehner, H. 156
Welte, D. H. 438, 504
Wiesenburg, D. A. 422
Williams, J. A. 524
Williams, P. F. V. 568
Winters, J. C. 3, 524
Wolff, G. A. 637
Woodhouse, G. W. 69, 76

Ypma, P. J. M. 99

Zumberge, J. E. 738

Index